Exploring ArcObjects™
Vol. I—Applications and Cartography

GIS by ESRI™

Edited by Michael Zeiler

PUBLISHED BY

ESRI

380 New York Street

Redlands, California 92373-8100

Contributing Writers

Julio Andrade, Eleanor Blades, Patrick Brennan, Tom Brown, Euan Cameron, Scott Campbell, Jillian Clark, Jim Clarke, Chris Davies, Cory Eicher, Ryan Gatti, Shelly Gill, Erik Hoel, Melita Kennedy, Allan Laframboise, Russell Louks, Keith Ludwig, Gary MacDougall, Glenn Meister, Sud Menon, Jason Pardy, Bruce Payne, Ghislain Prince, Sentha Shanmugam, Brad Taylor, Steve Van Esch, Aleta Vienneau, Michael Waltuch, Steve Wheatley, Larry Young, Michael Zeiler

ESRI

Exploring ArcObjects
Volume 1—Applications and cartography
ISBN: 1-58948-001-5 (Volume 1)
Volume 2—Geographic Data Management
ISBN: 1-58948-002-3 (Volume 2)
ISBN: 1-58948-000-7 (Set)

Contents

Introducing ArcObjects

Michael Waltuch, Euan Cameron, Allan Laframboise, Michael Zeiler

ESRI® ArcObjects™ is the development platform for the ArcGIS™ family of applications such as ArcMap™, ArcCatalog™, and ArcScene™. The ArcObjects software components expose the full range of functionality available in ArcInfo™ and ArcView® to software developers.

ArcObjects is a framework that lets you create domain-specific components from other components. The ArcObjects components collaborate to serve every data management and map presentation function common to most GIS applications. ArcObjects provides an infrastructure for application customization that lets you concentrate on serving the specific needs of your clients.

This chapter discusses: using this book and the other developer resources • reading the object model diagrams • getting started with ArcObjects and VBA • applying an ArcObjects problem-solving guide • examining the most commonly used components in ArcObjects with sample VBA code that solves a set of common tasks

ArcObjects is the development platform for ArcGIS Desktop.

ArcGIS Desktop is a suite of GIS software systems: ArcInfo, ArcEditor™, and ArcView. These systems serve GIS professionals with a spectrum of geographic data management, spatial editing, and cartographic visualization functionality.

The ArcGIS Desktop systems each contain a configuration of applications, such as ArcCatalog, ArcMap, ArcToolbox™, and ArcScene, and can host a variety of extension products such as ArcGIS Spatial Analyst, ArcGIS Geostatistical Analyst, ArcGIS 3D Analyst™, and others.

This book documents the core components of ArcObjects that comprise these two core applications: ArcMap and ArcCatalog.

THE ArcObjects FRAMEWORK

ArcObjects is built using Microsoft's Component Object Model (COM) technology. Therefore, it is possible to extend ArcObjects by writing COM components using any COM-compliant development language. You can extend every part of the ArcObjects architecture in exactly the same way as ESRI developers do.

CUSTOMIZING ArcGIS DESKTOP

The most common way that developers will customize the ArcGIS Desktop applications is through Visual Basic® for Applications (VBA), which is embedded within ArcCatalog and ArcMap.

Through VBA, you can leverage the application framework that already exists in ArcMap and ArcCatalog for general data management and map presentation tasks and extend ArcGIS with your own custom commands, tools, menus, and modules.

Using VBA inside ArcGIS Desktop, you can achieve the majority of your customization needs with relatively little development effort.

More advanced developers can further extend ArcGIS Desktop with custom map layers, renderers, property pages, and data sources.

For specialized applications, developers with sufficient skill can bypass the application framework of ArcMap and ArcCatalog and instead build their own targeted applications. The Map control, discussed in Appendix D, provides a good point of entry, allowing access to the remainder of ArcObjects.

ArcMap is used for mapping and editing tasks as well as map-based analysis.

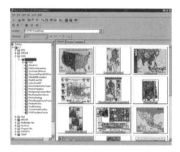

ArcCatalog is used for managing your spatial data holdings, defining your geographic data schemas, and recording and viewing metadata.

For more information on the products and applications that form the ArcGIS system, see the ESRI book What is ArcGIS?

Exploring ArcObjects is for anyone who wants to customize or extend the ArcMap and ArcCatalog applications.

Everyone should read the first two chapters for an overview of developing with ArcObjects. You can use the remainder of the two volumes as a reference to the core ArcObjects components in ArcMap and ArcCatalog.

To serve the greatest base of developers, most of the code samples in this book are written in VBA. As necessary, some code samples are written in Microsoft® Visual Basic (VB) or Visual C++®. All code is included on the ArcGIS CD at arcexe81\ArcObjects Developer kit\Samples\Exploring ArcObjects.

VOLUME 1—APPLICATIONS AND CARTOGRAPHY

The first volume documents the ArcObjects components directly used by the ArcMap and ArcCatalog applications, as well as the components used for cartographic presentation.

Chapter 1, 'Introducing ArcObjects', gives you an overview of using ArcObjects in the VBA environment, discusses how to read the object model diagrams, contains code examples for common tasks, and presents a problem-solving guide that can help you start with ArcObjects.

Chapter 2, 'Developing with ArcObjects', provides in-depth coverage of everything you need to know about applying COM, VBA, VB, Visual C++, and ATL to ArcObjects development.

Chapter 3, 'Customizing the user interface', discusses the general components and techniques for modifying the user interface of all ArcGIS Desktop applications.

Chapter 4, 'Composing maps', explains how views work in ArcMap and how to manipulate map layers, graphics, and elements of a map.

Chapter 5, 'Displaying graphics', documents the drawing of layers with feature renderers; working with colors, symbols, and annotation; and using the visual feedback components.

Chapter 6, 'Directing map output', describes how to send your maps to printing devices and graphics formats.

Chapter 7, 'Working with the Catalog', gives details on how to customize the ArcCatalog application to work with your geographic data.

VOLUME 2—GEOGRAPHIC DATA MANAGEMENT

The second volume documents the ArcObjects components that manage geographic data and auxiliary component subsystems, such as spatial reference and geometry.

Chapter 8, 'Accessing the geodatabase', provides the foundation for the core geographic data management components in ArcObjects.

Chapter 9, 'Shaping features with geometry', documents the rich geometric subsystem in ArcObjects that supports feature definition and graphic element interaction in ArcMap.

Chapter 10, 'Managing the spatial reference', discusses how to work with geographic data from a variety of coordinate systems.

Chapter 11, 'Editing features', explains how to perform customization of editing tasks in ArcMap.

Chapter 12, 'Solving linear networks', documents how to solve network tracing and allocation problems.

Chapter 13, 'Integrating raster data', discusses the use of raster data objects to provide a background display and perform analysis on image data.

Appendix A, 'Open data access in ArcGIS', discusses the use of universal data-access technology for accessing geographic data outside of ESRI® applications.

Appendix B, 'Geodatabase modeling with UML', gives the conceptual background for using the CASE functionality in ArcCatalog for data modeling.

Appendix C, 'Developing for ArcGIS deployments', discusses which functions in ArcObjects are available in the ArcInfo, ArcEditor, and ArcView systems.

Appendix D, 'Developing with the Map control', discusses how you can simplify external application development and access all of ArcObjects.

CORRECTIONS AND UPDATES

It is inevitable that a book of this scope and size will contain some errors of omission and fact. You will find corrections and late-breaking updates for this book at www.esri.com/arcobjectsonline.

You can report errors that you find or suggestions for future editions of this book to ArcObjects@esri.com. This e-mail address is not to be used for technical support queries. You can find resources for technical support on ESRI's Web site, www.esri.com.

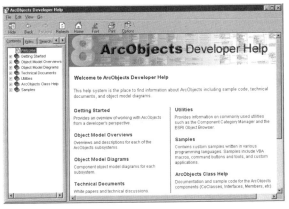

The ArcObjects Developer Help system main table of contents

The ArcObjects Developer Help system is an essential resource for both beginning and experienced ArcObjects developers. It lets you find detailed reference documentation about every coclass, class, interface, and enumeration within ArcObjects as well as sample code, technical documents, and object model diagrams.

You can start the ArcObjects Developer Help system by clicking the Windows Start button, clicking the Programs menu, pointing to ArcGIS, and clicking ArcObjects Developer Help.

The main table of contents outlines everything that you can find in the ArcObjects Developer Help system. The main table of contents also contains links to ArcObjects Online and ArcSDE™ Online.

Getting started with ArcObjects

The Getting Started page contains links to several documents that give you a conceptual foundation for developing with ArcObjects.

The ArcObjects and COM topic covers basic COM and ArcObjects terminology. It can be used as a quick reference for beginning COM programmers because it defines many terms and concepts related to COM programming.

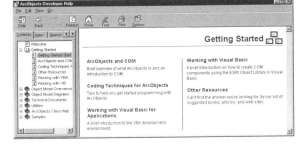

Some of the documents reached through the Getting Started page cover technical topics discussed in Chapter 2, 'Developing with ArcObjects'.

The Coding Techniques for ArcObjects topic describes how to use ArcObjects in VBA; it is a quick reference for beginner to intermediate-level ArcObjects programmers because it explains how to navigate the ArcObjects library and describes the general syntax, structures, and keywords required for COM programming in VBA.

The Working with Visual Basic for Applications topic describes how and where to write custom VBA macros inside ArcMap and ArcCatalog. You can learn about application-level variables and how to integrate VBA macros to control ArcMap and ArcCatalog. You can also learn where to write and save your code in the VBA environment.

The Working with Visual Basic topic is a general discussion about topics related to working with ArcObjects outside of the VBA environment. To get an overview of how to create an ActiveX DLL in VB, reference internal ArcObjects and start ArcMap from an external client.

The Other Resources topic links you to a page that lists recommended COM- and VBA-related books.

Object model overviews

The Object Model Overviews Start Page contains links to textual descriptions for each object model diagram.

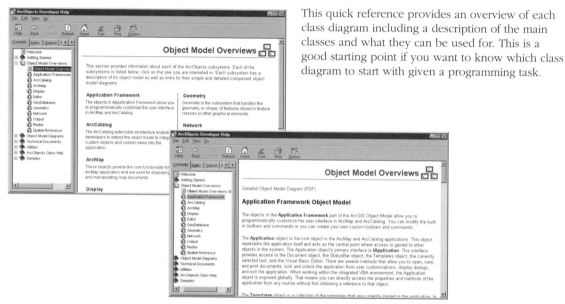

This quick reference provides an overview of each class diagram including a description of the main classes and what they can be used for. This is a good starting point if you want to know which class diagram to start with given a programming task.

Reading object model diagrams

The Diagrams Start Page in the Object Model Diagrams topic contains a list of links to each detailed object model diagram in PDF format.

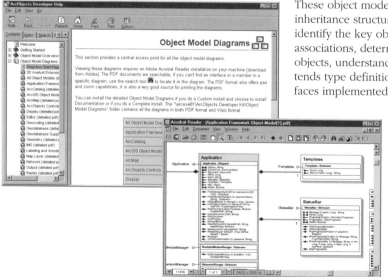

These object model diagrams visually present the inheritance structure of ArcObjects so that you can identify the key objects, see which objects have associations, determine which objects create other objects, understand how interface inheritance extends type definitions, and find the full list of interfaces implemented by a coclass.

Before studying these object model diagrams, you should read the object model diagram overview descriptions so that you understand the context of that package within the ArcObjects framework.

Accessing technical documents

The Technical Documents Start Page provides links to white papers and other technical documents.

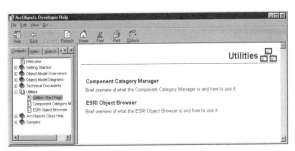

You can read these documents to gain background information and knowledge on specific technical concepts. This resource is recommended for all programmers.

Finding utility programs

The Utilities Start Page contains several programs useful to developers.

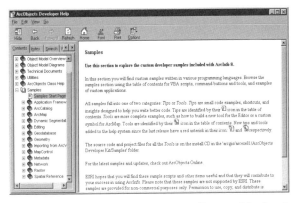

The Components Category Manager lets you associate software components that you have created and compiled into DLLs into the ArcObjects component categories for objects such as commands, snap agents, and extensions. This lets you integrate your custom components within the system.

The ESRI Object Browser is a custom-enhanced object browser that lets you search and locate ArcObjects coclasses, classes, interfaces, and enumerations. For more information, see Chapter 2, 'Developing with ArcObjects'.

These tools are useful for intermediate to advanced ArcObjects developers. The Visual Basic add-ins are discussed further in this section.

Browsing the ArcObjects Component Help

The ArcObjects Component Help system is a comprehensive online reference to all of ArcObjects. This is a vital resource for all ArcObjects programmers.

This system helps you find any given interface, coclass, or constant alphabetically. You can also easily find all the objects that implement a given interface.

Using developer samples

The Samples Page documents the structure of the sample code.

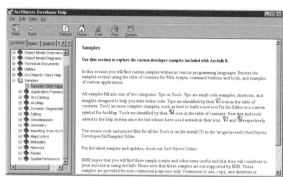

This page provides links to examples of how to use an assortment of ArcObjects classes and interfaces to accomplish a given task.

Tip samples provide "cut and paste" style code snippets, while tools provide more complete examples that generally require compilation and registration. These samples invite you to explore the interplay of interfaces and classes to solve real-world problems. These samples are an essential resource for all ArcObjects developers.

Finding objects alphabetically

The Index tab lets you search for objects by keywords and find all ArcObjects classes and interfaces through a tree view.

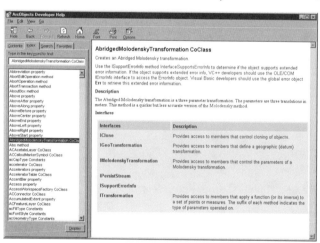

Using this tree view, you can display detailed information on classes, interfaces, methods, properties, and events.

Searching by keywords

The Search tab lets you type in a keyword and find all the documents in the ArcObjects Developer Help system containing that keyword.

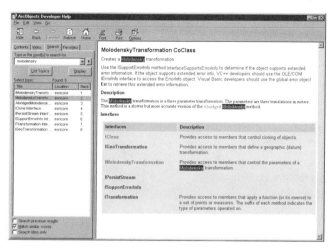

You can sort the list of documents by title, location, and rank. Selecting a document displays it in the contents view, with the keywords highlighted.

Using the Search tab is an effective way to quickly browse the object documentation and gain familiarity with ArcObjects.

Saving favorite documents

The Favorites tab lets you store and access links to documents of interest to you.

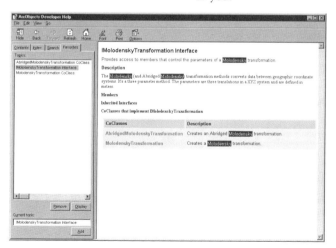

This tab has buttons that let you set and save shortcuts to useful help topics.

Reading the object model diagrams

Object model key

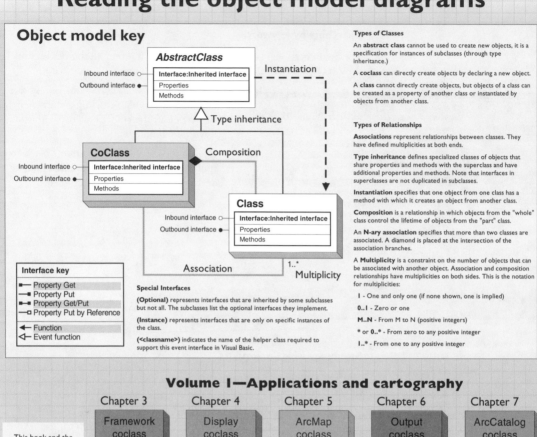

Types of Classes

An **abstract class** cannot be used to create new objects, it is a specification for instances of subclasses (through type inheritance.)

A **coclass** can directly create objects by declaring a new object.

A **class** cannot directly create objects, but objects of a class can be created as a property of another class or instantiated by objects from another class.

Types of Relationships

Associations represent relationships between classes. They have defined multiplicities at both ends.

Type inheritance defines specialized classes of objects that share properties and methods with the superclass and have additional properties and methods. Note that interfaces in superclasses are not duplicated in subclasses.

Instantiation specifies that one object from one class has a method with which it creates an object from another class.

Composition is a relationship in which objects from the "whole" class control the lifetime of objects from the "part" class.

An **N-ary association** specifies that more than two classes are associated. A diamond is placed at the intersection of the association branches.

A **Multiplicity** is a constraint on the number of objects that can be associated with another object. Association and composition relationships have multiplicities on both sides. This is the notation for multiplicities:

I - One and only one (if none shown, one is implied)

0..I - Zero or one

M..N - From M to N (positive integers)

* or 0..* - From zero to any positive integer

I..* - From one to any positive integer

Special Interfaces

(Optional) represents interfaces that are inherited by some subclasses but not all. The subclasses list the optional interfaces they implement.

(Instance) represents interfaces that are only on specific instances of the class.

(<classname>) indicates the name of the helper class required to support this event interface in Visual Basic.

Volume 1—Applications and cartography

This book and the inserted ArcGIS object model diagrams use this color code to denote the coclasses, classes, and abstract classes in the ArcObjects subsystems.

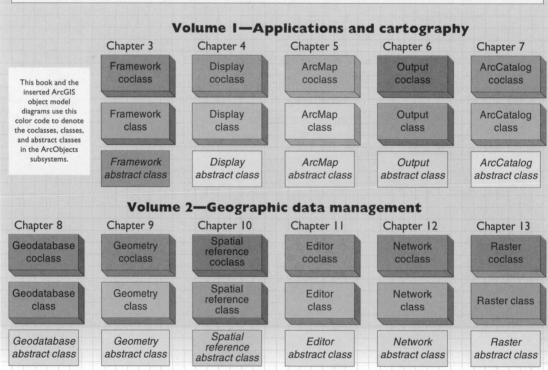

The diagram notation used in this book and the ArcObjects object model diagrams are based on the UML notation, an industry-diagramming standard for object-oriented analysis and design, with some modifications for documenting COM-specific constructs.

The object model diagrams are an important supplement to the information you receive in object browsers. The development environment, Visual Basic or other, lists all of the many classes and members but does not show the structure of those classes. These diagrams complete your understanding of the ArcObjects components.

Classes and objects

There are three types of classes shown in the UML diagrams: abstract classes, coclasses, and classes.

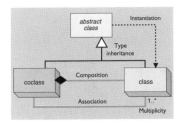

A *coclass* represents objects that you can directly create using the object declaration syntax in your development environment. In Visual Basic, this is written with the *Dim pFoo As New FooObject* syntax.

A *class* cannot directly create new objects, but objects of a class can be created as a property of another class or by functions from another class.

An *abstract class* cannot be used to create new objects, but it is a specification for subclasses. An example is that a "line" could be an abstract class for "primary line" and "secondary line" classes.

Relationships

Among abstract classes, coclasses, and classes, there are several types of class relationships possible.

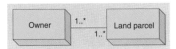

In this diagram, an owner can own one or many land parcels, and a land parcel can be owned by one or many owners.

Associations represent relationships between classes. They have defined multiplicities at both ends.

A *Multiplicity* is a constraint on the number of objects that can be associated with another object. This is the notation for multiplicities:

1—One and only one. Showing this multiplicity is optional; if none is shown, "1" is implied.

0..1—Zero or one

M..N—From M to N (positive integers)

* or 0..*—From zero to any positive integer

1..*—From one to any positive integer

Type inheritance

Type inheritance defines specialized classes that share properties and methods with the superclass and have additional properties and methods.

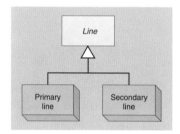

This diagram shows that a primary line (creatable class) and secondary line (creatable class) are types of a line (abstract class).

Instantiation

Instantiation specifies that one object from one class has a method with which it creates an object from another class.

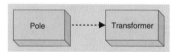

A pole object might have a method to create a transformer object.

Composition

Composition is a stronger form of aggregation in which objects from the "whole" class control the lifetime of objects from the "part" class.

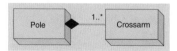

A pole contains one or many crossarms. In this design, a crossarm cannot be recycled when the pole is removed. The pole object controls the lifetime of the crossarm object.

The ESRI Object Browser lets you explore the structure of ArcObjects. It is a generic tool that ESRI created to address certain limitations of standard object browsers, such as the Microsoft OLEView tool or the Microsoft Visual Basic object browser.

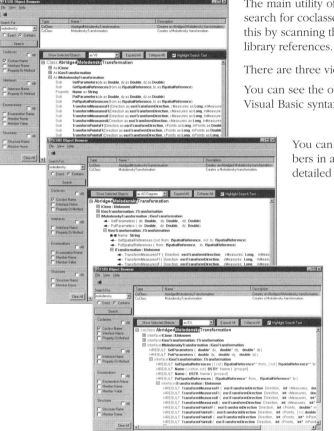

The main utility of the ESRI Object Browser is that it lets you search for coclasses that contain a specified interface. It does this by scanning the type libraries you've selected for object library references.

There are three views for the selected objects.

You can see the objects and their interfaces and members in Visual Basic syntax.

You can also view the objects, interfaces, and members in a style consistent with the notation of the detailed ArcObjects object model diagrams.

Developers using Visual C++ and other languages besides Visual Basic will find the most precise type definitions in the IDL view of the coclasses, interfaces, and members.

Using other languages, such as Visual Basic and Visual C++, is covered in Chapter 2, 'Developing with ArcObjects'.

VBA is available in ArcMap, ArcCatalog, and ArcScene applications. The examples in this quick-start tutorial all work within ArcMap, but the process of creating macros and commands for the other applications is the same.

You can use a variety of development languages with ArcObjects, but the easiest and quickest one to learn is included with your ArcGIS application, VBA. This chapter has many code examples, all of which can be easily executed from within the VBA environment.

What follows is a quick overview that illustrates the steps you will be taking when working with the samples later in this chapter. In this short tutorial you will learn how to add a toolbar to ArcMap, create a macro and execute it, add a command button to a toolbar, and create a tool that will allow you to interact with the display canvas.

The respective ArcGIS application user guides show how to carry out many of the customization tasks you want to accomplish without writing a single line of code. This tutorial provides a quick, guided tour of some of those same key tasks; details and explanations are left for later so that you can start to work as quickly as possible.

Let's get started.

1. To start this tutorial, click the Windows Start button, point to Programs, point to ArcGIS, and click ArcMap.

2. In the startup dialog box, click Start using ArcMap.

3. Add some sample data or your own data to the map.

Showing and hiding toolbars using the Customize dialog box

1. Click the Tools menu and click Customize.

   The Customize dialog box appears.

   You can also double-click any unoccupied area of any toolbar to display the Customize dialog box.

2. If it is not visible, click the Toolbars tab.

   The presence or absence of a check mark next to the toolbar name indicates its visible state.

3. Check and uncheck the check boxes.

Creating a new toolbar

1. In the Toolbars tab of the Customize dialog box, click New.

2. In the dialog box that appears, specify Chapter One Examples as the name of the new toolbar or use the default setting.

3. Store the toolbar in the document by changing the name of the Save in dropdown list from Normal.mxt to Untitled or the name of the current project.

4. Click OK.

The Customize dialog box

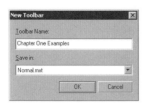

The New Toolbar dialog box

The newly created toolbar appears near the top of the application window.

Adding buttons to a toolbar

1. Make sure the toolbar you just created, Chapter One Examples, is visible.

2. If it is not visible, display the Customize dialog box.

3. Click the Commands tab of the Customize dialog box.

4. Select the Pan/Zoom category from the Categories list at the left of the dialog box.

Dragging a toolbar

5. Scroll to the bottom of the Commands list at the right of the dialog box.

6. Select the Zoom in command and drag it to the Chapter One Examples toolbar. Release the command when the arrow cursor with a small box below it appears.

Your Chapter One Examples toolbar might look like this.

7. Continue adding commands from the Pan/Zoom category until you have your own version of the built-in Tools toolbar.

   Note that you may switch to other categories to select commands.

8. Resize the toolbar so that its width allows the display of two commands per row.

   Note that you can dock the toolbar or drag it to any of the toolbar drop sites on the application window.

Renaming a toolbar

1. In the Toolbars tab, click the name of the toolbar whose name you want to change.

   In this case, select Chapter One Examples.

My Own Tools toolbar

2. Click the Rename button.

3. In the dialog box that appears, specify My Own Tools as the new name.

   Note that you can only rename toolbars you've created.

4. Click OK.

   If you decide not to rename the toolbar, click Cancel.

Removing buttons from a toolbar

1. Make sure the toolbar you just renamed, My Own Tools, is visible.

2. If it is not visible, display the Customize dialog box.

3. Drag some of the commands off the toolbar.

Even though you've removed the buttons from the toolbar, they are still available in the Customize dialog box.

Adding a menu to a toolbar

1. Make sure the My Own Tools toolbar is visible.

2. If it is not visible, display the Customize dialog box.

3. Click the Commands tab and choose the Menus category from the Categories list on the left-hand side of the dialog box.

4. In the Commands list at the right-hand side of the dialog box, click Selection.

5. Drag and drop it to the left of the Zoom In button on the My Own Tools toolbar.

Selection menu on the My Own Tools toolbar

6. Click Close in the Customize dialog box.

7. Click Selection on the My Own Tools toolbar and note the menu that appears.

Saving changes to a template

You can save your work to a document or template. Changes saved to a document are specific to the document, whereas changes saved to a template will be reflected in all documents based on the template.

1. Click the File menu and click Save As.

2. Navigate to the Templates folder of the <installation directory>\bin folder.

3. Click the Create New Folder button.

   Type a new name for the folder and double-click it. You'll see the folder name as a tab the next time you create a document from a template.

4. Type the template name, click ArcMap Templates (*.mxt) from the Save as type dropdown menu, then click Save.

WRITING MACROS IN VBA

You can use the VBA integrated development environment to create macros to help you automate tasks you perform repeatedly or to extend the application's built-in functionality.

Creating a macro

With the Visual Basic Editor, you can edit macros, copy macros from one module to another, rename the modules that store the macros, or rename the macros.

1. Click the Tools menu, point to Macros, then click Macros.

The Macros dialog box

2. In the Macros dialog, type MyZoomIn in the Macro name text box and click Create.

The application creates a new module named Module1 and stubs in the Sub procedure.

3. Enter the following code for *MyZoomIn:*

```
Sub MyZoomIn()
    '
    ' macro: MyZoomIn
    '
    Dim pDoc As IMxDocument
    Dim pEnv As IEnvelope
    Set pDoc = ThisDocument
    Set pEnv = pDoc.ActiveView.Extent
    pEnv.Expand 0.5, 0.5, True
    pDoc.ActiveView.Extent = pEnv
    pDoc.ActiveView.Refresh
End Sub
```

The first line of the macro declares a variable that represents the ArcMap document. At this point, we won't go into the coding techniques that are used with the ArcInfo COM-based object model. These techniques are discussed in greater detail in Chapter 2, 'Developing with ArcObjects'.

The second line declares a variable that represents a rectangle with sides parallel to a coordinate system defining the extent of the data. You'll use *pEnv* to define the visible bounds of the map.

The predefined variable, *ThisDocument*, is the *IDocument* interface to the *MxDocument* object that represents the ArcMap document.

The *ActiveView* property provides an *IActiveView* interface that links the document data to the current screen display of that data.

By reducing the size of the envelope that represents the extent of the map, the macro zooms in on the map's features once the screen display is refreshed.

4. Switch back to ArcMap by clicking the File menu, clicking Close, and clicking Return to ArcMap.

5. Click the Tools menu, point to Macros, then click Macros.

6. Select the *Module1.MyZoomIn* macro and click Run.

   The display zooms in.

Adding a macro to a toolbar

You'll want convenient access to the macros you write. You can add a macro to built-in toolbars or toolbars you've created.

1. Click the Tools menu and click Customize.

2. In the Toolbars tab, ensure that the toolbar you created is visible.

3. Click the Commands tab and select the Macros category.

The Customize dialog box

4. Click the name of your project in the Save in dropdown menu.

   The commands list to the right of the dialog box lists Project.Module1.MyZoomIn.

5. Drag the macro name to the My Own Tools toolbar you created.

   The macro appears with a default icon.

6. To change its properties, right-click the icon.

7. In the context menu that appears, click Change Button Image and choose a button from the palette of icons.

8. Close the Customize dialog box.

9. Click the button to run the macro.

Invoking the Visual Basic Editor directly

As an alternative to the Create button in the Macros dialog box, you can navigate directly to the Visual Basic Editor and create procedures on your own. In this section, you'll create a macro named *MyZoomOut* in the *Module1* module that will zoom out from the display. You can use the same code that you used for *MyZoomIn*, with only a minor modification to one line.

1. Press Alt+F11, which is the Visual Basic Editor keyboard accelerator.

2. Click Project Explorer in the Visual Basic Editor View menu.

3. In the Project Explorer, click the Project entry, then Modules, then Module1.

4. In the Code Window, copy the *MyZoomIn* code from the beginning of the Sub to the End Sub.

5. Paste the *MyZoomIn* Sub code below the existing code.

6. Change the name of the copied Sub to *MyZoomOut*.

7. Change the line:

   ```
   pEnv.Expand 0.5, 0.5, True
   ```
   to:
   ```
   pEnv.Expand 2.0, 2.0, True
   ```

8. Follow steps 1–9 of the 'Adding a macro to a toolbar' section of the tutorial to add and run your second macro.

Getting help in the Code Window

The two macros you've just completed perform operations similar to the Fixed Zoom In and Fixed Zoom Out commands on the Tools toolbar. You didn't really add any new functionality, but you've perhaps learned something about the object model and how to start to write some useful code. You can learn more about the methods with which you've worked by making use of the ArcObjects Class Help that's available in the Object Browser or in the Code Window.

1. Click the Tools menu, point to Macros, then click Visual Basic Editor.

2. Locate the *Module1* module. In the *MyZoomIn* Sub, click the method name *Expand* in the line:

   ```
   pEnv.Expand 0.5, 0.5, True
   ```

3. Press F1.

The ArcObjects Class Help window displays the help topic for *Expand*. In addition to ArcObjects Help, consult the ArcObjects Developer Help in the ArcGIS program group for object model diagrams, samples, tips, and tricks.

Calling built-in commands

If you've read any of the ArcGIS user guides, you know that the code you'll be writing will add functionality to what's already a rich environment. There may be instances in which you want to make use of several built-in commands executed in sequence or combine built-in commands with your own code.

Later you will learn that in ArcObjects many things are given unique identifiers.

Calling existing commands involves working with the *ArcID* module. Using the *Find* method, the code locates the unique identifier (UID) of the command in the *ArcID* module. If you want to look at the *ArcID* module in greater detail, it's in the Normal template of your application.

The Name of a command in the ArcID module can be derived using the following formula: Category In Customize Categories List + "_" + Command Caption in Customize Commands List. Any spaces are removed from the name.

The following steps outline how to write a macro that calls existing commands.

1. Click the Tools menu, point to Macros, then click Visual Basic Editor.

2. In the *Module1* module, create a Sub procedure with the following code:

   ```
   Sub FullExtentPlus()
     '
     ' macro: FullExtentPlus
     '
     Dim intAns As Integer
     Dim pItem As ICommandItem
     With ThisDocument.CommandBars
       Set pItem = .Find(ArcID.PanZoom_FullExtent)
       pItem.Execute
       intAns = MsgBox("Zoom to previous extent?", vbYesNo)
       If intAns = vbYes Then
         Set pItem = .Find(ArcID.PanZoom_ZoomToLastExtentBack)
         pItem.Execute
       End If
     End With
   End Sub
   ```

3. Add the *FullExtentPlus* macro to a toolbar or menu.

4. Run the *MyZoomIn* macro and then run *FullExtentPlus*.

Creating a command in VBA

Up to this point in the tutorial, you've only created macros. A command is similar to a macro but allows more customization in the way that it interacts with the user and provides ToolTips, descriptions, and so on. Once invoked, a command usually performs some direct action without user intervention. A command is a type of UIControls. You can read more about all the UIControls in Chapter 3, 'Customizing the user interface'.

The New UIControl dialog box

1. Click the Tools menu and click Customize.

2. In the Customize dialog box, click the Commands tab and change the Save in dropdown menu to the name of your project or to Untitled.

3. In the Categories list, select UIControls.

4. Click New UIControl.

5. In the dialog box that appears, choose UIButtonControl as the UIControl Type, then click Create and Edit.

Adding code for the UIToolControl

The following code assumes the UIButtonControl was named UIButtonControl1. If another name was used because this name was already in use, make the necessary changes to the code snippets.

The application adds an entry in the Object Box for the *UIButtonControl* and stubs in an event procedure for the *UIButtonControl's Click* event. You'll add code to this event to zoom the display to the extents of the dataset.

1. Add the following code to the *Click* event:

```
Private Sub UIButtonControl1_Click()
  Dim pDoc As IMxDocument
  Set pDoc = ThisDocument

  pDoc.ActiveView.Extent = pDoc.ActiveView.FullExtent
  pDoc.ActiveView.Refresh
End Sub
```

So far these is no difference to the macros you developed earlier. You will now add a ToolTip and message for the command.

2. Click Message in the Procedure combo box. This creates a stub function, to which you should add the following code:

```
Private Function UIButtonControl1_Message() As String
  UIButtonControl1_Message = _
    "Zooms the display to the full dataset extents"
End Function
```

3. Click ToolTip in the Procedure combo box. This creates a stub function, to which you should add the following code:

```
Private Function UIButtonControl1_ToolTip() As String
  UIButtonControl1_ToolTip= "Full Extent"
End Function
```

4. Click the Visual Basic Editor's File menu, click Close, then click Return to ArcMap.

5. Click the Tools menu, click Customize, then click the Commands tab.

6. In the Customize dialog box, click the Commands tab and change the Save in dropdown menu to the name of your project or to Untitled.

7. In the Categories list, choose UIControls and drag the *UIButtonControl* you created to a toolbar. Close the Customize dialog box.

Try the new command by zooming in on the map and clicking the button. Also, test the ToolTip and description properties. The ToolTip will display if you pause the cursor over the button, while the description will display in the status bar as the cursor moves over the button.

Creating a tool in VBA

Up to this point in the tutorial, you've only created commands, either with macros or *UIButtonControls*. As you've seen in the built-in toolbars and menus, users interact with other controls in addition to commands. As part of the customization environment, you can add sophisticated controls to toolbars and menus. In this section of the tutorial, you'll create a *UIToolControl* to interact with the ArcMap display.

1. Click the Tools menu and click Customize.

2. Click the Commands tab and change the Save in combo box to the name of your project or Untitled.

3. Choose UIControls from the Categories list.

4. Click New UIControl.

5. In the dialog box that appears, choose UIToolControl as the UIControl Type, then click Create and Edit.

Adding code for the *UIToolControl*

The following code assumes the UIToolControl was named UIToolControl1. If another name was used because this name was already in use, make the necessary changes to the code snippets.

The application adds an entry in the Object Box for the *UIToolControl* and stubs in an event procedure for the *UIToolControl*'s *Select* event. You won't add any code to the *Select* event procedure at this time; instead, select the *MouseDown* event in the Procedures combo box on the right-hand side of the Code Window. You'll add code to this event to enable you to drag a rectangle on the screen display; the application will zoom to the rectangle's extent.

1. Add the following code to the *MouseDown* event procedure:

```
Dim pDoc As IMxDocument
Dim pScreenDisp As IScreenDisplay
Dim pRubber As IRubberBand
Dim pEnv As IEnvelope
Set pDoc = ThisDocument
Set pScreenDisp = pDoc.ActiveView.ScreenDisplay
Set pRubber = New RubberEnvelope
```

```
Set pEnv = pRubber.TrackNew(pScreenDisp, Nothing)
pDoc.ActiveView.Extent = pEnv
pDoc.ActiveView.Refresh
```

The key line of the procedure is the one that contains the *TrackNew* method, which rubber bands a new shape on the specified screen. The code uses the *Envelope* object that the method returns to set the new extent for the map.

When you selected the *MouseDown* event procedure to add code to it, you may have noticed that *UIToolControl* supports several other events. The customization framework handles many of the details of coding for you, so you only have to code the event procedures you need. Later in Chapter 2, 'Developing with ArcObjects', you'll find that this is in contrast to what is required when implementing a tool as part of an ActiveX® DLL. A tool is not appropriate for all occasions. You can control when a tool or command is available by adding code to its Enabled event procedure.

2. Add the following code to the *UIToolControl1's Enabled* event procedure:

```
Private Function UIToolControl1_Enabled() As Boolean
  Dim pDoc As IMxDocument
  Set pDoc = ThisDocument
  UIToolControl1_Enabled = (pDoc.FocusMap.LayerCount <> 0)
End Function
```

3. Add the following code to the *CursorID* event procedure to control the cursor that appears when you use the tool:

```
Private Function UIToolControl1_CursorID() As Variant
  UIToolControl1_CursorID = 3 ' Crosshair
End Function
```

4. Add a ToolTip and message for the tool control as you did for *UIButtonControls* in the steps above.

5. Click the Visual Basic Editor File menu, click Close, then click Return to ArcMap.

6. Click the Tools menu, click Customize, then click the Commands tab.

7. In the Customize dialog box, click the Commands tab and change the Save in dropdown menu to the name of your project, or to Untitled.

8. In the Categories list, choose UIControls and drag the *UIToolControl* that you created to a toolbar. Close the Customize dialog box.

Try out the tool by selecting it and dragging a rectangle on the display. You can also see the *Enabled* event procedure code in action if you remove all layers from the map. Once you add data back to the map, the tool will be enabled again.

Changing button properties

You can change the image on any toolbar button or menu command, except for a button that displays a list or a menu when you click it. You can display text, an icon, or both on a toolbar button. You can also display either an icon and text or text only on a menu command. You can change the image that represents the tool and other properties by right-clicking the button.

1. Right-click any toolbar and click Customize in the context menu that appears. Context menus are available throughout ArcMap, ArcCatalog, and ArcScene. Click the right mouse button to determine whether a context menu is available.

2. Right-click the button whose properties you want to change.

3. In the context menu that appears, click Change Button Image and choose an image. The image you chose appears on the face of the button.

4. Close the Customize dialog box.

Congratulations! You now have the basic knowledge to tackle the example code samples later in this chapter. Along with each of these code samples is a hint about where best to develop the code, either in a macro, command, or tool.

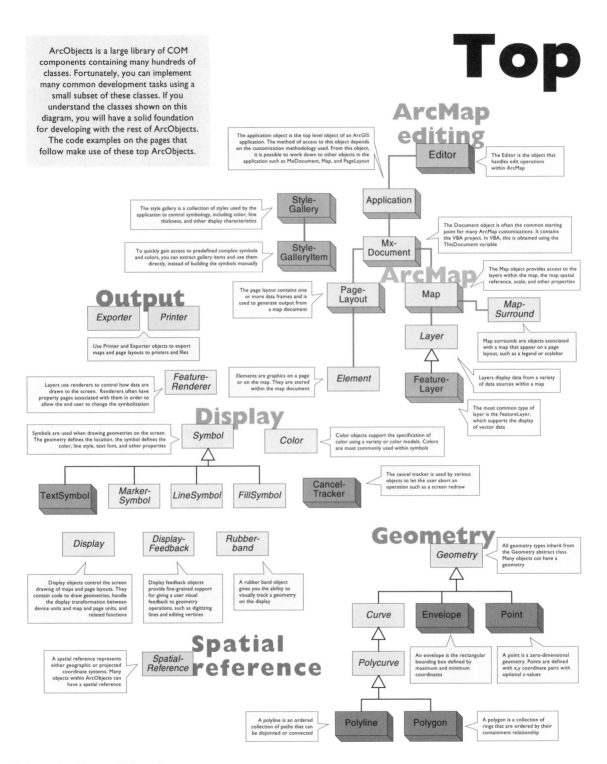

Top

ArcObjects is a large library of COM components containing many hundreds of classes. Fortunately, you can implement many common development tasks using a small subset of these classes. If you understand the classes shown on this diagram, you will have a solid foundation for developing with the rest of ArcObjects. The code examples on the pages that follow make use of these top ArcObjects.

ArcMap editing

The application object is the top level object of an ArcGIS application. The method of access to this object depends on the customization methodology used. From this object, it is possible to work down to other objects in the application such as MxDocument, Map, and PageLayout

Editor

The Editor is the object that handles edit operations within ArcMap

The style gallery is a collection of styles used by the application to control symbology, including color, line thickness, and other display characteristics

Style-Gallery

Application

The Document object is often the common starting point for many ArcMap customizations. It contains the VBA project. In VBA, this is obtained using the ThisDocument variable

To quickly gain access to predefined complex symbols and colors, you can extract gallery items and use them directly, instead of building the symbols manually

Style-GalleryItem

Mx-Document

The Map object provides access to the layers within the map, the map spatial reference, scale, and other properties

Output

Exporter

Printer

Use Printer and Exporter objects to export maps and page layouts to printers and files

The page layout contains one or more data frames and is used to generate output from a map document

Page-Layout

Map

ArcMap

Map-Surround

Map surrounds are objects associated with a map that appear on a page layout, such as a legend or scalebar

Layer

Layers use renderers to control how data are drawn to the screen. Renderers often have property pages associated with them in order to allow the end user to change the symbolization

Feature-Renderer

Elements are graphics on a page or on the map. They are stored within the map document

Element

Feature-Layer

Layers display data from a variety of data sources within a map

The most common type of layer is the FeatureLayer, which supports the display of vector data

Display

Symbols are used when drawing geometries on the screen. The geometry defines the location, the symbol defines the color, line style, text font, and other properties

Symbol

Color

Color objects support the specification of color using a variety or color models. Colors are most commonly used within symbols

TextSymbol

Marker-Symbol

LineSymbol

FillSymbol

Cancel-Tracker

The cancel tracker is used by various objects to let the user abort an operation such as a screen redraw

Display

Display-Feedback

Rubber-band

Geometry

Geometry

All geometry types inherit from the Geometry abstract class. Many objects can have a geometry

Display objects control the screen drawing of maps and page layouts. They contain code to draw geometries, handle the display transformation between device units and map and page units, and related functions

Display feedback objects provide fine-grained support for giving a user visual feedback to geometry operations, such as digitizing lines and editing vertices

A rubber band object gives you the ability to visually track a geometry on the display

Curve

Envelope

Point

Spatial reference

A spatial reference represents either geographic or projected coordinate systems. Many objects within ArcObjects can have a spatial reference

Spatial-Reference

Polycurve

An envelope is the rectangular bounding box defined by maximum and minimum coordinates

A point is a zero-dimensional geometry. Points are defined with x,y coordinate pairs with optional z-values

A polyline is an ordered collection of paths that can be disjointed or connected

Polyline

Polygon

A polygon is a collection of rings that are ordered by their containment relationship

ArcObjects

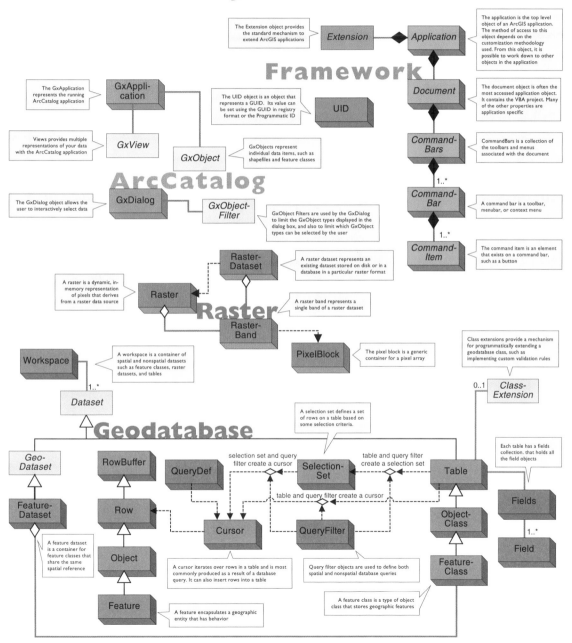

The Extension object provides the standard mechanism to extend ArcGIS applications

Extension

Application

The application is the top level object of an ArcGIS application. The method of access to this object depends on the customization methodology used. From this object, it is possible to work down to other objects in the application

Framework

The GxApplication represents the running ArcCatalog application

GxApplication

The UID object is an object that represents a GUID. Its value can be set using the GUID in registry format or the Programmatic ID

UID

Document

The document object is often the most accessed application object. It contains the VBA project. Many of the other properties are application specific

Views provides multiple representations of your data with the ArcCatalog application

GxView

GxObject

GxObjects represent individual data items, such as shapefiles and feature classes

Command-Bars

CommandBars is a collection of the toolbars and menus associated with the document

ArcCatalog

The GxDialog object allows the user to interactively select data

GxDialog

GxObject-Filter

GxObject Filters are used by the GxDialog to limit the GxObject types displayed in the dialog box, and also to limit which GxObject types can be selected by the user

1..*

Command-Bar

A command bar is a toolbar, menubar, or context menu

1..*

Command-Item

The command item is an element that exists on a command bar, such as a button

Raster-Dataset

A raster dataset represents an existing dataset stored on disk or in a database in a particular raster format

A raster is a dynamic, in-memory representation of pixels that derives from a raster data source

Raster

A raster band represents a single band of a raster dataset

Raster

Raster-Band

PixelBlock

The pixel block is a generic container for a pixel array

Class extensions provide a mechanism for programmatically extending a geodatabase class, such as implementing custom validation rules

Workspace

A workspace is a container of spatial and nonspatial datasets such as feature classes, raster datasets, and tables

1..*

Dataset

0..1

Class-Extension

A selection set defines a set of rows on a table based on some selection criteria.

Geodatabase

Each table has a fields collection. that holds all the field objects

Geo-Dataset

RowBuffer

QueryDef

selection set and query filter create a cursor

Selection-Set

table and query filter create a selection set

Table

Feature-Dataset

Row

Fields

A feature dataset is a container for feature classes that share the same spatial reference

table and query filter create a cursor

Cursor

QueryFilter

Object-Class

1..*

Object

A cursor iterates over rows in a table and is most commonly produced as a result of a database query. It can also insert rows into a table

Query filter objects are used to define both spatial and nonspatial database queries

Feature-Class

Field

Feature

A feature encapsulates a geographic entity that has behavior

A feature class is a type of object class that stores geographic features

Reading the illustrated code samples

The illustrated code samples in this section show you the fundamentals of programming with COM components in ArcObjects. Start by entering the VBA environment in ArcMap or ArcCatalog and type in the code. Step through the code in the VBA debugger. Look at these pages and study the relationships between coclasses and interfaces. A careful reading of the samples in this section gives you all the important concepts you need for developing with ArcObjects, as well as an introduction to the most important ArcObjects components.

The interface

IFeatureClass : IObjectClass

- AreaField: IField
- FeatureClassID: Long
- FeatureDataset: IFeatureDataset
- FeatureType: esriFeatureType
- LengthField: IField
- ShapeFieldName: String
- ShapeType: tagesriGeometryType

- CreateFeature: IFeature
- CreateFeatureBuffer: IFeatureBuffer
- FeatureCount (in QueryFilter: IQueryFilter) : Long
- GetFeature (in ID: Long) : IFeature
- GetFeatures (in fids: Variant, in Recycling: Boolean) : IFeatureCursor
- Insert (in useBuffering: Boolean) : IFeatureCursor
- Search (in Filter: IQueryFilter, in Recycling: Boolean) : IFeatureCursor
- Select (in QueryFilter: IQueryFilter, in selType: esriSelectionType, in selOption: esriSelectionOption, in selectionContainer: IWorkspace) : ISelectionSet
- Update (in Filter: IQueryFilter, in Recycling: Boolean) : IFeatureCursor

An interface is a specification of properties and methods. Many coclasses can implement the same interface. Interfaces allow a high degree of interoperability and shared behavior among a set of objects.

AreaField is a return property of type *IField. FeatureClassID* is of type *long.*

The *CreateFeature* method creates an object of type *IFeature. FeatureCount* takes in a query filter and returns a *long.*

QueryInterface

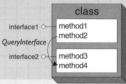

QueryInterface is a method in the *IUnknown* interface, which all COM objects inherit from. This method lets you query for and navigate to methods in other interfaces implemented by an object.

Type inheritance

Element

IClone
IElement
IElementProperties
IPersist
IPersistStream
IPropertySupport

IElement : IUnknown

- Geometry: IGeometry
- Locked: Boolean
- SelectionTracker:ISelectionTracker

- Activate (in Display: IDisplay)
- Deactivate
- Draw (in Display: IDisplay, in trackCancel: ITrackCancel)
- HitTest (in X: Double, in Y: Double, in Tolerance: Double) : Boolean
- QueryBounds (in Display: IDisplay, in Bounds: IEnvelope)
- QueryOutline (in Display: IDisplay, in Outline: IPolygon)

The object model diagrams reveal a structure not evident in standard object browsers. Shown here is an abstract class, *Element*, with six interfaces. The *IElement* interface is shown because a code sample made a call to it.

Graphic-Element

IGraphicElement
ITransform2D

A *GraphicElement* is an abstract class that specifies the two interfaces shown here as well as the six interfaces on the *Element* abstract class.

Interface inheritance

IFrameElement:IUnknown

- Background: IBackground
- Border: IBorder
- DraftMode: Boolean
- Object: Variant
- Thumbnail: Long

IMapFrame and *IMapSurroundFrame* inherit from *IFrameElement*. All properties and methods of *IFrameElement* are accessible to the developer who accesses *IMapFrame* or *IMapSurroundFrame.*

IMapFrame : IFrameElement

- Container: IGraphicsContainer
- ExtentType: esriExtentTypeEnum
- LocatorRectangleCount: Long
- Map: IMap
- MapBounds: IEnvelope
- MapScale: Double

- AddLocatorRectangle (in Locator: ILocatorRectangle)
- CreateSurroundFrame (in CLSID: IUID, in optionalStyle: IMapSurround) : IMapSurroundFrame
- LocatorRectangle (in Index: Long) : ILocatorRectangle
- RemoveAllLocatorRectangles
- RemoveLocatorRectangle (in Locator: ILocatorRectangle)

IMapSurroundFrame:IFrameElement

- MapFrame: IMapFrame
- MapSurround: IMapSurround

TextElement

IBoundsProperties
IElementEditVertices
IGroupSymbolElement
IPropertySupport
ITextElement
ITransformEvents

ITextElement : IUnknown

- ScaleText: Boolean
- Symbol: ITextSymbol
- Text: String

TextElement is a coclass that implements six interfaces in addition to the two from *GraphicElement* and six from *Element.*

This sample illustrates how to programmatically execute existing commands on command bars within ArcMap.

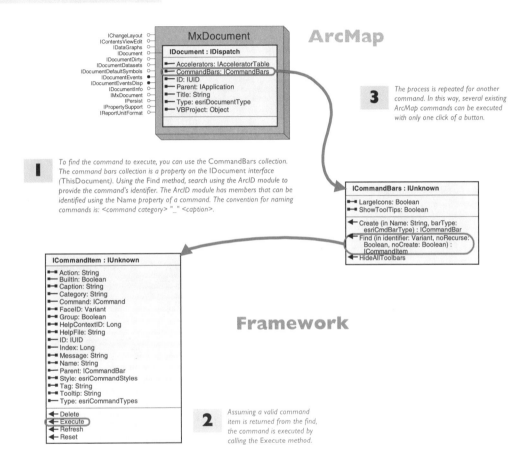

ArcMap

MxDocument

IDocument : IDispatch

IChangeLayout
IContentsViewEdit
IDataGraphs
IDocument
IDocumentDirty
IDocumentDatasets
IDocumentDefaultSymbols
IDocumentEvents
IDocumentEventsDisp
IDocumentInfo
IMxDocument
IPersist
IPropertySupport
IReportUnitFormat

- Accelerators: IAcceleratorTable
- CommandBars: ICommandBars
- ID: IUID
- Parent: IApplication
- Title: String
- Type: esriDocumentType
- VBProject: Object

3 The process is repeated for another command. In this way, several existing ArcMap commands can be executed with only one click of a button.

1 To find the command to execute, you can use the CommandBars collection. The command bars collection is a property on the IDocument interface (ThisDocument). Using the Find method, search using the ArcID module to provide the command's identifier. The ArcID module has members that can be identified using the Name property of a command. The convention for naming commands is: <command category> "_" <caption>.

ICommandBars : IUnknown

- LargeIcons: Boolean
- ShowToolTips: Boolean
- Create (in Name: String, barType: esriCmdBarType) : ICommandBar
- Find (in identifier: Variant, noRecurse: Boolean, noCreate: Boolean) : ICommandItem
- HideAllToolbars

ICommandItem : IUnknown

- Action: String
- BuiltIn: Boolean
- Caption: String
- Category: String
- Command: ICommand
- FaceID: Variant
- Group: Boolean
- HelpContextID: Long
- HelpFile: String
- ID: IUID
- Index: Long
- Message: String
- Name: String
- Parent: ICommandBar
- Style: esriCommandStyles
- Tag: String
- Tooltip: String
- Type: esriCommandTypes

- Delete
- Execute
- Refresh
- Reset

Framework

2 Assuming a valid command item is returned from the find, the command is executed by calling the Execute method.

Add this code to the Click event of a UIButtonControl in ArcMap.

```
Dim pCommandItem As ICommandItem
```

1
```
Set pCommandItem = ThisDocument.CommandBars.Find(ArcID.Query_ZoomToSelected)
If (pCommandItem Is Nothing) Then Exit Sub
```
2
```
pCommandItem.Execute
```

3
```
Set pCommandItem = ThisDocument.CommandBars.Find(ArcID.ReportObject_CreateReport)
If (pCommandItem Is Nothing) Then Exit Sub
pCommandItem.Execute
```

This sample uses a rubber banding line to obtain a digitized line geometry. With the geometry created, a symbol is created. The symbol is set as the current display symbol and the line is drawn. The color thickness and the style of the line symbol are set.

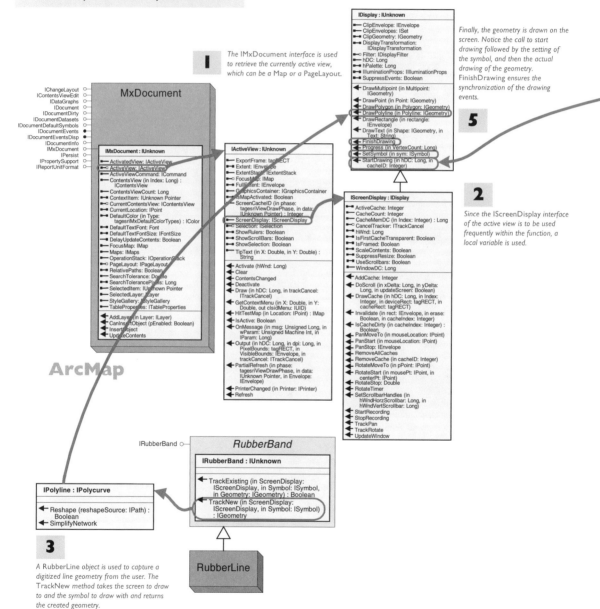

The IMxDocument interface is used to retrieve the currently active view, which can be a Map or a PageLayout.

Finally, the geometry is drawn on the screen. Notice the call to start drawing followed by the setting of the symbol, and then the actual drawing of the geometry. FinishDrawing ensures the synchronization of the drawing events.

Since the IScreenDisplay interface of the active view is to be used frequently within the function, a local variable is used.

A RubberLine object is used to capture a digitized line geometry from the user. The TrackNew method takes the screen to draw to and the symbol to draw with and returns the created geometry.

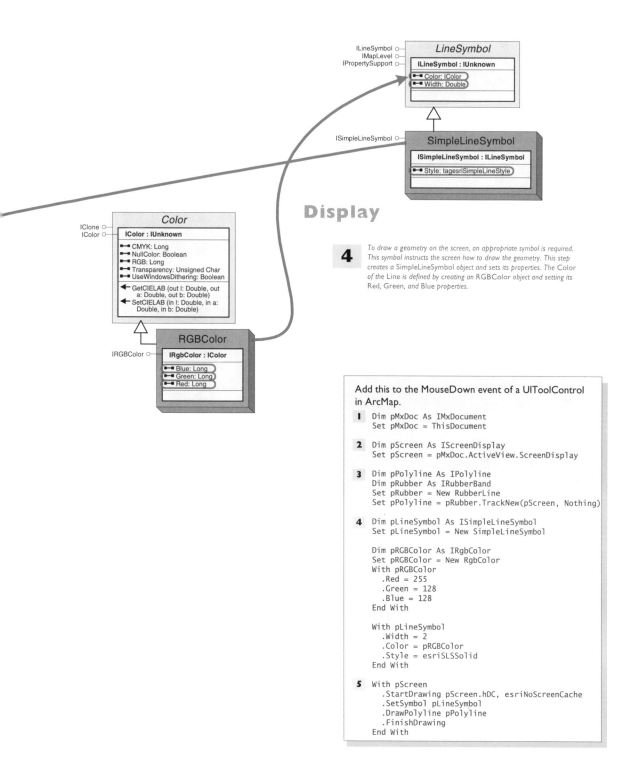

Display

4 To draw a geometry on the screen, an appropriate symbol is required. This symbol instructs the screen how to draw the geometry. This step creates a SimpleLineSymbol object and sets its properties. The Color of the Line is defined by creating an RGBColor object and setting its Red, Green, and Blue properties.

Add this to the MouseDown event of a UIToolControl in ArcMap.

```
1   Dim pMxDoc As IMxDocument
    Set pMxDoc = ThisDocument

2   Dim pScreen As IScreenDisplay
    Set pScreen = pMxDoc.ActiveView.ScreenDisplay

3   Dim pPolyline As IPolyline
    Dim pRubber As IRubberBand
    Set pRubber = New RubberLine
    Set pPolyline = pRubber.TrackNew(pScreen, Nothing)

4   Dim pLineSymbol As ISimpleLineSymbol
    Set pLineSymbol = New SimpleLineSymbol

    Dim pRGBColor As IRgbColor
    Set pRGBColor = New RgbColor
    With pRGBColor
      .Red = 255
      .Green = 128
      .Blue = 128
    End With

    With pLineSymbol
      .Width = 2
      .Color = pRGBColor
      .Style = esriSLSSolid
    End With

5   With pScreen
      .StartDrawing pScreen.hDC, esriNoScreenCache
      .SetSymbol pLineSymbol
      .DrawPolyline pPolyline
      .FinishDrawing
    End With
```

This sample opens a shapefile on the user's local disk and adds the contents to the map as a feature layer. The default symbology is used. This sample could easily be changed to support different data sources.

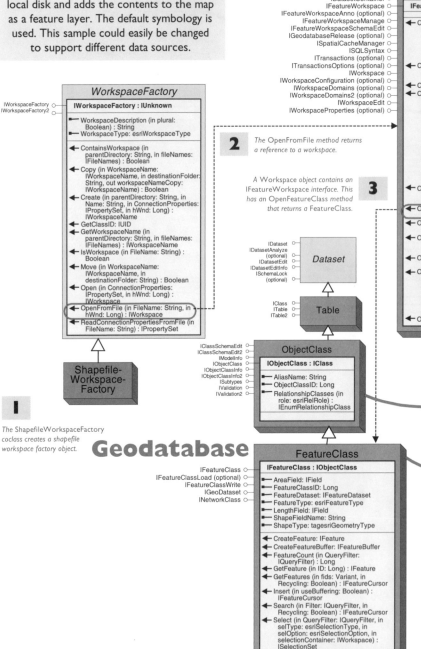

2 The OpenFromFile method returns a reference to a workspace.

A Workspace object contains an IFeatureWorkspace interface. This has an OpenFeatureClass method that returns a FeatureClass.

3

1 The ShapefileWorkspaceFactory coclass creates a shapefile workspace factory object.

Geodatabase

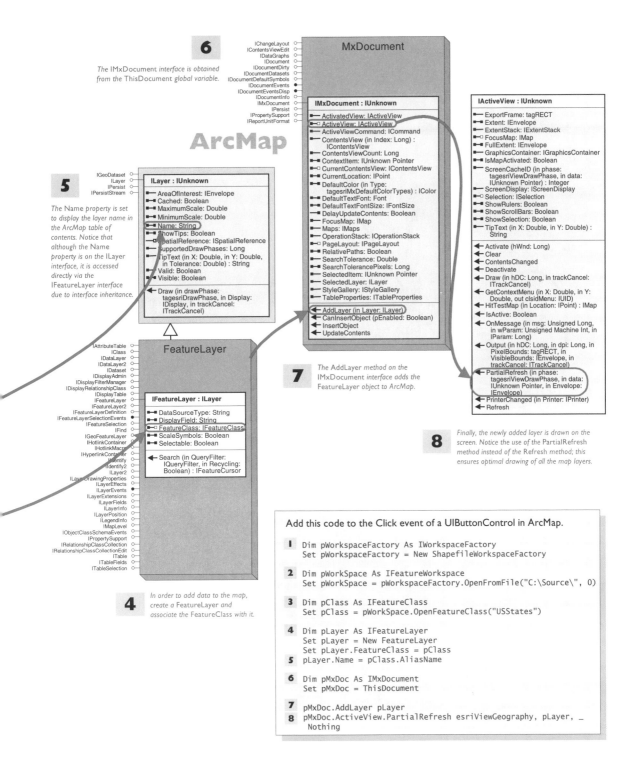

6

The IMxDocument interface is obtained from the ThisDocument global variable.

MxDocument

IChangeLayout
IContentsViewEdit
IDataGraphs
IDocument
IDocumentDirty
IDocumentDatasets
IDocumentDefaultSymbols
IDocumentEvents
IDocumentEventsDisp
IDocumentInfo
IMxDocument
IPersist
IPropertySupport
IReportUnitFormat

IMxDocument : IUnknown

- ActivatedView: IActiveView
- ActiveView: IActiveView
- ActiveViewCommand: ICommand
- ContentsView (in Index: Long) : IContentsView
- ContentsViewCount: Long
- ContextItem: IUnknown Pointer
- CurrentContentsView: IContentsView
- CurrentLocation: IPoint
- DefaultColor (in Type: tagesriMxDefaultColorTypes) : IColor
- DefaultTextFont: Font
- DefaultTextFontSize: IFontSize
- DelayUpdateContents: Boolean
- FocusMap: IMap
- Maps: IMaps
- OperationStack: IOperationStack
- PageLayout: IPageLayout
- RelativePaths: Boolean
- SearchTolerance: Double
- SearchTolerancePixels: Long
- SelectedItem: IUnknown Pointer
- SelectedLayer: ILayer
- StyleGallery: IStyleGallery
- TableProperties: ITableProperties

- AddLayer (in Layer: ILayer)
- CanInsertObject (pEnabled: Boolean)
- InsertObject
- UpdateContents

IActiveView : IUnknown

- ExportFrame: tagRECT
- Extent: IEnvelope
- ExtentStack: IExtentStack
- FocusMap: IMap
- FullExtent: IEnvelope
- GraphicsContainer: IGraphicsContainer
- IsMapActivated: Boolean
- ScreenCacheID (in phase: tagesriViewDrawPhase, in data: IUnknown Pointer) : Integer
- ScreenDisplay: IScreenDisplay
- Selection: ISelection
- ShowRulers: Boolean
- ShowScrollBars: Boolean
- ShowSelection: Boolean
- TipText (in X: Double, in Y: Double) : String

- Activate (hWnd: Long)
- Clear
- ContentsChanged
- Deactivate
- Draw (in hDC: Long, in trackCancel: ITrackCancel)
- GetContextMenu (in X: Double, in Y: Double, out clsidMenu: IUID)
- HitTestMap (in Location: IPoint) : IMap
- IsActive: Boolean
- OnMessage (in msg: Unsigned Long, in wParam: Unsigned Machine Int, in lParam: Long)
- Output (in hDC: Long, in dpi: Long, in PixelBounds: tagRECT, in VisibleBounds: IEnvelope, in trackCancel: ITrackCancel)
- PartialRefresh (in phase: tagesriViewDrawPhase, in data: IUnknown Pointer, in Envelope: IEnvelope)
- PrinterChanged (in Printer: IPrinter)
- Refresh

ArcMap

5

The Name property is set to display the layer name in the ArcMap table of contents. Notice that although the Name property is on the ILayer interface, it is accessed directly via the IFeatureLayer interface due to interface inheritance.

IGeoDataset
ILayer
IPersist
IPersistStream

ILayer : IUnknown

- AreaOfInterest: IEnvelope
- Cached: Boolean
- MaximumScale: Double
- MinimumScale: Double
- Name: String
- ShowTips: Boolean
- SpatialReference: ISpatialReference
- SupportedDrawPhases: Long
- TipText (in X: Double, in Y: Double, in Tolerance: Double) : String
- Valid: Boolean
- Visible: Boolean

- Draw (in drawPhase: tagesriDrawPhase, in Display: IDisplay, in trackCancel: ITrackCancel)

7

The AddLayer method on the IMxDocument interface adds the FeatureLayer object to ArcMap.

FeatureLayer

IAttributeTable
IClass
IDataLayer
IDataLayer2
IDataset
IDisplayAdmin
IDisplayFilterManager
IDisplayRelationshipClass
IDisplayTable
IFeatureLayer
IFeatureLayer2
IFeatureLayerDefinition
IFeatureLayerSelectionEvents
IFeatureSelection
IFind
IGeoFeatureLayer
IHotlinkContainer
IHotlinkMacro
IHyperlinkContainer
IIdentify
IIdentify2
ILayer2
ILayerDrawingProperties
ILayerEffects
ILayerEvents
ILayerExtensions
ILayerFields
ILayerInfo
ILayerPosition
ILegendInfo
IMapLevel
IObjectClassSchemaEvents
IPropertySupport
IRelationshipClassCollection
IRelationshipClassCollectionEdit
ITable
ITableFields
ITableSelection

IFeatureLayer : ILayer

- DataSourceType: String
- DisplayField: String
- FeatureClass: IFeatureClass
- ScaleSymbols: Boolean
- Selectable: Boolean

- Search (in QueryFilter: IQueryFilter, in Recycling: Boolean) : IFeatureCursor

8

Finally, the newly added layer is drawn on the screen. Notice the use of the PartialRefresh method instead of the Refresh method; this ensures optimal drawing of all the map layers.

4

In order to add data to the map, create a FeatureLayer and associate the FeatureClass with it.

Add this code to the Click event of a UIButtonControl in ArcMap.

```
1  Dim pWorkspaceFactory As IWorkspaceFactory
   Set pWorkspaceFactory = New ShapefileWorkspaceFactory

2  Dim pWorkSpace As IFeatureWorkspace
   Set pWorkSpace = pWorkspaceFactory.OpenFromFile("C:\Source\", 0)

3  Dim pClass As IFeatureClass
   Set pClass = pWorkSpace.OpenFeatureClass("USStates")

4  Dim pLayer As IFeatureLayer
   Set pLayer = New FeatureLayer
   Set pLayer.FeatureClass = pClass
5  pLayer.Name = pClass.AliasName

6  Dim pMxDoc As IMxDocument
   Set pMxDoc = ThisDocument

7  pMxDoc.AddLayer pLayer
8  pMxDoc.ActiveView.PartialRefresh esriViewGeography, pLayer, _
   Nothing
```

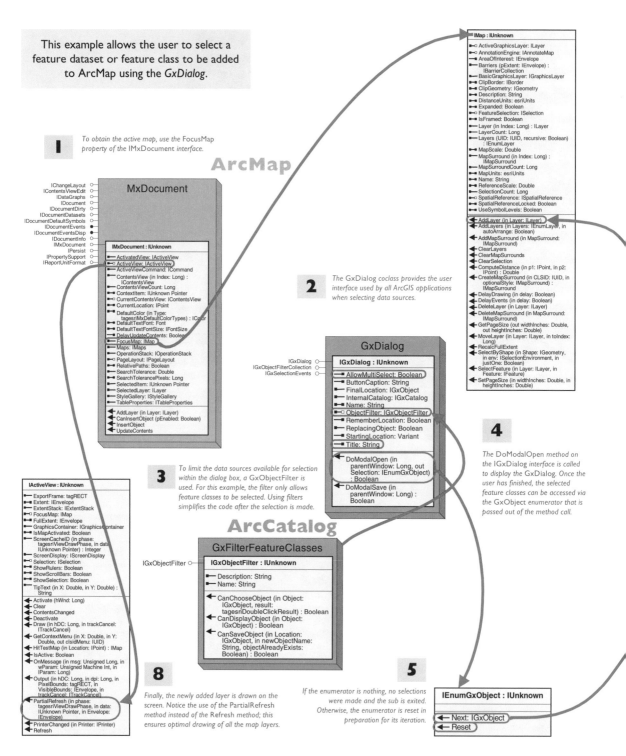

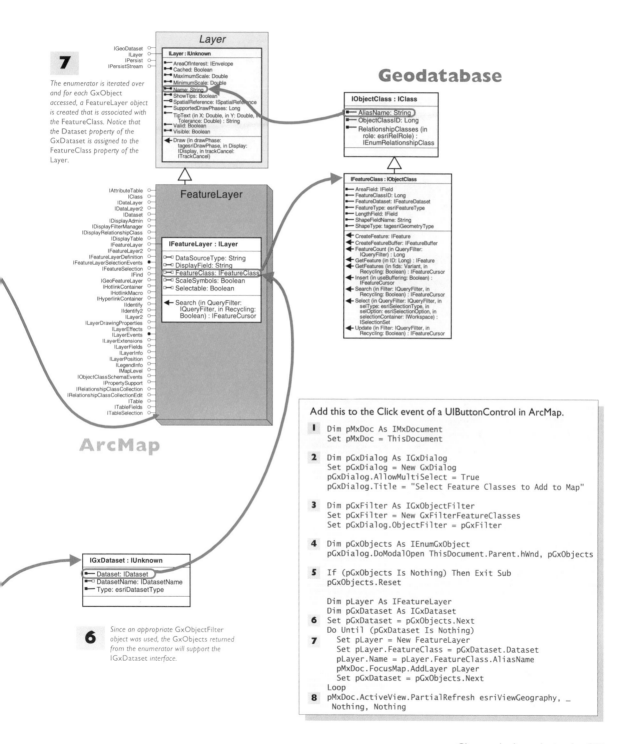

7

The enumerator is iterated over and for each GxObject accessed, a FeatureLayer object is created that is associated with the FeatureClass. Notice that the Dataset property of the GxDataset is assigned to the FeatureClass property of the Layer.

Layer

ILayer : IUnknown

- AreaOfInterest: IEnvelope
- Cached: Boolean
- MaximumScale: Double
- MinimumScale: Double
- Name: String
- ShowTips: Boolean
- SpatialReference: ISpatialReference
- SupportedDrawPhases: Long
- TipText (in X: Double, in Y: Double, in Tolerance: Double) : String
- Valid: Boolean
- Visible: Boolean

- Draw (in drawPhase: tagesriDrawPhase, in Display: IDisplay, in trackCancel: ITrackCancel)

IGeoDataset
ILayer
IPersist
IPersistStream

Geodatabase

IObjectClass : IClass

- AliasName: String
- ObjectClassID: Long
- RelationshipClasses (in role: esriRelRole) : IEnumRelationshipClass

IFeatureClass : IObjectClass

- AreaField: IField
- FeatureClassID: Long
- FeatureDataset: IFeatureDataset
- FeatureType: esriFeatureType
- LengthField: IField
- ShapeFieldName: String
- ShapeType: tagesriGeometryType

- CreateFeature: IFeature
- CreateFeatureBuffer: IFeatureBuffer
- FeatureCount (in QueryFilter: IQueryFilter) : Long
- GetFeature (in ID: Long) : IFeature
- GetFeatures (in fids: Variant, in Recycling: Boolean) : IFeatureCursor
- Insert (in useBuffering: Boolean) : IFeatureCursor
- Search (in Filter: IQueryFilter, in Recycling: Boolean) : IFeatureCursor
- Select (in QueryFilter: IQueryFilter, in selType: esriSelectionType, in selOption: esriSelectionOption, in selectionContainer: IWorkspace) : ISelectionSet
- Update (in Filter: IQueryFilter, in Recycling: Boolean) : IFeatureCursor

FeatureLayer

IAttributeTable
IClass
IDataLayer
IDataLayer2
IDataset
IDisplayAdmin
IDisplayFilterManager
IDisplayRelationshipClass
IDisplayTable
IFeatureLayer
IFeatureLayer2
IFeatureLayerDefinition
IFeatureLayerSelectionEvents
IFeatureSelection
IFind
IGeoFeatureLayer
IHotlinkContainer
IHotlinkMacro
IHyperlinkContainer
IIdentify
IIdentify2
ILayer2
ILayerDrawingProperties
ILayerEffects
ILayerEvents
ILayerExtensions
ILayerFields
ILayerInfo
ILayerPosition
ILegendInfo
IMapLevel
IObjectClassSchemaEvents
IPropertySupport
IRelationshipClassCollection
IRelationshipClassCollectionEdit
ITable
ITableFields
ITableSelection

IFeatureLayer : ILayer

- DataSourceType: String
- DisplayField: String
- FeatureClass: IFeatureClass
- ScaleSymbols: Boolean
- Selectable: Boolean

- Search (in QueryFilter: IQueryFilter, in Recycling: Boolean) : IFeatureCursor

ArcMap

IGxDataset : IUnknown

- Dataset: IDataset
- DatasetName: IDatasetName
- Type: esriDatasetType

6 *Since an appropriate GxObjectFilter object was used, the GxObjects returned from the enumerator will support the IGxDataset interface.*

Add this to the Click event of a UIButtonControl in ArcMap.

1
```
Dim pMxDoc As IMxDocument
Set pMxDoc = ThisDocument
```

2
```
Dim pGxDialog As IGxDialog
Set pGxDialog = New GxDialog
pGxDialog.AllowMultiSelect = True
pGxDialog.Title = "Select Feature Classes to Add to Map"
```

3
```
Dim pGxFilter As IGxObjectFilter
Set pGxFilter = New GxFilterFeatureClasses
Set pGxDialog.ObjectFilter = pGxFilter
```

4
```
Dim pGxObjects As IEnumGxObject
pGxDialog.DoModalOpen ThisDocument.Parent.hWnd, pGxObjects
```

5
```
If (pGxObjects Is Nothing) Then Exit Sub
pGxObjects.Reset

Dim pLayer As IFeatureLayer
Dim pGxDataset As IGxDataset
```

6
```
Set pGxDataset = pGxObjects.Next
Do Until (pGxDataset Is Nothing)
```

7
```
  Set pLayer = New FeatureLayer
  Set pLayer.FeatureClass = pGxDataset.Dataset
  pLayer.Name = pLayer.FeatureClass.AliasName
  pMxDoc.FocusMap.AddLayer pLayer
  Set pGxDataset = pGxObjects.Next
Loop
```

8
```
pMxDoc.ActiveView.PartialRefresh esriViewGeography, _
  Nothing, Nothing
```

This sample goes through all polygon layers in the map and attempts to match the symbology from the standard style set to the layer name. ArcMap does this by default. Therefore, to see a real difference before testing the tool, layer names should be changed to reflect suitable styles. For example, try changing a layer name to "Glacier" and executing this command.

2 *An enumerator is obtained from the style gallery for the style gallery's FillSymbol entries that, when accessed, will loop over all the FillSymbols.*

IStyleGallery : IUnknown
- ■— Categories (in ClassName: String) : IEnumBSTR
- ■— Class (in Index: Long) : IStyleGalleryClass
- ■— ClassCount: Long
- ■— Items (in ClassName: String, in styleSet: String, in Category: String) : IEnumStyleGalleryItem
- ◄— AddItem (in Item: IStyleGalleryItem)
- ◄— Clear
- ◄— ImportStyle (in FileName: String)
- ◄— LoadStyle (in FileName: String, in ClassName: String)
- ◄— RemoveItem (in Item: IStyleGalleryItem)
- ◄— SaveStyle (in FileName: String, in styleSet: String, in ClassName: String)
- ◄— UpdateItem (in Item: IStyleGalleryItem)

1 *To begin, you must gain access to the current document.*

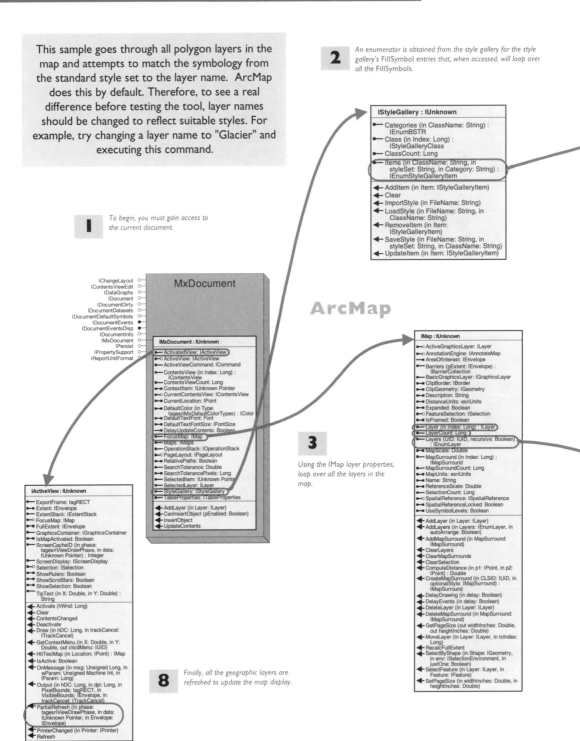

IChangeLayout
IContentsViewEdit
IDataGraphs
IDocument
IDocumentDirty
IDocumentDatasets
IDocumentDefaultSymbols
IDocumentEvents
IDocumentEventsDisp
IDocumentInfo
IMxDocument
IPersist
IPropertySupport
IReportUnitFormat

MxDocument

IMxDocument : IUnknown
- ■— ActivatedView: IActiveView
- ■— ActiveView: IActiveView
- ■— ActiveViewCommand: ICommand
- ■— ContentsView (in Index: Long) : IContentsView
- ■— ContentsViewCount: Long
- ■— ContextItem: IUnknown Pointer
- ■— CurrentContentsView: IContentsView
- ■— CurrentLocation: IPoint
- ■— DefaultColor (in Type: tagesriMxDefaultColorTypes) : IColor
- ■— DefaultTextFont: Font
- ■— DefaultTextFontSize: IFontSize
- ■— DelayUpdateContents: Boolean
- ■— FocusMap: IMap
- ■— Maps: IMaps
- ■— OperationStack: IOperationStack
- ■— PageLayout: IPageLayout
- ■— RelativePaths: Boolean
- ■— SearchTolerance: Double
- ■— SearchTolerancePixels: Long
- ■— SelectedItem: IUnknown Pointer
- ■— SelectedLayer: ILayer
- ■— StyleGallery: IStyleGallery
- ■— TableProperties: ITableProperties
- ◄— AddLayer (in Layer: ILayer)
- ◄— CanInsertObject (pEnabled: Boolean)
- ◄— InsertObject
- ◄— UpdateContents

ArcMap

3

Using the IMap layer properties, loop over all the layers in the map.

IMap : IUnknown
- ■—○ ActiveGraphicsLayer: ILayer
- ■—○ AnnotationEngine: IAnnotateMap
- ■— AreaOfInterest: IEnvelope
- ■— Barriers (pExtent: IEnvelope) : IBarrierCollection
- ■— BasicGraphicsLayer: IGraphicsLayer
- ■— ClipBorder: IBorder
- ■— ClipGeometry: IGeometry
- ■— Description: String
- ■— DistanceUnits: esriUnits
- ■— Expanded: Boolean
- ■— FeatureSelection: ISelection
- ■— IsFramed: Boolean
- ■— Layer (in Index: Long) : ILayer
- ■— LayerCount: Long
- ■— Layers (UID: IUID, recursive: Boolean) : IEnumLayer
- ■— MapScale: Double
- ■— MapSurround (in Index: Long) : IMapSurround
- ■— MapSurroundCount: Long
- ■— MapUnits: esriUnits
- ■— Name: String
- ■— ReferenceScale: Double
- ■— SelectionCount: Long
- ■— SpatialReference: ISpatialReference
- ■— SpatialReferenceLocked: Boolean
- ■— UseSymbolLevels: Boolean
- ◄— AddLayer (in Layer: ILayer)
- ◄— AddLayers (in Layers: IEnumLayer, in autoArrange: Boolean)
- ◄— AddMapSurround (in MapSurround: IMapSurround)
- ◄— ClearLayers
- ◄— ClearMapSurrounds
- ◄— ClearSelection
- ◄— ComputeDistance (in p1: IPoint, in p2: IPoint) : Double
- ◄— CreateMapSurround (in CLSID: IUID, in optionalStyle: IMapSurround) : IMapSurround
- ◄— DelayDrawing (in delay: Boolean)
- ◄— DelayEvents (in delay: Boolean)
- ◄— DeleteLayer (in Layer: ILayer)
- ◄— DeleteMapSurround (in MapSurround: IMapSurround)
- ◄— GetPageSize (out widthInches: Double, out heightInches: Double)
- ◄— MoveLayer (in Layer: ILayer, in toIndex: Long)
- ◄— RecalcFullExtent
- ◄— SelectByShape (in Shape: IGeometry, in env: ISelectionEnvironment, in justOne: Boolean)
- ◄— SelectFeature (in Layer: ILayer, in Feature: IFeature)
- ◄— SetPageSize (in widthInches: Double, in heightInches: Double)

IActiveView : IUnknown
- ■— ExportFrame: tagRECT
- ■— Extent: IEnvelope
- ■— ExtentStack: IExtentStack
- ■— FocusMap: IMap
- ■— FullExtent: IEnvelope
- ■— GraphicsContainer: IGraphicsContainer
- ■— IsMapActivated: Boolean
- ■— ScreenCacheID (in phase: tagesriViewDrawPhase, in data: IUnknown Pointer) : Integer
- ■— ScreenDisplay: IScreenDisplay
- ■—○ Selection: ISelection
- ■— ShowRulers: Boolean
- ■— ShowScrollBars: Boolean
- ■— ShowSelection: Boolean
- ■— TipText (in X: Double, in Y: Double) : String
- ◄— Activate (hWnd: Long)
- ◄— Clear
- ◄— ContentsChanged
- ◄— Deactivate
- ◄— Draw (in hDC: Long, in trackCancel: ITrackCancel)
- ◄— GetContextMenu (in X: Double, in Y: Double, out clsidMenu: IUID)
- ◄— HitTestMap (in Location: IPoint) : IMap
- ◄— IsActive: Boolean
- ◄— OnMessage (in msg: Unsigned Long, in wParam: Unsigned Machine Int, in lParam: Long)
- ◄— Output (in hDC: Long, in dpi: Long, in PixelBounds: tagRECT, in VisibleBounds: IEnvelope, in trackCancel: ITrackCancel)
- ◄— PartialRefresh (in phase: tagesriViewDrawPhase, in data: IUnknown Pointer, in Envelope: IEnvelope)
- ◄— PrinterChanged (in Printer: IPrinter)
- ◄— Refresh

8 *Finally, all the geographic layers are refreshed to update the map display.*

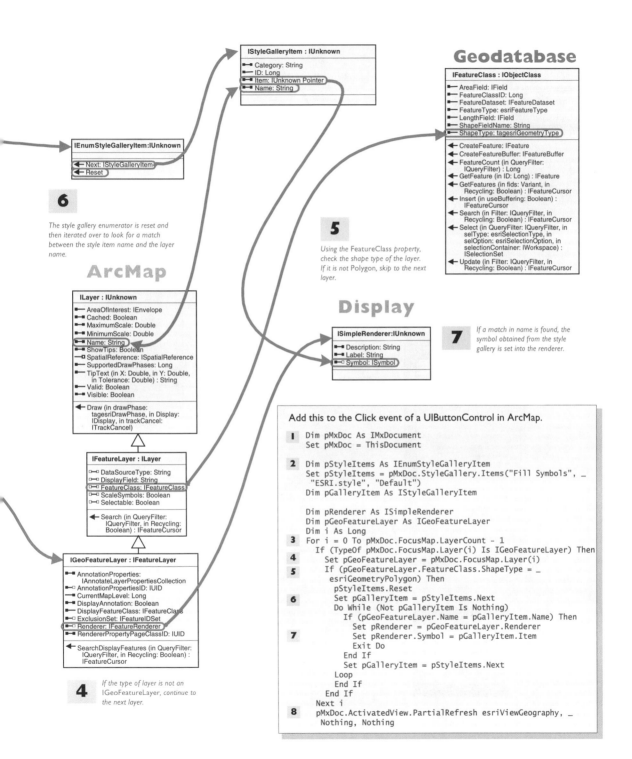

IStyleGalleryItem : IUnknown
- Category: String
- ID: Long
- Item: IUnknown Pointer
- Name: String

Geodatabase

IFeatureClass : IObjectClass
- AreaField: IField
- FeatureClassID: Long
- FeatureDataset: IFeatureDataset
- FeatureType: esriFeatureType
- LengthField: IField
- ShapeFieldName: String
- ShapeType: tagesriGeometryType
- CreateFeature: IFeature
- CreateFeatureBuffer: IFeatureBuffer
- FeatureCount (in QueryFilter: IQueryFilter) : Long
- GetFeature (in ID: Long) : IFeature
- GetFeatures (in fids: Variant, in Recycling: Boolean) : IFeatureCursor
- Insert (in useBuffering: Boolean) : IFeatureCursor
- Search (in Filter: IQueryFilter, in Recycling: Boolean) : IFeatureCursor
- Select (in QueryFilter: IQueryFilter, in selType: esriSelectionType, in selOption: esriSelectionOption, in selectionContainer: IWorkspace) : ISelectionSet
- Update (in Filter: IQueryFilter, in Recycling: Boolean) : IFeatureCursor

IEnumStyleGalleryItem:IUnknown
- Next: IStyleGalleryItem
- Reset

6

The style gallery enumerator is reset and then iterated over to look for a match between the style item name and the layer name.

5

Using the FeatureClass property, check the shape type of the layer. If it is not Polygon, skip to the next layer.

ArcMap

ILayer : IUnknown
- AreaOfInterest: IEnvelope
- Cached: Boolean
- MaximumScale: Double
- MinimumScale: Double
- Name: String
- ShowTips: Boolean
- SpatialReference: ISpatialReference
- SupportedDrawPhases: Long
- TipText (in X: Double, in Y: Double, in Tolerance: Double) : String
- Valid: Boolean
- Visible: Boolean
- Draw (in drawPhase: tagesriDrawPhase, in Display: IDisplay, in trackCancel: ITrackCancel)

Display

ISimpleRenderer:IUnknown
- Description: String
- Label: String
- Symbol: ISymbol

7

If a match in name is found, the symbol obtained from the style gallery is set into the renderer.

IFeatureLayer : ILayer
- DataSourceType: String
- DisplayField: String
- FeatureClass: IFeatureClass
- ScaleSymbols: Boolean
- Selectable: Boolean
- Search (in QueryFilter: IQueryFilter, in Recycling: Boolean) : IFeatureCursor

IGeoFeatureLayer : IFeatureLayer
- AnnotationProperties: IAnnotateLayerPropertiesCollection
- AnnotationPropertiesID: IUID
- CurrentMapLevel: Long
- DisplayAnnotation: Boolean
- DisplayFeatureClass: IFeatureClass
- ExclusionSet: IFeatureIDSet
- Renderer: IFeatureRenderer
- RendererPropertyPageClassID: IUID
- SearchDisplayFeatures (in QueryFilter: IQueryFilter, in Recycling: Boolean) : IFeatureCursor

4

If the type of layer is not an IGeoFeatureLayer, continue to the next layer.

Add this to the Click event of a UIButtonControl in ArcMap.

```
1   Dim pMxDoc As IMxDocument
    Set pMxDoc = ThisDocument

2   Dim pStyleItems As IEnumStyleGalleryItem
    Set pStyleItems = pMxDoc.StyleGallery.Items("Fill Symbols", _
      "ESRI.style", "Default")
    Dim pGalleryItem As IStyleGalleryItem

    Dim pRenderer As ISimpleRenderer
    Dim pGeoFeatureLayer As IGeoFeatureLayer
    Dim i As Long
3   For i = 0 To pMxDoc.FocusMap.LayerCount - 1
      If (TypeOf pMxDoc.FocusMap.Layer(i) Is IGeoFeatureLayer) Then
4       Set pGeoFeatureLayer = pMxDoc.FocusMap.Layer(i)
5       If (pGeoFeatureLayer.FeatureClass.ShapeType = _
          esriGeometryPolygon) Then
          pStyleItems.Reset
6         Set pGalleryItem = pStyleItems.Next
          Do While (Not pGalleryItem Is Nothing)
            If (pGeoFeatureLayer.Name = pGalleryItem.Name) Then
              Set pRenderer = pGeoFeatureLayer.Renderer
7             Set pRenderer.Symbol = pGalleryItem.Item
              Exit Do
            End If
            Set pGalleryItem = pStyleItems.Next
          Loop
        End If
      End If
    Next i
8   pMxDoc.ActivatedView.PartialRefresh esriViewGeography, _
    Nothing, Nothing
```

This sample loops through the selected features of the focus map. It loops using the *IEnumFeature* interface, which is reached through a *QueryInterface* from the *FeatureSelection* property of the map. For each feature it checks the geometry type and if *Polygon*, it performs a *QueryInterface* for the *IArea* interface. Using the *Area* property of the interface, it adds the area to a running total. At the end, it reports the total area via a message box.

Geodatabase

IFeatureSelection : IUnknown

- BufferDistance: Double
- CombinationMethod: esriSelectionResultEnum
- SelectionColor: IColor
- SelectionSet: ISelectionSet
- SelectionSymbol: ISymbol
- SetSelectionSymbol: Boolean

- Add (in Feature: IFeature)
- Clear
- SelectFeatures (in Filter: IQueryFilter, in Method: esriSelectionResultEnum, in justOne: Boolean)
- SelectionChanged

6 Obtain the IFeatureSelection interface by performing a QueryInterface to the IFeatureLayer interface.

IFeatureClass : IObjectClass

- AreaField: IField
- FeatureClassID: Long
- FeatureDataset: IFeatureDataset
- FeatureType: esriFeatureType
- LengthField: IField
- ShapeFieldName: String
- ShapeType: tagesriGeometryType

- CreateFeature: IFeature
- CreateFeatureBuffer: IFeatureBuffer
- FeatureCount (in QueryFilter: IQueryFilter) : Long
- GetFeature (in ID: Long) : IFeature
- GetFeatures (in fids: Variant, in Recycling: Boolean) : IFeatureCursor
- Insert (in useBuffering: Boolean) : IFeatureCursor
- Search (in Filter: IQueryFilter, in Recycling: Boolean) : IFeatureCursor
- Select (in Filter: IQueryFilter, in selType: esriSelectionType, in selOption: esriSelectionOption, in selectionContainer: IWorkspace) : ISelectionSet
- Update (in Filter: IQueryFilter, in Recycling: Boolean) : IFeatureCursor

5 If the shape type of the feature class is not a Polygon, the layer is skipped.

1 To obtain the layers of the map, you must first get access to the currently active map. Do this through the FocusMap property of the IMxDocument interface.

MxDocument

IChangeLayout
IContentsViewEdit
IDataGraphs
IDocument
IDocumentDirty
IDocumentDatasets
IDocumentDefaultSymbols
IDocumentEvents
IDocumentEventsDisp
IDocumentInfo
IMxDocument
IPersist
IPropertySupport
IReportUnitFormat

IMxDocument : IUnknown

- ActivatedView: IActiveView
- ActiveView: IActiveView
- ActiveViewCommand: ICommand
- ContentsView (in Index: Long) : IContentsView
- ContentsViewCount: Long
- ContextItem: IUnknown Pointer
- CurrentContentsView: IContentsView
- CurrentLocation: IPoint
- DefaultColor (in Type: tagesriMxDefaultColorTypes) : IColor
- DefaultTextFont: Font
- DefaultTextFontSize: IFontSize
- DelayUpdateContents: Boolean
- FocusMap: IMap
- Maps: IMaps
- OperationStack: IOperationStack
- PageLayout: IPageLayout
- RelativePaths: Boolean
- SearchTolerance: Double
- SearchTolerancePixels: Long
- SelectedItem: IUnknown Pointer
- SelectedLayer: ILayer
- StyleGallery: IStyleGallery
- TableProperties: ITableProperties

- AddLayer (in Layer: ILayer)
- CanInsertObject (pEnabled: Boolean)
- InsertObject
- UpdateContents

ArcMap

IMap : IUnknown

- ActiveGraphicsLayer: ILayer
- AnnotationEngine: IAnnotateMap
- AreaOfInterest: IEnvelope
- Barriers (pExtent: IEnvelope) : IBarrierCollection
- BasicGraphicsLayer: IGraphicsLayer
- ClipBorder: IBorder
- ClipGeometry: IGeometry
- Description: String
- DistanceUnits: esriUnits
- Expanded: Boolean
- FeatureSelection: ISelection
- IsFramed: Boolean
- Layer (in Index: Long) : ILayer
- LayerCount: Long
- Layers (UID: IUID, recursive: Boolean) : IEnumLayer
- MapScale: Double
- MapSurround (in Index: Long) : IMapSurround
- MapSurroundCount: Long
- MapUnits: esriUnits
- Name: String
- ReferenceScale: Double
- SelectionCount: Long
- SpatialReference: ISpatialReference
- SpatialReferenceLocked: Boolean
- UseSymbolLevels: Boolean

- AddLayer (in Layer: ILayer)
- AddLayers (in Layers: IEnumLayer, in autoArrange: Boolean)
- AddMapSurround (in MapSurround: IMapSurround)
- ClearLayers
- ClearMapSurrounds
- ClearSelection
- ComputeDistance (in p1: IPoint, in p2: IPoint) : Double
- CreateMapSurround (in CLSID: IUID, in optionalStyle: IMapSurround) : IMapSurround
- DelayDrawing (in delay: Boolean)
- DelayEvents (in delay: Boolean)
- DeleteLayer (in Layer: ILayer)
- DeleteMapSurround (in MapSurround: IMapSurround)
- GetPageSize (out widthInches: Double, out heightInches: Double)
- MoveLayer (in Layer: ILayer, in toIndex: Long)
- RecalcFullExtent
- SelectByShape (in Shape: IGeometry, in env: ISelectionEnvironment, in justOne: Boolean)
- SelectFeature (in Layer: ILayer, in Feature: IFeature)
- SetPageSize (in widthInches: Double, in heightInches: Double)

IFeatureLayer : ILayer

- DataSourceType: String
- DisplayField: String
- FeatureClass: IFeatureClass
- ScaleSymbols: Boolean
- Selectable: Boolean

- Search (in QueryFilter: IQueryFilter, in Recycling: Boolean) : IFeatureCursor

4 The layers enumerator is iterated over using the standard enumerator method, Next.

IEnumLayer : IUnknown

- Next: ILayer
- Reset

2 The UID helper object is used to represent the GUID for the IGeoFeatureLayer interface.

UID

IUID

IUID : IDispatch

- SubType: Long
- Value: Variant

- Compare (in otherID: IUID) : Boolean
- Generate

Framework

3 The UID object created previously is used to obtain an enumerator for all layers that support the IGeoFeatureLayer interface. Notice the resetting of the enumerator before its use.

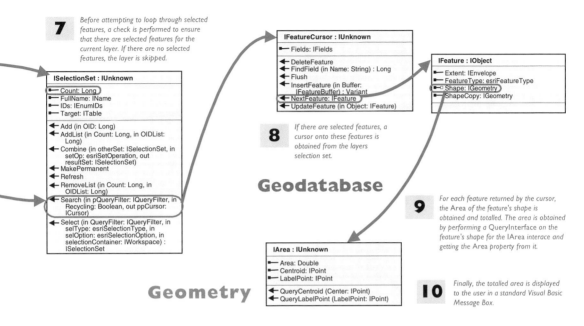

7 Before attempting to loop through selected features, a check is performed to ensure that there are selected features for the current layer. If there are no selected features, the layer is skipped.

IFeatureCursor : IUnknown
- Fields: IFields
- DeleteFeature
- FindField (in Name: String) : Long
- Flush
- InsertFeature (in Buffer: IFeatureBuffer) : Variant
- NextFeature: IFeature
- UpdateFeature (in Object: IFeature)

IFeature : IObject
- Extent: IEnvelope
- FeatureType: esriFeatureType
- Shape: IGeometry
- ShapeCopy: IGeometry

ISelectionSet : IUnknown
- Count: Long
- FullName: IName
- IDs: IEnumIDs
- Target: ITable
- Add (in OID: Long)
- AddList (in Count: Long, in OIDList: Long)
- Combine (in otherSet: ISelectionSet, in setOp: esriSetOperation, out resultSet: ISelectionSet)
- MakePermanent
- Refresh
- RemoveList (in Count: Long, in OIDList: Long)
- Search (in pQueryFilter: IQueryFilter, in Recycling: Boolean, out ppCursor: ICursor)
- Select (in QueryFilter: IQueryFilter, in selType: esriSelectionType, in selOption: esriSelectionOption, in selectionContainer: IWorkspace) : ISelectionSet

8 If there are selected features, a cursor onto these features is obtained from the layers selection set.

Geodatabase

9 For each feature returned by the cursor, the Area of the feature's shape is obtained and totalled. The area is obtained by performing a QueryInterface on the feature's shape for the IArea interace and getting the Area property from it.

IArea : IUnknown
- Area: Double
- Centroid: IPoint
- LabelPoint: IPoint
- QueryCentroid (Center: IPoint)
- QueryLabelPoint (LabelPoint: IPoint)

Geometry

10 Finally, the totalled area is displayed to the user in a standard Visual Basic Message Box.

Add this code to the Click event of a UIButtonControl in ArcMap.

```
1  Dim pMxDoc As IMxDocument
   Set pMxDoc = ThisDocument

2  Dim pUID As New UID
   pUID = "{E156D7E5-22AF-11D3-9F99-00C04F6BC78E}" 'IGeoFeatureLayer IID

3  Dim pEnumLayer As IEnumLayer
   Set pEnumLayer = pMxDoc.FocusMap.Layers(pUID, True)
   pEnumLayer.Reset

   Dim pFeatureLayer As IFeatureLayer
   Dim pFeatureSelection As IFeatureSelection
   Dim pFeatureCursor As IFeatureCursor
   Dim pFeature As IFeature
   Dim pArea As IArea
   Dim dTotalArea As Double

4  Set pFeatureLayer = pEnumLayer.Next
   Do Until (pFeatureLayer Is Nothing)
5    If (pFeatureLayer.FeatureClass.ShapeType = esriGeometryPolygon) Then
6      Set pFeatureSelection = pFeatureLayer

7      If (pFeatureSelection.SelectionSet.Count <> 0) Then
         pFeatureSelection.SelectionSet.Search Nothing, True, pFeatureCursor
8        Set pFeature = pFeatureCursor.NextFeature

         Do Until (pFeature Is Nothing)
9          Set pArea = pFeature.Shape
           dTotalArea = dTotalArea + pArea.Area
           Set pFeature = pFeatureCursor.NextFeature
         Loop
       End If
     End If
     Set pFeatureLayer = pEnumLayer.Next
   Loop

10 MsgBox "Total Area for selected polygon features = " & CStr(dTotalArea)
```

This sample builds a spatial query filter, gets a feature cursor based on the filter and then loops over all the features, totalling the number of points, lines, and areas, and reports these to the user.

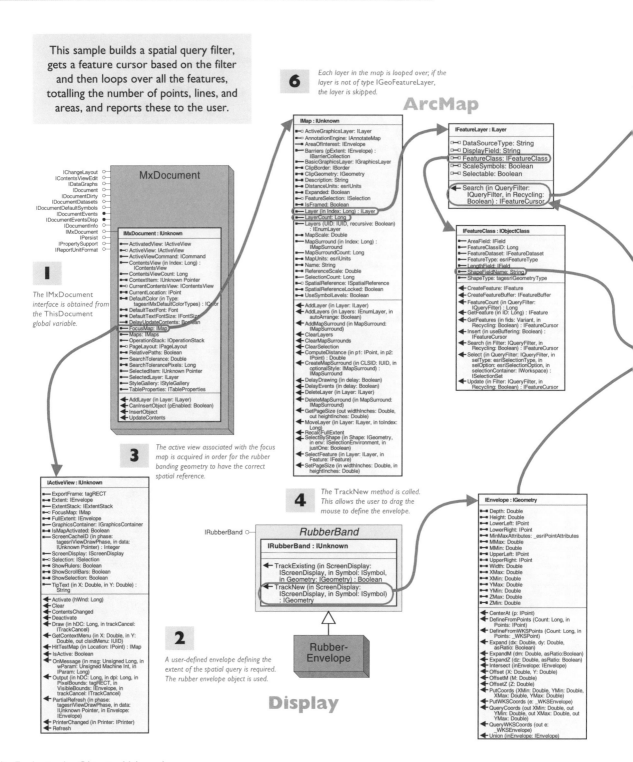

6 Each layer in the map is looped over; if the layer is not of type IGeoFeatureLayer, the layer is skipped.

ArcMap

1 The IMxDocument interface is obtained from the ThisDocument global variable.

3 The active view associated with the focus map is acquired in order for the rubber banding geometry to have the correct spatial reference.

4 The TrackNew method is called. This allows the user to drag the mouse to define the envelope.

2 A user-defined envelope defining the extent of the spatial query is required. The rubber envelope object is used.

Display

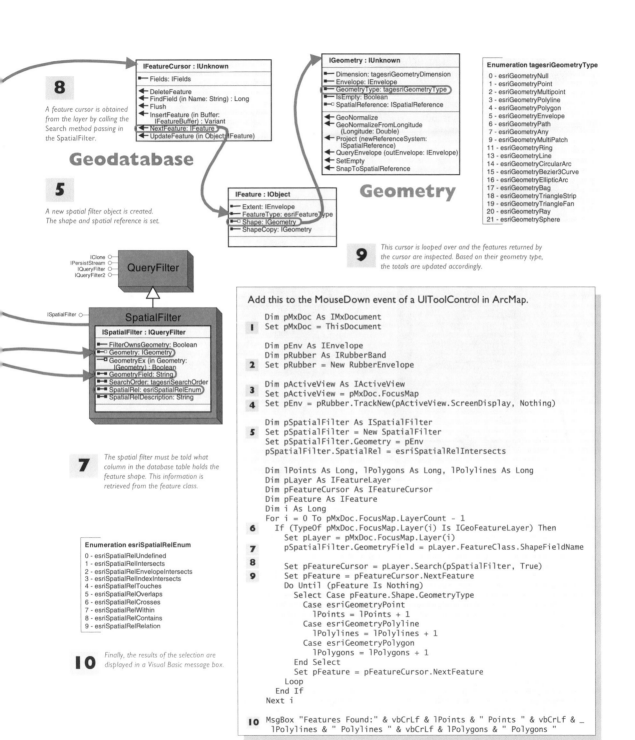

8

A feature cursor is obtained from the layer by calling the Search method passing in the SpatialFilter.

IFeatureCursor : IUnknown

- Fields: IFields
- DeleteFeature
- FindField (in Name: String) : Long
- Flush
- InsertFeature (in Buffer: IFeatureBuffer) : Variant
- NextFeature: IFeature
- UpdateFeature (in Object: IFeature)

Geodatabase

5

A new spatial filter object is created. The shape and spatial reference is set.

IGeometry : IUnknown

- Dimension: tagesriGeometryDimension
- Envelope: IEnvelope
- GeometryType: tagesriGeometryType
- IsEmpty: Boolean
- SpatialReference: ISpatialReference
- GeoNormalize
- GeoNormalizeFromLongitude (Longitude: Double)
- Project (newReferenceSystem: ISpatialReference)
- QueryEnvelope (outEnvelope: IEnvelope)
- SetEmpty
- SnapToSpatialReference

Enumeration tagesriGeometryType

0 - esriGeometryNull
1 - esriGeometryPoint
2 - esriGeometryMultipoint
3 - esriGeometryPolyline
4 - esriGeometryPolygon
5 - esriGeometryEnvelope
6 - esriGeometryPath
7 - esriGeometryAny
9 - esriGeometryMultiPatch
11 - esriGeometryRing
13 - esriGeometryLine
14 - esriGeometryCircularArc
15 - esriGeometryBezier3Curve
16 - esriGeometryEllipticArc
17 - esriGeometryBag
18 - esriGeometryTriangleStrip
19 - esriGeometryTriangleFan
20 - esriGeometryRay
21 - esriGeometrySphere

IFeature : IObject

- Extent: IEnvelope
- FeatureType: esriFeatureType
- Shape: IGeometry
- ShapeCopy: IGeometry

Geometry

9

This cursor is looped over and the features returned by the cursor are inspected. Based on their geometry type, the totals are updated accordingly.

QueryFilter

IClone
IPersistStream
IQueryFilter
IQueryFilter2

ISpatialFilter

SpatialFilter

ISpatialFilter : IQueryFilter

- FilterOwnsGeometry: Boolean
- Geometry: IGeometry
- GeometryEx (in Geometry: IGeometry) : Boolean
- GeometryField: String
- SearchOrder: tagesriSearchOrder
- SpatialRel: esriSpatialRelEnum
- SpatialRelDescription: String

7

The spatial filter must be told what column in the database table holds the feature shape. This information is retrieved from the feature class.

Enumeration esriSpatialRelEnum

0 - esriSpatialRelUndefined
1 - esriSpatialRelIntersects
2 - esriSpatialRelEnvelopeIntersects
3 - esriSpatialRelIndexIntersects
4 - esriSpatialRelTouches
5 - esriSpatialRelOverlaps
6 - esriSpatialRelCrosses
7 - esriSpatialRelWithin
8 - esriSpatialRelContains
9 - esriSpatialRelRelation

10

Finally, the results of the selection are displayed in a Visual Basic message box.

Add this to the MouseDown event of a UIToolControl in ArcMap.

```
    Dim pMxDoc As IMxDocument
 1  Set pMxDoc = ThisDocument

    Dim pEnv As IEnvelope
    Dim pRubber As IRubberBand
 2  Set pRubber = New RubberEnvelope

    Dim pActiveView As IActiveView
 3  Set pActiveView = pMxDoc.FocusMap
 4  Set pEnv = pRubber.TrackNew(pActiveView.ScreenDisplay, Nothing)

    Dim pSpatialFilter As ISpatialFilter
 5  Set pSpatialFilter = New SpatialFilter
    Set pSpatialFilter.Geometry = pEnv
    pSpatialFilter.SpatialRel = esriSpatialRelIntersects

    Dim lPoints As Long, lPolygons As Long, lPolylines As Long
    Dim pLayer As IFeatureLayer
    Dim pFeatureCursor As IFeatureCursor
    Dim pFeature As IFeature
    Dim i As Long
    For i = 0 To pMxDoc.FocusMap.LayerCount - 1
 6    If (TypeOf pMxDoc.FocusMap.Layer(i) Is IGeoFeatureLayer) Then
        Set pLayer = pMxDoc.FocusMap.Layer(i)
 7      pSpatialFilter.GeometryField = pLayer.FeatureClass.ShapeFieldName
 8
        Set pFeatureCursor = pLayer.Search(pSpatialFilter, True)
 9      Set pFeature = pFeatureCursor.NextFeature
        Do Until (pFeature Is Nothing)
          Select Case pFeature.Shape.GeometryType
            Case esriGeometryPoint
              lPoints = lPoints + 1
            Case esriGeometryPolyline
              lPolylines = lPolylines + 1
            Case esriGeometryPolygon
              lPolygons = lPolygons + 1
          End Select
          Set pFeature = pFeatureCursor.NextFeature
        Loop
      End If
    Next i

10  MsgBox "Features Found:" & vbCrLf & lPoints & " Points " & vbCrLf & _
      lPolylines & " Polylines " & vbCrLf & lPolygons & " Polygons "
```

This example adds legend map surround to a page layout and fills the legend with the layers of the map. Map surrounds are dynamically linked to their associated map; therefore, any changes to the map are reflected in the map surround.

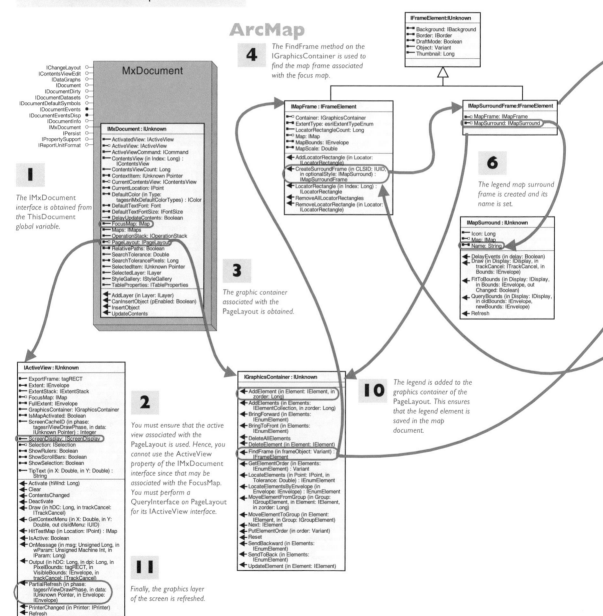

ArcMap

MxDocument

IChangeLayout
IContentsViewEdit
IDataGraphs
IDocument
IDocumentDirty
IDocumentDatasets
IDocumentDefaultSymbols
IDocumentEvents
IDocumentEventsDisp
IDocumentInfo
IMxDocument
IPersist
IPropertySupport
IReportUnitFormat

IMxDocument : IUnknown

- ActivatedView: IActiveView
- ActiveView: IActiveView
- ActiveViewCommand: ICommand
- ContentsView (in Index: Long) : IContentsView
- ContentsViewCount: Long
- ContextItem: IUnknown Pointer
- CurrentContentsView: IContentsView
- CurrentLocation: IPoint
- DefaultColor (in Type: tagesriMxDefaultColorTypes) : IColor
- DefaultTextFont: Font
- DefaultTextFontSize: IFontSize
- DelayUpdateContents: Boolean
- FocusMap: IMap
- Maps: IMaps
- OperationStack: IOperationStack
- PageLayout: IPageLayout
- RelativePaths: Boolean
- SearchTolerance: Double
- SearchTolerancePixels: Long
- SelectedItem: IUnknown Pointer
- SelectedLayer: ILayer
- StyleGallery: IStyleGallery
- TableProperties: ITableProperties

- AddLayer (in Layer: ILayer)
- CanInsertObject (pEnabled: Boolean)
- InsertObject
- UpdateContents

1

The IMxDocument interface is obtained from the ThisDocument global variable.

3

The graphic container associated with the PageLayout is obtained.

4

The FindFrame method on the IGraphicsContainer is used to find the map frame associated with the focus map.

IFrameElement:IUnknown

- Background: IBackground
- Border: IBorder
- DraftMode: Boolean
- Object: Variant
- Thumbnail: Long

IMapFrame : IFrameElement

- Container: IGraphicsContainer
- ExtentType: esriExtentTypeEnum
- LocatorRectangleCount: Long
- Map: IMap
- MapBounds: IEnvelope
- MapScale: Double
- AddLocatorRectangle (in Locator: ILocatorRectangle)
- CreateSurroundFrame (in CLSID: IUID, in optionalStyle: IMapSurround) : IMapSurroundFrame
- LocatorRectangle (in Index: Long) : ILocatorRectangle
- RemoveAllLocatorRectangles
- RemoveLocatorRectangle (in Locator: ILocatorRectangle)

IMapSurroundFrame:IFrameElement

- MapFrame: IMapFrame
- MapSurround: IMapSurround

6

The legend map surround frame is created and its name is set.

IMapSurround : IUnknown

- Icon: Long
- Map: IMap
- Name: String
- DelayEvents (in delay: Boolean)
- Draw (in Display: IDisplay, in trackCancel: ITrackCancel, in Bounds: IEnvelope)
- FitToBounds (in Display: IDisplay, in Bounds: IEnvelope, out Changed: Boolean)
- QueryBounds (in Display: IDisplay, in oldBounds: IEnvelope, newBounds: IEnvelope)
- Refresh

IActiveView : IUnknown

- ExportFrame: tagRECT
- Extent: IEnvelope
- ExtentStack: IExtentStack
- FocusMap: IMap
- FullExtent: IEnvelope
- GraphicsContainer: IGraphicsContainer
- IsMapActivated: Boolean
- ScreenCacheID (in phase: tagesriViewDrawPhase, in data: IUnknown Pointer) : Integer
- ScreenDisplay: IScreenDisplay
- Selection: ISelection
- ShowRulers: Boolean
- ShowScrollBars: Boolean
- ShowSelection: Boolean
- TipText (in X: Double, in Y: Double) : String

- Activate (hWnd: Long)
- Clear
- ContentsChanged
- Deactivate
- Draw (in hDC: Long, in trackCancel: ITrackCancel)
- GetContextMenu (in X: Double, in Y: Double, out clsidMenu: IUID)
- HitTestMap (in Location: IPoint) : IMap
- IsActive: Boolean
- OnMessage (in msg: Unsigned Long, in wParam: Unsigned Machine Int, in lParam: Long)
- Output (in hDC: Long, in dpi: Long, in PixelBounds: tagRECT, in VisibleBounds: IEnvelope, in trackCancel: ITrackCancel)
- PartialRefresh (in phase: tagesriViewDrawPhase, in data: IUnknown Pointer, in Envelope: IEnvelope)
- PrinterChanged (in Printer: IPrinter)
- Refresh

2

You must ensure that the active view associated with the PageLayout is used. Hence, you cannot use the ActiveView property of the IMxDocument interface since that may be associated with the FocusMap. You must perform a QueryInterface on PageLayout for its IActiveView interface.

11

Finally, the graphics layer of the screen is refreshed.

IGraphicsContainer : IUnknown

- AddElement (in Element: IElement, in zorder: Long)
- AddElements (in Elements: IElementCollection, in zorder: Long)
- BringForward (in Elements: IEnumElement)
- BringToFront (in Elements: IEnumElement)
- DeleteAllElements
- DeleteElement (in Element: IElement)
- FindFrame (in frameObject: Variant) : IFrameElement
- GetElementOrder (in Elements: IEnumElement) : Variant
- LocateElements (in Point: IPoint, in Tolerance: Double) : IEnumElement
- LocateElementsByEnvelope (in Envelope: IEnvelope) : IEnumElement
- MoveElementFromGroup (in Group: IGroupElement, in Element: IElement, in zorder: Long)
- MoveElementToGroup (in Element: IElement, in Group: IGroupElement)
- Next: IElement
- PutElementOrder (in order: Variant)
- Reset
- SendBackward (in Elements: IEnumElement)
- SendToBack (in Elements: IEnumElement)
- UpdateElement (in Element: IElement)

10

The legend is added to the graphics container of the PageLayout. This ensures that the legend element is saved in the map document.

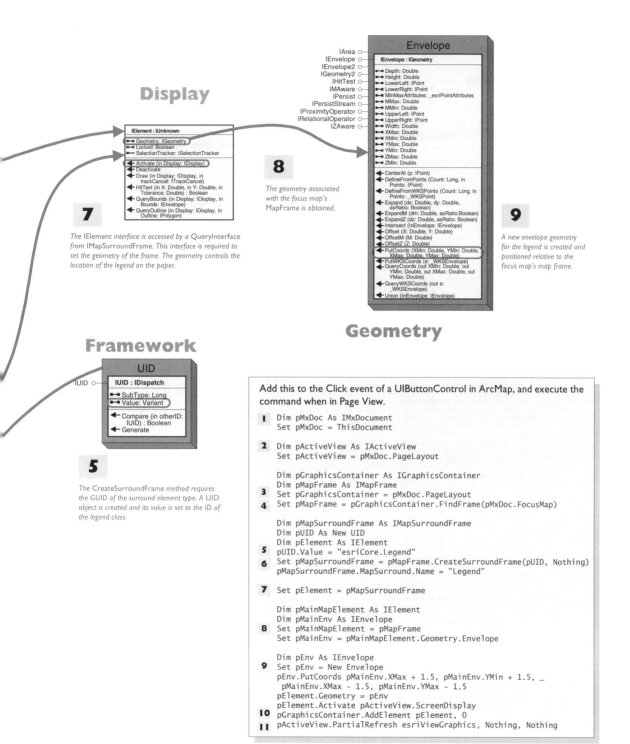

Display

IElement : IUnknown

- Geometry: IGeometry
- Locked: Boolean
- SelectionTracker: ISelectionTracker
- Activate (in Display: IDisplay)
- Deactivate
- Draw (in Display: IDisplay, in trackCancel: ITrackCancel)
- HitTest (in X: Double, in Y: Double, in Tolerance: Double) : Boolean
- QueryBounds (in Display: IDisplay, in Bounds: IEnvelope)
- QueryOutline (in Display: IDisplay, in Outline: IPolygon)

7

The IElement interface is accessed by a QueryInterface from IMapSurroundFrame. This interface is required to set the geometry of the frame. The geometry controls the location of the legend on the paper.

8

The geometry associated with the focus map's MapFrame is obtained.

Envelope

IArea
IEnvelope
IEnvelope2
IGeometry2
IHitTest
IMAware
IPersist
IPersistStream
IProximityOperator
IRelationalOperator
IZAware

IEnvelope : IGeometry

- Depth: Double
- Height: Double
- LowerLeft: IPoint
- LowerRight: IPoint
- MinMaxAttributes: _esriPointAttributes
- MMax: Double
- MMin: Double
- UpperLeft: IPoint
- UpperRight: IPoint
- Width: Double
- XMax: Double
- XMin: Double
- YMax: Double
- YMin: Double
- ZMax: Double
- ZMin: Double
- CenterAt (p: IPoint)
- DefineFromPoints (Count: Long, in Points: IPoint)
- DefineFromWKSPoints (Count: Long, in Points: _WKSPoint)
- Expand (dx: Double, dy: Double, asRatio: Boolean)
- ExpandM (dm: Double, asRatio:Boolean)
- ExpandZ (dz: Double, asRatio: Boolean)
- Intersect (inEnvelope: IEnvelope)
- Offset (X: Double, Y: Double)
- OffsetM (M: Double)
- OffsetZ (Z: Double)
- PutCoords (XMin: Double, YMin: Double, XMax: Double, YMax: Double)
- PutWKSCoords (e: _WKSEnvelope)
- QueryCoords (out XMin: Double, out YMin: Double, out XMax: Double, out YMax: Double)
- QueryWKSCoords (out e: _WKSEnvelope)
- Union (inEnvelope: IEnvelope)

9

A new envelope geometry for the legend is created and positioned relative to the focus map's map frame.

Geometry

Framework

UID

IUID : IDispatch

- SubType: Long
- Value: Variant
- Compare (in otherID: IUID) : Boolean
- Generate

5

The CreateSurroundFrame method requires the GUID of the surround element type. A UID object is created and its value is set to the ID of the legend class.

Add this to the Click event of a UIButtonControl in ArcMap, and execute the command when in Page View.

```
1  Dim pMxDoc As IMxDocument
   Set pMxDoc = ThisDocument

2  Dim pActiveView As IActiveView
   Set pActiveView = pMxDoc.PageLayout

   Dim pGraphicsContainer As IGraphicsContainer
   Dim pMapFrame As IMapFrame
3  Set pGraphicsContainer = pMxDoc.PageLayout
4  Set pMapFrame = pGraphicsContainer.FindFrame(pMxDoc.FocusMap)

   Dim pMapSurroundFrame As IMapSurroundFrame
   Dim pUID As New UID
   Dim pElement As IElement
5  pUID.Value = "esriCore.Legend"
6  Set pMapSurroundFrame = pMapFrame.CreateSurroundFrame(pUID, Nothing)
   pMapSurroundFrame.MapSurround.Name = "Legend"

7  Set pElement = pMapSurroundFrame

   Dim pMainMapElement As IElement
   Dim pMainEnv As IEnvelope
8  Set pMainMapElement = pMapFrame
   Set pMainEnv = pMainMapElement.Geometry.Envelope

   Dim pEnv As IEnvelope
9  Set pEnv = New Envelope
   pEnv.PutCoords pMainEnv.XMax + 1.5, pMainEnv.YMin + 1.5, _
     pMainEnv.XMax - 1.5, pMainEnv.YMax - 1.5
   pElement.Geometry = pEnv
   pElement.Activate pActiveView.ScreenDisplay
10 pGraphicsContainer.AddElement pElement, 0
11 pActiveView.PartialRefresh esriViewGraphics, Nothing, Nothing
```

This sample adds one of the more complicated types of graphic elements to a map or page layout, depending on the current view. The callout is added to the center of the view.

3 The IElement interface is used to set the geometry of the element. The IElement interface is obtained by performing a QueryInterface on the ITextElement interface.

2 A TextElement object is created and its Text property is set. This is the object that will be added to the graphics container.

1 The IMxDocument interface is obtained from the ThisDocument global variable.

ArcMap

5 The geometry of the text element is a point. A new Point object is created and the coordinates are set, then the Geometry property of the TextElement is assigned this newly created point.

Geometry

4 The center of the active view is calculated. This will be used to place the text element.

10 The graphics layer is redrawn to display the newly added text element. Once again, notice the use of the PartialRefresh method.

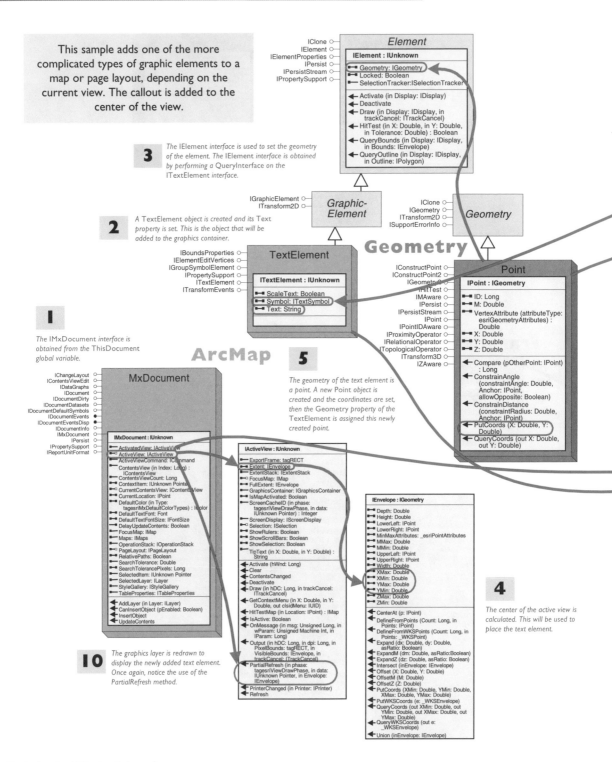

Element

IClone
IElement
IElementProperties
IPersist
IPersistStream
IPropertySupport

IElement : IUnknown
- Geometry: IGeometry
- Locked: Boolean
- SelectionTracker:ISelectionTracker

- Activate (in Display: IDisplay)
- Deactivate
- Draw (in Display: IDisplay, in trackCancel: ITrackCancel)
- HitTest (in X: Double, in Y: Double, in Tolerance: Double) : Boolean
- QueryBounds (in Display: IDisplay, in Bounds: IEnvelope)
- QueryOutline (in Display: IDisplay, in Outline: IPolygon)

Graphic-Element

IGraphicElement
ITransform2D

Geometry

IClone
IGeometry
ITransform2D
ISupportErrorInfo

TextElement

IBoundsProperties
IElementEditVertices
IGroupSymbolElement
IPropertySupport
ITextElement
ITransformEvents

ITextElement : IUnknown
- ScaleText: Boolean
- Symbol: ITextSymbol
- Text: String

Point

IConstructPoint
IConstructPoint2
IGeometry
IHitTest
IMAware
IPersist
IPersistStream
IPoint
IPointIDAware
IProximityOperator
IRelationalOperator
ITopologicalOperator
ITransform3D
IZAware

IPoint : IGeometry
- ID: Long
- M: Double
- VertexAttribute (attributeType: esriGeometryAttributes) : Double
- X: Double
- Y: Double
- Z: Double

- Compare (pOtherPoint: IPoint) : Long
- ConstrainAngle (constraintAngle: Double, Anchor: IPoint, allowOpposite: Boolean)
- ConstrainDistance (constraintRadius: Double, Anchor: IPoint)
- PutCoords (X: Double, Y: Double)
- QueryCoords (out X: Double, out Y: Double)

MxDocument

IChangeLayout
IContentsViewEdit
IDataGraphs
IDocument
IDocumentDirty
IDocumentDatasets
IDocumentDefaultSymbols
IDocumentEvents
IDocumentEventsDisp
IDocumentInfo
IMxDocument
IPersist
IPropertySupport
IReportUnitFormat

IMxDocument : IUnknown
- ActivatedView: IActiveView
- ActiveView: IActiveView
- ActiveViewCommand: ICommand
- ContentsView (in Index: Long) : IContentsView
- ContentsViewCount: Long
- ContextItem: IUnknown Pointer
- CurrentContentsView: IContentsView
- CurrentLocation: IPoint
- DefaultColor (in Type: tagesriMxDefaultColorTypes) : IColor
- DefaultTextFont: Font
- DefaultTextFontSize: IFontSize
- DelayUpdateContents: Boolean
- FocusMap: IMap
- Maps: IMaps
- OperationStack: IOperationStack
- PageLayout : IPageLayout
- RelativePaths: Boolean
- SearchTolerance: Double
- SearchTolerancePixels: Long
- SelectedItem: IUnknown Pointer
- SelectedLayer: ILayer
- StyleGallery: IStyleGallery
- TableProperties: ITableProperties

- AddLayer (in Layer: ILayer)
- CanInsertObject (pEnabled: Boolean)
- InsertObject
- UpdateContents

IActiveView : IUnknown
- ExportFrame: tagRECT
- Extent: IEnvelope
- ExtentStack: IExtentStack
- FocusMap: IMap
- FullExtent: IEnvelope
- GraphicsContainer: IGraphicsContainer
- IsMapActivated: Boolean
- ScreenCacheID (in phase: tagesriViewDrawPhase, in data: IUnknown Pointer) : Integer
- ScreenDisplay: IScreenDisplay
- Selection: ISelection
- ShowRulers: Boolean
- ShowScrollBars: Boolean
- ShowSelection: Boolean
- TipText (in X: Double, in Y: Double) : String

- Activate (hWnd: Long)
- Clear
- ContentsChanged
- Deactivate
- Draw (in hDC: Long, in trackCancel: ITrackCancel)
- GetContextMenu (in X: Double, in Y: Double, out clsidMenu: IUID)
- HitTestMap (in Location: IPoint) : IMap
- IsActive: Boolean
- OnMessage (in msg: Unsigned Long, in wParam: Unsigned Machine Int, in lParam: Long)
- Output (in hDC: Long, in dpi: Long, in PixelBounds: tagRECT, in VisibleBounds: IEnvelope, in trackCancel: ITrackCancel)
- PartialRefresh (in phase: tagesriViewDrawPhase, in data: IUnknown Pointer, in Envelope: IEnvelope)
- PrinterChanged (in Printer: IPrinter)
- Refresh

IEnvelope : IGeometry
- Depth: Double
- Height: Double
- LowerLeft: IPoint
- LowerRight: IPoint
- MinPointAttributes : _esriPointAttributes
- MMax: Double
- MMin: Double
- UpperLeft: IPoint
- UpperRight: IPoint
- Width: Double
- XMax: Double
- XMin: Double
- YMax: Double
- YMin: Double
- ZMax: Double
- ZMin: Double

- CenterAt (p: IPoint)
- DefineFromPoints (Count: Long, in Points: IPoint)
- DefineFromWKSPoints (Count: Long, in Points: _WKSPoint)
- Expand (dx: Double, dy: Double, asRatio: Boolean)
- ExpandM (dm: Double, asRatio: Boolean)
- ExpandZ (dz: Double, asRatio: Boolean)
- Intersect (inEnvelope: IEnvelope)
- Offset (X: Double, Y: Double)
- OffsetM (M: Double)
- OffsetZ (Z: Double)
- PutCoords (XMin: Double, YMin: Double, XMax: Double, YMax: Double)
- PutWKSCoords (e: _WKSEnvelope)
- QueryCoords (out XMin: Double, out YMin: Double, out XMax: Double, out YMax: Double)
- QueryWKSCoords (out e: _WKSEnvelope)
- Union (inEnvelope: IEnvelope)

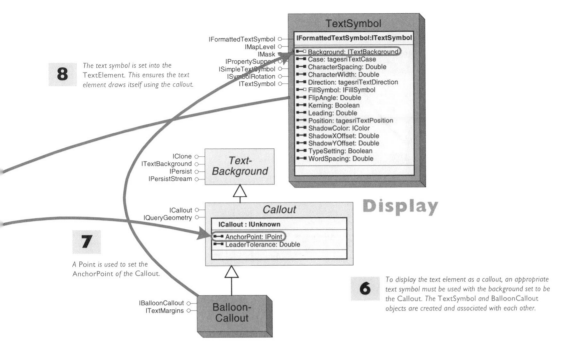

TextSymbol

IFormattedTextSymbol ○
IMapLevel ○
IMask ○
IPropertySupport ○
ISimpleTextSymbol ○
ISymbolRotation ○
ITextSymbol ○

IFormattedTextSymbol:ITextSymbol

- Background: ITextBackground
- Case: tagesriTextCase
- CharacterSpacing: Double
- CharacterWidth: Double
- Direction: tagesriTextDirection
- FillSymbol: IFillSymbol
- FlipAngle: Double
- Kerning: Boolean
- Leading: Double
- Position: tagesriTextPosition
- ShadowColor: IColor
- ShadowXOffset: Double
- ShadowYOffset: Double
- TypeSetting: Boolean
- WordSpacing: Double

8 *The text symbol is set into the TextElement. This ensures the text element draws itself using the callout.*

IClone ○
ITextBackground ○
IPersist ○
IPersistStream ○

Text-Background

Display

ICallout ○
IQueryGeometry ○

Callout

ICallout : IUnknown

- AnchorPoint: IPoint
- LeaderTolerance: Double

7

A Point is used to set the AnchorPoint of the Callout.

IBalloonCallout ○
ITextMargins ○

Balloon-Callout

6 *To display the text element as a callout, an appropriate text symbol must be used with the background set to be the Callout. The TextSymbol and BalloonCallout objects are created and associated with each other.*

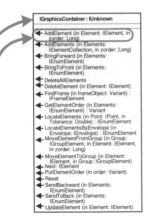

IGraphicsContainer : IUnknown

- AddElement (in Element: IElement, in zorder: Long)
- AddElements (in Elements: IElementCollection, in zorder: Long)
- BringForward (in Elements: IEnumElement)
- BringToFront (in Elements: IEnumElement)
- DeleteAllElements
- DeleteElement (in Element: IElement)
- FindFrame (in frameObject: Variant) : IFrameElement
- GetElementOrder (in Elements: IEnumElement) : Variant
- LocateElements (in Point: IPoint, in Tolerance: Double) : IEnumElement
- LocateElementsByEnvelope (in Envelope: IEnvelope) : IEnumElement
- MoveElementFromGroup (in Group: IGroupElement, in Element: IElement, in zorder: Long)
- MoveElementToGroup (in Element: IElement, in Group: IGroupElement)
- Next: IElement
- PutElementOrder (in order: Variant)
- Reset
- SendBackward (in Elements: IEnumElement)
- SendToBack (in Elements: IEnumElement)
- UpdateElement (in Element: IElement)

9

The graphics container associated with the active view of the document is obtained by performing a QueryInterface on the IActiveView interface. The TextElement is then added to the container. This ensures that the element is saved within the map document.

Add this code to the Click event of a UIButtonControl in ArcMap.

```
1   Dim pMxDoc As IMxDocument
    Set pMxDoc = ThisDocument

2   Dim pTextElement As ITextElement
    Set pTextElement = New TextElement

3   Dim pElement As IElement
    Set pElement = pTextElement
    pTextElement.Text = "Text in a callout" & vbCrLf & "In middle of screen"

4   Dim dMidX As Double, dMidY As Double, pPoint As IPoint
    dMidX = (pMxDoc.ActiveView.Extent.XMax + pMxDoc.ActiveView.Extent.XMin) / 2
    dMidY = (pMxDoc.ActiveView.Extent.YMax + pMxDoc.ActiveView.Extent.YMin) / 2
5   Set pPoint = New Point
    pPoint.PutCoords dMidX, dMidY
    pElement.Geometry = pPoint

    Dim pTextSymbol As IFormattedTextSymbol
    Set pTextSymbol = New TextSymbol
6   Dim pCallout As ICallout
    Set pCallout = New BalloonCallout
    Set pTextSymbol.Background = pCallout
7   pPoint.PutCoords dMidX - pMxDoc.ActiveView.Extent.Width / 4, _
      dMidY + pMxDoc.ActiveView.Extent.Width / 20
    pCallout.AnchorPoint = pPoint

8   pTextElement.Symbol = pTextSymbol
9   Dim pGraphicsContainer As IGraphicsContainer
    Set pGraphicsContainer = pMxDoc.ActiveView
    pGraphicsContainer.AddElement pElement, 0
    pElement.Activate pMxDoc.ActiveView.ScreenDisplay
10  pMxDoc.ActiveView.PartialRefresh esriViewGraphics, Nothing, Nothing
```

This sample takes the current cursor coordinates and converts them from pixels to map units. It then projects these map coordinates to a projected and geographic spatial reference system, displaying the results in the Status Bar.

Framework

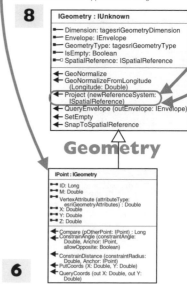

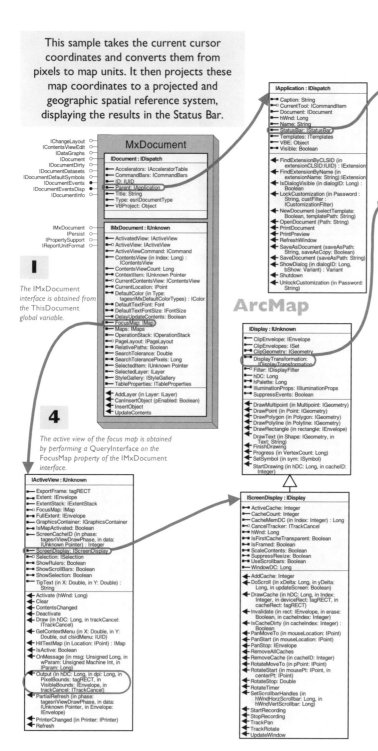

IStatusBar : IUnknown
- Message (in pane: Long) : String
- Panes: Long
- ProgressAnimation : IAnimationProgressor
- ProgressBar: IStepProgressor
- Visible: Boolean
- HideProgressAnimation
- HideProgressBar
- PlayProgressAnimation (in playAnim: Boolean)
- ShowProgressAnimation (in Message: String, in animationPath: String)
- ShowProgressBar (in Message: String, in min: Long, in max: Long, in Step: Long, in onePanel: Boolean)
- StepProgressBar

9

The string is displayed in the status bar of the ArcMap application.

IApplication : IDispatch
- Caption: String
- CurrentTool : ICommandItem
- Document: IDocument
- hWnd: Long
- Name: String
- StatusBar: IStatusBar
- Templates: ITemplates
- VBE: Object
- Visible: Boolean
- FindExtensionByCLSID (in extensionCLSID:IUID) : IExtension
- FindExtensionByName (in extensionName: String):IExtension
- IsDialogVisible (in dialogID: Long) : Boolean
- LockCustomization (in Password : String, custFilter : ICustomizationFilter)
- NewDocument (selectTemplate: Boolean, templatePath: String)
- OpenDocument (Path: String)
- PrintDocument
- PrintPreview
- RefreshWindow
- SaveAsDocument (saveAsPath: String, saveAsCopy: Boolean)
- SaveDocument (saveAsPath: String)
- ShowDialog (in dialogID: Long, bShow: Variant) : Variant
- Shutdown
- UnlockCustomization (in Password: String)

ArcMap

IDisplayTransformation:ITransformation
- Bounds: IEnvelope
- ConstrainedBounds: IEnvelope
- DeviceFrame: tagRECT
- FittedBounds: IEnvelope
- ReferenceScale: Double
- Resolution: Double
- Rotation: Double
- ScaleRatio: Double
- SpatialReference: ISpatialReference
- SuppressEvents: Boolean
- Units: esriUnits
- VisibleBounds: IEnvelope
- ZoomResolution: Boolean
- FromMapPoint (in mapPoint: IPoint, out X: Long, out Y: Long)
- FromPoints (in pointDistance: Double) : Double
- ToMapPoint (in X: Long, in Y: Long) : IPoint
- ToPoints (in mapDistance: Double) : Double
- TransformCoords (in mapPoints: _WKSPoint, in devPoints: tagPOINT, in numPoints: Long, in options: Long)
- TransformRect (in mapRect: IEnvelope, in devRect: tagRECT, in options: Long)

5

The cursor location in pixels (x,y) is converted to map units using a method on the IDisplay-Transformation interface, then stored in a Point object. This point object will have the same spatial reference as the map.

MxDocument

IDocument : IDispatch
- Accelerators: IAcceleratorTable
- CommandBars: ICommandBars
- ID: IUID
- Parent: IApplication
- Title: String
- Type: esriDocumentType
- VBProject: Object

IChangeLayout
IContentsViewEdit
IDataGraphs
IDocument
IDocumentDirty
IDocumentDatasets
IDocumentDefaultSymbols
IDocumentEvents
IDocumentEventsDisp
IDocumentInfo

IMxDocument
IPersist
IPropertySupport
IReportUnitFormat

1

The IMxDocument interface is obtained from the ThisDocument global variable.

IMxDocument : IUnknown
- ActivatedView: IActiveView
- ActiveView: IActiveView
- ActiveViewCommand: ICommand
- ContentsView (in Index: Long) : IContentsView
- ContentsViewCount: Long
- CurrentContentsView : IContentsView
- CurrentLocation: IPoint
- DefaultColor (in Type: tagesriMxDefaultColorTypes) : IColor
- DefaultTextFont: Font
- DefaultTextSize: IFontSize
- DelayUpdateContents: Boolean
- FocusMap: IMap
- Maps: IMaps
- OperationStack: IOperationStack
- PageLayout: IPageLayout
- RelativePaths: Boolean
- SearchTolerance: Double
- SearchTolerancePixels: Long
- SelectedItem: IUnknown Pointer
- SelectedLayer: ILayer
- StyleGallery: IStyleGallery
- TableProperties: ITableProperties
- AddLayer (in Layer: ILayer)
- CanInsertObject (pEnabled: Boolean)
- InsertObject
- UpdateContents

The cursor point is projected from the Cassini coordinate system into the WGS 84 reference system and the coordinates are appended to a string.

8

IGeometry : IUnknown
- Dimension: tagesriGeometryDimension
- Envelope: IEnvelope
- GeometryType: tagesriGeometryType
- IsEmpty: Boolean
- SpatialReference: ISpatialReference
- GeoNormalize
- GeoNormalizeFromLongitude (Longitude: Double)
- Project (newReferenceSystem: ISpatialReference)
- QueryEnvelope (outEnvelope: IEnvelope)
- SetEmpty
- SnapToSpatialReference

4

The active view of the focus map is obtained by performing a QueryInterface on the FocusMap property of the IMxDocument interface.

IActiveView : IUnknown
- ExportFrame: tagRECT
- Extent: IEnvelope
- ExtentStack: IExtentStack
- FocusMap: IMap
- FullExtent: IEnvelope
- GraphicsContainer: IGraphicsContainer
- IsMapActivated: Boolean
- ScreenCacheID (in phase: tagesriViewDrawPhase, in data: IUnknown Pointer) : Integer
- ScreenDisplay: IScreenDisplay
- Selection: ISelection
- ShowRulers: Boolean
- ShowScrollBars: Boolean
- ShowSelection: Boolean
- TipText (in X: Double, in Y: Double) : String
- Activate (hWnd: Long)
- Clear
- ContentsChanged
- Deactivate
- Draw (in hDC: Long, in trackCancel: ITrackCancel)
- GetContextMenu (in X: Double, in Y: Double, out clsidMenu: IUID)
- HitTestMap (in Location: IPoint) : IMap
- IsActive: Boolean
- OnMessage (in msg: Unsigned Long, in wParam: Unsigned Machine Int, in lParam: Long)
- Output (in hDC: Long, in dpi: Long, in PixelBounds: tagRECT, in VisibleBounds: IEnvelope, in trackCancel: ITrackCancel)
- PartialRefresh (in phase: tagesriViewDrawPhase, in data: IUnknown Pointer, in Envelope: IEnvelope)
- PrinterChanged (in Printer: IPrinter)
- Refresh

IDisplay : IUnknown
- ClipEnvelope: IEnvelope
- ClipEnvelopes: ISet
- ClipGeometry: IGeometry
- DisplayTransformation: IDisplayTransformation
- Filter: IDisplayFilter
- hDC: Long
- hPalette: Long
- IlluminationProps: IIlluminationProps
- SuppressEvents: Boolean
- DrawMultipoint (in Multipoint: IGeometry)
- DrawPoint (in Point: IGeometry)
- DrawPolygon (in Polygon: IGeometry)
- DrawPolyline (in Polyline: IGeometry)
- DrawRectangle (in rectangle: IEnvelope)
- DrawText (in Shape: IGeometry, in Text: String)
- FinishDrawing
- Progress (in VertexCount: Long)
- SetSymbol (in sym: ISymbol)
- StartDrawing (in hDC: Long, in cacheID: Integer)

IScreenDisplay : IDisplay
- ActiveCache: Integer
- CacheCount: Integer
- CacheMemDC (in Index: Integer) : Long
- CancelTracker: ITrackCancel
- hWnd: Long
- IsFirstCacheTransparent: Boolean
- IsFramed: Boolean
- ScaleContents: Boolean
- SuppressResize: Boolean
- UseScrollbars: Boolean
- WindowDC: Long
- AddCache: Integer
- DoScroll (in xDelta: Long, in yDelta: Long, in updateScreen: Boolean)
- DrawCache (in hDC: Long, in Index: Integer, in deviceRect: tagRECT, in cacheRect: tagRECT)
- Invalidate (in rect: IEnvelope, in erase: Boolean, in cacheIndex: Integer)
- IsCacheDirty (in cacheIndex: Integer) : Boolean
- PanMoveTo (in mouseLocation: IPoint)
- PanStart (in mouseLocation: IPoint)
- PanStop: IEnvelope
- RemoveAllCaches
- RemoveCache (in cacheID: Integer)
- RotateMoveTo (in pPoint: IPoint)
- RotateStart (in mousePt: IPoint, in centerPt: IPoint)
- RotateStop: Double
- RotateTimer
- SetScrollbarHandles (in hWndHorzScrollbar: Long, in hWndVertScrollbar: Long)
- StartRecording
- StopRecording
- TrackPan
- TrackRotate
- UpdateWindow

Geometry

IPoint : IGeometry
- ID: Long
- M: Double
- VertexAttribute (attributeType: esriGeometryAttributes) : Double
- X: Double
- Y: Double
- Z: Double
- Compare (pOtherPoint: IPoint) : Long
- ConstrainAngle (constraintAngle: Double, Anchor: IPoint, allowOpposite: Boolean)
- ConstrainDistance (constraintRadius: Double, Anchor: IPoint)
- PutCoords (X: Double, Y: Double)
- QueryCoords (out X: Double, out Y: Double)

6

The cursor point is projected from the map coordinates into the Cassini coordinate system and the projected coordinates are written to a string.

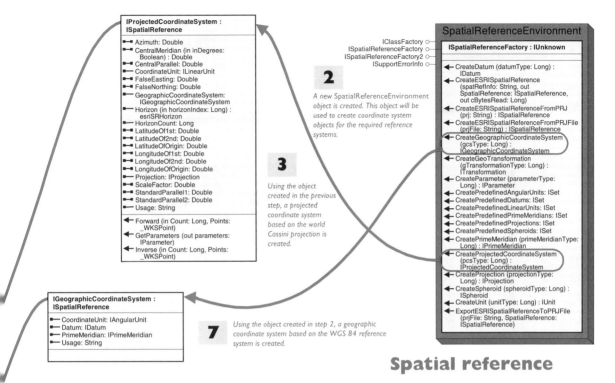

IProjectedCoordinateSystem :
ISpatialReference

- Azimuth: Double
- CentralMeridian (in inDegrees:
  Boolean) : Double
- CentralParallel: Double
- CoordinateUnit: ILinearUnit
- FalseEasting: Double
- FalseNorthing: Double
- GeographicCoordinateSystem:
  IGeographicCoordinateSystem
- Horizon (in horizonIndex: Long) :
  esriSRHorizon
- HorizonCount: Long
- LatitudeOf1st: Double
- LatitudeOf2nd: Double
- LatitudeOfOrigin: Double
- LongitudeOf1st: Double
- LongitudeOf2nd: Double
- LongitudeOfOrigin: Double
- Projection: IProjection
- ScaleFactor: Double
- StandardParallel1: Double
- StandardParallel2: Double
- Usage: String

- Forward (in Count: Long, Points:
  _WKSPoint)
- GetParameters (out parameters:
  IParameter)
- Inverse (in Count: Long, Points:
  _WKSPoint)

SpatialReferenceEnvironment

IClassFactory
ISpatialReferenceFactory
ISpatialReferenceFactory2
ISupportErrorInfo

ISpatialReferenceFactory : IUnknown

- CreateDatum (datumType: Long) :
  IDatum
- CreateESRISpatialReference
  (spatRefInfo: String, out
  SpatialReference: ISpatialReference,
  out cBytesRead: Long)
- CreateESRISpatialReferenceFromPRJ
  (prj: String) : ISpatialReference
- CreateESRISpatialReferenceFromPRJFile
  (prjFile: String) : ISpatialReference
- CreateGeographicCoordinateSystem
  (gcsType: Long) :
  IGeographicCoordinateSystem
- CreateGeoTransformation
  (gTransformationType: Long) :
  ITransformation
- CreateParameter (parameterType:
  Long) : IParameter
- CreatePredefinedAngularUnits: ISet
- CreatePredefinedDatums: ISet
- CreatePredefinedLinearUnits: ISet
- CreatePredefinedPrimeMeridians: ISet
- CreatePredefinedProjections: ISet
- CreatePredefinedSpheroids: ISet
- CreatePrimeMeridian (primeMeridianType:
  Long) : IPrimeMeridian
- CreateProjectedCoordinateSystem
  (pcsType: Long) :
  IProjectedCoordinateSystem
- CreateProjection (projectionType:
  Long) : IProjection
- CreateSpheroid (spheroidType: Long) :
  ISpheroid
- CreateUnit (unitType: Long) : IUnit
- ExportESRISpatialReferenceToPRJFile
  (prjFile: String, SpatialReference:
  ISpatialReference)

2

A new SpatialReferenceEnvironment
object is created. This object will be
used to create coordinate system
objects for the required reference
systems.

3

Using the object
created in the previous
step, a projected
coordinate system
based on the world
Cassini projection is
created.

IGeographicCoordinateSystem :
ISpatialReference

- CoordinateUnit: IAngularUnit
- Datum: IDatum
- PrimeMeridian: IPrimeMeridian
- Usage: String

7 Using the object created in step 2, a geographic
coordinate system based on the WGS 84 reference
system is created.

Spatial reference

Add this code to the MouseMove event of a UIToolControl in ArcMap.

```
1  Dim pMxDoc As IMxDocument
   Set pMxDoc = ThisDocument

2  Dim pSpatialRefFactory As ISpatialReferenceFactory
   Set pSpatialRefFactory = New SpatialReferenceEnvironment

   Dim pProjectedCoodinateSystem As IProjectedCoordinateSystem
3  Set pProjectedCoodinateSystem =
   pSpatialRefFactory.CreateProjectedCoordinateSystem(esriSRProjCS_World_Cassini)

4  Dim pActiveView As IActiveView
   Set pActiveView = pMxDoc.FocusMap

5  Dim pPoint As IPoint
   Set pPoint = pActiveView.ScreenDisplay.DisplayTransformation.ToMapPoint(x, y)

6  pPoint.Project pProjectedCoordinateSystem
   Dim sMessage As String
   sMessage = "Cassini : " & CStr(Round(pPoint.x, 2)) & ", " & _
   CStr(Round(pPoint.y, 2))

7  Dim pGeographicCoordinateSystem As IGeographicCoordinateSystem
   Set pGeographicCoordinateSystem = _
   pSpatialRefFactory.CreateGeographicCoordinateSystem(esriSRGeoCS_WGS1984)

8  pPoint.Project pGeographicCoordinateSystem
   sMessage = sMessage & " and WGS84 : " & CStr(Round(pPoint.x, 2)) & ", " &
   CStr(Round(pPoint.y, 2))
9  ThisDocument.Parent.StatusBar.Message(0) = sMessage
```

This sample displays the pixel value of the first raster layer in the map. This sample will display multiplane data in the form "(value 1, value 2, value 3)" for three planes.

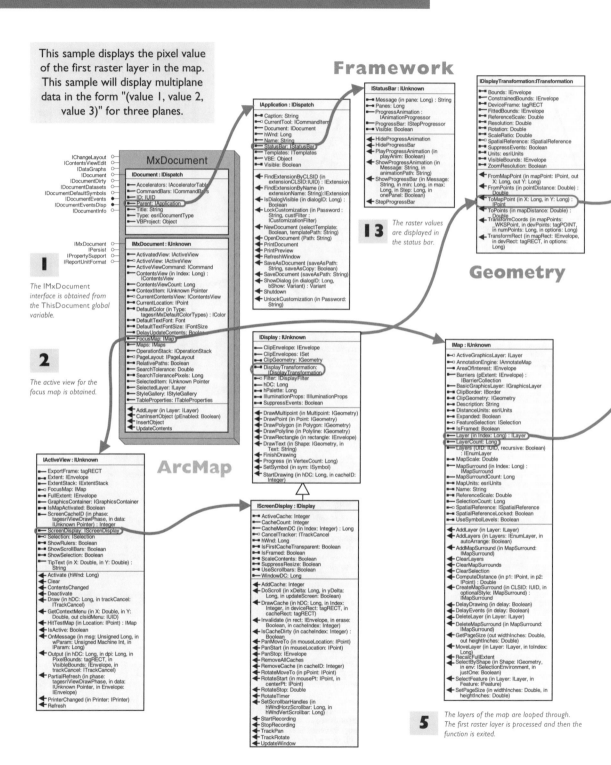

Framework

IStatusBar : IUnknown
- Message (in pane: Long) : String
- Panes: Long
- ProgressAnimation : IAnimationProgressor
- ProgressBar : IStepProgressor
- Visible: Boolean
- HideProgressAnimation
- HideProgressBar
- PlayProgressAnimation (in playAnim: Boolean)
- ShowProgressAnimation (in Message: String, in animationPath: String)
- ShowProgressBar (in Message: String, in min: Long, in max: Long, in Step: Long, in onePanel: Boolean)
- StepProgressBar

IApplication : IDispatch
- Caption: String
- CurrentTool: ICommandItem
- Document: IDocument
- hWnd: Long
- Name: String
- StatusBar : IStatusBar
- Templates : ITemplates
- VBE: Object
- Visible: Boolean
- FindExtensionByCLSID (in extensionCLSID:IUID) : IExtension
- FindExtensionByName (in extensionName: String):IExtension
- IsDialogVisible (in dialogID: Long) : Boolean
- LockCustomization (in Password : String, custFilter : ICustomizationFilter)
- NewDocument (selectTemplate: Boolean, templatePath: String)
- OpenDocument (Path: String)
- PrintDocument
- PrintPreview
- RefreshWindow
- SaveAsDocument (saveAsPath: String, saveAsCopy: Boolean)
- SaveDocument (saveAsPath: String)
- ShowDialog (in dialogID: Long, bShow: Variant) : Variant
- Shutdown
- UnlockCustomization (in Password: String)

IDisplayTransformation:ITransformation
- Bounds: IEnvelope
- ConstrainedBounds: IEnvelope
- DeviceFrame: tagRECT
- FittedBounds: IEnvelope
- ReferenceScale: Double
- Resolution: Double
- Rotation: Double
- ScaleRatio: Double
- SpatialReference: ISpatialReference
- SuppressEvents: Boolean
- Units: esriUnits
- VisibleBounds: IEnvelope
- ZoomResolution: Boolean
- FromMapPoint (in mapPoint: IPoint, out X: Long, out Y: Long)
- FromPoints (in pointDistance: Double) : IPoint
- ToMapPoint (in X: Long, in Y: Long) : IPoint
- ToPoints (in mapDistance: Double) : Double
- TransformCoords (in mapPoints: WKSPoint, in devPoints: tagPOINT, in numPoints: Long, in options: Long)
- TransformRect (in mapRect: IEnvelope, in devRect: tagRECT, in options: Long)

|13| The raster values are displayed in the status bar.

Geometry

MxDocument

IChangeLayout
IContentsViewEdit
IDataGraphs
IDocument
IDocumentDirty
IDocumentDatasets
IDocumentDefaultSymbols
IDocumentEvents
IDocumentEventsDisp
IDocumentInfo

IDocument : IDispatch
- Accelerators: IAcceleratorTable
- CommandBars: ICommandBars
- ID: IUID
- Parent: IApplication
- Title: String
- Type: esriDocumentType
- VBProject: Object

|1| The IMxDocument interface is obtained from the ThisDocument global variable.

IMxDocument
IPersist
IPropertySupport
IReportUnitFormat

IMxDocument : IUnknown
- ActivatedView: IActiveView
- ActiveView: IActiveView
- ActiveViewCommand: ICommand
- ContentsView (in Index: Long) : IContentsView
- ContentsViewCount: Long
- ContextItem: IUnknown Pointer
- CurrentContentsView: IContentsView
- CurrentLocation: IPoint
- DefaultColor (in Type: tagesriMxDefaultColorTypes): IColor
- DefaultTextFont: Font
- DefaultTextFontSize: IFontSize
- DelayUpdateContents: Boolean
- FocusMap: IMap
- Maps: IMaps
- OperationStack: IOperationStack
- PageLayout: IPageLayout
- RelativePaths: Boolean
- SearchTolerance: Double
- SearchTolerancePixels: Long
- SelectedItem: IUnknown Pointer
- SelectedLayer: ILayer
- StyleGallery: IStyleGallery
- TableProperties: ITableProperties
- AddLayer (in Layer: ILayer)
- CanInsertObject (pEnabled: Boolean)
- InsertObject
- UpdateContents

|2| The active view for the focus map is obtained.

IDisplay : IUnknown
- ClipEnvelope: IEnvelope
- ClipEnvelopes: ISet
- ClipGeometry: IGeometry
- DisplayTransformation: IDisplayTransformation
- Filter: IDisplayFilter
- hDC: Long
- hPalette: Long
- IlluminationProps: IIlluminationProps
- SuppressEvents: Boolean
- DrawMultipoint (in Multipoint: IGeometry)
- DrawPoint (in Point: IGeometry)
- DrawPolygon (in Polygon: IGeometry)
- DrawPolyline (in Polyline: IGeometry)
- DrawRectangle (in rectangle: IEnvelope)
- DrawText (in Shape: IGeometry, in Text: String)
- FinishDrawing
- Progress (in VertexCount: Long)
- SetSymbol (in sym: ISymbol)
- StartDrawing (in hDC: Long, in cacheID: Integer)

IMap : IUnknown
- ActiveGraphicsLayer: ILayer
- AnnotationEngine: IAnnotateMap
- AreaOfInterest: IEnvelope
- Barriers (pExtent: IEnvelope) : IBarrierCollection
- BasicGraphicsLayer: IGraphicsLayer
- ClipBorder: IBorder
- ClipGeometry: IGeometry
- Description: String
- DistanceUnits: esriUnits
- Expanded: Boolean
- FeatureSelection: ISelection
- IsFramed: Boolean
- Layer (in Index: Long) : ILayer
- LayerCount: Long
- Layers (UID: IUID, recursive: Boolean) : IEnumLayer
- MapScale: Double
- MapSurround (in Index: Long) : IMapSurround
- MapSurroundCount: Long
- MapUnits: esriUnits
- Name: String
- ReferenceScale: Double
- SelectionCount: Long
- SpatialReference: ISpatialReference
- SpatialReferenceLocked: Boolean
- UseSymbolLevels: Boolean
- AddLayer (in Layer: ILayer)
- AddLayers (in Layers: IEnumLayer, in autoArrange: Boolean)
- AddMapSurround (in MapSurround: IMapSurround)
- ClearLayers
- ClearMapSurrounds
- ClearSelection
- ComputeDistance (in p1: IPoint, in p2:) : Double
- CreateMapSurround (in CLSID: IUID, in optionalStyle: IMapSurround): IMapSurround
- DelayDrawing (in delay: Boolean)
- DelayEvents (in delay: Boolean)
- DeleteLayer (in Layer: ILayer)
- DeleteMapSurround (in MapSurround: IMapSurround)
- GetPageSize (out widthInches: Double, out heightInches: Double)
- MoveLayer (in Layer: ILayer, in toIndex: Long)
- RecalcFullExtent
- SelectByShape (in Shape: IGeometry, in env: ISelectionEnvironment, in justOne: Boolean)
- SelectFeature (in Layer: ILayer, in Feature: IFeature)
- SetPageSize (in widthInches: Double, in heightInches: Double)

IActiveView : IUnknown
- ExportFrame: tagRECT
- Extent: IEnvelope
- ExtentStack: IExtentStack
- FocusMap: IMap
- FullExtent: IEnvelope
- GraphicsContainer: IGraphicsContainer
- IsMapActivated: Boolean
- ScreenCacheID (in phase: tagesriViewDrawPhase, in data: IUnknown Pointer) : Integer
- ScreenDisplay: IScreenDisplay
- Selection: ISelection
- ShowRulers: Boolean
- ShowScrollBars: Boolean
- ShowSelection: Boolean
- TipText (in X: Double, in Y: Double) : String
- Activate (hWnd: Long)
- Clear
- ContentsChanged
- Deactivate
- Draw (in hDC: Long, in trackCancel: ITrackCancel)
- GetContextMenu (in X: Double, in Y: Double, out clsidMenu: IUID)
- HitTestMap (in Location: IPoint) : IMap
- IsActive: Boolean
- OnMessage (in msg: Unsigned Long, in wParam: Unsigned Machine Int, in lParam: Long)
- Output (in hDC: Long, in dpi: Long, in PixelBounds: tagRECT, in VisibleBounds: IEnvelope, in trackCancel: ITrackCancel)
- PartialRefresh (in phase: tagesriViewDrawPhase, in data: IUnknown Pointer, in Envelope: IEnvelope)
- PrinterChanged (in Printer: IPrinter)
- Refresh

ArcMap

IScreenDisplay : IDisplay
- ActiveCache: Integer
- CacheCount: Integer
- CacheMemDC (in Index: Integer) : Long
- CancelTracker: ITrackCancel
- hWnd: Long
- IsFirstCacheTransparent: Boolean
- IsFramed: Boolean
- ScaleContents: Boolean
- SuppressResize: Boolean
- UseScrollbars: Boolean
- WindowDC: Long
- AddCache: Integer
- DoScroll (in xDelta: Long, in yDelta: Long, in updateScreen: Boolean)
- DrawCache (in hDC: Long, in Index: Integer, in deviceRect: tagRECT, in cacheRect: tagRECT)
- Invalidate (in rect: IEnvelope, in erase: Boolean, in cacheIndex: Integer)
- IsCacheDirty (in cacheIndex: Integer) : Boolean
- PanMoveTo (in mouseLocation: IPoint)
- PanStart (in mouseLocation: IPoint)
- PanStop: IEnvelope
- RemoveAllCaches
- RemoveCache (in cacheID: Integer)
- RotateMoveTo (in pPoint: IPoint)
- RotateStart (in mousePt: IPoint, in centerPt: IPoint)
- RotateStop: Double
- RotateTimer
- SetScrollbarHandles (in hWndHorzScrollbar: Long, in hWndVertScrollbar: Long)
- StartRecording
- StopRecording
- TrackPan
- TrackRotate
- UpdateWindow

|5| The layers of the map are looped through. The first raster layer is processed and then the function is exited.

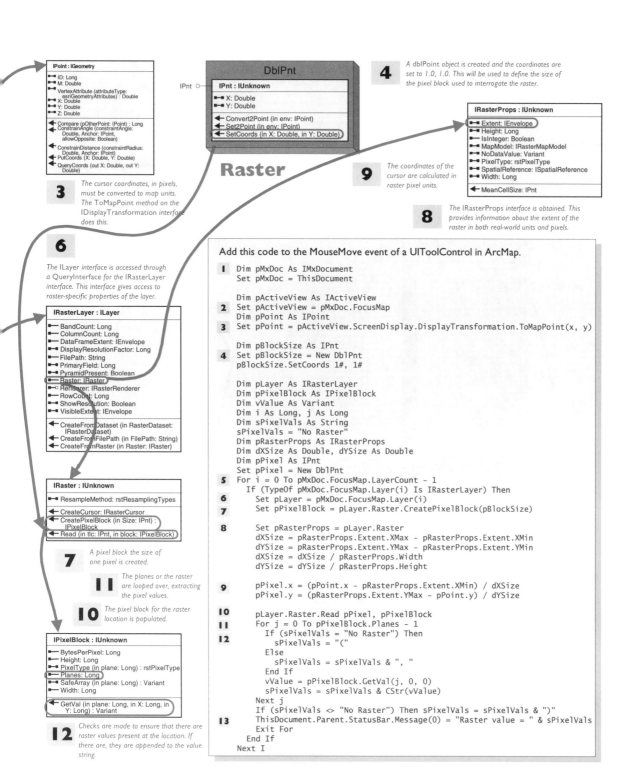

IPoint : IGeometry

- ID: Long
- M: Double
- VertexAttribute (attributeType: esriGeometryAttributes) : Double
- X: Double
- Y: Double
- Z: Double

- Compare (pOtherPoint: IPoint) : Long
- ConstrainAngle (constraintAngle: Double, Anchor: IPoint, allowOpposite: IPoint)
- ConstrainDistance (constraintRadius: Double, Anchor: IPoint)
- PutCoords (X: Double, Y: Double)
- QueryCoords (out X: Double, out Y: Double)

IPnt ○—

DblPnt

IPnt : IUnknown

- X: Double
- Y: Double

- Convert2Point (in env: IPoint)
- Set2Point (in env: IPoint)
- SetCoords (in X: Double, in Y: Double)

4 A dblPoint object is created and the coordinates are set to 1.0, 1.0. This will be used to define the size of the pixel block used to interrogate the raster.

Raster

9 The coordinates of the cursor are calculated in raster pixel units.

IRasterProps : IUnknown

- Extent: IEnvelope
- Height: Long
- IsInteger: Boolean
- MapModel: IRasterMapModel
- NoDataValue: Variant
- PixelType: rstPixelType
- SpatialReference: ISpatialReference
- Width: Long

- MeanCellSize: IPnt

3 The cursor coordinates, in pixels, must be converted to map units. The ToMapPoint method on the IDisplayTransformation interface does this.

8 The IRasterProps interface is obtained. This provides information about the extent of the raster in both real-world units and pixels.

6

The ILayer interface is accessed through a QueryInterface for the IRasterLayer interface. This interface gives access to raster-specific properties of the layer.

IRasterLayer : ILayer

- BandCount: Long
- ColumnCount: Long
- DataFrameExtent: IEnvelope
- DisplayResolutionFactor: Long
- FilePath: String
- PrimaryField: Long
- PyramidPresent: Boolean
- Raster: IRaster
- Renderer: IRasterRenderer
- RowCount: Long
- ShowResolution: Boolean
- VisibleExtent: IEnvelope

- CreateFromDataset (in RasterDataset: IRasterDataset)
- CreateFromFilePath (in FilePath: String)
- CreateFromRaster (in Raster: IRaster)

IRaster : IUnknown

- ResampleMethod: rstResamplingTypes

- CreateCursor: IRasterCursor
- CreatePixelBlock (in Size: IPnt) : IPixelBlock
- Read (in tlc: IPnt, in block: IPixelBlock)

7 A pixel block the size of one pixel is created.

11 The planes or the raster are looped over, extracting the pixel values.

10 The pixel block for the raster location is populated.

IPixelBlock : IUnknown

- BytesPerPixel: Long
- Height: Long
- PixelType (in plane: Long) : rstPixelType
- Planes: Long
- SafeArray (in plane: Long) : Variant
- Width: Long

- GetVal (in plane: Long, in X: Long, in Y: Long) : Variant

12 Checks are made to ensure that there are raster values present at the location. If there are, they are appended to the value string.

Add this code to the MouseMove event of a UIToolControl in ArcMap.

```
 1   Dim pMxDoc As IMxDocument
     Set pMxDoc = ThisDocument

     Dim pActiveView As IActiveView
 2   Set pActiveView = pMxDoc.FocusMap
     Dim pPoint As IPoint
 3   Set pPoint = pActiveView.ScreenDisplay.DisplayTransformation.ToMapPoint(x, y)

     Dim pBlockSize As IPnt
 4   Set pBlockSize = New DblPnt
     pBlockSize.SetCoords 1#, 1#

     Dim pLayer As IRasterLayer
     Dim pPixelBlock As IPixelBlock
     Dim vValue As Variant
     Dim i As Long, j As Long
     Dim sPixelVals As String
     sPixelVals = "No Raster"
     Dim pRasterProps As IRasterProps
     Dim dXSize As Double, dYSize As Double
     Dim pPixel As IPnt
     Set pPixel = New DblPnt
 5   For i = 0 To pMxDoc.FocusMap.LayerCount - 1
       If (TypeOf pMxDoc.FocusMap.Layer(i) Is IRasterLayer) Then
 6       Set pLayer = pMxDoc.FocusMap.Layer(i)
 7       Set pPixelBlock = pLayer.Raster.CreatePixelBlock(pBlockSize)

 8       Set pRasterProps = pLayer.Raster
         dXSize = pRasterProps.Extent.XMax - pRasterProps.Extent.XMin
         dYSize = pRasterProps.Extent.YMax - pRasterProps.Extent.YMin
         dXSize = dXSize / pRasterProps.Width
         dYSize = dYSize / pRasterProps.Height

 9       pPixel.x = (pPoint.x - pRasterProps.Extent.XMin) / dXSize
         pPixel.y = (pRasterProps.Extent.YMax - pPoint.y) / dYSize

10       pLayer.Raster.Read pPixel, pPixelBlock
11       For j = 0 To pPixelBlock.Planes - 1
12         If (sPixelVals = "No Raster") Then
             sPixelVals = "("
           Else
             sPixelVals = sPixelVals & ", "
           End If
           vValue = pPixelBlock.GetVal(j, 0, 0)
           sPixelVals = sPixelVals & CStr(vValue)
         Next j
         If (sPixelVals <> "No Raster") Then sPixelVals = sPixelVals & ")"
13       ThisDocument.Parent.StatusBar.Message(0) = "Raster value = " & sPixelVals
         Exit For
       End If
     Next I
```

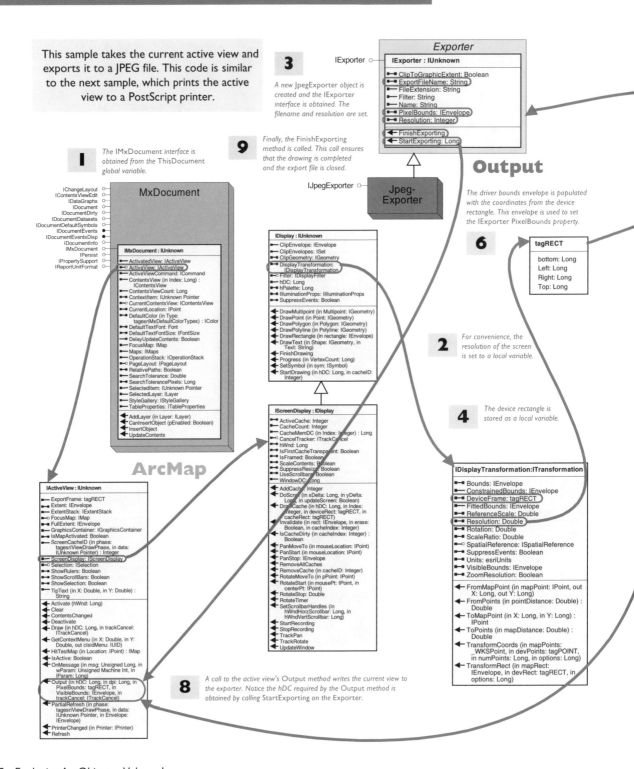

This sample takes the current active view and exports it to a JPEG file. This code is similar to the next sample, which prints the active view to a PostScript printer.

3 A new JpegExporter object is created and the IExporter interface is obtained. The filename and resolution are set.

Exporter

IExporter ○──

IExporter : IUnknown
- ClipToGraphicExtent: Boolean
- ExportFileName: String
- FileExtension: String
- Filter: String
- Name: String
- PixelBounds: IEnvelope
- Resolution: Integer
← FinishExporting
← StartExporting: Long

9 Finally, the FinishExporting method is called. This call ensures that the drawing is completed and the export file is closed.

IJpegExporter ○──

Jpeg-Exporter

Output

1 The IMxDocument interface is obtained from the ThisDocument global variable.

IChangeLayout ○
IContentsViewEdit ○
IDataGraphs ○
IDocument ○
IDocumentDirty ○
IDocumentDatasets ○
IDocumentDefaultSymbols ○
IDocumentEvents ●
IDocumentEventsDisp ○
IDocumentInfo ○
IMxDocument ○
IPersist ○
IPropertySupport ○
IReportUnitFormat ○

MxDocument

IMxDocument : IUnknown
- ActivatedView: IActiveView
- ActiveView: IActiveView
- ActiveViewCommand: ICommand
- ContentsView (in Index: Long) : IContentsView
- ContentsViewCount: Long
- ContextItem: IUnknown Pointer
- CurrentContentsView: IContentsView
- CurrentLocation: IPoint
- DefaultColor (in Type: tagesriMxDefaultColorTypes) : IColor
- DefaultTextFont: Font
- DefaultTextFontSize: IFontSize
- DelayUpdateContents: Boolean
- FocusMap: IMap
- Maps: IMaps
- OperationStack: IOperationStack
- PageLayout: IPageLayout
- RelativePaths: Boolean
- SearchTolerance: Double
- SearchTolerancePixels: Long
- SelectedItem: IUnknown Pointer
- SelectedLayer: ILayer
- StyleGallery: IStyleGallery
- TableProperties: ITableProperties
← AddLayer (in Layer: ILayer)
← CanInsertObject (pEnabled: Boolean)
← InsertObject
← UpdateContents

ArcMap

IActiveView : IUnknown
- ExportFrame: tagRECT
- Extent: IEnvelope
- ExtentStack: IExtentStack
- FocusMap: IMap
- FullExtent: IEnvelope
- GraphicsContainer: IGraphicsContainer
- IsMapActivated: Boolean
- ScreenCacheID (in phase: tagesriViewDrawPhase, in data: IUnknown Pointer) : Integer
- ScreenDisplay: IScreenDisplay
- Selection: ISelection
- ShowRulers: Boolean
- ShowScrollBars: Boolean
- ShowSelection: Boolean
- TipText (in X: Double, in Y: Double) : String
← Activate (hWnd: Long)
← Clear
← ContentsChanged
← Deactivate
← Draw (in hDC: Long, in trackCancel: ITrackCancel)
← GetContextMenu (in X: Double, in Y: Double, out clsidMenu: IUID)
← HitTestMap (in Location: IPoint) : IMap
← IsActive: Boolean
← OnMessage (in msg: Unsigned Long, in wParam: Unsigned Machine Int, in lParam: Long)
← Output (in hDC: Long, in dpi: Long, in PixelBounds: tagRECT, in VisibleBounds: IEnvelope, in trackCancel: ITrackCancel)
← PartialRefresh (in phase: tagesriViewDrawPhase, in data: IUnknown Pointer, in Envelope: IEnvelope)
← PrinterChanged (in Printer: IPrinter)
← Refresh

IDisplay : IUnknown
- ClipEnvelope: IEnvelope
- ClipEnvelopes: ISet
- ClipGeometry: IGeometry
- DisplayTransformation: IDisplayTransformation
- Filter: IDisplayFilter
- hDC: Long
- hPalette: Long
- IlluminationProps: IIlluminationProps
- SuppressEvents: Boolean
← DrawMultipoint (in Multipoint: IGeometry)
← DrawPoint (in Point: IGeometry)
← DrawPolygon (in Polygon: IGeometry)
← DrawPolyline (in Polyline: IGeometry)
← DrawRectangle (in rectangle: IEnvelope)
← DrawText (in Shape: IGeometry, in Text: String)
← FinishDrawing
← Progress (in VertexCount: Long)
← SetSymbol (in sym: ISymbol)
← StartDrawing (in hDC: Long, in cacheID: Integer)

IScreenDisplay : IDisplay
- ActiveCache: Integer
- CacheCount: Integer
- CacheMemDC (in Index: Integer) : Long
- CancelTracker: ITrackCancel
- hWnd: Long
- IsFirstCacheTransparent: Boolean
- IsFramed: Boolean
- ScaleContents: Boolean
- SuppressResize: Boolean
- UseScrollbars: Boolean
- WindowDC: Long
← AddCache: Integer
← DoScroll (in xDelta: Long, in yDelta: Long, in updateScreen: Boolean)
← DrawCache (in hDC: Long, in Index: Integer, in drawRect: tagRECT, in cacheRect: tagRECT)
← Invalidate (in rect: IEnvelope, in erase: Boolean, in cacheIndex: Integer)
← IsCacheDirty (in cacheID: Integer) : Boolean
← PanMoveTo (in mouseLocation: IPoint)
← PanStart (in mouseLocation: IPoint)
← PanStop: IEnvelope
← RemoveAllCaches
← RemoveCache (in cacheID: Integer)
← RotateMoveTo (in pPoint: IPoint)
← RotateStart (in mousePt: IPoint, in centerPt: IPoint)
← RotateStop: Double
← RotateTimer
← SetScrollbarHandles (in hWndHorzScrollbar: Long, in hWndVertScrollbar: Long)
← StartRecording
← StopRecording
← TrackPan
← TrackRotate
← UpdateWindow

2 For convenience, the resolution of the screen is set to a local variable.

4 The device rectangle is stored as a local variable.

6 tagRECT

bottom: Long
Left: Long
Right: Long
Top: Long

The driver bounds envelope is populated with the coordinates from the device rectangle. This envelope is used to set the IExporter PixelBounds property.

IDisplayTransformation:ITransformation
- Bounds: IEnvelope
- ConstrainedBounds: IEnvelope
- DeviceFrame: tagRECT
- FittedBounds: IEnvelope
- ReferenceScale: Double
- Resolution: Double
- Rotation: Double
- ScaleRatio: Double
- SpatialReference: ISpatialReference
- SuppressEvents: Boolean
- Units: esriUnits
- VisibleBounds: IEnvelope
- ZoomResolution: Boolean
← FromMapPoint (in mapPoint: IPoint, out X: Long, out Y: Long)
← FromPoints (in pointDistance: Double) : Double
← ToMapPoint (in X: Long, in Y: Long) : IPoint
← ToPoints (in mapDistance: Double) : Double
← TransformCoords (in mapPoints: _WKSPoint, in devPoints: tagPOINT, in numPoints: Long, in options: Long)
← TransformRect (in mapRect: IEnvelope, in devRect: tagRECT, in options: Long)

8 A call to the active view's Output method writes the current view to the exporter. Notice the hDC required by the Output method is obtained by calling StartExporting on the Exporter.

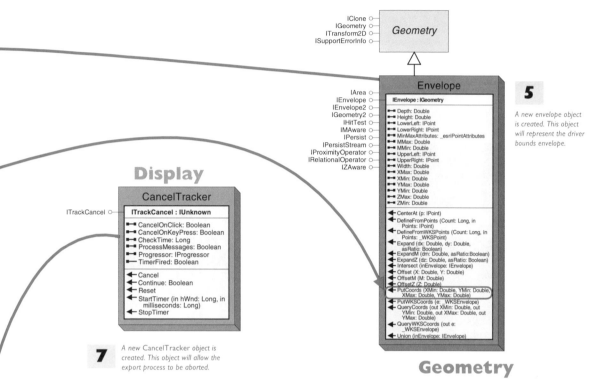

Geometry

Geometry
IClone ○—
IGeometry ○—
ITransform2D ○—
ISupportErrorInfo ○—

Envelope
IEnvelope : IGeometry
▪— Depth: Double
▪— Height: Double
▪— LowerLeft: IPoint
▪— LowerRight: IPoint
▪— MinMaxAttributes: _esriPointAttributes
▪— MMax: Double
▪— MMin: Double
▪— UpperLeft: IPoint
▪— UpperRight: IPoint
▪— Width: Double
▪— XMax: Double
▪— XMin: Double
▪— YMax: Double
▪— YMin: Double
▪— ZMax: Double
▪— ZMin: Double
◀— CenterAt (p: IPoint)
◀— DefineFromPoints (Count: Long, in Points: IPoint)
◀— DefineFromWKSPoints (Count: Long, in Points: _WKSPoint)
◀— Expand (dx: Double, dy: Double, asRatio: Boolean)
◀— ExpandM (dm: Double, asRatio:Boolean)
◀— ExpandZ (dz: Double, asRatio: Boolean)
◀— Intersect (inEnvelope: IEnvelope)
◀— Offset (X: Double, Y: Double)
◀— OffsetM (M: Double)
◀— OffsetZ (Z: Double)
◀— PutCoords (XMin: Double, YMin: Double, XMax: Double, YMax: Double)
◀— PutWKSCoords (e: _WKSEnvelope)
◀— QueryCoords (out XMin: Double, out YMin: Double, out XMax: Double, out YMax: Double)
◀— QueryWKSCoords (out e: _WKSEnvelope)
◀— Union (inEnvelope: IEnvelope)

The left side lists interfaces:
IArea, IEnvelope, IEnvelope2, IGeometry2, IHitTest, IMAware, IPersist, IPersistStream, IProximityOperator, IRelationalOperator, IZAware

5

A new envelope object is created. This object will represent the driver bounds envelope.

Display

CancelTracker
ITrackCancel : IUnknown
▪— CancelOnClick: Boolean
▪— CancelOnKeyPress: Boolean
▪— CheckTime: Long
▪— ProcessMessages: Boolean
▪— Progressor: IProgressor
▪— TimerFired: Boolean
◀— Cancel
◀— Continue: Boolean
◀— Reset
◀— StartTimer (in hWnd: Long, in milliseconds: Long)
◀— StopTimer

ITrackCancel ○—

7 *A new CancelTracker object is created. This object will allow the export process to be aborted.*

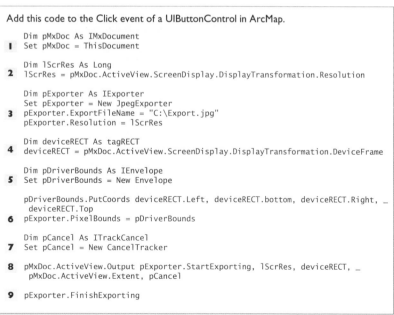

```
Add this code to the Click event of a UIButtonControl in ArcMap.

    Dim pMxDoc As IMxDocument
1   Set pMxDoc = ThisDocument

    Dim lScrRes As Long
2   lScrRes = pMxDoc.ActiveView.ScreenDisplay.DisplayTransformation.Resolution

    Dim pExporter As IExporter
    Set pExporter = New JpegExporter
3   pExporter.ExportFileName = "C:\Export.jpg"
    pExporter.Resolution = lScrRes

    Dim deviceRECT As tagRECT
4   deviceRECT = pMxDoc.ActiveView.ScreenDisplay.DisplayTransformation.DeviceFrame

    Dim pDriverBounds As IEnvelope
5   Set pDriverBounds = New Envelope

    pDriverBounds.PutCoords deviceRECT.Left, deviceRECT.bottom, deviceRECT.Right, _
      deviceRECT.Top
6   pExporter.PixelBounds = pDriverBounds

    Dim pCancel As ITrackCancel
7   Set pCancel = New CancelTracker

8   pMxDoc.ActiveView.Output pExporter.StartExporting, lScrRes, deviceRECT, _
      pMxDoc.ActiveView.Extent, pCancel

9   pExporter.FinishExporting
```

This sample takes the currently active view and prints the file to a PostScript printer. This code is similar to the previous sample, which exports the active view to a JPEG file.

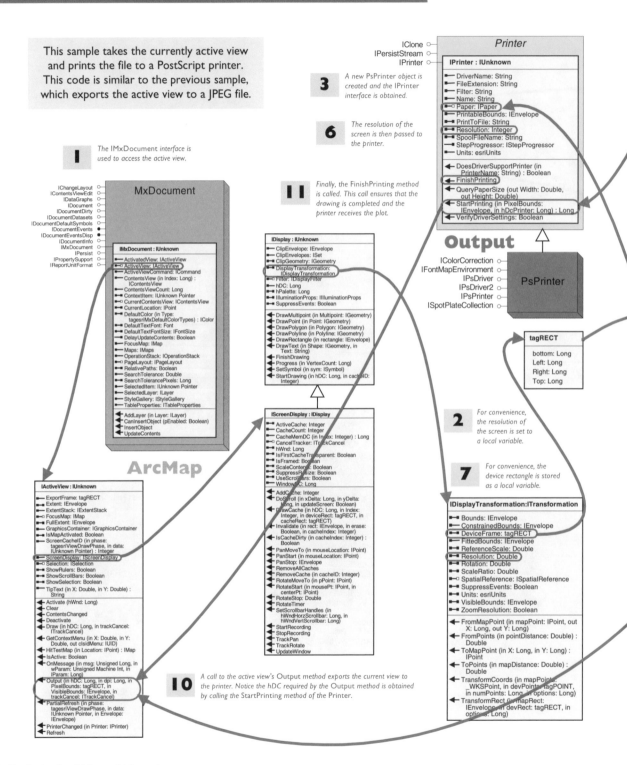

1 The IMxDocument interface is used to access the active view.

3 A new PsPrinter object is created and the IPrinter interface is obtained.

6 The resolution of the screen is then passed to the printer.

11 Finally, the FinishPrinting method is called. This call ensures that the drawing is completed and the printer receives the plot.

2 For convenience, the resolution of the screen is set to a local variable.

7 For convenience, the device rectangle is stored as a local variable.

10 A call to the active view's Output method exports the current view to the printer. Notice the hDC required by the Output method is obtained by calling the StartPrinting method of the Printer.

Printer

IClone
IPersistStream
IPrinter

IPrinter : IUnknown

- DriverName: String
- FileExtension: String
- Filter: String
- Name: String
- Paper: IPaper
- PrintableBounds: IEnvelope
- PrintToFile: String
- Resolution: Integer
- SpoolFileName: String
- StepProgressor: IStepProgressor
- Units: esriUnits
- DoesDriverSupportPrinter (in PrinterName: String) : Boolean
- FinishPrinting
- QueryPaperSize (out Width: Double, out Height: Double)
- StartPrinting (in PixelBounds: IEnvelope, in hDcPrinter: Long) : Long
- VerifyDriverSettings: Boolean

Output

PsPrinter

IColorCorrection
IFontMapEnvironment
IPsDriver
IPsDriver2
IPsPrinter
ISpotPlateCollection

tagRECT

bottom: Long
Left: Long
Right: Long
Top: Long

MxDocument

IChangeLayout
IContentsViewEdit
IDataGraphs
IDocument
IDocumentDirty
IDocumentDatasets
IDocumentDefaultSymbols
IDocumentEvents
IDocumentEventsDisp
IDocumentInfo
IMxDocument
IPersist
IPropertySupport
IReportUnitFormat

IMxDocument : IUnknown

- ActivatedView: IActiveView
- ActiveView: IActiveView
- ActiveViewCommand: ICommand
- ContentsView (in Index: Long) : IContentsView
- ContentsViewCount: Long
- ContextItem: IUnknown Pointer
- CurrentContentsView: IContentsView
- CurrentLocation: IPoint
- DefaultColor (in Type: tagesriMxDefaultColorTypes) : IColor
- DefaultTextFont: Font
- DefaultTextFontSize: IFontSize
- DelayUpdateContents: Boolean
- FocusMap: IMap
- Maps: IMaps
- OperationStack: IOperationStack
- PageLayout: IPageLayout
- RelativePaths: Boolean
- SearchTolerance: Double
- SearchTolerancePixels: Long
- SelectedItem: IUnknown Pointer
- SelectedLayer: ILayer
- StyleGallery: IStyleGallery
- TableProperties: ITableProperties
- AddLayer (in Layer: ILayer)
- CanInsertObject (pEnabled: Boolean)
- InsertObject
- UpdateContents

ArcMap

IDisplay : IUnknown

- ClipEnvelope: IEnvelope
- ClipEnvelopes: ISet
- ClipGeometry: IGeometry
- DisplayTransformation: IDisplayTransformation
- Filter: IDisplayFilter
- hDC: Long
- hPalette: Long
- IlluminationProps: IIlluminationProps
- SuppressEvents: Boolean
- DrawMultipoint (in Multipoint: IGeometry)
- DrawPoint (in Point: IGeometry)
- DrawPolygon (in Polygon: IGeometry)
- DrawPolyline (in Polyline: IGeometry)
- DrawRectangle (in rectangle: tagRECT)
- DrawText (in Shape: IGeometry, in Text: String)
- FinishDrawing
- Progress (in VertexCount: Long)
- SetSymbol (in sym: ISymbol)
- StartDrawing (in hDC: Long, in cacheID: Integer)

IScreenDisplay : IDisplay

- ActiveCache: Integer
- CacheCount: Integer
- CacheMemDC (in Index: Integer) : Long
- CancelTracker: ITrackCancel
- hWnd: Long
- IsFirstCacheTransparent: Boolean
- IsFramed: Boolean
- ScaleContents: Boolean
- SuppressResize: Boolean
- UseScrollBars: Boolean
- WindowDC: Long
- AddCache: Integer
- DoScroll (in xDelta: Long, in yDelta: Long, in updateScreen: Boolean)
- DrawCache (in hDC: Long, in Index: Integer, in deviceRect: tagRECT, in cacheRect: tagRECT)
- Invalidate (in rect: IEnvelope, in erase: Boolean, in cacheIndex: Integer)
- IsCacheDirty (in cacheIndex: Integer) : Boolean
- PanMoveTo (in mouseLocation: IPoint)
- PanStart (in mouseLocation: IPoint)
- PanStop: IEnvelope
- RemoveAllCaches
- RemoveCache (in cacheID: Integer)
- RotateMoveTo (in pPoint: IPoint)
- RotateStart (in mousePt: IPoint, in centerPt: IPoint)
- RotateStop: Double
- RotateTimer
- SetScrollbarHandles (in hWndHorzScrollbar: Long, in hWndVertScrollbar: Long)
- StartRecording
- StopRecording
- TrackPan
- TrackRotate
- UpdateWindow

IActiveView : IUnknown

- ExportFrame: tagRECT
- Extent: IEnvelope
- ExtentStack: IExtentStack
- FocusMap: IMap
- FullExtent: IEnvelope
- GraphicsContainer: IGraphicsContainer
- IsMapActivated: Boolean
- ScreenCacheID (in phase: tagesriViewDrawPhase, in data: IUnknown Pointer) : Integer
- ScreenDisplay: IScreenDisplay
- Selection: ISelection
- ShowRulers: Boolean
- ShowScrollBars: Boolean
- ShowSelection: Boolean
- TipText (in X: Double, in Y: Double) : String
- Activate (hWnd: Long)
- Clear
- ContentsChanged
- Deactivate
- Draw (in hDC: Long, in trackCancel: ITrackCancel)
- GetContextMenu (in X: Double, in Y: Double, out clsidMenu: IUID)
- HitTestMap (in Location: IPoint) : IMap
- IsActive: Boolean
- OnMessage (in msg: Unsigned Long, in wParam: Unsigned Machine Int, in lParam: Long)
- Output (in hDC: Long, in dpi: Long, in PixelBounds: tagRECT, in VisibleBounds: IEnvelope, in trackCancel: ITrackCancel)
- PartialRefresh (in phase: tagesriViewDrawPhase, in data: IUnknown Pointer, in Envelope: IEnvelope)
- PrinterChanged (in Printer: IPrinter)
- Refresh

IDisplayTransformation:ITransformation

- Bounds: IEnvelope
- ConstrainedBounds: IEnvelope
- DeviceFrame: tagRECT
- FittedBounds: IEnvelope
- ReferenceScale: Double
- Resolution: Double
- Rotation: Double
- ScaleRatio: Double
- SpatialReference: ISpatialReference
- SuppressEvents: Boolean
- Units: esriUnits
- VisibleBounds: IEnvelope
- ZoomResolution: Boolean
- FromMapPoint (in mapPoint: IPoint, out X: Long, out Y: Long)
- FromPoints (in pointDistance: Double) : Double
- ToMapPoint (in X: Long, in Y: Long) : IPoint
- ToPoints (in mapDistance: Double) : Double
- TransformCoords (in mapPoints: _WKSPoint, in devPoints: tagPOINT, in numPoints: Long, in options: Long)
- TransformRect (in mapRect: IEnvelope, in devRect: tagRECT, in options: Long)

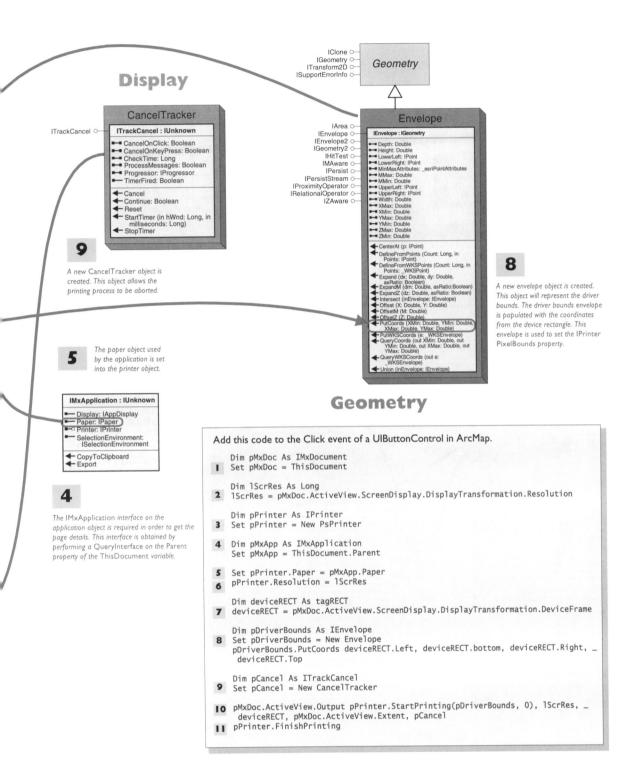

Display

CancelTracker

ITrackCancel

ITrackCancel : IUnknown

- CancelOnClick: Boolean
- CancelOnKeyPress: Boolean
- CheckTime: Long
- ProcessMessages: Boolean
- Progressor: IProgressor
- TimerFired: Boolean

- Cancel
- Continue: Boolean
- Reset
- StartTimer (in hWnd: Long, in milliseconds: Long)
- StopTimer

9

A new CancelTracker object is created. This object allows the printing process to be aborted.

Geometry

IClone
IGeometry
ITransform2D
ISupportErrorInfo

Geometry

Envelope

IArea
IEnvelope
IEnvelope2
IGeometry2
IHitTest
IMAware
IPersist
IPersistStream
IProximityOperator
IRelationalOperator
IZAware

IEnvelope : IGeometry

- Depth: Double
- Height: Double
- LowerLeft: IPoint
- LowerRight: IPoint
- MinMaxAttributes: _esriPointAttributes
- MMax: Double
- MMin: Double
- UpperLeft: IPoint
- UpperRight: IPoint
- Width: Double
- XMax: Double
- XMin: Double
- YMax: Double
- YMin: Double
- ZMax: Double
- ZMin: Double

- CenterAt (p: IPoint)
- DefineFromPoints (Count: Long, in Points: IPoint)
- DefineFromWKSPoints (Count: Long, in Points: _WKSPoint)
- Expand (dx: Double, dy: Double, asRatio: Boolean)
- ExpandM (dm: Double, asRatio:Boolean)
- ExpandZ (dz: Double, asRatio: Boolean)
- Intersect (inEnvelope: IEnvelope)
- Offset (X: Double, Y: Double)
- OffsetM (M: Double)
- OffsetZ (Z: Double)
- PutCoords (XMin: Double, YMin: Double, XMax: Double, YMax: Double)
- PutWKSCoords (e: _WKSEnvelope)
- QueryCoords (out XMin: Double, out YMin: Double, out XMax: Double, out YMax: Double)
- QueryWKSCoords (out e: _WKSEnvelope)
- Union (inEnvelope: IEnvelope)

8

A new envelope object is created. This object will represent the driver bounds. The driver bounds envelope is populated with the coordinates from the device rectangle. This envelope is used to set the IPrinter PixelBounds property.

5

The paper object used by the application is set into the printer object.

IMxApplication : IUnknown

- Display: IAppDisplay
- Paper: IPaper
- Printer: IPrinter
- SelectionEnvironment: ISelectionEnvironment

- CopyToClipboard
- Export

4

The IMxApplication interface on the application object is required in order to get the page details. This interface is obtained by performing a QueryInterface on the Parent property of the ThisDocument variable.

Add this code to the Click event of a UIButtonControl in ArcMap.

```
    Dim pMxDoc As IMxDocument
1   Set pMxDoc = ThisDocument

    Dim lScrRes As Long
2   lScrRes = pMxDoc.ActiveView.ScreenDisplay.DisplayTransformation.Resolution

    Dim pPrinter As IPrinter
3   Set pPrinter = New PsPrinter

    Dim pMxApp As IMxApplication
    Set pMxApp = ThisDocument.Parent

5   Set pPrinter.Paper = pMxApp.Paper
6   pPrinter.Resolution = lScrRes

    Dim deviceRECT As tagRECT
7   deviceRECT = pMxDoc.ActiveView.ScreenDisplay.DisplayTransformation.DeviceFrame

    Dim pDriverBounds As IEnvelope
8   Set pDriverBounds = New Envelope
    pDriverBounds.PutCoords deviceRECT.Left, deviceRECT.bottom, deviceRECT.Right, _
    deviceRECT.Top

    Dim pCancel As ITrackCancel
9   Set pCancel = New CancelTracker

10  pMxDoc.ActiveView.Output pPrinter.StartPrinting(pDriverBounds, 0), lScrRes, _
    deviceRECT, pMxDoc.ActiveView.Extent, pCancel
11  pPrinter.FinishPrinting
```

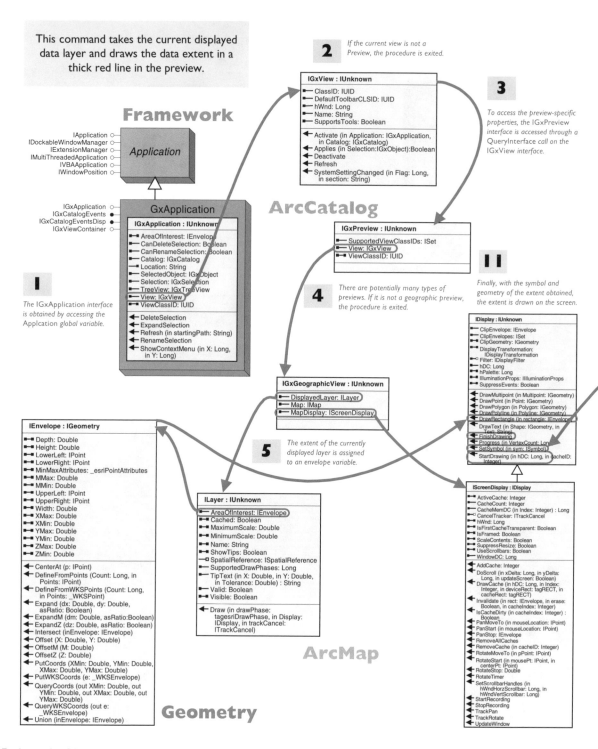

This command takes the current displayed data layer and draws the data extent in a thick red line in the preview.

2 *If the current view is not a Preview, the procedure is exited.*

IGxView : IUnknown
- ClassID: IUID
- DefaultToolbarCLSID: IUID
- hWnd: Long
- Name: String
- SupportsTools: Boolean
- Activate (in Application: IGxApplication, in Catalog: IGxCatalog)
- Applies (in Selection:IGxObject):Boolean
- Deactivate
- Refresh
- SystemSettingChanged (in Flag: Long, in section: String)

3 *To access the preview-specific properties, the IGxPreview interface is accessed through a QueryInterface call on the IGxView interface.*

Framework

IApplication
IDockableWindowManager
IExtensionManager
IMultiThreadedApplication
IVBAApplication
IWindowPosition

Application

ArcCatalog

IGxApplication
IGxCatalogEvents
IGxCatalogEventsDisp
IGxViewContainer

GxApplication

IGxApplication : IUnknown
- AreaOfInterest: IEnvelope
- CanDeleteSelection: Boolean
- CanRenameSelection: Boolean
- Catalog: IGxCatalog
- Location: String
- SelectedObject: IGxObject
- Selection: IGxSelection
- TreeView: IGxTreeView
- View: IGxView
- ViewClassID: IUID
- DeleteSelection
- ExpandSelection
- Refresh (in startingPath: String)
- RenameSelection
- ShowContextMenu (in X: Long, in Y: Long)

1 *The IGxApplication interface is obtained by accessing the Application global variable.*

IGxPreview : IUnknown
- SupportedViewClassIDs: ISet
- View: IGxView
- ViewClassID: IUID

4 *There are potentially many types of previews. If it is not a geographic preview, the procedure is exited.*

11 *Finally, with the symbol and geometry of the extent obtained, the extent is drawn on the screen.*

IDisplay : IUnknown
- ClipEnvelope: IEnvelope
- ClipEnvelopes: ISet
- ClipGeometry: IGeometry
- DisplayTransformation: IDisplayTransformation
- Filter: IDisplayFilter
- hDC: Long
- hPalette: Long
- IlluminationProps: IIlluminationProps
- SuppressEvents: Boolean
- DrawMultipoint (in Multipoint: IGeometry)
- DrawPoint (in Point: IGeometry)
- DrawPolygon (in Polygon: IGeometry)
- DrawPolyline (in Polyline: IGeometry)
- DrawRectangle (in rectangle: IEnvelope)
- DrawText (in Shape: IGeometry, in Text: String)
- FinishDrawing
- Progress (in VertexCount: Long)
- SetSymbol (in sym: ISymbol)
- StartDrawing (in hDC: Long, in cacheID: Integer)

IGxGeographicView : IUnknown
- DisplayedLayer: ILayer
- Map: IMap
- MapDisplay: IScreenDisplay

5 *The extent of the currently displayed layer is assigned to an envelope variable.*

Geometry

IEnvelope : IGeometry
- Depth: Double
- Height: Double
- LowerLeft: IPoint
- LowerRight: IPoint
- MinMaxAttributes: _esriPointAttributes
- MMax: Double
- MMin: Double
- UpperLeft: IPoint
- UpperRight: IPoint
- Width: Double
- XMax: Double
- XMin: Double
- YMax: Double
- YMin: Double
- ZMax: Double
- ZMin: Double
- CenterAt (p: IPoint)
- DefineFromPoints (Count: Long, in Points: IPoint)
- DefineFromWKSPoints (Count: Long, in Points: _WKSPoint)
- Expand (dx: Double, dy: Double, asRatio: Boolean)
- ExpandM (dm: Double, asRatio:Boolean)
- ExpandZ (dz: Double, asRatio: Boolean)
- Intersect (inEnvelope: IEnvelope)
- Offset (X: Double, Y: Double)
- OffsetM (M: Double)
- OffsetZ (Z: Double)
- PutCoords (XMin: Double, YMin: Double, XMax: Double, YMax: Double)
- PutWKSCoords (e: _WKSEnvelope)
- QueryCoords (out XMin: Double, out YMin: Double, out XMax: Double, out YMax: Double)
- QueryWKSCoords (out e: _WKSEnvelope)
- Union (inEnvelope: IEnvelope)

ArcMap

ILayer : IUnknown
- AreaOfInterest: IEnvelope
- Cached: Boolean
- MaximumScale: Double
- MinimumScale: Double
- Name: String
- ShowTips: Boolean
- SpatialReference: ISpatialReference
- SupportedDrawPhases: Long
- TipText (in X: Double, in Y: Double, in Tolerance: Double) : String
- Valid: Boolean
- Visible: Boolean
- Draw (in drawPhase: tagesriDrawPhase, in Display: IDisplay, in trackCancel: ITrackCancel)

IScreenDisplay : IDisplay
- ActiveCache: Integer
- CacheCount: Integer
- CacheMemDC (in Index: Integer) : Long
- CancelTracker: ITrackCancel
- hWnd: Long
- IsFirstCacheTransparent: Boolean
- IsFramed: Boolean
- ScaleContents: Boolean
- SuppressResize: Boolean
- UseScrollbars: Boolean
- WindowDC: Long
- AddCache: Integer
- DoScroll (in xDelta: Long, in yDelta: Long, in updateScreen: Boolean)
- DrawCache (in hDC: Long, in Index: Integer, in deviceRect: tagRECT, in cacheRect: tagRECT)
- Invalidate (in rect: IEnvelope, in erase: Boolean, in cacheIndex: Integer)
- IsCacheDirty (in cacheIndex: Integer) : Boolean
- PanMoveTo (in mouseLocation: IPoint)
- PanStart (in mouseLocation: IPoint)
- PanStop: IEnvelope
- RemoveAllCaches
- RemoveCache (in cacheID: Integer)
- RotateMoveTo (in pPoint: IPoint)
- RotateStart (in mousePt: IPoint, in centerPt: IPoint)
- RotateStop: Double
- RotateTimer
- SetScrollbarHandles (in hWndHorzScrollbar: Long, in hWndVertScrollbar: Long)
- StartRecording
- StopRecording
- TrackPan
- TrackRotate
- UpdateWindow

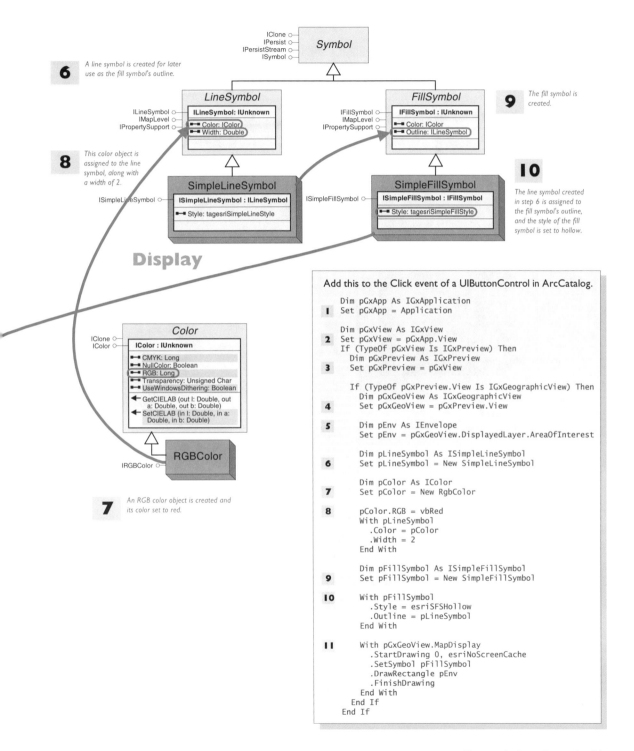

6 A line symbol is created for later use as the fill symbol's outline.

8 This color object is assigned to the line symbol, along with a width of 2.

9 The fill symbol is created.

10 The line symbol created in step 6 is assigned to the fill symbol's outline, and the style of the fill symbol is set to hollow.

7 An RGB color object is created and its color set to red.

Display

```
Add this to the Click event of a UIButtonControl in ArcCatalog.

     Dim pGxApp As IGxApplication
  1  Set pGxApp = Application

     Dim pGxView As IGxView
  2  Set pGxView = pGxApp.View
     If (TypeOf pGxView Is IGxPreview) Then
        Dim pGxPreview As IGxPreview
  3     Set pGxPreview = pGxView

        If (TypeOf pGxPreview.View Is IGxGeographicView) Then
           Dim pGxGeoView As IGxGeographicView
  4        Set pGxGeoView = pGxPreview.View

  5        Dim pEnv As IEnvelope
           Set pEnv = pGxGeoView.DisplayedLayer.AreaOfInterest

           Dim pLineSymbol As ISimpleLineSymbol
  6        Set pLineSymbol = New SimpleLineSymbol

           Dim pColor As IColor
  7        Set pColor = New RgbColor

  8        pColor.RGB = vbRed
           With pLineSymbol
              .Color = pColor
              .Width = 2
           End With

           Dim pFillSymbol As ISimpleFillSymbol
  9        Set pFillSymbol = New SimpleFillSymbol

  10       With pFillSymbol
              .Style = esriSFSHollow
              .Outline = pLineSymbol
           End With

  11       With pGxGeoView.MapDisplay
              .StartDrawing 0, esriNoScreenCache
              .SetSymbol pFillSymbol
              .DrawRectangle pEnv
              .FinishDrawing
           End With
        End If
     End If
```

This code sample inspects the selected objects in the ArcCatalog browser and if they are feature classes in a geodatabase, makes an edit to their alias name.

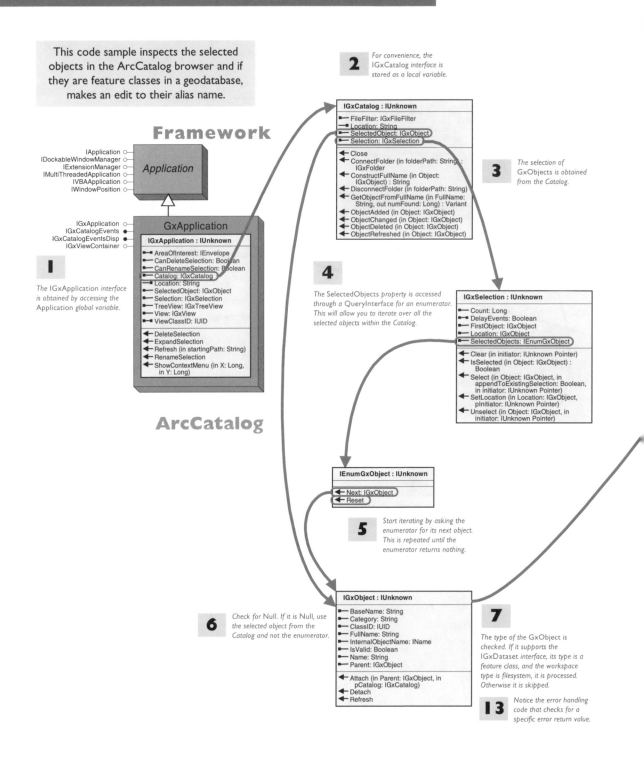

2 For convenience, the IGxCatalog interface is stored as a local variable.

Framework

IGxCatalog : IUnknown
- FileFilter: IGxFileFilter
- Location: String
- SelectedObject: IGxObject
- Selection: IGxSelection

- Close
- ConnectFolder (in folderPath: String) : IGxFolder
- ConstructFullName (in Object: IGxObject) : String
- DisconnectFolder (in folderPath: String)
- GetObjectFromFullName (in FullName: String, out numFound: Long) : Variant
- ObjectAdded (in Object: IGxObject)
- ObjectChanged (in Object: IGxObject)
- ObjectDeleted (in Object: IGxObject)
- ObjectRefreshed (in Object: IGxObject)

3 The selection of GxObjects is obtained from the Catalog.

Application

- IApplication
- IDockableWindowManager
- IExtensionManager
- IMultiThreadedApplication
- IVBAApplication
- IWindowPosition

GxApplication

- IGxApplication
- IGxCatalogEvents
- IGxCatalogEventsDisp
- IGxViewContainer

IGxApplication : IUnknown
- AreaOfInterest: IEnvelope
- CanDeleteSelection: Boolean
- CanRenameSelection: Boolean
- Catalog: IGxCatalog
- Location: String
- SelectedObject: IGxObject
- Selection: IGxSelection
- TreeView: IGxTreeView
- View: IGxView
- ViewClassID: IUID

- DeleteSelection
- ExpandSelection
- Refresh (in startingPath: String)
- RenameSelection
- ShowContextMenu (in X: Long, in Y: Long)

1

The IGxApplication interface is obtained by accessing the Application global variable.

4

The SelectedObjects property is accessed through a QueryInterface for an enumerator. This will allow you to iterate over all the selected objects within the Catalog.

IGxSelection : IUnknown
- Count: Long
- DelayEvents: Boolean
- FirstObject: IGxObject
- Location: IGxObject
- SelectedObjects: IEnumGxObject

- Clear (in initiator: IUnknown Pointer)
- IsSelected (in Object: IGxObject) : Boolean
- Select (in Object: IGxObject, in appendToExistingSelection: Boolean, in initiator: IUnknown Pointer)
- SetLocation (in Location: IGxObject, pInitiator: IUnknown Pointer)
- Unselect (in Object: IGxObject, in initiator: IUnknown Pointer)

ArcCatalog

IEnumGxObject : IUnknown
- Next: IGxObject
- Reset

5 Start iterating by asking the enumerator for its next object. This is repeated until the enumerator returns nothing.

6 Check for Null. If it is Null, use the selected object from the Catalog and not the enumerator.

IGxObject : IUnknown
- BaseName: String
- Category: String
- ClassID: IUID
- FullName: String
- InternalObjectName: IName
- IsValid: Boolean
- Name: String
- Parent: IGxObject

- Attach (in Parent: IGxObject, in pCatalog: IGxCatalog)
- Detach
- Refresh

7

The type of the GxObject is checked. If it supports the IGxDataset interface, its type is a feature class, and the workspace type is filesystem, it is processed. Otherwise it is skipped.

13 Notice the error handling code that checks for a specific error return value.

IClassSchemaEdit : IUnknown

- AlterAliasName (in Name: String)
- AlterClassExtensionCLSID (in ClassExtensionCLSID: IUID, in classExtensionProperties:IPropertySet)
- AlterDefaultValue (in FieldName: String, in Value: Variant)
- AlterDomain (in FieldName: String, in Domain: IDomain)
- AlterFieldAliasName (in FieldName: String, in AliasName: String)
- AlterFieldModelName (in FieldName: String, in ModelName: String)
- AlterInstanceCLSID (in InstanceCLSID: IUID)
- AlterModelName (in Name: String)
- RegisterAsObjectClass (in suggestedOIDFieldName: String, in ConfigKeyword: String) : Long

9

The method to edit the schema is on the IClassSchemaEdit interface. This is accessed through a QueryInterface from the IObjectClass interface.

ISchemaLock : IUnknown

- ChangeSchemaLock (in schemaLock: esriSchemaLock)
- GetCurrentSchemaLocks (out schemaLockInfo: IEnumSchemaLockInfo)

11 The schema edit is made.

12 The exclusive lock is released.

10 It is possible that when we ask the database for an exclusive lock it will fail because another user is editing, hence we must prepare for this with a specialized error handler.

IObjectClass : IClass

- AliasName: String
- ObjectClassID: Long
- RelationshipClasses (in role: esriRelRole) : IEnumRelationshipClass

8 To make the schema change, you must have a schema lock. The schema lock interface is accessed through a QueryInterface from the IObjectClass interface.

IGxDataset : IUnknown

- Dataset: IDataset
- DatasetName: IDatasetName
- Type: esriDatasetType

IDataset : IUnknown

- BrowseName: String
- Category: String
- FullName: IName
- Name: String
- PropertySet: IPropertySet
- Subsets: IEnumDataset
- Type: esriDatasetType
- Workspace: IWorkspace
- CanCopy: Boolean
- CanDelete: Boolean
- CanRename: Boolean
- Copy (in copyName:String,in copyWorkspace:IWorkspace):IDataset
- Delete
- Rename (in Name: String)

Enumeration esriDatasetType

1 - esriDTAny
2 - esriDTContainer
3 - esriDTGeo
4 - esriDTFeatureDataset
5 - esriDTFeatureClass
6 - esriDTPlanarGraph
7 - esriDTGeometricNetwork
9 - esriDTText
10 - esriDTTable
11 - esriDTRelationshipClass
12 - esriDTRasterDataset
13 - esriDTRasterBand
14 - esriDTTin
15 - esriDTCadDrawing
16 - esriDTRasterCatalog

IWorkspace : IUnknown

- ConnectionProperties: IPropertySet
- DatasetNames (in DatasetType: esriDatasetType) : IEnumDatasetName
- Datasets (in DatasetType: esriDatasetType) : IEnumDataset
- PathName: String
- Type: esriWorkspaceType
- WorkspaceFactory: IWorkspaceFactory
- ExecuteSQL (in sqlStmt: String)
- Exists: Boolean
- IsDirectory: Boolean

Enumeration esriWorkspaceType

0 - esriFileSystemWorkspace
1 - esriLocalDatabaseWorkspace
2 - esriRemoteDatabaseWorkspace

Geodatabase

Add this to the Click event of a UIButtonControl in ArcCatalog.

```
Dim pGxApp As IGxApplication
1   Set pGxApp = Application

Dim pGxCatalog As IGxCatalog
2   Set pGxCatalog = pGxApp.Catalog

Dim pGxSelection As IGxSelection
3   Set pGxSelection = pGxCatalog.Selection

Dim pGxObjects As IEnumGxObject
4   Set pGxObjects = pGxSelection.SelectedObjects
    pGxObjects.Reset

Dim pGxObject As IGxObject
5   Set pGxObject = pGxObjects.Next

    If (pGxObject Is Nothing) Then Set pGxObject =
6   pGxCatalog.SelectedObject

Dim pGxDataset As IGxDataset
Dim pObjectClass As IObjectClass
Dim pClassSchemaEdit As IClassSchemaEdit
Dim pSchemaLock As ISchemaLock
Do Until (pGxObject Is Nothing)
    If (TypeOf pGxObject Is IGxDataset) Then
7     Set pGxDataset = pGxObject
      If ((pGxDataset.Type = esriDTFeatureClass) And _
          (pGxDataset.Dataset.Workspace.Type <> _
          esriFileSystemWorkspace)) Then
8         Set pObjectClass = pGxDataset.Dataset
9         Set pSchemaLock = pObjectClass

10        Set pClassSchemaEdit = pObjectClass
          On Error GoTo lockDB
11        pSchemaLock.ChangeSchemaLock esriExclusiveSchemaLock
          On Error GoTo 0
          pClassSchemaEdit.AlterAliasName "ArcObjects Updated Alias"

12        pSchemaLock.ChangeSchemaLock esriSharedSchemaLock
      End If
    End If
    Set pGxObject = pGxObjects.Next
Loop

Exit Sub

lockDB:

If (Err.Number = FDO_E_SCHEMA_LOCK_CONFLICT) Then
13  MsgBox "Unable to obtain exclusive database lock",
    vbExclamation + vbOKOnly, "Database Lock Error"
Else
    MsgBox "Unknown error getting schema lock", vbExclamation +
    vbOKOnly, "Database Error"
End If
Err.Clear
```

Steps of the ArcObjects problem solving guide

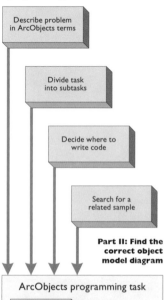

Part I: Define the ArcObjects programming task

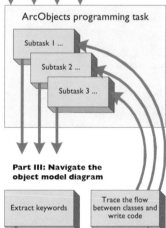

The ArcObjects library is a comprehensive set of COM components designed to provide developers with the ability to extend and customize ArcGIS applications such as ArcMap and ArcCatalog. The ArcObjects library consists of over 1,000 classes and 2,000 interfaces that are visually documented in several dozen object model diagrams.

With this extensive set of classes, you can create a wide variety of customizations and custom applications to extend existing ArcGIS applications. However, as you begin developing with ArcObjects, you may find the extent of the ArcObjects library overwhelming, and it may be difficult to know where to begin. The goal of this problem-solving guide is to present a methodology to help you solve real-world ArcObjects programming tasks.

The guide helps you describe and categorize your task and documents how to use the help resources and tools to solve the problem programmatically. In the end, the guide will not only help solve individual problems but will also help you understand and navigate the structure of ArcObjects.

The guide is broken into three parts. Part one is designed to help you define the ArcObjects programming task as clearly as possible. Part two illustrates how to use the help resources to locate the correct object model diagram you should start with. Part three provides an example of how to navigate the object model diagrams in order to assemble the code required to solve the task.

The following steps outline each part of the problem-solving guide:

PART ONE: DEFINE THE ARCOBJECTS PROGRAMMING TASK

1. Describe the problem in ArcObjects terms.
2. Identify subtasks.
3. Decide where to write the code.
4. Search for a related sample or recommended methodology.

PART TWO: LOCATE THE CORRECT OBJECT MODEL

1. Identify a subtask.
2. Extract keywords.
3. Search for the correct object model diagrams.
4. Review all related documentation.

PART THREE: NAVIGATE THE OBJECT MODEL DIAGRAM

1. Review the structure of the object model diagram.
2. Trace the flow between classes and assemble code.

Although there are three parts, this type of problem solving is really one continuous process. You may find it necessary to revisit some steps as you gain knowledge about a particular topic by reading the pages in this book and by exploring the wide variety of code samples available.

ARE YOU READY?

Before getting started with this problem-solving guide, you should be familiar with the basic terminology behind COM and ArcObjects, and you should know how to use the available help resources and tools. Here is a checklist of some topics discussed earlier in this chapter that should already be familiar to you:

- How to program with COM interfaces and classes in Visual Basic

- How to use the ArcObjects Developer Help system

- How to read and interpret the ArcObjects object model diagrams with Acrobat® Reader

- How to use ESRI's object browser, *EOBrowser*, to inspect the structure of ArcObjects not visible with other object browsers

- How to navigate this book using the index, table of contents, and inserted ArcGIS object model diagrams

- How to access continually updated information at ESRI's technical resource Web site, www.esri.com/arcobjectsonline

It is particularly important to understand the previous section in this chapter along with the illustrated code samples before starting with this problem-solving guide.

USING THE ArcObjects PROBLEM-SOLVING GUIDE

This problem-solving guide uses a real-world ArcObjects programming problem to explain the details of each step. To learn the methodology behind this guide, first follow the instructions and complete the real-world programming task defined below, then define your own problem and use these steps to solve your own development task.

This problem-solving guide will solve this example task: *Add a dataset called States to ArcMap.*

PART ONE: DEFINE THE ArcObjects PROGRAMMING TASK

The most important aspect of successfully using the problem-solving guide is being able to define the task itself. A task may originate from a real-world GIS problem at your workplace or may be the result of an enhancement you would like to make to the existing ArcGIS system. A task may be as simple as adding a *UIToolControl* to the user interface of ArcMap to zoom in on the map or as detailed as creating a custom feature for the geodatabase. In either case, in order to define the task as completely as possible, you should consider the following steps:

1. Describe the problem using ArcGIS terminology.

2. Divide the task into smaller subtasks.

3. Decide where to compile the source code.

4. Find an existing sample or recommended methodology.

The best way to learn ArcObjects is to first become familiar with the fundamental ArcGIS and COM terminology and concepts, then learn how to effectively use all of the help resources, tools, documentation, and samples that are at your disposal. This book provides a good foundation for the basic terms and concepts, and this section focuses specifically on how to use the help resources to solve ArcObjects-related programming tasks.

If you are not comfortable with any of these topics, concepts, resources, or tools, go back and review the previous sections of this chapter. For more detailed information on Visual Basic and COM programming techniques, you can also reference Chapter 2, 'Developing with ArcObjects'.

This guide does not attempt to provide an all-encompassing method for every ArcObjects programming task. It simply provides a methodology that can help you clearly define your initial objective and make effective use of the many resources and tools available.

To become familiar with basic ArcGIS terminology, refer to these ESRI books: Getting Started with ArcGIS, Building a Geodatabase, *and* Modeling Our World, *as well as the other resources mentioned earlier.*

Describe the problem in ArcGIS terms

When defining the problem, it is useful to frame the task with ArcGIS terminology and to describe the actions as completely as possible. This will help you find topics in the help system and the relevant components in ArcObjects.

In many cases, this step will also force you to go back and review important background topics and reading materials related to the task at hand. From this research, you will gain further insight about how a particular task can be solved.

For this example, the original task description is *Add a dataset called States to ArcMap.*

Using ArcGIS terminology, this statement could be expanded like this: *Access the States feature class from a personal geodatabase and add it to ArcMap.*

The most noticeable change to the description is that it has been expanded by identifying the datasets involved and by using the proper ArcObjects terminology. For example, the dataset named States has been more accurately defined as a feature class that resides in an existing personal geodatabase (stored in a Microsoft Access database).

Another important change is that the actions in the description have also been more completely defined. It now reveals the fact that it will be necessary to open the database first and then add a feature class in it to ArcMap. As you will see in the next step, it is important to identify these actions, as they can be treated as two separate programming tasks when building the final code.

Define subtasks

This step forces you to revisit the original task description and determine if it can be broken down into smaller, more manageable subtasks. This process allows you to focus on smaller parts of the original problem at one time and, therefore, smaller sections of the ArcObjects object model diagrams when it comes time to write code. The easiest way to identify subtasks is to look for verbs or action words that are hidden in the description. From the original task description, two subtasks can be easily identified.

From our expanded statement—*Access the States feature class from a personal geodatabase and add it to ArcMap*—we can identify two subtasks:

- *Access the States feature class.*

- *Add the new layer to the map.*

Each subtask will be solved individually as you traverse through parts two and three of this guide. This is important because it enables you to focus on small parts of the problem and smaller sections of the object model diagrams.

Decide where to write the code

You should always begin by trying to write ArcObjects code in the VBA environment in ArcMap or ArcCatalog. If necessary, this code can be moved to a different development environment before final compilation and distribution.

With the problem description and subtasks defined, you need to decide where to write the code and how to provide the functionality to end users.

Remember that where you test code and where you write the final code are two different issues. During the testing and initial design phase, it is always recommended to start writing code as a VBA macro in either ArcMap or ArcCatalog. There, you can easily assemble, test, and debug the source and experiment with any number of classes or interfaces. After completing the testing phase, you can then decide to leave the code as a VBA macro or move it to another format.

Deciding where to write the final application code can be a complicated matter, and as you gain experience developing with ArcObjects, your decision making will improve. In general, the answer is governed by the type of application you are developing and how you want to deliver the functionality to end users.

In general, there are three ways to write ArcObjects code:

- As a VBA macro in an ArcGIS application

- As an ActiveX COM component such as a DLL or OCX

- As a standalone EXE

You should also note that browsing the samples and associated documentation might help you determine where to locate your code. This is covered in detail in the next step.

Writing VBA macros in ArcGIS applications

For information about how to get started with the VBA environment, see the VBA topic in this chapter as well as related topics in the ArcObjects Developer Help system.

As mentioned, you should start development by using the VBA environment in one of the existing ArcGIS applications. VBA is a simple programming language with many utilities, such as design time code completion and the Object Browser, that will help you assemble code quickly.

Here are some more reasons to choose the VBA environment:

- It's fast and easy to create, test, and debug macros inside ArcMap and ArcCatalog.

- The standard ESRI type libraries are already referenced for you.

- Important global variables, such as the *Application* and *Document*, are available.

- It's simple to assemble UI forms using VBA and ActiveX® components.

- It's straightforward to integrate VBA code with new ArcObjects UIControls.

- It's relatively easy to migrate VBA code to VB ActiveX DLL projects.

- Many code samples available in the help system are macros that can be cut, pasted, and run with the VBA environment.

After the testing phase, you can easily save the VBA code into a Normal.mxt, Project.mxd, or custom Project.mxt file. Projects, documents, and templates can then be delivered to end users so they can take advantage of the new functionality your application provides. (See the topic on customizing with documents and templates in Chapter 3, 'Customizing the user interface'.)

Writing ActiveX COM components

This approach of writing ActiveX COM components must be taken if you wish to extend the existing ArcObjects architecture. Custom components can reside at the application or geodatabase level.

If you wish to use a programming language other than VBA or if you want to package ArcObjects functionality into a COM DLL, EXE, or OCX, you will have to work outside of the VBA development environment. This approach generally requires creating a project, referencing the ArcObjects type library, adding code, then compiling the source into a binary file.

Writing ActiveX COM components should be done when you want to extend the existing ArcObjects architecture by adding new custom components. The process requires implementing one or more ArcObjects interfaces in the new object (see the topic on creating COM components in Chapter 2, 'Developing with ArcObjects').

Unlike working in the VBA environment, all new components require Component Category registration in order to work correctly (see the topic on the Component Category manager in Chapter 2, 'Developing with ArcObjects').

These are some advantages of building custom components:

- They can be easily delivered to end users via custom setup programs.

- You can hide ArcObjects code in a binary file and then deliver the functionality to end users with a setup program.

- You can extend and customize virtually every aspect of the ArcGIS technology.

Components can be broadly categorized into two areas of customization: those that reside at the application level, such as custom buttons, toolbars, windows, and extensions, and those that reside at the geodatabase level, such as custom feature class extensions and custom features. Some of these more advanced customizations cannot be accomplished through the VBA environment.

The main disadvantage of working outside of the VBA environment is that you will have to acquire and use another COM-compliant development tool. Another consideration is the fact that you do not have direct access to the *Application* and *ThisDocument* global variables.

The development tool you choose must support the creation of new components as well as the implementation of COM interfaces in order to acquire a hook back into the ArcGIS applications (for more details, see Chapter 3, 'Customizing the user interface'). Interfaces that provide this functionality will allow you to acquire references to the *Application* and *ThisDocument* global variables, just as if you were working in the VBA environment. Another disadvantage is that it is often more difficult to debug the code (see the topic on getting started with VBA in Chapter 2, 'Developing with ArcObjects').

Standalone applications

ArcObjects can be used to write standalone applications. This generally requires creating a project, referencing the ArcObjects type library, then assembling the required code to support the functionality of the application.

These are some advantages of building standalone applications:

- You can use the ESRI ArcObjects Map control to simplify the embedding of ArcObjects functionality in your application.
- You can design a highly customized user interface specific to your application.
- You can quickly create small, lightweight applications.

These are the disadvantages of building standalone applications:

- You cannot take advantage of the extensive functionality that ESRI has built into the existing ArcGIS applications such as ArcMap or ArcCatalog.
- If you are not using the Map control, you will have to provide your own map display for visual applications.
- You will have to design your own data loading and layer management tools.
- You cannot use ArcMap documents or templates to their fullest capacity.
- You cannot take advantage of the components that give you the ability to extend the existing ArcMap and ArcCatalog framework.
- None of the extensions, including the *Editor*, can be used.

Although it is possible, it is not recommended to create standalone applications if the functionality you desire can be realized by extending existing ArcGIS applications such as ArcMap and ArcCatalog. All ArcGIS applications share the same application framework, designed to be extended by third-party developers.

If you create a standalone application, you have a significantly higher development effort. The Map control mitigates, but does not eliminate, this additional effort. Standalone applications are appropriate only for highly specialized implementations.

Of the three options for writing code—as VBA macros in ArcMap or ArcCatalog, as ActiveX COM components, or as standalone applications— the example used in this problem-solving guide, adding a dataset called States to ArcMap, will simply be run as a VBA macro stored in a map document (.mxd file).

Find a related sample or recommended methodology

The last step is to search all of the available resources for a code sample and to look for any documentation that may be related to the task at hand. To accomplish this, you will need to make use of the help resources and tools. As you may already know, there is often more than one way to accomplish a programming task. The recommendation here is to search the available resources for similar implementations in order to help you decide how to go about solving the problem.

The easiest way to locate a sample is to search using the ArcObjects Developer Help system.

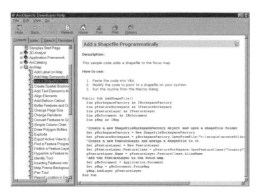

1. Start the ArcObjects Developer Help system.

2. Click the Search tab and type "Add".

3. Sort by clicking the "Title" field. You can sort by location as well.

4. Browse down until you find "samples" and until you locate the "Add a shapefile programmatically" sample. Open the page and study the sample.

5. Click the Contents tab. This reveals the location of the sample. Browse the other samples in this folder structure. Make note of the location of the sample.

6. Click the Favorites tab, give the current topic a title, and add the sample to your favorites list.

The Samples in the ArcObjects Developer Help system fall into two categories: Tips and Tools. Tips are smaller examples of ArcObjects code that you can generally cut and paste and then run as a VBA script in ArcMap or ArcCatalog. Tools are more complete examples of applications that often require compilation and component category registration. Many of the tools are COM components themselves. If you find a tip or tool that may be useful, be sure to store it in the Favorites tab for future reference.

Unfortunately, in this case it was not possible to find a sample that solves the exact problem, but a sample was found that relates to the problem. The sample found illustrates how to open and load a shapefile into ArcMap. Since you are not ready to write code at this point, the sample was simply stored in the favorites list so that it can be referenced later on. This will still prove to be a valuable step later on when writing code in the final steps.

Whether a sample was located or not, it is a good idea to look for background information related to the current task. The ArcObjects Developer Help system contains some topics that you might find valuable in the

Getting Started section. These pages provide some useful information, such as the basic principles related to working with ArcObjects in VB and VBA. Although the documentation doesn't relate to the problem description, it still relates to the overall task since this example will be written as a VBA macro. Therefore, it is a good idea to review this documentation.

1. Open the Getting Started Page in the ArcObjects Develop Help system.

2. Review the documentation related to working with Visual Basic for Applications.

If nothing is found that directly relates to the task at hand, it is a good idea to visit the other documentation available. You can check some other resources, such as the ArcGIS Desktop Help and ESRI books, such as *What is ArcGIS?*, *Building a Geodatabase*, and *Modeling Our World*.

Summary of part one

Now that you have more clearly defined the various components of the task and have done some research on the topic, it is possible to move on to the next step, which will help identify which object model diagram to start with.

Here is all of the task-related information found in part one of the problem-solving guide for the current example:

Task defined in ArcGIS terminology: *Access the States feature class from an existing Access personal geodatabase and add it to ArcMap.*

Subtask 1: *Access the States feature class.*

Subtask 2: *Add the new layer to the map.*

Where to write the code: *As a VBA macro in ArcMap.*

Located sample: *Add a shapefile to ArcMap programmatically.*

PART TWO: FIND THE CORRECT OBJECT MODEL DIAGRAM

This section explains how to use the help resources and tools to locate the correct object model diagram required to solve a task. As a reminder, the remaining steps in parts two and three are designed to work through one subtask at a time. Therefore, you will need to proceed through all of the remaining steps with subtask 1, then come back here to solve subtask 2.

Identify a subtask

Start with the first subtask defined in part one.

Original task: *Access the States feature class from an existing Access personal geodatabase and add it to ArcMap.*

Subtask 1: *Access the States feature class.*

Subtask 2: *Add the new layer to ArcMap.*

Extract keywords

It is important to use the correct ArcObjects terminology when describing the original task so that it is possible to extract meaningful keywords from each subtask. These keywords are important because they can be used later on to search for topics in the help system and to search for classes in the object model diagrams.

This step requires that you extract keywords from the subtask description. This is not an exact science, but the more ArcObjects terms used in the original description, the more success you will have here. Therefore, it should be evident that it is critical to define the initial task correctly in the first step of part one.

Two terms can be extracted from the previously defined subtask: *"Access"* and *"feature class"*.

Search for the correct object model diagram

The objective of this step is to use the keywords defined above to identify the correct object model diagram. The easiest way to find the object model diagram is to use Adobe® Acrobat Reader to search the ArcGIS object model PDF file. Searching the entire ArcGIS object model should lead you to one or more words or classes that are directly associated with an object model diagram.

The ArcGIS object model is a simplified version of the entire ArcObjects library. This object model contains subsystems that are composed of one or more object model diagrams. Each subsystem is clearly marked with a number that associates it with one of the chapters in the two volumes of this book.

The methodology here is to search the object model with the keywords defined in the last step, identify the appropriate subsystem or object model diagram, then go directly to the associated chapter in the book to learn more about the related classes. The chapters of the book provide both a detailed description of the classes and a number of helpful code samples.

The ArcGIS Object Model.pdf file contains subsystems that contain one or more object model diagrams. This diagram only shows those classes that are documented in the ArcObjects book. To search against the entire ArcObjects library, you can also use the AllOMDs.pdf file.

Another valuable resource is the AllOMDs.pdf file. This diagram contains all of the object model diagrams with expanded interfaces, members, and enumerations. It can be searched using Acrobat Reader just like the ArcGIS object model diagram, but since it contains considerably more detail, expect the search to point to many more hits. The advantage of using this object model diagram is that it will cover virtually every class and interface in the entire ArcObjects library at one time.

Use the Find tool in Acrobat Reader to search for the keywords in the ArcGIS Object Model PDF.

1. Open the ArcGIS Object Model diagram.

2. Use the Find tool to search for each word from the keyword list. Try to search until you identify a class. *Searching for the keywords "Access" and "Feature class" yields hits in the Geodatabase section of the ArcGIS object model diagram.*

3. Write down the object model diagram or subsystem to which the majority of the searches point. *For this example, both keywords point to the geodatabase object model diagram.*

4. Identify the chapter in the book that is associated with the OMD. *The geodatabase section of the ArcGIS object model diagram is labeled with the number 8; therefore, you can find that subsystem documented in Volume 2, Chapter 8, 'Accessing the geodatabase'.*

If you were unsuccessful at finding a diagram, repeat the steps using the AllOMDs.pdf file.

In this example, all of the search results point to descriptive text or an actual class associated with the geodatabase object model diagram. Therefore, this clearly indicates that you should start with this diagram to solve the subtask.

Review the documentation

With the object model diagram identified, the last step in part two is to review the available ArcObjects documentation. The best place to start is with the Object Model Overviews section of the ArcObjects Developer Help system. The Object Model Overviews Start Page provides a brief description of each subsystem that composes the ArcObjects library. At a minimum, you will find an overview of each subsystem that provides a description of the main classes associated with each subsystem.

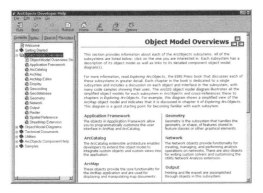

Review the appropriate Object Model Overview page in the ArcObjects Developer Help system.

1. Go to the ArcObjects Developer Help system and click Object Model Overviews.

2. From the Object Model Overviews Start Page, click the desired object model. *For this example, click Geodatabase.*

3. Read the overview information available to learn about the classes that belong to the selected object model diagram.

The object model diagram overviews provide some background information for the most important classes in each object model diagram. From this, you should be able to identify new keywords that you may have missed or even class names that are directly related to the current subtask. Add these keywords to the existing keyword list to improve your ability to navigate through the object model diagram.

From the Geodatabase overview page, you should have been able to identify the following keywords: "Access", "Feature class", "Workspace", and "Factory".

Next, go to the *Exploring ArcObjects* book and read the chapter associated with the geodatabase object model diagram. *For this subtask, you should go to Volume 2, Chapter 8, 'Accessing the geodatabase'.*

Reviewing this chapter should provide you with a solid understanding of what the main classes and interfaces are for as well as some good code samples. This last step is one of the most important parts of the entire problem-solving guide.

PART THREE: NAVIGATE THE OBJECT MODEL DIAGRAM

The last part of the guide involves navigating the object model diagrams and assembling the required code to solve each subtask. This is generally the most difficult step because it involves the use of many of the help resources and tools and is generally not a linear process. As you become more familiar with the help tools and the object model diagrams, this process will become easier.

Review the structure of the object model diagram

It is a good idea to familiarize yourself with the general structure of the object model diagram before proceeding. The easiest way to accomplish this is to use Acrobat Reader to zoom in and pan around the model.

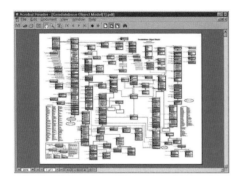

1. Open the geodatabase object model diagram with Acrobat Reader.

2. Zoom in and pan around the diagram to view the overall structure.

Another way to become familiar with the object model diagram is to examine the relationship between classes and interfaces of an existing sample. It is recommended that you physically trace the flow between the classes and interfaces to understand how the classes relate to one another. This knowledge will be useful as it will help you assemble your own code in the next step.

In part one, step 4, the "Add a shapefile to ArcMap programmatically" sample was located. Use this to start exploring the geodatabase object model diagram.

1. Click the Favorites tab where you saved the link to this sample in the ArcObjects Developer Help system. Make note of the classes used in this sample.

2. Open the geodatabase object model diagram and search for the main classes used in the sample.

3. Follow the inheritance symbols all the way to the feature class.

When searching the object model diagrams, it is important to pay attention to the UML symbols that identify relationships between classes. If there is no obvious relationship joining two classes, or if they are located in completely different parts of the model, you should keep in mind that they are still likely associated with each other in some way. It's also important to inspect all of the interfaces associated with the classes since they may contain members that are references to other classes.

4. Pay special attention to any inheritance relationships that may exist.

Trace the flow between the classes and assemble code

In this step you will search for classes in the object model diagram based on the keywords identified for the current subtask. After locating some potential classes to start with, you will go to the ArcObjects Developer Help system and look for any help topics that may be available. The last step is to start writing the code based on the knowledge you have gained from these steps.

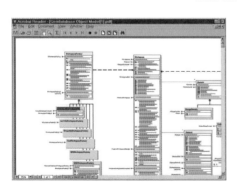

Start with the first subtask by searching for the keywords in the geodatabase object model diagram.

Subtask 1: *Access the States feature class.*

Keyword List: *Access, Feature Class, Workspace, Factory*

1. Using Acrobat Reader, zoom in to about 75 percent and search the geodatabase object model diagram for the first keyword in the list: *Access.*

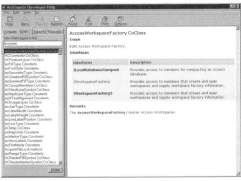

You should find the *AccessWorkspaceFactory* class.

2. Once you find the class, go back to the ArcObjects Developer Help system and use the Index tab to search for all instances of *AccessWorkspaceFactory*. Once a help topic is located, browse the available information along with any examples. To determine what interfaces the class supports, expand the Interfaces hyperlink on the page. Identify these below.

AccessWorkspaceFactory supports the following interfaces: *IWorkspaceFactory, IWorkspaceFactory2,* and *ILocal-DatabaseCompact.*

If no help topic is available, use the Search tab to find all related help documents in the system, such as samples, you might have missed in the initial steps.

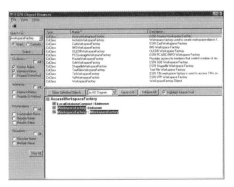

3. Now, return to the object model diagram and follow the inheritance symbols that connect the *AccessWorkspaceFactory* class to *WorkspaceFactory*. Note that the abstract class supports the *IWorkspaceFactory* interface. This information is valuable because it indicates that *AccessWorkspaceFactory* also must implement *IWorkspaceFactory*. It is important to note that this inheritance information can only be derived from the object model diagram itself or from the discussions in the associated chapters in this book.

At this point, you might also be interested in discovering what other coclasses implement *IWorkspaceFactory*. The easiest way is to look at the coclasses that inherit from *Workspace* on the object model diagram, but this can also be discovered two other ways. The first is to use the ArcObjects Developer Help system and click the Index tab to search for *IWorkspaceFactory*. Expand the 'CoClasses that implement IWorkspaceFactory' hyperlink to list the classes that support the interface.

This will list all of the coclasses for you. The second way is to use the ESRI EOBrowser application to search for all of the coclasses that implement the same interface. The coclasses are listed below.

4. With the information you have gathered from the object model diagram, the sample, the help system, and the EOBrowser, you should be able write some basic code to cocreate an instance of the *AccessWorkspaceFactory* class. At this point, you could also go back to the ArcObjects Help system and look for an example on the same page that was located for the *AccessWorkspaceFactory* search. With this information and from browsing the object model diagram, the code could be assembled like this:

```
' Subtask 1. Access the States feature class
Dim pWSF as IWorkspaceFactory
Set pWSF = New AccessWorkspaceFactory
```

5. Now, inspect the members of the *IWorkspaceFactory* interface and try to identify which one can be used to open the database. Again, this information can be acquired using multiple tools. You can:

- Read and interpret the members on the object model diagram.

- Search for the interface in the ArcObjects Developer Help system by expanding the Members hyperlink.

It is possible to view the members of an interface by using a number of tools, such as the ArcObjects Developer Help, the VB/VBA IntelliSense or Object Browser, and the ESRI EOBrowser. In most cases, however, it is recommended to use the ArcObjects Developer Help since it provides a more complete description of the members and often provides an example of how to use them.

- Display the members in VB/VBA using IntelliSense or by pressing F2 to view the Object Browser.

- Search for the interface using the ESRI EOBrowser and expand it to inspect all of its members.

Although there are many avenues to take, it is generally recommended to use the ArcObjects Developer Help system since it provides a description of each member, the required parameters, and often a code sample.

6. After inspecting the members of *IWorkspaceFactory*, it should be obvious that there are multiple members that can be used to open a geodatabase. In this case, since the file path of the database is known to be "C:\data\US.mdb", the *IWorkspaceFactory::OpenFromFile* member can be used. Since the *IWorkspaceFactory::OpenFromFile* member returns a reference to an *IWorkspace* interface, it will be necessary to store this return value.

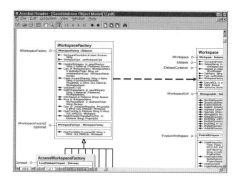

The code so far might look like this:

```
' Subtask 1. Access the States feature class
Dim pWSF as IWorkspaceFactory
Dim pWS as IWorkspace

Set pWSF = New AccessWorkspaceFactory
Set pWS = pWSF.OpenFromFile("c:\data\US.mdb")
```

7. If you inspect the *IWorkspace* interface, you will see that it will take several calls to search and open the "states" feature class if *IWorkspace::Datasets* or *IWorkspace::DatasetNames* are used. In this case it will be necessary to loop through all of the feature classes available just to identify the "states" feature class in the enumeration. Since you already know the name of the feature class to open, you should look for a way to optimize this process. The best resource at this point would be Volume 2, Chapter 8, 'Accessing the geodatabase', but if you inspect the class carefully, you might find it immediately.

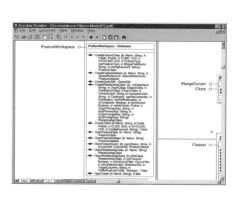

8. If you look at the *Workspace* class on the object model diagram or if you review Volume 2, Chapter 8, 'Accessing the geodatabase', you will notice that this class also supports the *IFeatureWorkspace* interface. This interface is designed to provide feature class-level access to a workspace. It supports an *IFeatureWorkspace::OpenFeatureClass* member, which takes a string name directly and returns an *IFeatureClass* reference.

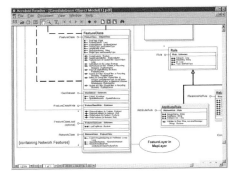

Since you can provide the name as a string and directly return a reference, you should use this interface to return a reference to the "states" feature class. To access the interface, it will be necessary to use *QueryInterface* against the *IWorkspace* reference. It should also be noted that the return value must be stored as an *IFeatureClass* reference.

You should recognize that there is often more than one way to solve a problem using the numerous classes and interfaces available in the ArcObjects library. When this is the case, you should research the documentation and test to find out which set of classes and interfaces work most optimally to solve your particular programming task.

After assembling the code it might look like this:

```
' Subtask 1. Access the States feature class
Dim pWSF as IWorkspaceFactory
Dim pWS as IWorkspace
Dim pFWS as IFeatureWorkspace
Dim pFC as IFeatureClass


Set pWSF = New AccessWorkspaceFactory
Set pWS = pWSF.OpenFromFile("c:\data\US.mdb")
Set pFWS = pWS ' QI
Set pFC = pFWS.OpenFeatureClass("States")
```

To optimize the code even further, rewrite it as follows:

```
' Subtask 1. Access the States feature class
Dim pWSF as IWorkspaceFactory
Dim pFWS as IFeatureWorkspace
Dim pFC as IFeatureClass


Set pWSF = New AccessWorkspaceFactory
Set pFWS = pWSF.OpenFromFile("c:\data\US.mdb")
Set pFC = pFWS.OpenFeatureClass("States")
```

Now that the code for the first subtask has been completed, you must return to part two of the problem-solving guide to assemble the code for the last subtask.

Return to part two, step 1 of this problem-solving guide and find the correct object model diagram for the next subtask.

Subtask two is "Add the new layer to the map."

Go to part two, step 2 and extract keywords.

The keywords are "Layer" and "Map".

Go to part two, step 3 and search for the correct object model diagram. Use the Find tool in Acrobat Reader to search for the keywords in the ArcGIS Object Model PDF.

The object model that contains these keywords is the ArcMap object model.

Go to part two, step 4 and identify the chapter in the book that is associated with the object model diagram. *Chapter 4, 'Composing maps', documents the ArcMap object model.*

Go to step 4 and review the appropriate object model overview page.

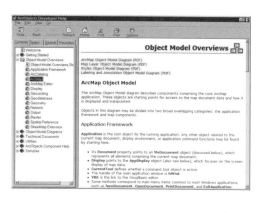

1. Start the ArcObjects Developer Help system and click Object Model Overviews.

2. Click the Object Model Overviews Start Page. *For this subtask, select ArcMap.*

3. Read the overview information available to learn about the classes.

From the overview, it should be obvious that a number of new keywords need to be added to the list. You may want to sort the list as well.

New keyword list: *Application, MxDocument, Map, FeatureLayer, Add*

Go to the *Exploring ArcObjects* book and read the associated chapter. *For this subtask, read Chapter 4, 'Composing maps'.*

With the information gained from the help system and the chapter in the book, you may be able to assemble the required code at this point; otherwise, continue on to the next part.

Return to part three, step 1. Review the structure of the object model diagram.

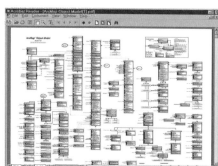

If you return to the sample that was identified in part one, step 4, you will notice that there are classes and interfaces that have not yet been located on an object model diagram. Take this time to look for these classes on the ArcMap object model diagram.

1. Using the ArcObjects Developer Help system, click the Favorites tab where you saved the link to this sample. View the sample.

2. Open the ArcMap object model diagram with Acrobat Reader and start tracing the flow between the classes by searching for the class names with the Find tool. Start with the *Application* class.

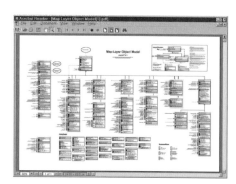

3. Follow the classes all the way to the *Map* class. Notice that there is a wormhole associated with the *Map* class that indicates it will be necessary to go to the map layer object model diagram to view the layer classes.

4. Now, open the map layer object model diagram with Acrobat Reader and follow the diagram until you locate the *FeatureLayer* class.

This step reveals that it will be necessary to traverse the map layer object model diagram to access the layers associated with a

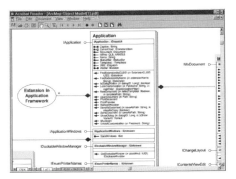

map. This information is also available from the Overview Start Page in the ArcObjects Developer Help system.

Go to step 2, trace the flow between the classes, and assemble code. Start this process by searching for the keywords for the current subtask.

Subtask 2: *Add the layer to ArcMap.*

Keyword List: *Application, MxDocument, Map, FeatureLayer, Add*

1. Using Acrobat Reader, search the relevant object model diagram for each keyword. *For Application, you should find the Application class.*

Inspect the interfaces that the class supports.

2. Once you find the class, go back to the ArcObjects Developer Help system and use the Index to search for that class. For this first keyword, click *Application* (esriMx). Read the information available. The help documentation reveals that *Application* is the primary object for ArcMap and ArcCatalog. Select the Interfaces hyperlink and view the interfaces associated with the *Application* class. Click *IApplication* to view the information available. Look for an example and then write code to access the *Application*.

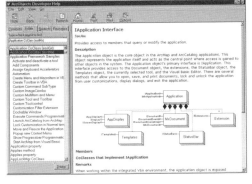

```
' Subtask 2. Add the new layer to the map
Dim pApp as IApplication
Set pApp = Application
```

Now expand the members of *IApplication* with the Members hyperlink. This information reveals that it is possible to access the current document with the *IApplication::Document* member. The code could be updated as follows:

```
' Subtask 2. Add the new layer to the map
Dim pApp as IApplication
Dim pDoc as IDocument
Set pApp = Application
Set pDoc = pApp.Document
```

3. Now return to the object model diagram and find the *MxDocument* class. Inspect the interfaces associated with this class. Notice that *IDocument* does not provide a member to access the *Map* class, but the *IMxDocument* interface does. Navigate the diagram to find the *Map* class.

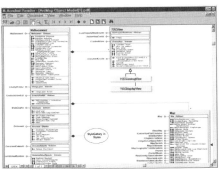

4. Go back to the ArcObjects Developer Help system and use the Index to search for *MxDocument*. Read the information available. Click the Interfaces hyperlink. Click *IMxDocument* and expand the members. Notice that the *IMxDocument* interface supports the *FocusMap* member and returns a reference to *IMap*. Use this member to access the *Map* class.

Update the code to get a reference to the document's map.

```
' Subtask 2. Add the new layer to the map

Dim pApp as IApplication
Dim pDoc as IDocument
Dim pMxDoc as IMxDocument
Dim pMap as IMap

Set pApp = Application
Set pDoc = pApp.Document
Set pMxDoc = pDoc 'QI
Set pMap = pMxDoc.FocusMap
```

5. Go back to the ArcObjects Developer Help system and use the Index to search for the *Map* coclass. Select the Interfaces hyperlink and the *IMap* interface. Expand the members and locate the *AddLayer* member. This member will be used later to add a layer to the map, but first we need to create the new layer and associate it with the "states" data.

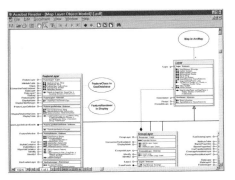

6. Locate the wormhole in the ArcMap object model diagram that connects the *Map* class to the map layer object model diagram. Open the map layer object model diagram and browse the contents. Search for the "FeatureLayer" keyword until you find the class. Inspect the inheritance relationship between *Feature-Layer* and *Layer*. Also, identify the interface inheritance between *IFeatureLayer* and *ILayer*.

The interface inheritance information can also be acquired if you go back to the ArcObjects Developer Help system and use the Index to search for the *FeatureLayer* coclass. Expand the Interfaces hyperlink and notice that it supports the *ILayer* interface.

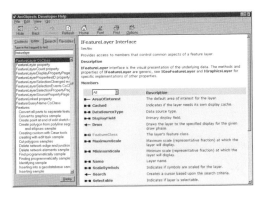

7. Now, inspect the members of *IFeatureLayer* more closely by using the ArcObjects Developer Help system or the object model diagram. Notice it supports an *IFeatureLayer::FeatureClass* member property. From the documentation and the information in Chapter 4, 'Composing maps', it should be obvious that you need to use this property to connect the *FeatureClass* class to the *Feature-Layer* class. The feature class contains a reference to the "states" dataset that was acquired in Subtask 1. Also, set the name of the layer to *IFeatureClass::AliasName*. The last step is to add the new layer to the *Map*.

```
' Subtask 2. Add the new layer to the map

Dim pApp as IApplication
Dim pDoc as IDocument
Dim pMxDoc as IMxDocument
Dim pMap as IMap
Dim pFL as IFeatureLayer

Set pApp = Application
Set pDoc = pApp.Document
Set pMxDoc = pDoc ' QI
Set pMap = pMxDoc.FocusMap
Set pFL = New FeatureLayer
Set pFL.FeatureClass = pFC ' pFC From Subtask 1.
pFL.Name = pFC.AliasName
pMap.AddLayer pFL
```

8. Now that you understand the relationship between the classes and interfaces, the code can be optimized. Rewrite the code as follows:

```
' Subtask 2. Add the new layer to the map

Dim pApp as IApplication
Dim pDoc as IMxDocument
Dim pFL as IFeatureLayer
Set pApp = Application
```

```
Set pMxDoc = pApp.Document
Set pFL = New FeatureLayer
Set pFL.FeatureClass = pFC ' pFC From Subtask 1.
pFL.Name = pFC.AliasName
pMxDoc.FocusMap.AddLayer pFL
```

9. Now, assemble all of the code from subtasks 1 and 2. It will look like this:

```
' Subtask 1. Access the states feature class.
Dim pWSF as IWorkspaceFactory
Dim pFWS as IFeatureWorkspace
Dim pFC as IFeatureClass

Set pWSF = New AccessWorkspaceFactory
Set pFWS = pWSF.OpenFromFile("c:\data\US.mdb")
Set pFC = pFWS.OpenFeatureClass("States")


' Subtask 2. Add the new layer to the map
Dim pApp as IApplication
Dim pDoc as IMxDocument
Dim pFL as IFeatureLayer

Set pApp = Application
Set pMxDoc = pApp.Document
Set pFL = New FeatureLayer
Set pFL.FeatureClass = pFC ' pFC from Subtask 1.
pFL.Name = pFC.AliasName
pMxDoc.FocusMap.AddLayer pFC
```

SUMMARY

It should be clear now that there are several ways to solve ArcObjects programming problems. The similarities between all of them, however, are being able to use the help documents and resources effectively and being able to read the object model diagrams. Hopefully this guide has provided you with an opportunity to visit the main resources that are available and exercise their use in order to solve this real-world problem.

2

Developing with ArcObjects

Euan Cameron

ArcObjects is based on Microsoft's Component Object Model (COM). End users of ArcGIS applications don't necessarily have to understand COM, but if you're a developer intent on developing applications based on ArcObjects or extending the existing ArcMap and ArcCatalog applications using ArcObjects, an understanding of COM is a requirement. The level of understanding required depends on the depth of customization or development you wish to undertake.

Although this chapter does not cover the entire COM environment, it provides both Visual Basic (VB) and Visual C++ developers with sufficient knowledge to be effective in using ArcObjects. There are many coding tips and guidelines that should make your work with ArcObjects more effective. The chapter ends with a bibliography if you're looking for more indepth detail not offered in this book.

Before discussing COM specifically, it is worth considering the wider use of software components in general. There are a number of factors driving the motivation behind software components, but the principal one is the fact that software development is a costly and time-consuming venture.

In an ideal world, it should be possible to write a piece of code once and then reuse it again and again using a variety of development tools, even in circumstances that the original developer did not foresee. Ideally, changes to the code's functionality made by the original developer could be deployed without requiring existing users to change or recompile their code.

Early attempts at producing reusable chunks of code revolved around the creation of class libraries, usually developed in C++. These early attempts suffered from several limitations, notably difficulty of sharing parts of the system (it is very difficult to share binary C++ components—most attempts have only shared source code), problems of persistence and updating C++ components without recompiling, lack of good modeling languages and tools, and proprietary interfaces and customization tools.

To counteract these and other problems, many software engineers have adopted component-based approaches to system development. A software component is a binary unit of reusable code.

Several different but overlapping standards have emerged for developing and sharing components. For building interactive desktop applications, Microsoft's COM is the de facto standard. On the Internet, JavaBeans™ is viable technology. At a coarser grain appropriate for application-level interoperability, the Object Management Group (OMG) has specified the common object request broker architecture (CORBA).

ESRI chose COM as the component technology for ArcGIS because it is a mature technology that offers good performance, many of today's development tools support it, and there are a multitude of third-party components that can be used to extend the functionality of ArcObjects.

To understand COM (and therefore all COM-based technologies), it's important to realize that it isn't an object-oriented language but a protocol or standard. COM is more than just a technology; it is a methodology of software development. COM defines a protocol that connects one software component, or module, with another. By making use of this protocol, it's possible to build reusable software components that can be dynamically interchanged in a distributed system.

COM also defines a programming model, known as interface-based programming. Objects encapsulate the manipulation methods and the data that characterize each instantiated object behind a well-defined interface. This promotes structured and safe system development since the client of an object is protected from knowing any of the details of how a particular method is implemented. COM doesn't specify how an application should be structured. As an application programmer working with COM, language, structure, and implementation details are left up to you.

The key to the success of components is that they implement, in a very practical way, many of the object-oriented principles now commonly accepted in software engineering. Components facilitate software reuse because they are self-contained building blocks that can easily be assembled into larger systems.

COM does specify an object model and programming requirements that enable COM objects to interact with other COM objects. These objects can be within a single process, in other processes, or even on remote machines. They can be written in other languages and may have been developed in very different ways. That is why COM is referred to as a binary specification or standard—it is a standard that applies after a program has been translated to binary machine code.

COM allows these objects to be reused at a binary level, meaning that third party developers do not require access to source code, header files, or object libraries in order to extend the system even at the lowest level.

COMPONENTS, OBJECTS, CLIENTS, AND SERVERS

Different texts use the terms components, objects, clients, and servers to mean different things (to add to the confusion, various texts refer to the same thing using all of these terms). Therefore, it is worthwhile to define the terminology that this book will use.

COM is a client/server architecture. The server (or object) provides some functionality, and the client uses that functionality. COM facilitates the communication between the client and the object. An object can at the same time be a server to a client and be a client of some other object's services.

Objects are instances of COM classes that make services available for use by a client. Hence it is normal to talk of clients and objects instead of clients and servers. These objects are often referred to as COM objects and component objects. This book will refer to them simply as objects.

The client and its servers can exist in the same process or in a different process space. In-process servers are packaged in Dynamic Link Library (DLL) form, and these DLLs are loaded into the client's address space when the client first accesses the server. Out-of-process servers are packaged in executables (EXE) and run in their own address space. COM makes the differences transparent to the client.

When creating COM objects, the developer must be aware of the type of server that the objects will sit inside, but if the creator of the object has implemented them correctly the packaging does not affect the use of the objects by the client.

There are pros and cons to each method of packaging that are symmetrically opposite. DLLs are faster to load into memory, and calling a DLL function is faster. EXEs, on the other hand, provide a more robust solution (if the server fails, the client will not crash), and security is better handled since the server has its own security context.

In a distributed system, EXEs are more flexible, and it does not matter if the server has a different byte ordering than the client. The majority of ArcObjects servers are packaged as in-process servers (DLLs). Later, you will see the performance benefits associated with in-process servers.

In a COM system, the client, or user of functionality, is completely isolated from the provider of that functionality, the object. All the client needs to know is that the functionality is available; with this knowledge, the client can make method calls to the object and expect the object to honor them. In this way, COM is said to act as a contract between client and object. If the object breaks that contract, the behavior of the system will be unspecified. In this way, COM development is based on trust between the implementer and the user of functionality.

Client and server

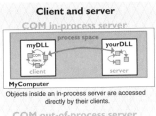

Objects inside an in-process server are accessed directly by their clients.

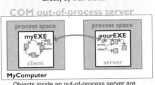

Objects inside an out-of-process server are accessed by COM-supplied proxy objects which make access transparent to the client

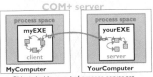

Objects inside an out-of-process server are accessed by COM-supplied proxy objects which make access transparent to the client. The COM run-time handles the remoting layer

In the ArcGIS applications there are many objects that provide, via their interfaces, thousands of properties and methods. When you use the ESRI object libraries you can assume that all these properties and interfaces have been fully implemented, and if they are present on the object diagrams, they are there to use.

CLASS FACTORY

Within each server there is an object called a class factory that the COM runtime interacts with in order to instantiate objects of a particular class. For every corresponding COM class there is a class factory. Normally, when a client requests an object from a server, the appropriate class factory creates a new object and passes out that object to the client.

While this is the normal implementation, it is not the only implementation possible. The class factory can also create an instance of the object the first time and, with subsequent calls, pass out the same object to clients. This type of implementation creates what is known as a singleton object since there is only one instance of the object per process.

GLOBALLY UNIQUE IDENTIFIERS

A distributed system potentially has many thousands of interfaces, classes, and servers, all of which must be referenced when locating and binding clients and objects together at runtime. Clearly, using human-readable names would lead to the potential for clashes, hence COM uses Globally Unique Identifiers (GUIDs), 128 bit numbers that are virtually guaranteed to be unique in the world. It is possible to generate 10 million GUIDs per second until the year 5770 A.D., and each one would be unique.

The COM API defines a function that can be used to generate GUIDs; in addition, all COM-compliant development tools automatically assign GUIDs when appropriate. GUIDs are the same as Universally Unique Identifiers (UUIDs), defined by the Open Group's Distributed Computing Environment (DCE) specification. Below is a sample GUID in registry format.

{E6BDAA76-4D35-11D0-98BE-00805F7CED21}

COM CLASSES AND INTERFACES

Developing with COM means developing using interfaces, the so-called interface-based programming model. All communication between objects is made via their interfaces. COM interfaces are abstract, meaning there is no implementation associated with an interface; the code associated with an interface comes from a class implementation. The interface sets out what requests can be made of an object that chooses to implement the interface.

How an interface is implemented differs between objects. Thus the objects inherit the type of interface, not its implementation, which is called type inheritance. Functionality is modeled abstractly with the interfaces and implemented within a class implementation. Classes and

A server is a binary file that contains all the code required by one or more COM classes. This includes both the code that works with COM to instantiate objects into memory and the code to perform the methods supported by the objects contained within the server.

GUIDGEN.EXE is a utility that ships with Microsoft's Visual Studio and provides an easy-to-use user interface for generating GUIDs. It can be found in the directory <VS Install Dir>\Common\Tools.

The acronym GUID is commonly pronounced "gwid".

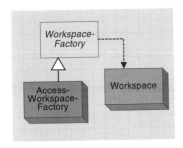

This is a simplified portion of the geodatabase object model showing type inheritance among abstract classes and coclasses and instantiation of classes.

interfaces are often referred to as the "What" and "How" of COM. The interface defines what an object can do, and the class defines how it is done.

COM classes provide the code associated with one or more interfaces, thus encapsulating the functionality entirely within the class. Two classes can both have the same interface, but they may implement them quite differently. By implementing these interfaces in this way, COM displays classic object-oriented polymorphic behavior. COM does not support the concept of multiple inheritance; however, this is not a shortcoming since individual classes can implement multiple interfaces. See the diagram to the left on polymorphic behavior.

Within ArcObjects are three types of classes that the developer must be aware of: abstract classes, coclasses, and classes. An abstract class cannot be created; it is solely a specification for instances of subclasses (through type inheritance). ArcObjects Dataset or Geometry classes are examples of abstract classes. An object of type Geometry cannot be created, but an object of type Polyline can. This Polyline object in turn implements the interfaces defined within the Geometry base class, hence any interfaces defined within object-based classes are accessible from the coclass.

A coclass is a publicly creatable class. In other words, it is possible for COM to create an instance of that class and give the resultant object to the client in order for the client to use the services defined by the interfaces of that class. A class cannot be publicly created, but objects of this class can be created by other objects within ArcObjects and given to clients to use.

To the left is a diagram that illustrates the polymorphic behavior exhibited in COM classes when implementing interfaces. Notice that both the *Human* and *Parrot* classes implement the *ITalk* interface. The *ITalk* interface defines the methods and properties, such as *StartTalking*, *StopTalking*, or *Language*, but clearly the two classes implement these differently.

INSIDE INTERFACES

COM interfaces are how COM objects communicate with each other. When working with COM objects, the developer never works with the COM object directly but gains access to the object via one of its interfaces. COM interfaces are designed to be a grouping of logically related functions. The virtual functions are called by the client and implemented by the server; in this way an object's interfaces are the contract between the client and object. The client of an object is holding an interface pointer onto that object. This interface pointer is referred to as an opaque pointer since the client cannot gain any knowledge of the implementation details within an object or direct access to an object's state data. The client must communicate through the member functions of the interface. This allows COM to provide a binary standard through which all objects can effectively communicate.

Interfaces allow developers to model functionality abstractly. Visual C++ developers see interfaces as a collection of pure virtual functions, while Visual Basic developers see an interface as a collection of properties, functions, and sub routines.

This diagram shows how common behavior, expressed as interfaces, can be shared among multiple objects, animals in this example, to support polymorphism.

The concept of the interface is fundamental in COM. The COM Specification (Microsoft, 1995) emphasizes these four points when discussing COM interfaces:

1. An interface is not a class. An interface cannot be instantiated by itself since it carries no implementation.

2. An interface is not an object. An interface is a related group of functions and is the binary standard through which clients and objects communicate.

3. Interfaces are strongly typed. Every interface has its own interface identifier, thereby eliminating the possibility of a collision between interfaces of the same human-readable name.

4. Interfaces are immutable. Interfaces are never versioned. Once defined and published, an interface cannot be changed.

Once an interface has been published, it is not possible to change the external signature of that interface. It is possible at any time to change the implementation details of an object that exposes an interface. This change may be a minor bug fix or a complete reworking of the underlying algorithm; the clients of the interface do not care since the interface appears the same to them. This means that when upgrades to the servers are deployed in the form of new DLLs and EXEs, existing clients need not be recompiled to make use of the new functionality. If the external signature of the interface is no longer sufficient, a new interface is created to expose the new functions. Old or deprecated interfaces are not removed from a class to ensure all existing client applications can continue to communicate with the newly upgraded server. Newer clients will have the choice of using the old or new interfaces.

An interface's permanence is not restricted to simply its method signatures, but it extends to its semantic behavior as well. For example, an interface defines two methods, A and B, with no restrictions placed on their use. It breaks the COM contract if at a subsequent release Method A requires that Method B be executed first. A change like this would force possible recompilations of clients.

THE *IUNKNOWN* INTERFACE

All COM interfaces derive from the *IUnknown* interface, and all COM objects must implement this interface. The *IUnknown* interface performs two tasks: it controls object lifetime and provides run-time type support. It is through the *IUnknown* interface that clients maintain a reference on an object while it is in use—leaving the actual lifetime management to the object itself.

The name IUnknown came from a 1988 internal Microsoft paper called Object Architecture: Dealing with the Unknown – or – Type Safety in a Dynamically Extensible Class Library.

Object lifetime is controlled with two methods, *AddRef* and *Release*, and an internal reference counter. Every object must have an implementation of *IUnknown* in order to control its own lifetime. Anytime an interface pointer is created or duplicated, the *AddRef* method is called, and when the client no longer requires this pointer, the corresponding *Release* method is called. When the reference count reaches zero, the object destroys itself.

Clients also use *IUnknown* to acquire other interfaces on an object. *QueryInterface* is the method that a client calls when another interface on the object is required. When a client calls *QueryInterface,* the object provides an interface and calls *AddRef.* In fact, it is the responsibility of any COM method that returns an interface to increment the reference count for the object on behalf of the caller. The client must call the *Release* method when the interface is no longer needed. The client calls *AddRef* explicitly only when an interface is duplicated.

When developing a COM object, the developer must obey the rules of *QueryInterface*. These rules dictate that interfaces for an object are symmetric, transitive, and reflexive and are always available for the lifetime of an object. For the client this means that, given a valid interface to an object, it is always valid to ask the object, via a call to *QueryInterface*, for any other interface on that object including itself. It is not possible to support an interface and later deny access to that interface, perhaps because of time or security constraints. Other mechanisms must be used to provide this level of functionality. Some classes support the concept of optional interfaces. Depending on the coclass, they may optionally implement an interface; this does not break this rule since the interface is either always available or always not available on the class.

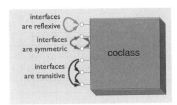

The rules of QueryInterface dictate that interfaces of an object are reflexive, symmetric, and transitive. It is always possible, holding a valid interface pointer on an object, to get any other interface on that object.

When requested for a particular interface, the *QueryInterface* method can return an already assigned piece of memory for that requested interface, or it can allocate a new piece of memory and return that. The only case when the same piece of memory must be returned is when the *IUnknown* interface is requested. When comparing two interface pointers to see if they point to the same object, it is important that a simple comparison not be performed. To correctly compare two interface pointers to see if they are for the same object, they both must be queried for their *IUnknown*, and the comparison must be performed on the *IUnknown* pointers. In this way, the *IUnknown* interface is said to define a COM object's identity.

The method QueryInterface is often referred to by the abbreviation QI.

It's good practice in Visual Basic to call *Release* explicitly by assigning an interface equal to *Nothing* to release any resources it's holding. Even if you don't call *Release*, Visual Basic will automatically call it when you no longer need the object—that is, when it goes out of scope. With global variables, you must explicitly call *Release*. In Visual Basic, the system performs all these reference-counting operations for you, making the use of COM objects relatively straightforward.

Since IUnknown is fundamental to all COM objects, in general there are no references to IUnknown in any of the ArcObjects documentation and class diagrams.

In C++, however, you must increment and decrement the reference count to allow an object to correctly control its own lifetime. Likewise, the *QueryInterface* method must be called when asking for another interface. In C++ the use of smart pointers simplifies much of this. These smart pointers are class-based and hence have appropriate constructors, destructors, and overloaded operators to automate much of the reference counting and query interface operations.

Smart pointers are a class-based smart type and are covered in detail later in this chapter.

INTERFACE DEFINITION LANGUAGE

Microsoft Interface Definition Language (MIDL) is used to describe COM objects including their interfaces. This MIDL is an extension of the IDL defined by the Distributed Computing Environment (DCE), where it used to define

MIDL is commonly referred to simply as IDL.

The IDL defines the public interface that developers use when working with ArcObjects. When compiled, the IDL creates a type library.

remote procedure calls between clients and servers. The MIDL extensions include most of the Object Definition Language (ODL) statements and attributes. ODL was used in the early days of OLE Automation for the creation of type libraries.

TYPE LIBRARY

A type library is best thought of as a binary version of an Interface Definition Language (IDL) file. It contains a binary description of all coclasses, interfaces, methods, and types contained within a server or servers.

There are several COM interfaces provided by Microsoft that work with type libraries. Two of these interfaces are *ITypeInfo* and *ITypeLib*. By utilizing these standard COM interfaces, various development tools and compilers can gain information about the coclasses and interfaces supported by a particular library.

In order to support the concept of a language-independent development set of components, all relevant data concerning the ArcObjects libraries is shipped inside type libraries. There are no header files, source files, or object files supplied or needed by external developers.

INBOUND AND OUTBOUND INTERFACES

Interfaces can be either inbound or outbound. An inbound interface is the most common kind—the client makes calls to functions within the interface contained on an object. An outbound interface is one where the object makes calls to the client—a technique analogous to the traditional callback mechanism.

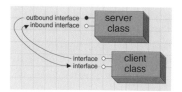

In the diagrams in this book and the ArcObjects object model diagrams, outbound interfaces are depicted with a solid circle on the interface jack.

There are differences in the way these interfaces are implemented. The implementer of an inbound interface must implement all functions of the interface; failure to do so breaks the contract of COM. This is also true for outbound interfaces. If you use Visual Basic, you don't have to implement all functions present on the interface since it provides stub methods for the methods you don't implement. On the other hand, if you use C++ you must implement all the pure virtual functions to compile the class.

Connection points is a specific methodology for working with outbound COM interfaces. The connection point architecture defines how the communication between objects is set up and taken down. Connection points are not the most efficient way of initializing bidirectional object communication, but they are in common use because many development tools and environments support them.

Dispatch event interfaces

There are some objects with ArcObjects that support two outbound event interfaces that look similar to the methods they support. An example of two such interfaces are the *IDocumentEvents* and the *IDocumentEventsDisp*. The "Disp" suffix denotes a pure Dispatch interface. These dispatch interfaces are used by VBA when dealing with certain application events, such as loading documents. A VBA programmer works with the dispatch interfaces, while a developer using another development language uses the nonpure dispatch interface. Since these dispatch event interfaces are application specific, the details are discussed in the application chapters of the book, not the framework chapter.

Default interfaces

Every COM object has a default interface that is returned when the object is created if no other interface is specified. All the objects within the ESRI object libraries have *IUnknown* as their default interface, with a few exceptions.

The reason for making IUnknown *the default interface is because the VB object browser hides information for the default interface. The fact that it hides* IUnknown *is not important for VB developers.*

The default interface of the *Application* object for both ArcCatalog and ArcMap is the *IApplication* interface. These uses of non*IUnknown* default interfaces are a requirement of Visual Basic for Applications and are found on the ArcMap and ArcCatalog application-level objects.

This means that variables that hold interface pointers must be declared in a certain way. For more details, see the coding sections later in this chapter. When COM objects are created, any of the supported interfaces can be requested at creation time.

IDispatch interface

COM supports three types of binding:

Binding is the term given to the process of matching the location of a function given a pointer to an object.

1. Late. This is where type discovery is left until runtime. Method calls made by the client but not implemented by the object will fail at execution time.
2. ID. Method IDs are stored at compile time, but execution of the method is still performed through a higher-level function.
3. Custom vTable (early). Binding is performed at compile time. The client can then make method calls directly into the object.

The *IDispatch* interface supports late- and ID-binding languages. The *IDispatch* interface has methods that allow clients to ask the object what methods it supports.

Binding type	In process DLL	Out of process DLL
Late binding	22,250	5,000
Custom vTable binding	825,000	20,000

This table shows the number of function calls that can be made per second on a typical Pentium® III machine.

Assuming the required method is supported, the client executes the method by calling the *IDispatch::Invoke* method. This method, in turn, calls the required method and returns the status and any parameters back to the client on completion of the method call.

Clearly, this is not the most efficient way to make calls on a COM object. Late binding requires a call to the object to retrieve the list of method IDs; the client must then construct the call to the *Invoke* method and call it. The *Invoke* method must then unpack the method parameters and call the function.

All these steps add significant overhead to the time it takes to execute a method. In addition, every object must have an implementation for *IDispatch*, which makes all objects larger and adds to their development time.

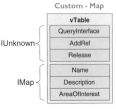

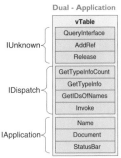

These diagrams summarize the custom and IDispatch interfaces for two classes in ArcObjects. The layout of the vTable displays the differences. It also illustrates the importance of implementing all methods—if one method is missing, the vTable will have the wrong layout, and hence the wrong function pointer would be returned to the client, resulting in a system crash.

Interfaces that directly inherit from an interface other than IUnknown cannot be implemented in VB.

ID binding offers a slight improvement over late binding in that the method IDs are cached at compile time, which means the initial call to retrieve the IDs is not required. However, there is still significant call overhead because the *IDispatch::Invoke* method is still called in order to execute the required method on the object.

Early binding, often referred to as custom vTable binding, does not use the *IDispatch* interface. Instead, a type library provides the required information at compile time to allow the client to know the layout of the server object. At runtime, the client makes method calls directly into the object. This is the fastest method of calling object methods and also has the benefit of compile-time type checking.

Objects that support both *IDispatch* and custom vTable are referred to as dual interface objects. The object classes within the ESRI object libraries do not implement the *IDispatch* interface; this means that these object libraries cannot be used with late-binding scripting languages such as JavaScript™ or VBScript since these languages require that all COM servers accessed support the *IDispatch* interface.

Careful examination of the ArcGIS class diagrams indicates that the *Application* objects support *IDispatch* because there is a requirement in VBA for the *IDispatch* interface.

All ActiveX controls support *IDispatch*. This means it is possible to use the various ActiveX controls shipped with ArcObjects to access functionality from within scripting environments.

INTERFACE INHERITANCE

An interface consists of a group of methods and properties. If one interface inherits from another, then all of the methods and properties in the parent are directly available in the inheriting object.

The underlying principle here is interface inheritance, rather than the implementation inheritance you may have seen in languages such as SmallTalk and C++. In implementation inheritance, an object inherits actual code from its parent; in interface inheritance, it's the definitions of the methods of the object that are passed on. The coclass that implements the interfaces must provide the implementation for all inherited interfaces.

Implementation inheritance is not supported in a heterogeneous development environment because of the need to access source and header files. For reuse of code, COM uses the principles of aggregation and containment. Both of these are binary-reuse techniques.

AGGREGATION AND CONTAINMENT

For a third-party developer to make use of existing objects, using either containment or aggregation, the only requirement is that the server housing the contained or aggregated object is installed on both the developer and target release machines. Not all development languages support aggregation.

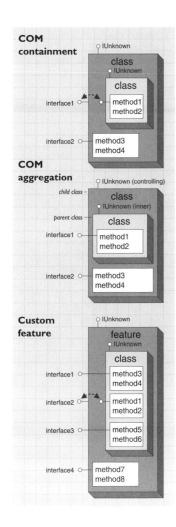

COM containment

COM aggregation

Custom feature

Although an understanding of Apartments and threading is not essential in the use of ArcObjects, basic knowledge will help you understand some of the implications with certain development environments highlighted later in this chapter.

The simplest form of binary reuse is containment. Containment allows modification of the original object's method behavior but not the method's signature. With containment, the contained object (inner) has no knowledge that it is contained within another object (outer). The outer object must implement all the interfaces supported by the inner. When requests are made on these interfaces, the outer object simply delegates them to the inner. To support new functionality, the outer object can either implement one of the interfaces without passing the calls on or implement an entirely new interface in addition to those interfaces from the inner object.

COM aggregation involves an outer object that controls which interfaces it chooses to expose from an inner object. Aggregation does not allow modification of the original object's method behavior. The inner object is aware that it is being aggregated into another object and forwards any *QueryInterface* calls to the outer (controlling) object so that the object as a whole obeys the laws of COM.

To the clients of an object using aggregation, there is no way to distinguish which interfaces the outer object implements and which interfaces the inner object implements.

Custom features make use of both containment and aggregation. The developer aggregates the interfaces where no customizations are required and contains those that are to be customized. The individual methods on the contained interfaces can then either be implemented in the customized class, thus providing custom functionality, or the method call can be passed to the appropriate method on the contained interface.

Aggregation is important in this case since there are some hidden interfaces defined on a feature that cannot be contained. For more information on custom features, see Volume 2, Chapter 8, 'Accessing the geodatabase'.

Visual Basic 6 does not support aggregation, so it can't be used to create custom features.

THREADS, APARTMENTS, AND MARSHALLING

A thread is a process flow through an application. There are potentially many threads within Windows applications. An apartment is a group of threads that work with contexts within a process. With COM+, a context belongs to one apartment. There are potentially many types of context; security is an example of a type of context. Before successfully communicating with each other, objects must have compatible contexts.

COM supports two types of apartments: single-threaded apartment (STA) and multithreaded apartment (MTA). COM+ supports the additional thread-neutral apartment (TNA). A process can have any number of STAs; each process creates one STA called the main apartment. Threads that are created as apartment threaded are placed in an STA. All user-interface code is placed in an STA to prevent deadlock situations. A process can only have one MTA. A thread that is started as multithreaded is placed in the MTA. The TNA has no threads permanently associated with it; rather, threads enter and leave the apartment when appropriate.

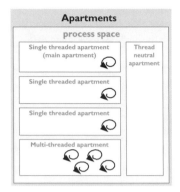

Apartments

Think of the SCM (pronounced scum) as the COM runtime environment. The SCM interacts with objects, servers, and the operating system and provides the transparency between clients and the objects that they work with.

In-process objects have an entry in the registry, the ThreadingModel, that informs the COM Service Control Manager (SCM) into which apartment to place the object. If the object's requested apartment is compatible with the creator's apartment, the object is placed in that apartment; otherwise, the SCM will find or create the appropriate apartment. If no threading model is defined, the object will be placed in the main apartment of the process. The ThreadingModel registry entry can have the following values:

1. *Apartment*. Object must be executed within the STA. Normally used by UI objects.

2. *Free*. Object must be executed within the MTA. Objects creating threads are normally placed in the MTA.

3. *Both*. Object is compatible with all apartment types. The object will be created in the same apartment as the creator.

4. *Neutral*. Objects must execute in the TNA. Used by objects to ensure there is no thread switch when called from other apartments. This is only available under COM+.

Marshalling enables a client to make interface-function calls to objects in other apartments transparently. Marshalling can occur between COM apartments on different machines, between COM apartments in different process spaces, and between COM apartments in the same process space (STA to MTA, for example). COM provides a standard marshaller that handles function calls that use automation-compliant data types (see table below). Nonautomation data types can be handled by the standard marshaller as long as proxy stub code is generated; otherwise, custom-marshalling code is required.

Type	Description
Boolean	Data item that can have the value True or False
unsigned char	8-bit unsigned data item
double	64-bit IEEE floating-point number
float	32-bit IEEE floating-point number
int	Signed integer, whose size is system dependent
long	32-bit signed integer
short	16-bit signed integer
BSTR	Length-prefixed string
CURRENCY	8-byte, fixed-point number
DATE	64-bit, floating-point fractional number of days since Dec 30, 1899
SCODE	For 16-bit systems - Built-in error that corresponds to VT_ERROR
Typedef enum myenum	Signed integer, whose size is system dependent
Interface IDispatch *	Pointer to the IDispatch interface
Interface IUnknown *	Pointer to an interface that does not derive from IDispatch
dispinterface Typename *	Pointer to an interface derived from IDispatch
Coclass Typename *	Pointer to a coclass name (VT_UNKNOWN)
[oleautomation] interface Typename *	Pointer to an interface that derives from IDispatch
SAFEARRAY(TypeName)	TypeName is any of the above types. Array of these types
TypeName*	TypeName is any of the above types. Pointer to a type
Decimal	96-bit unsigned binary integer scaled by a variable power of 10. A decimal data type that provides a size and scale for a number (as in coordinates)

COMPONENT CATEGORY

Component categories are used by client applications to find all COM classes of a particular type that are installed on the system efficiently. For example, a client application may support a data export function in which you can specify the output format—a component category could be used to find all the data export classes for the various formats. If component categories are not used, the application has to instantiate each object and interrogate it to see if it supports the required functionality, which is not a practical approach. Component categories support the extensibility of COM by allowing the developer of the client application to create and work with classes that belong to a particular category. If at a later date a new class is added to the category, the client application need not be changed to take advantage of the new class; it will automatically pick up the new class the next time the category is read.

COM AND THE REGISTRY

COM makes use of the Windows® system registry to store information about the various parts that compose a COM system. The classes, interfaces, DLLs, EXEs, type libraries, and so forth, are all given unique identifiers (GUIDs) that the SCM uses when referencing these components. To see an example of this, run regedit, then open HKEY_CLASSES_ROOT. This opens a list of all the classes registered on the system.

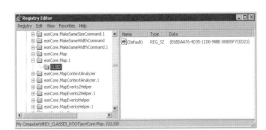

ESRI keys in the Windows system registry

COM makes use of the registry for a number of housekeeping tasks, but the most important and most easily understood is the use of the registry when instantiating COM objects into memory. In the simplest case, that of an in-process server, the steps are as follows:

1. Client requests the services of a COM object.

2. SCM looks for the requested objects registry entry by searching on the class ID (a GUID).

The function DllGetClassObject is the function that makes a DLL a COM DLL. Other functions, such as DllRegisterServer and DllUnregisterServer, are nice to have but not essential for a DLL to function as a COM DLL.

3. DLL is located and loaded into memory. The SCM calls a function within the DLL called *DllGetClassObject*, passing the desired class as the first argument.

4. The class object normally implements the interface *IClassFactory*. The SCM calls the method *CreateInstance* on this interface to instantiate the appropriate object into memory.

5. Finally, the SCM asks the newly created object for the interface that the client requested and passes that interface back to the client. At this stage, the SCM drops out of the equation, and the client and object communicate directly.

From the above sequence of steps, it is easy to imagine how changes in the object's packaging (DLL versus EXE) make little difference to the client of the object. COM handles these differences.

AUTOMATION

Automation is the technology used by individual objects or entire applications to provide access to their encapsulated functionality via a late-bound language. Commonly, automation is thought of as writing macros, where these macros can access many applications in order for a task to be done. ArcObjects, as already stated, does not support the *IDispatch* interface; hence, it cannot be used alone by an automation controller.

It is possible to instantiate an instance of ArcMap by cocreating the document object and then making calls into ArcMap via the document object or one of its connected objects. There are, however, problems with this approach since the automation controller instance and the ArcMap instance are running in separate processes. Many of the objects contained within ArcObjects are process dependent, and therefore simple Automation will not work. Using other techniques outlined in Chapter 4, 'Composing maps', it is possible to interact with ArcMap in a way analogous to OLE Automation.

Any language that supports COM can be used to develop with ArcObjects. The guidelines and advice in this section are useful for any programmer working with ArcObjects. The subsequent sections of this chapter deal specifically with Visual Basic, Visual Basic for Applications, and Visual C++. The main reason for this is that the majority of the samples accompanying the software are written in these environments, and these development tools are well suited for the creation of COM software components.

CODING STANDARDS

Each of the language-specific sections begins with a section on coding standards for that language. These standards are used internally at ESRI and are followed by the samples that ship with the software.

For simplicity, some samples will not follow the coding standards. As an example, it is recommended that when coding in Visual Basic, all types defined within the ESRI object library are prefixed with the library name esriCore. This is only done in samples where a name clash will occur. Omitting this text makes the code easier to understand for developers new to ArcObjects.

To understand why standards and guidelines are important, consider that in any large software development project, there are many backgrounds represented by the team members. Each programmer has personal opinions concerning how code should look and be built. If each programmer engineers code differently, it becomes increasingly difficult to share work and ideas. On a successful team, the developers adapt their coding styles to the tone set by the group. Often, this means adapting one's code to match the style of existing code in the system.

Initially, this may seem burdensome, but adopting a uniform programming style and set of techniques invariably increases software quality. When all the code in a project conforms to a standard set of styles and conventions, less time is wasted learning the particular syntactic quirks of individual programmers, and more time can be spent reviewing, debugging, and extending the code. Even at a social level, uniform style encourages team-oriented, rather than individualist, outlooks—leading to greater team unity, productivity and, ultimately, better software.

GENERAL CODING TIPS AND RESOURCES

This section on general coding tips will benefit all developers working with ArcObjects no matter what language they are using.

Class diagrams

Getting help with the object model is fundamental to successfully working with ArcObjects. Chapter 1, 'Introducing ArcObjects', started the process of introducing the class diagrams and showing many of the common routes through the objects. The class diagrams are most useful if viewed in the early learning process in printed form. This allows developers to appreciate the overall structure of the object model implemented by ArcObjects. When you are comfortable with the overall structure, the PDF files included with the software distribution can be more effective to work with. The PDF files are searchable; you can use the Search dialog box in Acrobat Reader to find classes and interfaces quickly.

Object browsers

In addition to the class diagram PDF files, the type library information can be viewed using a number of object browsers. Visual Basic has a built-in Object Browser; OLEView (a free utility from Microsoft) also displays type library information. The best object viewer to use is the ESRI object viewer. This object viewer can be used to view type information for any type library but defaults to the ESRI Object Library. Information on the classes and interfaces can be displayed in Visual Basic, Visual C++, or object diagram format.

The object browsers can view coclasses and classes but cannot be used to view abstract classes. Abstract classes are only viewable on the object diagrams, where their use is solely to simplify the models.

Component help

All interfaces and coclasses are documented in the component help file. This is a compiled HTML file that can be viewed by itself or when using an integrated developer environment (IDE). In Visual C++ and Visual Basic, if the cursor is over an ESRI type when the F1 key is pressed, the appropriate page in the ArcObjects Class Help in the ArcObjects Developer Help system is displayed in the compiled HTML viewer. Ultimately, this will be the help most commonly accessed when you get to know the object models better.

Code wizards

There are a number of Code Generation Wizards available to help with the creation of boiler plate code, both in Visual C++ and Visual Basic. While these wizards are useful in removing the tediousness in common tasks, they do not excuse you as the developer from understanding the underlying principles of the generated code. The main objective should be to read the accompanying documentation and understand the limitations of these tools.

Indexing of collections

All collection-like objects in ArcObjects are zero-based for their indexing. This is not the case with all development environments; Visual Basic has both zero- and one-based collections. As a general rule, if the collection base is not known, assume that the collection base is zero. This ensures that a runtime error will be raised when the collection is first accessed (assuming the access of the collection does not start at zero). Assuming a base of one means the first element of a zero-based collection would be missed and an error would only be raised if the end of the collection were reached when the code is executed.

Accessing collection elements

When accessing elements of a collection sequentially, it is best to use an enumerator interface. This provides the fastest method of walking through the collection. The reason for this is that each time an element is requested by index, internally an enumerator is used to locate the

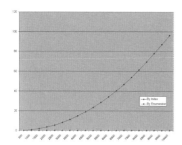

This graph shows the performance benefits of accessing a collection using an enumerator opposed to the elements index. As expected, the graph shows a classic power trend line ($y=cx^b$). The client (VB) and Server (VC++) code used to generate these metrics are included in the book samples.

element. Hence, if the collection is looped over getting each element in turn, the time taken increases by power ($y=cx^b$).

Enumerator use

When requesting an enumerator interface from an object, the client has no idea how the object has implemented this interface. The object may create a new enumerator, or it may decide for efficiency to return a previously created enumerator. If a previous enumerator is passed to the client, the position of the element pointer will be at the last accessed element. To ensure that the enumerator is at the start of the collection, the client should reset the enumerator before use.

Error handling

Exception handling is language specific and, since COM is language neutral, exceptions are not supported.

All methods of interfaces, in other words, methods callable from other objects, should handle internal errors and signify success or failure via an appropriate *HRESULT*. COM does not support passing exceptions out of interface method calls. COM supports the notion of a COM exception. A COM exception utilizes the COM error object by populating it with relevant information and then returning an appropriate *HRESULT* to signify failure. Clients, on receiving the *HRESULT*, can then interrogate the COM *Error* object for contextual information about the error. Languages such as Visual Basic implement their own form of exception handling. For more information, see the section on the Visual Basic Virtual Machine.

Notification interfaces

There are a number of interfaces in ArcObjects that have no methods. These are known as notification interfaces. Their purpose is to inform the application framework that the class that implements them supports a particular set of functionality. For instance, the Application Framework uses these interfaces to determine if a menu object is a root-level menu (*IRootLevelMenu*) or a context menu (*IShortcutMenu*).

Clientside storage

Some ArcObjects methods expect interface pointers to point to valid objects prior to making the method call. This is known as client storage since the client allocates the memory needed for the object before the method call. Let's say you have a polygon and you want to get its bounding box. To do this, use the *QueryEnvelope* method on *IPolygon*. If you write the following code:

```
Dim pEnv As IEnvelope
pPolygon.QueryEnvelope pEnv
```

you'll get an error because the *QueryEnvelope* method expects you (the client) to create the *Envelope*. The method will modify the envelope you pass in and return the changed one back to you. The correct code is shown below.

```
Dim pEnv As IEnvelope
Set pEnv = New Envelope
```

```
pPolygon.QueryEnvelope pEnv
```

How do you know when to create and when not to create? In general, all methods that begin with "Query", such as *QueryEnvelope*, expect you to create the object. If the method name is *GetEnvelope*, then an object will be created for you. The reason for this clientside storage is performance. Where it is anticipated that the method on an object will be called in a tight loop, the parameters need only be created once and simply populated. This is faster than creating new objects inside the method each time.

Property by value and by reference

Occasionally, you will see a property that can be set by value or by reference, meaning that it has both a *put_XXX* and a *putref_XXX* method. On first appearance this may seem odd—why does a property need to support both? A Visual C++ developer sees this as simply giving the client the opportunity to pass ownership of a resource over to the server (using the *putref_XXX* method). A Visual Basic developer will see this as quite different; indeed, it is likely because of the Visual Basic developer that both *By Reference* and *By Value* are supported on the property.

To illustrate this, assume there are two text boxes on a form, Text1 and Text2. With a *propput*, it is possible to do the following in Visual Basic:

```
Text1.text = Text2.text
```

It is also possible to write this:

```
Text1.text = Text2
```

or this:

```
Text1 = Text2
```

DISPIDs are unique IDs given to properties and methods in order for the IDispatch interface to efficiently call the appropriate method using the Invoke method.

All these cases make use of the *propput* method to assign the text string of text box Text2 to the text string of text box Text1. The second and third cases work because since no specific property is stated, Visual Basic looks for the property with a *DISPID* of 0.

This all makes sense assuming that it is the text string property of the text box that is manipulated. What happens if the actual object referenced by the variable Text2 is to be assigned to the variable Text1? If there was only a *propput* method it would not be possible, hence the need for a *propputref* method. With the *propputref* method, the following code will achieve the setting of the object reference.

Notice the use of the "Set".

```
Set Text1 = Text2
```

Initializing Outbound interfaces

When initializing an Outbound interface, it is important to only initialize the variable if the variable does not already listen to events from the server object. Failure to follow this rule will result in an infinite loop.

As an example, assume there is a variable *ViewEvents* that has been dimensioned as:

```
Private WithEvents ViewEvents As Map
```

To correctly sink this event handler, you can write code within the *OnClick* event of a UI button control, like this:

```
Private Sub UIButtonControl1_Click()
  Dim pMxDoc As IMxDocument
  Set pMxDoc = ThisDocument

  ' Check to see that the map is different than what is currently connected
  If (Not ViewEvents Is pMxDoc.FocusMap) Then
    ' Sink the event since listener has not been initialised with this map
    Set ViewEvents = pMxDoc.FocusMap
  End If
End Sub
```

Notice in the above code the use of the *Is* keyword to check for object identity.

DATABASE CONSIDERATIONS

When programming against the database, there are a number of rules that must be followed to ensure that the code will be optimal. These rules are detailed below.

If you are going to edit data programmatically, that is, not use the editing tools in ArcMap, you need to follow these rules in order to ensure that custom object behavior (such as network topology maintenance or triggering of custom-feature-defined methods) is correctly invoked in response to the changes your application makes to the database. You must also follow these rules in order to ensure that your changes are made within the multiuser editing (long transaction) framework.

Edit sessions

Make all changes to the geodatabase within an edit session, which is bracketed between *StartEditing* and *StopEditing* method calls on the *IEditWorkspace* interface found on the *Workspace* object.

This behavior is required for any multiuser update of the database. Starting an edit session gives the application a state of the database that is guaranteed not to change, except for changes made by the editing application.

In addition, starting an edit session turns on behavior in the geodatabase such that a query against the database is guaranteed to return a reference to an existing object in memory if the object was previously retrieved and is still in use.

This behavior is required for correct application behavior when navigating between a cluster of related objects while making modifications to objects. In other words, when you are not within an edit session, the database can create a new instance of a COM object each time the application requests a particular object from the database.

Edit operations

Group your changes into edit operations, which are bracketed between the *StartEditOperation* and *StopEditOperation* method calls on the *IEditWorkspace* interface.

You may make all your changes within a single edit operation if so required. Edit operations can be undone and redone. If you are working with data stored in ArcSDE, creating at least one edit operation is a requirement. There is no additional overhead to creating an edit operation.

Recycling and nonrecycling cursors

Use nonrecycling search cursors to select objects or fetch objects that are to be updated. Recycling cursors should only be used for read-only operations, such as drawing and querying features.

Nonrecycling cursors within an edit session create new objects only if the object to be returned does not already exist in memory.

Fetching properties using query filters

Always fetch all properties of the object; query filters should always use "*". For efficient database access, the number of properties of an object retrieved from the database can be specified. As an example, drawing a feature requires only the *OID* and the *Shape* of the feature, hence the simpler renderers only retrieve these two columns from the database. This optimization speeds up drawing but is not suitable when editing features.

If all properties are not fetched, then object-specific code that is triggered may not find the properties that the method requires. For example, a custom feature developer might write code to update attributes A and B whenever the geometry of a feature changes. If only the geometry was retrieved, then attributes A and B would be found to be missing within the *OnChanged* method. This would cause the *OnChanged* method to return an error, which would cause the *Store* to return an error and the edit operation to fail.

Marking changed objects

After changing an object, mark the object as changed (and guarantee that it is updated in the database) by calling *Store* on the object. Delete an object by calling the *Delete* method on the object. Set versions of these calls also exist and should be used if the operation is being performed on a set of objects to ensure optimal performance.

Calling these methods guarantees that all necessary polymorphic object behavior built into the geodatabase is executed (for example, updating of network topology or updating of specific columns in response to changes in other columns in ESRI-supplied objects). It also guarantees that developer-supplied behavior is correctly triggered.

Update and insert cursors

Never use update cursors or insert cursors to update or insert objects into object and feature classes in an already loaded geodatabase that has active behavior.

Update and insert cursors are bulk cursor APIs for use during initial database loading. If used on an object or feature class with active behavior, they will bypass all object-specific behavior associated with object creation (such as topology creation) and with attribute or geometry updating (such as automatic recalculation of other dependent columns).

Shape and ShapeCopy geometry property

Make use of a *Feature* object's *Shape* and *ShapeCopy* properties to optimally retrieve the geometry of a feature. To better understand how these properties relate to a feature's geometry, refer to the diagram to the left to see how features coming from a data source are instantiated into memory for use within an application.

Features are instantiated from the data source using the following sequence:

1. The application requests a *Feature* object from a data source by calling the appropriate geodatabase API method calls.

2. The geodatabase makes a request to COM to create a vanilla COM object of the desired COM class (normally this class is *esriCore.Feature*).

3. COM creates the *Feature* COM object.

4. The geodatabase gets attribute and geometry data from a data source.

5. The vanilla *Feature* object is populated with appropriate attributes.

6. The *Geometry* COM object is created and a reference is set in the *Feature* object.

7. The *Feature* object is passed to the application.

8. The *Feature* object exists in the application until it is no longer required.

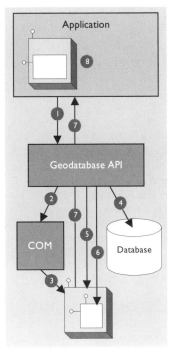

The diagram above clearly shows that the Feature, which is a COM object, has another COM object for its geometry. The Shape property of the feature simply passes the IGeometry interface pointer to this geometry object out to the caller that requested the shape. This means that if more than one client requested the shape, all clients point to the same geometry object. Hence, this geometry object must be treated as read-only. No changes should be performed on the geometry returned from this property, even if the changes are temporary. Anytime a change is to be made to a feature's shape, the change must be made on the geometry returned by the ShapeCopy property, and the updated geometry should subsequently be assigned to the Shape property.

USING A TYPE LIBRARY

Since objects from ArcObjects do not implement *IDispatch*, it is essential to make use of a type library in order for the compiler to early-bind to the correct data types. This applies to all development environments, although for both Visual Basic and Visual C++ there are wizards that help you set this reference.

The type library required by the core ArcObjects is located in the ArcGIS install\bin folder and is called esriCore.olb. Many different files can contain type library information, including EXEs, DLLs, OCXs, and OLBs.

COM DATA TYPES

COM objects talk via their interfaces, and hence all data types used must be supported by IDL. IDL supports a large number of data types; however, not all languages that support COM support these data types. Because of this, ArcObjects does not make use of all the data types available in IDL but limits the majority of interfaces to the data type supported by Visual Basic. The table below shows the data types supported by IDL and their corresponding types in a variety of languages.

Language	IDL	Microsoft C++	Visual Basic	Microsoft Java
Base types	boolean	unsigned char	unsupported	char
	byte	unsigned char	unsupported	char
	small	char	unsupported	char
	short	short	Integer	short
	long	long	Long	int
	hyper	__int64	unsupported	long
	float	float	Single	float
	double	double	Double	double
	char	unsigned char	unsupported	char
	wchar_t	wchar_t	Integer	short
	enum	enum	Enum	int
	Interface Pointer	Interface Pointer	Interface Ref.	Interface Ref.
Extended types	VARIANT	VARIANT	Variant	ms.com.Variant
	BSTR	BSTR	String	java.lang.String
	VARIANT_BOOL	short (-1/0)	Boolean	[true/false]

Note the extended data types at the bottom of the table: *VARIANT, BSTR,* and *VARIANT_BOOL*. While it is possible to pass strings using data types like *char* and *wchar_t*, these are not supported in languages such as Visual Basic. Visual Basic uses *BSTRs* as its text data type. A *BSTR* is a length-prefixed wide character array, where the pointer to the array points to the text contained within it and not the length prefix. Visual C++ maps *VARIANT_BOOL* values onto 0 and –1 for the *False* and *True* values, respectively. This is different from the normal mapping of 0 and 1. Hence, when writing C++ code, be sure to use the correct macros— *VARIANT_FALSE* and *VARIANT_TRUE*—not *False* and *True*.

USING COMPONENT CATEGORIES

Component categories are used extensively in ArcObjects so that developers can extend the system without requiring any changes to the ArcObjects code that will work with the new functionality.

ArcObjects uses component categories in two ways. The first requires classes to be registered in the respective component category at all times, for example, ESRI Mx Extensions. Classes, if present in that component category, have an object that implements *IExtension* interface and are instantiated when the ArcMap application is started. If the class is removed from the component category, the extension will not load, even if the map document (MXD file) is referencing that extension.

The second use is when the application framework uses the component category to locate classes and display them to a user to allow some user customization to occur. Unlike the first method, the application remembers (inside its map document) the objects being used and will subsequently load them from the map document. An example of this is the commands used within ArcMap. ArcMap reads the ESRI Mx Commands category when the Customization dialog box is displayed to the user. This is the only time the category is read. Once the user selects a command and adds it to a toolbar, the map document is used to determine what commands should be instantiated. Later, when this chapter covers debugging Visual Basic code, you'll see the importance of this.

Now that you've seen two uses of component categories, you will see how to get your classes registered into the correct component category. Development environments have various levels of support for component categories; ESRI provides two ways of adding classes to a component category. The first can only be used for Commands and command bars that are added to either ArcMap or ArcCatalog. Using the Add From File button on the Customize dialog box (shown to the left), it is possible to select a server. All classes in that server are then added to either the ESRI Gx Commands or the ESRI Mx Commands, depending on the application being customized. While this utility is useful, it is limited since it adds all the classes found in the server. It is not possible to remove classes, and it only supports two of the many component categories implemented within ArcObjects.

The Customize dialog box in ArcMap and ArcCatalog

Distributed with ArcGIS applications is a utility application called the Component Category Manager, shown to the left. This small application allows you to add and remove classes from any of the component categories on your system, not just ArcObjects ones. Expanding a category displays a list of classes in the category. You can then use the Add Object button to display a checklist of all the classes found in the server. You check the required classes, and these checked classes are then added to the category.

The Component Category Manager

Using these ESRI tools is not the only method to interact with component categories. During the installation of the server on the target user's machine, it is possible to add the relevant information to the Registry using a registry script. Below is one such script. The first line tells windows for which version of regedit this script is intended. The last line, starting with "[HKEY_LOCAL_", executes the registry command—all the other lines are comments in the file.

```
REGEDIT4
; This Registry Script enters coclasses into their appropriate Component Category
; Use this script during installation of the components

; CoClass: Exporter.ExportingExtension
; CLSID: {E233797D-020B-4AD4-935C-F659EB237065}
; Component Category: ESRI Mx Extensions
[HKEY_LOCAL_MACHINE\SOFTWARE\Classes\CLSID\{E233797D-020B-4AD4-935C-
F659EB237065}\Implemented Categories\{B56A7C45-83D4-11D2-A2E9-080009B6F22B}]
```

The last line in the code above is one continuous line in the script.

The last method is for the self-registration code off the server to add the relevant classes within the server to the appropriate categories. Not all development environments allow this to be set up. Visual Basic has no support for component categories, although there is an add-in that adds this functionality. See the sections on Visual Basic Developer Add-ins and ATL later in this chapter.

WHICH DEVELOPMENT ENVIRONMENT

You have already learned that developing with ArcObjects does not restrict you to a proprietary development environment and that any compiler capable of working with COM can be used. This section highlights some of the considerations when choosing a development environment. The choice is not restricted to which compiler; there are broader issues including which application framework to use—ArcMap, ArcCatalog, or your own. These broader issues are not within the scope of this book.

The choice of development environment is not a simple task and is influenced by many factors. Many developers will be selecting either Visual Basic for Applications, Visual Basic, or Visual C++, while others will use Delphi, C++ Builder, and so on. The primary driving force is the experience and skill level of the developers that will write the code. Other issues worth considering are the requirements, performance, development process, and security of code.

The performance issues of choosing the development language are not as significant as you might think. Since the majority of the work will be performed within the ArcObjects objects, which are all written in C++, the developer's customization language is for the most part used to control the program flow and user interface interaction. Since Visual Basic uses the same optimized back-end compiler technology that Visual C++ uses, the generated machine code performs at a comparable level. Tests have shown that to perform typical actions on features contained within a database (drawing, querying, editing, and so on), Visual Basic is approximately 2 percent slower than optimized Visual C++ code, and Visual Basic for Applications is 2 percent slower than Visual Basic.

Visual Basic is a very productive tool, especially for user interface development, but there are limitations to what can be done in Visual Basic. In the majority of cases, these limitations will not affect developers customizing and extending ArcObjects, with the exception of Custom Features. Many of the limitations have to do with the development environment itself. Debugging Visual Basic code is not as flexible as Visual C++. Using Visual Basic in a large development environment with many developers is not as productive as Visual C++ since partial compilations of projects are not supported. If one file is changed in a Visual Basic project, all the files must be recompiled. Since Visual Basic hides much of the interaction with COM away inside the Visual Basic Virtual Machine, low-level COM plumbing code cannot be written in Visual Basic.

Since Visual Basic for Applications does not support the creation of DLLs, all the source code must be shipped inside a document. It is possible to lock the source code projects with a document to stop third parties from seeing the customization code; however, this locking of the project also prevents third parties from using VBA to customize the application further. VBA is an ideal prototyping environment that provides the means for deploying lightweight customizations but, for other more involved customizations, Visual Basic should be considered. VBA also suffers from having its own form designer, meaning the UI source cannot be shared between VB and Visual Basic. In addition, the controls used by VBA do not expose their window handles, which further limits their use.

The tables below summarize suggested naming standards for the various elements of your Visual Basic projects.

Module Type	Prefix
Form	frm
Class	cls
Standard	bas
Project	prj

Name your modules according to the overall function they provide; do not leave any with default names (such as "Form1", "Class1", or "Module1"). Additionally, prefix the names of forms, classes, and standard modules with three letters that denote the type of module, as shown in the table above.

Control Type	Prefix
Check box	chk
Combo box	cbo
Command button	cmd
Common dialog	cdl
Form	frm
Frame	fra
Graph	gph
Grid	grd
Image	img
Image list	iml
Label	lbl
List box	lst
List view	lvw
Map control	map
Masked edit	msk
Menu	mnu
OLE client	ole
Option button	opt
Picture box	pic
Progress bar	pbr
Rich text box	rtf
Scroll bar	srl
Slider	sld
Status bar	sbr
Tab strip	tab
Text box	txt
Timer	tmr
Tool bar	tbr
Tree view	tvw

As with modules, name your controls according to the function they provide; do not leave them with default names since this leads to decreased maintainability. Use the three-letter prefixes above to identify the type of the control.

This section is intended for both VB and VBA developers. Differences in the development environments are clearly marked throughout the text.

USER-INTERFACE STANDARDS

Consider preloading forms to increase the responsiveness of your application. Be careful not to preload too many (preloading three or four forms is fine).

Use resource files (.res) instead of external files when working with bitmap files, icons, and related files.

Make use of constructors and destructors to set variable references that are only set when the class is loaded. These are the VB functions: *Class_Initialize()* and *Class_Terminate()*, or *Form_Load()* and *Form_Unload()*. Set all variables to *Nothing* when the object is destroyed.

Make sure the tab order is set correctly for the form. Do not add scroll bars to the tabbing sequence; it is too confusing.

Add access keys to those labels that identify controls of special importance on the form (use the *TabIndex* property).

Use system colors where possible instead of hard-coded colors.

Variable declaration

- Always use *Option Explicit* (or turn on Require Variable Declaration in the VB Options dialog box). This forces all variables to be declared before use and thereby prevents careless mistakes.

- Use *Public* and *Private* to declare variables at module scope and *Dim* in local scope. (*Dim* and *Private* mean the same at *Module* scope; however, using *Private* is more informative.) Do not use *Global* anymore; it is available only for backward compatibility with VB 3.0 and earlier.

- Always provide an explicit type for variables, arguments, and functions. Otherwise, they default to *Variant*, which is less efficient.

- Only declare one variable per line unless the type is specified for each variable.

This line causes *count* to be declared as a *Variant*, which is likely to be unintended.

```
Dim count, max As Long
```

This line declares both *count* and *max* as *Long*, the intended type.

```
Dim count As Long, max As Long
```

These lines also declare *count* and *max* as *Long* and are more readable.

```
Dim count As Long
Dim max As Long
```

Parentheses

Use parentheses to make operator precedence and logic comparison statements easier to read.

Use the following notation for naming variables and constants:

[<libraryName.>][<scope_>]<type><name>

<name> describes how the variable is used or what it contains. The <scope> and <type> portions should always be lowercase, and the <name> should use mixed case.

Library Name	Library
esriCore	ESRI Object Library
stdole	Standard OLE COM Library
<empty>	Simple variable datatype

<libraryName>

Prefix	Variable scope
c	constant within a form or class
g	public variable defined in a class form or standard module
m	private variable defined in a class or form
<empty>	local variable

<scope>

Prefix	Data Type
b	Boolean
by	byte or unsigned char
d	double
fn	function
h	handle
i	int (integer)
l	long
p	a pointer
s	string

<type>

```
Result = ((x * 24) / (y / 12)) + 42
If ((Not pFoo Is Nothing) And (Counter > 200)) Then
```

Order of conditional determination

Visual Basic, unlike languages such as C and C++, performs conditional tests on all parts of the condition, even if the first part of the condition is *False*. This means you must not perform conditional tests on objects and interfaces that had their validity tested in an earlier part of the conditional statement.

```
' The following line will raise a runtime error if pFoo is NULL
If ((Not pFoo Is Nothing) And (TypeOf pFoo.Thing Is IBar)) then
End If


' The correct way to test this code is
If (Not pFoo Is Nothing) Then
  If (TypeOf pFoo.Thing Is IBar) Then
    ' Perform action on IBar thing of Foo
  End If
End If
```

Indentation

Use two spaces for indentation or a tab width of two. Since there is only ever one editor for VB code, formatting is not as critical an issue as it is for C++ code.

Default properties

Avoid using default properties except for the most common cases. They lead to decreased legibility.

Intermodule referencing

When accessing intermodule data or functions, always qualify the reference with the module name. This makes the code more readable and results in more efficient runtime binding.

Multiple property operations

When performing multiple operations against different properties of the same object, use a *With ... End With* statement. It is more efficient than specifying the object each time.

```
With frmHello
  .Caption = "Hello world"
  .Font = "Playbill"
  .Left = (Screen.Width - .Width) / 2
  .Top  = (Screen.Height - .Height) / 2
End With
```

Arrays

For arrays, never change *Option Base* to anything other than zero (which is the default). Use *LBound* and *UBound* to iterate over all items in an array.

```
myArray = GetSomeArray
For i = LBound(myArray) To UBound(myArray)
  MsgBox cstr(myArray(i))
Next I
```

Bitwise operators

Since *And, Or,* and *Not* are bitwise operators, ensure that all conditions using them test only for Boolean values (unless, of course, bitwise semantics are what is intended).

```
If (Not pFoo Is Nothing) Then
  ' Valid Foo do something with it
End If
```

Type suffixes

Refrain from using type suffixes on variables or function names (such as *myString$* or *Right$(myString)*), unless they are needed to distinguish 16-bit from 32-bit numbers.

Ambiguous type matching

For ambiguous type matching, use explicit conversion operators (such as *CSng, CDbl,* and *CStr*), instead of relying on VB to pick which one will be used.

Simple image display

Use an *ImageControl* rather than a *PictureBox* for simple image display. It is much more efficient.

Error handling

Recovery Statement	Frequency	Meaning
Exit Sub	usually	Function failed, pass control back to caller
Raise	often	Raise a new error code in the caller's scope
Resume	rarely	Error condition removed, re-attempt offending statement
Resume Next	very rarely	Ignore error and continue with next statement

Always use *On Error* to ensure fault-tolerant code. For each function that does error checking, use *On Error* to jump to a single error handler for the routine that deals with all exceptional conditions that are likely to be encountered. After the error handler processes the error—usually by displaying a message—it should proceed by issuing one of the recovery statements shown on the table to the left.

Error handling in Visual Basic is not the same as general error handling in COM (see the section Working with HRESULTs).

Event functions

Refrain from placing more than a few lines of code in event functions to prevent highly fractured and unorganized code. Event functions should simply dispatch to reusable functions elsewhere.

Memory management

To ensure efficient use of memory resources, the following points should be considered:

• Unload forms regularly. Do not keep many forms loaded but invisible since this consumes system resources.

- Be aware that referencing a form-scoped variable causes the form to be loaded.

- Set unused objects to *Nothing* to free up their memory.

- Make use of *Class_Initialize()* and *Class_Terminate()* to allocate and destroy resources.

While Wend constructs

Avoid *While ... Wend* constructs. Use the *Do While ... Loop* or *Do Until ... Loop* instead because you can conditionally branch out of this construct.

```
pFoos.Reset
Set pFoo = pFoos.Next
Do While (Not pFoo Is Nothing)
  If (pFoo.Answer = "Done") Then Exit Loop
  Set pFoo = pFoos.Next
Loop
```

The Visual Basic Virtual Machine

The VBVM was called the VB Runtime in earlier versions of the software.

The Visual Basic Virtual Machine (VBVM) contains the intrinsic Visual Basic controls and services, such as starting and ending a Visual Basic application, required to successfully execute all Visual Basic developed code.

The VBVM is packaged as a DLL that must be installed on any machine wanting to execute code written with Visual Basic, even if the code has been compiled to native code. If the dependencies of any Visual Basic compiled file are viewed, the file msvbvm60.dll is listed; this is the DLL housing the Virtual Machine.

For more information on the services provided by the VBVM, see the sections Interacting with the *IUnknown* interface and Working with HRESULTs in this chapter.

Interacting with the *IUnknown* interface

The section on COM contains a lengthy section on the *IUnknown* interface and how it forms the basis on which all of COM is built. Visual Basic hides this interface from developers and performs the required interactions (*QueryInterface, AddRef,* and *Release* function calls) on the developer's behalf. It achieves this because of functionality contained within the VBVM. This simplifies development with COM for many developers, but to work successfully with ArcObjects you must understand what the VBVM is doing.

Visual Basic developers are used to dimensioning variables as follows:

```
Dim pColn as New Collection   'Create a new collection object
PColn.Add "Foo", "Bar"        'Add element to collection
```

It is worth considering what is happening at this point. From a quick inspection of the code it looks like the first line creates a collection object and gives the developer a handle on that object in the form of *pColn*. The developer then calls a method on the object *Add*. Earlier in the chapter you learned that objects talk via their interfaces, never through a direct handle on the object itself. Remember, objects expose their services via their interfaces. If this is true, something isn't adding up.

What is actually happening is some "VB magic" performed by the VBVM and some trickery by the Visual Basic Editor in the way that it presents objects and interfaces. The first line of code instantiates an instance of the collection class, then assigns the default interface for that object, *_Collection*, to the variable *pColn*. It is this interface, *_Collection*, that has the methods defined on it. Visual Basic has hidden the fact of interface-based programming to simplify the developer experience. This is not an issue if all the functionality implemented by the object can be accessed via one interface, but it is an issue when there are multiple interfaces on an object that provides services.

The Visual Basic editor backs this up by hiding default interfaces from the IntelliSense completion list and the object browser. By default, any interfaces that begin with an underscore, "_", are not displayed in the object browser (to display these interfaces turn Show Hidden Member on, although this will still not display default interfaces).

You have already learned that the majority of ArcObjects have *IUnknown* as their default interface and that Visual Basic does not expose any of *IUnknown*'s methods, namely, *QueryInterface, AddRef,* and *Release*. Assume you have a class *Foo* that supports three interfaces, *IUnknown* (the default interface), *IFoo,* and *IBar*. This means that if you were to dimension the variable *pFoo* as below, the variable *pFoo* would point to the *IUnknown* interfaces.

```
Dim pFoo As New Foo      ' Create a new Foo object
pFoo.??????
```

Since Visual Basic does not allow direct access to the methods of *IUnknown,* you would immediately have to *QI* for an interface with methods on it that you can call. Because of this, the correct way to dimension a variable that will hold pointers to interfaces is as follows:

```
Dim pFoo As IFoo  ' Variable will hold pointer to IFoo interface
Set pFoo = New Foo ' Create Instance of Foo object and QI for IFoo
```

Now that you have a pointer to one of the object's interfaces, it is an easy matter to request from the object any of its other interfaces.

```
Dim pBar as IBar  'Dim variable to hold pointer to interface
Set pBar = pFoo   'QI for IBar interface
```

By convention, most classes have an interface with the same name as the class with an "I" prefix; this tends to be the interface most commonly used when working with the object. You are not restricted to which interface you request when instantiating an object; any supported interface can be requested, hence the code below is valid.

```
Dim pBar as IBar
Set pBar = New Foo  'CoCreate Object
Set pFoo = pBar     'QI for interface
```

Objects control their own lifetime, which requires clients to call *AddRef* anytime an interface pointer is duplicated by assigning it to another variable and to call *Release* anytime the interface pointer is no longer required. Ensuring that there are a matching number of *AddRefs* and *Releases* is important and, fortunately, Visual Basic performs these calls automatically. This ensures that objects do not "leak". Even when interface pointers are reused, Visual Basic will correctly call release on the old interface before assigning the new interface to the variable. The code below illustrates these concepts; note the reference count on the object at the various stages of code execution.

```
Private Sub VBMagic()
  ' Dim a variable to the IUnknown interface on the simple object
  Dim pUnk As IUnknown

  ' Co Create simpleobject asking for the IUnknown interface
  Set pUnk = New SimpleObject 'refCount = 1

  ' We need access to methods lets QI for a useful interface
  ' Define the interface we are to request
  Dim pMagic As ISimpleObject

  ' Perform the QI operation
  Set pMagic = punk 'refCount = 2

  ' Dim another variable to hold another interface on the object
  Dim pMagic2 As IAnotherInterface

  ' QI for that interface
  Set pMagic2 = pMagic 'refCount = 3

  ' Release the interface pointer
  Set pMagic2 = Nothing 'refCount = 2

  ' Release the interface
  Set pMagic = Nothing 'refCount = 1

  ' Now reuse the pUnk variable - what will VB do for this?
  Set pUnk = New SimpleObject 'refCount = 1, then 0, then 1

  ' Let the interface variable go out of scope and VB to tidy up
End Sub    'refCount = 0
```

See Visual Basic Magic sample on the disk for this code. You are encouraged to run the sample and step though the code. This object also uses an ATL C++ project to define the SimpleObject and its interfaces; you are encouraged to look at this code to learn a simple implementation of a C++ ATL object.

Often interfaces have properties that are actually pointers to other interfaces. Visual Basic allows you to access these properties in a shorthand fashion by chaining interfaces together. For instance, assume that you have a pointer to the *IFoo* interface, and that interface has a property called *Gak* that is an *IGak* interface with the method *DoSomething()*. You have a choice on how to access the *DoSomething* method. The first method is the long-handed way.

```
Dim pGak as IGak
Set pGak = pFoo        'Assign IGak interface to local variable
pGak.DoSomething       'Call method on IGak interface
```

Alternatively, you can chain the interfaces and accomplish the same thing on one line of code.

```
pFoo.Gak.DoSomething  'Call method on IGak interface
```

When looking at the sample code, you will see both methods. Normally the former method is used on the simpler samples, as it explicitly tells you what interfaces are being worked with. More complex samples use the shorthand method.

This technique of chaining interfaces together can always be used to get the value of a property, but it cannot always be used to set the value of a property. Interface chaining can only be used to set a property if all the interfaces in the chain are set by reference. For instance, the code below would execute successfully.

```
Dim pMxDoc As ImxDocument
Set pMxDoc = ThisDocument
pMxDoc.FocusMap.Layers(0).Name = "Foo"
```

The above example works because both the *Layer* of the *Map* and the *Map* of the document are returned by reference. The lines of code below would not work since the *Extent* envelope is set by value on the active view.

```
pMxDoc.ActiveView.Extent.Width = 32
```

The reason that this does not work is that the VBVM expands the Interface chain in order to get the end property. Because an interface in the chain is dealt with by value, the VBVM has its own copy of the variable, not the one chained. To set the *Width* property of the extent envelope in the above example, the VBVM must write code similar to this:

```
Dim pActiveView as IActiveView
Set pActiveView = pMxDoc.ActiveView

Dim pEnv as IEnvelope
Set pEnv = pActiveView.Extent  ' This is a get by value,

PEnv.Extent = 32   ' The VBVM has set its copy of the Extent and not
                   ' the copy inside the ActiveView
```

For this to work the VBVM requires the extra line below.

```
Set pActiveView.Extent = pEnv  ' This is a set by value,
```

Accessing ArcObjects

You will now see some specific uses of the create instance and query interface operations that involve ArcObjects. To use an ArcGIS object in Visual Basic or VBA, you must first reference the ESRI object library. In a standalone Visual Basic application, always reference esriCore.olb. Inside of ArcMap or ArcCatalog, a reference is automatically made to the esriMx.olb and esriGx.olb libraries when you start the application, so no external referencing to esriCore.olb is required.

You will start by identifying a simple object and an interface that it supports. In this case, you will use a *Point* object and the *IPoint* interface. One way to set the coordinates of the point is to invoke the *PutCoords* method on the *IPoint* interface and pass in the coordinate values.

```
Dim pPt As IPoint
Set pPt = New Point
pPt.PutCoords 100, 100
```

IID is short for Interface Identifier, a GUID.

The first line of this simple code fragment illustrates the use of a variable to hold a reference to the interface that the object supports. The line reads the *IID* for the *IPoint* interface from the ESRI object library. You may find it less ambiguous (as per the coding guidelines), particularly if you reference other object libraries in the same project to precede the interface name with the library name, for example:

```
Dim pPt As esriCore.IPoint
```

That way, if there happens to be another *IPoint* referenced in your project, there won't be any ambiguity as to which one you are referring to.

Coclass is an abbreviation of component object class.

The second line of the fragment creates an instance of the object or coclass, then performs a *QI* operation for the *IPoint* interface that it assigns to *pPt*.

A QI is required since the default interface of the object is IUnknown. Since the pPt variable was declared as type IPoint, the default IUnknown interface was QI'd for the IPoint interface.

With a name for the coclass as common as *Point*, you may want to precede the coclass name with the library name, for example:

```
Set pPt = New esriCore.Point
```

The last line of the code fragment invokes the *PutCoords* method. If a method can't be located on the interface, an error will be shown at compile time.

Working with HRESULTs

So far you have seen that all COM methods signify success or failure via an *HRESULT* that is returned from the method; no exceptions are raised outside of the interface. You have also learned that Visual Basic raises exceptions when errors are encountered. In Visual Basic, *HRESULTs* are never returned from method calls and, to confuse you further when errors do occur, Visual Basic throws an exception. How can this be? The answer lies with the Visual Basic Virtual Machine. It is the VBVM that receives the *HRESULT*; if this is anything other than *S_OK*, the VBVM throws the exception. If it was able to retrieve any worthwhile error information from the COM error object, it populates the Visual Basic *Err* object with that information. In this way, the VBVM handles all *HRESULTs* returned from the client.

This is the compilation error message shown when a method or property is not found on an interface.

When implementing interfaces in Visual Basic, it is good coding practice to raise an *HRESULT* error to inform the caller that an error has occurred. Normally, this is done when a method has not been implemented.

```
' Defined in Module
Const E_NOTIMPL = &H80004001 'Constant that represents HRESULT
```

```
'Added to any method not implemented
On Error GoTo 0
Err.Raise E_NOTIMPL
```

You must also write code to handle the possibility that an *HRESULT* other than *S_OK* is returned. When this happens, an error handler should be called and the error dealt with. This may mean simply telling the user, or perhaps it may mean automatically dealing with the error and continuing with the function. The choice depends on the circumstances. Below is a very simple error handler that will catch any error that occurs within the function and report it to the user. Note the use of the *Err* object to provide the user with some description of the error.

```
Private Sub Test()
 On Error GoTo ErrorHandler
 ' Do something here
 Exit Sub    ' Must exit sub here before error handler
ErrorHandler:
 Msgbox "Error In Application - Description " & Err.Description
End Sub
```

Working with properties

Some properties refer to specific interfaces in the ESRI object library, and other properties have values that are standard data types, such as strings, numeric expressions, Boolean values, and so forth. For interface references, declare an interface variable and use the *Set* statement to assign the interface reference to the property. For other values, declare a variable with an explicit data type or use Visual Basic's *Variant* data type. Then, use a simple assignment statement to assign the value to the variable.

Properties that are interfaces can either be set by reference or set by value. Properties that are set by value do not require the *Set* statement.

```
Dim pEnv As IEnvelope
Set pEnv = pActiveView.Extent   'Get extent property of view
pEnv.Expand 0.5, 0.5, True      'Shrink envelope
pActiveView.Extent = pEnv       'Set By Value extent pack on IActiveView


Dim pFeatureLayer as IfeatureLayer
Set pFeatureLayer = New FeatureLayer    'Create New Layer
Set pFeatureLayer.FeatureClass = pClass 'Set ByRef a class into layer
```

As you might expect, some properties are read-only, others are write-only, and still others are read/write. All the object browsers and the ArcObjects Class Help (found in the ArcObjects Developer Help system) provide this information. If you attempt to use a property and either forget or misuse the *Set* keyword, Visual Basic will fail the compilation of the source code with a method or data member not found error message. This error may seem strange since it may be given for trying to assign a value to a read-only property. The reason for the message is that Visual Basic is attempting to find a method in the type library that maps to the property name. In the above examples, the underlying method calls in the type library are *put_Extent* and *putref_FeatureClass*.

Working with methods

Methods perform some action and may or may not return a value. In some instances, a method returns a value that's an interface; for example, in the code fragment below, *EditSelection* returns an enumerated feature interface:

```
Dim pApp As IApplication
Dim pEditor As IEditor
Dim pEnumFeat As IEnumFeature 'Holds the selection
Dim pID As New UID
'Get a handle to the Editor extension
pID = "esriCore.Editor"
Set pApp = Application
Set pEditor = pApp.FindExtensionByCLSID(pID)
'Get the selection
Set pEnumFeat = pEditor.EditSelection
```

In other instances, a method returns a Boolean value that reflects the success of an operation or writes data to a parameter; for example, the *DoModalOpen* method of *GxDialog* returns a value of *True* if a selection occurs and writes the selection to an *IEnumGxObject* parameter.

Be careful not to confuse the idea of a Visual Basic return value from a method call with the idea that all COM methods must return an *HRESULT*. The VBVM is able to read type library information and setup the return value of the VB method call to be the appropriate parameter of the COM method.

Working with events

Events let you know when something has occurred. You can add code to respond to an event. For example, a command button has a *Click* event. You add code to perform some action when the user clicks the control. You can also add events that certain objects generate. VBA and Visual Basic let you declare a variable with the keyword *WithEvents*. *WithEvents* tells the development environment that the object variable will be used to respond to the object's events. This is sometimes referred to as an "event sink". The declaration must be made in a class module or a form. Here's how you declare a variable and expose the events of an object in the *Declarations* section:

```
Private WithEvents m_pViewEvents as Map
```

Visual Basic only supports one outbound interface (marked as the default outbound interface in the IDL) per coclass. To get around this limitation, the coclasses that implement more than one outbound interface have an associated dummy coclass that allows access to the secondary outbound interface. These coclasses have the same name as the outbound interface they contain, minus the I.

```
Private WithEvents m_pMapEvents as MapEvents
```

Once you've declared the variable, search for its name in the Object combo box at the top left of the Code window. Then, inspect the list of events you can attach code to in the Procedure/Events combo box at the top right of the Code window.

Not all procedures of the outbound event interface need to be stubbed out, as Visual Basic will stub out any unimplemented methods. This is different from inbound interfaces, where all methods must be stubbed out for compilation to occur.

Before the methods are called, the hookup between the event source and sink must be made. This is done by setting the variable that represents the sink to the event source.

```
Set m_pMapEvents = pMxDoc.FocusMap
```

Pointers to valid objects as parameters

Some ArcGIS methods expect interfaces for some of their parameters. The interface pointers passed can point to an instanced object before the method call or after the method call is completed.

For example, if you have a polygon (*pPolygon*) whose center point you want to find, you can write code like this:

```
Dim pArea As IArea
Dim pPt As IPoint
Set pArea = pPolygon        ' QI for IArea on pPolygon
Set pPt = pArea.Center
```

You don't need to create *pPt* because the *Center* method creates a *Point* object for you and passes back a reference to the object via its *IPoint* interface. Only methods that use clientside storage require you to create the object prior to the method call.

Passing data between modules

When passing data between modules it is best to use accessor and mutator functions that manipulate some private member variable. This provides data encapsulation, which is a fundamental technique in object-oriented programming. Public variables should never be used.

For instance, you might have decided that a variable has a valid range of 1–100. If you were to allow other developers direct access to that variable, they could set the value to an illegal value. The only way of coping with these illegal values is to check them before they get used. This is both error prone and tiresome to program. The technique of declaring all variables private member variables of the class and providing accessor and mutator functions for manipulating these variables will solve this problem.

In the example below, these properties are added to the default interface of the class. Notice the technique used to raise an error to the client.

```
Private m_lPercentage As Long

Public Property Get Percentage() As Long
```

```
  Percentage = m_lPercentage
End Property
```

```
Public Property Let Percentage(ByVal lNewValue As Long)
  If (lNewValue >= 0) And (lNewValue <= 100) Then
    m_lPercentage = lNewValue
  Else
    Err.Raise vbObjectError + 29566, "MyProj.MyObject", _
    "Invalid Percentage Value. Valid values (0 -> 100)"
  End If
End Property
```

When you write code to pass an object reference from one form, class, or module to another, for example:

```
Private Property Set PointCoord(ByRef pPt As IPoint)
  Set m_pPoint = pPt
End Property
```

Your code passes a pointer to an instance of the *IPoint* interface. This means that you are only passing the reference to the interface, not the interface itself; if you add the *ByVal* keyword (as follows), the interface is passed by value.

```
Private Property Let PointCoord(ByVal pPt As IPoint)
  Set m_pPoint = pPt
End Property
```

In both of these cases the object pointed to by the interfaces is always passed by reference. In order to pass the object by value, a clone of the object must be made, and that is passed.

Using the *TypeOf* keyword

To check whether an object supports an interface, you can use Visual Basic's *TypeOf* keyword. For example, given an item selected in the ArcMap table of contents, you can test whether it is a *FeatureLayer* using the following code:

```
Dim pDoc As IMxDocument
Dim pUnk As IUnknown
Dim pFeatLyr As IGeoFeatureLayer
Set pDoc = ThisDocument
Set pUnk = pDoc.SelectedItem
If TypeOf pUnk Is IGeoFeatureLayer Then  ' can we QI for IGeoFeatureLayer?
  Set pFeatLyr = pUnk                    ' actually QI happens here
  ' Do something with pFeatLyr
End If
```

Using the *Is* operator

If your code requires you to compare two interface reference variables, you can use the *Is* operator. Typically, you can use the *Is* operator in the following circumstances:

To check if you have a valid interface.

```
Dim pPt As IPoint
Set pPt = New Point
If (Not pPt Is Nothing) Then 'a valid pointer?
    ...    ' do something with pPt
End If
```

To check if two interface variables refer to the same actual object, say you've got two interface variables of type *IPoint*, *pPt1*, and *pPt2*. Are they pointing to the same object? If they are, then *pPt1* Is *pPt2*.

The *Is* keyword works with the COM identity of an object. Below is an example that illustrates the use of the *Is* keyword when finding out if a certain method on an interface returns a copy of or a reference to the same real object.

In the following example, the *Extent* property on a map (*IMap*) returns a copy, while the *ActiveView* property on a document (*IMxDocument*) always returns a reference to the real object.

```
Dim pDoc As IMxDocument
Dim pEnv1 As IEnvelope, pEnv2 as IEnvelope
Dim pActView1 As IActiveView
Dim pActView2 as IActiveView
Set pDoc = ThisDocument
Set pEnv1 = pDoc.ActiveView.Extent
Set pEnv2 = pDoc.ActiveView.Extent
Set pActView1 = pDoc.ActiveView
Set pActView2 = pDoc.ActiveView
' Extent returns a copy,
' so pEnv1 Is pEnv2 returns False
Debug.Print pEnv1 Is pEnv2
' ActiveView returns a reference,
' so pActView1 Is pActView2
Debug.Print pActView1 Is pActView2
```

Iterating through a collection

Enumerators can support other methods, but these two methods are common amongst all enumerators.

In your work with ArcMap and ArcCatalog, you'll discover that in many cases you'll be working with collections. You can iterate through these collections with an enumerator. An enumerator is an interface that provides methods for traversing a list of elements. Enumerator interfaces typically begin with *IEnum* and have two methods: *Next* and *Reset*. *Next* returns the next element in the set and advances the internal pointer, and *Reset* resets the internal pointer to the beginning.

Here is some VBA code that loops through the selected features (*IEnumFeature*) in a map. To try the code, add the States sample layer to the map and use the Select tool to select multiple features (drag a rectangle to do this). Add the code to a VBA macro, then execute the macro. The name of each selected state will be printed in the debug window.

```
Dim pDoc As IMxDocument
```

```
Dim pEnumFeat As IEnumFeature
Dim pFeat As IFeature
Set pDoc = ThisDocument
Set pEnumFeat = pDoc.FocusMap.FeatureSelection
Set pFeat = pEnumFeat.Next
Do While (Not pFeat Is Nothing)
  Debug.Print pFeat.Value(pFeat.Fields.FindField("state_name"))
  Set pFeat = pEnumFeat.Next
Loop
```

Some collection objects, the Visual Basic Collection being one, implement a special interface called _NewEnum. This interface, because of the _ prefix, is hidden, but Visual Basic developers can still use it to simplify iterating through a collection. The Visual Basic *For Each* construct works with this interface to perform the *Reset* and *Next* steps through a collection.

```
Dim pColn as Collection
Set pColn = GetCollection()' Collection returned from some function


Dim thing as Variant      ' VB uses methods on _NewEnum to step through
For Each thing in pColn  ' an enumerator.
  MsgBox Cstr(thing)
Next
```

This section of the chapter discusses how to program in the VBA environment to control either ArcMap, ArcCatalog, or ArcScene by accessing the objects they expose. Your code manipulates the objects by getting and setting properties on their interfaces, such as setting the *MaximumScale* and *MinimumScale* of a *Map*'s *FeatureLayer*, invoking methods on the interfaces, such as adding a vertex to a polyline, or setting a field's value. The code runs when an event occurs, for example, when a user opens a document, clicks a button, or alters data by modifying an edit sketch.

First, though, you'll see the aspects of the VBA development environment in which you'll do your work that are specific to the ESRI applications. Consult the Visual Basic Reference, the online help file that displays when you click Microsoft Visual Basic Help in the Help menu of the VBA Editor for generic help on the user interface, conceptual topics, how-to topics, language reference topics, customizing the Visual Basic Editor, and user forms and controls.

In the VBA development environment you can add modules, class modules, and user forms to the default project contained in every ArcGIS application document. A project can consist of as many modules, class modules, and user forms as your work requires. A project is a collection of items to which you add code. A module is a set of declarations followed by procedures—a list of instructions that your code performs. A class module is a special type of module that contains the definition of a class, including its property and method definitions. A user form is a container for user interface controls, such as command buttons and text boxes.

ArcMap has a default project associated with its document that's listed in the Project Explorer as Project followed by its filename. In addition, you'll see another project listed in the Project Explorer called Normal (Normal.mxt).

Normal is, in fact, a template for all documents. It's always loaded into the document. It contains all the user-interface elements that users see, as well as the class module named ArcID, which contains all the UIDs for the application's commands.

Since any modifications made to Normal will be reflected every time you create or open a document, you should be careful when making changes to Normal.

In ArcMap, users can start by opening a template other than the default template. These templates are available to them in the New dialog box. From a developer's perspective this is a base template, a document that loads an additional project into the document; it is listed in the Project Explorer as the *TemplateProject* followed by its filename. This project can store code in modules, class modules, forms, and any other customizations, such as maps with data, page layout frames, and so on. Any modifications or changes made to this base template are reflected only in documents that are derived from it.

In ArcCatalog, Normal (Normal.gxt) is the only project that appears in the Project Explorer. There is no default Project in ArcCatalog, and you can't load any templates. You can, of course, add code to Normal.gxt inside modules, class modules, or forms, but again, be careful when making changes.

Once you've invoked the Visual Basic Editor, you can insert a module, class module, or user form. Then you insert a procedure or enter code for an existing event procedure in the item's Code window, where you can write, display, and edit code. You can open as many Code windows as you have modules, class modules, and user forms, so you can easily view the code and copy and paste between Code windows. In addition to creating your own modules, you can import other modules, class modules, or user forms from disk.

If your work requires it, you can add an external object library or type library reference to your project. This makes another application's objects available in your code. Once a reference is set, the referenced objects are displayed in the development environment's Object Browser.

Getting started with VBA

To begin programming with VBA in ArcMap or ArcCatalog, you start the Visual Basic Editor.

To start the Visual Basic Editor

1. Start ArcMap or ArcCatalog.

2. Click the Tools menu, point to Macros, then click Visual Basic Editor. You can also use the shortcut keys Alt+F11 to display the Visual Basic Editor. To navigate among the projects in the Visual Basic Editor, use the Project Explorer. It displays a list of the document's modules, class modules, and user forms.

To add a macro to a module

ArcMap and ArcCatalog both provide a shortcut for creating a simple macro in a module.

1. Click the Tools menu, point to Macros, then click Macros.

2. Type the name of the macro you want to create in the Macro name text box. If you don't specify a module name, the application creates a module called *modulexx* and stores the macro in that module. If no module is specified after you specify a module, and a module is already active, the macro is placed in that module. Preceding a macro's name with a name and a dot stores it in a module with the specified name. If the module doesn't exist, the application creates it.

3. Click the dropdown arrow of the Macros in the combo box and choose the VBA project in which you want to create the macro.

4. Press the Enter key or click Create.

5. The stub for a Sub procedure for the macro appears in the Code window.

Adding modules and class modules

All ArcGIS application documents contain the class module *ThisDocument*, a custom object that represents the specific document associated with a VBA project. The document object is called *MxDocument* in ArcMap and *GxDocument* in ArcCatalog. The *IDocument* interface provides access to the document's title, type, accelerator table, command bars collection, parent application, and Visual Basic project.

Modules and class modules can contain more than one type of procedure: sub, function, or property. You can choose the procedure type and its scope when you insert a procedure. Inserting a procedure is like creating a code template into which you enter code.

Every procedure has either private or public scope. Procedures with private scope are limited to the module that contains them—only a procedure within the same module can call a private procedure. If you declare the procedure public, other programs and modules can call it.

Variables in your procedures may either be local or global. Global variables exist during the entire time the code executes, whereas local variables exist only while the procedure in which they are declared is running. The next time you execute a procedure, all local variables are reinitialized. However, you can preserve the value of all local variables in a procedure for the code's lifetime by declaring them static, thereby fixing their value.

To add a procedure to an existing module

1. In the Project Explorer, double-click the ArcMap Objects, ArcCatalog Objects, or Modules folder, then choose the name of a module. Ensure that the code view of the module is active by clicking the View Code button.

2. Click the Insert menu and click Procedure.

3. Type the name of the procedure in the Name text box.

4. Click the Type dropdown arrow and click the type of procedure: Sub, Function, or Property.

5. Click the Scope dropdown arrow and click Public or Private.

6. To declare all local variables static, check the All Local variables as Statics check box.

7. Click OK. VBA stubs in a procedure into the item's Code window into which you can enter code. The stub contains the first and last lines of code for the type of procedure you've added.

8. Enter code into the procedure.

For more information about procedures, see the Microsoft Visual Basic online help reference.

Adding user forms

If you want your code to prompt the user for information, or you want to display the result of some action performed when the user invokes an ArcGIS application command or tool or in response to some other event, use VBA's user forms. User forms provide a context in which you can provide access to a rich set of integrated controls. Some of these controls are similar to the *UIControls* that are available as part of the Customize dialog box's Commands tab. In addition to text boxes or command buttons, you have access to a rich set of additional controls. A user form is a container for user-interface controls, such as command buttons and text boxes. A control is a Visual Basic object you place on a user form that has its own properties, methods, and events. You use controls to receive user input, display output, and trigger event procedures. You can set the form to be either modal, in which case the user must respond before using any other part of the application, or modeless, in which case subsequent code is executed as it's encountered.

To add and start coding in a user form

1. In the Project Explorer, select the Project to which you want to add a user form.

2. Click the Insert menu and click UserForm.

3. VBA inserts a user form into your project and opens the Controls Toolbox.

4. Click the controls that you want to add to the user interface from the Controls Toolbox.

5. Add code to the user form or to its controls.

For more information about adding controls, see the Microsoft Visual Basic online help reference.

To display the Code window for a user form or control, double-click the user form or control. Then, choose the event you want your code to trigger from the dropdown list of events and procedures in the Code window and start typing your code. Or, just as in a module or class module, insert a procedure and start typing your code.

To display the form during an ArcMap or ArcCatalog session in response to some action, invoke its *Show* method, as in this example:

```
UserForm1.Show vbModeless 'show modeless
```

Some VBA project management techniques

To work efficiently in the ArcGIS application's VBA development environment and reduce the amount of work you have to do every time you start a new task, make use of several techniques that will streamline your work:

Reusing modules, class modules, and user forms

To add an existing module or form to the Normal template, the Project, or a TemplateProject, click the name of the destination in the Project Explorer, then choose Import File from the File menu. You can choose any VBA module, user form, or class module to add a copy of the file to your project. To export an item from your project so that it is available for importing into other projects, select the item you want to export in the Project Explorer, choose Export File from the File menu, then navigate to where you want to save the file. Exporting an item does not remove it from your project.

Removing project items

When you remove an item, it is permanently deleted from the project list—you can't undo the Remove action; however, this action doesn't delete a file if it exists on disk. Before removing an item, make sure the remaining code in other modules and user forms doesn't refer to code in the removed item. To remove an item, select it in the Project Explorer, then choose Remove <Name> from the File menu. Before you remove the item, you'll be asked whether you want to export it. If you click Yes in the message box, the Export File dialog box opens. If you click No, VBA deletes the item.

Protecting your code

To protect your code from alteration and viewing by users, you can lock a Project, a TemplateProject, or even Normal. When you lock one of these items, you set a password that must be entered before it can be viewed in the Project Explorer. To lock one of these items, right-click Project, TemplateProject, or Normal in the Project Explorer, then click the Properties item in the context menu that appears. In the Properties dialog box, click the Protection tab and click the option to Lock Project for Viewing. Enter a password and confirm it. Finally, save your ArcMap or ArcCatalog file and close it. The next time you or anyone else opens the file, the project is locked. If anyone wants to view or edit the project, they must enter the password.

Saving a VBA project

VBA projects are stored in a file that can be a base template (*.mxt), the Normal template, or a document (*.mxd). When a user creates a new ArcMap document from a base template, the new document references the base template's VBA project and its items. To save your ArcMap document and your VBA project, click Save from the ArcMap File menu or Save <File Name> from the File menu in the Visual Basic Editor. Both commands save your file with the project and any items stored in it. After saving the file, its filename is displayed in the Project Explorer in parentheses after the project name. To save the document as a template, click Save As from the ArcMap File menu and specify ArcMap Templates (*.mxt) as the File type.

Running VBA code

As you build and refine your code, you can run it within VBA to test and debug it. This section discusses running your code in the Visual Basic Editor during design time. For more information about running and debugging a VBA program, such as adding break points, adding watch expressions, and stepping into and out of execution, see Microsoft Visual Basic online help.

To run your code in the Visual Basic Editor or from the Macros dialog box

1. Click the Tools menu and click Macros.

2. In the Macro list, click the macro you want and click Run.

If the macro you want is not listed, make sure you've chosen the appropriate item: either Normal, Project, or TemplateProject in the Macros In box. Private procedures do not appear in any menus or dialog boxes.

To run only one procedure in the Visual Basic Editor

1. In the Project Explorer, open the module that contains the procedure that you want to run.

2. In the Code window, click an insertion point in the procedure code.

3. Click the Run menu and click Run Sub/UserForm.

Only the procedure in which your cursor is located runs.

After you've finished writing your code

After you have finished writing code, users can run it from ArcMap or ArcCatalog. To do this, they choose Macros and then Macros from the Tools menu. You can also associate the code with a command or tool, or it can run in response to events or in other ways that you design.

Using the Global Application objects

Since ArcCataog does not support the use of documents, the ThisDocument global variable is not available to developers. However, the Application *variable is available if a developer wishes to access IGxApplication or IApplication.*

Application and *ThisDocument* are examples of global system variables that can be accessed by any module or class in the VBA environment while ArcMap is running. This variable is automatically set to reference the current document when ArcMap opens the document. You can use *ThisDocument* as a shortcut when programming in VBA to access the current document. Here is an example of how to use both the *Application* and *ThisDocument*:

```
Dim pMxDoc as IMxDocument
Set pMxDoc = Application.Document
'or
Set pMxDoc = ThisDocument
```

Both methods illustrated above result in a reference being set to the local document.

In the previous section of this chapter, we focused primarily on how to write code in the VBA development environment embedded within ArcMap and ArcCatalog. This section focuses on particular issues related to creating ActiveX DLLs that can be added to the applications and writing external standalone applications using the Visual Basic development environment. More details of using Visual Basic are given with the documentation that accompanies ArcObjects Developer Controls.

Creating COM components

Most developers use Visual Basic to create a COM component that works with ArcMap or ArcCatalog. Earlier in this chapter you learned that since the ESRI applications are COM clients—their architecture supports the use of software components that adhere to the COM specification—you can build components with different languages including Visual Basic. These components can then be added to the applications easily. For information about packaging and deploying COM components that you've built with Visual Basic, see the last section of this chapter.

This section is not intended as a Visual Basic tutorial; rather, it highlights aspects of Visual Basic that you should know in order to be effective when working with ArcObjects.

In Visual Basic you can build a COM component that will work with ArcMap or ArcCatalog by creating an ActiveX DLL. This section will review the rudimentary steps involved. Note that these steps are not all-inclusive. Your project may involve other requirements.

1. Start Visual Basic. In the New Project dialog box, create an ActiveX DLL Project.

2. In the Properties window, make sure that the Instancing property for the initial class module and any other class modules you add to the Project is set to 5—MultiUse.

3. Reference the ESRI Object Library.

The ESRI VB Add-In interface implementer can be used to automate steps 3 and 4.

4. Implement the required interfaces. When you implement an interface in a class module, the class provides its own versions of all the public procedures specified in the type library of the interface. In addition to providing a mapping between the interface prototypes and your procedures, the *Implements* statement causes the class to accept COM *QueryInterface* calls for the specified interface ID. You must include all the public procedures involved. A missing member in an implementation of an interface or class causes an error. If you don't put code in one of the procedures in a class you are implementing, you can raise the appropriate error (*Const E_NOTIMPL = &H80004001*). That way, if someone else uses the class, they'll understand that a member is not implemented.

5. Add any additional code that's needed.

Visual Basic automatically generates the necessary GUIDs for the classes, interfaces, and libraries. Setting binary compatibility forces VB to reuse the GUIDs from a previous compilation of the DLL. This is essential since ArcMap stores the GUIDs of commands in the document for subsequent loading.

6. Establish the Project Name and other properties to identify the component. In the Project Properties dialog box, the Project Name you specify will be used as the name of the component's type library. It can be combined with the name of each class the component provides to produce unique class names (these names are also called ProgIDs). These names appear in the Component Category Manager. Save the project.

7. Compile the DLL.

8. Set the component's Version Compatibility to binary. As your code evolves, it's good practice to set the components to Binary Compatibility so, if you make changes to a component, you'll be warned that you're breaking compatibility. For additional information, see the 'Binary compatibility mode' help topic in the Visual Basic online help.

9. Save the project.

10. Make the component available to the application. You can add a component to a document or template by clicking the Add from file button in the Customize dialog box's Commands tab. In addition, you can register a component in the Component Category Manager.

Implementing interfaces

You implement interfaces differently in Visual Basic depending if they are inbound or outbound interfaces. An outbound interface is seen by Visual Basic as an event source and is supported through the *WithEvents* keyword. To handle the outbound interface, *IActiveViewEvents*, in Visual Basic (the default outbound interface of the *Map* class), use the *WithEvents* keyword and provide appropriate functions to handle the events.

```
Private WithEvents ViewEvents As Map

Private Sub ViewEvents_SelectionChanged()
  ' User changed feature selection update my feature list form
  UpdateMyFeatureForm
End Sub
```

Inbound interfaces are supported with the *Implements* keyword. However, unlike the outbound interface, all the methods defined on the interface must be stubbed out. This ensures that the vTable is correctly formed when the object is instantiated. Not all of the methods have to be fully coded, but the stub functions must be there. If the implementation is blank, an appropriate return code should be given to any client to inform them that the method is not implemented (see the section *Working with HRESULTs*). To implement the *IExtension* interface, code similar to that below is required. Note that all the methods are implemented.

```
Private m_pApp As IApplication
Implements IExtension
```

```
Private Property Get IExtension_Name() As String
  IExtension_Name = "Sample Extension"
End Property


Private Sub IExtension_Startup(ByRef initializationData As Variant)
  Set m_pApp = initializationData
End Sub


Private Sub IExtension_Shutdown()
  Set m_pApp = Nothing
End Sub
```

Setting references to the ESRI object libraries

The principal difference between working with the VBA development environment embedded in the applications and working with Visual Basic is that the latter environment requires that you load the appropriate object libraries so that any object variables that you declare can be found. If you don't add the reference, you'll get the error message to the left. In addition, the global variables *ThisDocument* and *Application* are not available to you.

To add a reference to an object library

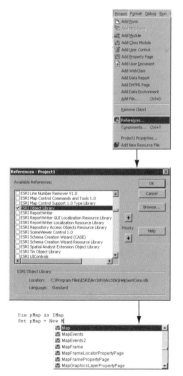

In all cases, you'll need to load the ESRI Object Library esriCore.olb. Depending on what you want your code to do, you may add other ESRI object libraries, perhaps for one of the extensions.

To display the References dialog box in which you can set the references you need, select References in the Visual Basic Project menu.

After you set a reference to an object library by selecting the check box next to its name, you can find a specific object and its methods and properties in the Object Browser.

If you are not using any objects in a referenced library, you should clear the check box for that reference to minimize the number of object references Visual Basic must resolve, thus reducing the time it takes your project to compile. You should not remove a reference for an item that is used in your project.

You can't remove the "Visual Basic for Applications" and "Visual Basic objects and procedures" references because they are necessary for running Visual Basic.

Referring to a document

Each VBA project (Normal, Project, TemplateProject) has a class called *ThisDocument*, which represents the document object. Anywhere you write code in VBA you can reference the document as *ThisDocument*. Further, if you are writing your code in the *ThisDocument* Code window, you have direct access to all the methods and properties on *IDocument*. This is not available in Visual Basic. You must first get a reference to the *Application* and then the document. When adding both extensions and

After the ESRI Object Library is referenced, all the types contained within it are available to Visual Basic. IntelliSense will also work with the contents of the object library.

commands to ArcGIS applications, a pointer to the *IApplication* interface is provided. For code samples that show you how to get a handle on the application, see Chapter 3, 'Customizing the user interface'.

```
Implements IExtension
Private m_pApp As IApplication

Private Sub IExtension_Startup(ByRef initializationData As Variant)
  Set m_pApp = initializationData    ' Assign IApplication
End Sub

Implements ICommand
Private m_pApp As IApplication

Private Sub ICommand_OnCreate(ByVal hook As Object)
  Set m_pApp = hook                    ' QI for IApplication
End Sub
```

Now that a reference to the application is in an *IApplication* pointer member variable, the document, and hence all other objects, can be accessed from any method within the class.

```
Dim pDoc as IDocument
Set pDoc = m_pApp.Document
MsgBox pDoc.Name
```

Getting to an object

In the previous example, navigating around the objects within ArcMap is a straightforward process since a pointer to the *Application* object, the root object of most of the ArcGIS application's objects, is passed to the object via one of its interfaces. This, however, is not the case with all interfaces that are implemented within the ArcObjects application framework. There are cases when you may implement an object that exists within the framework and there is no possibility to traverse the object hierarchy from that object. This is because very few objects support a reference to their parent object (the *IDocument* interface has a property named *Parent* that references the *IApplication* interface). In order to give developers access to the application object, there is a singleton object that provides a pointer to the running application object. The code below illustrates its use.

Singletons are objects that only support one instance of the object. These objects have a class factory that ensures that anytime an existing object is requested, a pointer to an already existing object is returned.

```
Dim pAppRef As New AppRef
Dim pApp as IApplication
Set pApp = pAppRef
```

You must be careful to ensure that this object is only used where the implementation will only ever run within ArcMap and ArcCatalog. For instance, it would not be a good idea to make use of this function from within a custom feature since that would restrict what applications could be used to view the feature class.

Running ArcMap with a command line argument

You can start ArcMap from the command line and pass it an argument that is either the pathname of a document (.mxd) or the pathname of a template (.mxt). In the former case, ArcMap will open the document; in the latter case, ArcMap will create a new document based on the template specified.

In Visual Basic, it is not possible to determine the command line used to start the application. There is a sample on disk that provides this functionality. It can be found at \arcgis\arcexe81\ArcObjects Developer Kit\samples\COM Techniques\Command Line.

You can also pass an argument and create an instance of ArcMap by supplying arguments to the Win32 API's *ShellExecute* function or Visual Basic's *Shell* function as follows:

```
Dim ret As Variant
ret = Shell("d:\arcexe81\bin\arcmap.exe _
    d:\arcexe80\bin\templates\LetterPortrait.mxt", vbNormalFocus)
```

By default, *Shell* runs other programs asynchronously. This means that ArcMap might not finish executing before the statements following the *Shell* function are executed.

To execute a program and wait until it is terminated, you must call three Win32 API functions. First, call the *CreateProcessA* function to load and execute ArcMap. Next, call the *WaitForSingleObject* function, which forces the operating system to wait until ArcMap has been terminated. Finally, when the user has terminated the application, call the *CloseHandle* function to release the application's 32-bit identifier to the system pool.

DEBUGGING VISUAL BASIC CODE

Visual Basic has a debugger integrated into its development environment. This is in many cases a valuable tool when debugging Visual Basic code; however, in some cases it is not possible to use the VB debugger. The use of the debugger and these special cases are discussed below.

Running the code within an application

It is possible to use the Visual Basic debugger to debug your ArcObjects-based source code even when ActiveX DLLs are the target server. The application that will host your DLL must be set as the Debug application. To do this, select the appropriate application, ArcMap.exe, for instance, and set it as the Start Program in the Debugging Options of the Project Properties.

Using commands on the Debug toolbar, ArcMap can be started and the DLL loaded and debugged. Break points can be set, lines stepped over, functions stepped into, and variables checked. Moving the line pointer in the left-hand margin can also set the current execution line.

Visual Basic debugger issues

In many cases, the Visual Basic debugger will work without any problems; however, there are two problems when using the debugger that is supplied with Visual Basic 6. Both of these problems exist because of the way that Visual Basic implements its debugger.

Normally when running a tool within ArcMap, the DLL is loaded into ArcMap address space, and calls are made directly into the DLL. When debugging, this is not the case. Visual Basic makes changes to the registry so that the CLSID for your DLL does not point to your DLL but, instead, it points to the Visual Basic Debug DLL (VB6debug.dll). The Debug DLL must then support all the interfaces implemented by your class on the fly. With the VB Debug DLL loaded into ArcMap, any method calls that come into the DLL are forwarded on to Visual Basic, where the code to be debugged is executed. The two problems with this are caused by the changes made to the Registry and the cross-process space method calling. When these restrictions are first encountered, it can be confusing since the object works outside the debugger or at least until it hits the area of problem code.

Since the method calls made from ArcMap to the custom tool are across apartments, there is a requirement for the interfaces to be marshalled. This marshalling causes problems in certain circumstances. Most data types can be automatically marshaled by the system, but there are a few that require custom code because the standard marshaler does not support the data types. If one of these data types is used by an interface within the custom tool and there is no custom marshalling code, the debugger will fail with an "Interface not supported error".

The registry manipulation also breaks the support for component categories. Any time there is a request on a component category, the category manager within COM will be unable to find your component because, rather than asking whether your DLL belongs to the component category, COM is asking whether the VB debugger DLL belongs to the component category, which obviously it doesn't. What this means is that anytime a component category is used to automate the loading of a DLL, the DLL cannot be debugged using the Visual Basic debugger.

This obviously causes problems for many of the ways to extend the framework. The most common way to extend the framework is to add a command or tool. Previously it was discussed how component categories were used in this instance. Remember the component category was only used to build the list of commands in the dialog box. This means that if the command to be debugged is already present on a toolbar, the Visual Basic debugger can be used. Hence, the procedure for debugging Visual Basic objects that implement the *ICommand* interface is to ensure that the command is added to a toolbar when ArcMap is executed standalone and then, after saving the document, loading ArcMap through the debugger.

In some cases, such as extensions and property pages, it is not possible to use the Visual Basic debugger. If you have access to the Visual C++ Debugger, you can use one of the options outlined below. Fortunately, there are a number of ESRI Visual Basic Add-ins that make it possible to track down the problem quickly and effectively. The add-ins described below, in the section 'Visual Basic Developer Add-Ins', provide error log information including line and module details. A sample output from an error log is given below; note the call stack information along with line numbers.

```
Error Log saved on : 8/28/2000 - 10:39:04 AM
Record Call Stack Sequence - Bottom line is error line.

  chkVisible_MouseUp C:\Source\MapControl\Commands\frmLayer.frm Line : 196
  RefreshMap C:\Source\MapControl\Commands\frmLayer.frm Line : 20
```

```
Description
  Object variable or With block variable not set
```

Alternatives to the Visual Basic debugger

If the Visual Basic debugger and add-ins do not provide enough information, the Visual C++ debugger can be used, either on its own or with C++ ATL wrapper classes. The Visual C++ debugger does not run the object to be debugged out of process from ArcMap, which means that none of the above issues apply. Common debug commands are given in the section 'Debugging tips in Visual Studio'. Both of the techniques below require the Visual Basic project to be compiled with Debug Symbol information.

The Visual C++ Debugger can work with this symbolic debug information and the source files.

Visual C++ Debugger

It is possible to use the Visual C++ debugger directly by attaching to a running process that has the Visual Basic object to be debugged loaded and then setting a break point in the Visual Basic file. When the line of code is reached, the debugger will halt execution and step you into the source file at the correct line. The required steps are shown below.

1. Start an appropriate application, such as ArcMap.exe.

2. Start Microsoft Visual C++.

3. Attach to the ArcMap process using Menu option Build -> Start Debug -> Attach to process.

4. Load the appropriate Visual Basic Source file into the Visual C++ debugger and set the break point.

5. Call the method within ArcMap.

No changes can be made to the source code within the debugger, and variables cannot be inspected, but code execution can be viewed and altered. This is often sufficient to determine what is wrong, especially with logic-related problems.

ATL Wrapper Classes

Using the Active Template Library (ATL), you can create a class that implements the same interfaces as the Visual Basic Class. When you create the ATL Object, you create the Visual Basic object. All method calls are then passed to the Visual Basic Object for execution. You

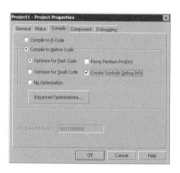

Create Debug Symbol information using the Create Symbolic Debug info option on the Compile tab of the Project Properties dialog box.

debug the contained object by setting a break point in the appropriate C++ wrapper method, and when the code reaches the break point, the debugger is stepped into the Visual Basic Code. For more information on this technique, look at the ATL Debugger sample in the Developer Samples of the ArcObjects Developer Help system.

The Add-Ins menu provides access to numerous developer tools that help ArcObjects developers be more productive.

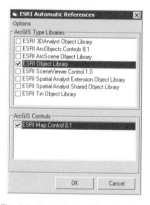

This dialog box is displayed faster than the Visual Basic Reference dialog box, making it the interface of choice when setting references to ESRI type libraries and controls.

The Compile and Register add-in enhances VB by adding support for component categories.

The ESRI add-ins automate some of the tasks performed by the software engineer when developing with ArcObjects, as well as provide tools that make debugging code easier.

What is a Visual Basic add-in?

A Visual Basic add-in extends the functionality provided through the MS Visual Basic Integrated Development Environment (IDE). An add-in typically automates repetitive tasks performed by a software engineer.

Add-ins register themselves with Visual Basic. After an add-in is installed it will appear automatically on the Add-Ins menu. The menu to the left shows the Add-In menu with the ESRI add-ins loaded.

Automatic references

When you develop with Visual Basic, you must reference all the external type libraries in order for the compiler to locate all the object types, interface types, and so on. The IntelliSense mechanism also makes use of this type library information.

In all cases when developing ArcObjects-based applications, you'll need to load the ESRI Object Library esriCore.olb. Depending on what you want your code to do, you may add other ESRI object libraries, perhaps for one of the extensions.

Normally, to add references to external libraries in Visual Basic you would display the References dialog box in the Visual Basic Project menu, then check on the required libraries. Depending on the number of libraries installed on your system, it can take a few seconds to display the References dialog box and locate the appropriate libraries. This Visual Basic add-in simplifies the process, and, if enabled, will automate this reference setting for all Visual Basic Projects.

To access the add-in, click ESRI Automatic References on the Add-Ins pulldown menu. Only the ArcObjects type libraries and controls are listed in the interface. To the left is the add-in's user interface.

Compile and register

This Visual Basic add-in supports the building of components and the subsequent registration of these components into the appropriate component category. To access the add-in, click ESRI Compile and Register on the Add-Ins pulldown menu. Not all the ESRI component categories are supported; however, the add-in supports the categories that are used commonly by the application framework and the geodatabase. To the left is the add-in's user interface.

The add-in lists all the classes defined within the VB project in the left column and lists all the available component categories in the right column. The developer selects a class in the left column and checks the appropriate component categories in the right. When a project is loaded, the interface updates to reflect the project's classes, and if these classes are within component categories, the categories list also updates. If the class has not been registered in a category, all items in the list will be unchecked.

When each class has the appropriate component category selected, the project can be built. Clicking the Compile button builds the project. Upon completion of a successful compile, the classes are registered into the required component category. If a class' component category changes, the class is removed from the old component category. If a class is not marked as a member of any category, it will be removed from any of the supported categories in which it is currently registered. If the developer has displayed the form once or the class already exists within the category, the Compile command can be executed directly by holding down the Ctrl key when selecting the add-in from the menu.

The Options menu has three items: Display Dialogs, Unregister on Error, and Set Binary Compatibility. Display Dialogs, if enabled, displays dialog boxes informing the developer of the operations that are being performed: saving the source files, compiling and registering the component, and so on. Unregister On Error sets the behavior if an error is encountered during the compilation and registration process. If checked when an error occurs at any time during the execution of the add-in, the component is unregistered from the system. Set Binary Compatibility, if checked, will automatically set the project's component compatibility to be Binary with the newly compiled DLL. The states of these menu items are saved in the registry and loaded on subsequent uses of the tool. By default, they are all enabled.

Before compiling the project, all source files within the project are saved. If a module has never been saved, the developer is prompted to save the project via the standard VB interface. This ability to save source files prior to a compile gives functionality that is not present in Visual Basic. Visual Basic only saves source files prior to building executables; it does not save source files when building DLLs.

If the current Visual Basic project has a class that is marked to go into either the ESRI Mx Command Bars or ESRI Gx Command Bars, the class can be marked as a premier toolbar.

To flag a toolbar class as a premier toolbar, you must display the Premier Toolbar Classes check list by clicking the Premier Toolbars button. This displays the list box shown on the left. All classes that are in the appropriate component category will be placed in this list. If the classes are already in the registry as premier toolbars, they will be automatically checked. To remove them from the registry, uncheck the class and compile the project. All classes checked will be added to the registry as premier toolbars. When developing the project, you must be aware that after every compile the toolbar will act like a fresh install when ArcMap or ArcCatalog is next started (that is, even if the toolbar was previously hidden, it will appear).

It is not a good idea to have classes that have a ProgID of project1.class1. This will be the result if the default project name and class name are not changed before compilation. Any classes that have a ProgID that is project1.class1 will not automatically be loaded in the right column of the form.

Remember, component categories are used by client applications to efficiently find all components of a particular type that are installed on the system. For example, ArcMap uses component categories extensively to efficiently locate installed components on a user's system. Component categories support the extensibility of COM by allowing the developer of the client application to create and work with classes that belong to a particular category. If at a later date a new class is added to the category, the client application need not be changed to take advantage of the new class; it will automatically pick up the new class the next time the category is read.

Premier toolbars are toolbars that are displayed the first time ArcMap or ArcCatalog is started after their installation. Once the user has hidden them for the first time, they are no longer displayed. This is good way of highlighting the installation of customizations to the user.

The required changes to the registry are made at compile time. An entry is also made in the registry script to ensure that the class is also marked as a Premier toolbar at install time.

Since the process of component category registration is tied to the compilation, these classes will only be registered in the categories on the developer's machine. To help with the installation of components on third-party machines, the compilation process also generates a Registry Script file. The file has the same name as the project with a .reg extension and is located in the VB Project directory. A sample script is shown below.

```
REGEDIT4

; This Registry Script enters CoClasses Into their appropriate Component Category ; Use this script during installation of the components

; CoClass: prjDisplay.ZoomIn ; CLSID: {FC7EC05F-6B1B-4A59-B8A2-37CE33738728}
; Component Category: ESRI Mx Commands
[HKEY_LOCAL_MACHINE\SOFTWARE\Classes\CLSID\{FC7EC05F-6B1B-4A59-B8A2-37CE33738728}\Implemented Categories\{B56A7C42-83D4-11D2-A2E9-080009B6F22B}]
; CoClass: prjDisplay.ZoomOut ; CLSID: {2C120434-0248-43DB-AD8E-BD4523A93DF8} ; Component Category: ESRI Mx Commands
[HKEY_LOCAL_MACHINE\SOFTWARE\Classes\CLSID\{2C120434-0248-43DB-AD8E-BD4523A93DF8}\Implemented Categories\{B56A7C42-83D4-11D2-A2E9-080009B6F22B}]
```

The Component Categories dialog box allows you to configure the component categories supported by the add-in.

The Components menu has two items. Select Component Categories displays the dialog box shown on the left. Using this dialog box, it is possible to select the Component Categories that the add-in displays in its Component Categories list. To reset the list back to the default settings, use the Reset Component Categories menu command.

Interface implementer

When implementing interfaces in Visual Basic, the developer is forced to stub out all the methods of the interface; unfortunately, Visual Basic does not automate this process. Thus, when you implement two interfaces, such as *ICommand* and *ITool*, it can mean carrying out a repetitive task for more than 20 method calls. Fortunately, this add-in automates this task.

To access the add-in, select the ESRI Interface Implementer menu item on the Add-Ins pulldown menu. When creating a COM server, this add-in can be used to generate the stub functions. In addition to generating the stub functions, the DLL also adds a reference to the ESRI Object Library and adds a module that contains a generic error-handling routine. For more details on this error-handling module, see the Error Handler add-in. A reference to the error handler is also added to the project.

By default, all stub functions are created with an error handler; this can be overridden by unchecking Generate Error Handlers on the Options menu. The state of this menu is saved in the registry. The Options menu has one other entry, Raise E_NOTIMPL, that defaults to unchecked. When this is checked, all functions disable error handling and raise the standard error *E_NOTIMPL* to indicate to clients that the function has

The Interface Implementer dialog box has facilities to select interfaces from shortcut combo boxes, a full list of the interfaces in the selected type library, and a search facility.

not been implemented. A constant is also added to the module that defines the variable *E_NOTIMPL*. The two lines of code added when this option is checked are shown below.

```
On Error GoTo 0
  Err.Raise E_NOTIMPL
```

Developers must remove these two lines when they implement the function.

The interface implementer interface can be seen to the left. The two combo boxes at the top of the form offer a shortcut to many of the ArcObjects interfaces that are commonly implemented. The combo boxes divide the interfaces into two broad groups: application and geodatabase interfaces.

If the required interface is not in one of the combo boxes, all the interfaces that are available in the selected type library are listed in the list below. You can scroll down the list, selecting all the interfaces required, then click OK or Apply. This will add the stub functions for all selected interfaces in one action.

You can also search the list using the search facility. To search the interface the developer types the name of the required interface in the text box below the list. The first interface that matches the entered text is displayed at the top of the list box. The search is not case sensitive by default. A popup menu, available on the text entry field, can enable a case-sensitive search if required. Click OK or Apply with an interface highlighted to implement the interface. You don't have to check the check box; the first selected interface is automatically selected. Thus, by simply typing in the text box and clicking Apply, multiple interfaces can be implemented very quickly.

Interfaces can only be generated in class modules. The module used is the currently selected module in the project browser, not necessarily the currently active code window. If the selected module and code window do not match, the developer is warned that the code will be placed in the selected class module and not the current window.

The tool will only implement an interface once per module.

If an error-handling module already exists within the project, a new one will not be added. If the error-handling module is an out-of-date version, the tool updates the module to match the latest installed error handler.

When the add-in displays the form, the text search field allows you to start searching for the required interface immediately.

Introduction screen

Step 1

Step 2

Step 3

Step 4

Command Creation Wizard

The Command Creation Wizard facilitates the creation of a command or tool for use within ArcMap, ArcCatalog, the Map control, or a combination of these. For instance, a tool written for ArcMap may also be suitable for the Map control. It is possible to quickly develop commands and tools without this wizard using the interface implementer and the Compile and Register Add-ins, but this wizards has many features that make the addition of commands straightforward.

To access the add-in, click ESRI Command Wizard from the Add-Ins pulldown menu. An introduction screen will display.

This screen has information about the wizard. When you complete the wizard, it compiles and registers the project automatically. The project will only be saved to file if you select this option at the start of the wizard.

The first step of the wizard displays only if the project was not saved prior to executing the wizard. It is advisable to save the project at the start of the wizard, as this will also ensure that the project is saved on completion.

When you save a project using the wizard, if no filenames have been assigned to modules, you are prompted to enter the filenames. In addition, you can elect to check for default names. If you enabled these options, the wizard checks the names of modules and, if a default name is detected, you are prompted to enter a new name. Default names are not a good idea since there is less chance that the programmable ID will be unique.

The wizard always performs the next step, project compilation, either after you save the project or when the wizard starts. If the project fails to compile, the wizard displays step 2. You have no other choice but to fix the compilation error and rerun the wizard.

The next step involves selecting the target application in which the command will operate. Not all commands are suitable for all application environments. For example, a Select tool used to select features on a map could be used within the Map control or the ArcMap application since the topmost object that must be accessed is the *Map*, and both these environments expose a map object; however, a Select tool may not be suitable for ArcCatalog since it does not expose a *Map* object.

The graphic panel on the left illustrates the choices made. You must select at least one application in order to continue on to the next step.

Step 4 of the wizard allows you to determine various properties of the code that the wizard generates.

You can add the generated source code to an existing class within your project. This option is only enabled if there is a suitable class module within your active project. The wizard disregards any class that already implements the *ICommand* interface. If the wizard does create a new class, it assigns the class the name of the Commands caption, minus any spaces, preceded by "cls".

Step 5

Step 6

Step 7

Step 8

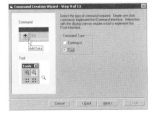

Step 9

The Error Handlers option controls whether the wizard adds error-handling code to the functions. All functions should have an error handler, but if you do not wish to use the generic ESRI error handler you can disable the creation of the error handlers and add your own.

Verbose comments can be helpful when starting out with Command development. With this option enabled, several hundred lines of comment code are added.

A number of objects within the ArcObjects object model support outbound event interfaces. To work with these interfaces, a certain amount of plumbing code is required to ensure that the event source and sink are connected. The wizard supports all three common event sources: the *MxDocument, PageLayout,* and *Map* objects. None of these options are available if ArcCatalog is set as a target application. When the Map control is selected, the choice is limited to the *Map* object. ArcMap supports all three event sources.

The stub functions the wizard creates will, by default, contain no lines of code other than error-handling code. The exceptions to this are the functions where code was added because it was required to perform an action, such as setting member variables when the command is created. If the function does not contain automatically generated code, you can add a message box to the function. This allows you to see when the application framework calls the function. This can be very helpful when you start to work with events. If the wizard creates a tool, a message box is not added to the *OnClick* event.

The wizard displays step 5 only if you chose to add the code to a class already in the project. If there is only one class, the wizard displays the class in the list with its check box selected; otherwise, you must select a class before continuing.

The wizard displays step 6 only if you chose to listen to *Document* events in step 4. The *NewDocument* and *OpenDocument* events are mandatory as these are required to maintain the source sink connection as new documents are created or loaded.

If you do not select an event to implement, it is straightforward to add the event later. You must select the variable *DocumentEvents* in the Object combo box of the Visual Basic editor, and the required event is selected in Visual Basic's Procedure combo box.

The wizard displays step 7 only if you chose to listen to *Map* events in step 4. The wizard assigns the event handler to the variable *MapActiveViewEvents.*

The wizard displays step 8 only if you chose to listen to PageLayout events in step 4. The wizard assigns the event handler to the variable *PageActiveViewEvents.*

Step 9 allows you to select whether to create a command or a tool. A command has the majority of the functionality coded within the *OnClick* event, whereas a tool is used to handle user interaction with the

Step 10

Step 11

Step 12

ActiveView (*Map* or *PageLayout*). Typically this involves handling mouse events, such as mouse down, mouse move, and mouse up.

Both commands and tools must implement the *ICommand* interface. Step 10 allows you to specify the properties of the *ICommand* interface. The name of the command is automatically generated from the category and caption entries. This can be changed if required. If the command has a bitmap, it can be added by selecting a bitmap file. If the bitmap uses a masking color, this can also be selected by clicking in the Mask color box on the form.

The bitmap is added to an image list named using the class name prepended with "iml", and the image is keyed with the string "Bitmap". The image list is added to a form module with the name *frmResources*. If the module is not present in the project, the wizard adds a form module. The wizard remembers the path of the bitmap file and will open the bitmap file browser at that path on subsequent calls.

The option to Enable conditionally allows you to select when the command will be enabled with the application based on some preset conditions. Step 11 covers these options. The Checked when active option is only available for commands since tools are automatically checked by the application when they are the active tool. When a button on a toolbar is checked, the button appears depressed; when the button is on a menu, a small checkmark is placed to the left of the caption.

The wizard displays step 11 only if you selected the option to Enable conditionally in step 10. These conditions are Data View, Layout View, Data Present, and Edit Status. Data View and Layout View are mutually exclusive. The conditions that you can choose to base the enabling on can be AND'd or OR'd together. If some other combination is required, you must edit the generated source code.

The wizard displays step 12 if you are creating a tool. It is a common function of a tool to generate a geometry object through input from the user; the object is then used in a subsequent action. To support this, you can elect to support Display Feedback, which can be in one of the four geometry types. Pressing the mouse button down and moving the cursor creates the *Envelope* and *Circle* geometries. When you release the mouse, the wizard creates the geometry. You can create polygon and polyline geometries by pressing the mouse button; each successive button press creates a vertex on the geometry. Double-clicking creates the geometry.

A tool normally is in one of two states: passive or active. When the user interacts with the tool, normally by pressing a key or mouse button, the tool is in its active state. When the user is not directly interacting with the tool and the tool is simply the current tool in use, the tool is in its passive state. You can associate cursors with these two states. The cursors are added to an image list named using the class name preceded with "iml", and the images are keyed with the strings "Active" and "Passive". The wizard adds the image list to a form module with the name

Step 13

frmResources. If the module is not present in the project, a form module is added. The wizard remembers the path of the cursor file and will open the cursor file browser at that path on subsequent calls.

The last panel of the wizard has two options that control the compiling and registration stage and an option to save all the settings selected during the wizard execution as the defaults. These settings include all check boxes and options but do not include the command string properties or the bitmap and icons.

After the wizard generates all the source code, it compiles the project into a DLL. The wizard then registers the DLL on the system and places the newly created class in the appropriate component categories. Only the newly created command is placed in a component category. If there are other classes, the Compile and Register Wizard can be used to register these and create the Registry script for use later with an install program. If required after the successful compile, you can direct the wizard to set the project's version compatibility mode to the newly compiled DLL by checking the Set Binary Compatibility option. You can view the progress of these various stages by checking the Display Progress Dialogs check box.

Error handler generator

This Visual Basic add-in automates the generation of error handling code. To access the add-in select the ESRI ErrorHandler Generator menu item on the Add-Ins menu. There are two parts to this add-in: the generation of the error handling code and the execution of the code when a runtime error is created.

The add-in creates the error handlers automatically; you don't ever have to write the error handler manually (unless a specialized handler is required). It is often better to wrap particular function calls with a specialized handler but still have the generic handler in use for the majority of the function.

The DLL can generate the error handlers in one of three ways:

1. Generate an error handler for the current function.

2. Generate error handlers for all the functions within the current module.

3. Generate error handlers for all source files within the active project.

The message box shown to the left asks for the method to use. This message box can be bypassed by pressing a combination of the Ctrl and Shift keys when executing the tool. The message box also allows the setting of four options.

• Update Error Handlers—Default is *True*. Forces the error handlers, generated by the add-in, in the function(s) to be rewritten even if they are already there. Use this option to ensure that the error handlers match the latest version or if you make a change to the dependency requirements. This ensures the correct arguments are passed to the *ErrorHandler* function.

Error Handler add-in dialog box

- Update Error Module—Default is *True*. Regenerates the ErrorHandler.bas module added to the project each time the add-in is executed. Typically this would be toggled off if you change the strings used by the various user interfaces. This should be toggled on if there is a change in the dependency requirements.

- No Dependency—Default is *False*. Error handler has no runtime dependency on the ErrorHandlerUI.DLL file. The error log user interface is not available, but the error is simply handled and the call stack displayed to the user in a message box.

- Parent Error Forms—Default is *False*. Parents the various forms using the *m_ParentHWND* module variable.

In addition to the error handler it adds to the functions, the add-in, depending on the options, declares one or two variables in the module: *c_ModuleFileName* and *m_ParentHWND*. The first, a constant, holds a string identifying the filename of the module on disk. If the add-in is executed before the file is saved, this string will be blank. To update the constant you can either enter the name manually or run the add-in again—this will update the constant value. The second is a variable that can hold a window handle that will be used to parent the various user interfaces used by the runtime error handlers. By default, all the error handler interfaces use the desktop as their parent window. Setting the member variable *m_ParentHWND*, defined at the top of the module, to a valid window handle will parent the error dialogs to this window. By default, the member variable *m_ParentHWND* is not added to the module, and all interfaces use the desktop as their parent.

The error handling code makes use of the same generic error handler module that is included with the Interface implementation tool. By default, every time the Error Handler tool executes, this module is regenerated. This means that any changes made to the module will be lost. The generic error handling function *HandleError* takes ten arguments.

Name	Data type	Description
bTopProcedure	Boolean	States whether the error handling function was called from a top-level function or not. Public methods, events and properties and friends are all top-level functions. Private methods called from within the same module are not top-level functions
sProcedureName	string	Encapsulates the function and module name, and any line number information available
lErrNumber	long	ErrorNumber (retrieved from Err object)
sErrSource	string	ErrorSource (retrieved from Err object)
sErrDescription	string	ErrorDescription (retrieved from Err object)
version	long	VersionOfFunction (optional Default 1)
parentHWND	long	Parent hWnd for error dialogs, NULL is valid (option is NULL)
reserved1	variant	Reserved
reserved2	variant	Reserved
reserved3	variant	Reserved

Depending on the first parameter, the *HandleError* function either presents the error to the user using a variety of interfaces or raises the error. A top-level error handler will eventually catch this raised error. In this way, the call stack can be created. For this mechanism to function correctly, all functions should implement this error handler.

Version 1 error log

Version 4 information message box

Version 4 error log

Error log with line number information

Error Handler Remover dialog box

The sixth parameter controls the user interface. You can choose to display either a simple Message Box, as shown in the figure to the left, with the error information contained within it (Version 1), or a more comprehensive error handling facility (Version 3). Version 2 is provided for backward compatibility, but its use is deprecated. The message box displayed when an error is raised using Version 1 is shown in the dialog box on the left. Notice the call stack and the original error description.

Version 4 of the Error Handler displays a message box to the user informing the user that an unexpected error has occurred, along with the error log showing the error message, number, and call stack. Neither of these forms are modal. The forms are implemented as singleton objects, meaning that no matter how many modules make use of the error handler, the errors will all be written to the same error log. If the error log is already displayed, the information message box is not shown. The error log is brought to the front of the display and the error appended to the text already there.

The contents of the error log can either be saved to a text file for later viewing or printed out. Save and Print options are available on the File menu.

Although the call stack information is useful, the error log displays the most information when combined with Line numbers. In order to obtain line number information in the error log, the source files must be annotated using the Line Number Generator add-in. If line number information is available, the error log displays data similar to that shown to the left.

Error Handler Remover

This add-in removes the error handlers from the source files. To access the add-in, click the Add-Ins menu and click ESRI Error Handler Remover. The add-in displays the message box to the left, which allows the developer to select the files within a project that should have their error handlers removed. You can bypass the dialog box by pressing the Shift and Ctrl keys when the add-in is executed.

Only ESRI error handlers are removed. If all the handlers for a module are removed, the two constants added to the top of the source file are also removed. If the error handlers are removed from all the source files of a project, the error handler module is removed from the project, but the file is not deleted from disk.

Line Number Generator

The Error Handler add-in can display line number information if there is any line number data available within the source file. Visual Basic supports the extraction of line number information, but only when lines are explicitly labeled with line numbers. This add-in adds line numbers to the appropriate lines within the source files of the active project. Line numbers are added only to those lines that support labeling.

Line Number Generator dialog box

To access the add-in, click the Add-Ins menu and click ESRI Line Number Generator. The add-in displays the dialog box to the left, which lets you select to which files within a project line numbers should be added. You can bypass the dialog box by pressing the Shift and Ctrl keys when the add-in is executed. To update the line number information after edits have been made, reexecute the add-in.

Line number labels in the source code can be obtrusive, making the code difficult to read. Hence you should only add them to debug code when tracing down a problem; remove them after the problem is found. A sample of these labels placed in the source code is shown below.

```
Dim pSourceFeature As IFeature
Dim pTargetFeature As IFeature
Dim i As Long
53: Set pSourceFeature = pFeatureCursor.NextFeature

55: Do While (Not pSourceFeature Is Nothing)
56: Set pTargetFeature = pTargetClass.CreateFeature

58: Set pTargetFeature.Shape = pSourceFeature.ShapeCopy

60: For i = 0 To pTargetClass.Fields.FieldCount - 1
61: If ((pTargetClass.Fields.Field(i).Type <> esriFieldTypeGeometry) And _
(pTargetClass.Fields.Field(i).Type <> esriFieldTypeOID)) Then

63: pTargetFeature.Value(i) = Now End If

65: Next i
66: pTargetFeature.Store

68: Set pSourceFeature = pFeatureCursor.NextFeature
69: Loop
```

Using a combination of the error handler add-in and this line number generator, it is possible to ship software that will provide rich error information in the event of runtime errors within a released product. Even if the line number labels are not placed in the source code during the majority of the development, it is valid to create the release build with the line numbers in place. In this way, if an end user encounters an error, rich context error information is available to investigate the error.

Line Number Remover

Line Number Remover dialog box

This add-in removes the line numbers from the source files. To access the add-in, click the Add-Ins menu and click ESRI Line Number Remover. The add-in displays the message box to the left to let you select the files within a project whose line number labels should be removed. You can bypass the dialog box by pressing the Shift and Ctrl keys when the add-in is executed.

Align Control Creation with Tab index

When hosting VB user interfaces within applications not created by VB, the Tab index of forms may not be honored. To correct this problem, the controls within a form should be created in their Tab index order.

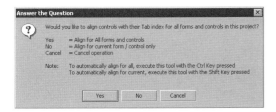

This add-in ensures that the creation of controls in a form occurs in the same order as the control's Tab index. To access the add-in, click the Add-Ins menu and click ESRI Align Controls with Tab Index. The add-in displays the message box on the left to let you select the modules within a project that have a user interface whose controls you want to align. You can bypass the dialog box by pressing the Shift and Ctrl keys when the add-in is executed.

To achieve the correct creation sequence, the z order of the controls are altered to match the Tab index. Therefore, if you have controls containing controls, you must ensure that you have the Tab index correct, otherwise the controls may "disappear" behind other controls.

In some cases, it may not be possible to change the creation sequence because of the z ordering restriction. In these cases, you must write code within the load sequence of the user interface component that sets the tab sequence.

This section provides coding guidelines when using C++. It also has useful information when debugging projects in Visual Studio. It finishes with a section on developing using the ATL.

Naming conventions

Name variables and constants using the following format (this is an abridged Hungarian notation):

[<scope>_]<type><name>

Prefix	Variable scope
m	Instance class members
c	Static class member (including constants)
g	Globally static variable
<empty>	local variable or struct or public class member

<type>

Prefix	Data Type
b	Boolean
by	byte or unsigned char
cx / cy	short used as size
d	double
dw	DWORD, double word or unsigned long
f	float
fn	function
h	handle
i	int (integer)
ip	smart pointer
l	long
p	a pointer
s	string
sz	ASCIIZ null-terminated string
w	WORD unsigned int
x, y	short used as coordinates

<name> describes how the variable is used or what it contains. The <scope> and <type> portions should always be lowercase, and the <name> should use mixed case:

Variable Name	Description
m_hWnd	a handle to a HWND
ipEnvelope	a smart pointer to a COM interface
m_pUnkOuter	a pointer to an object
c_isLoaded	a static class member
g_pWindowList	a global pointer to an object

Type names

All type names (*class, struct, enum,* and *typedef*) begin with an uppercase letter and use mixed case for the rest of the name:

```
class Foo : public CObject { . . .};
struct Bar { . . .};
enum ShapeType { . . . };
typedef int* FooInt;
```

Typedefs for function pointers (callbacks) append Proc to the end of their names.

```
typedef void (*FooProgressProc)(int step);
```

Enumeration values all begin with a lowercase string that identifies the project; in the case of ArcObjects this is esri, and each string occurs on separate lines:

```
typedef enum esriQuuxness
{
  esriQLow,
  esriQMedium,
  esriQHigh
} esriQuuxness;
```

Function names

Name functions using the following conventions:

For simple accessor and mutator functions, use Get<Property> and Set<Property>:

```
int GetSize();
void SetSize(int size);
```

If the client is providing storage for the result, use Query<Property>:

```
void QuerySize(int& size);
```

For state functions, use Set<State and Is<State> or Can<State>:

```
bool IsFileDirty();
void SetFileDirty(bool dirty);
bool CanConnect();
```

Where the semantics of an operation are obvious from the types of arguments, leave type names out of the function names.

Instead of

```
AddDatabase(Database& db);
```

consider using

```
Add(Database& db);
```

Instead of

```
ConvertFoo2Bar(Foo* foo, Bar* bar);
```

consider using

```
Convert(Foo* foo, Bar* bar)
```

If a client relinquishes ownership of some data to an object, use Give<Property>. If an object relinquishes ownership of some data to a client, use Take<Property>:

```
void GiveGraphic(Graphic* graphic);
Graphic* TakeGraphic(int itemNum);
```

Use function overloading when a particular operation works with different argument types:

```
void Append(const CString& text);
void Append(int number);
```

Argument names

Use descriptive argument names in function declarations. The argument name should clearly indicate what purpose the argument serves:

```
bool Send(int messageID, const char* address, const char* message);
```

True and false

There are at least three different sets of keywords for indicating the truth value of an expression. C++ has a built-in data-type *bool*, with keywords *true* and *false*. Win32 defines *TRUE* and *FALSE* macros. VB compatible COM programming requires the use of the Automation type *VARIANT_BOOL*, with macros *VARIANT_TRUE* and *VARIANT_FALSE*.

These keyword macros have one thing in common. *True* evaluates to a nonzero value, and *False* evaluates to zero. *VARIANT_TRUE* is defined as -1, which means that the correct macros and keywords must be used when comparing variables.

Class design

Conforming to a class design standard leads to easy-to-use and maintainable C++ class implementations.

Class layout

Organize class definitions in the following manner:

```
class MyClass : public CObject, private MyPrivateClass
{
// The public description of the class goes here. It describes what
// the class represents (from a client's perspective), and highlights
// which methods are the most important. Optionally, it shows examples
// of how to use the class.

public:
// Nested class and struct definitions.
// Enumerations, typedefs and constants.
```

```
MyClass()          {}
virtual ~MyClass() {}

// Public operations.

// Public accessor/mutator functions.

protected:
  // Protected description of the class goes here. This documentation
  // usually consists of instructions to potential subclassers on how to
  // subclass the class correctly.

  // Nested class and struct definitions.
  // Enumerations, typedefs and constants.
  // Protected data members.

  // Subclass-accessible operations. These are usually virtual.

private:
  // Nested class definitions.
  // Enumerations, typedefs, and constants.
  // Private data members.

  // Private operations.
};
```

Organizing classes this way helps clients of the class since it groups public operations and functions at the beginning. All the proprietary implementation details occur at the end of the class definition since clients do not need to know about them.

Public data

Do not make data members public unless the class is intended to be a semi-intelligent structure. One of the major benefits to using objects is the ability to encapsulate and hide implementation details from clients.

Class size

Keep classes small to decrease their complexity and increase their reusability. If you cannot summarize what the class does in a paragraph or less, chances are it is too complex and should be broken up into multiple classes.

Inline methods

Use inline methods only for empty implementations or for those containing only a few statements. Do not add a semicolon after the function body, but do add spaces to offset the brackets when there are statements in the function body. When several methods are inlined, line up the function bodies on the same column.

```
MyClass() : m_count(0)      {}
void SetCount(int count)    { m_count = count; }
```

Comments

To increase class legibility, add comments after the method or data member. If the comment fits to the right, place it there; otherwise, add it afterwards as an indented comment.

```
public:
  void SetCount(int count);
  //
  // Sets the count property of the object. Use this method only
  // when you are resetting the object.

  int GetCount();          // Gets the current count.

private:
  int    m_count;          // The current count.
  bool   m_inited;
  //
  // This property indicates whether or not the object is
  // currently being inited.
```

Construction

Be sure to provide a copy constructor and overload for the operator if the default structure-wise copy will result in an invalid object. Alternatively, consider hiding both by making them private.

```
MyClass(const MyClass& rhs);
MyClass& operator=(const MyClass& rhs);
```

Initialization versus assignment in constructors

When the constructor is invoked for an instance of a class, the following operations occur in the following order (storage is allocated for the entire instance):

- The constructor is invoked for the base class (in superclass to subclass order for all classes in the hierarchy).

- The constructors for any data members that are class variables are invoked in the order of their declaration in the interface specification.

- Execution of code defined within the constructor body occurs.

To avoid redundant operators, the following approach to constructor definition is suggested:

- Explicitly specify the call to the base class in the initialized list even if the default constructor is intended. This makes it more likely that errors can be detected during walk-throughs.

- Always initialize data members that are class variables using the initialization list, and initialize them in the order in which they are declared in the interface specification. This avoids unnecessary calls to default constructors and prevents unexpected side effects due to order of initialization.

- Initialize any primitive data types and pointers in either the initializer list or the body of the constructor.

Assignment operators

The assignment operators (=) should be explicitly defined for all classes. The automatic member-wise copy provided by the compiler is adequate only for shallow copy situations. Even if it works for initial development, it is likely to be inadequate when maintenance is performed. The following precautions should always be taken:

- The assignment operator should always return a reference to itself. The return type will be Type&, and the return value will be *this.

- The "other" assignment operators (+=, -=, *=, and so on) should conform to the same behavior as the primary assignment operator.

- Always check for self-assignment. The following example format should always be used for the simple assignment operator.

```
Type& Type::operator = (const Type& rhs)
{
  if (this != &rhs)
  {
    ... code to perform copy goes here ...
  }
  return *this;
}
```

- Assign base variables by invoking the base assignment operator. The following example indicates appropriate behavior:

```
DerivedType& DerivedType::operator = (const DerivedType& rhs)
{
  if (this != &rhs)
  {
    BaseType::operator = (rhs);
    ... code to perform copy goes here ...
  }
  return *this;
}
```

Casting

In general, all casts should now use one of the following explicit castings.

```
static_cast<>()
const_caset<>()
dynamic_cast<>()
reinterpret_cast<>()
```

The new style casts are preferred because they are more explicit and more visible.

const Methods

Make methods *const* when they do not change the object in any way.

```
int GetCount() const          { return m_count; }
```

If a method is conceptually *const* from the client's viewpoint, but internally the implementation needs to adjust some private data member, make the function *const* but cast away its *const*-like quality in the implementation.

```
int GetCount() const;

int MyClass::GetCount() const
{
MyClass* self = const_cast<MyClass*> this; // Cast away const-ness

if (self->m_countLoaded)
  self->LoadCount();

return m_count;
}
```

The keyword *mutable* can explicitly exempt data elements from *const*-like quality.

Using the *const* modifier

The *const* modifier is used in variable declaration to indicate that the variable cannot be modified after initialization. If the variable is declared with program, file, or function scope, it must be initialized when it is declared. When a pointer variable is declared, there are five possible options, as shown to the left.

When using reference variables, the reference may never be modified. The *const* modifier only refers to the referenced data.

When *const* is used as a keyword following a class-member function, it indicates that the member function will not modify any class member variables. The *const* keyword must be used in both the interface definition and the implementation.

Statement	Meaning
Foo* pFoo	Both the pointer and the referenced data may be modified
const Foo* pFoo	The pointer may be modified, but not the referenced data
const Foo& pFoo	The referenced data may not be modified
Foo* const pFoo	The referenced data may be modified, but not the pointer
const Foo* const pFoo	Neither the pointer or referenced data may be modified

const options for pointer variables

Type definitions and constants

If a constant or a type definition (*class, struct, enum,* or *typedef*) conceptually belongs to another class (that is, its only use is within the interface or implementation of another class), place it within the public, protected, or private scope of that class.

```
class Foo : public CObject
{
public:
  struct Bar
  {
    int   width;
    int   height;
  };

  typedef int ProgressLevel;
```

```
protected:
  typedef enum esriProgress
  {
   esriPIdle,
   esriPRunning,
   esriPCompleted
  } esriProgress;
};
```

Syntactic guidelines

The following syntactic guidelines make code more readable; they help maintainability and group development.

Indentation

Use tabs for indentation and set the tab size equal to two spaces. Do not replace tabs with spaces.

Implementation organization

Organize .cpp files as follows:

```
// Include precompiled header.
// Other includes.

// Macro definitions.

// Global data.
// Static class members.

// Constructor(s).
// Destructor.

// Public operations.
//   These should occur in the same order as the class definition.

// Protected operations.
//   These should occur in the same order as the class definition.

// Private operations.
//   These should occur in the same order as the class definition.
```

Avoid macros

Where possible, use *const* definitions instead of macros.

Instead of

```
#define MAX_COUNT    10
```

use

```
const int   g_maxCount   = 10;
```

Instead of

```
#define DEFAULT_USER TEXT("Moe")
```

use

```
const TCHAR* g_defaultUser = TEXT("Moe");
```

Comments

Use C++-style comments rather than C comments, unless you are writing a file that needs to be compiled by the C compiler.

```
// This is a C++ comment and should be used in all C++ code.
/* This is a C comment and should only be used in C code. */
```

White space

Arguments should be separated by a comma and single space. Spaces should not occur between the function name and the initial parenthesis or between the parentheses and the arguments.

```
result = MyFunction(count, name, &context);
```

Separate functions with at least one blank line.

```
void MyClass::MyFunction1()
{
}

void MyClass::MyFunction2()
{
}
```

Operators

Surround all operators with a space to the left and right.

```
size += sizeof(address);
i = j / 10 - 25;
```

Do not use extra spaces with these operators: !, #, ->, ., ++, and -.

```
if (!fileIsDirty) return;
#define DEBUG_ME
AfxGetApp()->ParseCommandLine(cmdInfo);
theConnection.Close();
if (i++ > 10 && j- < 100)
```

Operator precedence

Where operator precedence is not immediately obvious, use parentheses to indicate order of execution.

```
result = (i - (10 - count)) / 42;
```

Nested *if* statements

Avoid deeply nested blocks of *if* statements. They are difficult to read and debug.

```
if (i < 10)
{
  if (i != 5)
  {
    if (j == 42)
    {
      MyFunc(i, j);
    }
  }
}
```

Instead, use algorithmically equivalent *else-if* blocks that check the reverse conditions and are not deeply nested:

```
if (i >= 10)
{
}
else if (i == 5)
{
}
else if (j == 42)
{
  MyFunc(i, j);
}
```

Function declarations

Whenever possible, place function declarations on a single line:

```
bool ConnectToDatabase(const char* machineName, const char* databaseName);
```

If the declaration is too long, break it up into multiple indented lines, with all argument names positioned in the same column:

```
bool Connection::ConnectToDatabase(
        const char*        machineName,
        const char*        databaseName,
        const char*        userName,
        const char*        password,
        unsigned long      timeout,
        int&               connectionID);
```

When calling functions, try to place all arguments on a single line. If this is not possible, break them up into multiple lines, with each line indented one tab stop in from the leftmost character of the function name:

```
bool connectionResult = myConnection.ConnectToDatabase(machine, database,
                        user, password, timeout,
                        connectionID);
```

Global scope

Use :: to indicate global scope.

```
result = ::AfxMessageBox(errMsg, MB_OK, 0);
```

Brackets

Brackets should occupy an entire line by themselves.

```
for (int i = 0; i < 10; i++)
{
}

if (i <= 10)
{
}
else
{
}
```

Variable declaration

Where possible, declare variables where they are used, rather than grouping them together at the beginning of a function.

```
void MyFunc()
{
  . . .
 CString database;
 theDB.QueryDatabaseName(database);
  . . .
}
```

Where possible, declare loop variables in the first line of a *for* statement.

```
for (int i = 0; i < 10; i++)
{
  . . .
}
```

Avoid declaring multiple local variables on a single line.

```
int    connCount, connSuccess, passwordHandle, securityAttributes;
```

Instead, put them on separate lines, or at least group together only those that are logically related.

```
int    connCount, connSuccess;
int    passwordHandle, securityAttributes;
```

When declaring pointers, place the asterisk directly next to the type and leave a space before the variable, argument, or function name.

Instead of

```
char *myText;
```

use

```
char* myText;
```

Instead of

```
void *MyFunc(int *arg);
```

use

```
void* MyFunc(int* arg);
```

Bit-fields

Use bit-fields where possible to promote efficiency.

```
unsigned                m_flagA:1;
unsigned                m_flagB:1;
unsigned:0;                          // pads to integer boundary
```

Nested headers

Avoid including headers in other headers. Use forward declarations where possible.

```
class Bar;
class Foo
{
public:
```

```
   Bar*        m_bar;
};
```

Switch Statements

Construct a switch statement as follows. Note that the case and break keywords are indented one level, and the statements are all indented two levels.

```
switch (code)
{
 case firstCase:
   . . .
 break;

 case secondCase:
   . . .
 break;

 default:
   . . .
 break;
}
```

When an individual case contains many statements, move them into a separate function or enclose them with additional brackets.

```
case nthCase:
{
   . . .
}
break;
```

Always provide a default case within switch statements, even if the result is to log an error message and terminate. Always provide a break or return statement for each case path or an explicit comment on the justification for fall-through behavior.

Use references

Use references instead of pointers unless a NULL pointer value is needed. This is because the semantics of passing a pointer in C and C++ is very ambiguous.

```
void MyFunc(int* s);
```

The parameters of the function above could represent any of the following:

- A single *int*

- An array of *int* of a certain length

- An input-only parameter

- An output-only parameter

- Both an input and an output parameter

By using references (and const), these ambiguities are avoided.

```
void MyFunc(int& s);
void MyFunc(const int[]& s);
void MyFunc(const int& s);
void MyFunc(int& s);
```

Initialization

Use initialization syntax to initialize all data members to their default values, unless the initialization is conditional. Do not leave any members uninitialized. Place each data member on its own separate line.

```
MyClass()
  : m_count(0),
    m_name(0)
{
}
```

NULL initialization

Use 0 instead of *NULL*. In C++, the value 0 can be used to initialize any numeric or pointer variable.

Exceptions

A class should handle the exceptions thrown by objects that it uses and should define and throw its own exceptions when an unrecoverable situation occurs.

Avoid global data

Global data is inherently dangerous in a multithreaded environment. Where possible, try to embed all data in objects. In situations where data represents a shared resource, be sure to protect access to it with a critical section.

Avoid macros

C++ provides language constructs that in many cases obviate the need for macros. The constructs are integrated into the compiler and debugger. Thus, you gain type safety and ease of debugging.

Instead of doing this:

```
#define MyConstant 10
```

do this:

```
const long s_MyConstant = 10
```

Instead of doing this:

```
#define MyHelper(a, b) \
  a = 1;                \
  b = 2;                \
  a = b + a;            \
```

do this:

```
inline double MyHelper(double a, double b) {...}
```

About the only time you need macros is to adjust behavior in accordance with build settings:

```
#ifdef _DEBUG
OutputDebugString("I'm Here");
#endif
```

Using C++ with MFC and Win32

Standard C++ data types

Windows Type	Description
BYTE	unsigned char
SHORT	signed 16-bit integer
LONG	signed 32-bit integer
WORD	unsigned 16-bit integer
DWORD	unsigned 32-bit integer

Windows data types

Use standard C++ data types (*int, short, long, bool, void,* and others) unless the exact size of the data is critical to the behavior of the function, as with serialization or file I/O. In these cases, use Windows data types that are explicitly signed/unsigned and have an unambiguous size.

Use ASSERT and VERIFY

The *ASSERT* and *VERIFY* macros are invaluable debugging aids that should be used liberally throughout your code to check for entry and exit conditions or any other exceptional situations.

```
ASSERT(pWnd);
VERIFY(loading && userCount > 2);
```

Use *ASSERT* during the development phase to ensure that clients are adhering to rules for your interfaces. An assertion failure during development indicates that the contract between caller and callee has been broken.

The *VERIFY* macro does not go away in release builds. Use this only to check for catastrophic failure.

ASSERT and *VERIFY* behave identically in debug builds. However, in release builds, *ASSERT* compiles into nothing, whereas the arguments to *VERIFY* get treated as regular statements.

```
ASSERT(wnd && loading);                 // NOP in release build.
VERIFY(contents->LoadContextMenu());  // LoadContextMenu happens in
                                        // release build!
```

Use WIN32_ASSERT

If MFC is not available, consider using one of the string smart types covered later in this chapter.

Any Win32 call that sets an error code can use *WIN32_ASSERT* to throw an exception that displays the result of *GetLastError()*. However, this macro behaves the same as *VERIFY*, in that the side effect remains even in a release build, so be sure that this is the behavior you want.

Character strings

Consider using *CString* for all string data that you track and manipulate, instead of managing your own character arrays.

- Since *CString* is entirely *TCHAR*-based, Unicode is handled transparently with no extra work on your part.

- *CString* is very efficient with memory—where the same string value is passed from one *CString* to the next, no new storage is allocated until the second string is modified.

Application settings

Use the Windows registry to store and retrieve application settings. Do not use .ini files.

Windows and MFC function calls

Calls to all Windows and global MFC functions should use :: to indicate global scope.

Localization requirements

When developing an application intended for use in more than one language, a number of issues must be considered that will make the localization of the software an easier process.

Use string resources

Never place string constants in the code; instead, define them in a resource file from which they are loaded at runtime.

```
CString errorMessage;
errorMessage.LoadString(IDS_FILE_NOT_FOUND);
```

The only exceptions are debugging strings—they may reside directly in the code since they do not affect the released product and need not be localized.

Store all string constants together in a standard module to facilitate translation to other languages.

Support Unicode

All code should be Unicode-compliant; therefore, use arrays of *TCHAR* (instead of *char*) to represent character strings. Depending on the compilation settings, *TCHAR* expands either into single-character strings (ANSI) or wide-character strings (Unicode).

For string literals, use the *TEXT* macro to force the string or character to be Unicode compliant.

ANSI Function	Unicode-compliant macro
strlen	_tcslen
strcat	_tcscat
strncpy	_tcsncpy
strchr	_tcschr
strncmp	_tcsncmp
strstr	_tcsstr
atoi	_ttoi
atol	_ttol
splitpath	_tsplitpath

```
TCHAR dirSep = TEXT('\');
CString driveName(TEXT("C:"), 2);
```

Instead of the standard ANSI string functions, use the generic text mapping macros. A list of the more common string-handling functions, along with the correct macro to use, appears on the table to the left.

For a complete list of generic text-mapping macros, refer to the Visual C++ online help, in C/C++ Run-Time Library Reference, in the 'Generic Text Mappings' chapter.

SMART TYPES

Smart types are objects that behave like types. They are C++ class implementations that encapsulate a data type, wrapping it with operators and functions that make working with the underlying type easier and less error prone but transparent. When these smart types encapsulate an interface pointer, they are referred to as smart pointers. Smart pointers

DTC was an initiative from Microsoft to make COM C++ programming more like Visual Basic. To achieve this, DTC provides a set of classes and compiler extensions that shipped initially with Visual Studio 5.

work by working with the *IUnknown* interface to ensure that resource allocation and deallocation are correctly managed. They accomplish this by various functions, construct and destruct methods, and overloaded operators. There are numerous smart types available to the C++ programmer. The two main types of smart types covered here are defined by Direct-To-COM (DTC) and the Active Template Library. The relevant Direct-To-COM compiler extensions for the ArcObjects developer will be covered in the Active Template Library section later in this chapter.

Smart types can make the task of working with COM interfaces and data types easier since many of the API calls are moved into a class implementation; however, they must be used with caution and never without a clear understanding of how they are interacting with the encapsulated data type.

Direct-To-COM

The smart type classes supplied with DTC are known as the Compiler COM Support Classes and consist of:

- *_com_error*—this class represents an exception condition in one of the COM support classes. This object encapsulates the *HRESULT* and the *IErrorInfo* COM exception object.

- *_com_ptr_t*—this class encapsulates a COM interface pointer. See below for common uses.

- *_bstr_t*—this class encapsulates the *BSTR* data type. The functions and operators on this class are not as rich as the ATL *BSTR* smart type, hence this is not normally used.

- *_variant_t*—this class encapsulates the *VARIANT* data type. The functions and operators on this class are not as rich as the ATL *VARIANT* smart type, hence this is not normally used.

To define a smart pointer for an interface, you can use the macro *_COM_SMARTPTR_TYPEDEF* like this:

```
_COM_SMARTPTR_TYPEDEF(IFoo, __uuidof(IFoo));
```

The compiler expands this as such:

```
typedef _com_ptr_t<_com_IIID<IFoo, __uuidof(IFoo)> > IFooPtr;
```

Once declared, it is simply a matter of declaring a variable as the type of the interface and appending *Ptr* to the end of the interface. Below are some common uses of this smart pointer that you will see in the numerous C++ samples.

```
// Get a CLSID GUID constant
extern "C" const GUID __declspec(selectany) CLSID_Foo = \
   {0x2f3b470c,0xb01f,0x11d3,{0x83,0x8e,0x00,0x00,0x00,0x00,0x00,0x00}};

// Declare Smart Pointers for IFoo, IBar and IGak interfaces
_COM_SMARTPTR_TYPEDEF(IFoo, __uuidof(IFoo));
_COM_SMARTPTR_TYPEDEF(IBar, __uuidof(IBar));
_COM_SMARTPTR_TYPEDEF(IGak, __uuidof(IGak));

STDMETHODIMP SomeClass::Do ()
```

```
{
    // Create Instance of Foo class and QI for IFoo interface
    IFooPtr      ipFoo(CLSID_Foo);
    if (ipFoo == 0) return E_NOMEMORY

    // Call method on IFoo to get IBar
    IBarPtr      ipBar;
    HRESULT hr = ipFoo->get_Bar(&ipBar);
    if (FAILED(hr)) return hr;

    // QI IBar interface for IGak interface
    IGakPtr      ipGak(ipBar);

    // Call method on IGak
    hr  = ipGak->DoSomething()
    if (FAILED(hr)) return hr;

    // Explicitly call Release()
    ipGak = 0
    ipBar = 0

    // Let destructor call IFoo's Release
    return S_OK;
}
```

Active Template Library

ATL defines various smart types, as seen in the list below. You are free to combine both the ATL and DTC smart types in your code.

ATL smart types:

- *CComPtr*—class encapsulates a COM interface pointer by wrapping the *AddRef* and *Release* methods of the *IUnknown* interface.

- *CComQIPtr*—class encapsulates a COM interface and supports all three methods of the *IUnknown* interface: *QueryInterface, AddRef,* and *Release*.

- *CComBSTR*—class encapsulates the *BSTR* data type.

- *CComVariant*—class encapsulates the *VARIANT* data type.

- *CRegKey*—class provides methods for manipulating Windows registry entries.

- *CComDispatchDriver*—class provides methods for getting and setting properties and calling methods through an object's *IDispatch* interface.

- *CSecurityDescriptor*—Class provides methods for setting up and working with the Discretionary Access Control List (DACL).

This section examines the first four smart types and their uses. The example code below, written with ATL smart pointers, looks like the following:

```
// Get a CLSID GUID constant
```

```
extern "C" const GUID __declspec(selectany) CLSID_Foo = \
  {0x2f3b470c,0xb01f,0x11d3,{0x83,0x8e,0x00,0x00,0x00,0x00,0x00,0x00}};

STDMETHODIMP SomeClass::Do ()
{
  // Create Instance of Foo class and QI for IFoo interface
  CComPtr<IFoo>      ipFoo;
  HRESULT hr = CoCreateInstance(CLSID_Foo, NULL, CLSCTX_INPROC_SERVER,
                          IID_IFoo, (void **)& ipFoo);
  if (FAILED(hr)) return hr

  // Call method on IFoo to get IBar
  CComPtr<IBar>      ipBar;
  HRESULT hr = ipFoo->get_Bar(&ipBar);
  if (FAILED(hr)) return hr;

  // IBar interface for IGak interface
  CComQIPtr<IGak>       ipGak(ipBar);

  // Call method on IGak
  hr  = ipGak->DoSomething()
  if (FAILED(hr)) return hr;

  // Explicitly class Release()
  ipGak = 0
  ipBar = 0

  // Let destructor call Foo's Release
  return S_OK;
}
```

When reassigning an ATL smart pointer, a debug ASSERT is raised if the previous interface pointer is not explicitly released.

The most common smart pointer seen in the samples is the *DTC* type. In the examples below, which illustrate the *BSTR* and *VARIANT* data types, the *DTC* pointers are used. When working with *CComBSTR*, use the text mapping L"<string>", for example, L"name", to declare constant *OLECHAR* strings. *CComVariant* derives directly from the *VARIANT* data type, meaning that there is no overloading with its implementation, which in turn simplifies its use. It has a rich set of constructors and functions that make working with *VARIANTs* straightforward; there are even methods for reading and writing from streams. Be sure to call the *Clear* method before reusing the variable.

```
IFeaturePtr ipFeature(GetControllingUnknown()); // Get IFeature interface

// Get IFields interface and find index of Name field
long*        lIndex;
IFieldsPtr   ipFields;
```

```
HRESULT hr;

hr = ipFeature->get_Fields(&ipFields);
if (FAILED(hr)) return hr;

hr = ipFields->FindField(CComBSTR(L"Name"), &lIndex);
if (FAILED(hr)) return hr;

// Get OID change its type to String and set Name
// then set it back onto the feature
CComVariant   vID;
hr = ipFeature->get_Value(0, &vID);
if FAILED(hr)) return hr;

// Change its data type
hr = vID.ChangeType(VT_BSTR);
if (FAILED(hr)) return hr;

hr = ipFeature->put_Value(lIndex, vID);
if (FAILED(hr)) return hr;
hr = ipFeature->Store();
if (FAILED(hr)) return hr;
```

When working with *CComBSTR* and *CComVariant*, the *Detach()* function returns the underlying data type and should be used when passing a pointer as an [out] parameter of a method. The use of the *Detach* method is shown below.

```
void GetName(BSTR* name)
{
  CComBSTR bsName(L"FooBar");
  *name = bsName.Detach();
}
```

USEFUL C++ TIPS

These C++ tips are included here as tips for better development and should not be seen as a set of rules.

A better callback model

Instead of passing function pointers and opaque context data to implement callbacks, consider defining an abstract notification class that encapsulates the various notification events that can be fired. Clients can then subclass and instantiate this class to register for notification.

To see how this might work, consider the following example. It shows how to implement a traditional callback mechanism between an object (*Bar*) and a client (*Foo*).

```
class Foo : public CObject
{
public:
  Foo(Bar& bar) { bar.m_client = this; bar.m_clientProc = BarStub; }
```

```
    int Bar(char* string)  { printf("%s", string); }

    static int BarStub(void* client, char* string)
               { ((Foo*)client) ->Bar(string); }
};

class Bar
{
public:
  typedef int (*BarProc)(void* client, char* string);

  void*    m_client;
  BarProc  m_clientProc;

  void InvokeCallback()
    { if (m_clientProc) (*m_clientProc)(m_client, string); }
};
```

The *Bar* class defines the prototype for the callback function and has two member
variables: the address of the function to invoke and the object (stored as a *void**)
to pass along to the callback. Furthermore, at the *Foo* end, an additional static
stub routine (*BarStub*) is needed that casts the opaque pointer to a *Foo* object
before the real *Foo* method (*Bar*) is invoked. This seems like a lot of overhead for
such a simple task. It is also dangerous because it casts the *void** into a *Foo**.

However, there is a better way. By taking advantage of abstract classes in C++,
the relationship between *Foo* and *Bar* can be much more cleanly implemented:

```
class Foo : public CObject, public BarInterface
{
public:
  Foo(Bar& bar)        { bar.m_client = this; }
  int Bar(char* string) { printf("%s", string); }
};

class BarInterface
{
public:
  virtual int Bar(void* client, char* string) = 0;
};

class Bar
{
public:
  BarInterface*   m_client;

  void InvokeCallback() { if (m_client) m_client->Bar(string); }
};
```

The difference in this solution is that an abstract class, *BarInterface*, has been
introduced. It lives alongside the *Bar* class, like before, and contains virtual
methods that must be overridden by subclasses. These methods represent the
events (callbacks) that the *Bar* class sends. The events are handled when a client

provides a subclass that implements them. In this example, *Foo* derives both from *CObject* and from *BarInterface* and implements the *BarInterface* method, *Bar*.

There are several advantages to this approach. First of all, type safety is always maintained, unlike the former example; objects are never cast to *void** and then cast back to objects. Also, when a class provides multiple callbacks (which is often the case), they can all be encapsulated together in the abstract callback class. Some or all of them may be tagged with = 0, indicating that they must be overridden; this prevents clients from unwittingly implementing one callback while forgetting another, which is vital for proper functioning. One can also provide default implementations for the callbacks, should a subclass choose not to implement one. (Providing defaulted functions under the traditional model is difficult and error-prone.) Lastly, by using virtual functions directly, there is no need for static stub functions.

DEBUGGING TIPS IN DEVELOPER STUDIO

Visual C++ comes with a feature-rich debugger. These tips will help you get the most from your debugging session.

Backing up after failure

When a function call has failed and you'd like to know why (by stepping into it), you don't have to restart the application. Use the Set Next Statement command to reposition the program cursor back to the statement that failed (right-click on the statement to bring up the debugging context menu). Then, just step into the function.

Unicode string display

Set your debugger options to display Unicode strings (click the Tools menu, click Options, click Debug, then check the Display Unicode Strings check box).

Variable value display

Pause the cursor over a variable name in the source code to see its current value. If it is a structure, click it and bring up the QuickWatch dialog box (the Eyeglasses icon or Shift+F9) or drag and drop it into the Watch window.

Undocking windows

If the Output window (or any docked window, for that matter) seems too small to you, try undocking it to make it a real window. Just right-click it and toggle the Docking View item.

Conditional break points

Use conditional break points when you need to stop at a break point only once some condition is reached (a for-loop reaching a particular counter value). To do so, set the break point normally, then bring up the Breakpoints window (Ctrl+B or Alt+F9). Select the specific break point you just set and then click the Condition button to display a dialog in which you specify the break point condition.

Preloading DLLs

You can preload DLLs that you wish to debug before executing the program. This allows you to set break points up front rather than wait until the DLL has been loaded during program execution. (Project -> Settings... -> Debug -> Category -> Additional DLLs.) Then, click in the list area below to add any DLLs you wish to have preloaded.

Changing display formats

You can change the display format of variables in the QuickWatch dialog box or in the Watch window using the formatting symbols in the following table.

Symbol	Format	Value	Displays
d, i	signed decimal integer	0xF000F065	-268373915
u	unsigned decimal integer	0x0065	101
o	unsigned octal integer	0xF065	0170145
x, X	hexadecimal integer	61541	0x0000F065
l, h	long or short prefix for d, l, u, o, x, X	00406042, hx	0x0C22
f	signed floating-point	3./2.	1.500000
e	signed scientific notation	3./2.	1.500000e+00
g	e or f, whichever is shorter	3./2.	1.5
c	single character	0x0065	'e'
s	string	0x0012FDE8	"Hello"
su	Unicode string		"Hello"
hr	string	0	S_OK

To use a formatting symbol, type the variable name followed by a comma and the appropriate symbol. For example, if var has a value of 0x0065, and you want to see the value in character form, type var,c in the Name column on the tab of the Watch window. When you press ENTER, the character-format value appears: var,c = 'e'. Likewise, assuming that *hr* is a variable holding *HRESULTS*, view a human-readable form of the *HRESULT* by typing "hr,hr" in the Name column.

You can use the formatting symbols shown in the following table to format the contents of memory locations.

Symbol	Format	Value
ma	64 ASCII characters	0x0012ffac .4...0...".0W&.. .....IW&.0.:W..I ....".I.JO&.I.2 .."..I...0y....I
m	16 bytes in hex, followed by 16 ASCII characters	0x0012ffac B3 34 CB 00 84 30 94 80 FF 22 8A 30 57 26 00 00 .4...0....".0W&..
mb	16 bytes in hex, followed by 16 ASCII characters	0x0012ffac B3 34 CB 00 84 30 94 80 FF 22 8A 30 57 26 00 00 .4...0....".0W&..
mw	8 words	0x0012ffac 34B3 00CB 3084 8094 22FF 308A 2657 0000
md	4 double-words	0x0012ffac 00CB34B3 80943084 308A22FF 00002657
mu	2-byte characters (Unicode)	0x0012fc60 8478 77f4 ffff ffff 0000 0000 0000 0000

With the memory location formatting symbols, you can type any value or expression that evaluates to a location. To display the value of a character array as a string, precede the array name with an ampersand, *&yourname*. A formatting character can also follow an expression:

- *rep+1,x*
- *alps[0],mb*
- *xloc,g*
- *count,d*

To watch the value at an address or the value pointed to by a register, use the *BY, WO,* or *DW* operator:

- *BY* returns the contents of the byte pointed at.
- *WO* returns the contents of the word pointed at.
- *DW* returns the contents of the doubleword pointed at.

Follow the operator with a variable, register, or constant. If the *BY, WO,* or *DW* operator is followed by a variable, then the environment watches the byte, word, or doubleword at the address contained in the variable.

You can also use the context operator *{ }* to display the contents of any location.

To display a Unicode string in the Watch window or the QuickWatch dialog box, use the su format specifier. To display data bytes with Unicode characters in the Watch window or the QuickWatch dialog box, use the mu format specifier.

MFC Class Autoexpand

Microsoft Developer Studio has an autoexpand capability for Microsoft Foundation Class library classes. The string (or other information) between the braces ({ }) is automatically expanded.

Keyboard shortcuts

There are numerous keyboard shortcuts that make working with the Visual Studio editor faster. Some of the more useful keyboard shortcuts follow.

The text editor uses many of the standard shortcut keys used by Windows applications, such as Word. Some specific source code editing shortcuts are listed below.

Shortcut	Action
Alt+F8	Correct indent selected code based on surrounding lines.
Ctrl+]	Find the matching brace.
Ctrl+J	Display list of members.
Ctrl+Spacebar	Complete the word, once the number of letters entered allows the editor to recognize it. Use full when completing function and variable names.
Tab	Indents selection one tab stop to the right.
Shift+Tab	Indents selection one tab stop to the left.

Below is a table of common keyboard shortcuts used in the debugger.

Shortcut	Action
F9	Add or remove breakpoint from current line.
Ctrl+Shift+F9	Remove all breakpoints.
Ctrl+F9	Disable breakpoints.
Ctrl+Alt+A	Display auto window and move cursor into it.
Ctrl+Alt+C	Display call stack window and move cursor into it.
Ctrl+Alt+L	Display locals window and move cursor into it.
Ctrl+Alt+A	Display auto window and move cursor into it.
Shift+F5	End debugging session.
F11	Execute code one statement at a time, stepping into functions.
F10	Execute code one statement at a time, stepping over functions.
Ctrl+Shift+F5	Restart a debugging session.
Ctrl+F10	Resume execution from current statement to selected statement.
F5	Run the application.
Ctrl+F5	Run the application without the debugger.
Ctrl+Shift+F10	Set the next statement.
Ctrl+Break	Stop execution.

Loading the following shortcuts can greatly increase your productivity with the Visual Studio development environment.

Shortcut	Action
ESC	Close a menu or dialog box, cancel an operation in progress, or place focus in the current document window.
CTRL+SHIFT+N	Create a new file.
CTRL+N	Create a new project.
CTRL+F6 or CTRL+TAB	Cycle through the MDI child windows one window at a time.
CTRL+ALT+A	Display the auto window and move the cursor into it
CTRL+ALT+C	Display the call stack window and move the cursor into it
CTRL+ALT+T	Display the document outline window and move the cursor into it
CTRL+H	Display the find window.
CTRL+F	Display the find window. If there is no current Find criteria, put the word under your cursor in the find box.
CTRL+ALT+I	Display the immediate window and move the cursor into it. Not available if you are in the text editor window.
CTRL+ALT+L	Display the locals window and move the cursor into it.
CTRL+ALT+O	Display the output window and move the cursor into it
CTRL+ALT+J	Display the project explorer and move the cursor into it.
CTRL+ALT+P	Display the properties window and move the cursor into it.
CTRL+SHIFT+O	Open a file.
CTRL+O	Open a project.
CTRL+P	Print all or part of the document.
CTRL+SHIFT+S	Save all of the files, projects, or documents.
CTRL+S	Select all.
CTRL+A	Save the current document or selected item or items.

Navigating through online Help topics

Right-click a blank area of a toolbar to display a list of all the available toolbars. The Infoviewer toolbar contains up and down arrows that allow you to cycle through help topics in the order in which they appear in the table of contents. The left and right arrows cycle through help topics in the order that you visited them.

This section on the ATL cannot hope to cover all the topics that a developer working with ATL should know in order to become an effective ATL C++ developer, but it will serve as an introduction to getting started with ATL. ATL helps you implement COM objects, and it saves typing, but it does not excuse you from knowing C++ and how to develop COM objects.

This section will introduce ATL by working through the creation of a project that implements one object to Zoom In to the ArcMap display by a factor of 2. Each stage of the project is explained including how to automatically generate code. You are encouraged to look at the bibliography at the end of this chapter in order to seek more in depth reference materials.

ATL IN BRIEF

ATL is a set of C++ template classes designed to be small, fast, and extensible, based loosely on the Standard Template Library (STL). ATL provides a set of wizards that extend the Visual Studio development environment. These wizards automate some of the tedious plumbing code that all ATL projects must have. The wizards include, but are not limited to, the following:

- Application—used to initialize an ATL C++ project.

- Object—used to create COM objects. Both C++ and IDL code is generated, along with the appropriate code to support the creation of the objects at runtime.

- Property—used to add properties to interfaces.

- Method—used to add methods to interfaces; both the Property and Method Wizards require you to know some IDL syntax.

- Interface Implementation—used to implement stub functions for existing interfaces.

ATL provides base classes for implementing COM objects, as well as implementations for some of the common COM interfaces, including *IUnknown, IDispatch,* and *IClassFactory.* There are also classes that provide support for ActiveX controls and their containers.

ATL provides the required services for exposing ATL-based COM objects—these being registration, server lifetime, and class objects.

These template classes build a hierarchy that sandwiches your class. These inheritances are shown below. The *CComxxxThreadModel* supports thread-safe access to global, instance, and static data. The *CComObjectRootEx* provides the behavior for the *IUnknown* methods. The interfaces at the second level represent the interfaces that the class will implement; these come in two varieties. The *IxxxImpl* is an ATL-supplied interface that also includes an implementation; the other interfaces have pure virtual functions that must be fully implemented within your class. The *CComObject* class inherits your class; this class provides the implementation of the *IUnknown* methods along with the object instantiation and lifetime control.

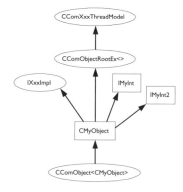

The hierarchical layers of ATL

This layer structure allows changes to be made that affect the interaction of the Object and COM, with only minimal changes to your source files. Only the inherited classes must change.

ATL AND DTC

In addition to the smart types covered earlier in this chapter, DTC provides some useful compiler extensions you can use when creating ATL-based objects. The functions __declspec and __uuidof are two such functions, but the most useful is the #import command.

COM interfaces are defined in IDL, then compiled by the Microsoft IDL compiler (MIDL.exe). This results in the creation of a type library and header files. The project uses these files automatically when compiling software that references these interfaces. This approach is limited in that when working with interfaces you must have access to the IDL files. As a developer of ArcObjects, you only have access to the type library information contained in the esriCore.olb or equivalent file. While it is possible to engineer a header file from a type library, it is a tedious process, especially when using a large type library such as the ESRI Object Library. The #import command automates the creation of the necessary files required by the compiler. Since the command was developed to support DTC when using it to import the ESRI Object Library, there are a number of parameters that must be passed so that the correct import takes place.

```
#import "esriCore.olb" \              \\ Typelib to generate C++ mapping
raw_interfaces_only, \                \\ Don't add raw_ to method names
raw_native_types, \                   \\ Don't map to DTC smart types
no_namespace, \                       \\ Don't wrap with C++ name space
named_guids, \                        \\ Named guids and declspecs
exclude("OLE_COLOR", "OLE_HANDLE") \\ Exclude conflicting types
```

This importing of the type library creates the smart pointers and CLSID constants seen in the section on Smart Types. The exclude ("OLE_COLOR", "OLE_HANDLE") is required because Windows defines these to be unsigned longs, which conflicts with the ArcObjects definition of long—this was required to support Visual Basic as a client of ArcObjects since Visual Basic has no support for unsigned types. There are no issues with excluding these.

HANDLING ERRORS IN ATL

If possible, you should always raise these COM exceptions to ensure that clients have access to this rich error information if required.

It is possible to return an *HRESULT* as the only signaling of failure in a method; however, as we saw with Visual Basic, not all development environments have comprehensive support for *HRESULT*s. In addition, simply returning *HRESULT*s to Visual Basic clients raises the "Automation Error – Unspecified Error". ATL provides a simple mechanism for working with the COM exception object in order to provide more context when methods fail.

When creating an ATL object, the Object Wizard has an option to support *ISupportErrorInfo*. If you toggle the option on, when the wizard runs your object will implement the interface *ISupportErrorInfo*, and a method will be added that looks something like this:

```
STDMETHODIMP MyClass::InterfaceSupportsErrorInfo(REFIID riid)
 {
  static const IID* arr[] =
   {
   &IID_IMyClass,
   };

  for (int i = 0; i < sizeof(arr) / sizeof(arr[0]); i++)
   {
   if (InlineIsEqualGUID(*arr[i], riid))
     return S_OK;
   }

  return S_FALSE;
 }
```

It is now possible to return rich error messages by calling one of the ATL error functions. These functions even work with resource files to ensure easy internationalization of the message strings.

```
// Return a simple string
AtlReportError(CLSID_MyClass, _T("No connection to Database."),
  IID_IMyClass, E_FAIL);

 // Get the Error Text from a resource string
AtlReportError(CLSID_MyClass, IDS_DBERROR, IID_IMyClass, E_FAIL,
  _Module.m_hInstResource);
```

LINKING ATL CODE

One of the primary purposes of ATL is to support the creation of small fast objects for distribution over the Internet. To support this, the ATL development team gives the developer a number of choices when compiling and linking the source code. Choices must be made about how to link or dynamically access the C runtime (CRT) libraries, the registration code, and the various ATL utility functions. If no CRT calls are made in the code, this can be removed from the link. If CRT calls are made and the linker switch *_ATL_MIN_CRT* is not removed from the link line, the error shown below will generate during the link stage of the build. When compiling a debug build, there will probably not be a problem; however, depending on the code written, there may be problems when compiling a release build. If you receive this error, either remove the CRT calls or change the linker switches.

```
LIBCMT.lib(crt0.obj) : error LNK2001: unresolved external symbol _main
ReleaseMinSize/History.dll : fatal error LNK1120: 1 unresolved externals
Error executing link.exe.
```

If the Utilities code is dynamically loaded at runtime, you must ensure that the appropriate DLL (ATL.DLL) is installed and registered on the user's system. The following table shows the various choices and the related linker switches.

	Symbols	CRT	Utilities	Registrar
Debug		yes	static	dynamic
RelMinDepend	_ATL_MIN_CRT _ATL_STATIC_REGISTRY	no	static	static
RelMinSize	_ATL_MIN_CRT _ATL_DLL	no	dynamic	dynamic

DEBUGGING ATL CODE

In addition to the standard Visual Studio facilities, ATL provides a number of debugging options that provide specific support for debugging COM objects. The output of these debugging options is displayed in the Visual C++ Output window. The *QueryInterface* call can be debugged by setting the symbol *_ATL_DEBUG_QI*, *AddRef*, and *Release* calls with the symbol *_ATL_DEBUG_INTERFACES*, and leaked objects can be traced by monitoring the list of leaked interfaces at termination time when the *_ATL_DEBUG_INTERFACES* symbol is defined. The leaked interfaces list has entries like the following:

```
INTERFACE LEAK: RefCount = 1, MaxRefCount = 3, {Allocation = 10}
```

On its own, this does not tell you much apart from the fact that one of your objects is leaking because an interface pointer has not been released. However, the *Allocation* number allows you to automatically break when that interface is obtained by setting the *m_nIndexBreakAt* member of the *CComModule* at server startup time. This, in turn, calls the function *DebugBreak()* to force the execution of the code to stop at the relevant place in the debugger. For this to work the program flow must be the same, but it can be very useful.

```
extern "C"
BOOL WINAPI DllMain(HINSTANCE hInstance, DWORD dwReason, LPVOID /
  *lpReserved*/)
{
  if (dwReason == DLL_PROCESS_ATTACH)
    {
      _Module.Init(ObjectMap, hInstance, &LIBID_HISTORYLib);
      DisableThreadLibraryCalls(hInstance);
      _Module.m_nIndexBreakAt = 10
    }
  else if (dwReason == DLL_PROCESS_DETACH)
    {
      _Module.Term();
    }
  return TRUE;    // ok
}
```

CREATING AN ATL COM SERVER AND OBJECT

This example will create a COM in-process server, a DLL, and add one object to that server that implements the *ICommand* interface to allow it to be used within ArcMap. Not all aspects of the process or options available will be explained; you are encouraged to use the Visual Studio online Help to find more information.

1. Start Visual C++.

2. Open the New Project form by clicking File and clicking New.

This example uses the project name DisplayCommands.

3. Click ATL COM AppWizard, then enter the project name and location of the source files. The project name will be the name given to the server file. Click OK.

Application Wizard

4. On the next dialog box, accept the defaults and click OK. Click OK on the Information dialog box. The skeleton project is now created and loaded into the editor.

5. Close inspection of the file view in the workspace window will show that an IDL file, along with a CPP file, has been created for the server, along with files to support precompiled header files and resources. The server file has the implementations of the exported DLL functions:

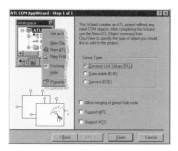

Server-type step in the Application Wizard

- *DllMain*

- *DllCanUnloadNow*

- *DllGetClassObject*

- *DllRegisterServer*

- *DllUnregisterServer*

The majority of these functions simply delegate to the *CComModule* class, defined as *_Module*.

```
/////////////////////////////////////////////////////////////////
// DllRegisterServer - Adds entries to the system registry

STDAPI DllRegisterServer(void)
{
    // registers object, typelib and all interfaces in typelib
    return _Module.RegisterServer(TRUE);
}
```

The IDL file only contains the library GUID and two importlibs for the standard COM API calls.

```
[
uuid(D8FBD63B-E107-43BE-A493-E71A8A467561),
version(1.0),
helpstring("DisplayCommands 1.0 Type Library")
]
library DISPLAYCOMMANDSLib
{
importlib("stdole32.tlb");
```

```
    importlib("stdole2.tlb");

};
```

6. With the Server code present the ATL COM objects can be added. This is done using the ATL Object Wizard. Start this wizard by clicking the Insert menu and clicking New ATL Object. Click Next to define a simple object.

The wizard can also be accessed via the ATL toolbar or the context menu in the class view of the workspace window.

7. Give the object a name and confirm that the automatically generated names are concise but informative.

This example names the coclass ZoomIn.

8. Click the Attributes tab and set the Interface type to Custom. This ensures that the interface *IZoomIn* inherits directly from *IUnknown* and not *IDispatch*, which is the default—in this way it is the same as all the other ArcObjects interfaces. While this is not necessary, it reduces the size of the COM object when it is instantiated for better memory management.

ATL Object Wizard

9. Click OK when finished. This creates three new files, ZoomIn.cpp, ZoomIn.h, and ZoomIn.rgs, and changes the existing files, DisplayCommands.idl, DisplayCommands.cpp, DisplayCommands.rc, and Resource.h.

The *ZoomIn* coclass and the *IZoomIn* interfaces are added to the IDL, and the coclass is added to the DisplayCommands.cpp file to the object map. This table has an entry for every coclass in the server. ATL makes extensive use of tables to hold information about the COM object and has various macros that initialize and add entries to these tables.

```
BEGIN_OBJECT_MAP(ObjectMap)
OBJECT_ENTRY(CLSID_ZoomIn, CZoomIn)
END_OBJECT_MAP()
```

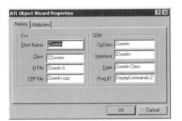

Name allocation step of the ATL Object Wizard

The three *ZoomIn* files that are specific to the *ZoomIn* class are the registry script, the header, and the implementation files. The registry script file ZoomIn.rgs is shown below. This registry script will be executed when the server is registered and unregistered. If required, you can enter other information into the registry by editing this script.

```
HKCR
{
  DisplayCommands.ZoomIn.1 = s 'ZoomIn Class'
  {
    CLSID = s '{52442231-E144-4B7C-94EF-70ABB17476E5}'
  }
  DisplayCommands.ZoomIn = s 'ZoomIn Class'
  {
    CLSID = s '{52442231-E144-4B7C-94EF-70ABB17476E5}'
    CurVer = s 'DisplayCommands.ZoomIn.1'
  }
  NoRemove CLSID
  {
    ForceRemove {52442231-E144-4B7C-94EF-70ABB17476E5} = s 'ZoomIn Class'
```

Defining the characteristics of your COM object

The registry script parser is very particular, hence care must be exercised when editing this file.

```
      {
        ProgID = s 'DisplayCommands.ZoomIn.1'
        VersionIndependentProgID = s 'DisplayCommands.ZoomIn'
        InprocServer32 = s '%MODULE%'
          {
          val ThreadingModel = s 'Apartment'
          }
        'TypeLib' = s '{D8FBD63B-E107-43BE-A493-E71A8A467561}'
        }
      }
    }
```

At this stage, the CPP implementation file is empty, except for some includes. The header file contains the C++ class definition. Notice the inheritance list of the class.

All publicly created classes (coclasses) must inherit from the class CComCoClass.

```
/////////////////////////////////////////////////////////////
// CZoomIn
class ATL_NO_VTABLE CZoomIn :
..public CComObjectRootEx<CComSingleThreadModel>,
..public CComCoClass<CZoomIn, &CLSID_ZoomIn>,
..public IZoomIn
  {
public:
..CZoomIn()
..{
..}

DECLARE_REGISTRY_RESOURCEID(IDR_ZOOMIN)

DECLARE_PROTECT_FINAL_CONSTRUCT()

BEGIN_COM_MAP(CZoomIn)
..COM_INTERFACE_ENTRY(IZoomIn)
END_COM_MAP()

// IZoomIn
public:
  };
```

A map is used to drive the query interface implementation. The interface map must list all the interfaces supported by the object. ATL's implementation of *QueryInterface* uses these entries in the COM_MAP. Two other macros are present: *DECLARE_REGISTRY_RESOURCEID (IDR_ZOOMIN)*, which binds the registry script to the class, and *DECLARE_PROTECT_FINAL_CONSTRUCT()*, which stops reference counting problems during the execution of the *FinalConstruct* method, primarily when aggregating objects.

10. Confirm that everything has been successful by pressing F7 to compile the project.

Interface Implementation Wizard

11. Click Class View in the Workspace browser.

Additional type libraries can be selected to access their interfaces.

Locate and check required interfaces and click OK.

This path will vary depending on your installation.

12. Select the class *CZoomIn* and display the context menu. This menu allows access to various wizards including the Method and Property Wizards. Click Implement Interface to display the list of available type libraries.

You will be implementing the *ICommand* interface defined within the ESRI Object Library; this means you must select this type library before continuing by clicking the Add Typelib button.

Next, select the *ICommand* interface and click OK. Changes are made to the ZoomIn.h file.

The Interface Implementation tool only updates the header file for the class. Therefore, the interface that has just been implemented should also be added to the coclass *ZoomIn* defined in the IDL file. You can also take this opportunity to mark the IUnknown interface as the default interface of the coclass.

```
coclass ZoomIn
{
[default] interface IUnknown;
interface IZoomIn;
interface ICommand;
};
```

If you try to compile the IDL file at this point (using the Workspace Browser context menu with the IDL file selected in the Workspace Browser), an error will be raised stating there is an unresolved forward declaration *ICommand*. The esriCore.olb file must be included in the library section of the IDL, in a similar way that the standard COM libraries are. Another cause of the forward declaration error that you may encounter in your ATL development is that an interface method uses a type included within the ESRI Object Library. By default, interface definitions are placed before the library section of the IDL file. To fix the compile error, the interface definition must be moved inside the library section after the importlib directive.

```
library DISPLAYCOMMANDSLib
{
importlib("stdole32.tlb");
importlib("stdole2.tlb");
importlib("C:\arcexe81\ArcObjects Developer Kit\Help\esriCore.olb");
```

13. The header file is where most of the code has been placed. Several changes must be made: some are required, while others are simply good coding practices.

The *ICommand* interface has been added to the inheritance list of the C++ class as well as the COM_MAP.

```
class ATL_NO_VTABLE CZoomIn :
  public CComObjectRootEx<CComSingleThreadModel>,
  public CComCoClass<CZoomIn, &CLSID_ZoomIn>,
  public IZoomIn,
  public ICommand
  {
```

```
public:
  CZoomIn()
  {
  }

DECLARE_REGISTRY_RESOURCEID(IDR_ZOOMIN)

DECLARE_PROTECT_FINAL_CONSTRUCT()

BEGIN_COM_MAP(CZoomIn)
  COM_INTERFACE_ENTRY(IZoomIn)
  COM_INTERFACE_ENTRY(ICommand)
END_COM_MAP()
```

14. The wizard also added the stub functions for the *ICommand* interface to the header file. These functions should be moved to the CPP file, leaving only the function prototypes in the header file. The listing below shows the changes required for each function.

The wizard creates this function in the header file.

```
STDMETHOD(get_Enabled)(VARIANT_BOOL * Enabled)
  {
    if (Enabled == NULL)
      return E_POINTER;

    return E_NOTIMPL;
  }
```

The header file prototype should look like this:

```
STDMETHOD(get_Enabled)(VARIANT_BOOL * Enabled);
```

The implementation file should look like this:

```
STDMETHODIMP CZoomIn::get_Enabled(VARIANT_BOOL * Enabled)
  {
    if (Enabled == NULL)
      return E_POINTER;

    return E_NOTIMPL;
  }
```

15. Next, the #import that imports the ESRI Object Library into the class must be edited. The reverse engineering of the type library takes a few seconds so, for more efficient compilation in the future, remove this #import line from the header and add it to the precompiled header file stdafx.h. Remember to exclude both OLE_COLOR and OLE_HANDLE from the import.

```
#pragma warning(push)
#pragma warning(disable : 4146)
#pragma warning(disable : 4192)
#import "C:\arcexe81\ArcObjects Developer Kit\Help\esriCore.olb" \
  raw_interfaces_only, \
  raw_native_types, \
  no_namespace, \
```

This path will vary depending on your installation.

```
    named_guids, \
    exclude("OLE_COLOR", "OLE_HANDLE")
#pragma warning(pop)
```

Several warnings will appear. These can be safely disabled using the #pragma statement. It is advisable to push and pop the warning stack so that the warnings are only disabled for this import.

16. Add a member variable to hold a bitmap resource used by the Command button; this involves changes to the *ZoomIn* header file and the creation of a Bitmap resource in the resource editor. From the main menu, click Insert, click Resource, then click Import. Navigate to the .bmp file you wish to use as the *ZoomIn* icon. Click OK when finished. Using the properties for the resource, set the name of the resource to "IDB_ZOOMIN". Add the following member variable to the ZoomIn.h header file.

```
private:
    HBITMAP          m_hBitmap;
```

This member variable is initialized in the class constructor and released in the class destructor. Notice the use of the *_Module* for access to the application instance handle. The IDB_ZOOMIN is a bitmap resource defined in the resource editor.

```
CZoomIn()
{
    m_hBitmap = ::LoadBitmap(_Module.m_hInst, MAKEINTRESOURCE(IDB_ZOOMIN));
}

~CZoomIn()
{
    DeleteObject(m_hBitmap);
}
```

17. Next, add a member variable that will hold a reference to the application. This reference is the *IApplication* interface, which is passed to the command when it is created.

```
IApplicationPtr        m_ipApp;
```

The member variable does not need to be initialized in the class initialization list since it is a smart pointer. Smart pointers are initialized, by default, to *NULL*. If this were a standard interface pointer, it would have to be initialized in the constructor's initialization list.

18. The final change to the header file involves the automatic registration of the class into the appropriate Component Category. This is an optional step, but one that makes installation of the server easier. It means that the end user will see the new command in the Customize dialog box the first time ArcMap is started after the DLL is registered.

For your convenience, a header file is provided that defines constants for all the CATIDs used by ArcGIS. You could also have retrieved this information from the registry and created your own constants.

This path will vary depending on your installation.

```
#include "C:\arcexe81\ArcObjects Developer Kit\Kits\CATIDS\h\ArcCATIDs.h"
```

The category map is used to drive this registration information:

```
BEGIN_CATEGORY_MAP(CZoomIn)
  IMPLEMENTED_CATEGORY(__uuidof(CATID_MxCommands))
END_CATEGORY_MAP()
```

19. Now all that is left to do is for the implementation code to be added to the cpp file.

Below are some of the methods of the *ICommand* interface, with a comment.

Note the use of *VARIANT_TRUE*.

```
STDMETHODIMP CZoomIn::get_Enabled(VARIANT_BOOL * Enabled)
{
  if (Enabled == NULL)
    return E_POINTER;

  *Enabled = VARIANT_TRUE;   // Enable the tool always

  return S_OK;
}
```

Note the use of the API calls used to create a *BSTR*.

```
STDMETHODIMP CZoomIn::get_Name(BSTR * Name)
{
  if (Name == NULL)
    return E_POINTER;

  *Name = ::SysAllocString(L"Exploring ArcObjects_Zoom In");
  return S_OK;
}
```

A simple cast is all that is required here to coerce the bitmap handle into an *OLE_HANDLE* variable.

```
STDMETHODIMP CZoomIn::get_Bitmap(OLE_HANDLE * Bitmap)
{
  if (Bitmap == NULL)
    return E_POINTER;

  *Bitmap = (OLE_HANDLE) m_hBitmap;

  return S_OK;
}
```

The *OnCreate* method is passed the *IDispatch* interface of the object. Using the *QueryInterface* support of the smart pointer, it is a simple matter to set the member variable to be the hook. The smart pointer handles the *QI*.

```
STDMETHODIMP CZoomIn::OnCreate(IDispatch * hook)
{
  m_ipApp = hook;
```

```
    return S_OK;
}
```

The *OnClick* method is implemented to zoom the display by a factor of two. There is no error checking to simplify the code.

```
STDMETHODIMP CZoomIn::OnClick()
{
  // HRESULT checking omitted for clarity
  IDocumentPtr      ipDoc;
  m_ipApp->get_Document(&ipDoc);

  IMxDocumentPtr    ipMxDoc(ipDoc);
  IActiveViewPtr    ipActiveView;

  ipMxDoc->get_ActiveView(&ipActiveView);

  IEnvelopePtr      ipEnv;
  ipActiveView->get_Extent(&ipEnv);

  ipEnv->Expand(0.5, 0.5, VARIANT_TRUE);

  ipActiveView->put_Extent(ipEnv);

  ipActiveView->Refresh();

    return S_OK;
}
```

20. Now, compile the project by pressing F7. Load the command into ArcMap and test.

The above example illustrates many of the tasks that you will perform when implementing COM objects using ATL. You are encouraged to look at the other samples included with the software.

This section looks at what is involved with packaging developments and deploying these on other machines. Exactly what must be packaged depends on the type of development; the typical steps are outlined below.

WHAT GETS PACKAGED

The obvious things to package are the server DLLs; however, you should also consider the following:

- With VBA developments, all code required is packaged in the *Map* document file.

- Type Libraries. If the DLLs do not have type information contained within them, the type libraries associated with the DLLs should also be packaged.

- Object Diagrams. Since you have developed using COM, other developers are free to work with your code in the same way that you work with ArcObjects. Object diagrams and help within the DLLs are good ways of supplying developers with information.

- Other files to package can include data files, help files, documentation, and so on.

Both Visual Basic- and ATL-generated DLLs contain type library information. Often when many DLLs are involved it is better to extract the type library information into one file, which is exactly what is done with the esriCore.olb. This means that when working with many DLLs, only one reference is required.

The server deployment is the most involved, so the rest of this section will cover the process of packaging and deploying a DLL server that contains one or more coclass implementations.

It is very important not to package any of the core ArcObjects DLLs or type libraries into your package. If you did this and the user uninstalled your software, there would be a danger that they might uninstall some of the files ArcGIS requires to function correctly.

JUST THE DLL

It is possible to simply give the user a copy of the DLL with instructions on how to register the DLL on the system. Normally, this involves the use of the Windows Utility RegSvr32.EXE. To register a DLL, the user must type a command line similar to that below.

```
RegSvr32 MyServer.DLL
```

To unregister a server, the command is run with the /U switch.

```
RegSvr32 /U MyServer.DLL
```

A dialog box appears when the operation completes. When running regsvr32 on several files, it is advisable to run it in silent mode with the /S switch—this disables the dialog box.

Depending on how the DLL was developed, registering the DLL may not be the only task. The coclasses contained with the DLL may have to be added to the appropriate component categories. If ATL was used, as shown in the ATL section, this can be made automatic on server registration. Other alternatives include the facility in the applications for commands; the Category Manager utility application; and the *ComponentCategoryManager* coclass, which is part of the framework subsystem or the creation of a registry script.

Included in the Utilities directory of the ArcObjects Developers Kit folder is a small registry script called reg_in_menu.reg. The registry script adds options to the Windows Explorer context menu when DLL, EXE, OLB, and OCX files are selected. The five options provide support for registering and unregistering the files. The context menu is shown in the figure to the left.

USING REGISTRY SCRIPTS

Although the Package and DeploymentWizard only works with Visual Basic projects, it is possible to create an empty project and add files of any type in order to package non-Visual Basic developments.

After the server is registered on the system, registry scripts provide a good mechanism for adding supplemental information about the server to the registry including the component category information. These registry scripts can either be written by hand or generated from the Compile and Register Visual Basic Add-In. A sample script is shown below. The lines beginning "[HKEY" must all be on one line in the file.

REGEDIT4

Step 1

```
; This Registry Script enters CoClasses Into their appropriate Component
Category ; Use this script during installation of the components

; CoClass: prjDisplay.ZoomIn ; CLSID: {FC7EC05F-6B1B-4A59-B8A2-37CE33738728}
; Component Category: ESRI Mx Commands
[HKEY_LOCAL_MACHINE\SOFTWARE\Classes\CLSID\{FC7EC05F-6B1B-4A59-B8A2-
37CE33738728}\Implemented Categories\{B56A7C42-83D4-11D2-A2E9-080009B6F22B}]
; CoClass: prjDisplay.ZoomOut ; CLSID: {2C120434-0248-43DB-AD8E-
BD4523A93DF8} ; Component Category: ESRI Mx Commands
[HKEY_LOCAL_MACHINE\SOFTWARE\Classes\CLSID\{2C120434-0248-43DB-AD8E-
BD4523A93DF8}\Implemented Categories\{B56A7C42-83D4-11D2-A2E9-080009B6F22B}]
```

USING AN INSTALLATION PROGRAM

Step 2

Most setup packages work well with registry scripts. For example, the Visual Basic Package and Deployment Wizard provides a straightforward way of creating setup programs. To create a setup program for your server follow the following steps:

1. Click the Start menu and click the Package and Deployment Wizard. The dialog box to the left is displayed. Select the Visual Basic project to be packaged and choose the package option. This will build the setup program and gather all files required by the setup program into a support directory for easy regeneration of the package. The wizard then performs some checks to ensure that the server created by the Visual Basic project is up-to-date with its source files. If not, you are given the option to recompile the project.

Step 3

2. Next, the package type is selected; this will normally be a Standard Setup Package.

3. The next step allows you to specify the folder where the package is created. This folder will contain the Setup executable and cabinet files and a supporting folder with all the files used to build the package.

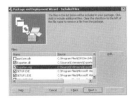

Step 4

4. Ensure that the files list shown doesn't include any Core ArcObjects files and that any other files required by the installation are added.

Step 5

Step 6

Step 7

Step 8

Step 9

Step 10

The additional files normally include a registry script to perform advanced registration, along with help files, and so on. Notice in the illustration that the esriCore.olb file has been unchecked, and the registry script has been added.

5. The next panel depends on whether a registry file was added in the previous step. If the file was added, the dialog box to the left is shown. If no file was added, go to step 6. The simplest option is to accept the default. This will cause the registry script to be executed when the setup program has registered the servers on the target machine but will not copy the registry script to the machine.

6. The wizard then asks if one or multiple cabinet files will be created. This depends on whether or not the setup program will span multiple floppy disks.

7. Next, follow a couple of panels asking for the Installation Screen title and where on the Windows Start menu the setup program should group files. Often when installing DLLs it is not appropriate to define an entry on the Start menu. Sometimes, even with DLLs, it may be desirable to add access to documents containing help information.

8. The next panel allows the user to define the location of the various files after they have been installed. Various macros are defined that will point to different locations, depending on the configuration of the target machine.

9. The next panel allows files to be marked as shared. Any files of the installation that will be used by other programs or installations must be marked as shared. This ensures that the uninstall program does not remove them automatically, which would break the other programs.

10. Finally, the Finish panel is displayed. Click Finish to assemble the package. The three files in the package directory—setup, cabinet, and list files—can then be given to third parties for a seamless install.

This is just one method of packaging COM developments. Whatever method you use, the setup procedure must be as simple as possible and involve as few decisions as possible in order to avoid user frustration.

This bibliography is not intended as a complete resource, but it does contain many of the everyday references that ESRI developers use when developing C++ and Visual Basic code and ArcObjects. It is not necessary to buy all these books before starting to program in COM; rather, look at these books and others that are available, and perhaps buy the one most suitable to your development track. The books listed below cover COM and developing with COM in Visual C++, mainly using ATL and Visual Basic. The books listed are from various companies; however, there are many other companies producing books for developers of COM components. You are encouraged to look at these other books, too.

ATL

Grimes, Richard. *ATL COM Programmer's Reference*. Chicago: Wrox Press Inc., 1998.

Grimes, Richard. *Professional ATL COM Programming*. Chicago: Wrox Press Inc., 1998.

Grimes, Richard, and Reilly Stockton, and Alex Stockton, and Julian Templeman. *Beginning ATL 3 COM Programming*. Chicago: Wrox Press Inc., 1999.

King, Brad and George Shepherd. *Inside ATL*. Redmond, WA: Microsoft Press, 1999.

Rector, Brent, and Chris Sells, and Jim Springfield. *ATL Internals*. Reading, MA: Addison–Wesley, 1999.

C++

Lippman, Stanley. *C++ Primer: Second Edition*. Reading, MA: Addison–Wesley, 1991.

Lippman, Stanley. *Inside the C++ Object Model*. Reading, MA: Addison–Wesley, 1996.

Meyers, Scott. *Effective C++: 50 Specific Ways to Improve Your Programs and Designs*. Reading, MA: Addison–Wesley, 1992.

Meyers, Scott. *More Effective C++: 35 New Ways to Improve Your Programs and Designs*. Reading, MA: Addison–Wesley, 1996.

Shepard, George and David Kruglinski. *Inside Visual C++: Fifth Edition*. Redmond, WA: Microsoft Press, 1998.

Stroustrup, Bjarne. *The C++ Programming Language: Third Edition*. Reading, MA: Addison–Wesley, 1997.

COM

Box, Don. *Essential COM*. Reading, MA: Addison–Wesley, 1998.

Chappell, David. *Understanding ActiveX and OLE: A Guide for Developers and Managers*. Redmond, WA: Microsoft Press, 1996.

Effective COM: 50 Ways to Improve Your COM and MTS-Based Applications. Edited by Don Box, Keith Brown, Tim Ewald, and Chris Sells. Reading, MA: Addison–Wesley, 1998.

Major, Al. *COM IDL and Interface Design.* Chicago: Wrox Press Inc., 1999.

Platt, David S. *Understanding COM+.* Redmond, WA: Microsoft Press, 1999.

Rogerson, Dale. *Inside COM: Microsoft's Component Object Model.* Redmond, WA: Microsoft Press, 1997.

SOFTWARE ENGINEERING

Gamma, Erich, and Richard Helm, and Ralph Johnson, and John Vlissides. *Design Patterns: Elements of Reusable Object-Oriented Software.* Reading, MA: Addison–Wesley, 1995.

The New Hacker's Dictionary: Second Edition. Edited by Eric Raymond. Cambridge, MA: MIT Press, 1993.

VBA

Cummings, Steve. *VBA For Dummies.* New York: IDG Books Worldwide, 1999.

Getz, Ken and Mike Gilbert. *VBA Developer's Handbook.* San Francisco: Sybex, 1997.

Lomax, Paul. *VB and VBA in a Nutshell: The Language.* Sebastopol, CA: O'Reilly & Associates, 1998.

VISUAL BASIC

Lewis, Thomas. *VB COM.* Chicago: Wrox Press Inc., 1999.

Microsoft Visual Basic 6.0 Programmer's Guide. Redmond, WA: Microsoft Press, 1998.

Pattison, Ted. *Programming Distributed Applications with COM and Microsoft Visual Basic 6.0.* Redmond, WA: Microsoft Press, 1998.

Wright, Peter. *Beginning Visual Basic 6 Objects.* Chicago: Wrox Press Inc., 1998.

WINDOWS DEVELOPMENT

Petzold, Charles. *Programming Windows 95: The Definitive Developer's Guide to the Windows 95 API.* Redmond, WA: Microsoft Press, 1996.

Shepard, George and Scot Wingo. *MFC Internals: Inside the Microsoft Foundation Class Architecture.* Reading, MA: Addison–Wesley, 1996.

3 Customizing the user interface

Eleanor Blades, Euan Cameron

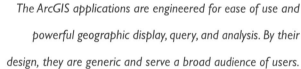

The ArcGIS applications are engineered for ease of use and powerful geographic display, query, and analysis. By their design, they are generic and serve a broad audience of users.

With the ArcObjects application framework, you have unlimited freedom to customize the user interface for your users' business needs. You can add new toolbars, buttons, tools, commands, and other elements. You can deliver advanced functions through custom commands. You can augment the functionality of applications through extensions, and you can selectively propagate customizations through templates.

This chapter discusses the application framework object model and how to employ these objects to deliver custom applications that are at once simple and powerful.

Application framework

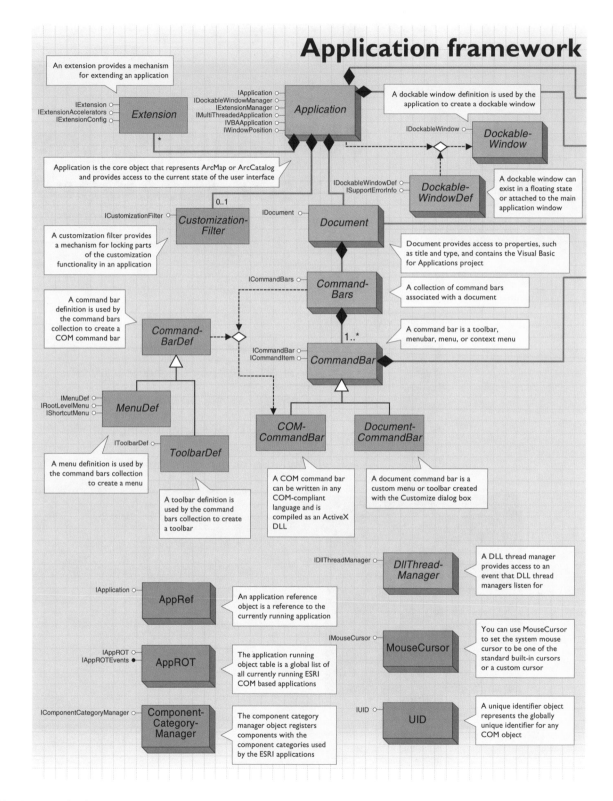

An extension provides a mechanism for extending an application

IExtension
IExtensionAccelerators
IExtensionConfig

Extension

IApplication
IDockableWindowManager
IExtensionManager
IMultiThreadedApplication
IVBAApplication
IWindowPosition

Application

A dockable window definition is used by the application to create a dockable window

IDockableWindow

Dockable-Window

Application is the core object that represents ArcMap or ArcCatalog and provides access to the current state of the user interface

IDockableWindowDef
ISupportErrorInfo

Dockable-WindowDef

A dockable window can exist in a floating state or attached to the main application window

ICustomizationFilter

Customization-Filter

IDocument

Document

A customization filter provides a mechanism for locking parts of the customization functionality in an application

Document provides access to properties, such as title and type, and contains the Visual Basic for Applications project

A command bar definition is used by the command bars collection to create a COM command bar

Command-BarDef

ICommandBars

Command-Bars

A collection of command bars associated with a document

A command bar is a toolbar, menubar, menu, or context menu

ICommandBar
ICommandItem

CommandBar

IMenuDef
IRootLevelMenu
IShortcutMenu

MenuDef

IToolbarDef

ToolbarDef

COM-CommandBar

Document-CommandBar

A menu definition is used by the command bars collection to create a menu

A toolbar definition is used by the command bars collection to create a toolbar

A COM command bar can be written in any COM-compliant language and is compiled as an ActiveX DLL

A document command bar is a custom menu or toolbar created with the Customize dialog box

IDllThreadManager

DllThread-Manager

A DLL thread manager provides access to an event that DLL thread managers listen for

IApplication

AppRef

An application reference object is a reference to the currently running application

IMouseCursor

MouseCursor

You can use MouseCursor to set the system mouse cursor to be one of the standard built-in cursors or a custom cursor

IAppROT
IAppROTEvents

AppROT

The application running object table is a global list of all currently running ESRI COM based applications

IComponentCategoryManager

Component-Category-Manager

The component category manager object registers components with the component categories used by the ESRI applications

IUID

UID

A unique identifier object represents the globally unique identifier for any COM object

objects

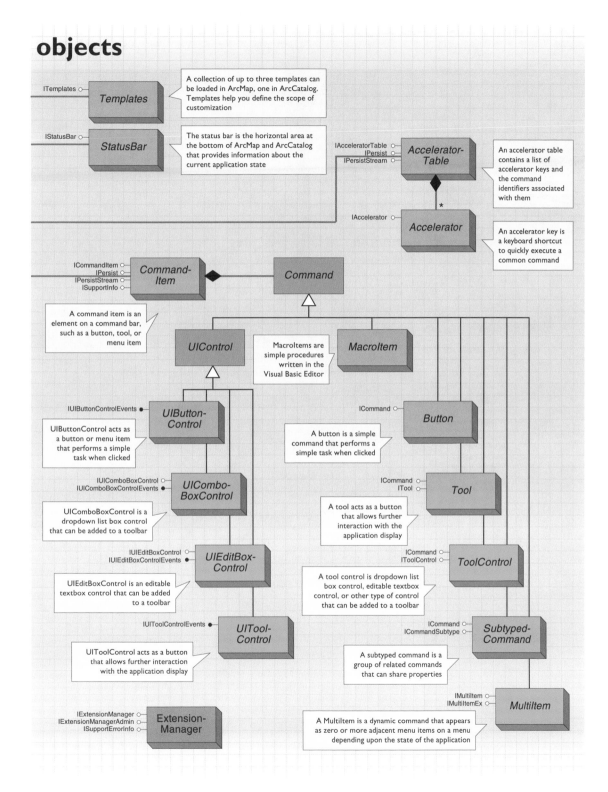

ITemplates ○—

Templates

A collection of up to three templates can be loaded in ArcMap, one in ArcCatalog. Templates help you define the scope of customization

IStatusBar ○—

StatusBar

The status bar is the horizontal area at the bottom of ArcMap and ArcCatalog that provides information about the current application state

IAcceleratorTable ○—
IPersist ○—
IPersistStream ○—

Accelerator-Table

An accelerator table contains a list of accelerator keys and the command identifiers associated with them

IAccelerator ○—

Accelerator

An accelerator key is a keyboard shortcut to quickly execute a common command

ICommandItem ○—
IPersist ○—
IPersistStream ○—
ISupportInfo ○—

Command-Item

Command

A command item is an element on a command bar, such as a button, tool, or menu item

UIControl

MacroItems are simple procedures written in the Visual Basic Editor

MacroItem

IUIButtonControlEvents ●—

UIButton-Control

UIButtonControl acts as a button or menu item that performs a simple task when clicked

ICommand ○—

Button

A button is a simple command that performs a simple task when clicked

IUIComboBoxControl ○—
IUIComboBoxControlEvents ●—

UICombo-BoxControl

UIComboBoxControl is a dropdown list box control that can be added to a toolbar

ICommand ○—
ITool ○—

Tool

A tool acts as a button that allows further interaction with the application display

IUIEditBoxControl ○—
IUIEditBoxControlEvents ●—

UIEditBox-Control

UIEditBoxControl is an editable textbox control that can be added to a toolbar

ICommand ○—
IToolControl ○—

ToolControl

A tool control is dropdown list box control, editable textbox control, or other type of control that can be added to a toolbar

IUIToolControlEvents ●—

UITool-Control

UIToolControl acts as a button that allows further interaction with the application display

ICommand ○—
ICommandSubtype ○—

Subtyped-Command

A subtyped command is a group of related commands that can share properties

IMultiItem ○—
IMultiItemEx ○—

MultiItem

IExtensionManager ○—
IExtensionManagerAdmin ○—
ISupportErrorInfo ○—

Extension-Manager

A MultiItem is a dynamic command that appears as zero or more adjacent menu items on a menu depending upon the state of the application

You can help your users work more quickly and efficiently by building a custom user interface that rearranges the standard user interface and adds new custom commands.

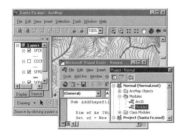

The customization framework in ArcObjects lets you programmatically customize the user interface of ArcMap, ArcCatalog, and other ArcGIS applications. You can manipulate the elements of the user interface—toolbars, menus, commands, and so on—and customize your application in accordance with the Windows user interface guidelines.

Most of the objects in the customization framework correspond to items in the various applications.

DOCUMENTS AND TEMPLATES

Whenever you are using ArcMap, you have a map document open. The document stores the map state, custom user interface settings, and a Visual Basic for Applications project.

Understanding documents and templates is the key to understanding customization with ArcObjects in ArcGIS applications.

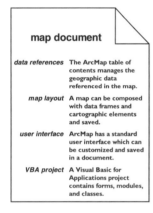

map document	
data references	The ArcMap table of contents manages the geographic data referenced in the map.
map layout	A map can be composed with data frames and cartographic elements and saved.
user interface	ArcMap has a standard user interface which can be customized and saved in a document.
VBA project	A Visual Basic for Applications project contains forms, modules, and classes.

Each document and template contains a persistent state of the user interface, a Visual Basic for Applications project, and other application-specific information, such as cartographic layouts for ArcMap documents.

The structure and function of documents and templates vary from one application to another. Because of this variation, it is best to discuss them in the context of each respective application. ArcMap employs the full structure of documents and templates.

CUSTOMIZING ARCMAP

You can customize ArcMap in several ways:

- You can add references to geographic data and define how the data is displayed.

- You can create a map layout with a spatial reference and ancillary cartographic elements.

- You can add, remove, or rearrange elements of the standard user interface.

- You can write code in a Visual Basic for Applications project.

All customization in ArcMap is stored in a map document or a map template.

The changes you make to the ArcMap table of contents, the layout of a map, the toolbars and their command items, and the VBA code you write all get saved to the map document.

A map document can reside anywhere on your file system; it has a file extension of .mxd.

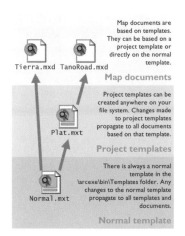

Map documents are based on templates. They can be based on a project template or directly on the normal template.

Map documents

Project templates can be created anywhere on your file system. Changes made to project templates propagate to all documents based on that template.

Project templates

There is always a normal template in the \arcexe\bin\Templates folder. Any changes to the normal template propagate to all templates and documents.

Normal template

ArcMap automatically creates a Normal template if one does not exist. If you have applied unintended customizations, such as removing toolbars and command items, you can simply remove the Normal.mxt file and a new one with the standard user interface will be generated. This is easier than undoing a set of unintended customizations.

This is how the three loaded templates in ArcMap—normal, project template, and project (current document)—appear in the VBA project explorer.

Map templates

You can use map templates to disseminate customization throughout an organization—globally, by project, or by document.

A map template is a kind of map document. In nearly every respect, map templates are structurally identical to map documents. The functional difference is that ArcMap recognizes and uses templates as a starting point to create new map documents. This is similar to how you work with templates in Microsoft Office applications.

Any customization of the user interface or the VBA project becomes part of the newly created map document. Furthermore, any changes to a template will propagate to template-based documents when they are next loaded.

There are three levels of templates and documents in ArcMap. You can save changes to any level to control how widely your customizations are used.

Custom map documents

When you are working with a map, you are setting references to data, designing a map layout, customizing the user interface, and writing VBA code, all with the lifetime of the document.

Selective customization with project templates

Other projects and other users can share the customizations that you make through templates. A template is a kind of map document that is specified to be a starting point for a new map document. The new map document will inherit all of the customizations from the template (data references, map layout, user interface state, and VBA project).

Global customizations with the normal template

ArcMap has a special template called Normal that stores any personal settings you have made to the user interface that you want loaded every time you start ArcMap. Any customizations that you save to the Normal template will get propagated to all the other map documents when they are next opened.

When you first start ArcMap after installing the software, a Normal template is automatically created and put in your profiles location, which is one of the following folders depending on your operating system.

For Windows NT®:

`C:\WINNT\Profiles\<your username>\Application Data\ESRI\ArcMap\Templates\`

For Windows 2000:

`C:\Documents and Settings\<your username>\Application Data\ESRI\ArcMap\Templates\`

This is the default Normal template that contains all the standard toolbars and commands and places the toolbars and the table of contents in their default positions. Any customizations that you save in your Normal template get saved to this file.

If you want to make changes that appear every time you open ArcMap, save them in the Normal template.

Suppose your administrator has custom toolbars or tools to which she would like everyone in your organization to have access. Your administrator could create a customized Normal template and allow everyone in your organization to use that Normal template instead of the default Normal template. To accomplish this, your administrator would customize her Normal template and then copy that Normal.mxt file to the \ArcGIS\arcexe81\bin\Templates folder. Everyone would then start with this Normal template instead of the default Normal template. The following is an explanation of how this works.

If there is no Normal.mxt file in your profiles location when you start ArcMap, the application will look in the \ArcGIS\arcexe81\bin\Templates folder. If a Normal.mxt file exists in the \ArcGIS\arcexe81\bin\Templates folder, that file will be copied to your profiles location and will then be treated as your personal Normal template. Therefore, you start off with a copy of your organization's customized Normal template, but from that point on you can save your own customizations to it.

If a Normal.mxt file is not found in your profiles location or in the \ArcGIS\arcexe81\bin\Templates folder, then a new default Normal.mxt file will be created and placed in your profiles location.

CUSTOMIZING ArcCatalog

You can customize ArcCatalog in several ways:

- You can add, remove, or rearrange elements of the standard user interface.

- You can write code in a Visual Basic for Applications project.

ArcCatalog does not employ the full structure of documents and templates like ArcMap does. The ArcCatalog application does not use documents or base templates; it only uses a Normal template. Therefore, all customizations to the ArcCatalog user interface are stored in the Normal template.

When you first start ArcCatalog after installing the software, a Normal template called Normal.gxt is automatically created and put in your profiles location, which is one of the following folders depending on your operating system.

For Windows NT:

`C:\WINNT\Profiles\<your username>\Application Data\ESRI\ArcCatalog\`

For Windows 2000:

`C:\Documents and Settings\<your username>\Application Data\ESRI\ArcCatalog\`

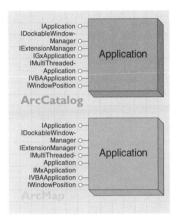

ArcCatalog

Application

ArcMap

Application is the core object that represents an ArcGIS application (ArcMap, ArcCatalog, or other). Through this object, you can access properties and methods for the application and navigate to other elements, such as the document, window handle, and status bar.

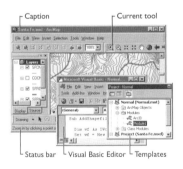

- Caption
- Current tool
- Status bar
- Visual Basic Editor
- Templates

Extensions are subsystems that add significant functionality to an application. ArcGIS Spatial Analyst is an example of an extension to an application.

Documents contain custom user interface settings, a VBA project, and other settings, such as layers and map extent. You can open or save documents.

Each running ArcGIS application is represented by an instance of an *Application* object—ArcCatalog by *Application* from the ESRI ArcCatalog object library (esriGx.olb), and ArcMap by *Application* from the ESRI ArcMap object library (esriMx.olb).

The *IGxApplication* is documented in Chapter 7, 'Working with the Catalog'. The *IMxApplication* is documented in Chapter 4, 'Composing maps'. The *IApplication* interface is shared by both *Application* classes.

The *Application* object is instantiated in VBA when an ArcGIS application is launched. It is always available as a global object, and you can inspect properties of *Application* in this way:

```
MsgBox Application.Caption
```

You can also launch the ArcMap application in Visual Basic or other COM-compliant language. For example, to launch ArcMap from VB, create a new project, add a reference to the ESRI core library (esriCore), add this code to a Sub, then execute the Sub:

```
Dim m_doc As IDocument
Set m_doc = New MxDocument 'start ArcMap
```

Visual C++ programmers use the #import directive to obtain type information. Importing esriCore.olb will automatically build "smart pointer" classes for ArcGIS interfaces. With smart pointers, an instance of ArcMap can then be created in C++ as follows:

```
// Example : Creating an instance of ArcMap
IDocumentPtr ipDoc (CLSID_MxDocument);
```

IApplication : IDispatch	Provides access to members that query or modify the application.
■—● Caption: String	The caption of this application.
■—□ CurrentTool: ICommandItem	The currently selected tool.
■— Document: IDocument	The document that is currently loaded in the application.
■— hWnd: Long	The handle of the application's window.
■— Name: String	The name of this application.
■— StatusBar: IStatusBar	The statusbar of this application.
■— Templates: ITemplates	The templates collection.
■— VBE: Object	The Visual Basic Environment.
■—■ Visible: Boolean	Indicates if the application window is visible.
← FindExtensionByCLSID (in extensionCLSID: IUID) : IExtension	Finds an extension by its CLSID.
← FindExtensionByName (in extensionName: String) : IExtension	Finds an extension by its name.
← IsDialogVisible (in dialogID: Long) : Boolean	Indicates if the specified dialog is visible in the application.
← LockCustomization (in Password: String, custFilter: ICustomizationFilter)	Locks the application's user interface against any customizations.
← NewDocument (selectTemplate: Boolean, templatePath: String)	Creates a new document in this application.
← OpenDocument (Path: String)	Opens a document in this application.
← PrintDocument	Displays the Print dialog.
← PrintPreview	Displays how the document will look like when it is printed.
← RefreshWindow	Redraws the application window.
← SaveAsDocument (saveAsPath: String, saveAsCopy: Boolean)	Saves the document that is currently open in this application to a different file.
← SaveDocument (saveAsPath: String)	Saves the document that is currently open in this application.
← ShowDialog (in dialogID: Long, bShow: Variant) : Variant	Displays the specified dialog in the application.
← Shutdown	Terminates the application.
← UnlockCustomization (in Password: String)	Unlocks previous user interface customization lock.

The *IApplication* interface provides access to the *Document* object, the extensions, the *StatusBar* object, the *Templates* object, the currently selected tool, and the Visual Basic Editor.

There are several methods that allow you to open, save, and print documents; lock and unlock the application from user customizations; display dialog boxes; and exit the application.

The *NewDocument, OpenDocument, PrintDocument, PrintPreview,* and *SaveAsDocument* methods are not implemented in ArcCatalog. The *SaveDocument* method in ArcCatalog saves the Normal template rather than saving a document.

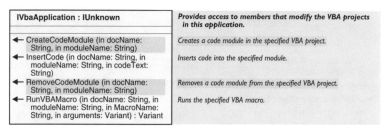

The *Application* object implements the *IVbaApplication* interface, which allows you to programmatically insert, remove, and run VBA code without actually opening the Visual Basic Editor.

To get access to this interface, do a *QueryInterface* (*QI*) on *Application*. The *IVbaApplication* interface has methods to create a new module, insert code into a specific module, remove a module, and run a macro.

The following code shows how to create a new VBA module, insert a VBA macro into that module, and run the macro.

```
Dim pVbaApp As IVbaApplication
Dim s As String
Set pVbaApp = Application
pVbaApp.CreateCodeModule "Project", "MyModule"
s = "Public Sub MyMacro" & vbNewLine & _
    " Msgbox Application.Document.Title" & vbNewLine & "End Sub"
pVbaApp.InsertCode "Project", "MyModule", s
pVbaApp.RunVBAMacro "Project", "MyModule", "MyMacro", Nothing
```

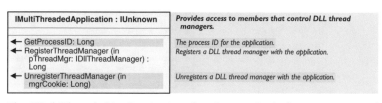

For more information on threading, read Threads, Apartments, and Marshalling in Chapter 2, 'Developing with ArcObjects'.

The *IMultiThreadedApplication* interface has methods for registering and unregistering thread managers with the application and returning the process ID of the application.

Multithreading refers to a software configuration where independent paths of execution are in use simultaneously in an application. Each thread has its own stack and its own CPU state.

The *Application* object implements the *IMultiThreadedApplication* interface, which provides a simple callback mechanism for registering user created thread manager objects. A thread manager object is any object that implements the *IDllThreadManager* interface. The thread manager object will be notified prior to application shutdown so that all currently running threads can be exited cleanly before the *Application* process actually shuts down.

If you are developing components that will create threads and will be used in any of the ArcGIS application processes, the DLL that contains these components must also contain an object that implements *IDll-ThreadManager*. Also, you must use the *IMultiThreadedApplication* interface to register this thread manager object with that application.

IDllThreadManager : IUnknown	Provides access to an event that DLL thread managers listen for.
← OnShutdown	Occurs when the application is shutting down. DLL threads should be terminated upon receiving this message.

The *IDllThreadManager* interface has an *OnShutdown* method that notifies the DLL thread manager object that the application is shutting down so that the DLL thread manager can terminate any threads that were created by the components in that DLL.

IWindowPosition : IUnknown	Provides access to members that query or modify a window's position, size and state.
■—■ Height: Long	The height of the window.
■—■ Left: Long	The distance between the internal left edge of the window and screen.
■—■ State: tagesriWindowState	The state of the window.
■—■ Top: Long	The distance between the internal top edge of the window and screen.
■—■ Width: Long	The width of the window.
← Move (in Left: Long, in Top: Long, Width: Long, Height: Long)	Moves and optionally resizes the windows in a single function.

The *IWindowPosition* interface has methods to move and resize a window. Any window object can implement this interface. All the ArcGIS application windows implement this interface; you can *QI* from the application to *IWindowPosition*.

The *Left* and *Top* properties determine the position of the window in screen coordinates relative to the upper-left corner of the display screen.

The *Height* and *Width* properties determine the size of the window.

Use the *Move* method to set these four properties at the same time.

Enumeration tagesriWindowState	Application window states.
0 - esriWSNormal	The window is restored.
1 - esriWSMinimize	The window is minimized.
2 - esriWSMaximize	The window is maximized.

The *esriWindowState* enumeration specifies whether the window is normal, minimized, or maximized.

The following code in the *ThisDocument* code window in the Normal template forces the application window to always open with the specified size and position.

```
Private Function MxDocument_NewDocument() As Boolean
  Dim pWindPos As IWindowPosition
  Set pWindPos = Application
  pWindPos.Move 10, 10, 600, 500
End Function


Private Function MxDocument_OpenDocument() As Boolean
  Dim pWindPos As IWindowPosition
  Set pWindPos = Application
  pWindPos.Move 10, 10, 600, 500
End Function
```

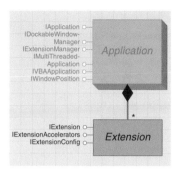

An extension provides a mechanism for extending an application.

Extensions provide the developer with a powerful mechanism for extending the core functionality of the ArcGIS applications. An extension can provide a toolbar with new tools, listen for and respond to events, perform feature validation, and so on.

Extensions act as a central point of reference for developers when they are creating commands and tools for use within the applications. Often these commands and tools must share data or access common UI components. An extension is the logical place to store this data and develop the UI components. The main reason for this is that there is only ever one instance of an extension per running application and, given an *IApplication* interface, it is always possible to locate the extension and work with it.

Any extension that is registered with an application is automatically loaded and unloaded by the application; the end user does nothing to load or unload. For example, an extension that has been added to the "ESRI Mx Extensions" component category will be started when ArcMap is started and shut down when ArcMap is shut down.

When customizing an ArcGIS application, you can deliver these customizations in a generic or locked down user environment. Generic and locked down environments are often referred to as Extension and OEM products, respectively.

These two environments, Generic and Locked Down, are often referred to as Extension and OEM products. There is much more to the creation of an OEM product besides writing software, which is beyond the scope of this book. For more details on OEM development, you should contact ESRI.

With a generic environment, you, as a developer, have no control over the end user's environment. Your customizations must live harmoniously with potentially many other ArcGIS customizations that the user has installed. This is the type of extension that ESRI supplies. With a locked down environment, you, as the developer of that environment, have complete control over the setup of the application and how the user interacts with that environment.

Because the mechanisms for customization are the same for both of the above environments, it is important to follow a set of rules when developing a generic application. If, as a developer, you initially develop customizations for a locked down environment for a custom application, you cannot deliver these customizations to a generic ArcGIS user. In order to deliver this functionality to generic ArcGIS users, you must develop a generic solution in addition to the locked down solution.

GENERIC APPLICATION DEVELOPMENT RULES

If in doubt about whether a rule applies to your development or not, you should not remove anything that does not belong to you. In this way, generic customizations act as extensions to a user's ArcGIS system. Below are the rules for creating generic customizations:

Extensions are the best mechanism for delivering professionally built application customizations. However, any customizations you make must follow the rules given here to ensure that conflicting customizations are not created.

- Do not remove UI components, including buttons, tools, and property pages, that do not belong to you.

- Your extension should not use customization filters unless the filter is applied to a specific document.

- Do not make changes in document persistence that will invalidate previously saved documents.

- Do not abort document events by returning *True* from these events.

- If your extension works with a license, your extension must implement *IExtensionConfig* and follow the conventions used by the ArcGIS extension. For more information, refer to the discussion on *IExtensionConfig* later in this chapter.

LOCKED DOWN APPLICATION DEVELOPMENT RULES

Although none of the generic application rules apply to the creation of a locked down application, it is good programming practice to write your code defensively. That way, the code will fail gracefully if a conflict does occur.

As an example, extensions designed for locked applications can use customization filters. However, when applying a customization filter you should always be prepared for the case of a filter already being in operation. The following code displays an error message if the attempt to apply the customization filter fails.

```
Private Function m_pDoc_OpenDocument() As Boolean
  On Error GoTo FilterErr

  ' Reset the Lock when a document is opened.
  m_pApp.LockCustomization "mylock", m_MyFilter
  Exit Function
FilterErr:
  MsgBox "Attempt To Lock Document With Filter Failed", _
    vbOKOnly + vbExclamation, "Extension Error"
End Function
```

WORKING WITH AND CREATING EXTENSIONS

The *Application* object implements the *IExtensionManager* interface, which has properties to get a reference to a particular extension and to get a count of how many extensions are currently loaded.

IExtensionManager : IUnknown	Provides access to members that query extension.
■— Extension (in Index: Long) : IExtension	*The extension at the specified index.*
■— ExtensionCount: Long	*The number of extensions loaded in the application.*

To get access to the application extension manager, do a *QI* for *IExtensionManager* on *Application*. Note that other types of objects can also implement *IExtensionManager*. For example, the Editor toolbar in ArcMap is an extension that manages editor extensions. Therefore, the *Editor* object also implements *IExtensionManager*.

This VBA code uses the application extension manager to loop through all of the extensions that are currently loaded in the application, then reports the name of the extensions.

```
Dim pExtMgr As IExtensionManager, pExt As IExtension
Dim i as Integer
Set pExtMgr = Application
For i = 0 To pExtMgr.ExtensionCount - 1
```

```
    Set pExt = pExtMgr.Extension(i)
    MsgBox pExt.Name
  Next
```

To ensure that there is not the potential for a name clash, the use of the FindExtensionByCLSID method is encouraged.

This is not the only way to get a reference to an extension; the *IApplication* interface has *FindExtensionByCLSID* and *FindExtensionByName* methods.

To create your own extension, implement the *IExtension* interface. You can also optionally implement *IExtensionConfig* and *IExtensionAccelerators*.

IExtension : IUnknown	*Provides access to members that define an extension.*
▬— Name: String	*The name of the extension.*
◀— Shutdown	*Shuts down the extension.*
◀— Startup (in initializationData: Variant)	*Starts up the extension with the given initialization data.*

For more information on creating COM components, see Chapter 2, 'Developing with ArcObjects'.

The *IExtension* interface allows you to set the name of the extension and specify what action takes place when the extension is started or shut down.

The following code demonstrates how to create a custom ArcMap extension that can perform some action when the document events occur. When this extension is loaded, a message box appears when a new document is created and when a document is opened.

To use this extension in ArcMap, register it in the "ESRI Mx Extensions" component category.

```
Implements IExtension

Dim m_pApp As IApplication
' Need to listen for the MxDocument events
Dim WithEvents m_pDocEvents As MxDocument

Private Property Get IExtension_Name() As String
  IExtension_Name = "My Extension"
End Property

Private Sub IExtension_Shutdown()
  ' Clear the reference to the Application and MxDocument
  Set m_pApp = Nothing
  Set m_pDocEvents = Nothing
  Set m_pDoc = Nothing
End Sub

Private Sub IExtension_Startup(initializationData As Variant)
  Set m_pApp = initializationData
  'Start listening for the MxDocument events.
  Set m_pDocEvents = m_pApp.Document
  Set m_pDoc = m_pApp.Document
End Sub

Private Function pDoc_NewDocument() As Boolean
  MsgBox "Creating a new document."
End Function
```

```
Private Function pDoc_OpenDocument() As Boolean
  MsgBox "Opening a document"
End Function
```

The Extensions dialog box allows you to turn extensions on and off.

IExtensionConfig : IUnknown	Provides access to members that describe an extension.
■— Description: String	Detailed description of the extension.
■— ProductName: String	Name of the extension.
■—■ State: esriExtensionState	The state of the extension.

If you want your extension to be exposed in the Extensions dialog box, you should implement the *IExtensionConfig* interface. The Extensions dialog box allows users to turn extensions on and off. The *IExtensionConfig* interface provides the Extension dialog box with the name of the extension and a description of the extension; it also specifies the state of the extension.

Enumeration esriExtensionState	Extension availability states.
1 - esriESEnabled	Enabled for use.
2 - esriESDisabled	Disabled by the user.
4 - esriESUnavailable	Unavailable - not licensed.

The *esriExtensionState* enumeration is used to specify whether the extension is enabled, disabled, or unavailable. The state of the extension is user-based. When an extension is installed, its default state is unchecked (*esriESDisabled*), and the user must knowingly check the extension on in the Extensions dialog box.

With a custom extension, you have full control over what happens when your extension is turned on or off. However, it is a good idea to follow the same design as the ArcGIS extensions. The following notes explain how the ArcGIS extensions work when they are turned on or off in the Extensions dialog box.

When a user checks one of the ArcGIS extensions in the Extensions dialog box, the following things occur:

- The checked state of the extension is saved to the user settings in the registry. (This occurs automatically by the application—it is not something a developer needs to do.)

- The extension requests a license from the license manager.

- If a license is available, the tools are enabled on the toolbar delivered by the extension.

- If a license is not available, the tools are disabled on the toolbar delivered by the extension. Also, text stating that the license is unavailable is displayed to the right of the extension name in the Extensions dialog box.

When a user unchecks one of the ArcGIS extensions in the Extensions dialog box, the following things occur:

- The extension verifies that it is not being used within that application.

- If the extension is being used within the application, the extension does not allow itself to be unchecked and a warning message is given.

- If the extension is not being used within the application, the uncheck completes successfully and the remaining steps occur.

- The unchecked state for the extension is saved in the user settings in the registry. (This occurs automatically by the application—it is not something a developer needs to do.)

- If the toolbar for the extension is active, the appropriate tools are disabled.

- The *Extension* lets the license manager know it is no longer using the extension license within the application, and the license manager releases the license for that extension.

The *IExtensionConfig* interface is independent of ESRI's licensing approach, so as a developer you can incorporate a custom licensing solution. Alternatively, if your extension doesn't work with a license manager, you don't have to worry about requesting and releasing a license. You can implement *IExtensionConfig* to enable and disable the tools on your extension's toolbar accordingly.

The following excerpt of code from a class module that also implements *IExtension* shows you how you can use the *IExtensionConfig* interface.

```
Implements IExtensionConfig
Private m_pExtState As esriExtensionState

Private Property Get IExtensionConfig_Description() As String
  IExtensionConfig_Description = "This is the sample extension."
End Property

Private Property Let IExtensionConfig_State(ByVal RHS As _
    esriCore.esriExtensionState)
  m_pExtState = RHS
End Property

Private Property Get IExtensionConfig_ProductName() As String
  IExtensionConfig_ProductName = "Sample Extension"
End Property

Private Property Get IExtensionConfig_State() As _
    esriCore.esriExtensionState
  IExtensionConfig_State = m_pExtState
End Property
```

The application has a mechanism for dealing with extension-specific data in an ArcMap document. For example, some of the ArcGIS extensions have their own types of layers saved in the document. When a user opens such a document and the extension-specific layer is loaded, an attempt is made to create the layer. Creation may fail for one of three reasons:

- The extension has not been installed.

- The extension is not checked on in the Extension dialog box.

- The extension is checked on, but a license for the extension is currently not available.

In each of these failure cases, a warning will be issued stating what the problem is. The document is then opened but without the extension-specific layer. However, if the extension is installed, checked on in the Extension dialog box, and an extension license was successfully obtained, the document opens successfully.

If you want any of the commands in your extension to have keyboard accelerators associated with them, your extension needs to implement *IExtensionAccelerators*.

The *IExtensionAccelerators* interface has one method called *CreateAccelerators* that creates the accelerators for the extension. This method is called when the accelerator table is created during application startup, when a new document is created, or when a document is opened. Accelerators and the accelerator table are discussed later in this chapter.

When you use the *CreateAccelerators* method to assign an accelerator to one of the commands in your extension, check to make sure that no other command is currently using the key combination that you want to use.

The following code excerpt from a class module that also implements *IExtension* shows you how you can use the *IExtensionAccelerators* interface.

```
Implements IExtensionAccelerators

Private m_pDoc As IDocument

Private Sub IExtensionAccelerators_CreateAccelerators()
  Dim pAccelTable As IAcceleratorTable
  Dim pAccel As IAccelerator
  Dim u As New UID
  Set pAccelTable = m_pDoc.Accelerators
  Set pAccel = pAccelTable.FindByKey(vbKeyH, True, False, False)
  ' Create accelerator only if nothing else is using it
  If pAccel Is Nothing Then
    'The clsid of one of the commands in the ext
```

If one of the ArcGIS applications fails to start after you have registered a custom extension in one of the ESRI extension component categories, then you should check for errors in your extension. If there are any problems in your extension, this may cause the application startup sequence to abort.

```
  u.Value = "CustomCOMCommands.clsICommand"
  pAccelTable.Add u, vbKeyH, True, False, False
 End If
End Sub
```

APPLICATION STARTUP SEQUENCE

When working with extensions, customization filters, and document events, it is important to have an understanding of the application startup sequence. The basic startup sequence is:

1. User starts application.

2. *Application* object created.

3. *Document* object created.

4. Extensions are loaded.

5. If a document file is specified on the command line or if ArcMap is started by double-clicking a document file, then the document is loaded.
   If not, a new document is created. If the user then chooses to open an existing document, that document is loaded.

6. Application startup completed.

The order of extension loading cannot be controlled. The extensions are loaded in CLSID order using the appropriate component category. In certain circumstances, you may want to share data between extensions. In such circumstances, the data should not be associated with one extension but with another helper class. Each extension can check to see if the helper object has been created, and if not, the extension can create it. Once the helper object is created by the first initialized extension, the other extensions can access the data it contains.

Any document-specific code, such as customization filters, should not be placed in the extension-loading stage. The extensions are loaded before any map document is opened. This ensures that any extensions referred to in the map document are present when the document is opened. If you had a customization filter that was initialized during its extension startup, it would only operate until a document was opened or a new document was created. This is because customization filters are tied to individual documents. To get around this problem, event handlers can be initialized during extension startup, and the document-specific code can be added to the appropriate events. For example, when the open or new document events occur, the customization filter can be applied.

HANDLING GLOBAL APPLICATION DATA

When developing components for use within the ArcGIS suite of applications, it is often desirable to share data between components. As stated in the introduction, an extension is the logical place to store this data. For example, you might define public variables in the extension class and then access these variables directly.

Using public variables is not a good practice, since as creator of the variable you lose control over that variable when you add your component into the system. A better technique is to provide accessor and mutator functions. This allows for data encapsulation within the extension.

In Visual Basic, these functions are defined as a property on the default interface of the class. To locate the property, you must locate the extension, then *QI* the *Extension* object for its default interface. Then, you can call the properties on that interface.

The following VB code shows a class that implements the *IExtension* interface with a member variable that holds a Zoom Percentage, which has a valid range of 0–100. Also, a piece of code from the *OnClick* event of a command that uses that percentage to Zoom the display is provided.

This is a piece of code for *clsDisplayExtension*:

```
Implements IExtension

Private m_lZoomPercentage As Long
Private m_pApp As IApplication

Private Property Get IExtension_Name() As String
  IExtension_Name = "Display Extension"
End Property

Private Sub IExtension_Startup(ByRef initializationData As Variant)
  Set m_pApp = initializationData

  ' Initialize the Percentage value
  m_lZoomPercentage = 50
End Sub

Private Sub IExtension_Shutdown()
  Set m_pApp = Nothing
End Sub

Public Property Get ZoomPercentage() As Long
  ZoomPercentage = m_lZoomPercentage
End Property

Public Property Let ZoomPercentage(ByVal lPercentage As Long)
  If (lPercentage >= 0) And (lPercentage <= 100) Then
    m_lZoomPercentage = lPercentage
  Else
    Err.Raise vbObjectError + 29566, "MyProj.MyObject", _
    "Invalid Percentage Value. Valid values (0 -> 100)"
  End If
End Property
```

The following code is for the *OnClick* event of the command:

```
Private Sub ICommand_OnClick()
  Dim pExtension As clsDisplayExtension

  Dim pUID As New UID
  pUID.Value = "prjDisplay.clsDisplayExtension"

  ' QI IExtension for interface _clsDisplayExtension
  Set pExtension = m_pApp.FindExtensionByCLSID(pUID)

  ' Get Extent
  Dim pActiveView As IActiveView
  Set pActiveView = m_pMxDoc.ActiveView

  Dim pEnv As IEnvelope
  Set pEnv = pActiveView.Extent

  ' Zoom Extent and refresh the screen
  pEnv.Expand pExtension.ZoomPercentage / 100, _
    pExtension.ZoomPercentage / 100, True
  pActiveView.Extent pEnv
  pActiveView.Refresh
End Sub
```

PERSISTENCE

The state of the application is persisted inside an OLE2 document. For instance, ArcMap saves its state in an .mxd file and its various template files, which are documents themselves.

Not every object is given the opportunity to save information within the document. The application framework knows which objects can be saved. When the user clicks Save on the File menu, the application framework creates a document storage and then asks these objects to save themselves to the document.

The framework works with the objects by calling *QueryInterface* for an appropriate persistence interface; if it finds a suitable interface, it calls the appropriate methods, passing a suitable storage medium—normally a stream. The object is then responsible for serializing its state into the storage medium. The framework is not concerned with what is written to the medium; this is the sole concern of the object. When loading the state of an object from the storage medium, the object is able to read the serialized data and rehydrate itself.

An ArcObjects developer has two methods of saving data into the document—through an *Extension* or through a supported persistable object class. Persistable objects classes are classes such as layers, renderers, and so on. Commands and tools are not given the opportunity to persist information they are maintaining. For these and other objects which the framework will not automatically persist, an application extension must be used. When creating an extension, you need to implement a suitable persistence interface in addition to the *IExtension* interface. The persistence interface is *IPersistStream* if developing in Visual C++ or *IPersistVariant* if developing in Visual Basic.

IPersistVariant : IUnknown	Provides access to members used for storage of an object through VARIANTs.
■— ID: IUID	The ID of the object.
← Load (in Stream: IVariantStream)	Loads the object properties from the stream.
← Save (in Stream: IVariantStream)	Saves the object properties to the stream.

The *IPersistVariant* interface has one property, the class ID of the object being persisted, and two methods—*Load* and *Save*—that perform the loading and saving from the stream. It is good practice to version the persisted data so that the data can evolve over time in a way that allows backwards compatibility. It is important to load and save the data in the same order since access to the stream is always sequential. Below is a very simple example of an extension that implements persistence. It displays a message box when a document is opened that informs the user how many times the document has been saved.

```
Option Explicit

Implements IExtension
Implements IPersistVariant

Const c_lVersion = 1
Private m_lNumSaves As Long
Private m_pApp As IApplication

Private Property Get IExtension_Name() As String
  IExtension_Name = "Persistence Example Extension"
End Property

Private Sub IExtension_Startup(ByRef initializationData As Variant)
  Set m_pApp = initializationData
End Sub

Private Sub IExtension_Shutdown()
  Set m_pApp = Nothing
End Sub

Private Property Get IPersistVariant_ID() As esriCore.IUID
  IPersistVariant_ID.Value = "PersistenceSample.clsPersistExtension"
End Property

Private Sub IPersistVariant_Load(ByVal Stream As esriCore.IVariantStream)
  Dim version As Long
  version = Stream.Read

  If (version > c_lVersion) Then Exit Sub
```

```
  m_lNumSaves = Stream.Read
  MsgBox "Document Saved " & CStr(m_lNumSaves) & " Times"
End Sub

Private Sub IPersistVariant_Save(ByVal Stream As esriCore.IVariantStream)
  Stream.Write c_lVersion

  m_lNumSaves = m_lNumSaves + 1
  Stream.Write m_lNumSaves
End Sub
```

IVariantStream : IUnknown	Provides access to members that store values to and retrieve values from a stream.
◄— Read: Variant	Reads a value from a stream.
◄— Write (in Value: Variant)	Writes a value to a stream.

Notice the use of the *Write* and *Read* methods on the *IVariantStream* interfaces in the above code. These methods take variants, meaning they can save most data types. If an object, such as a layer, has a persistence interface, the object can be passed to these methods via one of its interfaces, and the object will be persisted.

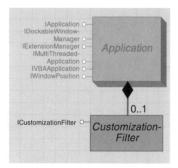

A customization filter locks parts of customized functionality of ArcGIS applications.

A customization filter provides a mechanism to lock parts of the customization functionality in the ArcGIS applications. If you use an extension to enable a customization filter, you should do so only in locked down applications where you have complete control over the application setup and how the users interact with that application. In generic applications, you can use customization filters if they are applied to a specific document.

To create a customization filter, implement the *ICustomizationFilter* interface in a class module. To activate your customization filter, pass it into the *IApplication::LockCustomization* method. You can make the call to *LockCustomization* in a simple VBA macro, in the *MxDocument_OpenDocument* or *MxDocument_NewDocument* event in VBA, or in an extension. If this is done in a macro or the open document event in VBA, make sure that the VBA project has a reference to the class that implements the customization filter.

If the customization filter is applied in an extension, you must be aware of the application startup sequence in order for this to work correctly. Refer to the Application startup sequence discussion earlier in this chapter. Also, be aware that if your customization filter is applied by an extension, it may override other locking logic that might be saved in an existing ArcMap document; also, another extension might activate a customization filter before your extension is even loaded. There can only be one active customization filter in a running application.

ICustomizationFilter : IUnknown	**Provides access to members that define a customization filter.**
← OnCustomizationEvent (in custEventType: esriCustomizationEvent, in eventCtx: Variant) : Boolean	*Occurs when certain types of customization occur.*

The *ICustomizationFilter* interface has an *OnCustomizationEvent* event that occurs whenever a user attempts any type of customization.

The *custEventType* parameter of *OnCustomizationEvent* specifies what type of customization event has just happened. The types of customization events are defined by the *esriCustomizationEvent* constants.

Enumeration esriCustomizationEvent	**Customization event types.**
0 - esriCEAddCategory	*Occurs when the Categories list on the Customize dialog is populated.*
1 - esriCEAddCommand	*Occurs when the Commands list on the Customize dialog is populated.*
2 - esriCEShowCustDlg	*Occurs when the Customize dialog is requested to be opened.*
3 - esriCEShowVBAIDE	*Occurs when the Visual Basic Editor is requested to be opened.*
4 - esriCEInvokeCommand	*Occurs when a command on a commandbar is about to be executed.*
5 - esriCEShowCustCtxMenu	*Occurs when the Customize context menu is popped up for a command item.*

The following lists additional things that the customization events can be used for:

- *esriCEAddCategory* can be used to remove categories from the Categories list in the Customize dialog box.

- *esriCEAddCommand* can be used to remove commands from the Commands list in the Customize dialog box.

- *esriCEShowCustDlg* can be used to prevent the Customize dialog box from being opened.

- *esriCEShowVBAIDE* can be used to prevent the Visual Basic Editor from being opened.

- *esriCEInvokeCommand* can be used to prevent a particular command from being executed.

- *esriCEShowCustCtxMenu* can be used to prevent the Customize context menu from being displayed when you right-click a command item when the Customize dialog box is open.

The *eventCtx* parameter of *OnCustomizationEvent* provides event context information for each type of customization event. To see what type of information is provided by *eventCtx* for each customization event type, refer to the table below.

CustEventType	eventCtx
esriCEAddCategory	string representing category name
esriCEAddCommand	UID or string identifying a command
esriCEShowCustDlg	nothing
esriCEShowVBAIDE	nothing
esriCEInvokeCommand	CommandItem
esriCEShowCustCtxMenu	nothing

The following VB class module defines a customization filter. This filter locks the following three areas of customization:

- Prevents the Visual Basic Editor from being opened.

- Locks the Map and Edit categories. These categories will not appear in the Categories list on the Commands panel of the Customize dialog box. This prevents users from dragging the commands in these categories onto toolbars.

- Locks the What's This command. This command will not show up in the Commands list for the Help category on the Commands panel of the Customize dialog box. This prevents users from dragging this command onto a toolbar but still gives them access to the other commands in the Help category.

Use the IApplication::LockCustomization
method to activate the customization filter.

```
Implements ICustomizationFilter

Private Function ICustomizationFilter_OnCustomizationEvent _
    (ByVal custEventType As esriCore.esriCustomizationEvent, _
    ByVal eventCtx As Variant) As Boolean
  ' Lock the Visual Basic editor.
  ' custEventType is esriCEShowVBAIDE
  ' eventCtx is nothing
  If custEventType = esriCEShowVBAIDE Then
    ICustomizationFilter_OnCustomizationEvent = True
```

```
    ' Lock the Map and Edit categories.
    ' custEventType is esriCEAddCategory
    ' eventCtx is a string representing the category name
    ElseIf custEventType = esriCEAddCategory Then
        Select Case eventCtx
        Case "Map"
            ICustomizationFilter_OnCustomizationEvent = True
        Case "Edit"
            ICustomizationFilter_OnCustomizationEvent = True
        Case Else
            ICustomizationFilter_OnCustomizationEvent = False
        End Select
    ' Lock the What's This Help command.
    ' custEventType is esriCEAddCommand
    ' eventCtx can be either a UID or a string identifier
    ' for a command.
    ElseIf custEventType = esriCEAddCommand Then
        'UID for What's This Help command
        Dim u As New UID
        u.Value = "esriCore.HelpTool"
        If u = eventCtx Then
            ICustomizationFilter_OnCustomizationEvent = True
        End If
    End If
End Function
```

Another common use of a customization filter is to restrict access to functionality by trapping *Invoke* calls. For example, the customization filter can prevent the execution of a command when a user tries to execute that command. To simplify the coding, a collection of disallowed commands can be created; then, when each command is invoked, it can be tested against this collection. These collections can be built on a user-by-user basis to provide user-level customization locking.

Below is an example of a class that implements the *ICustomizationFilter* to support this functionality.

```
Option Explicit
Implements ICustomizationFilter

Private m_pBlockedCommands As Collection

Private Sub Class_Initialize()
  Set m_pBlockedCommands = New Collection

  Dim pUID As IUID
  ' Add Commands to Disable
  Set pUID = New UID
  pUID.Value = "esriCore.StartEditingCommand"
  m_pBlockedCommands.Add pUID.Value, pUID.Value

  Set pUID = New UID
```

```
 pUID.Value = "esriCore.AddDataCommand"
 m_pBlockedCommands.Add pUID.Value, pUID.Value
End Sub

Private Sub Class_Terminate()
  Set m_pBlockedCommands = Nothing
End Sub

Private Function IsCommandBlocked(pItemUID As IUID) As Boolean
  IsCommandBlocked = True

  Dim tmpStr As String
  On Error GoTo Missing
  tmpStr = m_pBlockedCommands.Item(pItemUID.Value)
  Exit Function
Missing:
  IsCommandBlocked = False
  Err.Clear
End Function

Private Function ICustomizationFilter_OnCustomizationEvent _
  (ByVal custEventType As esriCore.esriCustomizationEvent, _
   ByVal eventCtx As Variant) As Boolean
  If (custEventType = esriCEInvokeCommand) Then
    Dim pItem As ICommandItem
    Set pItem = eventCtx
    ICustomizationFilter_OnCustomizationEvent = IsCommandBlocked(pItem.ID)
  End If
End Function
```

If you wanted to create an extension to apply one of these customization filters, the class of the extension could be coded as follows:

```
Implements IExtension

Dim m_pApp As IApplication
Dim m_MyFilter As ICustomizationFilter

' Need to listen for the MxDocument events so that the Lock
' can be set on OpenDocument and NewDocument events.
Dim WithEvents m_pDoc As MxDocument

Private Property Get IExtension_Name() As String
  IExtension_Name = "MyFilterExt"
End Property

Private Sub IExtension_Shutdown()
  Set m_pApp = Nothing
  Set m_pDoc = Nothing
End Sub
```

To use this extension in ArcMap, register it in the ESRI Mx Extensions component category.

```
Private Sub IExtension_Startup(initializationData As Variant)
  If TypeOf initializationData Is IMxApplication Then
    Set m_pApp = initializationData

    'Start listening for the MxDocument events.
    If Not m_pDoc Is m_pApp.Document Then
      Set m_pDoc = m_pApp.Document
    End If
    ' Replace MyFilter with the class name of your filter
    Set m_MyFilter = New clsMyFilter
  End If
End Sub


Private Function m_pDoc_NewDocument() As Boolean
  On Error GoTo FilterErr

  ' Set the Lock when a new document is created.
  m_pApp.LockCustomization "mylock", m_MyFilter

  Exit Function
FilterErr:
  MsgBox "Attempt To Lock Document With Filter Failed", _
    vbOKOnly + vbExclamation, "Extension Error"
End Function


Private Function m_pDoc_OpenDocument() As Boolean
  On Error GoTo FilterErr

  ' Reset the Lock when a document is opened.
  m_pApp.LockCustomization "mylock", m_MyFilter

  Exit Function
FilterErr:
  MsgBox "Attempt To Lock Document With Filter Failed", _
    vbOKOnly + vbExclamation, "Extension Error"
End Function
```

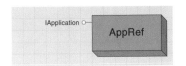

The application reference object, AppRef, is a reference to the currently running ArcGIS application.

If for some reason you can't easily get a reference to the *Application* object in your code, you can create a new *AppRef* object. For example, there are cases where you may implement an object that exists within the application framework, but there is no way to traverse the application hierarchy from that object.

In order to provide developers with access to the *Application* object, there is a singleton object that provides a pointer to the running application object. The code below illustrates its use.

```
Dim pApp As IApplication
Set pApp = New AppRef
```

You can only use the *AppRef* object if your code is running inside one of the ArcGIS application processes.

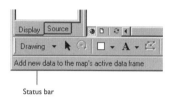

The status bar is the horizontal area at the bottom of an ArcGIS application window. It provides information about the current state of the application.

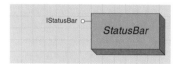

Status bar

The status bar provides information about the selected command. For example, if you select a layer in the table of contents in ArcMap, the status bar will tell you how many features are currently selected. It may also display a progress bar while something is being processed.

The *StatusBar* property on the *IApplication* interface can be used to get a reference to the *StatusBar* object.

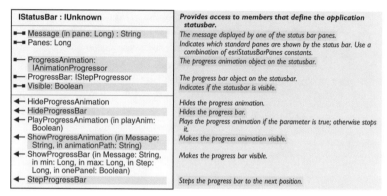

IStatusBar : IUnknown	Provides access to members that define the application statusbar.
■—■ Message (in pane: Long) : String	The message displayed by one of the status bar panes.
■—■ Panes: Long	Indicates which standard panes are shown by the status bar. Use a combination of esriStatusBarPanes constants.
■— ProgressAnimation: IAnimationProgressor	The progress animation object on the statusbar.
■— ProgressBar: IStepProgressor	The progress bar object on the statusbar.
■—■ Visible: Boolean	Indicates if the statusbar is visible.
◄— HideProgressAnimation	Hides the progress animation.
◄— HideProgressBar	Hides the progress bar.
◄— PlayProgressAnimation (in playAnim: Boolean)	Plays the progress animation if the parameter is true; otherwise stops it.
◄— ShowProgressAnimation (in Message: String, in animationPath: String)	Makes the progress animation visible.
◄— ShowProgressBar (in Message: String, in min: Long, in max: Long, in Step: Long, in onePanel: Boolean)	Makes the progress bar visible.
◄— StepProgressBar	Steps the progress bar to the next position.

The *IStatusBar* interface allows you to set the properties of the status bar. The status bar is divided into sections called panes. The *Panes* property specifies which panes of the status bar are currently visible.

Enumeration esriStatusBarPanes	Status bar panes.
0 - esriStatusMain	Leftmost pane where application messages are displayed.
1 - esriStatusAnimation	Pane showing an animated icon.
2 - esriStatusPosition	Pane showing mouse position in map coordinates.
4 - esriStatusPagePosition	Pane showing mouse position in page coordinates.
8 - esriStatusSize	Pane showing object size.
16 - esriStatusCapsLock	Pane showing caps lock indicator.
32 - esriStatusNumLock	Pane showing num lock indicator.
64 - esriStatusScrollLock	Pane showing scroll lock indicator.
128 - esriStatusClock	Pane showing clock.

The *esriStatusBarPanes* constants define which panes are shown. The *Panes* property is a bit field; this means that you can use a combination of the *esriStatusBarPanes* constants. Add up the values of the panes you want shown and set the *Panes* property to the total.

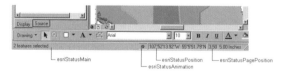

esriStatusMain   esriStatusPosition   esriStatusPagePosition
esriStatusAnimation

Only the default panes are shown in the status bar.

The default value of *Panes* is 7; this means that the main (0), animation (1), position (2), and page position (4) panes are visible (0 + 1 + 2 + 4 = 7). You can set the *Panes* property to 255 to show all panes.

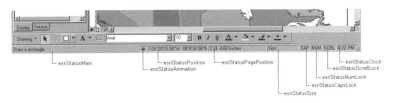

All the panes are shown in the status bar.

The step progressor bar is the blue moving line that displays the percentage of completeness.

The *Message* property allows you to display text in the status bar. Most commonly, the main pane is used for the display of messages; however, any pane can be used.

The *ProgressBar* property and the *HideProgressBar, ShowProgressBar,* and *StepProgressBar* methods are used to control the step progress bar on the status bar. The step progress bar displays in the main status bar pane.

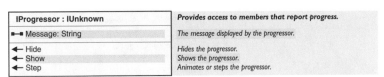

IProgressor : IUnknown	Provides access to members that report progress.
▪━▪ Message: String	The message displayed by the progressor.
◀━ Hide	Hides the progressor.
◀━ Show	Shows the progressor.
◀━ Step	Animates or steps the progressor.

The *IProgressor* interface is a generic interface for progressors. There are methods to show, step, and hide the progressor and a property to set the message of the progressor.

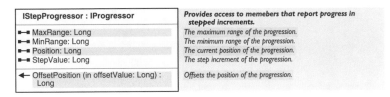

IStepProgressor : IProgressor	Provides access to memebers that report progress in stepped increments.
▪━▪ MaxRange: Long	The maximum range of the progression.
▪━▪ MinRange: Long	The minimum range of the progression.
▪━▪ Position: Long	The current position of the progression.
▪━▪ StepValue: Long	The step increment of the progression.
◀━ OffsetPosition (in offsetValue: Long) : Long	Offsets the position of the progression.

The *IStepProgressor* interface has properties for setting the properties of the step progress bar, such as the message, the minimum and maximum values, and the step size. Use the *IStatusBar::ProgressorBar* interface to get access to the step progress bar. Alternatively, the *IStatusBar::Show-ProgressBar* method provides shortcuts to the properties of the step progress bar. This method allows you to set the message, minimum and maximum values, and the step size of the step progress bar and also display the step progress bar. Therefore, it is unnecessary to use *IStep-Progressor* to do this.

The following code displays a step progress bar and steps in a loop from 1 to 900,000.

```
Public Sub StepProg()
    Dim pStatusBar As IStatusBar
    Dim i As Long
    Dim pProgbar As IStepProgressor
    Set pStatusBar = Application.StatusBar
    Set pProgbar = pStatusBar.ProgressBar
```

The animation progressor is the spinning globe on the status bar. You could also display a custom animation here.

```
  pProgbar.Position = 0
  pStatusBar.ShowProgressBar "Loading...", 0, 900000, 1, True
  For i = 0 To 900000
    pStatusBar.StepProgressBar
  Next
  pStatusBar.HideProgressBar
End Sub
```

On the *IStatusBar* interface, the *ProgressAnimation* property and the *HideProgressAnimation, ShowProgressAnimation,* and *PlayProgressAnimation* methods control the animation progressor (spinning globe) on the status bar. The animation progressor displays in the animation pane. You can use the default spinning globe for the animation progressor or specify your own animation file (.avi).

IAnimationProgressor : IProgressor	Provides access to members that report progress using an animation.
■─■ Animation: esriAnimations	The animation displayed by the progressor as one of the esriAnimation constants. (Not implemented).
◄─ OpenPath (in animationPath: String)	Opens the AVI file specified in the path and displays its first frame. The AVI file specified must not contain audio.
◄─ Play (frameFrom: Long, frameTo: Long, repeat: Long)	Plays the animation.
◄─ Seek (in frameTo: Long)	Moves to the specified frame of the animation. The animation starts at this frame the next time it is played.
◄─ Stop	Stops the animation.

The *IProgressAnimation* interface has methods for controlling the animation progessor, such as setting the path to the avi file and showing and playing the animation progressor.

Use the *IStatusBar::AnimationProgressor* interface to get access to the animation progressor.

Alternatively, the *IStatusBar::ShowProgressAnimation* method provides a shortcut to the *OpenPath* and *Show* methods of the animation progressor.

The *IStatusBar::PlayProgressAnimation* method provides a shortcut to the *Play* and *Stop* methods of the animation progressor.

The *Animation* property on *IAnimationProgressor* is not implemented.

The following code plays the animation progressor on the status bar.

```
Public Sub AnimProg()
  Dim pStatusBar As IStatusBar
  Dim i As Long
  Dim pProgAnim As IAnimationProgressor
  Set pStatusBar = Application.StatusBar
  Set pProgAnim = pStatusBar.ProgressAnimation
  pProgAnim.Show
  pStatusBar.PlayProgressAnimation True
  For i = 0 To 10000
    pStatusBar.Message(0) = "Counting..." & Str(i)
  Next
  pStatusBar.PlayProgressAnimation False
  pProgAnim.Hide
End Sub
```

The document in ArcMap stores objects such as map layers and elements. The document in ArcCatalog is actually default user interface settings in the Normal template.

This *Document* object only represents the generic document properties common to all ArcGIS applications. Each application has its own document object.

The document object in ArcMap is called *MxDocument*; for further discussion, see Chapter 4, 'Composing maps'. The document object in ArcCatalog is called *GxDocument*; for further discussion, see Chapter 7, 'Working with the Catalog'.

Even though ArcCatalog doesn't use documents, it has a document object associated with it. The document provides access to the user interface elements and the VBA project. The *GxDocument* is really just the Normal template, Normal.gxt.

Use the *Document* property of the *IApplication* interface to get a reference to the document.

In the Visual Basic Editor, each VBA project contains a VBA class module called *ThisDocument*. This class represents the document object. When you are working in the *ThisDocument* code window in VBA, you have direct access to the properties and methods on the *IDocument* interface.

IDocument : IDispatch	Provides access to other objects in the document.
■— Accelerators: IAcceleratorTable	*The accelerator table for this document.*
■— CommandBars: ICommandBars	*The commandbars collection in this document.*
■— ID: IUID	*The unique id for this document.*
■— Parent: IApplication	*The application in which this document is open.*
■— Title: String	*The title of this document.*
■— Type: esriDocumentType	*The type of this document.*
■— VBProject: Object	*The VBProject for this document.*

The *IDocument* interface provides access to the document's title, type, accelerator table, command bars collection, parent application, and Visual Basic for Applications project.

Use the *Document* property of the *IApplication* interface to get a reference to the document.

The following VBA code will report the title of the document:

```
Dim pDoc As IDocument
Set pDoc = Application.Document
MsgBox pDoc.Title
```

Enumeration esriDocumentType	Document types.
0 - esriDocumentTypeNormal	*The Normal template.*
1 - esriDocumentTypeTemplate	*The base template.*
2 - esriDocumentTypeDocument	*The current document.*

The *esriDocumentType* enumeration is used by the *Type* property on the *IDocument* interface. Use this enumeration to determine whether the document object is the current document, a base template, or the Normal template.

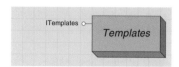

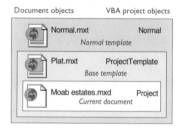

The templates collection references the template objects that are currently loaded with the application.

Scope of applying customizations

The ArcMap package contains an object called Template that is unrelated to the Templates collection.

A template is a document that is used as a starting point for creating new documents. It carries customizations of several types—user interface, VBA project, and application-specific data.

ArcMap has two or three templates loaded with an application. If the document is based on the Normal template, two items are in the templates collection. If the document is based on a project template, three items are in the templates collection. ArcCatalog always has one item in the templates collection; this item represents Normal.gxt.

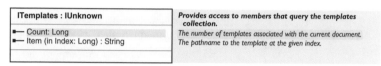

The *ITemplates* interface has a *Count* property that returns the number of currently loaded templates. The *Item* property returns the full filename of the specified template. This provides a convenient way to find out where the Normal template, project template, or document is stored on disk.

This VBA code will report the name of the project template that is loaded in ArcMap, if there is one loaded:

```
Dim pTemplates As ITemplates
Set pTemplates = Application.Templates
If pTemplates.Count = 3 Then
  MsgBox pTemplates.Item(1)
End If
```

A dockable window is an auxiliary window that can display data. This window is treated as a modeless child window of the application.

A dockable window is a window that can exist in a floating state or attached to the main application window. The table of contents in ArcMap and the tree view in ArcCatalog are examples of dockable windows.

IDockableWindowManager : IUnknown	Provides access to a method that finds a dockable window in the application.
◄— GetDockableWindow (in dockWnd: IUID) : IDockableWindow	Finds a dockable window looking first in the collection and then in the category.

The *Application* object implements the *IDockableWindowManager* interface that is used to get access to a particular dockable window. The *GetDockableWindow* method finds a dockable window using the *UID* of the dockable window. To get access to this interface, do a *QI* on *Application*.

IDockableWindow : IUnknown	Provides access to members that define and control a dockable window.
■—■ Caption: String	The caption of the dockable window.
■— ID: IUID	The unique id for this dockable window.
■— Name: String	The name of the dockable window.
■— UserData: Variant	User defined data.
◄— Dock (in dockFlags: esriDockFlags)	Docks or undocks this docking window.
◄— IsVisible: Boolean	Indicates if this docking window is visible.
◄— Show (in Show: Boolean)	Hides or shows the dockable window.

The *IDockableWindow* interface queries the properties of a dockable window, such as the *Caption, Name,* and *ID*. This interface also has methods to return whether the window is currently visible, to display the window, and to dock the window in a particular location on the application.

The following VBA code finds the ArcMap table of contents and, if it's currently visible, docks it on the right side of the application.

```
Dim pDocWinMgr As IDockableWindowManager
Dim pTOC As IDockableWindow
Set pDocWinMgr = Application  'QI
Set pTOC = pDocWinMgr.GetDockableWindow(arcid.TableofContents)
If pTOC.IsVisible Then
  pTOC.Dock esriDockRight
End If
```

IDockableWindowDef ○—
ISupportErrorInfo ○—
**Dockable-
WindowDef**

A dockable window definition is used by the application to create a dockable window.

IDockableWindowDef : IUnknown	Provides access to members that define a dockable window.
■— Caption: String	The caption of the dockable window.
■— ChildHWND: Long	The hWnd of the window to be embedded in a dockable window.
■— Name: String	The name of the dockable window.
■— UserData: Variant	User defined data.
◄— OnCreate (in hook: Object)	Occurs when this dockable window is created and provides access to the application.
◄— OnDestroy	Occurs when the docking window is about to be destroyed.

To create your own dockable window, implement the *IDockableWindow-Def* interface. This interface allows you to set properties, such as caption and name. You use the *ChildHWND* property to define what the window will consist of by passing in an *hWnd* of a control, such as a form, listbox, and so on. The *OnCreate* method provides a hook to the application and allows you to perform any necessary initialization of the window. The *OnDestroy* method is called when the window is about to be destroyed.

The class you create is a definition for a dockable window; it is not actually a dockable window object. Once your class is registered in one of the dockable window component categories, the application uses the definition of the dockable window in your class to create the actual dockable window.

The following VB class module defines a dockable window that displays a list of layers with their selection count and updates that list whenever the selection changes.

```
Implements IDockableWindowDef
Dim m_pApp As IApplication
Dim m_pMXDoc As IMxDocument
Dim WithEvents m_pMapEvent As Map

Private Property Get IDockableWindowDef_Caption() As String
  IDockableWindowDef_Caption = "Selected Features Count"
End Property

Private Property Get IDockableWindowDef_ChildHWND() As _
esriCore.OLE_HANDLE
  IDockableWindowDef_ChildHWND = frmDockWin.lstDockWin.hWnd
End Property

Private Property Get IDockableWindowDef_Name() As String
  IDockableWindowDef_Name = "Selection Count"
End Property

Private Sub IDockableWindowDef_OnCreate(ByVal hook As Object)
  Set m_pApp = hook
  Set m_pMXDoc = m_pApp.Document
  Set m_pMapEvent = m_pMXDoc.FocusMap
End Sub

Private Sub IDockableWindowDef_OnDestroy()
  Set m_pMapEvent = Nothing
  Set m_pMXDoc = Nothing
  Set m_pApp = Nothing
End Sub

Private Property Get IDockableWindowDef_UserData() As Variant
End Property

Private Sub m_pMapEvent_SelectionChanged()
  Dim pMap As IMap
  Dim i As Integer
  Dim pFLayer As IFeatureLayer
```

To use your dockable window in one of the ArcGIS applications, you have to register it in the appropriate component category. For example, if your dockable window was designed to be used in ArcMap, you would register it in the ESRI Mx DockableWindows component category. You also have to have code to display that window in ArcMap. Use the IDockableWindowManager and IDockableWindow interfaces to do this.

```
Dim pSel As IFeatureSelection
Set pMap = m_pMapEvent
frmDockWin.lstDockWin.Clear
For i = 0 To pMap.LayerCount - 1
  If TypeOf pMap.Layer(i) Is IFeatureSelection Then
    Set pFLayer = pMap.Layer(i)
    Set pSel = pFLayer
    frmDockWin.lstDockWin.AddItem pFLayer.Name & ": " &
pSel.SelectionSet.Count
  End If
Next
End Sub
```

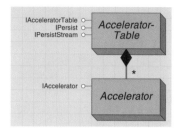

An accelerator is a mapping between a particular keyboard combination and a command. When you press the combination of keys on the keyboard, the command is executed. For example, Ctrl+C is a well-known accelerator for copying something in Windows.

└─ Accelerator table   └─ Accelerator

Some commands in the application already have accelerators assigned to them, but you can also assign additional accelerators to these commands.

The *AcceleratorTable* is an object with a list of accelerator keys and the command identifiers associated with them. You can get a reference to the *AcceleratorTable* of a document using the *Accelerators* property of *IDocument*.

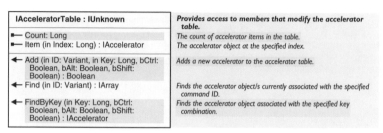

The *IAcceleratorTable* interface is used to add or find accelerators in an *AcceleratorTable*.

The following VBA code assigns the Ctrl+Shift+A accelerator to the Add Data command if this accelerator is not already assigned to another command.

```
Dim pAccelTbl As IAcceleratorTable
Set pAccelTbl = Application.Document.Accelerators
If pAccelTbl.FindByKey(vbKeyA, True, False, True) Is Nothing Then
  pAccelTbl.Add ArcID.File_AddData, vbKeyA, True, False, True
End If
```

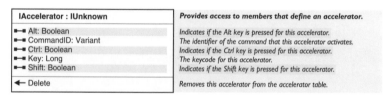

The *IAccelerator* interface defines the properties of an accelerator. Use the *Add* method in the *IAcceleratorTable* interface to create an accelerator.

The following VBA code removes all accelerators currently assigned to the Add Data command. The *Find* method on the *IAcceleratorTable* interface returns an array of all the accelerators for a particular command.

```
Dim pAccelTbl As IAcceleratorTable
Dim pAccelArray As IArray, pAccel As IAccelerator
Dim i as Integer
Set pAccelTbl = Application.Document.Accelerators
Set pAccelArray = pAccelTbl.Find(ArcID.File_AddData)

For i = 0 To pAccelArray.Count - 1
  Set pAccel = pAccelArray.Element(i)
  pAccel.Delete
Next
```

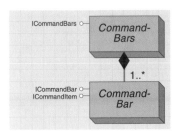

A command bar is a toolbar, menubar, menu, or context menu. CommandBars is a collection of all the toolbars available to a document.

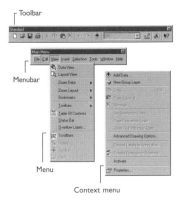

CommandBars is a collection of the command bars associated with a document.

CommandBar represents a toolbar, menubar, menu, or context menu.

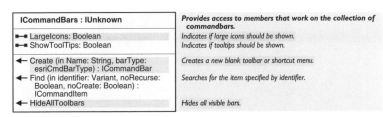

ICommandBars : IUnknown	Provides access to members that work on the collection of commandbars.
■–■ LargeIcons: Boolean	Indicates if large icons should be shown.
■–■ ShowToolTips: Boolean	Indicates if tooltips should be shown.
◄– Create (in Name: String, barType: esriCmdBarType) : ICommandBar	Creates a new blank toolbar or shortcut menu.
◄– Find (in identifier: Variant, noRecurse: Boolean, noCreate: Boolean) : ICommandItem	Searches for the item specified by identifier.
◄– HideAllToolbars	Hides all visible bars.

The *ICommandBars* interface allows you to set properties for the *CommandBars* and to create, find, or hide *CommandBars*. Use the *CommandBars* property of *IDocument* to get a reference to the *CommandBars* collection.

Enumeration esriCmdBarType	Commandbar types.
0 - esriCmdBarTypeToolbar	Toolbar commandbar type.
1 - esriCmdBarTypeMenu	Menu commandbar type.
2 - esriCmdBarTypeShortcutMenu	Context menu commandbar type.

The *esriCmdBarType* enumeration specifies the type of command bar. Use this enumeration with the *ICommandBars::Create* method to create a new toolbar or shortcut menu. Do not use the *esriCmdBarTypeMenu* enumeration with the *ICommandBars::Create* method to create a new menu; use the *ICommandBar::CreateMenu* method instead.

Use the *Find* method in *ICommandBars* to get a reference to a particular *CommandBar*.

There is a built-in module called *ArcID* in the VBA project for the Normal template in both ArcMap and ArcCatalog. This module is a utility for finding the UID of the built-in commands and toolbars. Pass the name of a command or toolbar in as an argument to *ArcID*, and the *UID* of that item is returned. The *ArcID* module is regenerated every time the Normal template is loaded; the registry is read to get the GUIDs of all the commands and toolbars that are currently used by the application.

The following code shows how you can use the ArcID module to find the Standard toolbar in ArcMap.

```
Dim pCmdBars As ICommandBars
Dim pStdBar As ICommandBar
Set pCmdBars = Application.Document.CommandBars
Set pStdBar = pCmdBars.Find(arcid.Standard_Toolbar)
```

ICommandBar : IUnknown	Provides access to members that modify a commandbar.
■— Count: Long	The number of items contained within this commandbar.
■— Item (in Index: Long) : ICommandItem	The command item on this commandbar at the specified index.
◄— Add (in cmdID: IUID, Index: Variant) : ICommandItem	Adds a new command to this commandbar.
◄— CreateMacroItem (in Name: String, FaceID: Variant, Action: String, Index: Variant) : ICommandItem	Creates a new macro item on this commandbar at the specified position.
◄— CreateMenu (in Name: String, Index: Variant) : ICommandBar	Creates a new blank menu on this commandbar at the specified position.
◄— Dock (in dockFlags: esriDockFlags, referenceBar: ICommandBar)	Docks or undocks this commandbar.
◄— Find (in identifier: Variant, noRecurse: Boolean) : ICommandItem	Finds a command on this commandbar.
◄— IsVisible: Boolean	Indicates if this commandbar is visible.
◄— Popup (X: Long, Y: Long) : ICommandItem	Displays this commandbar as a popup menu at the specified location.

The *ICommandBar* interface lets you modify a *CommandBar* by adding a command, menu, or macro item to it.

The *Count* property returns the number of command items on the command bar, and the *Item* property allows you get a reference to the command item at the specified index.

The *IsVisible* method determines whether or not the command bar is currently visible.

Use the *Dock* method to show or hide the command bar and to put it in a floating state or place it in a particular location on the application window.

Enumeration esriDockFlags	Toolbar docking flags.
0 - esriDockHide	Hides the toolbar.
1 - esriDockShow	Shows the toolbar.
2 - esriDockLeft	Docks the toolbar on the left side of the application.
4 - esriDockRight	Docks the toolbar on the right side of the application.
8 - esriDockTop	Docks the toolbar on the top of the application.
16 - esriDockBottom	Docks the toolbar on the bottom of the application.
32 - esriDockFloat	Floats the toolbar.
64 - esriDockToggle	Toggles the toolbar visibility.

The *esriDockFlags* enumeration is used with the *Dock* method to specify where the command bar should be placed.

You can write VBA code to create custom toolbars or menus; however, these toolbars and menus are only stored in memory; they are never written out to any document or template. Use the *Create* method in *ICommandBars* to create a new toolbar or shortcut menu. Use the *CreateMenu* method in *ICommandBar* to create a new menu.

The following VBA macro creates a new toolbar, puts a new menu on it, adds an item to the menu, and places the toolbar at the top of the application below the Standard toolbar.

```
Sub CreateBar()
  Dim pCommandBars As ICommandBars
  Dim pNewBar As ICommandBar
  Dim pNewMenu As ICommandBar
  Dim pCmdBars As ICommandBars
```

```
    Set pCommandBars = Application.Document.CommandBars
    'Create the new toolbar
    Set pNewBar = pCommandBars.Create("MyToolbar", esriCmdBarTypeToolbar)
    'Create the new menu on the new toolabr
    Set pNewMenu = pNewBar.CreateMenu("MyMenu")
    'Add an item to the menu
    pNewMenu.Add arcid.File_AddData
    Set pCmdBars = Application.Document.CommandBars
    'Place the new toolbar at the top of the app below the Standard toolbar
    pNewBar.Dock esriDockBottom, pCmdBars.Find(arcid.Standard_Toolbar)
End Sub
```

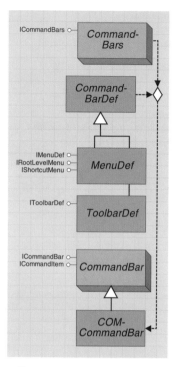

You can create custom document command bars using the Customize dialog box in ArcMap or ArcCatalog. To create a custom toolbar, use the New button on the Toolbars panel. To create a custom menu, go to the New Menu category on the Commands panel and drag the New Menu command to any toolbar or menu. These types of toolbars and menus are stored in a specific document or template and can only be used in that document or template.

There are two basic types of custom command bars that you can create—document command bars and COM command bars. Document command bars can be created using built-in functionality in the applications. COM command bars can be created by defining menus or toolbars in any COM-compliant language and compiling them into an ActiveX DLL.

The command bars collection uses command bar definitions (either *ToolBarDef* or *MenuDef*) to create command bars. For example, a class that implements *IToolbarDef* is only a definition for a toolbar; it is not actually a toolbar object. Once this class is registered in one of the command bar component categories, the command bars collection uses the definition of the toolbar in your class to create the actual command bar.

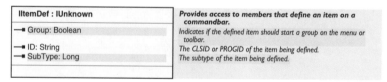

IToolBarDef: IUnknown	Provides access to members that define a toolbar.
Caption: String	The caption of this toolbar.
ItemCount: Long	The number of items in this toolbar.
Name: String	The name of this toolbar.
GetItemInfo (in pos: Long, in itemDef: IItemDef)	The CLSID for the item on this toolbar at the specified index.

To create a custom toolbar, implement *IToolbarDef*. The *IToolbarDef* interface is used to define the properties of a custom toolbar. You can set the caption and name of the toolbar and specify what command items are on the toolbar.

IItemDef : IUnknown	Provides access to members that define an item on a commandbar.
Group: Boolean	Indicates if the defined item should start a group on the menu or toolbar.
ID: String	The CLSID or PROGID of the item being defined.
SubType: Long	The subtype of the item being defined.

The *IItemDef* interface defines a command item on a toolbar or menu. Use the *IItemDef* interface with the *GetItemInfo* method on either the *IToolbarDef* or the *IMenuDef* interface to define the items on the toolbar or menu. This interface specifies the identifier (CLSID or ProgID) of the command and its subtype if there is one. It also determines whether this item begins a group on the toolbar or menu.

```
Implements IToolBarDef

Private Property Get IToolBarDef_Caption() As String
    IToolBarDef_Caption = "MyToolbar"
End Property

Private Sub IToolBarDef_GetItemInfo(ByVal pos As Long, _
        ByVal itemDef As esriCore.IItemDef)
    Select Case pos
    Case 0
        itemDef.ID = "esriCore.AddDataCommand"
        itemDef.Group = False
```

```
   Case 1
     itemDef.ID = "esriCore.FullExtentCommand"
     itemDef.Group = True
   End Select
End Sub

Private Property Get IToolBarDef_ItemCount() As Long
   IToolBarDef_ItemCount = 2
End Property

Private Property Get IToolBarDef_Name() As String
   IToolBarDef_Name = "MyToolbar"
End Property
```

*In the registry, a custom toolbar has been added
to PremierToolbars.*

When an end user installs your custom toolbar, you may want this toolbar immediately available in the application so that the user doesn't have to manually display that toolbar before using it. You can add a registry setting to make this toolbar automatically appear the first time the application is run after the installation of your toolbar. In the setup program for your toolbar, create a new key under:

HKEY_CURRENT_USER\Software\ESRI\ArcMap\Settings\PremierToolbars

The key name should be the CLSID of the toolbar. You don't have to set a value for this key.

*If you are working in Visual Basic, you can use
the ESRI Compile and Register Add-in to set up
this registry key. For more information, refer to
Chapter 2, 'Developing with ArcObjects'.*

The PremierToolbars setting is only used the first time the application is started; if the user subsequently hides the toolbar, no further attempts will be made to show the toolbar on application startup. After the application is started, the value of your PremierToolbars key is set to 1 and is then ignored by the application.

IMenuDef : IUnknown	*Provides access to members that define a menu.*
▪— Caption: String ▪— ItemCount: Long ▪— Name: String	*The caption of this menu.* *The number of items in this menu.* *The name of this menu.*
◄— GetItemInfo (in pos: Long, in itemDef: IItemDef)	*The CLSID for the item on this menu at the specified index.*

To create a custom menu, implement *IMenuDef*. The *IMenuDef* interface is identical to the *IToolbarDef* interface except that it is used to indicate to the application that this is a menu.

IRootLevelMenu : IUnknown	*Identifies a root level menu.*

If you are creating a root menu (a menu that will appear in the Menus command category in the Customize dialog box), implement both *IMenuDef* and *IRootLevelMenu*. *IRootLevelMenu* is an indicator interface that is only used to indicate to the application that the menu should be treated as a root menu.

IShortcutMenu : IUnknown	Identifies a context menu.

If you are creating a context menu, implement both *IMenuDef* and *IShortcutMenu*. *IShortcutMenu* is an indicator interface that is only used to indicate to the application that this menu should be treated as a context menu.

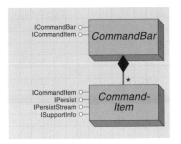

A command item is any item on a command bar. For example, button, tools, and menu items that appear on command bars are all command items.

A *CommandItem* class represents any item on a command bar.

ICommandItem : IUnknown	Provides access to members that define a command item.
■━■ Action: String	The name of the VBA macro this command should run when pressed.
■━ BuiltIn: Boolean	Indicates whether this command item is built-in or if it was implemented through VBA.
■━■ Caption: String	The caption of this command item.
■━ Category: String	The name of the category with which this command item is associated.
■━ Command: ICommand	A reference to the internal command object.
■━■ FaceID: Variant	The bitmap that is used as the icon on this command item.
■━■ Group: Boolean	Indicates if this command item begins a menu or toolbar group.
■━■ HelpContextID: Long	The help context ID associated with this command item.
■━■ HelpFile: String	The help file associated with this command item.
■━ ID: IUID	The unique integer ID associated with this command item.
■━ Index: Long	The positional index of this command item within its menu or toolbar.
■━■ Message: String	The status bar message for this command item.
■━■ Name: String	The name of this command item.
■━ Parent: ICommandBar	The menu or toolbar that this command item currently resides on.
■━■ Style: esriCommandStyles	The display style of this command item.
■━■ Tag: String	The tag for this command item.
■━■ Tooltip: String	The tooltip for this command item.
■━ Type: esriCommandTypes	The type of this command item.
← Delete	Removes this object from the commandbar.
← Execute	Causes the command to execute.
← Refresh	Causes the command to be redrawn.
← Reset	Restores this command item's properties to that of the original.

The *ICommandItem* interface allows you to get or set the properties of the *CommandItem*, such as caption, button image, status bar message, ToolTip, display style, help context ID, and so on. You can obtain a reference to the command on which this item is based. The *ICommandItem* interface also provides methods to execute, delete, refresh, and reset the *CommandItem*.

Use the *Find* method from either *ICommandBars* or *ICommandBar* to obtain a reference to a particular *CommandItem*.

This VBA code changes the caption, button image, and display style of the Add Data button on the Standard toolbar. To change the button image, set the FaceID property to a custom bitmap on disk.

```
Dim pStdBar As ICommandBar
Dim pCmdItem As ICommandItem
Set pStdBar= Application.Document.CommandBars.Find(ArcID.Standard_Toolbar)
Set pCmdItem = pStdBar.Find(ArcID.File_AddData)
pCmdItem.Caption = "Add Layer..."
pCmdItem.FaceID = LoadPicture("c:\bitmaps\layer.bmp")
pCmdItem.Style = esriCommandStyleIconAndText
```

Enumeration esriCommandStyles	Command display styles.
0 - esriCommandStyleTextOnly	Display text only.
1 - esriCommandStyleIconOnly	Display icon only.
2 - esriCommandStyleIconAndText	Display icon and text.
4 - esriCommandStyleMenuBar	Display bar as main menu.

The *esriCommandStyles* enumeration is used with the *Style* property to set whether the *CommandItem* is displayed on a command bar using its caption, image, or both.

Enumeration esriCommandTypes	Command types.
0 - esriCmdTypeCommand	Built in command.
1 - esriCmdTypeMenu	Menu.
2 - esriCmdTypeToolbar	Toolbar.
3 - esriCmdTypeMacro	Macro Item.
4 - esriCmdTypeUIButtonCtrl	UIButtonControl.
5 - esriCmdTypeUIToolCtrl	UIToolControl.
6 - esriCmdTypeUIComboBoxCtrl	UIComboBoxControl.
7 - esriCmdTypeUIEditBoxCtrl	UIEditBoxControl.

The *esriCommandTypes* enumeration is used with the *Type* property to specify whether the *CommandItem* is a command, macro, or UI control.

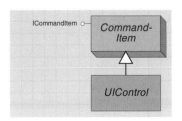

UI Controls represent buttons, combo boxes, edit boxes, or tools in a custom dialog box.

UIControls are VBA-based commands. This means that VBA code stored in a document or template defines and determines the behavior of this type of command. If a *UIControl* was created in a document, it can only be accessed in that document. If a *UIControl* was created in a template, it can be accessed in the template and any document that uses the template. If a *UIControl* was created in the Normal template, it can be accessed at all levels. There are four different types of *UIControl*: *UIButtonControl*, *UIComboBoxControl*, *UIEditBoxControl*, and *UIToolControl*.

To create a new *UIControl*, use the New *UIControl* button on the Customize dialog box in the ArcGIS applications; this creates a *UIControl* stub. While the Customize dialog box is still open, you can drag the new *UIControl* to any toolbar. You can then write the code that defines and determines the behavior of the *UIControl*. This code is written in the Visual Basic Editor in the *ThisDocument* code window for the document or template in which you created the *UIControl*.

The new *UIControl* is listed in the Object Box on the code window; select the *UIControl* in this list. Then, click one of the functions listed in the Procedures/Events box on the code window. This will stub out the function in the code window. You can now write your code. When the Visual Basic Editor is open, your *UIButtonControl* is in design mode. To fully test your button in ArcMap or ArcCatalog, you need to close the Visual Basic Editor.

The interfaces for *UIControls* are usable only in Visual Basic for Applications.

A UI button control acts as a button or menu item that performs a simple task when clicked. You can set properties such as status bar message, tooltip, enabled state, and checked state.

A *UIButtonControl* acts as a button or menu item that performs a simple task when clicked.

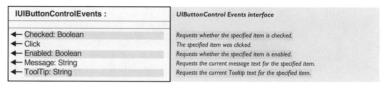

IUIButtonControlEvents :	UIButtonControl Events interface
← Checked: Boolean	*Requests whether the specified item is checked.*
← Click	*The specified item was clicked.*
← Enabled: Boolean	*Requests whether the specified item is enabled.*
← Message: String	*Requests the current message text for the specified item.*
← ToolTip: String	*Requests the current Tooltip text for the specified item.*

The *IUIButtonControlEvents* interface defines the properties of a *UIButtonControl*, such as the enabled state, checked state, ToolTip, and status bar message. This interface also has a *Click* method that defines what action occurs when the button is clicked.

The following VBA code is a full implementation of a *UIButtonControl* that reports the number of selected features in all the layers. This control is enabled only when there are layers in the map.

```vba
Private Function UIButtonControl1_Checked() As Boolean
  UIButtonControl1_Checked = False
End Function


Private Sub UIButtonControl1_Click()
  Dim pMxDoc As IMxDocument
  Dim SelCount As Long
  Set pMxDoc = Application.Document
  SelCount = pMxDoc.FocusMap.SelectionCount
  MsgBox SelCount
End Sub


Private Function UIButtonControl1_Enabled() As Boolean
  Dim pMxDoc As IMxDocument
  Dim LayerCount As Long
  Set pMxDoc = Application.Document
  LayerCount = pMxDoc.FocusMap.LayerCount
  If LayerCount > 0 Then
    UIButtonControl1_Enabled = True
  Else
    UIButtonControl1_Enabled = False
  End If
End Function


Private Function UIButtonControl1_Message() As String
  UIButtonControl1_Message = "Return selection count for all layers"
End Function


Private Function UIButtonControl1_ToolTip() As String
  UIButtonControl1_ToolTip = "Selection Count"
End Function
```

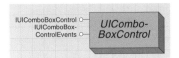

A UIComboBox control is a dropdown list box control that can be added to a toolbar.

A *UIComboBoxControl* has properties and methods that allow you to change, add, and remove items in the combo box list. The *EditChange*, *SelectionChange*, and *Keydown* events allow you to control what happens when a user changes the text or selection in the combo box.

IUIComboBoxControlEvents :	UIComboBoxControl Events interface
← EditChange	Occurs when the user types within the edit portion of the combobox.
← Enabled: Boolean	Requests whether the specified item is enabled.
← GotFocus	Occurs when UIComboBoxControl gets focus.
← KeyDown (in keyCode: Long, in shift: Long)	Occurs when the user presses a key.
← LostFocus	Occurs when UIComboBoxControl loses focus.
← Message: String	Requests the current message text for the specified item.
← SelectionChange (in newIndex: Long)	Occurs when the user selects an item in the combobox.
← ToolTip: String	Requests the current Tooltip text for the specified item.

The *IUIComboBoxControlEvents* interface defines the properties of a *UIComboBoxControl*, such as the enabled state, ToolTip, and status bar message. This interface also has *EditChange, KeyDown,* and *SelectionChange* methods that allow you to control what happens when a user changes the text or selection in the combo box.

The following VBA code displays a message box that reports the currently selected item when the selection changes in the combo box.

```
Private Sub UIComboBoxControl1_SelectionChange(ByVal newIndex As Long)
  MsgBox UIComboBoxControl1.Item(newIndex)
End Sub
```

IUIComboBoxControl : IDispatch	UIComboBox Control interface
■─■ EditText: String	Returns or sets the edit text within the combobox.
■─ Item (in index: Long) : String	Returns the text at the specified index.
■─ ItemCount: Long	Returns the number of items currently inside of the combobox.
■─■ ListIndex: Long	Returns or sets the selected index within the combobox.
← AddItem (in itemText: String, index: Variant)	Adds an item to the combobox, optionally at the specified index.
← DeleteItem (in index: Long)	Deletes an item from the combobox at the specified index.
← RemoveAll	Removes all items from the combobox.

The *IUIComboBoxControl* interface has properties and methods that allow you to change, edit, and remove items in the combo box list.

The following VBA macro adds items to *UIComboBoxControl1* and selects the first item in the list.

```
Public Sub PopulateComboBox()
  UIComboBoxControl1.AddItem "Red"
  UIComboBoxControl1.AddItem "Green"
  UIComboBoxControl1.AddItem "Blue"
  UIComboBoxControl1.AddItem "Yellow"
  UIComboBoxControl1.ListIndex = 0
End Sub
```

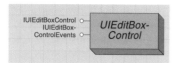

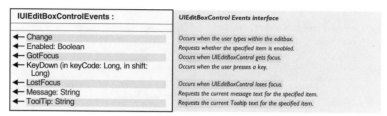

A UI edit box control is an editable text box control that can be added to a toolbar.

A *UIEditBox* has a property to set the text that appears in the edit box. The *Change* and *Keydown* events allow you to control what happens when a user changes the text in the edit box.

IUIEditBoxControlEvents :	UIEditBoxControl Events interface
← Change	Occurs when the user types within the editbox.
← Enabled: Boolean	Requests whether the specified item is enabled.
← GotFocus	Occurs when UIEditBoxControl gets focus.
← KeyDown (in keyCode: Long, in shift: Long)	Occurs when the user presses a key.
← LostFocus	Occurs when UIEditBoxControl loses focus.
← Message: String	Requests the current message text for the specified item.
← ToolTip: String	Requests the current Tooltip text for the specified item.

The *IUIEditBoxControlEvents* interface defines the properties of a *UIEditBoxControl*, such as the enabled state, ToolTip, and status bar message.

This interface also has *Change* and *KeyDown* methods that allow you to control what happens when a user changes the text in the edit box.

The following VBA code uses the *KeyDown* method to report the current text in the edit box if the Return key is pressed.

```
Private Sub UIEditBoxControl1_KeyDown(ByVal keyCode As Long, ByVal shift As Long)
  If keyCode = vbKeyReturn Then
    MsgBox UIEditBoxControl1.Text
  End If
End Sub
```

IUIEditBoxControl : IDispatch	UIEditBoxControl interface
■→ Text: String	Returns or sets the editbox text.
← Clear	Clears the contents of the editbox.

The *IUIEditBoxControl* interface has a *Text* property for getting and setting the text in the *UIEditBox* control and a *Clear* method for deleting the text.

The following VBA macro sets the text in a *UIEditBoxControl* called *UIEditBoxControl1*.

```
Public Sub SetText()
  UIEditBoxControl1.Text = "Hello"
End Sub
```

IUIToolControlEvents

*A UI tool control interacts with the
application's display.*

A *UIToolControl* is similar to a COM command that implements the *ITool* interface. This type of control can interact with the application's display. You can set all the properties that *UIButtonControls* have and define what occurs on events, including mouse move, mouse button press and release, keyboard key press and release, double-click, and right-click.

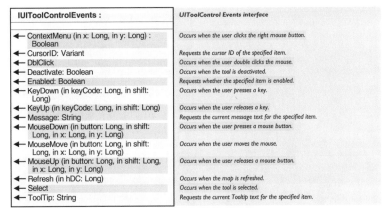

IUIToolControlEvents :	UIToolControl Events interface
← ContextMenu (in x: Long, in y: Long) : Boolean	*Occurs when the user clicks the right mouse button.*
← CursorID: Variant	*Requests the cursor ID of the specified item.*
← DblClick	*Occurs when the user double clicks the mouse.*
← Deactivate: Boolean	*Occurs when the tool is deactivated.*
← Enabled: Boolean	*Requests whether the specified item is enabled.*
← KeyDown (in keyCode: Long, in shift: Long)	*Occurs when the user presses a key.*
← KeyUp (in keyCode: Long, in shift: Long)	*Occurs when the user releases a key.*
← Message: String	*Requests the current message text for the specified item.*
← MouseDown (in button: Long, in shift: Long, in x: Long, in y: Long)	*Occurs when the user presses a mouse button.*
← MouseMove (in button: Long, in shift: Long, in x: Long, in y: Long)	*Occurs when the user moves the mouse.*
← MouseUp (in button: Long, in shift: Long, in x: Long, in y: Long)	*Occurs when the user releases a mouse button.*
← Refresh (in hDC: Long)	*Occurs when the map is refreshed.*
← Select	*Occurs when the tool is selected.*
← ToolTip: String	*Requests the current Tooltip text for the specified item.*

The *IUIToolControlEvents* interface defines the properties of a *UIToolControl*, such as the enabled state, cursor, ToolTip, and status bar message. This interface also has methods that allow you to control what happens on events, including mouse move, mouse button press and release, keyboard key press and release, double-click, and right-click.

The following VBA code displays the x,y coordinates of the left mouse button click in the ArcMap status bar message.

```
Private Sub UIToolControl1_MouseDown(ByVal button As Long, _
 ByVal shift As Long, ByVal x As Long, ByVal y As Long)
  ' Check for left button press
  If button = 1 Then
    ' Convert x and y to map units.
    Dim pPoint As IPoint
    Dim pMxApp As IMxApplication
    Set pMxApp = Application
    Set pPoint = pMxApp.Display.DisplayTransformation.ToMapPoint(x, y)
    ' Set the statusbar message
    Application.StatusBar.Message(0) = Str(pPoint.x) & "," & Str(pPoint.y)
  End If
End Sub
```

You can create COM commands in any development environment that supports COM—for example, Visual Basic, Visual C++, or Delphi®. COM-based commands are distributed in the form of ActiveX DLLs.

For more information on creating COM components, see Chapter 2, 'Developing with ArcObjects'.

The interfaces discussed in this section (*ICommand, ITool, IToolControl, ICommandSubtype,* and *IMultiItem*) are generally implemented to create custom commands. It is very rare that you would use these interfaces to query the properties of the command. In the application, all commands are exposed through command items, so you would use the *ICommandItem* interface to query the properties or to override some of the properties of the underlying command.

You can create the following types of commands: *Button, Tool, ToolControl, SubtypedCommand,* and *MultiItem.*

Buttons can be put on toolbars and menus. To create a custom button, you only have to implement *ICommand.*

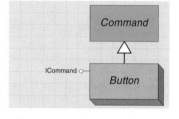

Buttons are simple commands that act as button or menu items and perform simple actions when clicked.

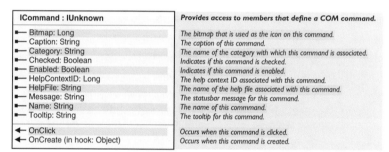

ICommand : IUnknown	Provides access to members that define a COM command.
■— Bitmap: Long	The bitmap that is used as the icon on this command.
■— Caption: String	The caption of this command.
■— Category: String	The name of the category with which this command is associated.
■— Checked: Boolean	Indicates if this command is checked.
■— Enabled: Boolean	Indicates if this command is enabled.
■— HelpContextID: Long	The help context ID associated with this command.
■— HelpFile: String	The name of the help file associated with this command.
■— Message: String	The statusbar message for this command.
■— Name: String	The name of this command.
■— Tooltip: String	The tooltip for this command.
◄— OnClick	Occurs when this command is clicked.
◄— OnCreate (in hook: Object)	Occurs when this command is created.

The *ICommand* interface must be implemented by all COM-based commands (except for *MultiItems*). This interface determines the behavior and properties of simple commands, such as buttons and menu items. For example, the *ICommand* interface sets command properties, such as caption, name, category, bitmap, status bar message, ToolTip, help context ID and help file, enabled state, and checked state. It also defines what action happens when the command is clicked.

The main concept to understand about implementing *ICommand* is the *OnCreate* method. This method occurs when the command is instantiated and provides a hook to the application object that instantiated the command. Once you have this reference to the application object, you can access the other objects in the application. The following VB code fragment from a class file that implements *ICommand* gets a reference to the application object and, from that, gets a reference to the document object.

```
Dim m_pApp As IApplication
Dim m_pMxDoc As IMxApplication
Private Sub ICommand_OnCreate(ByVal hook As Object)
  Set m_pApp = hook
  Set m_pMxDoc = m_pApp.Document
End Sub
```

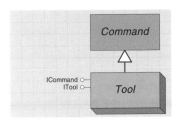

A tool acts as a button that allows further interaction with the application display. Tools can only be put on toolbars.

To create a custom *Tool* object, implement both *ICommand* and *ITool*. The Zoom In tool is a good example of a tool—you click or drag a rectangle over the map display to define the area on which to zoom.

ITool : IUnknown	Provides access to members that define a tool.
▪— Cursor: Long	The mouse pointer for this tool.
◄— Deactivate: Boolean	Causes the tool to no longer be the active tool.
◄— OnContextMenu (in X: Long, in Y: Long) : Boolean	Context menu event occured at the given xy location.
◄— OnDblClick	Occurs when a mouse button is double clicked when this tool is active.
◄— OnKeyDown (in keyCode: Long, in Shift: Long)	Occurs when a key on the keyboard is pressed when this tool is active.
◄— OnKeyUp (in keyCode: Long, in Shift: Long)	Occurs when a key on the keyboard is released when this tool is active.
◄— OnMouseDown (in Button: Long, in Shift: Long, in X: Long, in Y: Long)	Occurs when a mouse button is pressed when this tool is active.
◄— OnMouseMove (in Button: Long, in Shift: Long, in X: Long, in Y: Long)	Occurs when the mouse is moved when this tool is active.
◄— OnMouseUp (in Button: Long, in Shift: Long, in X: Long, in Y: Long)	Occurs when a mouse button is released when this tool is active.
◄— Refresh (in hDC: Long)	Occurs when a screen display in the application is refreshed.

The *ITool* interface is implemented by specialized commands that can interact with the application's display. Only one tool can be active in the application at a time. With the *ITool* interface, you can define what occurs on events, such as mouse move, mouse button press and release, keyboard key press and release, double-click, and right-click.

The following is a code excerpt from a class that implements *ICommand* and *ITool*. This ArcMap tool displays the x,y coordinates of the left moust button click in the status bar. The x,y coordinates that are passed in as arguments to this subprocedure are converted to map coordinates.

```
Private Sub ITool_OnMouseDown(ByVal Button As Long, ByVal Shift As Long, _
                              ByVal X As Long, ByVal Y As Long)
  ' Check to see if left button is pressed
 If Button = 1 Then
   ' Convert x and y to map units. m_pApp is set in ICommand_OnCreate.
   Dim pPoint As IPoint
   Dim pMxApp As IMxApplication
   Set pMxApp = m_pApp
   Set pPoint = pMxApp.Display.DisplayTransformation.ToMapPoint(x, y)
   ' Set the statusbar message.
   m_pApp.StatusBar.Message(0) = Str(pPoint.X) & "," & Str(pPoint.Y)
 End If
End Sub
```

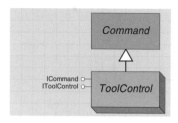

A tool control is a dropdown list box control, editable textbox control, or other type of control that can be added to a toolbar.

To create a custom ToolControl object, implement both ICommand and IToolControl.

Only one instance of a particular tool control is allowed to exist in the application at any one time.

A command that implements the *IToolControl* interface passes its window handle to the application using the *hWnd* property. The *OnDrop* method is used to specify on which type of command bar this tool control can be put. In most cases, tool controls can only be used on toolbars.

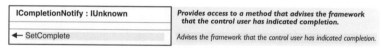

IToolControl : IUnknown	Provides access to members that define a toolcontrol.
■— hWnd: Long	The handle of the control.
◄— OnDrop (in barType: esriCmdBarType) : Boolean	Indicates if the drag-drop operation is valid.
◄— OnFocus (in complete: ICompletionNotify)	Occurs when the control gains focus.

The *IToolControl* interface is implemented by commands that act as edit box controls or combo box controls. A command that implements *IToolControl* passes its window handle to the application.

ICompletionNotify : IUnknown	Provides access to a method that advises the framework that the control user has indicated completion.
◄— SetComplete	Advises the framework that the control user has indicated completion.

The *ICompletionNotify* interface provides the *IToolControl* interface with a mechanism to report to the application that the tool control no longer needs focus.

When the *ToolControl* object gains focus, an *ICompletionNotify* object is passed to the tool control as the *complete* parameter in the *IToolControl* *OnFocus* method. The tool control needs to call the *ICompletionNotify* *SetComplete* method to let the application know that the control should lose focus.

In the following VB code, the *hWnd* property passes back the window handle of a combo box control on a form in the VB project. The *OnDrop* method specifies that the tool control can only be dropped onto toolbars. In the *OnFocus* method, a variable is set to the *ICompletionNotify* object so that *SetComplete* can be called when the tool control no longer needs focus. For example, if a combo box control loses focus after a user selects an item in the combo box, the combo box *Click* event calls *SetComplete*.

```
Implements IToolControl
Public pCompNotify As ICompletionNotify
Private Property Get IToolControl_hWnd  () As esriCore.OLE_HANDLE
  IToolControl_hWnd = Form1.Combo1.hWnd
End Property

Private Function IToolControl_OnDrop  (ByVal barType As _
                            esriCore.esriCmdBarType) As Boolean
  If barType = esriCmdBarTypeToolbar Then IToolControl_OnDrop = True
End Function

Private Sub IToolControl_OnFocus  (ByVal complete As _
                            esriCore.ICompletionNotify)
  Set pCompNotify = complete
End Sub
```

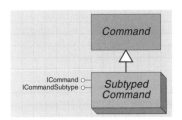

A subtyped command object is a group of related commands that can share properties. Subtyped commands can be put on toolbars and menus.

To create a custom *SubtypedCommand* class, implement the *ICommand* and *ICommandSubtype* interfaces.

ICommandSubType: IUnknown	Provides access to members that define a subtyped command.
← GetCount: Long	The number of commands defined with this CLSID.
← SetSubType (in SubType: Long)	The subtype of the command.

The *ICommandSubType* interface is used when you want more than one command in a single class. You would implement both *ICommand* and *ICommandSubType* in your class. The *ICommandSubType* interface lets you specify how many subtypes there are. Then, within the implementation of each *ICommand* property, you set the property for each subtype instead of implementing the *ICommand* interface multiple times.

This VB code fragment is from a class that implements *ICommand* and *ICommandSubType*; it specifies that the subtyped command contains two subtypes. In the *Caption* property of *ICommand*, a case statement is used to determine which subtype is being queried.

```
Dim m_lSubType As Long
Private Function ICommandSubType_GetCount() As Long
  ICommandSubType_GetCount = 2
End Function

Private Sub ICommandSubType_SetSubType(ByVal SubType As Long)
  m_lSubType = SubType
End Sub
Private Property Get ICommand_Caption() As String
  Select Case m_lSubType
  Case 1
     ICommand_Caption = "Command 1"
  Case 2
     ICommand_Caption = "Command 2"
  End Select
End Property
```

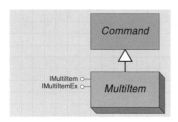

A MultiItem object is a dynamic command that appears as zero or more adjacent menu items on a menu, depending on the state of the application.

A *MultiItem* can be used when items on a menu can't be determined prior to run time or the items need to be modified based on the state of the system. A good example of this are the menu items at the bottom of the File menu, which represent the most recently used files.

IMultiItem : IUnknown	Provides access to members that define a multiitem.
■— Caption: String	*The caption of the multiitem.*
■— HelpContextID: Long	*The help context ID associated with this multiitem.*
■— HelpFile: String	*The name of the help file associated with this multiitem.*
■— ItemBitmap (in Index: Long) : Long	*The bitmap for the item at the specified index.*
■— ItemCaption (in Index: Long) : String	*The caption of the item at the specified index.*
■— ItemChecked (in Index: Long) : Boolean	*Indicates if item at the specified index is checked.*
■— ItemEnabled (in Index: Long) : Boolean	*Indicates if the item at the specified index is enabled.*
■— Message: String	*The status bar message for all items on the multiitem.*
■— Name: String	*The name of the multiitem.*
◄— OnItemClick (in Index: Long)	*Occurs when the item at the specified index is clicked.*
◄— OnPopup (in hook: Object) : Long	*Occurs when the menu that contains the multiitem is about to be displayed.*

The *IMultiItem* interface allows a single object to act like several adjacent menu items. During run time, the framework notifies *MultiItem* commands when their host menu is about to be shown. At this point, all the commands implementing *IMultiItem* can query the system to determine how many items should be represented and how each should appear. The *IMultiItem* interface allows you to assign properties, such as caption, bitmap, enabled state, and checked state, to each item. You do not implement the *ICommand* interface when creating a *MultiItem*.

The main concept to understand about implementing *IMultiItem* is the *OnPopup* method. This method occurs just before the menu containing the *MultiItem* is displayed. *OnPopup* provides a hook to the application object that instantiated the *MultiItem* and is also used to set the number of items in the *MultiItem*. The following VB code fragment gets a reference to the application object, document object, and map object. This particular *MultiItem* will contain an item corresponding to each layer in the map, so the map layer count is returned to specify the number of items.

```
Dim m_pApp As IApplication 'ArcMap application
Dim m_pMxDoc As IMxDocument    'ArcMap document
Dim m_pMap As IMap        'Current focus map
Dim m_pLayerCnt As Long     'Number of layers in the map

Private Function IMultiItem_OnPopup(ByVal hook As Object) As Long
  Set m_pApp = hook
  Set m_pMxDoc = m_pApp.Document
  Set m_pMap = m_pMxDoc.FocusMap
  m_pLayerCnt = m_pMap.LayerCount
  IMultiItem_OnPopup = m_pLayerCnt
End Function
```

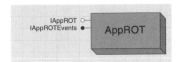

The application running object table is an instantiable class that gives you access to a list of all running ArcGIS applications.

The *AppROT* object represents the application running object table, which is a global list of all the currently running ArcGIS applications. *AppROT* only contains references to application objects that implement the *IApplication* interface. ArcMap, ArcCatalog, and other ArcGIS applications automatically register themselves in the running object table when starting and remove themselves from the table when terminating. (The *AppROT* object should not be confused with Microsoft's running object table, which contains all running COM objects.)

Advanced developers can create custom standalone applications with ArcObjects by creating their own implementation of *IApplication*. They can register and expunge application references in *AppROT* through the *Add* and *Remove* methods.

You can return the count of running applications and return application references. You can also add and remove application references.

IAppROT : IUnknown	Provides access to members that manipulate the ESRI application running object table, AppROT.
■— Count: Long	The count of application references within the running object table.
■— Item (in Index: Long) : IApplication	The application reference at the specified index in the running object table.
← Add (in pApp: IApplication) : Long	Adds an application reference to the running object table.
← Remove (in cookie: Long)	Removes an application reference from the running object table.

The *Add* method returns a long value called a cookie, which is a reference to an application. It should be kept by the client application for eventual use in the *Remove* method.

This VBA code iterates through all running applications and lists captions.

```
Dim pAppROT as AppROT
Set pAppRot = New AppROT
Dim i as Integer
For i = 0 to pApprot.Count - 1
  msgbox pAppROT.Item(i).Caption
Next
```

IAppROTEvents : IUnknown	Provides access to events that occur on the ESRI application running object table.
← AppAdded (in pApp: IApplication)	Occurs when an application reference is added to the table.
← AppRemoved (in pApp: IApplication)	Occurs when an application reference is removed from the table.

Whenever an ArcGIS application is started or dismissed, you can add custom code whenever that event is fired. Through this code, you can synchronize the behavior of many running applications.

The *AppROT* events let interested applications and components know when an ArcGIS application has been started or terminated. When an instance of an application starts or terminates, an event will automatically fire from *AppROT* to let all listeners know about it. This may be useful if listening components or applications need to maintain switch-to lists or if they want to synchronize representations between all running instances so that if something happens in one application, all others can be informed and update themselves appropriately. Such coordinating components need to know when new instances start and when existing ones terminate.

In the following VB code, the *StartListening* routine initializes the *m_pAppROT* variable, which will listen to the *IAppRotEvents*. The code in the events uses the *TypeOf* keyword to determine which application was started or shutdown, and reports a message with that information.

```
Dim WithEvents m_pAppROTEvents As AppROT

Public Sub StartListening()
  Set m_pAppROTEvents = New AppROT
End Sub

Private Sub m_pAppROTEvents_AppAdded(ByVal pApp As IApplication)
  If TypeOf pApp Is IMxApplication Then
    MsgBox "ArcMap started"
  ElseIf TypeOf pApp Is IGxApplication Then
    MsgBox "ArcCatalog started"
  End If
End Sub

Private Sub m_pAppROTEvents_AppRemoved(ByVal pApp As IApplication)
  If TypeOf pApp Is IMxApplication Then
    MsgBox "ArcMap shut down"
  ElseIf TypeOf pApp Is IGxApplication Then
    MsgBox "ArcCatalog shut down"
  End If
End Sub
```

Component categories are used by client applications to efficiently find all components of a particular type that are installed on the system.

The *ComponentCategoryManager* object provides a mechanism for you to programmatically add or remove new components to a particular category and create new component categories.

For example, ArcMap only supports commands that implement the *ICommand* interface. A component category, ESRI Mx Commands, is used to find all the command components that can be used inside ArcMap.

If component categories were not used, the application would have to instantiate each COM component and interrogate it to see if it supported the required functionality, which is not a practical approach. Component categories support the extensibility of COM by allowing the developer of the client application to create and work with classes that belong to a particular category. If at a later date a new class is added to the category, the client application need not be changed to take advantage of the new class; it will automatically pick up the new class the next time the category is read.

IComponentCategoryManager : IUnknown	Provides access to members that work with the component category manager.
← Create (in Name: String, in Category: IUID)	Creates a component category.
← Setup (in PathName: String, in ObjectType: IUID, in Category: IUID, in install: Boolean)	Installs or uninstalls the objects that match the object type into the given category.
← SetupObject (in PathName: String, in obj: IUID, in Category: IUID, in install: Boolean)	Installs or uninstalls the given object into the given category.

The *IComponentCategoryManager* interface has methods that allow you to create a new component category, add or remove a particular object to a category, and add or remove all objects of a certain type to a category. To get access to the *IComponentCategoryManager* interface, create a new instance of a *ComponentCategoryManager* object.

The following Visual Basic code registers a specific command contained in a DLL with the ArcMap commands component category.

```
Public Sub RegObj()
```

Set the path to the dll. Change this to the location of your dll.

```
    Dim dllPath As String
    dllPath = "D:\MyTools\MyCustomTool.dll"
```

Get a reference to the component category manager.

```
    Dim pCCMgr As IComponentCategoryManager
    Set pCCMgr = New ComponentCategoryManager
```

Get the UID for the object. This will be the UID for your command, the ProgID of your class.

```
    Dim objUID As New UID
    objUID.Value = "MyCustomTool.MyTool"
```

Get the UID of the category.

```
    Dim catUID As New UID
    catUID.Value = "{B56A7C42-83D4-11D2-A2E9-080009B6F22B}"
```

Register the objects with the category.

```
    pCCMgr.SetupObject dllPath, objUID, catUID, True
End Sub
```

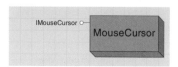

IMouseCursor ○──

MouseCursor

The mouse cursor object is a reference to the system mouse cursor object.

You can use *MouseCursor* to set the system mouse cursor to be one of the standard built-in cursors or a custom cursor. This is useful if you want to display a wait cursor while your code performs a large process.

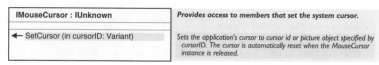

IMouseCursor : IUnknown	*Provides access to members that set the system cursor.*
← SetCursor (in cursorID: Variant)	*Sets the application's cursor to cursor id or picture object specified by cursorID. The cursor is automatically reset when the MouseCursor instance is released.*

The *IMouseCursor* interface has one method, *SetCursor*, which sets the system's cursor to the cursor ID or picture object specified by the *cursorID* parameter. The cursor is automatically reset when the *MouseCursor* instance is released. The instance is released when the calling procedure ends; when the variable that references the mouse cursor is set to nothing; or when something, such as the display of a message box, overrides Windows messaging.

The values of cursorID that can be used to set the mouse cursor to one of the built-in cursors.

The following VBA example uses the built-in wait cursor. The cursor is automatically reset when this subprocedure ends.

```
Public Sub WaitCurs()
  Dim pMouseCursor As IMouseCursor
  Dim i As Integer

  Set pMouseCursor = New MouseCursor
  pMouseCursor.SetCursor 2

  For i = 0 To 10000
    Application.StatusBar.Message(0) = Str(i)
  Next
End Sub
```

Instead of using one of the built-in cursors, you can set the cursor to a custom cursor; it can be either a cursor file (.cur) or icon file (.ico). You can store your custom cursor in an Image control on a form or use the Visual Basic *LoadPicture* function to load the cursor.

The following VBA example sets the cursor to the *Picture* property of an *Image* control called *Image1*, which is on *UserForm1*.

```
Dim pMouseCursor As IMouseCursor
Set pMouseCursor = New MouseCursor
pMouseCursor.SetCursor UserForm1.Image1.Picture
```

The following VBA example uses the *LoadPicture* function to set the cursor.

```
Dim pMouseCursor As IMouseCursor
Set pMouseCursor = New MouseCursor
pMouseCursor.SetCursor LoadPicture("D:\Cursors\Bullseye.cur")
```

A unique identifier represents the globally unique identifier for all COM objects.

A unique identifier object, or *UID*, represents the globally unique identifier (GUID) for any COM object.

COM interfaces and coclasses are identified by a GUID.

The GUID for an interface is called an interface ID (IID).

The GUID for a coclass is called a class ID (CLSID).

A ProgID is a text alias for a CLSID; the ProgID is a string composed of the project name and the class name of the coclass.

The *UID* object can be used to represent the GUID of an object.

IUID : IDispatch	**Provides access to members that work with globally unique identifier objects.**
■─■ SubType: Long	*The subtype of the UID object.*
■─■ Value: Variant	*The value of the UID object.*
← Compare (in otherID: IUID) : Boolean	*Indicates if the two UID objects represent the same globally unique identifier.*
← Generate	*Creates a new globally unique value for the UID object.*

The *IUID* interface has properties and methods that allow you to set the value of a *UID* object, set the subtype of the *UID* object, generate a new globally unique value, and compare two *UID* objects.

In the following VB example, *u* is defined as a new *UID* object and is set to the CLSID of the ArcMap AddData command. That way, *u* can be used in any of the methods that require an *IUID* object.

The *IUID* interface is the default interface for the UID coclass—you don't need to Dim the interface; you can cocreate this object in Visual Basic, as shown in the following code.

```
Dim u As New UID
u.Value = "{E1F29C6B-4E6B-11D2-AE2C-080009EC732A}"
```

In the following example, *u* is set to the ProgID of the ESRI Object Editor extension.

```
Dim u As New UID
u.Value = "esriCore.Editor"
```

Framework dialog box objects

IProgressDialogFactory — **Progress-Dialog-Factory**
> The Progress dialog box factory creates and displays a new progress dialog box

IProgressDialog
IProgressDialog2
IProgressor
IStepProgressor — *Progress-Dialog*
> A Progress dialog box displays animation and a step progressor bar

ICoordinateDialog — **Coordinate-Dialog**
> The Coordinate dialog box is used for getting user input in the form of x, y coordinates

IGetStringDialog — **GetString-Dialog**
> The Get String dialog is used for getting user input in the form of a string

IGetUserAndPasswordDialog — **GetUserAnd-Password-Dialog**
> The Get User and Password dialog is used for getting username and password information

IListDialog — **ListDialog**
> The List dialog box is used to present a list of options and allows the user to select one of the options

IMessageDialog — **Message-Dialog**
> The Message dialog box is used to display a message to the user

INumberDialog — **Number-Dialog**
> The Number dialog box is used for getting user input in the form of a number

The ArcGIS applications provide a set of simple dialog boxes for getting input from the user or for displaying information. For more elaborate dialog boxes, you can create your own forms in VB or VBA.

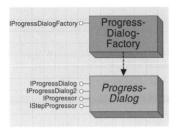

IProgressDialogFactory ○— **Progress-Dialog-Factory**

IProgressDialog ○—
IProgressDialog2 ○— **Progress-Dialog**
IProgressor ○—
IStepProgressor ○—

A progress dialog box displays an animation and a step progressor bar.

Instead of reporting the progress of an operation in the status bar, you can display a progress dialog box instead. The progress dialog box displays an animation and a step progress bar. The *ProgressDialogFactory* coclass creates and displays a new progress dialog.

IProgressDialogFactory : IUnknown	Provides access to a method that creates a progress dialog.
← Create (in trackCancel: ITrackCancel, in hWnd: Long) : IStepProgressor	*Creates a progress dialog.*

The *IProgressDialogFactory* interface has one method, *Create*, which creates and displays a progress dialog box. You can pass a *Cancel-Tracker* object into this method to allow the user to cancel the process.

IProgressDialog2 : IUnknown	Provides access to members that work with a progress dialog.
■—■ Animation: esriProgressAnimationTypes	*The animation type displayed in the dialog.*
■—■ CancelEnabled: Boolean	*Indicates if the Cancel button is enabled.*
■—■ Description: String	*The description displayed in the dialog.*
■—■ Title: String	*The caption displayed in the dialog.*
← HideDialog	*Hides the progress dialog.*
← ShowDialog	*Shows the progress dialog.*

The *IProgressDialog* interface is the original interface for the progress dialog box. However, you should use the more recent *IProgressDialog2* interface instead. The *IProgressDialog2* interface has methods for hiding and showing the progress dialog box.

The *Title* and *Description* properties can be used to provide the user with information about the process that the dialog box is tracking.

The *CancelEnabled* property specifies if the Cancel button is enabled. If *CancelEnabled* is set to *True*, you can use the *Continue* method on the *CancelTracker* object to determine if the user hit *Cancel* and the operations should be stopped.

The *Animation* property specifies the type of animation displayed in the dialog box.

Enumeration esriProgressAnimationTypes	Progress animation types.
0 - esriProgressGlobe	*Spinning globe animation.*
1 - esriDownloadFile	*Downloading file animation.*

The animation in the dialog box can either be the spinning globe animation or the downloading file animation.

The following VBA code creates and displays a progress dialog box and shows the progress of a loop counting to 10,000.

```
Sub ProgDialog()
  Dim pProDlgFact As IProgressDialogFactory
  Dim pStepPro As IStepProgressor
  Dim pProDlg As IProgressDialog2
  Dim pTrkCan As ITrackCancel
  Dim boolCont As Boolean
  Dim i As Long
```

The progress dialog box

```
' Create a CancelTracker
Set pTrkCan = New CancelTracker

' Create the ProgressDialog. This automatically displays the dialog
Set pProDlgFact = New ProgressDialogFactory
Set pProDlg = pProDlgFact.Create(pTrkCan, Application.hWnd)

' Set the properties of the ProgressDialog
pProDlg.CancelEnabled = True
pProDlg.Description = "This is counting to 10000."
pProDlg.Title = "Counting..."
pProDlg.Animation = esriDownloadFile

' Set the properties of the Step Progressor
Set pStepPro = pProDlg
pStepPro.MinRange = 0
pStepPro.MaxRange = 10000
pStepPro.StepValue = 1
pStepPro.Message = "Hello"

' Step. Do your big process here.
boolCont = True
For i = 0 To 10000
  Application.StatusBar.Message(0) = Str(i)
  'Check if the cancel button was pressed. If so, stop process
  boolCont = pTrkCan.Continue
  If Not boolCont Then
    Exit For
  End If
Next i

' Done

Set pTrkCan = Nothing
Set pStepPro = Nothing
Set pProDlg = Nothing
End Sub
```

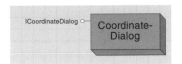

The Coordinate dialog box gets user input in the form of x,y coordinates.

To get access to the *ICoordinateDialog* interface, instantiate a new *CoordinateDialog* object.

ICoordinateDialog : IUnknown	Provides access to members that work with a dialog for getting coordinates.
■— X: Double	The X value entered in the dialog.
■— Y: Double	The Y value entered in the dialog.
◄— DoModal (in Title: String, in initialX: Double, in initialY: Double, in numDecs: Long, in hWnd: Long) : Boolean	Shows the dialog.

The GetCoordinateDialog

The *ICoordinateDialog* interface has a *DoModal* method for displaying the dialog box. There are parameters on this method for setting the dialog box title, the initial x-value, the initial y-value, and the number of decimal places in the values. If nonnumeric values were entered or if the dialog box was cancelled, the *DoModal* method returns *False*. The x and y properties allow you to get the x- and y-values that were entered in the dialog box.

The following VBA code shows a *CoordinateDialog* and reports the x- and y-values.

```
Public Sub CoordDlg()
  Dim pCoordDlg As ICoordinateDialog
  Dim boolValid As Boolean
  Set pCoordDlg = New CoordinateDialog
  boolValid = pCoordDlg.DoModal("Enter X & Y coordinates", 1, 1, _
      3, Application.hWnd)
  If boolValid Then
    MsgBox "X: " & pCoordDlg.X & vbNewLine & _
        "Y: " & pCoordDlg.Y
  Else
    MsgBox "Bad entries."
  End If
End Sub
```

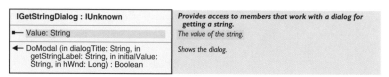

The get string dialog box gets user input in the form of a string.

To get access to the *IGetStringDialog* interface, instantiate a new *GetStringDialog* object.

IGetStringDialog : IUnknown	Provides access to members that work with a dialog for getting a string.
■— Value: String	*The value of the string.*
◄— DoModal (in dialogTitle: String, in getStringLabel: String, in initialValue: String, in hWnd: Long) : Boolean	*Shows the dialog.*

The *IGetStringDialog* interface has a *DoModal* method for displaying the dialog box. There are parameters on this method for setting the dialog box title, the label for the string, and the initial value for the string. If the dialog box was cancelled, the *DoModal* method returns *False*.

The *Value* property allows you to get the value of the string that was entered in the dialog box.

The get string dialog box

The following VBA code shows a *GetStringDialog* and reports the string value that was entered in the dialog box.

```
Public Sub GetStrDlg()
  Dim pGetStrDlg As IGetStringDialog
  Dim boolOK As Boolean
  Set pGetStrDlg = New GetStringDialog
  boolOK = pGetStrDlg.DoModal("Please enter a string", _
    "String:", "Hello", Application.hWnd)
  If boolOK Then
    MsgBox pGetStrDlg.Value
  Else
    MsgBox "Cancelled."
  End If
End Sub
```

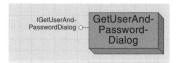

The get user and password dialog box gets username and password information.

To get access to the *IGetUserAndPasswordDialog* interface, instantiate a new *GetUserAndPasswordDialog* object.

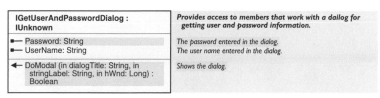

IGetUserAndPasswordDialog : IUnknown	Provides access to members that work with a dailog for getting user and password information.
■— Password: String	The password entered in the dialog.
■— UserName: String	The user name entered in the dialog.
◄— DoModal (in dialogTitle: String, in stringLabel: String, in hWnd: Long) : Boolean	Shows the dialog.

The *IGetUserAndPasswordDialog* interface has a *DoModal* method for displaying the dialog box. There are parameters on this method for setting the dialog box title and a message to be displayed in the dialog box. If the dialog box was cancelled, the *DoModal* method returns *False*.

The *UserName* property allows you to get the username that was entered in the dialog box.

The *Password* property allows you to get the password that was entered in the dialog box.

The get user and password dialog box

The following VBA code shows a *GetUserAndPasswordDialog* and validates the username and password that were entered in the dialog box.

```
Public Sub GetUserPassDlg()
  Dim pGetUserPassDlg As IGetUserAndPasswordDialog
  Dim boolOK As Boolean
  Set pGetUserPassDlg = New GetUserAndPasswordDialog
  boolOK = pGetUserPassDlg.DoModal("Login", _
      "Login for this document:", Application.hWnd)
  If boolOK Then
    If pGetUserPassDlg.UserName = "GISTeam" And _
    pGetUserPassDlg.Password = "guru" Then
      MsgBox "You're in!"
    Else
      MsgBox "Wrong username or password."
    End If
  Else
    MsgBox "Cancelled."
  End If
End Sub
```

The list dialog box presents a list of options and allows the user to select one of the options.

To get access to the *IListDialog* interface, instantiate a new *ListDialog* object.

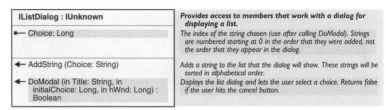

IListDialog : IUnknown	Provides access to members that work with a dialog for displaying a list.
Choice: Long	The index of the string chosen (use after calling DoModal). Strings are numbered starting at 0 in the order that they were added, not the order that they appear in the dialog.
AddString (Choice: String)	Adds a string to the list that the dialog will show. These strings will be sorted in alphabetical order.
DoModal (in Title: String, in initialChoice: Long, in hWnd: Long) : Boolean	Displays the list dialog and lets the user select a choice. Returns false if the user hits the cancel button.

The *IListDialog* interface has an *AddString* method for populating the list that is displayed in the dialog box, and a *DoModal* method for displaying the dialog box. The *DoModal* method has parameters for setting the title of the dialog and the initial selection. This method returns *False* if the dialog box was cancelled. When the dialog box is displayed, the items in the list are sorted in alphabetical order.

The ListDialog

The *Choice* property returns the index of the selected item in the list. The items are numbered starting at zero in the order that they were added, not in the order in which they appear in the dialog box.

The following VBA code shows a list in the dialog box, then reports the string associated with the selected item.

```
Public Sub ListDlg()
  Dim pListDlg As IListDialog
  Dim boolOK As Boolean
  Set pListDlg = New ListDialog
  pListDlg.AddString "California"
  pListDlg.AddString "Arizona"
  pListDlg.AddString "Utah"
  pListDlg.AddString "Nevada"
  boolOK = pListDlg.DoModal("The list", 0, Application.hWnd)
  If boolOK Then
    Select Case pListDlg.Choice
    Case 0
      MsgBox "California"
    Case 1
      MsgBox "Arizona"
    Case 2
      MsgBox "Utah"
    Case 3
      MsgBox "Nevada"
    End Select
  Else
    MsgBox "Cancelled."
  End If
End Sub
```

The message dialog box displays a message to the user.

To get access to the *IMessageDialog* interface, instantiate a new *Message-Dialog* object.

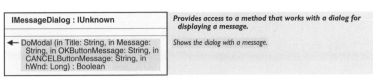

IMessageDialog : IUnknown	Provides access to a method that works with a dialog for displaying a message.
◄— DoModal (in Title: String, in Message: String, in OKButtonMessage: String, in CANCELButtonMessage: String, in hWnd: Long) : Boolean	Shows the dialog with a message.

The *IMessageDialog* interface has a *DoModal* method for displaying the dialog box. There are parameters on this method for setting the dialog box title, the message, the caption for the OK button, and the caption for the Cancel button. If the dialog box was cancelled, the *DoModal* method returns *False*.

The message dialog box

The following VBA code shows a *MessageDialog* and checks whether the user clicked OK or Cancel.

```
Public Sub MsgDlg()
  Dim pMsgDlg As IMessageDialog
  Dim boolYes As Boolean
  Set pMsgDlg = New MessageDialog
  boolYes = pMsgDlg.DoModal("Processing...", _
    "This will take awhile. Do you want to continue?", "YES", _
    "NO", Application.hWnd)
  If boolYes Then
    MsgBox "Continuing"
  Else
    MsgBox "Stopping."
  End If
End Sub
```

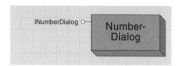

The number dialog box gets user input in the form of a number.

The number dialog box

To get access to the *INumberDialog* interface, instantiate a new *Number-Dialog* object.

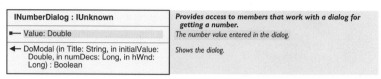

INumberDialog : IUnknown	Provides access to members that work with a dialog for getting a number.
■— Value: Double	The number value entered in the dialog.
◄— DoModal (in Title: String, in initialValue: Double, in numDecs: Long, in hWnd: Long) : Boolean	Shows the dialog.

The *INumberDialog* interface has a *DoModal* method for displaying the dialog box. There are parameters on this method for setting the dialog box title, an initial value for the number, and the number of decimal places. If a nonnumeric value was entered or if the dialog box was cancelled, the *DoModal* method returns *False*.

The *Value* property allows you to get the number that was entered in the dialog box.

The following VBA code shows a *NumberDialog* and reports the number that was entered in the dialog box.

```
Public Sub NumbDlg()
  Dim pNumbDlg As INumberDialog
  Dim boolValid As Boolean
  Set pNumbDlg = New NumberDialog
  boolValid = pNumbDlg.DoModal("Enter a number", 1, 3, _
      Application.hWnd)
  If boolValid Then
    MsgBox pNumbDlg.Value
  Else
    MsgBox "Bad entry."
  End If
End Sub
```

4

Composing maps

Steve Van Esch, Eleanor Blades, Sentha Shanmugam, Scott Campbell, Larry Young

The ArcMap application employs a presentation model that closely parallels our everyday experience of reading maps. You can customize the geographic expression of your user interface by programming the ArcMap object model.

The topics covered in this chapter include: controlling the application through the core map objects • affecting the ArcMap layout view with the page layout objects • adding graphics with the map element objects • augmenting the cartographic display with data window objects • drawing map features with the layer objects • providing spatial context to the map with map surround objects • standardizing symbology with style gallery objects • providing a visual measurement framework with map grid objects • showing quantitative information with the number objects • annotating the map with labeling objects

ArcMap core objects

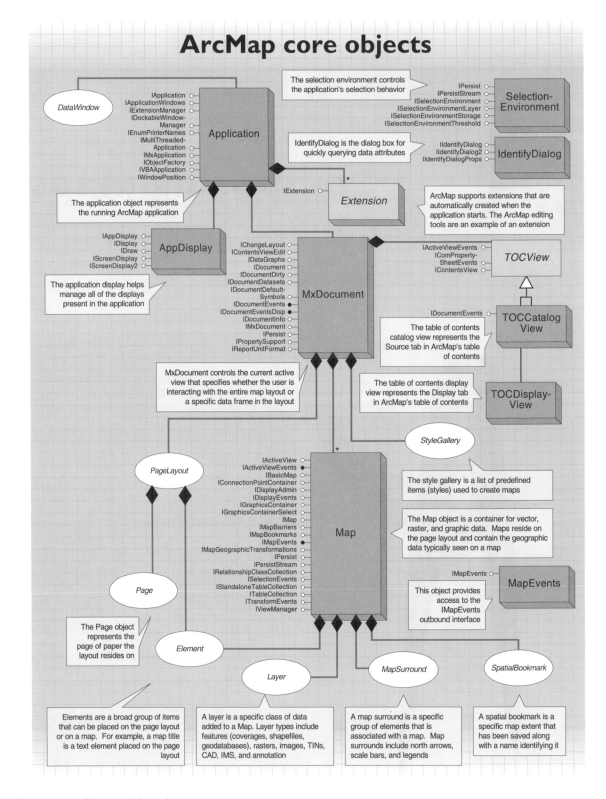

DataWindow

IApplication
IApplicationWindows
IExtensionManager
IDockableWindow-
Manager
IEnumPrinterNames
IMultiThreaded-
Application
IMxApplication
IObjectFactory
IVBAApplication
IWindowPosition

Application

The selection environment controls
the application's selection behavior

IPersist
IPersistStream
ISelectionEnvironment
ISelectionEnvironmentLayer
ISelectionEnvironmentStorage
ISelectionEnvironmentThreshold

**Selection-
Environment**

IdentifyDialog is the dialog box for
quickly querying data attributes

IIdentifyDialog
IIdentifyDialog2
IIdentifyDialogProps

IdentifyDialog

The application object represents
the running ArcMap application

IExtension

Extension

ArcMap supports extensions that are
automatically created when the
application starts. The ArcMap editing
tools are an example of an extension

IAppDisplay
IDisplay
IDraw
IScreenDisplay
IScreenDisplay2

AppDisplay

IChangeLayout
IContentsViewEdit
IDataGraphs
IDocument
IDocumentDirty
IDocumentDatasets
IDocumentDefault-
Symbols
IDocumentEvents
IDocumentEventsDisp
IDocumentInfo
IMxDocument
IPersist
IPropertySupport
IReportUnitFormat

MxDocument

IActiveViewEvents
IComProperty-
SheetEvents
IContentsView

TOCView

The application display helps
manage all of the displays
present in the application

IDocumentEvents

**TOCCatalog
View**

The table of contents
catalog view represents the
Source tab in ArcMap's table
of contents

MxDocument controls the current active
view that specifies whether the user is
interacting with the entire map layout or
a specific data frame in the layout

The table of contents display
view represents the Display tab
in ArcMap's table of contents

**TOCDisplay-
View**

StyleGallery

PageLayout

IActiveView
IActiveViewEvents
IBasicMap
IConnectionPointContainer
IDisplayAdmin
IDisplayEvents
IGraphicsContainer
IGraphicsContainerSelect
IMap
IMapBarriers
IMapBookmarks
IMapEvents
IMapGeographicTransformations
IPersist
IPersistStream
IRelationshipClassCollection
ISelectionEvents
IStandaloneTableCollection
ITableCollection
ITransformEvents
IViewManager

Map

The style gallery is a list of predefined
items (styles) used to create maps

The Map object is a container for vector,
raster, and graphic data. Maps reside on
the page layout and contain the geographic
data typically seen on a map

IMapEvents

MapEvents

Page

This object provides
access to the
IMapEvents
outbound interface

The Page object
represents the
page of paper the
layout resides on

Element

Layer

MapSurround

SpatialBookmark

Elements are a broad group of items
that can be placed on the page layout
or on a map. For example, a map title
is a text element placed on the page
layout

A layer is a specific class of data
added to a Map. Layer types include
features (coverages, shapefiles,
geodatabases), rasters, images, TINs,
CAD, IMS, and annotation

A map surround is a specific
group of elements that is
associated with a map. Map
surrounds include north arrows,
scale bars, and legends

A spatial bookmark is a
specific map extent that
has been saved along
with a name identifying it

To better comprehend programming against the ArcMap object model, it helps to understand the relationship between the ArcMap objects and the user interface. This illustration shows several important parts of the map that you can control with key objects. Compare this to the object model diagram on the facing page.

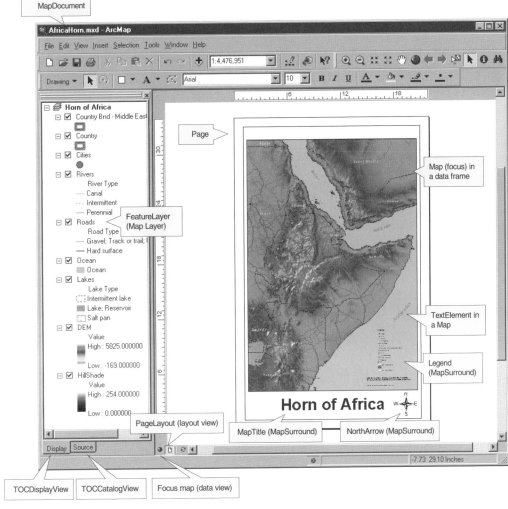

For more information about ArcMap user interface concepts, see *Using ArcMap*.

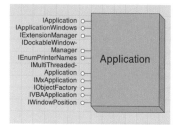

This object represents the running application and is the initial point of access to many other objects in the ArcMap application.

The *Application* object directly manages a collection of objects, including *MxDocument*, *AppDisplay*, *SelectionEnvironment*, and any registered extensions; it also manages a *StatusBar*, *Templates*, *Paper*, and printer object. For more information, see Chapter 3, 'Customizing the user interface' and Chapter 5, 'Displaying graphics'. When you first start ArcMap, the *Application* object is first created, and then it in turn instantiates all of the objects it manages.

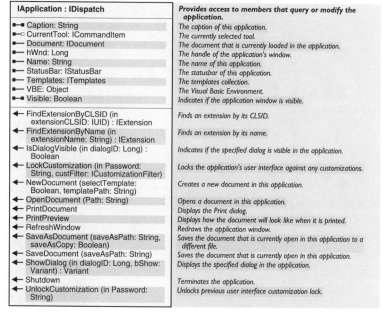

The *IApplication* interface provides access to the *MxDocument* object, the extensions, the *StatusBar* object, the *Templates* object, the currently selected tool, and the Visual Basic Editor. There are several methods that allow you to open, save, and print documents; lock and unlock the application from user customizations; display dialog boxes; and exit the application. For more details, see Chapter 3, 'Customizing the user interface'.

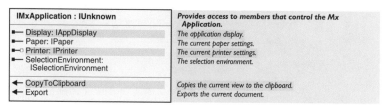

The *IMxApplication* interface provides access to the remainder of the objects the *Application* automatically creates, including *AppDisplay*, *Paper* CoClass, *Printer*, and *SelectionEnvironment*. Additionally, *IMxApplication* exposes methods for exporting the current map document or copying it to the system clipboard.

```
Dim pMxApp As IMxApplication
Set pMxApp = Application 'Query Interface
MsgBox pMxApp.SelectionEnvironment.SearchTolerance
```

IApplicationWindows : IUnknown	Provides access to members that control the DataWindow Container.
■— DataWindows: ISet	The data windows in the application.

IApplicationWindows provides access to the application's data windows. This interface has one property, *DataWindows*, which returns an *ISet* reference to a *Set* object. The *Set* object is used because it can hold a collection of heterogeneous objects and, as is the case here, one data window may be a magnifier window and another an overview window. All data windows implement the *IDataWindow* interface. The example below moves the first data window found to the top-left corner of the terminal display and makes it 500 x 500 screen pixels.

```
Public Sub AccessDataWindows()
  Dim pAppWindows As IApplicationWindows
  Dim pDataWindow As IDataWindow
  Dim pWindowsSet As ISet
  Set pAppWindows = Application 'QI
  Set pWindowsSet = pAppWindows.DataWindows
  pWindowsSet.Reset
  Set pDataWindow = pWindowsSet.Next
  If pDataWindow Is Nothing Then Exit Sub
  pDataWindow.PutPosition 0, 0, 500, 500
End Sub
```

IEnumPrinterNames : IUnknown	Provides access to an enumeration of all the Printers.
◄— Next: String	The next Printer Name.
◄— Reset	Reset the Enumeration to the beginning.

Use *IEnumPrinterNames* to loop through all of the available printers currently configured on your machine. The *Next* property returns the name of a printer, which can be passed to *IPaper::PrinterName* on the *Paper* object to change the current target printer.

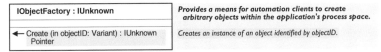

IObjectFactory : IUnknown	Provides a means for automation clients to create arbitrary objects within the application's process space.
◄— Create (in objectID: Variant) : IUnknown Pointer	Creates an instance of an object identified by objectID.

The *IObjectFactory* interface is a new interface released at ArcGIS 8.1 that allows users driving ArcMap through automation to create objects in the ArcMap process space. This eliminates marshalling between objects created in, for example, a Visual Basic application and ArcMap. Eliminating marshalling greatly improves performance as ArcMap can work directly with new objects instead of through intra-application communication.

For more information, see the topic on customizing ArcMap through automation at the end of this chapter.

For documentation on the *IDockableWindowManager, IExtensionManager, IMultiThreadedApplication,* and *IVBAApplication* interfaces, see Chapter 3, 'Customizing the user interface'.

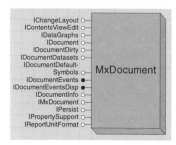

IChangeLayout
IContentsViewEdit
IDataGraphs
IDocument
IDocumentDirty
IDocumentDatasets
IDocumentDefault-
Symbols
IDocumentEvents
IDocumentEventsDisp
IDocumentInfo
IMxDocument
IPersist
IPropertySupport
IReportUnitFormat

MxDocument

Each running instance of ArcMap works with a current map document, which is represented by MxDocument.

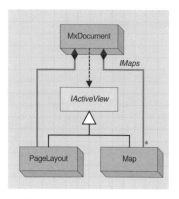

MxDocument controls the current active view, which specifies whether the user is interacting with the map as a whole through its page layout, or whether the user is viewing one of the maps in data view.

The ArcMap document is called *MxDocument*; its role is to control the representation of data. The ArcMap application automatically creates this object when the application first starts.

In the ArcMap object model, the *MxDocument* is cocreatable in case you are not customizing within an ArcMap session—instantiating a new *MxDocument* creates a new instance of the *Application* object, which in turn creates the *MxDocument* object. There is one *MxDocument* per session of ArcMap.

MxDocument specifically creates and manages the following objects: an empty *Map*, a *PageLayout*, the *TOCCatalogView*, the *TOCDisplayView*, the *StyleGallery*, and the *TableProperties*. You can obtain a reference to the *MxDocument* through *IApplication::Document*.

One of the most important aspects of *MxDocument* is the notion of its views. You can think of the view as the main application window, or the place where all data is drawn. ArcMap currently has two different views, data view and layout view—developers using C++ can create additional ones.

Objects implement the *IActiveView* interface to establish themselves as views. The data view corresponds to a *Map* object, and the layout view corresponds to the *PageLayout* object. Either of these objects can be set as the document's active view, and only one view is visible at a time. A map document can contain several *Map* objects, one per data frame. The data view always corresponds to the *Map* currently in focus.

Each view consists of a *ScreenDisplay* object, which performs the actual drawing. Each *ScreenDisplay* object in turn has a *DisplayTransformation* object, which manages the map to device transformation. When you need to draw features or get at a *Map*'s spatial reference, for example, it is very important you get a handle to the correct *ScreenDisplay*.

To help with this, ArcMap exposes the *AppDisplay* object, which has a handy property for returning the *ScreenDisplay* with focus. In addition, this object has its own implementation of *IScreenDisplay* and, in this case, if you draw or pan, the results will appear in all of the displays currently instantiated in the application. For more details, see the documentation on the *AppDisplay* object later in this chapter.

IMxDocument *is a starting point for accessing most of the other ArcMap objects including the views, the collection of maps, the page layout, the style gallery, and the table properties. This interface also manages many properties reflected in the running application including the current table of contents, the currently selected item in the table of contents, and the current mouse location.*

IMxDocument *is also useful when working with content views—the different tabs in the table of contents. Some members that work with content views are SelectedItem, ContextItem, and UpdateContents. Here are some common problems and solutions.*

I need to know what items are selected in the active content view. *Use the SelectedItem property to obtain a reference to the selected item in the TOC. This property returns an IUnknown because an item in the TOC can be any number of things. For example, when working in the Display tab, the reference could be to a Map object if you have a data frame selected, one of the Layer objects (FeatureLayer, FDOGraphicsLayer, or other) if you have a layer selected, or a LegendGroup if you have a unique value or heading selected. In the Source tab, the reference can be to any of the above objects plus a Table, FeatureDataset, or Workspace. In the case where more than one item is selected, the reference is to the Set object.*

I need to refresh the TOC because of changes I have made programmatically. *Use UpdateContents to automatically refresh the active TOC. Alternatively, you can use CurrentContentsView to get a reference to the active TOC and call IContentsView::Refresh.*

I'm creating a content menu and need to know which item was right-clicked. *ContextItem returns the last item that was right-clicked; it works the same as SelectedItem. The Map also has an Expanded property to collapse or open or close the map tree in the Contents view.*

IMxDocument : IUnknown	
■─■ ActivatedView: IActiveView	The activated view. This is the same as the active view unless a data frame is activated within a layout.
■─□ ActiveView: IActiveView	The active view.
■─■ ActiveViewCommand: ICommand	The command associated with the active view.
■─■ ContentsView (in Index: Long) : IContentsView	The contents view at the specified index.
■─■ ContentsViewCount: Long	The number of contents views in the document.
■─■ ContextItem: IUnknown Pointer	The last item that was right-clicked.
■─□ CurrentContentsView: IContentsView	The current contents view of the document.
■─□ CurrentLocation: IPoint	The current mouse location in map units.
■─■ DefaultColor (in Type: tagesriMxDefaultColorTypes) : IColor	The default color for the given type.
■─■ DefaultTextFont: Font	The default font for text.
■─■ DefaultTextFontSize: IFontSize	The default font size for text.
─■ DelayUpdateContents: Boolean	Indicates document update notifications should be ignored.
■─■ FocusMap: IMap	The current focus map.
■─■ Maps: IMaps	The collection of maps in the document.
■─■ OperationStack: IOperationStack	The operation stack.
■─□ PageLayout: IPageLayout	The page layout.
■─■ RelativePaths: Boolean	Indicates if path names are stored relative to the document.
■─■ SearchTolerance: Double	The global search tolerance in geographic units for selection.
■─■ SearchTolerancePixels: Long	The global search tolerance in pixels for selection.
■─■ SelectedItem: IUnknown Pointer	The selected item in the layer control.
■─■ SelectedLayer: ILayer	The selected layer in the layer control.
■─■ StyleGallery: IStyleGallery	Reference to the document's Style Gallery.
■─■ TableProperties: ITableProperties	Table properties, for Layers and Tables in ArcMap.
◄─ AddLayer (in Layer: ILayer)	Adds a layer to the current focus map.
◄─ CanInsertObject (pEnabled: Boolean)	Indicates if the document allows objects to be inserted.
◄─ InsertObject	Inserts an object into the document. Displays the insert object dialog.
◄─ UpdateContents	Notifies the document that the contents have been updated.

Provides access to members that control the Mx Document.

The following VBA code checks the type of active view:

```
Dim pMxDoc As IMxDocument
Set pMxDoc = Application.Document
If TypeOf pMxDoc.ActiveView Is IMap Then
  MsgBox "Active View is a Map"
ElseIf TypeOf pMxDoc.ActiveView Is IPageLayout Then
  MsgBox "Active view is the PageLayout"
End If
```

The following VBA code returns the total number of maps managed by the document:

```
Dim pMxDoc As IMxDocument
Set pMxDoc = Application.Document
MsgBox pMxDoc.Maps.Count
```

The following VBA code accesses the document's map, which has focus (though this is not necessarily the active view):

```
Dim pMxDoc As IMxDocument
Dim pMap As IMap
Set pMxDoc = Application.Document
Set pMap = pMxDoc.FocusMap
MsgBox pMap.LayerCount
```

ArcMap

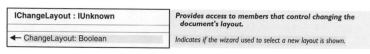

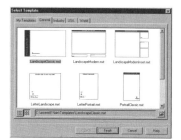

The Change Layout dialog box in ArcMap

IChangeLayout : IUnknown	Provides access to members that control changing the document's layout.
← ChangeLayout: Boolean	Indicates if the wizard used to select a new layout is shown.

Use the *IChangeLayout* interface to change the template the document is currently based on. A template is a type of map document that provides a quick way to create a new map. Templates often contain data, a custom interface, and a predefined layout that arranges map elements such as north arrows, scale bars, and logos. *IChangeLayout* has one member called *ChangeLayout* that launches a wizard from which a new template can be selected.

IContentsViewEdit : IUnknown	Provides access to members that control Contents View Edit.
← AddContentsView (in ContentsView: IContentsView)	Adds a contents view object to the TOC.
← ClearContentsViews	Removes all current contents views.

Use the *IContentsViewEdit* interface to manage the content views (tabs) in the table of contents. This interface has methods for adding new content views and removing existing ones. Custom content views are created by implementing the *IContentsView* interface. *IContentsViewEdit* also has a member that clears all of the content views. ArcMap ships with two content views, Display and Source. Use *IMxDocument::ContentsView* or *IMxDocument::CurrentContentsView* to obtain a reference to a particular contents view.

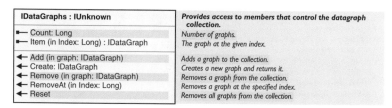

IDataGraphs : IUnknown	Provides access to members that control the datagraph collection.
■— Count: Long	Number of graphs.
■— Item (in Index: Long) : IDataGraph	The graph at the given index.
← Add (in graph: IDataGraph)	Adds a graph to the collection.
← Create: IDataGraph	Creates a new graph and returns it.
← Remove (in graph: IDataGraph)	Removes a graph from the collection.
← RemoveAt (in Index: Long)	Removes a graph at the specified index.
← Reset	Removes all graphs from the collection.

The *IDataGraphs* interface manages the collection of data graphs currently associated with the document. Use *IDataGraphs* to create new data graphs, clear old ones, or obtain a reference to a specific graph.

IDocumentDatasets : IUnknown	Provides access to members that control the Dataset Container.
■— Datasets: IEnumDataset	The datasets in the document.

Use the *IDocumentDatasets* interface to access the datasets currently loaded in the document. *IDocumentDatasets* has only one member, *Datasets,* which returns an *IEnumDataset* reference, which can be used to cycle through all of the datasets in the document.

```
Public Sub DocumentDatasets()
  Dim pDocumentDatasets As IDocumentDatasets
  Dim pEnumDataset As IEnumDataset
  Dim pDataset As IDataset
  Set pDocumentDatasets = Application.Document
```

```
  Set pEnumDataset = pDocumentDatasets.Datasets
  pEnumDataset.Reset
  Set pDataset = pEnumDataset.Next
  Do While Not pDataset Is Nothing
    MsgBox pDataset.Name
    Set pDataset = pEnumDataset.Next
  Loop
End Sub
```

IDocumentDefaultSymbols : IUnknown	Provides access to members that control Default Symbols for the document.
■–■ AreaPatch: IAreaPatch	Default Area Patch.
■–■ Callout: IFormattedTextSymbol	Default Callout.
■–■ CustomTOCFont: Font	Custom TOC Font.
■–■ CustomTOCFontSize: Double	Custom TOC Font Size in Points.
■–■ FillSymbol: IFillSymbol	Default Fill Symbol.
■–■ LinePatch: ILinePatch	Default Line Patch.
■–■ LineSymbol: ILineSymbol	Default Line Symbol.
■–■ MarkerSymbol: IMarkerSymbol	Default Marker Symbol.
■–■ PatchHeight: Double	Default Patch Height in Points.
■–■ PatchWidth: Double	Default Patch Width in Points.
■–■ TextSymbol: ITextSymbol	Default Text Symbol.

The *IDocumentDefaultSymbols* interface provides a central point for accessing and managing symbols used by many tools. For example, layout tools, such as the New Rectangle tool, rely on the symbols managed by this interface to symbolize the graphics they create; in this case, the New Rectangle tool creates a polygon graphic using the fill symbol stored in *IDocumentDefaultSymbols::FillSymbol*. The example below shows one method to change the default fill symbol.

```
Public Sub ChangeDefaultFillSymbol()
  Dim pDefaultSymbols As IDocumentDefaultSymbols
  Dim pFillSymbol As IFillSymbol
  Dim pColor As IRgbColor

  Set pDefaultSymbols = Application.Document
  Set pFillSymbol = pDefaultSymbols.FillSymbol
  Set pColor = New RgbColor
  pColor.Red = 255
  pFillSymbol.Color = pColor
  pDefaultSymbols.FillSymbol = pFillSymbol
End Sub
```

IDocumentEvents : IUnknown	Provides access to events that occur in ArcMap.
← ActiveViewChanged	Fired when the active view changes.
← BeforeCloseDocument: Boolean	Fired before a document is closed. Return True to abort the close process.
← CloseDocument	Fired when a document is closed.
← MapsChanged	Fired when a change is made to the map collection.
← NewDocument	Fired when a new document is created.
← OnContextMenu (in X: Long, in Y: Long, out handled: Boolean)	Indicates if a context menu should be displayed at the given xy location. Return true if handled.
← OpenDocument	Fired when a document is opened.

IDocumentEvents is the outbound interface on the *MxDocument* object. Use this interface to listen for specific events related to map documents.

For example, an event is fired whenever a map document is opened. For more details on map document events, see *IDocumentEventsDisp* below.

IDocumentEventsDisp : IDispatch	Provides access to events that occur in ArcMap.
← ActiveViewChanged: Boolean	Fired when the active view has changed.
← BeforeCloseDocument: Boolean	Fired before a document is closed. Return True to abort the close process.
← CloseDocument: Boolean	Fired when a document is closed.
← MapsChanged: Boolean	Fired when a change is made to the map collection.
← NewDocument: Boolean	Fired when a new document is created.
← OnContextMenu (in X: Long, in Y: Long) : Boolean	Indicates if a context menu should be displayed at the given xy location. Return true if handled.
← OpenDocument: Boolean	Fired when a document is opened.
← VBAReset: Boolean	Fired when VBA is reset.

IDocumentEvents and *IDocumentEventsDisp* are nearly identical except the latter is exposed automatically in the ArcMap VBA editor. When working in VBA, an *MxDocument* object is defined in all *ThisDocument* class modules. After selecting this object in the Object Box, you can select any of the *IDocumentEventsDisp* events by clicking on them in Procedure/Method Box. Selecting one of the events stubs out the event procedure in the class module.

In ArcMap, there can be up to three VBA projects (*Project, TemplateProject,* and *Normal*) loaded; each one has a *ThisDocument* class module. You can write code for each document event in each *ThisDocument* code window. It is important to know the order in which the document events for each VBA project get fired. For example, when the *NewDocument* event occurs, the code in the *MxDocument_NewDocument* function in *Project.ThisDocument* executes first, followed by code in *TemplateProject.ThisDocument*, and finally code in *Normal.ThisDocument*.

If an event function in *Project.ThisDocument* returns *True*, then the code for this event in *TemplateProject.ThisDocument* and *Normal.ThisDocument* does not get executed. This provides a mechanism for a document to override any code that might be in the base template or the *Normal* template.

The sample below asks the user for a username and password before providing complete access to the document. This sample's intent is to show how the open document event works, not how to secure a document.

```
Private Function MxDocument_OpenDocument() As Boolean
  Dim pGetUser As IGetUserAndPasswordDialog
  Dim pTemplates As ITemplates
  Dim sUserName As String
  Dim sPassword As String

  Set pTemplates = Application.Templates

  Set pGetUser = New GetUserAndPasswordDialog
  If pGetUser.DoModal("Enter Username and Password", " ", _
```

```
        Application.hWnd) Then
    sUserName = pGetUser.UserName
    sPassword = pGetUser.Password
    If Not UCase(sUserName) = UCase("GIS") Or _
      Not UCase(sPassword) = UCase("opensaysme") Then
      'Open new document
      MsgBox "Sorry, you do not have access to this document."
      Application.NewDocument False, pTemplates.Item(0)
    End If
  Else
    Application.NewDocument False, pTemplates.Item(0)
  End If
End Function
```

IDocumentInfo : IUnknown	Provides access to members that control the Document Info.
■–■ Author: String	The author of the document.
■–■ Category: String	The category of the document.
■–■ Comments: String	Comments for the document.
■–■ DocumentTitle: String	The title of the document.
■–■ HyperlinkBase: String	The hyperlink base of the document.
■–■ Keywords: String	The keywords for the document.
■–■ SavePreview: Boolean	Indicates if a preview of the document is saved when the document is saved.
■–■ Subject: String	The subject of the document.

All map documents have properties, such as who authored the document and what the document represents. The *IDocumentInfo* interface conveniently provides properties for entering map document metadata. *IDocumentInfo* also manages a few map document properties that are not metadata type information.

The *SavePreview* property specifies whether or not a thumbnail image of the layout is displayed in ArcCatalog when browsing map documents.

The *HyperlinkBase* property specifies the root Web address for hyperlink fields. For example, you can set a map document's *HyperlinkBase* property to www.esri.com and a Web-linked field on a feature to ArcObjectsOnline. When you turn on field hyperlinks for a layer and use the *Hyperlink* tool, the two are put together, and www.esri.com/ArcObjectsOnline becomes the hyperlink.

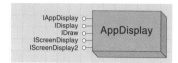

Because there are potentially multiple objects, each with its own ScreenDisplay object, the Application object also has an AppDisplay object to help manage all of these.

The *AppDisplay* object has its own implementation of *IScreenDisplay* whereby the properties and methods get applied to all of the display objects currently instantiated in the application. For example, if you draw or pan in this screen display, all of the screen displays in the application are forwarded the same call.

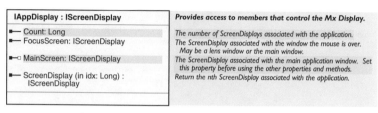

Views are not the only objects that have a *ScreenDisplay*; each *MapInsetWindow* has its own *ScreenDisplay* object. The *Pan* tool uses the *AppDisplay* object to pan the active view and all magnifier windows if they are not in snapshot mode. This *AppDisplay* object can also pass references to any individual *ScreenDisplay* object, the *ScreenDisplay* object currently with focus, or the main *ScreenDisplay* belonging to active view.

For documentation on the *IDisplay, IScreenDisplay,* and *IDraw* interfaces, see Chapter 5, 'Displaying graphics'.

The *Application* object directly manages the life of all application extensions. Application extensions are those extensions registered in the ESRI *MxExtension* objects; the editing tools in ArcMap are an example of an *MxExtension*. All extensions are automatically created and destroyed in synchronization with an *Application* object.

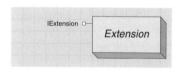

An extension is registered with an ArcGIS application to augment the application.

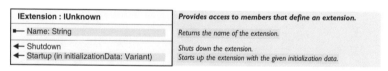

Use the *IExtension* interface to query the properties of an extension or implement this interface to create your own custom extension. There are other categories for extensions, such as ESRI Editor Extensions, that are not managed by the *Application* object, but they work in much the same fashion.

Use *IApplication::FindExtension* to get a reference to a particular extension.

```
Public Sub CheckEditState()
  Dim pEditor As IEditor
  Dim pUID As New UID

  pUID = "esriCore.Editor"
  Set pEditor = Application.FindExtensionByCLSID(pUID)

  If pEditor.EditState = esriStateEditing Then
    MsgBox "Active Edit Session Present"
  End If
End Sub
```

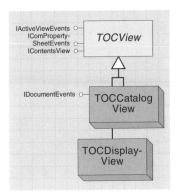

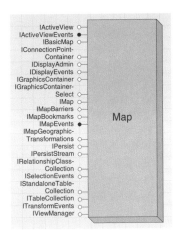

The Display tab in the ArcMap table of contents shows all the layers on the map and what the features in each layer represent.

The Source tab in the ArcMap table of contents shows all the layers on the map and from where they originate.

ArcMap

Contents views are tabs in the ArcMap table of contents. ArcMap ships with two contents views: display view and source view. The Display tab is the _TOCDisplayView_ object, and the Source tab is the _TOCCatalog-View_ object. Developers can add new contents views by creating their own custom object that implements the _IContentsView_ interface. All contents views must be registered in the 'ESRI Contents Views' component category.

All contents views are managed by the _MxDocument_ object. All contents views registered in the contents views component category are automatically created by an _MxDocument_ object when it is first created. However, only one contents view can be active at a time. Use the _IMxDocument:: CurrentContentsView_ property to set the current contents view and to get a reference to the current contents view.

Setting the current contents view automatically refreshes the table of contents (_IContentsView::Refresh_). The _MxDocument_ objects has two additional members for accessing the contents views: _IMxDocument::ContentsView_, which takes an index, and _IMxDocument::ContentsViewCount._

Contents views implement _IActiveViewEvents_. These objects are not sources for _IActiveViewEvents_; however, they are sinks. These objects are clients responding to the active view events fired by the _PageLayout_ and _Map_ objects.

IContentsView : IUnknown	Provides access to members that control table of contents views.
▪━ ContextItem: Variant	The context item (could be an enumerator).
▪━ hWnd: Long	The HWND of the contents view.
▪━ Name: String	The name of the contents view.
━▪ ProcessEvents: Boolean	Indicates if the view is currently responding to events.
▪━▪ SelectedItem: Variant	The selected item (could be an enumerator).
▪━▪ ShowLines: Boolean	Indicates if lines are shown in the TOC tree.
▪━▪ Visible: Boolean	Indicates if the view is visible.
◄━ Activate (in parentHWnd: Long, in Document: IMxDocument)	Activates the contents view.
◄━ AddToSelectedItems (in Item: Variant)	Adds to the selected items.
◄━ Deactivate	Deactivates the contents view.
◄━ Refresh (in Item: Variant)	Refreshes the contents view. If a non-null item is specified, it refreshes only that item and its children.
◄━ RemoveFromSelectedItems (in Item: Variant)	Removes an item from the selected items.

The _IContentsView_ interface provides the contract for the minimum behavior all contents views must support. Each contents view implements this interface slightly differently. For more information on their custom implementation, see the documentation on _TOCDisplayView_ and _TOCSourceView_.

Aside from implementing this interface to create a new contents view, this interface is rarely accessed by applications and, in many cases, contents views do not provide an implementation for several of the members. More commonly used members on this interface are _Name, SelectedItem,_ and _Visible._ In fact, accessing the currently selected item is actually much easier via _IMxDocument::SelectedItem_ off the _MxDocument_ object. This property will return the currently selected item on the active contents view.

When you work with the *SelectedItem* property, remember that it returns a reference to the currently selected item in the contents view you are working with. The return is a variant because there are several possible objects the selected item can be.

When working with the *TOCDisplayView* object, the reference could be to a *Map* object if you have a data frame selected, one of the *Layer* objects (*FeatureLayer, FDOGraphicsLayer,* or other) if you have a layer selected, or a *LegendGroup* if you have a unique value or heading selected.

If you are working with the *TOCSourceView* object, the reference can be to any of the above objects plus a *Table, FeatureDataset,* or *Workspace*.

If more than one item is selected, the reference is to a *Set* object. Again, it is much easier to use *IMxDocument::SelectedItem,* which returns an *IUnknown* instead of *IContentsView::SelectedItem,* which returns a *Variant*.

The *TOCDisplayView* object represents the Display tab in the ArcMap table of contents. For information about the capabilities inside the Display tab, see *Using ArcMap*. This object is creatable strictly because the *MxDocument* needs to create one when it is first created; there is generally no need for developers to create or access this object.

TOCDisplayView and *TOCSourceView* currently do not provide an implementation for these members: *IContentsView::put_SelectedItem, IContentsView::AddToSelectedItems, IContentsView::RemoveFromSelectedItems,* and *IActiveViewEvents::SelectionChanged*.

The *TOCSourceView* object represents the Source tab in the ArcMap table of contents. For information about this tab including its capabilities, consult *Using ArcMap*. Like the *TOCDisplayView* object, this object is creatable because the *MxDocument* creates one when it is first created; there is generally no need for developers to create or access this object. See the note in *TOCDisplayView* about which members are not currently implemented by this object.

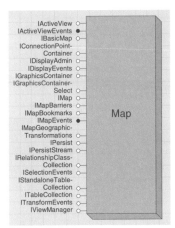

IActiveView
IActiveViewEvents
IBasicMap
IConnectionPoint-
Container
IDisplayAdmin
IDisplayEvents
IGraphicsContainer
IGraphicsContainer-
Select
IMap
IMapBookmarks
IMapEvents
IMapGeographic-
Transformations
IPersist
IPersistStream
IRelationshipClass-
Collection
ISelectionEvents
IStandaloneTable-
Collection
ITableCollection
ITransformEvents
IViewManager

Map

The Map *object is a container for map data—it manages layers of feature and graphic data. The* Map *object is a primary point for customization tasks because it not only manages layers of data, but it is also a view and has to manage the drawing of all its data. Typical tasks with the* Map *object include adding a new layer, panning the display, changing the view extent (zooming functions), changing the spatial reference, and getting the currently selected features and elements.*

Every map document contains at least one *Map* object. Only one *Map* can have focus at a time, and this *Map* is called the focus map. *IMxDocument* provides access to all of the *Map* objects loaded in the document; *IMxDocument::FocusMap* returns a reference to the *Map* currently with focus, and *IMxDocument.Maps* returns the entire collection of *Map* objects.

ArcMap comes with two different views: data view and layout view. Data view relates to a *Map* object, and layout view relates to the *PageLayout* object. A map document can contain any number of *Map* objects—the focus *Map* always represents the data view.

All of the layers in a map share the same spatial reference. A *Map*'s spatial reference is automatically set to the spatial reference of the first layer loaded. New layers loaded into a *Map* are projected to the *Map* object's spatial reference if their spatial reference is different.

In ArcMap, *Map* objects are always contained by *MapFrame* objects—the *PageLayout* object actually manages all the *MapFrame* objects, a type of element, and each *MapFrame* manages a *Map*. Note that for convenience, the *MxDocument* object passes a reference to the focus map and the *Map*'s collection. In reality, however, the *PageLayout* object manages these. Each *Map* object, in turn, manages a collection of *Layer* objects. Types of *Layer* objects include *FeatureLayers, FDOGraphicsLayers,* and *GroupLayers*.

Every *Map* also manages a *CompositeGraphicsLayer* object, which contains a collection of graphics layers. The default graphics layer is a *Map* object's basic graphics layer where all graphics, including labels, are drawn by default. The *Map* provides direct access to this layer with the property *IMap::BasicGraphicsLayer*. A *Map* object's basic graphics layer cannot be deleted from the *CompositeGraphicsLayer* object, though new graphics layers can be added and deleted.

The layer collection returned from the *IMap::Layers* property does not include the *Map* object's *CompositeGraphicsLayer*; to access this object, you must use the *IMap::BasicGraphicsLayer* property. The *Map* also has a shortcut to the basic graphics layer *IGraphicsContainer* interface; you can query an interface from any of the *Map* interfaces, for example, *IMap*, to *IGraphicsLayers*.

MapSurround objects are elements that are related to a *Map*. Types of map surrounds include *Legends, NorthArrows,* and *ScaleBars*. The *Map* object exposes several properties and methods for accessing the map surrounds associated with it. All map surrounds are actually contained by a *MapSurroundFrame* which, like a *MapFrame*, is ultimately managed by the *PageLayout* object.

The *Map* object is cocreatable so that new *Map* objects can be created and added to the document. Instantiating a new *Map* object automatically creates the following related objects on which it relies: a *ScreenDisplay* object, which every view uses to manage the drawing window, and a new *CompositeGraphicsLayer*, as discussed above.

ArcMap

IMap is the main interface to the Map coclass and is used for controlling the Map's data and associated elements.

IMap : IUnknown	Provides access to members that control the map.
■—□ ActiveGraphicsLayer: ILayer	The active graphics layer. If no graphic layers exist a basic memory graphics layer will be created.
■—□ AnnotationEngine: IAnnotateMap	The annotation (label) engine the map will use.
—■ AreaOfInterest: IEnvelope	Area of interest for the map.
■— Barriers (pExtent: IEnvelope) : IBarrierCollection	The list of barriers and their weight for labeling.
■— BasicGraphicsLayer: IGraphicsLayer	The basic graphics layer.
■—■ ClipBorder: IBorder	An optional border drawn around ClipGeometry.
■—■ ClipGeometry: IGeometry	A shape that layers in the map are clipped to.
■—■ Description: String	Description of the map.
■—■ DistanceUnits: esriUnits	The distance units for the map.
■—■ Expanded: Boolean	Indicates if the Map is expanded.
■—□ FeatureSelection: ISelection	The feature selection for the map.
■—■ IsFramed: Boolean	Indicates if map is drawn in a frame rather than on the whole window.
■— Layer (in Index: Long) : ILayer	The layer at the given index.
■— LayerCount: Long	Number of layers in the map.
■— Layers (UID: IUID, recursive: Boolean) : IEnumLayer	The layers in the map of the type specified in the uid. If recursive is true it will return layers in group layers.
■—■ MapScale: Double	The scale of the map as a representative fraction.
■— MapSurround (in Index: Long) : IMapSurround	The map surround at the given index.
■— MapSurroundCount: Long	Number of map surrounds associated with the map.
■—■ MapUnits: esriUnits	The units for the map.
■—■ Name: String	Name of the map.
■—■ ReferenceScale: Double	The reference scale of the map as a representative fraction.
■— SelectionCount: Long	Number of selected features.
■—□ SpatialReference: ISpatialReference	The spatial reference of the map.
■—■ SpatialReferenceLocked: Boolean	Prevents the spatial reference from being changed.
■—■ UseSymbolLevels: Boolean	Indicates if the Map draws using symbol levels.
← AddLayer (in Layer: ILayer)	Adds a layer to the map.
← AddLayers (in Layers: IEnumLayer, in autoArrange: Boolean)	Adds multiple layers to the map, arranging them nicely if specified.
← AddMapSurround (in MapSurround: IMapSurround)	Adds a map surround to the map.
← ClearLayers	Removes all layers from the map.
← ClearMapSurrounds	Removes all map surrounds from the map.
← ClearSelection	Clears the map selection.
← ComputeDistance (in p1: IPoint, in p2: IPoint) : Double	Computes the distance between two points on the map and returns the result.
← CreateMapSurround (in CLSID: IUID, in optionalStyle: IMapSurround) : IMapSurround	Create and initialize a map surround. An optional style from the style gallery may be specified.
← DelayDrawing (in delay: Boolean)	Suspends drawing.
← DelayEvents (in delay: Boolean)	Used to batch operations together to minimize notifications.
← DeleteLayer (in Layer: ILayer)	Deletes a layer from the map.
← DeleteMapSurround (in MapSurround: IMapSurround)	Deletes a map surround from the map.
← GetPageSize (out widthInches: Double, out heightInches: Double)	Gets the page size for the map.
← MoveLayer (in Layer: ILayer, in toIndex: Long)	Moves a layer to another position.
← RecalcFullExtent	Forces the full extent to be recalculated.
← SelectByShape (in Shape: IGeometry, in env: ISelectionEnvironment, in justOne: Boolean)	Selects features in the map given a shape and a selection environment (optional).
← SelectFeature (in Layer: ILayer, in Feature: IFeature)	Selects a feature.
← SetPageSize (in widthInches: Double, in heightInches: Double)	Sets the page size for the map (optional).

The *IMap* interface is a starting point for many of the tasks one does with a *Map*. For example, you can use *IMap* to add, delete, and access map layers containing data from various sources, including feature layers and graphics layers; associate map surround objects (legends, scale bars, and so on) with the *Map*; access the various properties of a *Map*, including the area of interest, the current map units, and the spatial reference; and select features and access the *Map* object's current selection.

```
Public Sub AddShapeFile()
  Dim pWorkspaceFactory As IWorkspaceFactory
  Dim pFeatureWorkspace As IFeatureWorkspace
  Dim pFeatureLayer As IFeatureLayer
  Dim pMxDocument As IMxDocument
  Dim pMap As IMap

  ' Create a new ShapefileWorkspaceFactory object and
  ' open a shapefile folder
  Set pWorkspaceFactory = New ShapefileWorkspaceFactory
  Set pFeatureWorkspace = pWorkspaceFactory.OpenFromFile _
    ("c:\arcgis\arcexe81\ArcObjects Developer Kit\Samples\Data\USA", 0)
  'Create a new FeatureLayer and assign a shapefile to it
  Set pFeatureLayer = New FeatureLayer
  Set pFeatureLayer.FeatureClass = _
    pFeatureWorkspace.OpenFeatureClass("States")
  pFeatureLayer.Name = pFeatureLayer.FeatureClass.AliasName
  'Add the FeatureLayer to the focus map
  Set pMxDocument = Application.Document
  Set pMap = pMxDocument.FocusMap
  pMap.AddLayer pFeatureLayer
End Sub
```

Use this code to get the currently selected feature.

```
Public Sub GetSelectedFeature()
  Dim pMxDoc As IMxDocument
  Dim pMap As IMap
  Dim pEnumFeature As IEnumFeature
  Dim pFeature As IFeature
  Set pMxDoc = Application.Document
  Set pMap = pMxDoc.FocusMap
  Set pEnumFeature = pMap.FeatureSelection
  pEnumFeature.Reset
  Set pFeature = pEnumFeature.Next
End Sub
```

This code shows how to select features by shape.

To use this sample, paste the code into a new UIToolControl's MouseDown event. Completely close VBA so that mouse events fire. Select the tool and drag out an envelope.

```
Private Sub UIToolControl1_MouseDown(ByVal button As Long, _
    ByVal shift As Long, ByVal x As Long, ByVal y As Long)
  Dim pMxApp As IMxApplication
  Dim pMxDoc As IMxDocument
  Dim pMap As IMap
  Dim pActiveView As IActiveView
  Dim pRubberEnv As IRubberBand
  Dim pEnvelope As IEnvelope

  Set pMxApp = Application 'QI
  Set pMxDoc = Application.Document
  Set pMap = pMxDoc.FocusMap
  Set pActiveView = pMap 'QI
  Set pRubberEnv = New RubberEnvelope
```

```
'Flag the area of the old selection to invalidate
pActiveView.PartialRefresh esriViewGeoSelection, Nothing, Nothing
'Use TrackNew to prompt user to drag out a square on the display
Set pEnvelope = pRubberEnv.TrackNew(pActiveView.ScreenDisplay, Nothing)
'Perform the selection
pMap.SelectByShape pEnvelope, pMxApp.SelectionEnvironment, False
'Flag the area of the new selection to invalidate
pActiveView.PartialRefresh esriViewGeoSelection, Nothing, Nothing
End Sub
```

IBasicMap : IUnknown	Provides access to members that control the basic map.
ActiveGraphicsLayer: ILayer	The active graphics layer. If no graphic layers exist a basic memory graphics layer will be created.
AreaOfInterest: IEnvelope	Area of interest for the map.
BasicGraphicsLayer: IGraphicsLayer	The basic graphics layer.
Description: String	Description of the map.
FeatureSelection: ISelection	The map's feature selection.
Layer (in Index: Long) : ILayer	The layer at the given index.
LayerCount: Long	Number of layers in the map.
Layers (UID: IUID, recursive: Boolean) : IEnumLayer	The layers in the map of the type specified in the uid. If recursive is true it will return layers in group layers.
Name: String	Name of the map.
SelectionCount: Long	Number of selected features in the map.
SpatialReference: ISpatialReference	The spatial reference of the map.
AddLayer (in pLayer: ILayer)	Adds a layer to the map.
AddLayers (in pLayers: IEnumLayer, in autoArrange: Boolean)	Adds multiple layers to the map, arranging them nicely if specified.
ClearLayers	Removes all layers from the map.
ClearSelection	Clears the map selection.
DeleteLayer (in pLayer: ILayer)	Deletes a layer from the map.
SelectByShape (in Shape: IGeometry, in env: ISelectionEnvironment, in justOne: Boolean)	Selects features in the map given a shape and a selection environment (optional).

IBasicMap is a subset of *IMap* that provides support for ArcScene. Both *Map* (2D) and *Scene* (3D) components implement this interface. These components are used by both ArcMap and ArcScene (such as *Table* coclass) QI for *IBasicMap* rather than *IMap*.

IGraphicsContainer : IUnknown	Provides access to members that control the Graphics Container.
← AddElement (in Element: IElement, in zorder: Long)	Add a new graphic element to the layer.
← AddElements (in Elements: IElementCollection, in zorder: Long)	Add new graphic elements to the layer.
← BringForward (in Elements: IEnumElement)	Move the specified elements one step closer to the top of the stack of elements.
← BringToFront (in Elements: IEnumElement)	Make the specified elements draw in front of all other elements.
← DeleteAllElements	Delete all the elements.
← DeleteElement (in Element: IElement)	Delete the given element.
← FindFrame (in frameObject: Variant) : IFrameElement	Find the frame that contains the specified object.
← GetElementOrder (in Elements: IEnumElement) : Variant	Private order object. Used to undo ordering operations.
← LocateElements (in Point: IPoint, in Tolerance: Double) : IEnumElement	Returns the elements at the given coordinate.
← LocateElementsByEnvelope (in Envelope: IEnvelope) : IEnumElement	Returns the elements that intersect with the given envelope.
← MoveElementFromGroup (in Group: IGroupElement, in Element: IElement, in zorder: Long)	Move the element from the group to the container.
← MoveElementToGroup (in Element: IElement, in Group: IGroupElement)	Move the element from the container to the group.
← Next: IElement	Returns the next graphic in the container.
← PutElementOrder (in order: Variant)	Private order object. Used to undo ordering operations.
← Reset	Reset internal cursor so that Next returns the first element.
← SendBackward (in Elements: IEnumElement)	Move the specified elements one step closer to the bottom of the stack of elements.
← SendToBack (in Elements: IEnumElement)	Make the specified elements draw behind all other elements.
← UpdateElement (in Element: IElement)	The graphic element's properties have changed.

The *Map* object is a graphics container somewhat like the *PageLayout* object.

Elements, such as a text element (label), can be added directly to a *Map*, or they can be stored in a database. For those elements stored in a *Map*, the *Map* actually manages a *CompositeGraphicsLayer* object to store all the elements. *CompositeGraphicsLayer* objects can have multiple layers in them.

One layer is the *Map*'s basic graphics layer, which is also the default graphics layer. Access this layer using *IMap::BasicGraphicsLayer*. The basic graphics layer is a special layer that cannot be deleted and is not reported in the *CompositeGraphicsLayer*'s layer count. Further, this layer's element count reports the total number of elements in all the *CompositeGraphicsLayer*'s layers. If you delete all elements in the *Map*'s basic graphics layer, you delete all elements in all target layers (annotation groups) in the *CompositeGraphicsLayer*. In the case where the *Map*'s *CompositeGraphicsLayer* does have multiple layers, use *IMap::ActiveGraphicsLayer* to set or get a reference to the active layer.

The active graphics layer does not always reference a layer in the *Map*'s *CompositeGraphicsLayer*; this is the case when a database layer containing elements is set as the active graphics layer. A feature-linked annotation layer (*FDOGraphicsLayer*) is a good example of this.

The *Map*'s *IGraphicsContainer* always returns a reference to the *Map*'s active graphics layer. Again, this can either be the basic graphics layer, a layer in the *Map*'s *CompositeGraphicsLayer*, or a feature layer such as an *FDOGraphicsLayer*.

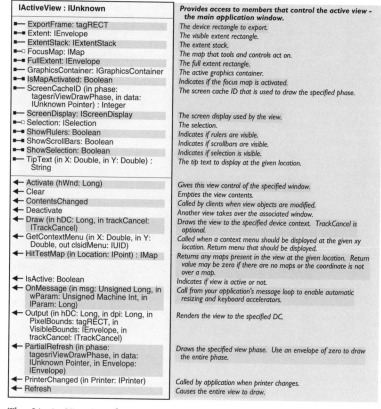

IGraphicsContainerSelect : IUnknown	Provides access to members that control graphic container selection.
▪—◻ DominantElement: IElement	Dominant element.
▪—◄ ElementSelectionCount: Long	Returns the number of selected elements.
▪—◄ SelectedElements: IEnumElement	Returns the selected elements.
▪—◄ SelectionBounds (in Display: IDisplay) : IEnvelope	Returns the bounds of the selection.
◄— ElementSelected (in Element: IElement) : Boolean	Indicates if the element is selected.
◄— SelectAllElements	Selects all elements.
◄— SelectedElement (in Index: Long) : IElement	Returns the nth selected element. Use Selection count to get the number of selected elements.
◄— SelectElement (in Element: IElement)	Selects the specified element.
◄— SelectElements (in Elements: IEnumElement)	Selects the specified elements.
◄— SelectionTracker (in Index: Long) : ISelectionTracker	Returns the tracker for the nth selected element. Use Selection count to get the number of selected elements.
◄— UnselectAllElements	Unselects all elements.
◄— UnselectElement (in Element: IElement)	Unselects the specified element.
◄— UnselectElements (in Elements: IEnumElement)	Unselects the specified elements.

The *IGraphicsContainerSelect* interface is documented with the *Page-Layout* object later in this chapter.

IActiveView : IUnknown	Provides access to members that control the active view - the main application window.
▪—◄ ExportFrame: tagRECT	The device rectangle to export.
▪—◄ Extent: IEnvelope	The visible extent rectangle.
▪—◄ ExtentStack: IExtentStack	The extent stack.
▪—◻ FocusMap: IMap	The map that tools and controls act on.
▪—◄ FullExtent: IEnvelope	The full extent rectangle.
▪—◄ GraphicsContainer: IGraphicsContainer	The active graphics container.
▪—◄ IsMapActivated: Boolean	Indicates if the focus map is activated.
▪—◄ ScreenCacheID (in phase: tagesriViewDrawPhase, in data: IUnknown Pointer) : Integer	The screen cache ID that is used to draw the specified phase.
▪—◄ ScreenDisplay: IScreenDisplay	The screen display used by the view.
▪—◻ Selection: ISelection	The selection.
▪—◄ ShowRulers: Boolean	Indicates if rulers are visible.
▪—◄ ShowScrollBars: Boolean	Indicates if scrollbars are visible.
▪—◄ ShowSelection: Boolean	Indicates if selection is visible.
▪—◄ TipText (in X: Double, in Y: Double) : String	The tip text to display at the given location.
◄— Activate (hWnd: Long)	Gives this view control of the specified window.
◄— Clear	Empties the view contents.
◄— ContentsChanged	Called by clients when view objects are modified.
◄— Deactivate	Another view takes over the associated window.
◄— Draw (in hDC: Long, in trackCancel: ITrackCancel)	Draws the view to the specified device context. TrackCancel is optional.
◄— GetContextMenu (in X: Double, in Y: Double, out clsidMenu: IUID)	Called when a context menu should be displayed at the given xy location. Return menu that should be displayed.
◄— HitTestMap (in Location: IPoint) : IMap	Returns any maps present in the view at the given location. Return value may be zero if there are no maps or the coordinate is not over a map.
◄— IsActive: Boolean	Indicates if view is active or not.
◄— OnMessage (in msg: Unsigned Long, in wParam: Unsigned Machine Int, in lParam: Long)	Call from your application's message loop to enable automatic resizing and keyboard accelerators.
◄— Output (in hDC: Long, in dpi: Long, in PixelBounds: tagRECT, in VisibleBounds: IEnvelope, in trackCancel: ITrackCancel)	Renders the view to the specified DC.
◄— PartialRefresh (in phase: tagesriViewDrawPhase, in data: IUnknown Pointer, in Envelope: IEnvelope)	Draws the specified view phase. Use an envelope of zero to draw the entire phase.
◄— PrinterChanged (in Printer: IPrinter)	Called by application when printer changes.
◄— Refresh	Causes the entire view to draw.

The *IActiveView* interface controls the main application window, including all drawing operations. Use this interface to change the extent of the view, access the associated *ScreenDisplay* object, show or hide rulers and scroll bars, and refresh the view. The *Map* object's implementation of the *IActiveView* is different from the *PageLayout* object's implementation. For more information about the different views, see the *MxDocument* topic in this chapter.

Two important methods on this interface are *Refresh* and *PartialRefresh*; see the discussion comparing these two methods later in this chapter.

This VBA script lets the user zoom in on the current active view:

```
Public Sub ZoomInCenter()
  Dim pMxDocument As IMxDocument
  Dim pActiveView As IActiveView
  Dim pDisplayTransform As IDisplayTransformation
  Dim pEnvelope As IEnvelope
  Dim pCenterPoint As IPoint

  Set pMxDocument = Application.Document
  Set pActiveView = pMxDocument.FocusMap
  Set pDisplayTransform = _
    pActiveView.ScreenDisplay.DisplayTransformation
  Set pEnvelope = pDisplayTransform.VisibleBounds
  ' IActiveView::Extent is a shortcut to the visible bounds
  Set pEnvelope = pActiveView.Extent

  Set pCenterPoint = New Point
  pCenterPoint.x = ((pEnvelope.XMax - pEnvelope.XMin) / 2) + _
    pEnvelope.XMin
  pCenterPoint.y = ((pEnvelope.YMax - pEnvelope.YMin) / 2) + _
    pEnvelope.YMin
  pEnvelope.Width = pEnvelope.Width / 2
  pEnvelope.Height = pEnvelope.Height / 2
  pEnvelope.CenterAt pCenterPoint
  pDisplayTransform.VisibleBounds = pEnvelope
  pActiveView.Refresh
End Sub
```

IActiveViewEvents : IUnknown	Provides access to events that occur when the state of the active view changes.
← AfterDraw (in Display: IDisplay, in phase: tagesriViewDrawPhase)	Fired after the specified phase is drawn.
← AfterItemDraw (in Index: Integer, in Display: IDisplay, phase: tagesriDrawPhase)	Fired after an individual view item is drawn. Example: view items include layers in a map or elements in a page layout.
← ContentsChanged	Fired when the contents of the view changes.
← ContentsCleared	Fired when the contents of the view is cleared.
← FocusMapChanged	Fired when a new map is made active.
← ItemAdded (in Item: Variant)	Fired when an item is added to the view.
← ItemDeleted (in Item: Variant)	Fired when an item is deleted from the view.
← ItemReordered (in Item: Variant, in toIndex: Long)	Fired when a view item is reordered.
← SelectionChanged	Fired when the selection changes.
← SpatialReferenceChanged	Fired when the spatial reference is changed.
← ViewRefreshed (in View: IActiveView, in phase: tagesriViewDrawPhase, in data: Variant, in Envelope: IEnvelope)	Fired when view is refreshed before draw happens.

The *IActiveViewEvents* interface is the default outbound interface on the *Map* object. It is exposed off the *Map* object so that clients may listen and respond to specific events related to the active view, such as

AfterDraw and *SelectionChanged*. Many coclasses implement this interface, and each of them fires events differently. For example, the *Map* object does not fire the *FocusMap* changed event, whereas the *PageLayout* object does. Similarly, the *Map* object fires the Item Deleted Event when a layer is removed from the *Map*, and the *PageLayout* object fires the same event when elements such as a map frame or graphic are deleted.

The *AfterViewDraw* event will not fire unless *IViewManager::VerboseEvents* is set to *True*. For more details, see the discussion on *IViewManager*.

The following VBA script is a simple example showing one possible way an event listener can be set up. Run the *SetUpEvents* routine to set up the listener. From that point on, whenever the focus *Map*'s selection changes, the *SelectionChanged* routine will be called.

```
Private WithEvents MapActiveViewEvents As Map

Public Sub SetUpEvents()
  Dim pMxDoc As IMxDocument
  Set pMxDoc = Application.Document
  Set MapActiveViewEvents = pMxDoc.FocusMap
End Sub

Private Sub MapActiveViewEvents_SelectionChanged()
  MsgBox "Selection Changed"
End Sub
```

Barriers are used by labeling engines to signal that a label should not be placed in a particular region. Barriers currently include annotation, graphical elements, and symbols generated from renderers. For example, a feature layer using a pie chart renderer doesn't want labels to appear directly above the pie chart's symbols. In this case, pie chart symbols act as barriers informing the label engine that no labels should be placed overtop of them.

IMapBarriers : IUnknown	Provides access to members that control map barriers.
■— Barriers2 (pExtent: IEnvelope, in pTrackCancel: ITrackCancel) : IBarrierCollection	The list of barriers and their weight for labeling.

The *IMapBarriers* interface returns a list of all the barriers and their weights from all the layers in the *Map*. Layers with barriers include those layers that implement *IBarrierProperties*—the *CompositeGraphicsLayer*, *CoverageAnnotationLayer*, and *FDOGraphicsLayer*. When creating a labeling engine, use this interface to conveniently access all the barriers from all the layers.

Bookmarks make it easy to jump to specific extents because they save map extents along with a name identifying them. There are two types of spatial bookmarks available in ArcMap: Area of Interest bookmarks and Feature bookmarks.

In ArcMap, bookmarks are accessible via the Bookmarks menu under the View menu. ArcMap also has a bookmark manager that allows users to delete undesired bookmarks.

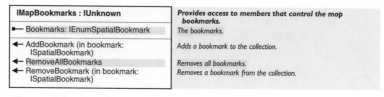

IMapBookmarks : IUnknown	Provides access to members that control the map bookmarks.
■— Bookmarks: IEnumSpatialBookmark	The bookmarks.
◄— AddBookmark (in bookmark: ISpatialBookmark)	Adds a bookmark to the collection.
◄— RemoveAllBookmarks	Removes all bookmarks.
◄— RemoveBookmark (in bookmark: ISpatialBookmark)	Removes a bookmark from the collection.

All spatial bookmarks are managed by a *Map* object and are persisted in the map document. A *Map*'s bookmarks are managed by the *IMapBookmarks* interface. Use *IMapBookmarks* to access existing bookmarks, add new ones, and delete old ones. Once you have a reference to a particular bookmark, you can make the *Map*'s extent equal to that stored in the bookmark.

This sample shows one method for creating a new Area of Interest bookmark:

```
Public Sub AddSpatialBookMark()
  Dim pMxDoc As IMxDocument
  Dim pMap As IMap
  Dim pActiveView As IActiveView
  Dim pAreaOfInterest As IAOIBookmark
  Dim pMapBookmarks As IMapBookmarks

  Set pMxDoc = Application.Document
  Set pMap = pMxDoc.FocusMap
  Set pActiveView = pMap

  'Create a new bookmark and set its location to the focus map's
  'current extent
  Set pAreaOfInterest = New AOIBookmark
  Set pAreaOfInterest.Location = pActiveView.Extent
  'Give the bookmark a name
  pAreaOfInterest.Name = "My bookmark"
  'Add the bookmark to the map's bookmark collection.This will add
  'the bookmark to the Bookmarks menu accessible from the View menu
  Set pMapBookmarks = pMap
  pMapBookmarks.AddBookmark pAreaOfInterest
End Sub
```

This sample shows one way to find an existing spatial bookmark and zoom to its stored extent:

```
Public Sub ZoomToBookmark()
  Dim pMxDoc As IMxDocument
  Dim pMapBookmarks As IMapBookmarks
  Dim pEnumBookmarks As IEnumSpatialBookmark
  Dim pBookmark As ISpatialBookmark

  Set pMxDoc = Application.Document
  Set pMapBookmarks = pMxDoc.FocusMap
  Set pEnumBookmarks = pMapBookmarks.Bookmarks
  pEnumBookmarks.Reset
  Set pBookmark = pEnumBookmarks.Next
  Do While Not pBookmark Is Nothing
    If pBookmark.Name = "My bookmark" Then
      pBookmark.ZoomTo pMxDoc.FocusMap
      pMxDoc.ActiveView.Refresh
      Exit Sub
    End If
    Set pBookmark = pEnumBookmarks.Next
  Loop
End Sub
```

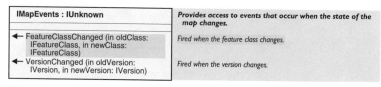

IMapEvents : IUnknown	Provides access to events that occur when the state of the map changes.
← FeatureClassChanged (in oldClass: IFeatureClass, in newClass: IFeatureClass)	Fired when the feature class changes.
← VersionChanged (in oldVersion: IVersion, in newVersion: IVersion)	Fired when the version changes.

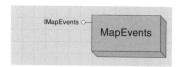

The MapEvents coclass provides access to the IMapEvents outbound interface.

The *IMapEvents* interface is exposed off the *Map* object, enabling clients to listen and respond to two events occurring inside a map: *FeatureClassChanged* and *VersionChanged*. Both of these events are related to changing the version the map's layers are working with. For example, if someone changes the version an edit session is working with, the *Editor* has to know about all the new feature classes so that it can reset the snapping environment.

The *Map* object's default outbound interface is *IActiveViewEvents*. Because Visual Basic can only handle one outbound interface per object, the *MapEvents* object has been created to give Visual Basic users a method for responding to the events grouped under *IMapEvents*.

The example demonstrates listening to map events. The event is declared on the *MapEvents* object instead of the *Map* object.

```
Private WithEvents MapEvents As MapEvents


Public Sub InitBookMark()
  Dim pMxDoc As IMxDocument
  Set pMxDoc = Application.Document
  Set MapEvents = pMxDoc.FocusMap
End Sub


Private Sub MapEvents_FeatureClassChanged(ByVal oldClass As _
    IFeatureClass, ByVal newClass As IFeatureClass)
  MsgBox "Feature Class Changed"
End Sub


Private Sub MapEvents_VersionChanged(ByVal oldVersion As _
    IVersion, ByVal newVersion As IVersion)
  MsgBox "Version Changed"
End Sub
```

ITableCollection : IUnknown	Provides access to members that control a table collection.
▪— Table (in Index: Long) : ITable	The table at the given index.
▪— TableCount: Long	Number of tables.
← AddTable (in Table: ITable)	Adds a table to the collection.
← RemoveAllTables	Removes all tables from the collection.
← RemoveTable (in Table: ITable)	Removes a table from the collection.

The *ITableCollection* interface is used to manage tables associated with a *Map*. Use this interface to add new tables to a map, remove old tables, or access a table already loaded. The following VBA macro loads a table into the focus map.

```
Public Sub AddTable()
  Dim pMxDoc As IMxDocument
```

```
    Dim pMap As IMap
    Dim pTable As ITable
    Dim pTableCollection As ITableCollection

    Set pMxDoc = Application.Document
    Set pMap = pMxDoc.FocusMap
    Set pTableCollection = pMap 'QI
    Set pTable = OpenTable("d:\data\usa\tables", "stdemog.dbf")
    If pTable Is Nothing Then Exit Sub
    pTableCollection.AddTable pTable
    pMxDoc.UpdateContents
End Sub

Private Function OpenTable(strWorkspace As String, _
    strTableName As String) As ITable
    On Error GoTo ErrorHandler
    Dim pShpWorkspaceName As IWorkspaceName
    Dim pDatasetName As IDatasetName
    Dim pName As IName

    'Create the workspace name object
    Set pShpWorkspaceName = New WorkspaceName
    pShpWorkspaceName.PathName = strWorkspace
    pShpWorkspaceName.WorkspaceFactoryProgID = _
      "esriCore.shapefileworkspacefactory.1"

    'Create the table name object
    Set pDatasetName = New TableName
    pDatasetName.Name = strTableName
    Set pDatasetName.WorkspaceName = pShpWorkspaceName

    'Open the table
    Set pName = pDatasetName
    Set OpenTable = pName.Open

    Exit Function 'exit to avoid error handler
ErrorHandler:
    Set OpenTable = Nothing
End Function
```

IViewManager : IUnknown	Provides access to members used to describe or define view behavior.
ConserveMemory: Boolean	Indicates whether to be conservative when allocating resources.
DelayBackgroundDraw: Boolean	Indicates if the background should draw immediately. Set to true to eliminate flashing during animation.
ElementSelection: ISelection	Object to use for element selection.
ExternalDrawing (in phase: tagesriViewDrawPhase) : Boolean	Indicates if external clients are drawing in response to the specified phase.
OutputBandSize: Long	Size allocated for each band when banding output.
TopFilterIndex: Long	Phase index that supplements TopFilterPhase. Clients should set the item index here if they draw in response to AfterDrawItem and they use a display filter. TopFilterPhase must also be specified.
TopFilterPhase: tagesriViewDrawPhase	The highest phase in the drawing order that uses a display filter. Clients should set this when they draw in response to AfterDraw and they use a display filter.
UsesPageCoordinates: Boolean	Indicates whether view uses page coordinates.
VerboseEvents: Boolean	Expand or limit the number of events that are fired. The following events are not fired if VerboseEvents is false: AfterDrawItem.

IViewManager is a low-level interface to the properties defining the behavior of the active view.

One commonly used property managed by the *IViewManager* interface is *VerboseEvents*. When *VerboseEvents* is set to *False*, the default, *IActiveViewEvents::AfterItemDraw*, is not fired. To listen for this event, you must set *VerboseEvents* equal to *True*.

The sample below buffers each selected feature and draws the result on the display. The buffer polygons have a black outline and a slanted red line fill.

```
Private WithEvents ActiveViewEvents As Map
Private m_pMxDoc As IMxDocument
Private m_pBufferPolygon As IPolygon
Private m_pLastBufferedExtent As IEnvelope
Private m_pFillSymbol As ISimpleFillSymbol
Public Sub InitEvents()
  Dim pViewManager As IViewManager
  Dim pRgbColor As IRgbColor

  Set m_pMxDoc = Application.Document
  Set pViewManager = m_pMxDoc.FocusMap
  pViewManager.VerboseEvents = True
  Set ActiveViewEvents = m_pMxDoc.FocusMap
  Set m_pActiveView = m_pMxDoc.FocusMap

  'Create a fill symbol
  Set m_pFillSymbol = New SimpleFillSymbol
  Set pRgbColor = New RgbColor
  pRgbColor.Red = 255
  m_pFillSymbol.Style = esriSFSForwardDiagonal
  m_pFillSymbol.Color = pRgbColor
End Sub
```

```
Private Sub ActiveViewEvents_AfterItemDraw(ByVal Index As Integer, _
    ByVal display As IDisplay, ByVal phase As esriDrawPhase)

  'Only draw in the geography phase
  If Not phase = esriDPGeography Then Exit Sub
  'Draw the buffered polygon
  If m_pBufferPolygon Is Nothing Then Exit Sub
  With display
    .SetSymbol m_pFillSymbol
    .DrawPolygon m_pBufferPolygon
  End With
End Sub

Private Sub ActiveViewEvents_SelectionChanged()
  Dim pActiveView As IActiveView
  Dim pEnumFeature As IEnumFeature
  Dim pFeature As IFeature
  Dim pPolygon As IPolygon
  Dim pTopoOperator As ITopologicalOperator
  Dim pGeometryBag As IGeometryCollection

  Set pActiveView = m_pMxDoc.FocusMap
  Set pGeometryBag = New GeometryBag

  'Flag last buffered region for invalidation
  If Not m_pLastBufferedExtent Is Nothing Then
    pActiveView.PartialRefresh esriViewGeography, Nothing, _
      m_pLastBufferedExtent
  End If

  If m_pMxDoc.FocusMap.SelectionCount = 0 Then
    'Nothing selected; don't draw anything; bail
    Set m_pBufferPolygon = Nothing
    Exit Sub
  End If

  'Buffer each selected feature
  Set pEnumFeature = m_pMxDoc.FocusMap.FeatureSelection
  pEnumFeature.Reset
  Set pFeature = pEnumFeature.Next

  Do While Not pFeature Is Nothing
    Set pTopoOperator = pFeature.Shape
    Set pPolygon = pTopoOperator.Buffer(0.1)
    pGeometryBag.AddGeometry pPolygon
    'Get next feature
    Set pFeature = pEnumFeature.Next
  Loop
```

```
'Union all the buffers into one polygon
Set m_pBufferPolygon = New Polygon
Set pTopoOperator = m_pBufferPolygon 'QI
pTopoOperator.ConstructUnion pGeometryBag

Set m_pLastBufferedExtent = m_pBufferPolygon.Envelope

'Flag new buffered region for invalidation
pActiveView.PartialRefresh esriViewGeography, Nothing, _
    m_pBufferPolygon.Envelope

End Sub
```

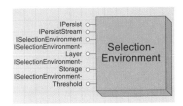

The selection environment controls the applications' selection behavior.

In the ArcMap application, most of the selection environment properties are available on the Selection/Options dialog box.

The *Application* object, which represents the running application, manages a *SelectEnvironment* object that controls several default properties related to creating and drawing selections. For example, when a selection is being performed, should previously selected objects be unselected, or should the newly selected object be appended to the original selection? The *SelectionEnvironment* object provides much more, including the default color all selections are drawn in. The one exception is the dominant element selection color.

A *SelectionEnvironment* object is automatically created by the *Application* object when the application starts. You may want to create your own *SelectionEnvironment* object if you want to perform a selection without changing the application's selection environment. Access to the *Application* object's *SelectionEnvironment* is through *IMxApplication:: SelectionEnvironment*. This property is read-only; you cannot substitute the *Application* object's *SelectionEnvironment* object with another.

The code below changes the default selection color to red; the default is cyan.

```
Public Sub ChangeDefaultSelectionColor()
    Dim pMxDoc As IMxDocument
    Dim pMxApp As IMxApplication
    Dim pSelectionEnv As ISelectionEnvironment
    Dim pRgbColor As IRgbColor

    Set pMxApp = Application 'QI
    Set pMxDoc = Application.Document

    'Obtain a reference to the application's selection environment
    Set pSelectionEnv = pMxApp.SelectionEnvironment

    'Change the selection color to red
    Set pRgbColor = New RgbColor
    pRgbColor.Red = 255
    Set pSelectionEnv.DefaultColor = pRgbColor
End Sub
```

ISelectionEnvironment : IUnknown	*Provides access to members that control the selection environment.*
■→■ AreaSearchDistance: Double	*Distance used for selecting areas by proximity.*
■→■ AreaSelectionMethod: esriSpatialRelEnum	*Selection method used for areas.*
■→■ CombinationMethod: esriSelectionResultEnum	*Combination method for the selection results.*
■→□ DefaultColor: IColor	*Search tolerance in device units.*
■→■ LinearSearchDistance: Double	*Distance used for selecting lines by proximity.*
■→■ LinearSelectionMethod: esriSpatialRelEnum	*Selection method used for lines.*
■→■ PointSearchDistance: Double	*Distance used for selecting points by proximity.*
■→■ PointSelectionMethod: esriSpatialRelEnum	*Selection method used for points.*
■→■ SearchTolerance: Long	*Search tolerance in device units.*

The *ISelectionEnvironment* interface is the primary interface the *SelectionEnvironment* object implements; the *SelectionEnvironment* object also provides defaults for the various types of selections made, including the combination method, selection color, selection method, and search tolerance. The *MxDocument*'s *SearchTolerance* property is a shortcut to the *SearchTolerance* property on the *Application*'s *SelectionEnvironment* object.

This code sample selects features based on the mouse down point location.

To use this sample, add a new UIToolControl onto a toolbar and paste this code into its mouse down event. Completely close VBA so that mouse events will fire. Select the tool and click the focus map to select features.

```
Private Sub UIToolControl1_MouseDown(ByVal button As Long, _
    ByVal shift As Long, ByVal x As Long, ByVal y As Long)
  Dim pMxApp As IMxApplication
  Dim pMxDoc As IMxDocument
  Dim pMap As IMap
  Dim pActiveView As IActiveView
  Dim pEnvelope As IEnvelope

  Set pMxApp = Application
  Set pMxDoc = Application.Document

  Set pMap = pMxDoc.FocusMap
  Set pActiveView = pMap

  Set pEnvelope = pMxDoc.CurrentLocation.Envelope
  pEnvelope.Expand pMxDoc.SearchTolerance, _
    pMxDoc.SearchTolerance, False

  'Refresh the old selection to erase it
  pActiveView.PartialRefresh esriViewGeoSelection, Nothing, Nothing

  'Perform the selection using a point created on mouse down
  pMap.SelectByShape pEnvelope, pMxApp.SelectionEnvironment, True

  'Refresh again to draw the new selection
  pActiveView.PartialRefresh esriViewGeoSelection, Nothing, Nothing
End Sub
```

Enumeration esriSelectionResultEnum	Selection result options.
0 - esriSelectionResultNew	*Creates a new selection.*
1 - esriSelectionResultAdd	*Adds to the current selection.*
2 - esriSelectionResultSubtract	*Subtracts from the current selection.*
3 - esriSelectionResultAnd	*Selects from the current selection.*
4 - esriSelectionResultXOR	*Performs an 'exclusive or' with the current selection.*

The *esriSelectionResultEnum* enumeration is used by *CombinationMethod* to specify the combination method when a new selection is being created. The default is to always create a new selection, but often you need to add new features to the current selection. To do this, change *ISelectionEnvironment::CombinationMethod* to *esriSelectionResultAdd* before performing the selection.

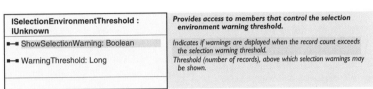

ISelectionEnvironmentStorage : IUnknown	Provides access to members that controls whether objects save their selections.
■—■ SaveSelections: Boolean	Indicates if objects save their selections.

The *ISelectionEnvironmentStorage* interface has one property, *SaveSelections*, that specifies whether each layer's current selection will be saved with the document or not. This property is set to *True* by default.

This interface is not automatically checked when creating a selection; instead, when creating a custom selection tool, you can optionally check the properties in the interface and determine, on your own, if a warning message should be displayed. For example, the ArcMap Select All command uses this interface, but the Select Features tool does not.

ISelectionEnvironmentThreshold : IUnknown	Provides access to members that control the selection environment warning threshold.
■—■ ShowSelectionWarning: Boolean	Indicates if warnings are displayed when the record count exceeds the selection warning threshold.
■—■ WarningThreshold: Long	Threshold (number of records), above which selection warnings may be shown.

The *ISelectionEnvironmentThreshold* interface holds properties that some selection tools use to determine if a warning should be displayed if the number of records reaches a certain threshold when performing large selections.

ArcMap

Each view has a ScreenDisplay object that performs drawing operations. The ScreenDisplay object also makes it possible for clients to create any number of caches. A cache is an off-screen bitmap representing the application's window. Instead of drawing directly to the screen, graphics are drawn into caches, then the caches are drawn on the screen. When the application's window is obscured and requires redrawing, it is done so from the caches instead of from a database. In this way, caches improve drawing performance—bitmap rendering is faster than reading and displaying data from a database.

In general, the *Map* creates three caches: one for all the layers, another for any annotation or graphics, and a third for any feature selections. A layer can create its own private cache if it sets *ILayer::Cached* equal to *True*. In this case, the *Map* will create a separate cache for the layer and groups the layers above and below it into different caches.

IActiveView::PartialRefresh uses its knowledge of the cache layout to invalidate as little as possible. *IActiveView::Refresh*, on the other hand, invalidates all the caches (which is inefficient). Use *PartialRefresh* whenever possible.

Both *PartialRefresh* and *Refresh* call *IScreenDisplay::Invalidate*; this sets a flag clients watch for. Clients draw a cache from scratch (the database) if its flag is set to *True*, and from cache if its flag is set to *False*.

This table shows the phases each view supports and what they map to.

Phase	Map	Layout
esriViewBackground	unused	page/snap grid
esriViewGeography	layers	unused
esriViewGeoSelection	feature selection	unused
esriViewGraphics	labels/graphics	graphics
esriViewGraphicSelection	graphic selection	element selection
esriViewForeground	unused	snap guides

Multiple draw phases may be or'd together. For example, this code specifies a phase of 6 to invalidate the geography (2) and the geo selection (4).

```
pActiveView.PartialRefresh esriViewGeography + _
    esriViewGeoSelection, Nothing, Nothing
```

which is the same as:

```
pActiveView.PartialRefresh 6, Nothing, Nothing
```

Use the data parameter to invalidate just a specific piece of data. For example, if a layer is loaded and its cache property is set to *True*, this layer alone can be invalidated. A tracking layer is a good example of this.

The rectangle parameter specifies a region to invalidate. For example, if a graphic element is added, it is usually only necessary to invalidate the immediate area surrounding the new graphic. Both the data and rectangle parameters are optional.

Here are several Visual Basic examples in ArcMap:

refresh layer
refresh all layers
refresh selection
refresh labels

```
pActiveView.PartialRefresh esriViewGeography, pLayer, Nothing
pActiveView.PartialRefresh esriViewGeography, Nothing, Nothing
pActiveView.PartialRefresh esriViewGeoSelection, Nothing, Nothing
pActiveView.PartialRefresh esriViewGraphics, Nothing, Nothing
```

Below are several Visual Basic examples in *PageLayout*.

refresh element
refresh all elements
refresh selection

```
pActiveView.PartialRefresh esriViewGraphics, pElement, Nothing
pActiveView.PartialRefresh esriViewGraphics, Nothing, Nothing
pActiveView.PartialRefresh esriViewGraphicSelection, Nothing, Nothing
```

When using *PartialRefresh*, it is often necessary that you call it twice if more than one region on the display is being worked with. For example, when moving features, you must invalidate the original area the features were in as well as the new area to wihch the features have moved. A similar and more common case is working with selections. Whenever a new selection is created, you must call *PartialRefresh* twice, once to invalidate the old selection and again to invalidate the new selection. The following VBA code excerpt shows an example of this. This code has been taken from a *UIToolControl* that selects features.

```
Private Sub UIToolControl1_MouseDown(ByVal button As Long, _
    ByVal shift As Long, ByVal x As Long, ByVal y As Long)
  Dim pMxApp As IMxApplication
  Dim pMxDoc As IMxDocument
  Dim pMap As IMap
  Dim pActiveView As IActiveView
  Dim pRubberEnv As IRubberBand
  Dim pEnvelope As IEnvelope

  Set pMxApp = Application 'QI
  Set pMxDoc = Application.Document
  Set pMap = pMxDoc.FocusMap
  Set pActiveView = pMap 'QI
  Set pRubberEnv = New RubberEnvelope

  'Flag the area of the old selection to invalidate
  pActiveView.PartialRefresh esriViewGeoSelection, Nothing, Nothing

  'Use TrackNew to prompt user to drag out a square on the display
  Set pEnvelope = pRubberEnv.TrackNew(pActiveView.ScreenDisplay, _
    Nothing)

  'Perform the selection
  pMap.SelectByShape pEnvelope, pMxApp.SelectionEnvironment, False

  'Flag the area of the new selection to invalidate
  pActiveView.PartialRefresh esriViewGeoSelection, Nothing, Nothing
End Sub
```

PartialRefresh just flags an area on the display that needs invalidating. The invalidatation doesn't immediately occur when *PartialRefresh* is called. Instead, a Windows flag is set, and only when Windows processes its message loop (after a routine like the one above is executed) does the actual invalidation occur. So, in the above example, calling *PartialRefresh* twice in a single routine simply tells Windows that there are two areas on the selection cache (bitmap) that require invalidating—the bounds of the old selection and the new selection.

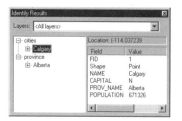

IdentifyDialog *is the dialog box for quickly querying data attributes.*

The Identify Results dialog box in ArcMap

Identifying features, raster cells, and so on, is simplified by the *Identify-Dialog* object. The *IdentifyDialog* object automatically performs a search on all the layers specified and populates a standard dialog box with the search results. This object makes identification easier because you don't have to manually call *IIdentify::Identify* on each desired layer—the *IdentifyDialog* does this automatically and populates the results in a standard dialog box.

To use the *IdentifyDialog* object, you must cocreate a new instance of it and set several of its properties—this hooks it up to the current application. The object is global, however, if an instance has already been created for the application. In this case, cocreating a new one really finds the one already available. It is important to remember that only one Identify dialog box may be opened per session in ArcMap.

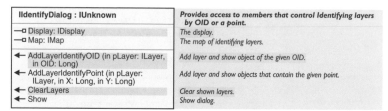

The primary interface on the *IdentifyDialog* object is the *IIdentifyDialog*. There are two properties, *Display* and *Map*, which must be set before the object can be used. These properties tie the object to the current application, enabling it to perform searches. Typically, the *Map* property is set to the document's focus map (*IMxDocument::FocusMap*), and the *Display* property is set to the focus map's *ScreenDisplay* object.

Features, rasters, and others are identified as they are added to the *IdentifyDialog* object. There are two methods for adding layers: *AddLayerIdentifyOID* and *AddLayerIdentifyPoint*. The first method searches for features based on a specific objectID (OID), and the latter searches for features based on an x,y location.

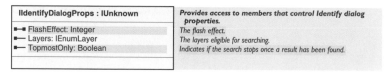

The *IdentifyDialog* object additionally implements *IIdentifyDialogProps*.

The primary member of this interface is the *Layers* property, which provides a list of all the layers in the *Map* specified to *IIdentifyDialog::Map*.

The *TopmostOnly* property is used internally by *IIdentifyDialog::AddLayerIdentifyPoint*. When set to *True*, the default, *AddLayerIdentifyPoint*, searches for features only in the top map layer. The only way to change this property is to change it in the Layers

The only way to change this property is to change it in the Layers combo box on the Identify dialog box. You cannot programmatically set this beforehand. The dropdown combo box has choices for specific layers, all visible layers, topmost layer, and all selectable layers.

The *FlashEffect* property is currently not implemented.

The script below searches from features around an input x,y location coming from a *UIToolControl*'s mouse down event.

```
Private Sub UIToolControl1_MouseDown(ByVal button As Long, _
    ByVal shift As Long, ByVal x As Long, ByVal y As Long)
  Dim pMxDoc As IMxDocument
  Dim pActiveView As IActiveView
  Dim pIdentifyDialog As IIdentifyDialog
  Dim pIdentifyDialogProps As IIdentifyDialogProps
  Dim pEnumLayer As IEnumLayer
  Dim pLayer As ILayer

  Set pMxDoc = Application.Document
  Set pActiveView = pMxDoc.FocusMap

  'Create a new IdentifyDialog and associate it
  'with the focus map and the map's display
  Set pIdentifyDialog = New IdentifyDialog
  Set pIdentifyDialogProps = pIdentifyDialog 'QI
  Set pIdentifyDialog.Map = pMxDoc.FocusMap
  Set pIdentifyDialog.display = pActiveView.ScreenDisplay

  'Clear the dialog on each mouse click
  pIdentifyDialog.ClearLayers

  'Perform an identify on all of the layers the dialog
  'says are searchable
  Set pEnumLayer = pIdentifyDialogProps.Layers
  pEnumLayer.Reset
  Set pLayer = pEnumLayer.Next

  Do While Not pLayer Is Nothing
    pIdentifyDialog.AddLayerIdentifyPoint pLayer, x, y
    Set pLayer = pEnumLayer.Next
  Loop

  pIdentifyDialog.Show

End Sub
```

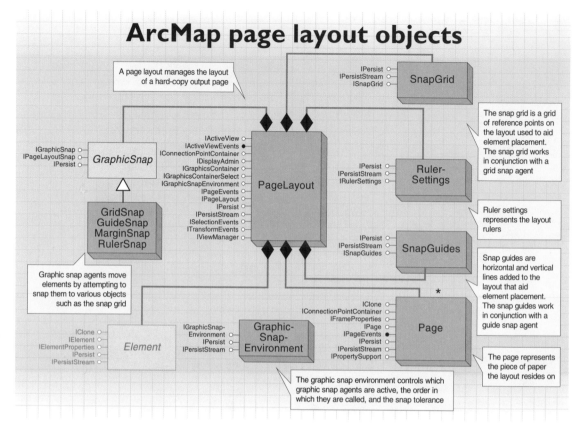

ArcMap page layout objects

A page layout manages the layout of a hard-copy output page

SnapGrid
- IPersist
- IPersistStream
- ISnapGrid

The snap grid is a grid of reference points on the layout used to aid element placement. The snap grid works in conjunction with a grid snap agent

GraphicSnap
- IGraphicSnap
- IPageLayoutSnap
- IPersist

PageLayout
- IActiveView
- IActiveViewEvents ●
- IConnectionPointContainer
- IDisplayAdmin
- IGraphicsContainer
- IGraphicsContainerSelect
- IGraphicSnapEnvironment
- IPageEvents
- IPageLayout
- IPersist
- IPersistStream
- ISelectionEvents
- ITransformEvents
- IViewManager

Ruler-Settings
- IPersist
- IPersistStream
- IRulerSettings

Ruler settings represents the layout rulers

GridSnap GuideSnap MarginSnap RulerSnap

SnapGuides
- IPersist
- IPersistStream
- ISnapGuides

Snap guides are horizontal and vertical lines added to the layout that aid element placement. The snap guides work in conjunction with a guide snap agent

Graphic snap agents move elements by attempting to snap them to various objects such as the snap grid

Element
- IClone
- IElement
- IElementProperties
- IPersist
- IPersistStream

Graphic-Snap-Environment
- IGraphicSnap-Environment
- IPersist
- IPersistStream

Page
- IClone
- IConnectionPointContainer
- IFrameProperties
- IPage
- IPageEvents ●
- IPersist
- IPersistStream
- IPropertySupport

The page represents the piece of paper the layout resides on

The graphic snap environment controls which graphic snap agents are active, the order in which they are called, and the snap tolerance

---

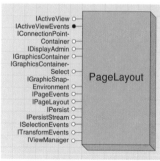

PageLayout
- IActiveView
- IActiveViewEvents ●
- IConnectionPoint-Container
- IDisplayAdmin
- IGraphicsContainer
- IGraphicsContainer-Select
- IGraphicSnap-Environment
- IPageEvents
- IPageLayout
- IPersist
- IPersistStream
- ISelectionEvents
- ITransformEvents
- IViewManager

The page layout manages the layout of a hardcopy output page. The view the page layout draws in the main application window depicts exactly what gets printed. A page layout typically consists of one or more maps, graphics, and a title. It facilitates the creation and management of these parts of a map.

The *PageLayout* object corresponds to the ArcMap layout view. A *PageLayout* object is automatically created by the document when you first start ArcMap. Access the ArcMap *PageLayout* object via *IMxDocument::PageLayout*. This property is read/write; you can instantiate your own *PageLayout* object and swap out the documents' existing *PageLayout*.

The *PageLayout* object is very similar to the *Map* object. Both are views, meaning they take control of the main application window; both are also graphics containers, meaning they can store graphical elements. If there is no map activated in layout view (*IMxDocument::ActivatedView*), all new graphic elements are added to the *PageLayout*. If a *Map* is activated, graphic elements are added to the focus map (*IMxDocument::FocusMap*). Although both the *PageLayout* and *Map* objects are graphics containers, the type of graphics they store is different. The *PageLayout* can additionally store frame elements such as a *MapFrame*, and both can store graphic elements, such as a *TextElement*.

Although the map document (*MxDocument*) can pass a reference to the focus map and the entire collection of maps in the document, the *PageLayout* object really manages all *Map* objects via *MapFrame* objects. In ArcMap, all *Maps* must be contained by a *MapFrame* element, which is directly managed by the *PageLayout*. It is only for convenience that map documents are able to pass a reference to *Maps*.

In order to present itself as a hard-copy output page, the *PageLayout* automatically creates these objects: *SnapGuides*, *SnapGrid*, *RulerSettings*, and *Page*.

The PageLayout object also implements IActiveView, which, like the Map class, you interact with to control the extents that are being viewed. But unlike the Map's active view, the reference system is in page units. Hence, all graphic elements are positioned in page units.

IPageLayout : IUnknown	Provides access to members that control the Page Layout.
■─■ AlignToMargins: Boolean	*Indicates if graphics will be aligned to the margins or to each other.*
■─ HorizontalSnapGuides: ISnapGuides	*The horizontal snapping guides.*
■─ Page: IPage	*The page.*
■─ RulerSettings: IRulerSettings	*The ruler settings.*
■─ SnapGrid: ISnapGrid	*The snapping grid.*
■─ VerticalSnapGuides: ISnapGuides	*The vertical snapping guides.*
■─ ZoomPercent: Double	*The current zoom percent. 100 means 1:1. 200 means twice normal size, etc.*
◄─ FocusNextMapFrame	*Focus the next map.*
◄─ FocusPreviousMapFrame	*Focus the previous map.*
◄─ ReplaceMaps (in Maps: IMaps)	*Replace the maps in the data frames with the specified maps. If there are more maps than frames, new frames are created. If there are fewer frames than maps, extra frames are cleared.*
◄─ ZoomToPercent (in percent: Long)	*Magnify the page by a certain percentage. 100 means actual size. 200 means twice normal size, etc.*
◄─ ZoomToWhole	*Fit the whole page in the window.*
◄─ ZoomToWidth	*Fit the width of the page to the screen.*

The *IPageLayout* interface is the primary interface implemented by the *PageLayout* object. Use this interface to access the *RulerSettings*, the *SnapGrid*, the *SnapGuides*, and the *Page* objects. *IPageLayout* also has methods for zooming the view and changing the focus map. This code demonstrates zooming.

```
Public Sub ZoomToPercent()
  Dim pPageLayout As IPageLayout
  Dim pMxDoc As IMxDocument
  Set pMxDoc = Application.Document
  Set pPageLayout = pMxDoc.PageLayout
  'Ensure the application is in layout view
  If Not pMxDoc.ActiveView Is pMxDoc.PageLayout Then
    Set pMxDoc.ActiveView = pMxDoc.PageLayout
  End If
  pPageLayout.ZoomToPercent 50  'Zoom the view to 50%
End Sub
```

IGraphicsContainer : IUnknown	Provides access to members that control the Graphics Container.
← AddElement (in Element: IElement, in zorder: Long)	Add a new graphic element to the layer.
← AddElements (in Elements: IElementCollection, in zorder: Long)	Add new graphic elements to the layer.
← BringForward (in Elements: IEnumElement)	Move the specified elements one step closer to the top of the stack of elements.
← BringToFront (in Elements: IEnumElement)	Make the specified elements draw in front of all other elements.
← DeleteAllElements	Delete all the elements.
← DeleteElement (in Element: IElement)	Delete the given element.
← FindFrame (in frameObject: Variant) : IFrameElement	Find the frame that contains the specified object.
← GetElementOrder (in Elements: IEnumElement) : Variant	Private order object. Used to undo ordering operations.
← LocateElements (in Point: IPoint, in Tolerance: Double) : IEnumElement	Returns the elements at the given coordinate.
← LocateElementsByEnvelope (in Envelope: IEnvelope) : IEnumElement	Returns the elements that intersect with the given envelope.
← MoveElementFromGroup (in Group: IGroupElement, in Element: IElement, in zorder: Long)	Move the element from the group to the container.
← MoveElementToGroup (in Element: IElement, in Group: IGroupElement)	Move the element from the container to the group.
← Next: IElement	Returns the next graphic in the container.
← PutElementOrder (in order: Variant)	Private order object. Used to undo ordering operations.
← Reset	Reset internal cursor so that Next returns the first element.
← SendBackward (in Elements: IEnumElement)	Move the specified elements one step closer to the bottom of the stack of elements.
← SendToBack (in Elements: IEnumElement)	Make the specified elements draw behind all other elements.
← UpdateElement (in Element: IElement)	The graphic element's properties have changed.

IGraphicsContainer provides access to the *PageLayout* object's graphic elements. Use this interface to add new elements or access existing ones. For example, a title at the top of a layout is a *TextElement* stored in the layout's graphics container.

The script below shows one method for adding a new text element onto the page layout. In this example, a *UIToolControl* is used to get a mouse down event so users can place the text element anywhere they desire on the page layout. The script will only add a new element if ArcMap is in layout view.

```
Private Sub UIToolControl1_MouseDown(ByVal button As Long, _
    ByVal shift As Long, ByVal x As Long, ByVal y As Long)
 Dim pMxDoc As IMxDocument
 Dim pPageLayout As IPageLayout
 Dim pActiveView As IActiveView
 Dim pGraphicsContainer As IGraphicsContainer
 Dim pTextElement As ITextElement
 Dim pElement As IElement
 Dim pPoint As IPoint

 Set pMxDoc = Application.Document
 Set pPageLayout = pMxDoc.PageLayout
 Set pActiveView = pPageLayout 'QI
 Set pGraphicsContainer = pPageLayout 'QI

 'Check that ArcMap is in layout view
 If Not TypeOf pMxDoc.ActiveView Is IPageLayout Then
   MsgBox "Tool works only in layout view"
```

```
      Exit Sub
    End If

    Set pTextElement = New TextElement
    Set pElement = pTextElement 'QI
    'Create a point from the x,y coordinate parameters
    Set pPoint = _
    pActiveView.ScreenDisplay.DisplayTransformation.ToMapPoint(x,y)
    pTextElement.Text = "My Map"
    pElement.Geometry = pPoint
    pGraphicsContainer.AddElement pTextElement, 0

    'Refresh only the pagelayout's graphics
    pActiveView.PartialRefresh esriViewGraphics, Nothing, Nothing
  End Sub
```

This script moves all the elements in the layout one inch to the right:

```
Public Sub MoveAllElements()
  Dim pMxDoc As IMxDocument
  Dim pPageLayout As IPageLayout
  Dim pActiveView As IActiveView
  Dim pGraphicsContainer As IGraphicsContainer
  Dim pElement As IElement
  Dim pTransform2D As ITransform2D

  Set pMxDoc = Application.Document
  Set pPageLayout = pMxDoc.PageLayout
  Set pActiveView = pPageLayout 'QI
  Set pGraphicsContainer = pPageLayout 'QI

  'Loop through all the elements and move each one 1 inch
  pGraphicsContainer.Reset
  Set pElement = pGraphicsContainer.Next
  Do While Not pElement Is Nothing
    Set pTransform2D = pElement
    pTransform2D.Move 1, 0
    Set pElement = pGraphicsContainer.Next
  Loop

  'Refresh only the pagelayout's graphics
  pActiveView.PartialRefresh esriViewGraphics, Nothing, Nothing
End Sub
```

IGraphicsContainerSelect : IUnknown	Provides access to members that control graphic container selection.
▪━○ DominantElement: IElement	Dominant element.
▪━ ElementSelectionCount: Long	Returns the number of selected elements.
▪━ SelectedElements: IEnumElement	Returns the selected elements.
▪━ SelectionBounds (in Display: IDisplay) : IEnvelope	Returns the bounds of the selection.
◄━ ElementSelected (in Element: IElement) : Boolean	Indicates if the element is selected.
◄━ SelectAllElements	Selects all elements.
◄━ SelectedElement (in Index: Long) : IElement	Returns the nth selected element. Use Selection count to get the number of selected elements.
◄━ SelectElement (in Element: IElement)	Selects the specified element.
◄━ SelectElements (in Elements: IEnumElement)	Selects the specified elements.
◄━ SelectionTracker (in Index: Long) : ISelectionTracker	Returns the tracker for the nth selected element. Use Selection count to get the number of selected elements.
◄━ UnselectAllElements	Unselects all elements.
◄━ UnselectElement (in Element: IElement)	Unselects the specified element.
◄━ UnselectElements (in Elements: IEnumElement)	Unselects the specified elements.

Most objects that are graphics containers, such as *PageLayout* and *Map*, implement the *IGraphicsContainerSelect* interface to expose additional members for managing their element selection. For example, *IGraphicsContainerSelect::UnselectAllElements* can be used to clear an object's graphic element selection.

The following simple VBA example returns the number of elements currently selected in the focus *Map* and the *PageLayout*:

```
Public Sub GraphicSelectionCount()
  Dim pMxDocument As IMxDocument
  Dim pMap As IMap
  Dim pPageLayout As IPageLayout
  Dim pMapGraphicsSelect As IGraphicsContainerSelect
  Dim pPageLayoutGraphicsSelect As IGraphicsContainerSelect

  Set pMxDocument = Application.Document
  Set pMap = pMxDocument.FocusMap
  Set pPageLayout = pMxDocument.PageLayout
  Set pMapGraphicsSelect = pMap
  Set pPageLayoutGraphicsSelect = pPageLayout
  MsgBox pMapGraphicsSelect.ElementSelectionCount
  MsgBox pPageLayoutGraphicsSelect.ElementSelectionCount
End Sub
```

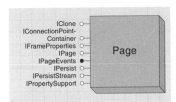

The page represents the piece of paper on which the layout resides. The page has many properties, including color, size, and orientation.

The *PageLayout* object automatically creates a *Page* object to manage the page of paper on which the layout resides. Aside from color, size, and orientation, the *Page* object manages additional layout properties, such as page units, border style, and printable bounds. Access the *PageLayout*'s *Page* object via *IPageLayout::Page*.

IPage : IUnknown	Provides access to members that control the Page.
■← Background: IBackground	The page background.
■← BackgroundColor: IColor	The page color.
■← Border: IBorder	The page border.
■← DelayEvents: Boolean	Indicates if the page stops firing IPageEvents until the flag is set to false.
■← FormID: esriPageFormID	The Page form.
■← IsPrintableAreaVisible: Boolean	Indicates if the printable area is visible.
■← Orientation: Integer	The Page orientation. 1 = portrait. 2 = landscape.
■← PageToPrinterMapping: esriPageToPrinterMapping	The page to printer mapping.
■← PrintableBounds: IEnvelope	The printable bounds.
■← StretchGraphicsWithPage: Boolean	Indicates if graphics should stretch with the page when the page size changes.
■← Units: esriUnits	The units used for the page and all associated coordinates.
←— DrawBackground (in Display: IDisplay)	Draw the page background.
←— DrawBorder (in Display: IDisplay)	Draw the page border.
←— DrawPaper (in Display: IDisplay, in eraseColor: IColor)	Draw the paper. EraseColor is the color of the area surrounding the page. Only the area around the page is drawn in order to eliminate flashing. Use EraseColor = 0 to simply draw page.
←— DrawPrintableArea (in Display: IDisplay)	Draw the printable area.
←— GetDeviceBounds (in Printer: IPrinter, in currentPage: Integer, in Overlap: Double, in Resolution: Integer, in deviceBounds: IEnvelope)	The number of printer pages spanned by the page.
←— GetPageBounds (in Printer: IPrinter, in currentPage: Integer, in Overlap: Double, in pageBounds: IEnvelope)	The number of printer pages spanned by the page.
←— PrinterChanged (in Printer: IPrinter)	Called by PageLayout when printer changes.
←— PrinterPageCount (in Printer: IPrinter, in Overlap: Double, out pageCount: Integer)	The number of printer pages spanned by the page.
←— PutCustomSize (in Width: Double, in Height: Double)	The size of the page in page units.
←— QuerySize (out Width: Double, out Height: Double)	The size of the page in page units.

IPage is the primary interface on the *Page* object. Use this interface to access all of the properties of an ArcMap page, including the page's border, background, background color, orientation, and size.

This code checks the current page size and, if it is 8.5" x 11", changes it to 5" x 5".

```
Public Sub CheckPageSize()
    Dim pMxDoc As IMxDocument
    Dim pPage As IPage
    Dim dHeight As Double
    Dim dWidth As Double

    Set pMxDoc = Application.Document
    Set pPage = pMxDoc.PageLayout.Page
    pPage.QuerySize dWidth, dHeight
    If dWidth = 8.5 And dHeight = 11 Then
        pPage.PutCustomSize 5, 5
    End If
End Sub

Public Sub ChangePageColor()
    Dim pMxDoc As IMxDocument
```

ArcMap

This code changes the page color to yellow.

```
Dim pPage As IPage
Dim pColor As IColor
Dim pRgbColor As IRgbColor

Set pMxDoc = Application.Document
Set pPage = pMxDoc.PageLayout.Page
Set pRgbColor = New RgbColor
pRgbColor.Blue = 204
pRgbColor.Red = 255
pRgbColor.Green = 255
pPage.BackgroundColor = pRgbColor
End Sub
```

Enumeration esriPageFormID	Forms support in Page.
0 - esriPageFormLetter	Letter - 8.5in x 11in.
1 - esriPageFormLegal	Legal - 8.5in x 14in.
2 - esriPageFormTabloid	Tabloid - 11in x 17in.
3 - esriPageFormC	C - 17in x 22in.
4 - esriPageFormD	D - 22in x 34in.
5 - esriPageFormE	E - 34in x 44in.
6 - esriPageFormA5	Metric A5 - 148mm x 210mm.
7 - esriPageFormA4	Metric A4 - 210mm x 297mm.
8 - esriPageFormA3	Metric A3 - 297mm x 420mm.
9 - esriPageFormA2	Metric A2 - 420mm x 594mm.
10 - esriPageFormA1	Metric A1 - 594mm x 841mm.
11 - esriPageFormA0	Metric A0 - 841mm x 1189mm.
12 - esriPageFormCUSTOM	Custom Page Size.
13 - esriPageFormSameAsPrinter	Page Form same as Printer Form.

The *esriPageFormID* enumeration provides a convenient list of preselected page sizes for use by the *Page* object. For example, to change the layout to standard legal page size, pass in *esriPageFormLegal* to *IPage::FormID*. This is much quicker than setting a custom size with *IPage::PutCustomSize*.

One important element in this enumeration is *esriPageFormSameAsPrinter*. When the *FormID* property has been set to this element, the layout's page size mimics the page size of the printer; whenever the printer page size changes, the layout's page size changes to match it. You can see this behavior in the ArcMap application on the Page Setup dialog box accessed from the File menu. Click the File menu and click Page Setup. If the Same as Printer check box is checked, the map setup will change to reflect any changes to the printer setup.

This sample uses the esriPageFormID enumeration to quickly change the page size.

```
Public Sub SetLegalPageSize()
  Dim pMxDoc As IMxDocument
  Dim pPageLayout As IPageLayout
  Dim pPage As IPage
  Dim x As Double, y As Double

  Set pMxDoc = Application.Document
  Set pPageLayout = pMxDoc.PageLayout
  Set pPage = pPageLayout.Page
  pPage.FormID = esriPageFormLegal
  pPage.QuerySize x, y

  MsgBox x & "  " & y
End Sub
```

ArcMap

Enumeration esriPageToPrinterMapping	Page to Printer Mapping.
0 - esriPageMappingCrop	Crop Page to Printer.
1 - esriPageMappingScale	Scale Page to Printer.
2 - esriPageMappingTile	Tile Page to Printer.

The *esriPageToPrinterMapping* enumeration tells the *Page* what to do when the layout's page size does not match the printer's page size. This is often the case when *IPage::FormID* is set to something other than *esriPageFormSameAsPrinter*. By default, ArcMap crops the page, but you can choose to either scale the page or tile it. In the ArcMap application, you can see these choices on the Print dialog box.

IPageEvents : IUnknown	Provides access to events that occur when the Page changes.
← PageColorChanged	Fired when the page color changes.
← PageMarginsChanged	Fired when the page margins change.
← PageSizeChanged	Fired when the page size changes.
← PageUnitsChanged	Fired when the units used by the page changes.

The *Page* object is the event source for page events. Page events are fired by the *Page* object to notify all clients that certain aspects of the page have changed. The page events are grouped under the *IPageEvents* interface and are *PageColorChanged, PageMarginsChanged, PageSizeChanged,* and *PageUnitsChanged*. Within ArcMap, there is only one client—the *Page-Layout* object—listening for these events. The *PageLayout* object listens for these events so it can modify its layout according to changes made to its page. For example, when the page units are changed, the page layout needs to update its transformation, update the snap tolerance and snap grid, update its snap guides, and convert its graphics to the new units.

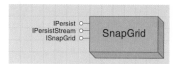

The layout view supports a snap grid, which is a grid of reference points on the layout used to help position elements. The grid may be used as a visual indicator of size and position, or it may be used to snap elements into position.

This image shows the snap grid.

In layout view, right-click the screen and click Grid. This lets you show or hide the snap grid, as well as enable or disable snapping to the grid. The *SnapGrid* object represents the snap grid. Although this object is cocreatable, there is generally no need to create one as the *PageLayout* object automatically creates one when it is created. Use *IPageLayout::SnapGrid* to get a reference to the snap grid currently associated with the layout view.

For information about enabling and disabling grid snapping, see the section on graphic snap agents.

The *SnapGrid* implements *IPersist* and *IPersistStream* to save the object's current settings in the current map document.

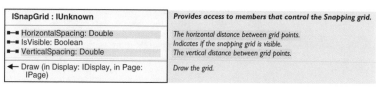

ISnapGrid : IUnknown	Provides access to members that control the Snapping grid.
■—■ HorizontalSpacing: Double	*The horizontal distance between grid points.*
■—■ IsVisible: Boolean	*Indicates if the snapping grid is visible.*
■—■ VerticalSpacing: Double	*The vertical distance between grid points.*
◄— Draw (in Display: IDisplay, in Page: IPage)	*Draw the grid.*

The primary interface on the *SnapGrid* object is *ISnapGrid*. Use this interface to change the grid's horizontal and vertical spacing and control whether or not the grid is visible. The sample below changes the snap grid's vertical and horizontal spacing to 0.5 inches and ensures the grid is visible.

```
Public Sub SnapGrid()
  Dim pMxDoc As IMxDocument
  Dim pSnapGrid As ISnapGrid
  Dim pActiveView As IActiveView

  Set pMxDoc = Application.Document
  Set pSnapGrid = pMxDoc.PageLayout.SnapGrid
  pSnapGrid.HorizontalSpacing = 0.5
  pSnapGrid.VerticalSpacing = 0.5
  pSnapGrid.IsVisible = True
  Set pActiveView = pMxDoc.PageLayout
  pActiveView.Refresh
End Sub
```

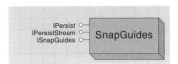

You can use rulers, guides, and grids in layout view to align elements on the page.

This image shows a vertical and a horizontal snap guide added to the layout.

The *PageLayout* object has two *SnapGuides* objects, one for managing horizontal guides, and one for managing vertical guides. Use *IPageLayout::VerticalSnapGuides* or *IPageLayout::HorizontalSnapguides* to obtain a reference to the desired *SnapGuides* object.

Each *SnapGuides* object manages an internal collection of individual guides. For example, the *SnapGuides* object that represents the horizontal snap guides may contain 10 individual guides.

ISnapGuides : IUnknown	Provides access to members that control the Snapping guides.
■—■ AreVisible: Boolean	Indicates if snapping guides are visible.
■—■ DrawLevel: tagesriViewDrawPhase	Level where guides are drawn.
■—■ Guide (in idx: Long) : Double	The nth guide. The position is specified in page units.
■— GuideCount: Long	The number of guides.
◄— AddGuide (in pos: Double)	Adds a guide at the specified position. The position is specified in page units.
◄— Draw (in Display: IDisplay, in isHorizontal: Boolean)	Draw a fine line showing exactly where objects will snap.
◄— DrawHighlight (in Display: IDisplay, in isHorizontal: Boolean)	Draw a highlight around the snap line for a nice visual effect.
◄— RemoveAllGuides	Removes all the guides.
◄— RemoveGuide (in idx: Long)	Removes the nth guide.

Use *ISnapGuides* to add a new guide, remove a guide, and turn the visibility of the guides on or off. The sample below adds a new horizontal guide 5 inches from the bottom of the page and then turns on the horizontal guides' visibility if they are turned off.

```
Public Sub AddHorizontalSnapGuide()
  'Add a horizontal snap guide 5 inches up the page
  Dim pMxDoc As IMxDocument
  Dim pHorizontalSnapGuides As ISnapGuides
  Dim pActiveView As IActiveView

  Set pMxDoc = Application.Document
  Set pHorizontalSnapGuides = pMxDoc.PageLayout.HorizontalSnapGuides
  pHorizontalSnapGuides.AddGuide 5
  If Not pHorizontalSnapGuides.AreVisible Then
    pHorizontalSnapGuides.AreVisible = True
    Set pActiveView = pMxDoc.PageLayout
    pActiveView.Refresh
  End If
End Sub
```

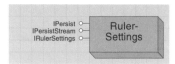

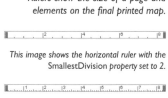

Rulers show the size of a page and elements on the final printed map.

This image shows the horizontal ruler with the SmallestDivision property set to 2.

This image shows the same ruler again but with the SmallestDivision property set to 0.1. Notice that there are now 10 markings between each inch.

The *PageLayout* object has a *RulerSettings* object that manages the ruler settings. Although this object is cocreatable, there is generally no need to create one because the *PageLayout* object automatically instantiates one when it is created. Use *IPageLayout::RulerSettings* to get a reference to the *RulerSettings* object currently associated with the layout view.

IRulerSettings : IUnknown	Provides access to members that control Ruler setup.
SmallestDivision: Double	The size of the smallest ruler division. The size is in page units.

The *IRulerSettings* interface only has one property, *SmallestDivision*. This property controls the size of the smallest ruler division in page units. For example, if the page size is 8.5 by 11 inches and the *SmallestDivision* is set to 2, the rulers in layout view will read off every 2 inches. If the property is set to .1, the rulers will read off every 1/10 of an inch.

```
Public Sub ChangeRulerSettings()

    Dim pMxDoc As IMxDocument
    Dim pRulerSettings As IRulerSettings

    Set pMxDoc = Application.Document
    Set pRulerSettings = pMxDoc.PageLayout.RulerSettings
    pRulerSettings.SmallestDivision = 2
    pMxDoc.ActiveView.Refresh
End Sub
```

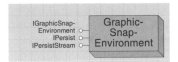

The graphic snap environment controls which graphic snap agents are active, the order in which they are called, and the snap tolerance.

To aid in aligning and positioning elements on a page, the layout view supports element snapping. Elements may be snapped to the snap grid, rulers, guides, and margins. Snapping is performed by a combination of efforts between snapping target objects and snap agents. The snap agents attempt to move a graphic to a position on a snapping target object. The *PageLayout* object manages the snap agents, snapping target objects, and the snapping environment.

The *GraphicSnapEnvironment* object manages the graphic snap agents. This object is cocreatable, but typically this is not necessary because *PageLayout* object automatically creates the object when it itself is created. The *PageLayout* actually aggregates a *GraphicSnapEnvironment* object, making it part of the *PageLayout* object.

To get a reference to the *GraphicSnapEnvironment* associated with the page layout, simply perform a query interface from any of the other interfaces on *PageLayout,* such as *IPageLayout.*

IGraphicSnapEnvironment : IUnknown	Provides access to members that control the Collection of snap agents used for snapping graphics.
■— SnapAgent (in Index: Long) : IGraphicSnap	Get a snap agent. The index argument is zero based.
■— SnapAgentCount: Long	The number of snap agents.
■—■ SnapAgentOrder: IArray	An array of IDs indicating how agents should be ordered.
■—■ SnapTolerance: Double	The snap tolerance in page units.
◄— AddSnapAgent (in SnapAgent: IGraphicSnap)	Add a new snap agent to the environment.
◄— ClearSnapAgents	Remove all snap agents.
◄— DeleteSnapAgent (in SnapAgent: IGraphicSnap)	Remove specified snap agent from the environment.
◄— SnapShape (in Shape: IGeometry)	Snap the shape using the agents in the environment.

Use the *IGraphicSnapEnvironment* interface to add or delete snap agents and to snap a graphic into place with *SnapShape*. The *SnapShape* method calls each snap agent's snap method until one of them returns *True,* indicating that they have moved the graphic. When a snap agent returns *True*, no other snap agents are called. You can also use the *SnapAgentOrder* property on this interface to control in which order the snap agents are called. With this interface, you can establish a snap agent priority—for example, you may decide snapping to the snap grid is more important than snapping to the page margins.

ArcMap

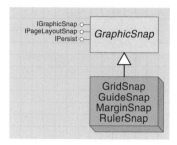

The grid snap moves graphics to the snap grid. The guide snap moves graphics to the horizontal and vertical guides. The margin snap snaps graphics to the layouts printable bounds. The ruler snap snaps graphics to the rulers.

Rulers, guides, and grids are layout objects that aid in aligning elements on a page. However, these objects are only half the story—there are also snap agents that snap to them. Layout snap agents include *GridSnap, GuideSnap, MarginSnap,* and *RulerSnap.* There is a one-to-one correlation between the snap agents and the objects to which they snap. For example, the *GridSnap* snap agent attempts to snap graphic elements to the snap grid created by the *SnapGrid* object. The exception is the *MarginSnap* snap agent, which simply snaps to the layout's printable bounds (*IPage::PrintableBounds*).

Graphics are snapped into place by calling *IGraphicSnapEnvironment:: SnapShape* on the *PageLayout* object. *SnapShape* in turn calls *IGraphicSnap::SnapX* and *IGraphicSnap::SnapY* on each active snap agent (in the order specified by *IGraphicSnapEnvironment::SnapOrder*) until one of the snap agents returns *True,* indicating that a new point has been found that meets the criteria of the snap agent. *SnapX* and *SnapY* are separate calls because some agents, such as guides, may only act in one direction.

GraphicSnap is an abstract class with the interface *IGraphicSnap,* which all graphic snap agents implement.

In ArcMap, a guide snap agent is automatically created and then snaps to vertical and horizontal snap guides. There is no need to create more than one type of snap agent. In ArcMap, you can access the snapping environment and snap agents by right-clicking in the layout view and clicking Options. On the Layout View tab, you can turn snap agents on or off, control the snap agent order, and set the snap tolerance.

IGraphicSnap : IUnknown	Provides access to members that control snapping graphics.
■─ Name: String	*The name of the snap agent.*
◄─ SnapX (in Shape: IGeometry, in Tolerance: Double) : Boolean	*Indicates if the point is snapped in the horizontal direction.*
◄─ SnapY (in Shape: IGeometry, in Tolerance: Double) : Boolean	*Indicates if the point is snapped in the vertical direction.*

All graphic snap agents implement the *IGraphicSnap* interface. This interface only has three members: *Name, SnapX,* and *SnapY. SnapX* and *SnapY* are unique and are used to determine if a graphic can be snapped. For example, the *GridSnap* agent's implementation of *SnapX* for polygon graphics checks if either the *Xmin* or *Xmax* of the graphics bounding rectangle is within snap tolerance of the snap grid. If either is, the graphic is moved the calculated distance between the two. *SnapX* and *SnapY* always return a Boolean, indicating whether or not the graphic was snapped. If any snap agent returns *True,* no other snap agents are called.

IPageLayoutSnap : IGraphicSnap	Provides access to members that control snap agents that are used with PageLayout.
─■ PageLayout: IPageLayout	*Sets the PageLayout that this snap agent is associated with.*

This interface is used to tie the snap agents to the *PageLayout* object. If this property is not set, the graphic snap agents will not work properly.

Because *IPageLayoutSnap* inherits from *IGraphicSnap*, all the methods on *IGraphicSnap* are directly available on *IPageLayoutSnap*.

The following sample demonstrates how a grid snap agent can be added to the layout:

```
Public Sub AddGridSnapAgent()
  Dim pMxDoc As IMxDocument
  Dim pPageLayout As IPageLayout
  Dim pSnapEnv As IGraphicSnapEnvironment
  Dim pPageLayoutSnap As IPageLayoutSnap

  Set pMxDoc = Application.Document
  Set pPageLayout = pMxDoc.PageLayout
  Set pSnapEnv = pPageLayout

  Set pPageLayoutSnap = New GridSnap
  pPageLayoutSnap.PageLayout = pPageLayout
  pSnapEnv.AddSnapAgent pPageLayoutSnap
End Sub
```

ArcMap map element objects

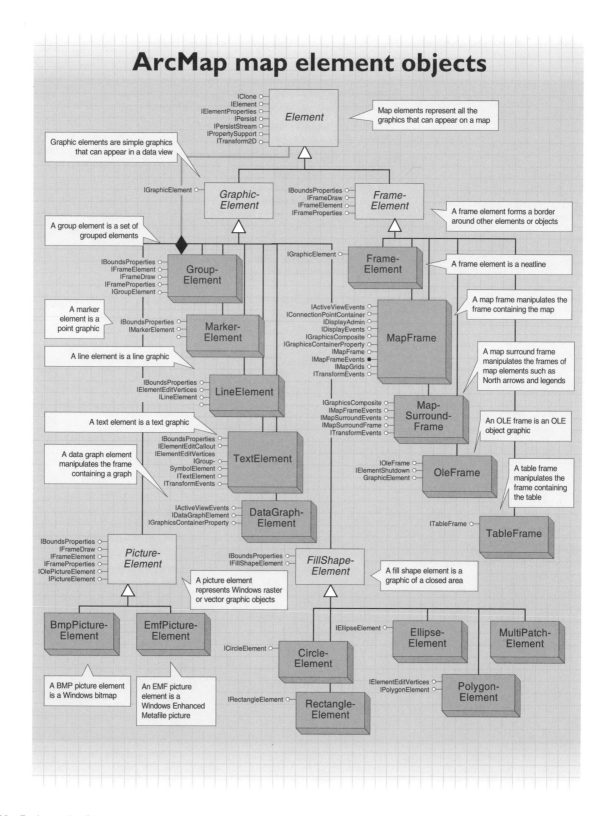

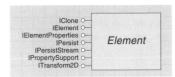

Element *is the abstract class on which all graphic elements and frames are based.*

A map layout and a data frame can both contain elements, but elements are most commonly manipulated as part of a map layout. Elements can basically be thought of as the nonfeature-based components of a map. The list of supported elements includes *FrameElements*, which hold maps; *MapSurroundFrames*, which hold North arrows, scale bar, and so on; and *GraphicElements*, which hold text, line, point, fillshape, and picture elements.

Elements are commonly accessed through the *IGraphicsContainer* interface implemented by the *Map* and *PageLayout* objects. Through this interface you can add, delete, update, and retrieve the individual elements within a *Map* or *PageLayout*. Use the *GroupElement* object to combine multiple elements into a single unit for manipulation by the user.

ArcMap

IElement : IUnknown	Provides access to members that control the Element.
■-■ Geometry: IGeometry	*Shape of the element as a geometry.*
■-■ Locked: Boolean	*Indicates if the element is in a read-only state.*
■— SelectionTracker: ISelectionTracker	*Selection tracker used by this element.*
◄— Activate (in Display: IDisplay)	*Prepare to display graphic on screen.*
◄— Deactivate	*ActiveView that graphics are displayed on is no longer visible.*
◄— Draw (in Display: IDisplay, in trackCancel: ITrackCancel)	*Draws the element into the given display object.*
◄— HitTest (in X: Double, in Y: Double, in Tolerance: Double) : Boolean	*Indicates if the given x and y coordinates are contained by the element.*
◄— QueryBounds (in Display: IDisplay, in Bounds: IEnvelope)	*Bounds of the element taking symbology into consideration.*
◄— QueryOutline (in Display: IDisplay, in Outline: IPolygon)	*Bounds of the element taking symbology into consideration.*

IElement is the generic interface implemented by all graphic elements and frames. Most methods that return graphics (various methods and properties of *IGraphicsContainer* and *IGraphicsContainerSelect*) return them as generic *IElement* objects. *IElement* gives the programmer access to the geometry of the object and employs methods for querying the object and drawing it. It is the programmer's responsibility to determine what type of object is hosting the *IElement* interface by performing a *QI*. In VB, check the elements in a page layout for a *PolygonElement* in the following manner:

```
Dim pDoc As IMxDocument, pPageLayout As IPageLayout
Dim pContainer As IGraphicsContainer, pElement As IElement
Set pDoc = ThisDocument
Set pPageLayout = pDoc.PageLayout
Set pContainer = pPageLayout
pContainer.Reset
Set pElement = pContainer.Next
Do While Not pElement Is Nothing
  If TypeOf pElement Is IPolygonElement Then
    MsgBox "This is a PolygonElement"
  End If
  Set pElement = pContainer.Next
Loop
```

The *SelectionTracker* property will return an *ISelectionTracker*, which can be used to reshape the element. Reshaping of elements is done via handles around the edges of the element. *QueryBounds* and

QueryOutline both require instantiated objects to be passed in. The results of each will be the same for line and point elements, but will vary for polygon elements (*QueryBounds* returns the bounding box, while *QueryOutline* will return an outline of the element).

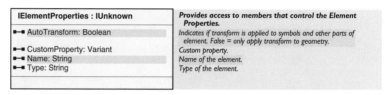

IElementProperties : IUnknown	Provides access to members that control the Element Properties.
■—■ AutoTransform: Boolean	Indicates if transform is applied to symbols and other parts of element. False = only apply transform to geometry.
■—■ CustomProperty: Variant	Custom property.
■—■ Name: String	Name of the element.
■—■ Type: String	Type of the element.

IElementProperties is a generic interface implemented by all graphic elements and frames. This interface allows the developer to attach custom properties to an element. The *Name* and *Type* properties allow the developer to categorize their custom properties.

AutoTransform is a Boolean value that indicates whether internal settings should be transformed along with the element's geometry when a transform is applied via *ITransform2D*. For instance, if you have a point element and you rotate it around a central location (the anchor point of the rotation being different from the point element itself), then the *AutoTransform* property is used to determine whether the orientation of the symbol associated to the element should also be rotated by the same amount.

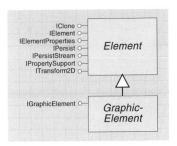

Descending from the Element abstract class, GraphicElement objects are elements that work in both a data frame and a map layout. This category of elements includes text, lines, points, polygons, and pictures.

Graphic elements are added to a data frame or map to highlight areas or provide detail beyond that of the geographic features. The process of redlining (marking areas for correction or notification) can be done by adding graphic elements to the map. Annotation, which is used to label features, is unique in that it is both a geographic feature and a graphic element (specifically a *TextElement*). Annotation is added to the map based on attribute values or other text strings.

IGraphicElement : IUnknown	Provides access to members that control the Graphic Element object.
▪─□ SpatialReference: ISpatialReference	*Spatial reference of the map.*

The *IGraphicElement* interface is a generic interface implemented by all graphic elements. This interface provides access to the spatial reference of the element. The spatial reference of the element reflects its location on the map.

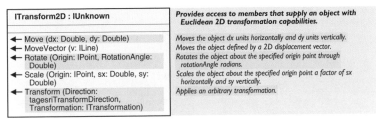

ITransform2D : IUnknown	Provides access to members that supply an object with Euclidean 2D transformation capabilities.
◄─ Move (dx: Double, dy: Double)	*Moves the object dx units horizontally and dy units vertically.*
◄─ MoveVector (v: ILine)	*Moves the object defined by a 2D displacement vector.*
◄─ Rotate (Origin: IPoint, RotationAngle: Double)	*Rotates the object about the specified origin point through rotationAngle radians.*
◄─ Scale (Origin: IPoint, sx: Double, sy: Double)	*Scales the object about the specified origin point a factor of sx horizontally and sy vertically.*
◄─ Transform (Direction: tagesriTransformDirection, Transformation: ITransformation)	*Applies an arbitrary transformation.*

The *ITransform2D* interface is implemented by elements and basic geometries (points, polylines, and so on) to aid in the repositioning of objects. This interface allows elements and geometries to be moved, rotated, scaled, and transformed to new locations. It is implemented for graphic elements so that they can move along with the geometries (features) by which they are placed. The *ITransform2D* interface is documented more fully in Volume 2, Chapter 9, 'Shaping features with geometry'.

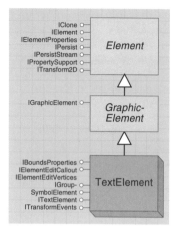

The TextElement coclass is a graphic element that supports text or annotation strings for labeling features and maps. Text elements range from the labeling on a street to the title of a map.

The ITextElement interface is the default interface for the TextElement coclass. This interface allows access to the text string and symbology for the element.

Annotation is both a geographic feature (stored in the geodatabase as a feature with attributes) and a *TextElement*. It is actually a custom feature within the geodatabase, and the *TextElement* is one of the components of that feature.

The following VBA code will access the *TextElement* in a selected set of annotation features:

```
Dim pDoc As IMxDocument, pMap As IMap
Set pDoc = ThisDocument
Set pMap = pDoc.FocusMap
Dim pFeatSel As IEnumFeature
Set pFeatSel = pMap.FeatureSelection
Dim pFeat As IFeature
Set pFeat = pFeatSel.Next
Do While Not pFeat Is Nothing
  If TypeOf pFeat Is IAnnotationFeature Then
    Dim pAnnoFeat As IAnnotationFeature, pElem As IElement
    Set pAnnoFeat = pFeat
    Set pElem = pAnnoFeat.Annotation
    Dim pTextEl As ITextElement
    Set pTextEl = pElem
  End If
  Set pFeat = pFeatSel.Next
Loop
```

ITextElement : IUnknown	Provides access to members that control the Text element.
▪━▪ ScaleText: Boolean	*Indicates if the text scales with the map.*
▪━▪ Symbol: ITextSymbol	*Text symbol this element uses to draw itself.*
▪━▪ Text: String	*Text being displayed by this element.*

Annotation feature classes have a reference scale stored with them so that the annotation automatically scales based on a desired size. For instance, if you want your annotation to be 10 pt. at a scale of 400 map units, you will make your reference scale 400 and set your symbol size to 10 pt. When the scale of your map is set to 200, the annotation will appear twice as large. The *ScaleText* property of *ITextElement* indicates whether the automatic scaling should take place for that particular element.

The IElementEditVertices interface is implemented by TextElement, LineElement, and PolygonElement to support the editing of vertices for these elements.

IElementEditVertices : IUnknown	Provides access to members that control the Element edit vertices object.
▪━▪ MovingVertices: Boolean	*Indicates if this element is moving its vertices.*
◀━ GetMoveVerticesSelectionTracker: ISelectionTracker	*Selection tracker to move points used by this element.*

The *MovingVertices* property tells *SelectionTracker* to hand out the normal selection tracker (*False*) or forward the call to *GetMoveVerticesSelectionTracker* (*True*).

IElementEditCallout : IUnknown	Callout editing interfaces for text elements.
▪━▪ EditingCallout: Boolean	*Returns or sets a flag indicating if this element is editing it's callout.*
◀━ GetMoveTextSelectionTracker: ISelectionTracker	*Returns the selection tracker to move the text used by this element.*

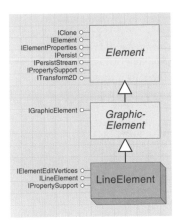

The LineElement coclass is a type of graphic element used to support line graphics within a data frame or map layout.

To determine whether a *GraphicElement* is a *LineElement*, check for the implementation of the *ILineElement* interface:

```
Dim pDoc As IMxDocument, pPageLayout As IPageLayout
Dim pContainer As IGraphicsContainer, pElement As IElement
Set pDoc = ThisDocument
Set pPageLayout = pDoc.PageLayout
Set pContainer = pPageLayout
pContainer.Reset
Set pElement = pContainer.Next
Do While Not pElement Is Nothing
  If TypeOf pElement Is ILineElement Then
    Dim pLineElem As ILineElement
    Set pLineElem = pElement
  End If
  Set pElement = pContainer.Next
Loop
```

ILineElement : IUnknown	Provides access to members that control the Line element.
▪━▪ Symbol: ILineSymbol	Line symbol this element uses to draw itself.

The *ILineElement* interface is the default interface for the *LineElement* coclass. This interface is only implemented for the *LineElement* coclass; it provides access to the symbology for the element.

Check for the implementation of the *IMarkerElement* interface to determine if your element is a *MarkerElement*:

```
Dim pDoc As IMxDocument, pPageLayout As IPageLayout
Dim pContainer As IGraphicsContainer, pElement As IElement
Set pDoc = ThisDocument
Set pPageLayout = pDoc.PageLayout
Set pContainer = pPageLayout
pContainer.Reset
Set pElement = pContainer.Next
Do While Not pElement Is Nothing
  If TypeOf pElement Is IMarkerElement Then
    Dim pMarkerElem As IMarkerElement
    Set pMarkerElem = pElement
  End If
  Set pElement = pContainer.Next
Loop
```

The MarkerElement coclass is a type of graphic element used to support point (marker) graphics within a data frame or map layout.

IMarkerElement : IUnknown	Provides access to members that control the Marker element.
▪━▪ Symbol: IMarkerSymbol	Marker symbol this element uses to draw itself.

The *IMarkerElement* interface is the default interface for the *MarkerElement* coclass. This interface is only implemented for the *MarkerElement* coclass and provides access to the symbology for the element.

ArcMap

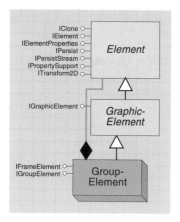

A group element is a creatable object that is composed of one or more element objects.

GroupElement objects are passed to the developer as *IElements* (by *IGraphicsContainer::Next* among other members). It is up to the developer to determine if the object supports *IGroupElement,* which would make it a *GroupElement* object. Use *GroupElement* objects when you want to move or rotate more than one element as a unit.

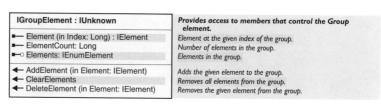

IGroupElement : IUnknown	Provides access to members that control the Group element.
■— Element (in Index: Long) : IElement	Element at the given index of the group.
■— ElementCount: Long	Number of elements in the group.
■—○ Elements: IEnumElement	Elements in the group.
◄— AddElement (in Element: IElement)	Adds the given element to the group.
◄— ClearElements	Removes all elements from the group.
◄— DeleteElement (in Element: IElement)	Removes the given element from the group.

IGroupElement is the interface for creating a group of element objects. It is implemented by the *GroupElement* object. This interface will allow the programmer to manipulate (*Add, Clear,* or *Delete*) a group of elements.

The following code uses *IGroupElement::DeleteElement* to remove the second element in a group:

```
Dim pDoc As IMxDocument, pPageLayout As IPageLayout
Dim pContainer As IGraphicsContainer, pElement As IElement
Set pDoc = ThisDocument
Set pPageLayout = pDoc.PageLayout
Set pContainer = pPageLayout
pContainer.Reset
Set pElement = pContainer.Next
Do While Not pElement Is Nothing
  If TypeOf pElement Is IGroupElement Then
    Dim pElem2 As IElement, pGroup As IGroupElement
    Set pGroup = pElement
    Set pElem2 = pGroup.Element(1)
    pGroup.DeleteElement pElem2
  End If
  Set pElement = pContainer.Next
Loop
```

DeleteElement removes the element from the group and deletes the element from the map. If you want to keep the element in the map but remove it from the group, you will need to readd the element to the map after deleting it from the group.

IFrameElement : IUnknown	Provides access to members that control the Frame element object.
■—■ Background: IBackground	Frame background used by this element.
■—■ Border: IBorder	Frame border used by this element.
■—■ DraftMode: Boolean	Indicates if this element is in draft mode, i.e., draws fast.
■— Object: Variant	Object framed by this element.
■— Thumbnail: Long	Small bitmap representation of this element.

The *IFrameElement* interface is a generic interface for manipulating the properties of the frame itself (not the object within the frame).

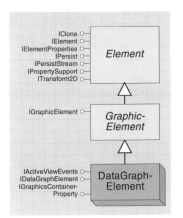

The DataGraphElement *object is a type of* Element *that supports graphs based on data in the map.*

Through the user interface, *DataGraphElement* objects are created by selecting the Show Graph on Layout option when creating a graph or the Show on Layout option after the graph has been created.

DataGraphElement objects can only appear on page layouts. The purpose of the class is to allow graphs to be displayed on the page layouts for outputting purposes.

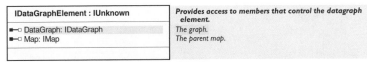

The *IDataGraphElement* interface is implemented only by the *DataGraphElement* coclass and provides access to the graph and the parent map. Through the parent map, you can access the layer or table that was used to generate the graph.

The following VBA code demonstrates how to loop through the elements in a page layout, find the elements that support *IDataGraphElement*, and change the selection set property on the graph to *True* (use the selected set):

```
Dim pDoc As IMxDocument, pPageLayout As IPageLayout
Dim pContainer As IGraphicsContainer, pElement As IElement
Set pDoc = ThisDocument
Set pPageLayout = pDoc.PageLayout
Set pContainer = pPageLayout
pContainer.Reset
Set pElement = pContainer.Next
Do While Not pElement Is Nothing
  If TypeOf pElement Is IDataGraphElement Then
    Dim pDataGraphEl As IDataGraphElement, pDataGraph As IDataGraph
    Set pDataGraphEl = pElement
    Set pDataGraph = pDataGraphEl.DataGraph
    pDataGraph.UseSelectedSet = True
  End If
  Set pElement = pContainer.Next
Loop
```

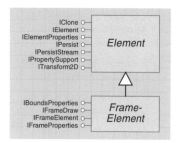

FrameElement *is the abstract class on which all frame element objects are based.*

The FrameElement *types include* FrameElement *(holds point, line, and polygon graphics),* OleFrame *(holds OLE objects such as Word documents),* MapFrame *(holds maps), and* MapSurroundFrame *(holds North arrows, scale bar, legends, and other map primitives).*

FrameElements contain other map elements—they serve as the background and border to these elements. The *MapFrame* element holds a map and allows the programmer access to that map along with the background and border properties of the container holding that map within a layout session.

IFrameElement : IUnknown	Provides access to members that control the Frame element object.
■—■ Background: IBackground	*Frame background used by this element.*
■—■ Border: IBorder	*Frame border used by this element.*
■—■ DraftMode: Boolean	*Indicates if this element is in draft mode, i.e., draws fast.*
■—■ Object: Variant	*Object framed by this element.*
■—■ Thumbnail: Long	*Small bitmap representation of this element.*

The *IFrameElement* interface is a generic interface for manipulating the properties of the frame itself (not the object within the frame). This interface provides access to the background and border properties of the frame, as well as access to the object within the frame.

The *Object* property returns the object within the frame, but it returns it as a variant. The programmer is required to determine what type of object it is. To get an *IMap* object, first determine if the *FrameElement* supports *IMapFrame*, then use the *Map* property of that interface.

The *Thumbnail* property returns a picture of the contents within the frame. This is useful for showing previews in other windows.

The *FrameElement* object does not house any particular type of element, but can be grouped with other elements that are not normally associated with frames. For example, *PointElement* does not support *IFrameElement* Interface, and so, by default, you do not have a frame for your point. However, there may be times when you want to make a point graphic stand out by placing it inside a border with a particular background. This can be accomplished by creating a *FrameElement* object and grouping it (*IGroupElement*) with your *PointElement*.

```
Dim pFrame as IFrameElement, pPointElement as IMarkerElement
Dim pGroup as IGroupElement
Set pFrame = New FrameElement
Set pGroup = New GroupElement
pGroup.AddElement pPointElement
pGroup.AddElement pFrame
```

IGraphicElement : IUnknown	Provides access to members that control the Graphic Element object.
■—○ SpatialReference: ISpatialReference	*Spatial reference of the map.*

The *IGraphicElement* interface is a generic interface implemented by all graphic elements and *OleFrame*. The purpose of the interface is to provide the spatial reference information for the element.

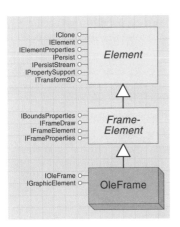

OleFrame *objects house OLE objects (Excel spreadsheets, Word documents, and so on) that have been added to a page layout.*

The *OleFrame* object allows for the embedding of standard OLE objects in a page layout. Check an element for the implementation of *IOleFrame* to determine if it is an *OleFrame* object.

IOleFrame : IUnknown	Graphic Element that holds an OLE object
■— OleClientItem	Valid only in MFC environment. Returns pointer to the COleClientItem representing the OLE object.
← CreateOleClientItem (oleDocument)	Valid only in MFC environment. Initialize the internal COleClientItem. Pass in a pointer to the application's COleDocument.
← Edit	Edit the object in-place.
← EditProperties: Boolean	Show the properties dialog for the object.
← Hide	Stop editing the object.
← Open	Edit the object in a separate application window.

The *IOleFrame* interface is implemented by the *OleFrame* coclass, which allows for the editing of embedded OLE objects. The interface allows for the standard manipulation of embedded OLE objects.

The *Edit* method allows for the editing of the object within the frame, while the *Open* method allows for editing of the object within its own domain.

C++ programmers can use the *CreateOleClientItem* method to initialize the internal *COleClientItem*. Pass in a pointer to the application's *COleDocument* when executing the method.

MapFrame objects are unique among the other frames and elements because they support events (*MapSurroundFrames* also support events) and reference grids. The *MapFrameResized* event is supported through *IMapFrameEvents* to allow for the updating of map grids (graticules) when the frame is resized. Map grids are only supported through the *MapFrame*, not on the map itself.

Check an element for the implementation of *IMapFrame* to determine if it is a *MapFrame* object.

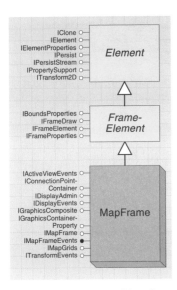

MapFrame *objects house IMap objects (data frames) within a page layout.*

IMapFrame : IFrameElement	Provides access to the members that control the map element object.
■—□ Container: IGraphicsContainer	The frame's container.
■—■ ExtentType: esriExtentTypeEnum	The way in which the map extent of the frame is specified.
■—□ LocatorRectangleCount: Long	The number of locator rectangles.
■—□ Map: IMap	The associated map.
■—■ MapBounds: IEnvelope	The bounds of the map displayed by the frame.
■—■ MapScale: Double	The scale at which the map should be displayed.
← AddLocatorRectangle (in Locator: ILocatorRectangle)	Add a new locator rectangle to the data frame.
← CreateSurroundFrame (in CLSID: IUID, in optionalStyle: IMapSurround) : IMapSurroundFrame	Returns the map surround frame element of the type given in clsid. An optional style object may be specified.
← LocatorRectangle (in Index: Long) : ILocatorRectangle	Returns the locator rectangle at the specified index.
← RemoveAllLocatorRectangles	Remove all the locator rectangles from the data frame.
← RemoveLocatorRectangle (in Locator: ILocatorRectangle)	Remove a locator rectangle from the data frame.

IMapFrame is the interface implemented only by the *MapFrame* coclass. The interface provides access to the map within the frame and also has the ability to create locator rectangles outlining the areas covered by other data frames. Among other things, locator rectangles can be used to highlight inset areas.

The *MapBounds* and *MapScale* properties can be used to update the extent of the map within the frame, but make sure the *ExtentType* is set to the correct option for the property you update.

The *Container* property provides access to the *PageLayout* object within which the *MapFrame* object resides. The back pointer to the *PageLayout* is needed so that the container can be refreshed when the *MapFrame* is updated via a connection point (not through the *PageLayout* itself).

The *CreateSurroundFrame* method should be used for creating map surround elements (North arrows, scale bars, and so on) that you want to be linked to the map frame. Surrounds created in this method will be updated when the map is updated (scale changed, and so on).

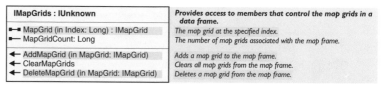

IMapFrameEvents : IUnknown	Provides access to the events that occur when the state of the map frame changes.
◄— MapFrameResized	Occurs when a map frame is resized.

The *IMapFrameEvents* interface is implemented by the *MapFrame* and *MapSurroundFrame* coclasses. This interface is used to notify related objects of changes in the size of the frame.

IMapGrids : IUnknown	Provides access to members that control the map grids in a data frame.
▪—▪ MapGrid (in Index: Long) : IMapGrid	The map grid at the specified index.
▪— MapGridCount: Long	The number of map grids associated with the map frame.
◄— AddMapGrid (in MapGrid: IMapGrid)	Adds a map grid to the map frame.
◄— ClearMapGrids	Clears all map grids from the map frame.
◄— DeleteMapGrid (in MapGrid: IMapGrid)	Deletes a map grid from the map frame.

The *IMapGrids* interface supports adding and deleting map grids (graticules) to a map frame. It is implemented by the *MapFrame* object and acts as a collection for map grids.

The *MapSurroundFrame* object is a type of *FrameElement* that holds surround objects such as North arrows, legends, and scale bars. Like the *MapFrame* coclass, *MapSurroundFrame* objects support the *MapFrameResized* event. Listening for the event allows for the updating of objects such as scale bars that may need to change when the map is resized.

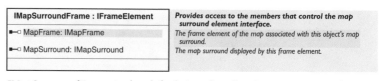

IMapSurroundFrame : IFrameElement	Provides access to the members that control the map surround element interface.
▪—□ MapFrame: IMapFrame	The frame element of the map associated with this object's map surround.
▪—□ MapSurround: IMapSurround	The map surround displayed by this frame element.

IMapSurroundFrame is the default interface for the *MapSurroundFrame* coclass. This interface permits access to the surround within the frame and the *IMapFrame* to which the surround is related.

The *MapFrame* property provides access to the frame to which the surround is linked.

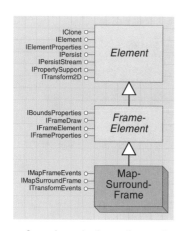

Surrounds are related to map frames so that changes in the map frame are reflected in the surround. For instance, if the map frame is rotated, then a North arrow linked to the frame should also be rotated.

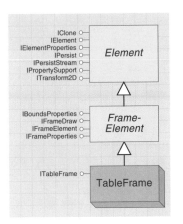

The TableFrame *object is a type of* FrameElement *that holds tables.*

Through the user interface, *TableFrame* objects are created by opening an attribute table and selecting Add table to layout from the Options pulldown menu.

The purpose of the object class is to allow attributes tables to be displayed with a page layout. *TableFrame* objects can only exist within a page layout; they can't be added to a map.

ITableFrame: IUnknown	Provides access to members that control table frames.
■—■ StartCol: Long	The first column to display.
■—■ StartRow: Long	The first row to display.
■—□ Table: ITable	The table (either standalone table or feature layer).
■—■ TableProperty: ITableProperty	The table property.
■—■ TableView: ITableView	The table view to show.

The *ITableFrame* interface is implemented only by the *TableFrame* coclass and provides access to the table held by the frame and the properties of that table. Through this interface, you can specify the starting column and row for the table being displayed and access the query filter and selection set for the table.

The following VBA code demonstrates how to loop through the elements in the page layout, find the ones that support *ITableFrame*, and set the starting row for each to 2:

```
Dim pDoc As IMxDocument, pPageLayout As IPageLayout
Dim pContainer As IGraphicsContainer, pElement As IElement
Set pDoc = ThisDocument
Set pPageLayout = pDoc.PageLayout
Set pContainer = pPageLayout
pContainer.Reset
Set pElement = pContainer.Next
Do While Not pElement Is Nothing
  If TypeOf pElement Is ITableFrame Then
    Dim pTab As ITableFrame
    Set pTab = pElement
    pTab.StartRow = 2
  End If
  Set pElement = pContainer.Next
Loop
```

Using the *TableView* property you can get an *ITableView* object and change properties of the table view such as *ShowSelected* (which determines whether all records or just the selected records are shown in the table).

The *Table* property will return to you the *ITable* object associated with the frame, but you can also get to this object by using the *Table* property on the *ITableProperty* object returned with the *TableProperty* property.

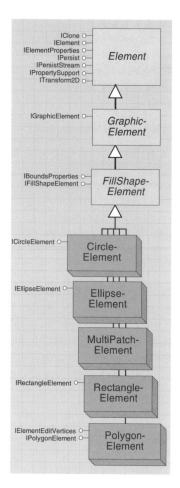

The *FillShapeElement* abstract class is a type of *Element*, but it is also an abstract class supporting *CircleElement*, *EllipseElement*, *PolygonElement*, and *RectangleElement*. Each of the supported elements represents a two-dimensional, closed-area graphic.

IFillShapeElement : IUnknown	Provides access to members that control the Fill Shape element.
■—■ Symbol: IFillSymbol	*Fill symbol this element uses to draw itself.*

IFillShapeElement is a generic interface supported by all *FillShapeElements*. This interface provides access to the symbology used in displaying the element.

IPropertySupport : IUnknown	Provides access to members that set a default property on an object.
■— Current (in pUnk: IUnknown Pointer) : IUnknown Pointer	*The object currently being used.*
◄— Applies (in pUnk: IUnknown Pointer) : Boolean	*Indicates if the receiver can apply the given object at any given time.*
◄— Apply (in NewObject: IUnknown Pointer) : IUnknown Pointer	*Applies the given property to the receiver and returns the old object.*
◄— CanApply (in pUnk: IUnknown Pointer) : Boolean	*Indicates if the receiver can apply the given object at that particular moment.*

IPropertySupport is the interface implemented by *Elements* and various other components (*DimensionLayer*, *FeatureLayer*, *TinEdgeRenderer*, and others) to provide access to generic properties of the object. The interface determines whether a certain property can be applied to an object, then allows that property to be applied when appropriate.

Applies indicates whether an object can be applied at all, while *CanApply* indicates whether an object can be applied at that particular moment (whether or not the object is currently editable).

Current will return the current object of the specified type. For instance, you may ask a *CircleElement* for its current *IColor* property.

ICircleElement : IUnknown	Provides access to members that control the Circle element.

A CircleElement is a type of FillShapeElement that supports circle graphics.

The *ICircleElement* interface is implemented only by the *CircleElement* coclass. The interface does not have any properties or methods and primarily exists for determining if an element is a circle.

IEllipseElement : IUnknown	Provides access to members that control the Ellipse element.

An EllipseElement is a type of FillShapeElement that supports ellipse graphics.

The *IEllipseElement* interface is implemented only by the *EllipseElement* coclass. The interface does not have any properties or methods and primarily exists for determining if an element is an ellipse.

A PolygonElement *is a type of* FillShapeElement *that supports polygon graphics.*

IPolygonElement : IUnknown	Provides access to members that control the Polygon element.

The *IPolygonElement* interface is implemented only by the *Polygon-Element* coclass. The interface does not have any properties or methods and primarily exists for determining if an element is a polygon.

A RectangleElement *is a type of* FillShapeElement *that supports rectangle graphics.*

IRectangleElement : IUnknown	Provides access to members that control the Rectangle element.

You can set a rectangle as the geometry for a RectangleElement, *but the geometry is actually stored and returned as a polygon.*

The *IRectangleElement* interface is implemented only by the *Rectangle-Element* coclass. The interface does not have any properties or methods and primarily exists for determining if an element is a rectangle.

IElementEditVertices : IUnknown	Provides access to members that control the Element edit vertices object.
■—■ MovingVertices: Boolean	*Indicates if this element is moving its vertices.*
◀— GetMoveVerticesSelectionTracker: ISelectionTracker	*Selection tracker to move points used by this element.*

The *MovingVertices* property tells *SelectionTracker* to hand out the normal selection tracker (*False*) or forward the call to *GetMoveVerticesSelectionTracker* (*True*).

ArcMap

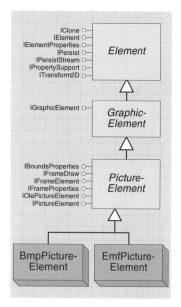

The PictureElement *abstract class is a type of graphic element that supports the* BmpPictureElement *and* EmfPicture-Element *coclasses.*

The BmpPictureElement *coclass supports bitmap files. Query* IPictureElement::Filter *to determine if your element is a* BmpPictureElement.

The EmfPictureElement *coclass supports .emf (Windows Enhanced Metafile) files. Query* IPictureElement::Filter *to determine if your element is an* Emf-PictureElement.

PictureElement objects are very similar to *OleFrame* objects. However, *PictureElements* are the elements themselves, while *OleFrames* are the frames around the object. More subtly, *OleFrame* objects can contain pictures (bmp files and others), but they can also contain other types of OLE objects (Word documents, Excel spreadsheets, and others). *PictureElement* objects can only contain pictures (.bmp or .emf files).

IPictureElement : IUnknown	Provides access to members that control the Picture element.
■— Filter: String	Filter used in CFileDialog.
■—■ MaintainAspectRatio: Boolean	Indicates if the resize box will maintain the picture's aspect ratio.
■— PictureAspectRatio: Double	Filter used in CFileDialog.
■— PictureDescription: String	Description of the Picture Element.
■—■ SavePictureInDocument: Boolean	Indicates if the Picture will be stored in the Document.
◆— ImportPictureFromFile (in Name: String)	File to be imported.

The *IPictureElement* interface is the generic interface implemented by *BmpPictureElement* and *EmfPictureElement* types.

Check for the implementation of the *IPictureElement* interface to determine if your element is a *PictureElement*. The following code demonstrates this.

```
Dim pMyElement As IPictureElement
Set pMyElement = New BmpPictureElement

If TypeOf pMyElement Is IPictureElement Then
  MsgBox ("pMyElement is IPictureElement")
Else
  MsgBox ("pMyElement is not IPictureElement")
End If
```

Use the *Filter* property to determine if the *PictureElement* is a *BmpPictureElement* or an *EmfPictureElement*. For instance, for the *EmfPictureElement*, the filter is "Windows Enhanced Metafile (*.emf)|*.emf|".

SavePictureInDocument specifies whether that actual picture will be saved with the document or just link to the picture on disk.

Make sure you have the correct filter set before using *ImportPictureFromFile*.

IOlePictureElement : IUnknown	Provides access to members that control the Ole Style Picture element.
◆— ImportPicture (in pictureDisp: Picture)	Import Picture from an IPictureDisp interface.

The *IOlePictureElement* interface is a generic interface implemented by *BmpPicture-Element* and *EmfPictureElement*. The interface is used to load a picture into one of these coclasses through an OLE *IPictureDisp*. To load a picture from a file, use *IPictureElement*.

The following VBA code adds a picture element to the layout. The code uses the *PictureAspectRatio* property of *IPictureElement* to ensure that the proper ratio is maintained. The ratio is given as change in x/change in y, so if you want your image to be two inches tall on the y-axis, then it would need to be 2 * *PictureAspectRatio* long on the x-axis.

```
Private Sub AddPicture()
  Dim pDoc As IMxDocument, pPageLayout As IPageLayout
  Dim pContainer As IGraphicsContainer, pElement As IElement, _
    pPic As IPictureElement
  Set pDoc = ThisDocument
  Set pPageLayout = pDoc.PageLayout
  Set pContainer = pPageLayout
  pContainer.Reset
  Set pPic = New BmpPictureElement
  pPic.ImportPictureFromFile
"d:\arcgis\arcexe81\symbols\stipples\woodland.bmp"
  pPic.MaintainAspectRatio = True

  Dim pEnv As IEnvelope
  Dim dXmin As Double, dYmin As Double, dXmax As Double, _
    dYmax As Double
  dXmin = 2
  dYmin = 2
  dXmax = 2 + (2 * pPic.PictureAspectRatio)
  dYmax = 2 + 2
  Set pEnv = New Envelope
  pEnv.PutCoords dXmin, dYmin, dXmax, dYmax
  Set pElement = pPic
  pElement.Geometry = pEnv
  pPic.MaintainAspectRatio = True

  pContainer.AddElement pPic, 0
  Dim pActive As IActiveView
  Set pActive = pPageLayout
  pActive.Refresh
End Sub
```

ArcMap

ArcMap data window objects

IDataWindow ○— **DataWindow**

Data windows are additional displays associated with the application

IClone ○—
IDataGraph ○—
IDataGraphAxis ○—
IDataGraphTicks ○—
IDataGraphAreaProperties ○—
IDataGraphBarProperties ○—
IDataGraphColorProperties ○—
IDataGraphHighLowCloseProperties ○—
IDataGraphOverlayProperties ○—
IDataGraphPieProperties ○—
IDataGraphProperties ○—
IPersistStream ○—
DataGraph

Data graphs represent ArcMap and ArcCatalog graphs

IActiveViewEvents ○—
IComPropertySheetEvents ○—
IDataGraphWindow ○—
IDocumentEvents ○—
IPersist ○—
IPersistStream ○—
DataGraph-Window

Data graph windows display graphs

A map inset window factory creates map inset windows

IDataWindow-Factory ○— **MapInset-Window-Factory**

IActiveViewEvents ○—
IDocumentEvents ○—
ILensWindow ○—
IMapInsetWindow ○—
IMapSurroundEvents ○—
IPersistStream ○—
MapInset-Window

Mapinset windows display a magnified view of the focus map

IDataWindowFactory ○— **Overview-Window-Factory**

An overview window factory creates overview windows

IActiveViewEvents ○—
IDocumentEvents ○—
IMapSurroundEvents ○—
IOverviewWindow ○—
IPersistStream ○—
Overview-Window

Overview windows display the full extent view of the focus map

ITableWindow ○—
ITableWindow2 ○—
Table-Window

Table windows display a table

 IClone ○—
ITableControl ○—
ITableControlInfo ○—
ITableControlWidth ○—
ITableOutput ○—
ITableView ○—
ITableView2 ○—
ITableViewTableFields ○—
TableView

A table view displays a table

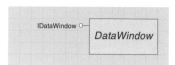

Data windows are additional displays associated with the application.

Data windows are additional windows associated with the ArcMap application; their purpose is to provide a separate window for displaying additional data. The data window framework provides an architecture for easily creating new data windows. ArcMap ships with a variety of data windows, including: *DataGraphWindow, TableWindow, TableView, MapInsetWindow,* and *OverviewWindow.*

The *Application* object manages all data windows; access to a particular window is available using the *IApplicationWindows* interface on the *Application* object.

All data windows implement the following interfaces: *IDataWindow, IActiveViewEvents,* and *IDocumentEvents*. However, custom data windows cannot be implemented in Visual Basic.

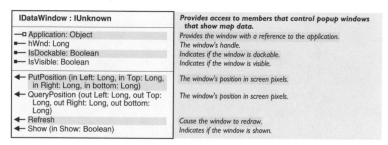

IDataWindow : IUnknown	Provides access to members that control popup windows that show map data.
—□ Application: Object	Provides the window with a reference to the application.
■— hWnd: Long	The window's handle.
■— IsDockable: Boolean	Indicates if the window is dockable.
■— IsVisible: Boolean	Indicates if the window is visible.
◀— PutPosition (in Left: Long, in Top: Long, in Right: Long, in bottom: Long)	The window's position in screen pixels.
◀— QueryPosition (out Left: Long, out Top: Long, out Right: Long, out bottom: Long)	The window's position in screen pixels.
◀— Refresh	Cause the window to redraw.
◀— Show (in Show: Boolean)	Indicates if the window is shown.

Use the *IDataWindow* interface to access the generic properties and methods each data window has, such as the following: is it visible, is it dockable, refresh the window, and change its position.

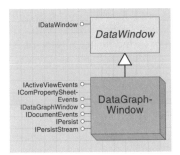

Data graph windows display graphs.

The *DataGraphWindow* wraps a *DataGraph* object that allows a data graph to appear in a separate data window. The *DataGraphElement* object also wraps the *DataGraph* object, but in this case it does so to enable a graph to be directly added to a layout. The example below shows one method for creating a new data graph window. This example creates a graph using the currently selected feature layer in the table of contents.

```
Public Sub CreateNewGraph()
    Dim pMxDoc As IMxDocument
    Dim pTable As ITable
    Dim pDataGraph As IDataGraph
    Dim pDataGraphProperties As IDataGraphProperties
    Dim pGraphWindow As IDataGraphWindow
    Dim pDataGraphs As IDataGraphs

    Set pMxDoc = Application.Document
    If pMxDoc.SelectedLayer Is Nothing Then Exit Sub
    If Not TypeOf pMxDoc.SelectedLayer Is IFeatureLayer Then Exit Sub
    Set pTable = pMxDoc.SelectedLayer

    'Create a new graph
    Set pDataGraph = New DataGraph

    'Set the default Table, DataGraph will select a default graph
    'type and some fields
    Set pDataGraph.Table = pTable

    'Specifically give the graph a name and title
    pDataGraph.Name = pMxDoc.SelectedLayer.Name & " Graph"
    Set pDataGraphProperties = pDataGraph 'QI
    pDataGraphProperties.Title = "Cool Graph"

    'Associate the data graph with a data graph window
    Set pGraphWindow = New DataGraphWindow
    Set pGraphWindow.DataGraph = pDataGraph
    Set pGraphWindow.Application = Application

    'Add the graph to the system
    Set pDataGraphs = pMxDoc 'QI
    pDataGraphs.Add pDataGraph
End Sub
```

IDataGraphWindow : IDataWindow	Provides access to members that control the DataGraph Window.
■─○ DataGraph: IDataGraph	*The DataGraph used by this window.*

Use the *IDataGraphWindow* interface to access or set the *DataGraph* object associated with the *DataGraphWindow*. For more information about the *DataGraph* object, see the section on elements.

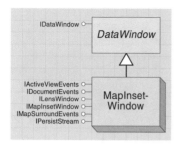

A map inset window displays a magnified view of the focus map.

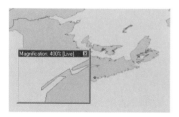

A magnification window with a zoom percent of 400

The *MapInsetWindow* object is the component behind the ArcMap magnifier window. This data window provides a zoomed view of the current focus map. To create a new magnifier window in ArcMap, click the Windows menu and click Magnifier. The *MapInsetWindow* object contains a *MapInset* (a type of map surround), which has the job of controlling the zoom and setting the bounds of the map. The *MapInsetWindow* allows the *MapInset* to appear in its own private window rather than on the page layout.

The *MapInsetWindow* object is not a directly creatable object. To create a new map inset window, you must call *IDataWindowFactory::Create* on a new *MapInsetWindowFactory* object. The example below shows one method for creating a new magnifier window.

```
Public Sub CreateMagnifierWindow()
  Dim pMapInset As IMapInset
  Dim pMapInsetWindow As IMapInsetWindow
  Dim pDataWindowFactory As IDataWindowFactory

  Set pDataWindowFactory = New MapInsetWindowFactory
  If pDataWindowFactory.CanCreate(Application) Then
    Set pMapInsetWindow = pDataWindowFactory.Create(Application)
    Set pMapInset = pMapInsetWindow.MapInset
    'Set the zoom percent to 200%
    pMapInset.ZoomPercent = 200
    pMapInsetWindow.Show True
  End If
End Sub
```

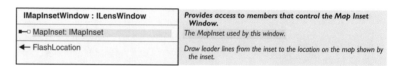

IMapInsetWindow : ILensWindow	Provides access to members that control the Map Inset Window.
●—○ MapInset: IMapInset	The MapInset used by this window.
◄— FlashLocation	Draw leader lines from the inset to the location on the map shown by the inset.

Use the *IMapInsetWindow* interface to access the *MapInset* object associated with the *MapInsetWindow*. *IMapInsetWindow* also contains a *FlashLocation* method, which pinpoints the bounds of the *MapInset* on the focus map.

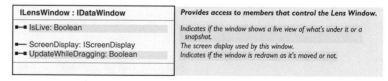

ILensWindow : IDataWindow	Provides access to members that control the Lens Window.
●—■ IsLive: Boolean	Indicates if the window shows a live view of what's under it or a snapshot.
●— ScreenDisplay: IScreenDisplay	The screen display used by this window.
●—■ UpdateWhileDragging: Boolean	Indicates if the window is redrawn as it's moved or not.

Use the *ILensWindow* interface to access and set other import properties of a magnifier window. For example, *ILensWindow* controls whether or not the magnifier window updates while it is being dragged over the focus map; *ILensWindow* also controls whether or not the window should contain a snapshot of a specific location. Of course, when a snapshot is in place, the *UpdateWhileDragging* property has no effect.

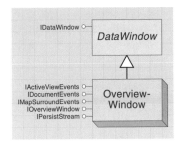

An overview window displays the full extent view of the focus map.

The *OverviewWindow* object is the component behind the ArcMap overview window. This data window provides an overview of the current focus map. To create a new overview window in ArcMap, click the Windows menu and click Overview.

The *OverviewWindow* object contains an *Overview* object—a type of map surround. This object controls the contents of the data window. The *OverviewWindow* allows the *Overview* to appear in its own private window rather than on the page layout.

ArcMap

IOverviewWindow : IDataWindow	Provides access to members that control the Overview Window.
◼─□ Overview: IOverview	The Overview used by this window.

The *OverviewWindow* object is not directly creatable. To make a new overview window, you must call *IDataWindowFactory::Create* on a new *OverviewWindowFactory* object. The code below shows one method for creating a new overview window.

An overview window

```
Public Sub CreateOverviewWindow()
  Dim pOverview As IOverview
  Dim pOverviewWindow As IOverviewWindow
  Dim pDataWindowFactory As IDataWindowFactory
  Dim pFillSymbol As ISimpleFillSymbol
  Dim pLineSymbol As ISimpleLineSymbol
  Dim pRgbColor As IRgbColor

  Set pDataWindowFactory = New OverviewWindowFactory
  If Not pDataWindowFactory.CanCreate(Application) Then Exit Sub
  'Create a new overview window
  Set pOverviewWindow = pDataWindowFactory.Create(Application)
  'Change the area of interterest fill symbol
  'to a hollow fill with a blue border
  Set pOverview = pOverviewWindow.Overview
  Set pFillSymbol = New SimpleFillSymbol
  Set pLineSymbol = New SimpleLineSymbol
  Set pRgbColor = New RgbColor
  pRgbColor.Blue = 255
  pLineSymbol.Color = pRgbColor
  pFillSymbol.Style = esriSFSNull
  pFillSymbol.Outline = pLineSymbol
  pOverview.AoiFillSymbol = pFillSymbol
End Sub
```

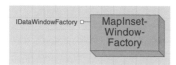

Use a map inset window factory to create a map inset window (magnification window).

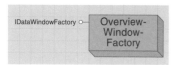

Use an overview window factory to create an overview window.

As discussed earlier, the *MapInsetWindow* and *OverviewWindow* objects are not directly creatable. You must use the related factory objects to create them.

IDataWindowFactory : IUnknown	Provides access to members that control the Factory for creating floating windows.
■— Name: String	The name of objects created by this factory.
◄— CanCreate (in app: Object) : Boolean	Indicates if the window is available given the current application state.
◄— Create (in app: Object) : IDataWindow	Create a new floating window.

The data window factory objects implement the *IDataWindowFactory* interface. Use this interface to check if the window object is creatable and, if it is, to create it. For example, map inset windows and overview windows cannot be created when ArcMap is in layout mode. For more information, see the *CreateMagnifierWindow* code sample documented with the *MapInsetWindow* class.

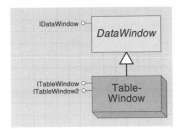

IDataWindow ○— *DataWindow*

ITableWindow ○—
ITableWindow2 ○— Table-Window

Table windows display tables.

ArcMap

The *TableWindow* object is a data window that presents a feature class attribute table or standalone table. Each *TableWindow* houses a *TableView*; for more information on *TableViews*, see Chapter 7, 'Working with the Catalog'. The *TableWindow* allows users to sort, summarize, edit, and get statistics on records in a table.

ITableWindow : IDataWindow	**Displays table window in ArcMap. This interface intergrates ITableView with ArcMap's events and selections.**
■—□ FeatureLayer: IFeatureLayer	Setup feature class to view/edit
■— SelectionSet: ISelectionSet	Current selection set of the table. Only valid for tables showing all rows.
■—■ ShowAliasNamesInColumnHeadings: Boolean	Show alias names or the real field name in column headings. Default False.
■—■ ShowSelected: Boolean	Show only features that are selected
■—□ Table: ITable	Setup table to view/edit
■— TableControl: ITableControl	Get table control. Table needs to be showing before you can get a valid pointer.
■—■ TableSelectionAction: tagesriTableSelectionActions	Action to perform when table selections are made
◄— FindViaFeatureLayer (in pFeatureLayer: IFeatureLayer, in ShowSelected: Boolean) : ITableWindow	Is table (of a featurelayer) already being displayed
◄— FindViaTable (in pTable: ITable, in ShowSelected: Boolean) : ITableWindow	Is table already being displayed
◄— UpdateSelection (in pSelection: ISelectionSet)	Updates current table selection. Does not update Mx feature layer selection.

ITableWindow is the primary interface on the *TableWindow* object. Use this interface to set or access the properties of a *TableWindow*, such as the feature layer or standalone table that is to be presented, in the data window. One interesting property on *ITableWindow* is *ShowSelected*; use this property to control whether all records or just the selected ones are displayed.

The example below opens the table associated with the currently selected feature layer or standalone table in the ArcMap table of contents. The code only creates a new table if it determines one has not already been created. To use this code, select a feature layer or standalone table in the table of contents and run this VBA macro.

```
Public Sub OpenTableWindow()
  Dim pMxDoc As IMxDocument
  Dim pUnknown As IUnknown
  Dim pFeatureLayer As IFeatureLayer
  Dim pStandaloneTable As IStandaloneTable
  Dim pTable As ITable
  Dim pTableWindow As ITableWindow
  Dim pExistingTableWindow As ITableWindow
  Dim bSetProperties As Boolean

  'Get the selected item from the current contents view
  Set pMxDoc = ThisDocument
  Set pTableWindow = New TableWindow
  Set pUnknown = pMxDoc.SelectedItem

  'Determine the selected item's type
  'Exit sub if item is not a feature layer or standalone table
  If pUnknown Is Nothing Then
```

```
                    Exit Sub
            ElseIf TypeOf pUnknown Is IFeatureLayer Then 'A featurelayer
              Set pFeatureLayer = pUnknown
              Set pExistingTableWindow = _
                  pTableWindow.FindViaFeatureLayer(pFeatureLayer, False)
              'Check if a table already exists; if not create one
              If pExistingTableWindow Is Nothing Then
                Set pTableWindow.FeatureLayer = pFeatureLayer
                bSetProperties = True
              End If
            ElseIf TypeOf pUnknown Is IStandaloneTable Then
              'A standalone table
              Set pStandaloneTable = pUnknown
              Set pTable = pStandaloneTable.Table
              Set pExistingTableWindow = _
                pTableWindow.FindViaTable(pTable, False)
              'Check if a table already exists; if not, create one
              If pExistingTableWindow Is Nothing Then
                Set pTableWindow.Table = pTable
                bSetProperties = True
              End If
            Else 'Cannot determine selected item type, exit sub
              Exit Sub
            End If

            If bSetProperties Then
              pTableWindow.TableSelectionAction = esriSelectFeatures
              pTableWindow.ShowSelected = False
              pTableWindow.ShowAliasNamesInColumnHeadings = True
              Set pTableWindow.Application = Application
            Else
              Set pTableWindow = pExistingTableWindow
            End If
            'Ensure table is visible
            If Not pTableWindow.IsVisible Then pTableWindow.Show True

          End Sub
```

ITableWindow2 : IDataWindow	This interface extends ITableWindow to work with ILayers
■—□ Layer: ILayer	*Setup layer attributes to view*
■—□ StandaloneTable: IStandaloneTable	*Sets the standalone table to view/edit*

ITableWindow2 extends table windows, making other layer types (such as raster layers) addable. With *ITableWindow*, only feature layers can be added to a table window.

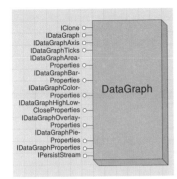

Data graphs present information about map features in an easy-to-understand manner. The information on a graph comes directly from the attribute information stored with the geographic data.

The *DataGraph* object is the main attribute graphing or charting generation object.

ArcMap

IDataGraph : IUnknown	Provides access to members that control the data graph.
■— CGraphHandle: Long	The CGraph handle. CGraph handle can only be used with C++ clients.
■—■ FieldSet1: String	First field set as a comma delimited list.
■—■ FieldSet2: String	Second field set as a comma delimited list.
■—■ FieldSet3: String	Third field set as a comma delimited list.
■—■ FieldSet4: String	Fourth field set as a comma delimited list.
■—■ MaxDataPoints: Long	Maximum number of data points.
■—■ Name: String	Name of the graph.
■—■ PreviewMode: Boolean	Indicates if the graph is in preview mode.
■—■ ReloadAlways: Boolean	Indicates if the graph should always be reloaded.
■—■ SeriesByRecord: Boolean	Indicates if the records or fields for the data series should be used.
■—□ Table: ITable	The graph's table.
■—■ UseSelectedSet: Boolean	Indicates if the selected set should be used.
■—■ Valid: Boolean	Indicates if the graph is currently valid.
←— Attach (in hWnd: Long)	Attaches the DataGraph to the input hWnd.
←— CopyToClipboard	Copys the graph to the clipboard.
←— Detach	Detaches the DataGraph from its current hWnd.
←— Draw	Updates the display of the graph based upon the associated map's current settings.
←— DrawToDC (in hDC: Long, in pRect: tagRECT)	Draws the graph to the input device context.
←— ExportToFile (in FileName: String)	Exports the graph to a file.
←— LoadFromFile (in FileName: String)	Load the graph from a file.
←— Print	Prints the graph.
←— Reload	Loads data values from a table.
←— Resize (in nType: Long, in Width: Long, in Height: Long)	Resizes the graph display.
←— SaveToFile (in FileName: String)	Saves the graph to a file.

The *IDataGraph* interface contains the most basic methods and properties common to all *DataGraph* objects.

Important properties of the *IDataGraph* interface include the *Table* property and the *FieldSet* properties (*FieldSet1, FieldSet2, FieldSet3,* and *FieldSet4*). The *FieldSet* properties strings contain comma-delimited lists of field names. Note that the different *FieldSets* are used differently depending on the graph type of the *DataGraph*. Other properties control how the graph is displayed in a *DataGraphWindow* or on the *PageLayout* CoClass.

IDataGraph methods perform operations such as reloading the *DataGraph* (*Reload* method), redrawing the graph (*Draw* method), drawing the graph to a particular Windows device context (*DrawToDC*), and loading a graph from a file or exporting the graph to a different file format (*SaveToFile, LoadFromFile,* and *ExportToFile*).

The *Attach* and *Detach* methods allow the graph to draw directly to a Window hWnd. This method can be used both by C++ and VB, as long as you have access to the control's *hWnd* property.

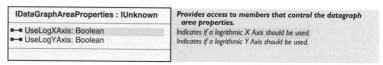

IDataGraphProperties : IUnknown	Provides access to members that control the datagraph properties.
GraphSubtype: esriDataGraphSubtypeEnum	Subtype of the graph.
GraphType: esriDataGraphTypeEnum	Type of graph.
LegendPosition: esriDataGraphLegendPositionEnum	The graph's legend position.
ShowDataLabels: Boolean	Indicates if the graph shows data labels.
ShowLegend: Boolean	Indicates if the graph shows a legend.
ShowXAxisLabels: Boolean	Indicates if the graph shows X axis labels.
SubTitle: String	Sub-title of the graph.
Title: String	Title of the graph.
XAxisLabelField: String	X axis label field.
EditAdvancedProperties	Edits the advanced properties for the graph.

The *IDataGraphProperties* interface contains additional general properties common to all graph types. The *GraphType* and *GraphSubType* properties allow you to set the graph type and graph subtype using enum values. Other properties control whether to show different types of labels, the values used for the title and subtitle, and the position and display status of the legend. The *EditAdvancedProperties* method invokes an additional set of property pages on the *DataGraph* object.

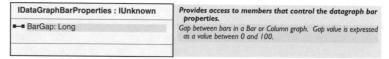

IDataGraphAreaProperties : IUnknown	Provides access to members that control the datagraph area properties.
UseLogXAxis: Boolean	Indicates if a logrithmic X Axis should be used.
UseLogYAxis: Boolean	Indicates if a logrithmic Y Axis should be used.

The *IDataGraphAreaProperties* interface contains properties specific to area type graphs. The two properties control if the area graph uses logarithms on the x- or y-axes when generating the graph display.

IDataGraphBarProperties : IUnknown	Provides access to members that control the datagraph bar properties.
BarGap: Long	Gap between bars in a Bar or Column graph. Gap value is expressed as a value between 0 and 100.

The *IDataGraphBarProperties* interface contains properties specific to bar type graphs. The *BarGap* property controls the gap between bars on the graph display.

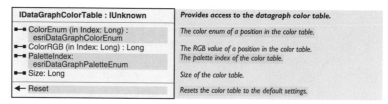

IDataGraphColorTable : IUnknown	Provides access to the datagraph color table.
ColorEnum (in Index: Long) : esriDataGraphColorEnum	The color enum of a position in the color table.
ColorRGB (in Index: Long) : Long	The RGB value of a position in the color table.
PaletteIndex: esriDataGraphPaletteEnum	The palette index of the color table.
Size: Long	Size of the color table.
Reset	Resets the color table to the default settings.

The *IDataGraphColorTable* interface contains properties and methods for controlling the graph's color table.

Note that *DataGraphs* have a very limited set of palettes. The *ColorRGB* property performs a color match to match the input color with the closest color from the current graph color palette. Other methods on the *IDataGraphColorTable* interface allow you to set the color palette, set a color table entry by an *esriDataGraphColorEnum*, or reset the color table to the default settings.

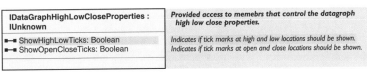

IDataGraphHighLowCloseProperties : IUnknown	Provided access to memebrs that control the datagraph high low close properties.
■─■ ShowHighLowTicks: Boolean	Indicates if tick marks at high and low locations should be shown.
■─■ ShowOpenCloseTicks: Boolean	Indicates if tick marks at open and close locations should be shown.

The *IDataGraphHighLowCloseProperties* interface contains properties specific to *HighLowClose* type graphs. The properties control whether the tick marks show at high and low locations and at open and close locations.

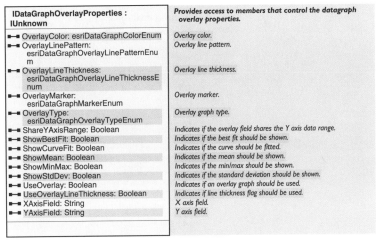

IDataGraphOverlayProperties : IUnknown	Provides access to members that control the datagraph overlay properties.
■─■ OverlayColor: esriDataGraphColorEnum	Overlay color.
■─■ OverlayLinePattern: esriDataGraphOverlayLinePatternEnum	Overlay line pattern.
■─■ OverlayLineThickness: esriDataGraphOverlayLineThicknessEnum	Overlay line thickness.
■─■ OverlayMarker: esriDataGraphMarkerEnum	Overlay marker.
■─■ OverlayType: esriDataGraphOverlayTypeEnum	Overlay graph type.
■─■ ShareYAxisRange: Boolean	Indicates if the overlay field shares the Y axis data range.
■─■ ShowBestFit: Boolean	Indicates if the best fit should be shown.
■─■ ShowCurveFit: Boolean	Indicates if the curve should be fitted.
■─■ ShowMean: Boolean	Indicates if the mean should be shown.
■─■ ShowMinMax: Boolean	Indicates if the min/max should be shown.
■─■ ShowStdDev: Boolean	Indicates if the standard deviation should be shown.
■─■ UseOverlay: Boolean	Indicates if an overlay graph should be used.
■─■ UseOverlayLineThickness: Boolean	Indicates if line thickness flag should be used.
■─■ XAxisField: String	X axis field.
■─■ YAxisField: String	Y axis field.

The *IDataGraphOverlayProperties* interface contains properties specific to graph overlays. A graph overlay is a separate set of graph features drawn on top of the primary graph features. The overlay graph properties control elements such as the type of overlay graph, the color of the overlay graph, line thickness or line pattern, and overlay marker symbol. They also control whether different types of statistical lines show along with the overlay graph.

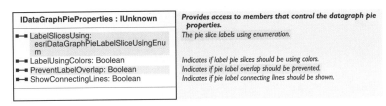

IDataGraphPieProperties : IUnknown	Provides access to members that control the datagraph pie properties.
■─■ LabelSlicesUsing: esriDataGraphPieLabelSliceUsingEnum	The pie slice labels using enumeration.
■─■ LabelUsingColors: Boolean	Indicates if label pie slices should be using colors.
■─■ PreventLabelOverlap: Boolean	Indicates if pie label overlap should be prevented.
■─■ ShowConnectingLines: Boolean	Indicates if pie label connecting lines should be shown.

The *IDataGraphPieProperties* interface contains properties specific to pie type graphs. The properties control different labeling options as well as whether or not to display lines connecting labels with their pie slices.

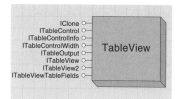

A table view (table control) holds a table.

In ArcMap, all tables are presented in a table data window. Table windows house a table view, also known as a table control. In ArcCatalog, there are no table windows; instead, a table view is directly displayed as a GX view. The table view object is cocreatable. For example, you can instantiate a new table view object, link it to a table, and display it in a custom form.

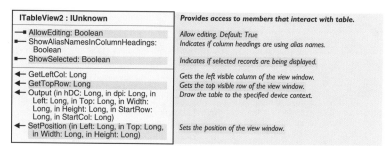

The primary interface on the table view objects is *ITableView*. Use this interface to link a table to the table view and display it.

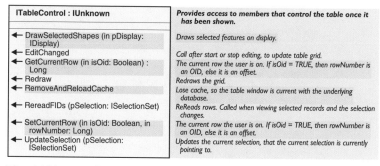

ITableView2 manages some additional table view properties such as whether the table can be edited or not. It also controls whether the table only shows selected records or all of the records.

ITableControl : IUnknown	Provides access to members that control the table once it has been shown.
← DrawSelectedShapes (in pDisplay: IDisplay)	Draws selected features on display.
← EditChanged	Call after start or stop editing, to update table grid.
← GetCurrentRow (in isOid: Boolean) : Long	The current row the user is on. If isOid = TRUE, then rowNumber is an OID, else it is an offset.
← Redraw	Redraws the grid.
← RemoveAndReloadCache	Lose cache, so the table window is current with the underlying database.
← RereadFIDs (pSelection: ISelectionSet)	ReReads rows. Called when viewing selected records and the selection changes.
← SetCurrentRow (in isOid: Boolean, in rowNumber: Long)	The current row the user is on. If isOid = TRUE, then rowNumber is an OID, else it is an offset.
← UpdateSelection (pSelection: ISelectionSet)	Updates the current selection, that the current selection is currently pointing to.

The *ITableControl* interface manages methods that apply to an existing displayed table. For example, use the methods managed by this interface to draw the features currently selected in the table, redraw the table after edits have been made, and set the current row in the table.

ITableControlWidth : IUnknown	Provides access to members that control the table once it has been shown.
■— FullTableWidth: Long	Table width of all columns, and scroll bars.
■— RecommendMinimumTableWidth: Long	Recommend minimum table width, that will ensure all controls can be seen.

The *ITableControlWidth* interface has two properties that aid in sizing the table when first displaying it. The *RecommendMinimumTableWidth* property returns the minimum width the table needs to be to see all columns. The *FullTableWidth* property returns the current table width.

ITableViewTableFields : IUnknown	Provides access to members that associate additional field properties with the table being displayed.
■—□ TableFields: ITableFields	The collection of field information for the table being viewed/edited.

The *ITableViewTableFields* interface has one property that provides access to the fields in the table.

ArcMap

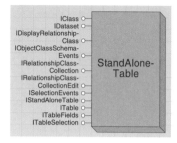

IClass ○—
IDataset ○—
IDisplayRelationship-
Class ○—
IObjectClassSchema-
Events ○—
IRelationshipClass-
Collection ○—
IRelationshipClass-
CollectionEdit ○—
ISelectionEvents ○—
IStandAloneTable ○—
ITable ○—
ITableFields ○—
ITableSelection ○—

StandAlone-
Table

A standalone table is not associated with a feature class, raster, or other dataset.

Not all the tabular data associated with a layer has to be stored in its attribute table. You may choose to store some data in separate tables. You can add this tabular data directly to your map as a table and use it in conjunction with the layers on your map. These tables don't display on your map, but they are listed in the table of contents on the Source tab. Work with these tables as you would any table based on geographic features. For example, you can view the table, add new fields, create graphs, and join it to other tables.

Use the *IStandaloneTableCollection* interface on the *Map* to get a reference to a *StandaloneTable*. Alternatively, if you have a *TableWindow*, you can use the *ITableWindow2::StandaloneTable* property to get the *StandaloneTable* that is displayed by that *TableWindow*.

This map contains a standalone table called STDEMOG. Standalone tables are listed on the Source tab.

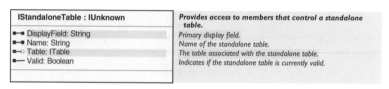

IStandaloneTable : IUnknown	**Provides access to members that control a standalone table.**
▪—▪ DisplayField: String	*Primary display field.*
▪—▪ Name: String	*Name of the standalone table.*
▪—○ Table: ITable	*The table associated with the standalone table.*
▪— Valid: Boolean	*Indicates if the standalone table is currently valid.*

The *IStandaloneTable* interface has properties to manage the table on which the standalone table is based.

Use *Table* property to set or get the underlying table object. There are also properties to specify the name and the display field.

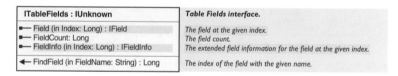

ITableFields : IUnknown	**Table Fields interface.**
▪— Field (in Index: Long) : IField	*The field at the given index.*
▪— FieldCount: Long	*The field count.*
▪— FieldInfo (in Index: Long) : IFieldInfo	*The extended field information for the field at the given index.*
◄— FindField (in FieldName: String) : Long	*The index of the field with the given name.*

You can use the *ITableFields* interface to return the field count and to get a particular field.

The *FieldInfo* property provides extended information on the field; it returns a *FieldInfo* object. For more information, refer to the discussion on the *FieldInfo* coclass later in this chapter.

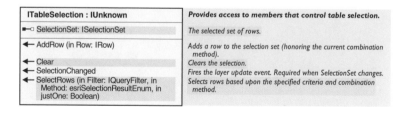

ITableSelection : IUnknown	**Provides access to members that control table selection.**
▪—○ SelectionSet: ISelectionSet	*The selected set of rows.*
◄— AddRow (in Row: IRow)	*Adds a row to the selection set (honoring the current combination method).*
◄— Clear	*Clears the selection.*
◄— SelectionChanged	*Fires the layer update event. Required when SelectionSet changes.*
◄— SelectRows (in Filter: IQueryFilter, in Method: esriSelectionResultEnum, in justOne: Boolean)	*Selects rows based upon the specified criteria and combination method.*

The *ITableSelection* interface lets you perform a selection on the table, add a row to the current selection, and clear the selection; it then notifies you that the selection changed. You can also specify the selection set using the *SelectionSet* property.

For information on the other interfaces on *StandaloneTable*, refer to the *FeatureLayer* coclass later in this chapter.

The following VBA code gets the first standalone table in the map, selects the rows that have a population greater that 10,000,000, and reports the number of selected rows:

```
Public Sub TableSel()
  Dim pMxDoc As IMxDocument
  Dim pMap As IStandaloneTableCollection
  Dim pStdAloneTbl As IStandaloneTable
  Dim pTableSel As ITableSelection
  Dim pQueryFilt As IQueryFilter
  Dim pSelSet As ISelectionSet

  ' Get the standalone table from the map
  Set pMxDoc = Application.Document
  Set pMap = pMxDoc.FocusMap
  Set pStdAloneTbl = pMap.StandaloneTable(0)
  Set pTableSel = pStdAloneTbl

  ' Make the query filter
  Set pQueryFilt = New QueryFilter
  pQueryFilt.WhereClause = "POP1990 > 10000000"

  ' Perform the selection
  pTableSel.SelectRows pQueryFilt, esriSelectionResultNew, False

  ' Report how many rows were selected
  Set pSelSet = pTableSel.SelectionSet
  MsgBox pSelSet.Count & " rows selected in " & pStdAloneTbl.Name
End Sub
```

After running this macro, the selection is shown in the table window. The message box reports how many rows were selected.

ArcMap

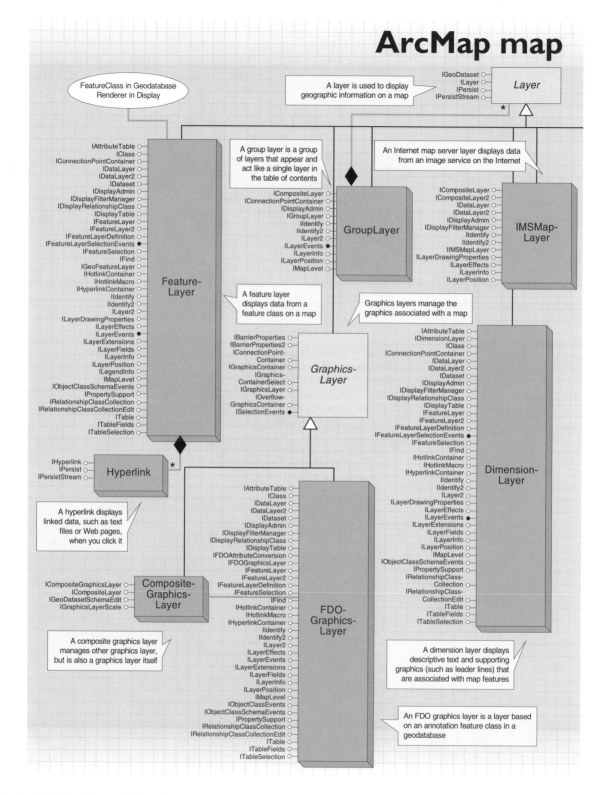

ArcMap map

FeatureClass in Geodatabase
Renderer in Display

A layer is used to display
geographic information on a map

IGeoDataset
ILayer
IPersist
IPersistStream

Layer

A group layer is a group
of layers that appear and
act like a single layer in
the table of contents

An Internet map server layer displays data
from an image service on the Internet

IAttributeTable
IClass
IConnectionPointContainer
IDataLayer
IDataLayer2
IDataset
IDisplayAdmin
IDisplayFilterManager
IDisplayRelationshipClass
IDisplayTable
IFeatureLayer
IFeatureLayer2
IFeatureLayerDefinition
IFeatureLayerSelectionEvents ●
IFeatureSelection
IFind
IGeoFeatureLayer
IHotlinkContainer
IHotlinkMacro
IHyperlinkContainer
IIdentify
IIdentify2
ILayer2
ILayerDrawingProperties
ILayerEffects
ILayerEvents ●
ILayerExtensions
ILayerFields
ILayerInfo
ILayerPosition
ILegendInfo
IMapLevel
IObjectClassSchemaEvents
IPropertySupport
IRelationshipClassCollection
IRelationshipClassCollectionEdit
ITable
ITableFields
ITableSelection

Feature-
Layer

ICompositeLayer
IConnectionPointContainer
IDisplayAdmin
IGroupLayer
IIdentify
IIdentify2
ILayer2
ILayerEvents ●
ILayerInfo
ILayerPosition
IMapLevel

GroupLayer

ICompositeLayer
ICompositeLayer2
IDataLayer
IDataLayer2
IDisplayAdmin
IDisplayFilterManager
IIdentify
IIdentify2
IIMSMapLayer
ILayerDrawingProperties
ILayerEffects
ILayerInfo
ILayerPosition

IMSMap-
Layer

A feature layer
displays data from a
feature class on a map

Graphics layers manage the
graphics associated with a map

IBarrierProperties
IBarrierProperties2
IConnectionPoint-
Container
IGraphicsContainer
IGraphics-
ContainerSelect
IGraphicsLayer
IOverflow-
GraphicsContainer
ISelectionEvents ●

*Graphics-
Layer*

IAttributeTable
IDimensionLayer
IClass
IConnectionPointContainer
IDataLayer
IDataLayer2
IDataset
IDisplayAdmin
IDisplayFilterManager
IDisplayRelationshipClass
IDisplayTable
IFeatureLayer
IFeatureLayer2
IFeatureLayerDefinition
IFeatureLayerSelectionEvents ●
IFeatureSelection
IFind
IHotlinkContainer
IHotlinkMacro
IHyperlinkContainer
IIdentify
IIdentify2
ILayer2
ILayerDrawingProperties
ILayerEffects
ILayerEvents ●
ILayerExtensions
ILayerFields
ILayerInfo
ILayerPosition
IMapLevel
IObjectClassSchemaEvents
IPropertySupport
IRelationshipClass-
Collection
IRelationshipClass-
CollectionEdit
ITable
ITableFields
ITableSelection

Dimension-
Layer

IHyperlink
IPersist
IPersistStream

Hyperlink

*

A hyperlink displays
linked data, such as text
files or Web pages,
when you click it

ICompositeGraphicsLayer
ICompositeLayer
IGeoDatasetSchemaEdit
IGraphicsLayerScale

Composite-
Graphics-
Layer

IAttributeTable
IClass
IDataLayer
IDataLayer2
IDataset
IDisplayAdmin
IDisplayFilterManager
IDisplayRelationshipClass
IDisplayTable
IFDOAttributeConversion
IFDOGraphicsLayer
IFeatureLayer
IFeatureLayer2
IFeatureLayerDefinition
IFeatureSelection
IFind
IHotlinkContainer
IHotlinkMacro
IHyperlinkContainer
IIdentify
IIdentify2
ILayer2
ILayerEffects
ILayerEvents
ILayerExtensions
ILayerFields
ILayerInfo
ILayerPosition
IMapLevel
IObjectClassEvents
IObjectClassSchemaEvents
IPropertySupport
IRelationshipClassCollection
IRelationshipClassCollectionEdit
ITable
ITableFields
ITableSelection

FDO-
Graphics-
Layer

A composite graphics layer
manages other graphics layer,
but is also a graphics layer itself

A dimension layer displays
descriptive text and supporting
graphics (such as leader lines) that
are associated with map features

An FDO graphics layer is a layer based
on an annotation feature class in a
geodatabase

layer objects

A CAD feature layer displays a CAD feature class from a drawing

IAttributeTable
ICadDrawingLayers
ICadTransformations
IClass
IConnectionPointContainer
IDataLayer
IDataLayer2
IDataset
IDisplayAdmin
IDisplayFilterManager
IDisplayRelationshipClass
IDisplayTable
IFeatureLayer
IFeatureLayer2
IFeatureLayerDefinition
IFeatureSelection
IFind
IGeoFeatureLayer
IHotlinkContainer
IHotlinkMacro
IHyperlinkContainer
IIdentify
IIdentify2
ILayer2
ILayerDrawingProperties
ILayerEffects
ILayerExtensions
ILayerFields
ILayerInfo
ILayerPosition
ILegendInfo
IMapLevel
IObjectClassSchemaEvents
IPropertySupport
IRelationshipClassCollection
IRelationshipClassCollectionEdit
ITable
ITableFields
ITableSelection

CadFeature-Layer

ICadLayer
ICad3DRenderMode
ICadDrawingLayers
ICadTransformations
IConnectionPointContainer
IDataLayer
IDataLayer2
IDisplayAdmin
IIdentify
ILayerEffects
ILayerExtensions
ILayerInfo
ILayerPosition

CadLayer

A CAD layer displays a CAD drawing

IConnectionPointContainer
IDataLayer
IDataLayer2
IDisplayAdmin
IIdentify
ILayerEffects
ILayerEvents
ILayerDrawingProperties
ILayerExtensions
ILayerInfo
ILayerPosition
ILegendInfo
IRasterCatalogLayer

Raster-CatalogLayer

Documented in chapter 13, "Integrating raster data"

IAttributeTable
IClass
IConnectionPointContainer
IDataLayer
IDataLayer2
IDataset
IDisplayAdmin
IDisplayRelationshipClass
IDisplayTable
IGeoReference
IIdentify
ILayerDrawingProperties
ILayerEffects
ILayerEvents
ILayerExtensions
ILayerFields
ILayerInfo
ILayerPosition
ILegendInfo
IObjectClass
IRasterLayer
IRelationshipClassCollection
IRelationshipClassCollectionEdit
ITable
ITableFields
ITableSelection

RasterLayer

Documented in chapter 13, "Integrating raster data"

IAttributeTable
IBarrierProperties
IBarrierProperties2
ICadDrawingLayers
ICadTransformations
ICoverageAnnotationLayer
ICoverageAnnotationLayer2
IDataLayer
IDataLayer2
IFeatureLayer
IFind
ILayerFields
ILayerInfo
ITableFields

Cad-Annotation-Layer

IConnectionPointContainer
IDataLayer
IDataLayer2
IDisplayAdmin
IDisplayFilterManager
IIdentify
ILayerDrawingProperties
ILayerEffects
ILayerEvents ●
ILayerExtensions
ILayerFields
ILayerInfo
ILayerPosition
ILegendInfo
ITableFields
ITinLayer

TinLayer

A TIN layer displays 3D surface data

A CadAnnotationLayer is used to control the symbology of the annotation features from a CAD layer

IAttributeTable
IBarrierProperties
IBarrierProperties2
ICoverageAnnotationLayer
ICoverageAnnotationLayer2
IDataLayer
IDataLayer2
IFeatureLayer
IFind
ILayerFields
ILayerInfo
ITableFields

Coverage-Annotation-Layer

A coverage annotation layer displays annotation from a coverage

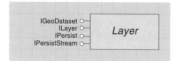

Geographic data is represented on a map as a layer. A layer might represent a particular type of feature, such as highways, lakes, or wildlife habitats, or it might represent a particular type of data, such as a satellite image, a computer-aided design (CAD) drawing, or a terrain elevation surface in a TIN.

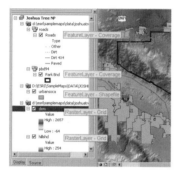

This map contains different types of layers.

For more information on caching, see the topic 'Refreshing the map versus partial refresh' earlier in this chapter.

Layers display geographic information on a map. A layer doesn't store the actual geographic data; it references the data contained in coverages, shapefiles, geodatabases, images, grids, and so on, then defines how to display this geographic data.

Each different type of layer object represents different types of data. Examples of layer objects include *FeatureLayer, GraphicsLayer, RasterLayer, TinLayer, CoverageAnnotationLayer,* and *GroupLayer.*

The *Map* object manages the collection of layers. You can use the *Layer* or the *Layers* property on the *IMap* interface to get a reference to a layer. To determine the type of layer to which you have a reference, query for specific interfaces. For example, if the layer object supports the *IGeoFeatureLayer* interface, then you know it is a *FeatureLayer* object. In Visual Basic, this might be coded as follows:

```
Dim pLayer as ILayer
Set player = pMap.Layer(0)
If TypeOf pLayer is IGeoFeatureLayer Then
  'pLayer is a FeatureLayer object
End If
```

ILayer : IUnknown	Provides access to members that work with all layers.
■— AreaOfInterest: IEnvelope	The default area of interest for the layer.
■—■ Cached: Boolean	Indicates if the layer needs its own display cache.
■—■ MaximumScale: Double	Maximum scale (representative fraction) at which the layer will display.
■—■ MinimumScale: Double	Minimum scale (representative fraction) at which the layer will display.
■—■ Name: String	Layer name.
■—■ ShowTips: Boolean	Indicates if the layer shows map tips.
—□ SpatialReference: ISpatialReference	Spatial reference for the layer.
■— SupportedDrawPhases: Long	Supported draw phases.
■— TipText (in X: Double, in Y: Double, in Tolerance: Double) : String	Map tip text at the specified location.
■—■ Valid: Boolean	Indicates if the layer is currently valid.
■—■ Visible: Boolean	Indicates if the layer is currently visible.
◀— Draw (in drawPhase: tagesriDrawPhase, in Display: IDisplay, in trackCancel: ITrackCancel)	Draws the layer to the specified display for the given draw phase.

All layer objects implement the *ILayer* and *IGeoDataset* interfaces. The *ILayer* interface has a method to draw the layer and properties to define the extent of the layer, the minimum and maximum display scale, the spatial reference, the name, the supported draw phases, and the map tip text. There are also properties that indicate whether the layer is visible, valid, or cached, and whether or not the layer shows map tips.

The *Cached* property indicates whether the layer requires its own display cache or not. If *Cached* is set to *True*, the *Map* will give a separate display cache to the layer so it can be refreshed independently of all other layers. A tracking layer is a good example of a custom layer that would set the *Cached* property to *True*.

Note that the *SpatialReference* property is used only for the map display; it does not change the spatial reference of the underlying data. It carries the map object's knowledge of the current on-the-fly projection back to the feature layer.

The following VB function finds and returns the layer with the specified name.

```
Function FindLayerByName(pMap As IMap, sName As String) As ILayer
  Dim i As Integer
  For i = 0 To pMap.LayerCount - 1
    If pMap.Layer(i).Name = sName Then
      Set FindLayerByName = pMap.Layer(i)
    End If
  Next
End Function
```

IGeoDataset : IUnknown	GeoDataset Interface.
■— Extent: IEnvelope ■— SpatialReference: ISpatialReference	*The extent of the GeoDataset.* *The spatial reference of the GeoDataset.*

The *IGeoDataset* interface specifies the extent and spatial reference of the underlying data. The *SpatialReference* property on *IGeoDataset* is read-only. The property is used to set the spatial reference of the *Map*; the *Map*'s spatial reference is automatically set to the spatial reference of the first layer loaded. For more information on this interface, refer to Volume 2, Chapter 8, 'Accessing the geodatabase'.

The following code reports the name of the spatial reference of the layer.

```
Sub ReportSpatRef()
  Dim pMxDoc As IMxDocument
  Dim pMap As IMap
  Dim pLayer As IGeoDataset
  Dim pSpatRef As ISpatialReference

  Set pMxDoc = Application.Document
  Set pMap = pMxDoc.FocusMap
  Set pLayer = pMap.Layer(0)
  Set pSpatRef = pLayer.SpatialReference
  MsgBox pSpatRef.Name
End Sub
```

The Coordinate System panel of Data Frame Properties is automatically set based on the spatial reference of the first layer added to the map.

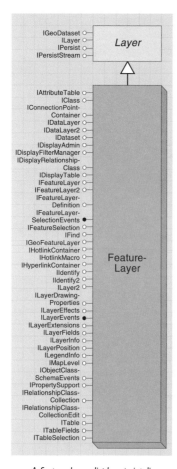

A feature layer displays point, line, or polygon geographic data.

This map contains feature layers.

A *FeatureLayer* is a layer based on a feature class in a vector geographic dataset—a geodatabase, coverage, or shapefile.

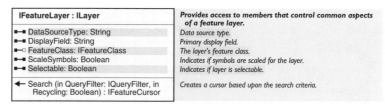

IFeatureLayer : ILayer	Provides access to members that control common aspects of a feature layer.
■—■ DataSourceType: String	Data source type.
■—■ DisplayField: String	Primary display field.
■—□ FeatureClass: IFeatureClass	The layer's feature class.
■—■ ScaleSymbols: Boolean	Indicates if symbols are scaled for the layer.
■—■ Selectable: Boolean	Indicates if layer is selectable.
◄— Search (in QueryFilter: IQueryFilter, in Recycling: Boolean) : IFeatureCursor	Creates a cursor based upon the search criteria.

The *IFeatureLayer* interface has properties that determine the feature class of the layer, the data source type, the display field, whether the symbols are scaled, and whether the layer is selectable. There is also a method for performing a search on the layer. If there is a definition query set on the layer, the *Search* method will work on the subset of the features in the layer that meet the definition criteria. However, the *Search* method will not work on joined fields. If the feature layer has any joins, use the *IGeoFeatureLayer::SearchDisplayFeatures* method instead.

The following code creates a feature layer from a shapefile and adds it to the map:

```
Sub AddLayer()
  Dim pShpWksFact As IWorkspaceFactory
  Dim pFeatWks As IFeatureWorkspace
  Dim pFeatClass As IFeatureClass
  Dim pFeatLayer As IFeatureLayer
  Dim pDataSet As IDataset
  Dim pMxDoc As IMxDocument
  Dim pMap As IMap

  Set pShpWksFact = New ShapefileWorkspaceFactory
  Set pFeatWks = pShpWksFact.OpenFromFile("D:\Data\Canada", 0)
  Set pFeatClass = pFeatWks.OpenFeatureClass("province")
  Set pFeatLayer = New FeatureLayer
  Set pFeatLayer.FeatureClass = pFeatClass
  Set pDataSet = pFeatClass
  pFeatLayer.Name = pDataSet.Name

  Set pMxDoc = Application.Document
  Set pMap = pMxDoc.FocusMap
  pMap.AddLayer pFeatLayer
End Sub
```

IGeoFeatureLayer : IFeatureLayer	Provides access to members that control geographic aspects of a feature layer.
■← AnnotationProperties: IAnnotateLayerPropertiesCollection	Annotation properties.
■□ AnnotationPropertiesID: IUID	The UID used for annotation properties.
─■ CurrentMapLevel: Long	Current map level for drawing symbols.
■← DisplayAnnotation: Boolean	Indicates if the layer displays annotation.
─■ DisplayFeatureClass: IFeatureClass	Feature class used for display operations (may include joined fields).
■□ ExclusionSet: IFeatureIDSet	Set of features that are excluded from drawing.
■← Renderer: IFeatureRenderer	Renderer used to draw the layer.
■← RendererPropertyPageClassID: IUID	Class id of the property page for the renderer.
←─ SearchDisplayFeatures (in QueryFilter: IQueryFilter, in Recycling: Boolean) : IFeatureCursor	Creates a cursor from the display feature class based upon the search criteria.

Only the *FeatureLayer* object uses the *IGeoFeatureLayer*. This interface has properties to set the annotation and renderer for the layer.

The *SearchDisplayFeatures* method allows you to search the feature layer to find features that meet the specified criteria. If there is a definition query set on the layer, the *SearchDisplayFeatures* method will work on the subset of the features in the layer that meet the definition criteria. This search method will also work on joined fields if you qualify the field names. For example, if you want to search on a joined field called "Pop1990" from a table called "Demog", you should use "Demog.Pop1990" as the field name in query filter used in the search method. The *IDisplayTable::SearchDisplayTable* method is a similar search method that will work on feature layers as well as other types of layers. If you want your code to be generic enough to work on different types of layers and standalone tables, you should perform searches using *IDisplayTable::SearchDisplayTable*.

The *IGeoFeatureLayer* interface inherits from the *IFeatureLayer* interface, and the *IFeatureLayer* interface inherits from the *ILayer* interface. This means that when you are working with the *IGeoFeatureLayer* interface, all the properties and methods in *IFeatureLayer* and *ILayer* are exposed. Therefore, when you are working with a feature layer object, you don't need to *QI* for *IFeatureLayer* or *ILayer*; if you *QI* for *IGeoFeatureLayer*, you will get everything from all of these three interfaces.

The following code performs a search on the first layer in the map. This layer is joined to a table named "Demog", and a joined field is used in the query filter for the search method. The name of each feature in the results is reported.

```
Sub GeoFeatLyrSearch()
    Dim pDoc As IMxDocument, pMap As IMap
    Dim pLayer As IGeoFeatureLayer
    Dim pQueryFilt As IQueryFilter
    Dim pFeatCursor As IFeatureCursor
    Dim pFeature As IFeature
    Set pDoc = Application.Document
    Set pMap = pDoc.FocusMap
    Set pLayer = pMap.Layer(0)
    ' Create the query filter and set the where clause. Note that
    ' this is a joined layer so you must qualify the field names.
    Set pQueryFilt = New QueryFilter
```

```
pQueryFilt.WhereClause = "DEMOG.Pop1991 > 1000000"

'Perform the search and report name of each feature in results
Set pFeatCursor = pLayer.SearchDisplayFeatures(pQueryFilt, True)
Set pFeature = pFeatCursor.NextFeature
MsgBox pFeature.Value(pFeatCursor.FindField("Province.Name"))
Do Until pFeature Is Nothing
  Set pFeature = pFeatCursor.NextFeature
  If Not pFeature Is Nothing Then
    MsgBox pFeature.Value(pFeatCursor.FindField("Province.Name"))
  End If
Loop
End Sub
```

IDataLayer : IUnknown	Provides access to members that control the data source properties of a layer.
■—• DataSourceName: IName	Name of the data object for the layer.
■— DataSourceSupported (in Name: IName) : Boolean	Indicates if the specified data object name is supported by the layer.
■—• RelativeBase: String	Base path used when storing relative path names.
←— Connect (in pOptRepairName: IName) : Boolean	Connects the layer to its data source. An optional name object can be specified to aid in repairing a lost connection.

The *IDataLayer* interface provides information about the data source of the layer, such as the data source name, the base path used in relative path names, and whether the layer supports the data source. There is also a method to connect to the data source if the connection has been lost. The following code reports the base path used in relative pathnames:

```
Public Sub GetRelativeBase()
  Dim pMxDoc As IMxDocument
  Dim pMap As IMap
  Dim pLayer As IDataLayer
  Set pMxDoc = Application.Document
  Set pMap = pMxDoc.FocusMap
  Set pLayer = pMap.Layer(0)
  MsgBox pLayer.RelativeBase
End Sub
```

IDisplayTable : IUnknown	Provides access to members that work with the display table associated with a standalone table.
■— DisplayTable: ITable	The display table.
←— SearchDisplayTable (in pQueryFilter: IQueryFilter, in Recycling: Boolean) : ICursor	Creates a cursor from the display table based upon the search criteria.
←— SelectDisplayTable (in pQueryFilter: IQueryFilter, in selType: esriSelectionType, in selOption: esriSelectionOption, in pSelWorkspace: IWorkspace) : ISelectionSet	Creates a selection set from the display table based upon the search criteria.

The display table is the table used for display purposes. This table differs from the table of the base feature class of the layer (*IFeatureLayer:: FeatureClass*) in that it may contain joined fields. The display table is the *RelQueryTable* object of the layer. The *IDisplayTable* interface has a property to get a reference to the display table and methods to perform searches and selections on the display table. If you want your code to be generic enough to work on different types of layers and standalone tables, you should perform selections and searches using the methods on *IDisplayTable* rather than similar methods on other interfaces.

The following code creates a selection set using the *SelectDisplayTable* method, then reports the number of selected features. It is necessary to create a scratch workspace to use for the selection. This code only creates a selection set; it doesn't show the selection on the display. To see how to show the selection on the display, refer to the *IFeatureSelection* interface.

```
Public Sub DpyTableSelect()
  Dim pDoc As IMxDocument
  Dim pMap As IMap
  Dim pDpyTable As IDisplayTable
  Dim pScratchWorkspace As IWorkspace
  Dim pScratchWorkspaceFactory As IScratchWorkspaceFactory
  Dim pQFilt As IQueryFilter
  Dim pSelSet As ISelectionSet

  Set pDoc = Application.Document
  Set pMap = pDoc.FocusMap
  Set pDpyTable = pMap.Layer(0)

  ' Create a scratch workspace to use for the selection
  Set pScratchWorkspaceFactory = New ScratchWorkspaceFactory
  Set pScratchWorkspace = _
  pScratchWorkspaceFactory.DefaultScratchWorkspace

  ' Create the query filter
  Set pQFilt = New QueryFilter
  pQFilt.WhereClause = "TYPE = 'Gravel'"

  ' Create the selection set
  Set pSelSet = pDpyTable.SelectDisplayTable(pQFilt, _
    esriSelectionTypeIDSet, esriSelectionOptionNormal, _
    pScratchWorkspace)

  ' Report number of selected features
  MsgBox pSelSet.Count
End Sub
```

IDisplayAdmin : IUnknown	Provides access to members that control display administration.
■— UsesFilter: Boolean	Indicates if the current object draws using a filter.

A display filter allows a rasterized version of the layer to be processed for drawing purposes. You can create your own display filter to display a layer using more raster-like effects, such as contrast and brightness adjustments.

The *IDisplayAdmin* interface indicates whether the layer uses a display filter.

IDisplayFilterManager : IDisplayAdmin	Provides access to members that control display filter management.
■—■ DisplayFilter: IDisplayFilter	The display filter.

The *IDisplayFilterManager* interface specifies what display filter object is currently being used.

IPropertySupport : IUnknown	Provides access to members that set a default property on an object.
■— Current (in pUnk: IUnknown Pointer) : IUnknown Pointer	The object currently being used.
◄— Applies (in pUnk: IUnknown Pointer) : Boolean	Indicates if the receiver can apply the given object at any given time.
◄— Apply (in NewObject: IUnknown Pointer) : IUnknown Pointer	Applies the given property to the receiver and returns the old object.
◄— CanApply (in pUnk: IUnknown Pointer) : Boolean	Indicates if the receiver can apply the given object at that particular moment.

Many objects implement the *IPropertySupport* interface to provide access to properties of the object. The interface has methods for determining whether a certain property can be applied to an object; it allows the property to be applied when appropriate. *FeatureLayer*'s implementation of *IPropertySupport* is used to check to see if the specified display filter object can be applied to the layer. The *Applies* method indicates whether the specified display filter object can be applied at all, while the *CanApply* method indicates whether the specified display filter object can be applied at that particular moment. The *Current* method will return the current display filter. *FeatureLayer* also uses *IPropertySupport* for some renderer objects.

IFeatureLayer2 : IUnknown	Additional interface to provides access to members that control common aspects of a feature layer.
■— ShapeType: tagesriGeometryType	The layer's shape type.

The *IFeatureLayer2* interface has a *ShapeType* property that uses the *esriGeometryType* enumeration to indicate the shape type of the features in the layer.

IFeatureLayerDefinition : IUnknown	Provides access to members that are used to create a selection layer from an existing FeatureLayer's selected features.
■—■ DefinitionExpression: String	Definition query expression for the existing layer.
■— DefinitionSelectionSet: ISelectionSet	Set of features defined by the existing layer's definition query expression.
■—□ RelationshipClass: IRelationshipClass	The current relationship class used to display related fields.
◄— CreateSelectionLayer (in LayerName: String, in useCurrentSelection: Boolean, in joinTableNames: String, in Expression: String) : IFeatureLayer	Creates a new feature layer from the existing layer based on the current selection and the specified query expression.

The *IFeatureLayerDefinition* interface can be used to set a definition query on the feature layer so that only the features that meet the specified criteria are displayed. The *CreateSelectionLayer* method allows you to create a new layer based on the current selection on the layer, the current definition query on the layer, or the combination of the two.

The *RelationshipClass* property returns a reference to the relationship class that defines the relationship between the layer and the table to which it is joined, if there is one. However, it's better to use the *RelationshipClass* property on the *IDisplayRelationshipClass* interface for this since you'll also have access to the other properties and methods that deal with joins.

The following code uses the *DefinitionExpression* property to assign a definition query to the feature layer. Only the features in the layer that have an area greater than 350,000 are displayed.

```
Sub DefineLayer()
    Dim pMxDoc As IMxDocument
    Dim pMap As IMap
    Dim pFeatLayerDef As IFeatureLayerDefinition
    Set pMxDoc = Application.Document
    Set pMap = pMxDoc.FocusMap
    Set pFeatLayerDef = pMap.Layer(0)
    pFeatLayerDef.DefinitionExpression = "Area > 350000"
    pMxDoc.ActiveView.PartialRefresh esriViewGeography, _
        Nothing, Nothing
End Sub
```

After running this macro, only the features that meet the specified criteria are shown in the display. The Definition Query panel of the layer's Properties dialog box shows the expression that was assigned by this macro.

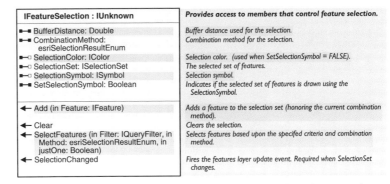

IFeatureLayerSelectionEvents : IUnknown	Provides access to events that occur when the selection changes.
← FeatureLayerSelectionChanged	Occurs when the selection changes.

The *IFeatureLayerSelectionEvents* interface has an event that occurs when the selection on the layer changes.

IFeatureSelection : IUnknown	Provides access to members that control feature selection.
■–■ BufferDistance: Double	Buffer distance used for the selection.
■–■ CombinationMethod: esriSelectionResultEnum	Combination method for the selection.
■–□ SelectionColor: IColor	Selection color. (used when SetSelectionSymbol = FALSE).
■–□ SelectionSet: ISelectionSet	The selected set of features.
■–□ SelectionSymbol: ISymbol	Selection symbol.
■–■ SetSelectionSymbol: Boolean	Indicates if the selected set of features is drawn using the SelectionSymbol.
← Add (in Feature: IFeature)	Adds a feature to the selection set (honoring the current combination method).
← Clear	Clears the selection.
← SelectFeatures (in Filter: IQueryFilter, in Method: esriSelectionResultEnum, in justOne: Boolean)	Selects features based upon the specifed criteria and combination method.
← SelectionChanged	Fires the features layer update event. Required when SelectionSet changes.

The *IFeatureSelection* interface has properties to set the selection color and symbol, buffer distance, and selection combination method. There are methods to perform a selection on the layer, add a feature to the current selection, clear the selection, and notify you that the selection changed. The *SelectFeatures* method performs the selection and automatically shows the selection in the display. Use the *SelectionSet* property to get the set of the selected features after the selection is performed. If you have created a selection set some other way, you can use the *SelectionSet* property to assign that selection set to the feature layer so that the selection shows up on the display.

This code selects all the features that have an area greater than 350,000 data units and reports the number of selected features.

```
Public Sub SelFeatures()
    Dim pMxDoc As IMxDocument
```

ArcMap

After running this macro, the selection is shown in the display, and the message box reports how many features were selected.

```
Dim pMap As IMap
Dim pFeatSel As IFeatureSelection
Dim pQueryFilt As IQueryFilter
Dim pSelSet As ISelectionSet

Set pMxDoc = Application.Document
Set pMap = pMxDoc.FocusMap
Set pFeatSel = pMap.Layer(0)

' Make the query filter
Set pQueryFilt = New QueryFilter
pQueryFilt.WhereClause = "AREA > 350000"

'Perform the selection and refresh the view
pFeatSel.SelectFeatures pQueryFilt, esriSelectionResultNew, False
pFeatSel.SelectionChanged
pMxDoc.ActiveView.PartialRefresh esriViewGeography, _
        Nothing, Nothing

'Report how many features were selected
Set pSelSet = pFeatSel.SelectionSet
MsgBox pSelSet.Count
End Sub
```

IIdentify : IUnknown	*Provides access to members that identify features.*
←— Identify (in pGeom: IGeometry) : IArray	*Identifies objects at the specified location.*

The *IIdentify* interface has a method that identifies features at the specified location. The *Identify* method returns an array of *FeatureIdentifyObj* objects.

ILayer2 : IUnknown	*Provides access to additional members that work with all layers.*
—■ AreaOfInterest: IEnvelope	*Area of interest for the layer.*
■— ScaleRangeReadOnly: Boolean	*Indicates if the minimum and maximum scale range values are read-only.*

The *ILayer2* interface contains additional *ILayer* properties that set the extent of the layer and lock the scale range.

ILayerDrawingProperties : IUnknown	*Provides access to members that control layer drawing properties.*
■—■ DrawingPropsDirty: Boolean	*Indicates if the layer drawing properties are dirty.*

The *ILayerDrawingProperties* interface is used internally by the Layer Properties dialog box to indicate whether any of the properties that determine how a layer is drawn have been changed. For example, if you set the minimum or maximum draw scale, set the renderer, turn on labeling, or change similar properties, then the *DrawingPropsDirty* property is automatically set to *True*. The map display is refreshed only if the layer's drawing properties are dirty after the Layer Properties dialog box is dismissed.

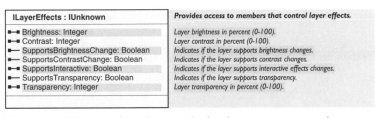

ILayerEffects : IUnknown	Provides access to members that control layer effects.
Brightness: Integer	Layer brightness in percent (0-100).
Contrast: Integer	Layer contrast in percent (0-100).
SupportsBrightnessChange: Boolean	Indicates if the layer supports brightness changes.
SupportsContrastChange: Boolean	Indicates if the layer supports contrast changes.
SupportsInteractive: Boolean	Indicates if the layer supports interactive effects changes.
SupportsTransparency: Boolean	Indicates if the layer supports transparency.
Transparency: Integer	Layer transparency in percent (0-100).

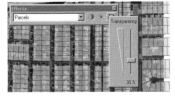

Setting a layer's transparency in ArcMap

The *ILayerEffects* interface changes the brightness, contrast, and transparency of the layer. The controls on the *Effects* toolbar use the *ILayerEffects* interface. Feature layers only support transparency changes. Raster layers support all three types of layer effects. Before you attempt to change a layer effect, you should check to see if the layer supports that type of change. To determine this, use the *SupportsBrightnessChange, SupportsContrastChange,* and *SupportsTransparency* properties. The display settings on your computer must be set to True Color in order for layer effects to work correctly.

The following VBA code changes the transparency of the first map layer:

```
Sub ChangeTransparency()
  Dim pMxDoc As IMxDocument
  Dim pMap As IMap
  Dim pLayerEffects As ILayerEffects
  Set pMxDoc = Application.Document
  Set pMap = pMxDoc.FocusMap
  Set pLayerEffects = pMap.Layer(0)
  If pLayerEffects.SupportsTransparency Then
    pLayerEffects.Transparency = 30
    pMxDoc.ActiveView.PartialRefresh esriViewGeography, _
      Nothing, Nothing
  End If
End Sub
```

When you set the *ILayerEffects::Transparency* property on a feature layer, a display filter is created and applied to the layer. You can accomplish the same effect by implementing *IDisplayFilter* and using *IDisplayFilterManager* to assign it to the layer.

ILayerEvents : IUnknown	Provides access to events that occur when layer visibility changes.
VisibilityChanged (in currentState: Boolean)	Occurs when layer visibility changes.

The *ILayerEvents* interface has an event that occurs when the visibility of the layer changes—either the layer is turned on (checked) or off (unchecked) in the table of contents. The *LayerEvents::VisibilityChanged* event occurs when the value of the *ILayer::Visible* property is changed. Note, *VisibilityChanged* does not occur when the visibility of the layer changes due to minimum or maximum scale properties.

ArcMap

The following code listens for the *VisibilityChanged* event. When the first feature layer in the map is turned on or off, a message box is displayed.

```
Dim WithEvents pLyrEvents As FeatureLayer
Sub StartListening()
  Dim pMxDoc As IMxDocument, pMap As IMap
  Set pMxDoc = Application.Document
  Set pMap = pMxDoc.FocusMap
  Set pLyrEvents = pMap.Layer(0)
End Sub

Private Sub pLyrEvents_VisibilityChanged(ByVal currentState As Boolean)
  Dim pLayer As ILayer
  Set pLayer = pLyrEvents
  MsgBox pLayer.name & " is visible: " & currentState
End Sub
```

ILayerExtensions : IUnknown	Provides access to members that manage layers used by the extensions.
■— Extension (in Index: Long) : IUnknown Pointer	The extension at the specified index.
■— ExtensionCount: Long	Number of extensions.
◄— AddExtension (in ext: IUnknown Pointer)	Adds a new extension.
◄— RemoveExtension (in Index: Long)	Removes the specified extension.

You can extend the existing layer implementation by implementing and registering layer extensions. For example, feature layers currently use extensions that implement *IFeatureLayerSourcePageExtension* to set a feature layer's data source.

ILayerFields : IUnknown	Provides access to members that work with a layer's fields.
■— Field (in Index: Long) : IField	The field at the specified index.
■— FieldCount: Long	The number of fields.
■— FieldInfo (in Index: Long) : IFieldInfo	Extended field information for the field at the specified index.
◄— FindField (in FieldName: String) : Long	Returns the index of the field with the specified name.

The *ILayerFields* interface has properties and methods for finding fields, returning the field count, and getting extended information on the field. The *FieldInfo* coclass provides this extended information.

ILegendInfo : IUnknown	Provides access to members that control legend information provided by a renderer.
■— LegendGroup (Index: Long) : ILegendGroup	Number of legend groups contained by the object.
■— LegendGroupCount: Long	Number of legend groups contained by the object.
■— LegendItem: ILegendItem	Optional. Defines legend formatting for layer rendered with this object.
■—■ SymbolsAreGraduated: Boolean	Indicates if symbols are graduated.

The *ILegendInfo* interface has properties that report legend information provided by a renderer. Each layer must implement *ILegendInfo*; normally, the implementation is delegated to the renderer.

ArcMap provides two ways to associate data stored in tables with the features in the layer: joins and relates. When you join a table to the layer's attribute table, you append the fields from the table to the layer's table. Joins can be used for one-to-one or many-to-one relationships between a layer and a table.

Relating the layer's table with another table defines a relationship between the two tables, but it doesn't append the fields of the table to the layer's table. Relates can be used for one-to-many or many-to-many relationships between a layer and a table. Relates defined in ArcMap are essentially the same as simple relationship classes defined in a geodatabase, except that they are saved with the map instead of in a geodatabase. If the feature class of the layer already has predefined relationship classes in the geodatabase, these relationships are automatically available for use in ArcMap (you do not have to relate the tables in ArcMap).

The *IDisplayRelationshipClass* interface is used to manage joins on the layer, and the *IRelationshipClassCollection* and *IRelationshipClassCollectionEdit* interfaces are used to manage relates on the layer.

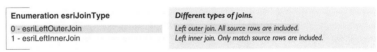

IDisplayRelationshipClass : IUnknown	Provides access to members that are used to set up joins.
→ JoinType: esriJoinType	Join type for the most recent join performed.
→ RelationshipClass: IRelationshipClass	Relationship class that defines how the tables are joined.
← DisplayRelationshipClass (in relClass: IRelationshipClass, in JoinType: esriJoinType)	Sets a join based on the specified relationship class and join type.

The *IDisplayRelationshipClass* interface is used to set up joins between the layer and other tables. The *DisplayRelationshipClass* method internally calls *RelQueryTable::Init* to perform a join. The relationship class that is used as input to the *DisplayRelationshipClass* method can be either a predefined relationship class in a geodatabase or a memory relationship class (*MemoryRelationshipClass* coclass). For more information on both types of relationship classes, refer to Volume 2, Chapter 8, 'Accessing the geodatabase'.

The *IDisplayRelationshipClass* interface also has a property that indicates the type of the most recent join and a property that returns the relationship class that defines the tables that are joined. The *RelationshipClass* property on the *IFeatureLayerDefinition* interface can also be used to get a reference to the relationship class. However, it's better to use the *IDisplayRelationshipClass* interface for this since you'll have access to the other properties and methods dealing with joins.

Enumeration esriJoinType	Different types of joins.
0 - esriLeftOuterJoin	Left outer join. All source rows are included.
1 - esriLeftInnerJoin	Left inner join. Only match source rows are included.

The *esriJoinType* enumeration indicates the join type. The join can either be a left-outer join, where all source rows are included, or a left-inner join, where only match source rows are included.

The following code performs a one-to-one, left-outer join on the first layer in the map and the first table in the map using a memory relationship class. The join field is "Code" in both the layer and the table. In the *IMemoryRelationshipClass::Init* method, it is important to use the layer's feature class as the *pOriginForeignClass* rather than the *pOriginPrimaryClass*.

```
Public Sub JoinTable()
  Dim pMxDoc As IMxDocument
  Dim pMap As IMap
  Dim pLayer As IGeoFeatureLayer
  Dim pDpyRC As IDisplayRelationshipClass
  Dim pTableCollection As ITableCollection
  Dim pTable As ITable
  Dim pMemRC As IMemoryRelationshipClass

  Set pMxDoc = Application.Document
  Set pMap = pMxDoc.FocusMap
```

The join called DEMOG is associated with the layer.

```
' Get a reference to the layer
Set pLayer = pMap.Layer(0)
Set pDpyRC = pLayer

' Get a reference to the table
Set pTableCollection = pMap
Set pTable = pTableCollection.Table(0)

' Create a relationship class in memory
Set pMemRC = New MemoryRelationshipClass
pMemRC.Init "ProvDemog", pTable, "CODE", pLayer.FeatureClass, _
        "CODE", "Province", "Demog", esriRelCardinalityOneToOne

' Perform the join
pDpyRC.DisplayRelationshipClass pMemRC, esriLeftOuterJoin
End Sub
```

The following code performs a join using a predefined relationship in a geodatabase:

```
Public Sub JoinWithGDBRelate()
  Dim pMxDoc As IMxDocument, pMap As IMap
  Dim pLayer As IGeoFeatureLayer
  Dim pDpyRC As IDisplayRelationshipClass
  Dim pFeatClass As IFeatureClass
  Dim pEnumRC As IEnumRelationshipClass
  Dim pRelClass As IRelationshipClass

  Set pMxDoc = Application.Document
  Set pMap = pMxDoc.FocusMap

  ' Get a reference to the layer
  Set pLayer = pMap.Layer(0)
  Set pDpyRC = pLayer

  ' Get the relationshipclass from the layer's featureclass
  Set pFeatClass = pLayer.FeatureClass
  Set pEnumRC = pFeatClass.RelationshipClasses(esriRelRoleAny)
  Set pRelClass = pEnumRC.Next

  ' Perform the join
  pDpyRC.DisplayRelationshipClass pRelClass, esriLeftOuterJoin
End Sub
```

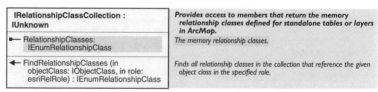

IRelationshipClassCollection : IUnknown	*Provides access to members that return the memory relationship classes defined for standalone tables or layers in ArcMap.*
▬ RelationshipClasses: IEnumRelationshipClass	*The memory relationship classes.*
◄ FindRelationshipClasses (in objectClass: IObjectClass, in role: esriRelRole) : IEnumRelationshipClass	*Finds all relationship classes in the collection that reference the given object class in the specified role.*

The *IRelationshipClassCollection* interface provides a method to get all the relationship classes associated with the layer and a method to find all the relationship classes that reference the given object class in the specified role.

Enumeration esriRelRole	Relationship Role.
1 - esriRelRoleAny	*Any.*
2 - esriRelRoleOrigin	*Origin.*
3 - esriRelRoleDestination	*Destination.*

The *esriRelRole* enumeration indicates the relationship role. The layer can be the origin or the destination in the relationship.

IRelationshipClassCollectionEdit : IUnknown	*Provides access to members that add and remove memory relationship classes from a standalone table or layer.*
← AddRelationshipClass (in RelationshipClass: IRelationshipClass)	*Adds the specified memory relationship class to a standalone table or layer.*
← RemoveAllRelationshipClasses	*Removes all memory relationship classes from a standalone table or layer.*
← RemoveRelationshipClass (in RelationshipClass: IRelationshipClass)	*Removes the specified memory relationship class from a standalone table or layer.*

The *IRelationshipClassCollectionEdit* interface provides members that manage the memory relationships (relates) associated with the layer. You can add relationship classes, remove a particular relationship class, or remove all relationship classes using the methods on this interface. The following code uses the *AddRelationshipClass* method to set up a relate between the first layer in the map and the first table in the map:

```
Public Sub RelateTable()
  Dim pMxDoc As IMxDocument
  Dim pMap As IMap
  Dim pLayer As IGeoFeatureLayer
  Dim pTableCollection As ITableCollection
  Dim pTable As ITable
  Dim pMemRC As IMemoryRelationshipClass
  Dim pRCCollectionEdit As IRelationshipClassCollectionEdit

  Set pMxDoc = Application.Document
  Set pMap = pMxDoc.FocusMap

  'Get a reference to the layer
  Set pLayer = pMap.Layer(0)
  Set pRCCollectionEdit = pLayer

  ' Get a reference to the table
  Set pTableCollection = pMap
  Set pTable = pTableCollection.Table(0)

  ' Create a relationship class in memory
  Set pMemRC = New MemoryRelationshipClass
  pMemRC.Init "ProvDemog", pTable, "CODE", pLayer.FeatureClass, _
      "CODE", "Province", "DEMOG", esriRelCardinalityOneToOne

  ' Perform the relate
  pRCCollectionEdit.AddRelationshipClass pMemRC
End Sub
```

The relate called ProvDemog *is associated with the layer.*

A hyperlink displays linked data, such as text files or Web pages, when you click it.

There are two types of hyperlinks that can be associated with a layer—dynamic hyperlinks, which can be created as you browse your data, and hotlinks, which are hyperlinks stored in a field in the feature layer. Both hyperlinks and hotlinks can be assigned to features in a layer to display a document or Web page when a feature is clicked using the Hyperlink tool.

Hotlinks use a field in the database to store the hyperlink address for a Web page, document, or some information used by a macro.

When hotlinks are assigned to a feature layer, every feature in the layer is linked to the item listed in its hotlink field. If the hotlink field is empty for a feature, that feature is not linked to anything. To set up hotlinks using the user interface in ArcMap, click the Display panel of the Layer Properties dialog box and check Support Hyperlinks using field. Click the field that contains the hyperlink information, then use the *IHotlinkContainer* interface on the *FeatureLayer* coclass to programmatically assign hotlinks.

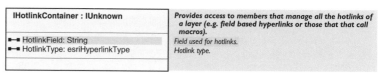

IHotlinkContainer : IUnknown	Provides access to members that manage all the hotlinks of a layer (e.g. field based hyperlinks or those that that call macros).
■→ HotlinkField: String	*Field used for hotlinks.*
■→ HotlinkType: esriHyperlinkType	*Hotlink type.*

The *IHotLinkContainer* interface is used to assign hotlinks to a layer. Using this interface, you can specify what field in the layer's attribute table contains the hotlink information; you can also specify the hotlink type.

Enumeration esriHyperlinkType	Hyperlink type.
0 - esriHyperlinkTypeDocument	*Document hyperlink type.*
1 - esriHyperlinkTypeURL	*URL hyperlink type.*
2 - esriHyperlinkTypeMacro	*Macro hyperlink type.*

The *esriHyperlinkType* enumeration specifies the type of hotlinks and hyperlinks—either document, URL, or macro—that are assigned to the layer.

The following code sets the hotlink field and type for the first layer in the map:

```
Sub AssignHotlinks()
  Dim pMxDoc As IMxDocument
  Dim pMap As IMap
  Dim pHotlinkContainer As IHotlinkContainer

  Set pMxDoc = Application.Document
  Set pMap = pMxDoc.FocusMap
  Set pHotlinkContainer = pMap.Layer(0)

  pHotlinkContainer.HotlinkField = "Canada-ID"
  pHotlinkContainer.HotlinkType = esriHyperlinkTypeDocument
End Sub
```

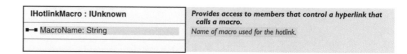

IHotlinkMacro : IUnknown	Provides access to members that control a hyperlink that calls a macro.
■→ MacroName: String	*Name of macro used for the hotlink.*

The *IHotlinkMacro* interface specifies the macro to be used by the hotlinks if the hyperlink type is *esriHyperlinkTypeMacro*. A hotlink macro has the following structure by default. The *pLink* argument is a

After running this code, the Display panel of the Layer Properties dialog box shows that the layer now supports hyperlinks using the Pictures field—the hyperlink type is macro.

When you click a feature with the Hyperlink tool, a window showing the picture specified in the hotlink field appears.

hyperlink object that is automatically created and has its *Link* property set to a value from the hotlink field.

```
Sub Hyperlink(pLink, pLayer)
  Dim pHyperlink As IHyperlink
  Set pHyperlink = pLink
  Dim pFLayer As IFeatureLayer
  Set pFLayer = pLayer
  ' Then do something with the hyperlink
End Sub
```

The following code sets up hotlinks for the first layer in the map using the Picture field. A macro called *PicHyperlink* is used for the hotlinks. When you click a feature with the Hotlink tool, the macro displays a form showing the picture specified in the hotlink field for that feature.

```
Sub AssignHotlinks()
  Dim pMxDoc As IMxDocument
  Dim pMap As IMap
  Dim pHotlinkContainer As IHotlinkContainer
  Dim pHotlinkMacro As IHotlinkMacro

  Set pMxDoc = Application.Document
  Set pMap = pMxDoc.FocusMap
  Set pHotlinkContainer = pMap.Layer(0)
  Set pHotlinkMacro = pHotlinkContainer

  pHotlinkContainer.HotlinkField = "Pictures"
  pHotlinkContainer.HotlinkType = esriHyperlinkTypeMacro
  pHotlinkMacro.MacroName = "Project.MyMacros.PicHyperlink"
End Sub


Sub PicHyperlink(pLink, pLayer)
  Dim pHyperlink As IHyperlink
  Set pHyperlink = pLink
  Dim pFLayer As IFeatureLayer
  Set pFLayer = pLayer
  If Not UserForm1.Visible Then
    UserForm1.Show vbModeless
  End If
  UserForm1.Picture = LoadPicture(pHyperlink.link)
End Sub
```

ArcMap

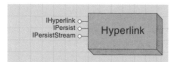

Hyperlinks are not dependent on a field and do not call macros. They are dynamic and more flexible than a hotlink in that they do not need to exist in a container.

Hyperlinks are generally assigned one feature at a time; unlike hotlinks, they are set up for an individual feature rather than an entire feature layer. The Identify dialog box in the user interface in ArcMap interactively sets up hyperlinks.

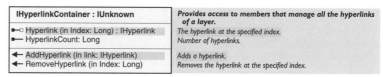

IHyperlinkContainer : IUnknown	Provides access to members that manage all the hyperlinks of a layer.
Hyperlink (in Index: Long) : IHyperlink	The hyperlink at the specified index.
HyperlinkCount: Long	Number of hyperlinks.
AddHyperlink (in link: IHyperlink)	Adds a hyperlink.
RemoveHyperlink (in Index: Long)	Removes the hyperlink at the specified index.

Use the *IHyperlinkContainer* interface on the *FeatureLayer* coclass with the *IHyperlink* interface on the *Hyperlink* coclass to programmatically assign hyperlinks.

The hyperlink container manages the hyperlinks for a feature layer. The *IHyperlinkContainer* interface has methods for adding hyperlinks to and removing hyperlinks from the layer. There is a property to get a count of all the hyperlinks on the layer and a property to get a reference to a specific hyperlink. To assign hyperlinks to a feature in the layer, you must first create a new *Hyperlink* object, then set the properties on the *IHyperlink* interface.

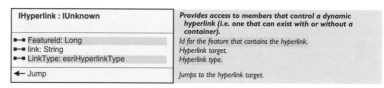

IHyperlink : IUnknown	Provides access to members that control a dynamic hyperlink (i.e. one that can exist with or without a container).
FeatureId: Long	Id for the feature that contains the hyperlink.
link: String	Hyperlink target.
LinkType: esriHyperlinkType	Hyperlink type.
Jump	Jumps to the hyperlink target.

The *IHyperlink* interface defines a hyperlink. Use this interface to set the ID of the feature with which the hyperlink is associated, the name of the file or URL to which it is to be linked, and the type of hyperlink it is.

The following code creates a hyperlink for the selected feature in the layer. The link type is URL, and the link is set to ESRI's Web page. The *IHyperlinkContainer::AddHyperlink* method assigns the hyperlink to the layer.

After running this code, the Identify dialog box shows that the hyperlink was assigned to the selected feature.

```
Sub AddHyperlink()
  Dim pMxDoc As IMxDocument
  Dim pMap As IMap
  Dim pLayer As IGeoFeatureLayer
  Dim pFeatureSel As IFeatureSelection
  Dim pSelSet As ISelectionSet
  Dim pEnumIDs As IEnumIDs
  Dim pFID As Long
  Dim pHyperlink As IHyperlink
  Dim pHyperlinkContainer As IHyperlinkContainer

  Set pMxDoc = Application.Document
  Set pMap = pMxDoc.FocusMap
  Set pLayer = pMap.Layer(0)
```

```
'Get the feature id of first selected feature
Set pFeatureSel = pLayer
Set pSelSet = pFeatureSel.SelectionSet
If pSelSet.Count = 0 Then
  MsgBox "Please select a feature."
  Exit Sub
End If
Set pEnumIDs = pSelSet.IDs
pFID = pEnumIDs.Next

'Create a new hyperlink and set its properties
Set pHyperlink = New Hyperlink
pHyperlink.link = "www.esri.com"
pHyperlink.LinkType = esriHyperlinkTypeURL
pHyperlink.FeatureId = pFID

'Assign the hyperlink to the layer
Set pHyperlinkContainer = pLayer
pHyperlinkContainer.AddHyperlink pHyperlink
End Sub
```

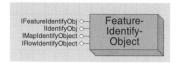

A FeatureIdentifyObject *provides shortcuts to some of the properties of the identified feature.*

A *FeatureIdentifyObject* object provides access to the identified feature and has methods that can operate on that feature.

IFeatureIdentifyObj : IUnknown	Provides access to a member that sets the feature used by the identify object.
■→ Feature: IFeature	The feature to be identified.

The *IFeatureIdentifyObj* interface sets the feature to be identified.

IIdentifyObj : IUnknown	Provides access to members that control feature identification for a layer.
■— hWnd: Long	The window handle.
■— Layer: ILayer	Target layer for identification.
■— Name: String	Name of the identify object.
←— CanIdentify (in pLayer: ILayer) : Boolean	Indicates if the object can identify the specified layer.
←— Flash (in pDisplay: IScreenDisplay)	Flashes the identified object on the screen.
←— PopUpMenu (in X: Long, in Y: Long)	Displays a context sensitive popup menu at the specified location.

The *IIdentifyObj* interface returns the window handle, layer, and name of the feature; it has methods to flash the feature in the display and to display a context menu at the Identify location.

The following *UIToolControl* code uses the *IIdentify::Identify* method to get the *FeatureIdentifyObject* objects at the mouse-click location. Then, some of the properties of the feature first identified are reported.

```
Private Sub UIToolControl1_MouseDown(ByVal button As Long, _
    ByVal shift As Long, ByVal x As Long, ByVal y As Long)
 Dim pMxApp As IMxApplication, pDoc As IMxDocument
 Dim pMap As IMap, pIdentify As IIdentify
 Dim pPoint As IPoint, pIDArray As IArray
 Dim pFeatIdObj As IFeatureIdentifyObj, pIdObj As IIdentifyObj

 Set pMxApp = Application
 Set pDoc = Application.Document
 Set pMap = pDoc.FocusMap
 Set pIdentify = pMap.Layer(0)

 ' Convert x and y to map units
 Set pPoint = pMxApp.Display.DisplayTransformation.ToMapPoint(x, y)
 Set pIDArray = pIdentify.Identify(pPoint)

 'Get the FeatureIdentifyObject
 If Not pIDArray Is Nothing Then
   Set pFeatIdObj = pIDArray.Element(0)
   Set pIdObj = pFeatIdObj
   pIdObj.Flash pMxApp.Display

   ' Report info from FeatureIdentifyObject
   MsgBox "Layer: " & pIdObj.Layer.Name & vbNewLine & _
         "Feature: " & pIdObj.Name
 Else
   MsgBox "No feature identified."
 End If
End Sub
```

FieldInfo *provides extend information on a field.*

The *FieldInfo* coclass has an interface called *IFieldInfo* that allows you to set an alias for the field, set the number format if the field is numeric, set the visibility flag for the field, and return a string representation of a value in the field.

IFieldInfo : IUnknown		Provides access to properties that give extended information on the field.
▪—▪	Alias: String	The alias for the field.
▪—	AsString (in Value: Variant) : String	The string representation of a given value based on the current field information.
▪—○	NumberFormat: INumberFormat	The number format for the field (invalid if non-numeric field).
▪—▪	Visible: Boolean	Indicates if the field is visible.

This code uses the *ILayerFields::FindField* method to get the index of the specified field and then uses the *FieldInfo* property to access the *FieldInfo* object for that field. The field's visible property is set to *False* so that the field is no longer visible in the attribute table of the layer.

```
Public Sub HideField()
    Dim pDoc As IMxDocument
    Dim pMap As IMap
    Dim pLayerFlds As ILayerFields
    Dim pFldInfo As IFieldInfo
    Set pDoc = Application.Document
    Set pMap = pDoc.FocusMap
    Set pLayerFlds = pMap.Layer(0)
    Set pFldInfo = pLayerFlds.FieldInfo(pLayerFlds.FindField("Area"))
    pFldInfo.Visible = False
End Sub
```

After running this code, the Fields panel of the Layer Properties dialog box shows that the Area field has been made invisible.

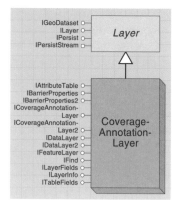

Annotation is a unique coverage feature class that stores labels used to describe other geographic features.

Annotation is only used for display purposes; it is not used in analysis. The labels are stored as text strings along with the text symbol numbers used to draw them and their location and positioning specifications. A coverage annotation feature class can use more than one symbol to define how the annotation is to be displayed.

The Levels panel of the coverage annotation's Layer Properties dialog box shows that this layer has six levels and shows which levels are visible.

The Symbols panel of the coverage annotation's Layer Properties dialog box shows that this layer has four symbols and shows their properties.

Annotation can be organized into annotation levels and subclasses. For example, a coverage storing roads may have street names in one annotation level, highway names in another level, and place names in a third level. Alternatively, the roads coverage might have two subclasses, one for street names, Anno.Street, and one for highway names, Anno.Hwy. Each subclass may contain several levels for specific annotation text sizes.

A *CoverageAnnotationLayer* is a layer that is based on a coverage annotation feature class. If an annotation coverage has no subclasses, then there is only one layer for this coverage. However, if the annotation coverage has subclasses, each subclass is treated as a separate layer. A *CoverageAnnotationLayer* may have more than one level.

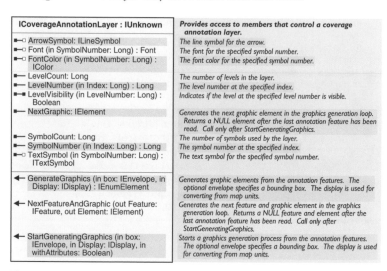

The *ICoverageAnnotationLayer* interface controls the display of coverage annotation. Use the *LevelCount* property to get the number of levels in the layer and the *LevelVisibility* property to specify whether a specific level is visible in the layer.

Use the *SymbolCount* property to get the number of symbols defined for the layer. The *ArrowSymbol, Font, FontColor,* and *TextSymbol* properties allow you to change the properties of a specific symbol in the layer.

The *ICoverageAnnotationLayer* interface also has methods for converting the annotation to graphics.

The following VBA code reports how many levels and symbols there are in the coverage annotation layer. It loops through all the levels and reports whether the level is visible. It also loops through all the symbols and reports the font size of that symbol.

```
Public Sub AnnoReport()
  Dim pMxDoc As IMxDocument
  Dim pMap As IMap
  Dim pCovAnnoLyr As ICoverageAnnotationLayer
  Dim i As Integer
```

```
Set pMxDoc = Application.Document
Set pMap = pMxDoc.FocusMap
Set pCovAnnoLyr = pMap.Layer(0)

' Report the count of levels and symbols
MsgBox "This layer has " & pCovAnnoLyr.LevelCount & _
    " levels and " & pCovAnnoLyr.SymbolCount & " symbols."

' Loop through the levels and report whether level is visible
For i = 0 To pCovAnnoLyr.LevelCount - 1
  MsgBox "Level " & pCovAnnoLyr.LevelNumber(i) & _
    " is visible: " & pCovAnnoLyr.LevelVisibility(i)
Next

' Loop through the symbols and report the font size
For i = 0 To pCovAnnoLyr.SymbolCount - 1
  MsgBox "Symbol " & pCovAnnoLyr.SymbolNumber(i) & ": " & _
  pCovAnnoLyr.Font(i).Size
Next
End Sub
```

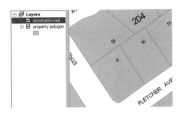

This map contains a coverage annotation layer called annotation.red.

IBarrierProperties2 : IUnknown	*Provides access to members that control how objects (text, features, graphics) act as barriers for labelling with the cancel tracker*
■— Barriers2 (in Display: IDisplay, in pBarriers: IGeometryCollection, in Extent: IEnvelope, in trackCancel: ITrackCancel)	*List of barriers within the specified extent, or all barriers if no extent given.*
■—■ Weight: Long	*Weight of the barriers for this layer.*

Barriers are used by labeling engines to signal that a label should not be placed in a particular location. Barriers currently include annotation, graphical elements, and symbols generated from renderers. A layer uses barriers to let other layers know where its elements are so that nothing gets displayed on top of those elements.

The *IBarrierProperties2* interface has a *QueryBarriers* method for getting the collection of geometries (the *pBarriers* parameter) that represent the barriers for the layer. The *trackCancel* parameter is used to get the *CancelTracker* object; this allows the drawing of labels to be stopped during the barriers loading phase. The *IBarriersProperties2* interface also has a *Weight* property that specifies the weight of the barriers in the layer.

The *IBarriersProperties* interface is the original version of this interface. You should always use *IBarriersProperties2*.

You can use the *IMapBarriers* interface on *Map* to conveniently access all the barriers from all the layers in the map; this interface returns a collection of barriers.

The following VBA macro reports the number of barriers in the current extent of the data view. You have to create a valid geometry collection object and pass this object into the *QueryBarriers* method, which will populate the collection. The resulting collection will consist of the geometries that represent the barriers in the current extent.

```
Public Sub Barriers()
  Dim pMxDoc As IMxDocument
  Dim pMap As IMap
  Dim pActiveView As IActiveView
  Dim pCovAnnoLyr As ICoverageAnnotationLayer
```

```
Dim i As Integer

Set pMxDoc = Application.Document
Set pMap = pMxDoc.FocusMap
Set pActiveView = pMap
Set pCovAnnoLyr = pMap.Layer(0)

Dim pBarrierProp As IBarrierProperties2
Set pBarrierProp = pCovAnnoLyr

' Create a geometry collection to pass into the method
Dim pGeomCol As IGeometryCollection
Set pGeomCol = New GeometryBag

' Use the QueryBarriers method to populate the geometry collection
pBarrierProp.QueryBarriers pActiveView.ScreenDisplay, pGeomCol, _
        pActiveView.Extent, Nothing
MsgBox pGeomCol.GeometryCount
End Sub
```

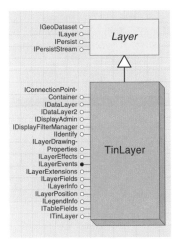

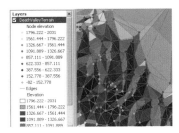

TIN layers are used to display three-dimensional surface data.

This map has a TIN layer called DeathValleyTerrain. Three different renderers are used to display this layer.

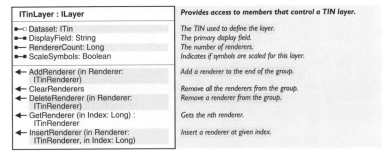

The Symbology panel of the TIN layer Properties dialog box shows which renderers are used by the layer, and allows you to add and remove renderers and set the properties of the renderers.

TINs represent continuous surfaces, such as terrain elevation or temperature gradient. Typically, you display a TIN using color-shaded relief. This lets you easily see the ridges, valleys, and hillsides, along with their respective heights. You can display any one of three surface characteristics—slope, aspect, and elevation—on your map and even simulate shaded relief. You can also display the internal structure of a TIN—for example, nodes and breaklines—independently or on top of the shaded relief display.

A *TinLayer* is a layer that is based on TIN. A *TinLayer* can use more than one renderer for its display.

ITinLayer : ILayer	Provides access to members that control a TIN layer.
■–□ Dataset: ITin	The TIN used to define the layer.
■–■ DisplayField: String	The primary display field.
■– RendererCount: Long	The number of renderers.
■–■ ScaleSymbols: Boolean	Indicates if symbols are scaled for this layer.
← AddRenderer (in Renderer: ITinRenderer)	Add a renderer to the end of the group.
← ClearRenderers	Remove all the renderers from the group.
← DeleteRenderer (in Renderer: ITinRenderer)	Remove a renderer from the group.
← GetRenderer (in Index: Long) : ITinRenderer	Gets the nth renderer.
← InsertRenderer (in Renderer: ITinRenderer, in Index: Long)	Insert a renderer at given index.

The *ITinLayer* interface defines how the TIN is displayed in the layer.

The *Dataset* property returns the TIN dataset on which the layer is based.

The *RendererCount* property returns the number of renderers currently used by the TinLayer.

Use the *AddRenderer, InsertRenderer, GetRenderer, ClearRenderers,* and *DeleteRenderers* methods to define the set of renderers associated with the layer.

The following VBA code reports the name of each renderer used by the *TinLayer*:

```
Public Sub RendererReport()
  Dim pMxDoc As IMxDocument
  Dim pMap As IMap
  Dim pTinLayer As ITinLayer
  Dim pTinRend As ITinRenderer
  Dim i As Integer

  Set pMxDoc = Application.Document
  Set pMap = pMxDoc.FocusMap
  Set pTinLayer = pMap.Layer(0)

  For i = 0 To pTinLayer.RendererCount - 1
    Set pTinRend = pTinLayer.GetRenderer(i)
    MsgBox pTinRend.Name
  Next
End Sub
```

ArcMap

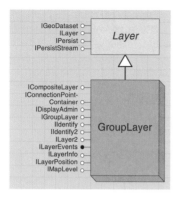

A group layer is a group of several layers that appear and act like a single layer in the table of contents in ArcMap.

This map contains a group layer called Water Systems, which consists of two layers—rivers and lakes.

When you want to work with several layers as one layer, gather them together into a group layer. Suppose you have two layers on a map, with one representing rivers and the other lakes. You might choose to group these layers together and name the resulting layer "water systems". Turning off a group layer turns off all its component layers. The properties of the group layer override any conflicting properties of its constituent layers. However, you can still work with the individual layers in the group.

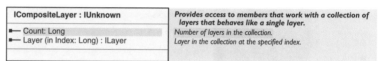

IGroupLayer : ILayer	Provides access to members that control a collection of layers that behaves like a single layer.
▪◾ Expanded: Boolean	Indicates if the group's entry is expanded in the TOC.
◀ Add (in Layer: ILayer)	Adds a layer to the end of the group.
◀ Clear	Removes all layers from the group.
◀ Delete (in Layer: ILayer)	Removes the specified layer from the group.

The *IGroupLayer* interface provides methods for managing the contents of group layers.

The *Add* method adds the specified layer to the group, the *Remove* method removes the specified layer from the group, and the *Clear* method removes all the layers from the group.

The *Expanded* property indicates whether or not the group layer is expanded in the map's table of contents.

ICompositeLayer : IUnknown	Provides access to members that work with a collection of layers that behaves like a single layer.
▪— Count: Long	Number of layers in the collection.
▪— Layer (in Index: Long) : ILayer	Layer in the collection at the specified index.

The *ICompositeLayer* is a generic interface for working with a layer that contains other layers.

The *Count* property returns the number of layers in the group, and the *Layer* property returns the layer at the specified index.

The following VBA code creates a new group layer, moves two layers from the map into this group layer, adds the group layer to the map, then reports the number of layers in the new group layer.

```
Sub CreateGroupLayer()
  Dim pMxDoc As IMxDocument
  Dim pMap As IMap
  Dim pRiverLayer As IGeoFeatureLayer
  Dim pLakeLayer As IGeoFeatureLayer
  Dim i As Integer
  Dim pGroupLayer As IGroupLayer
  Dim pCompLayer As ICompositeLayer

  Set pMxDoc = Application.Document
  Set pMap = pMxDoc.FocusMap

  ' Get references to the rivers and lakes layers.
```

```
For i = 0 To pMap.LayerCount - 1
  If pMap.Layer(i).Name = "rivers" Then
    Set pRiverLayer = pMap.Layer(i)
  End If
  If pMap.Layer(i).Name = "lakes" Then
    Set pLakeLayer = pMap.Layer(i)
  End If
Next

' Create the group layer and add the layers to it.
Set pGroupLayer = New GroupLayer
pGroupLayer.Name = "Water Systems"
pGroupLayer.Add pRiverLayer
pGroupLayer.Add pLakeLayer

' Remove the rivers and lakes layers from the map,
' add the group layer to the map, and refesh the TOC.
pGroupLayer.Expanded = True
pMap.DeleteLayer pRiverLayer
pMap.DeleteLayer pLakeLayer
pMap.AddLayer pGroupLayer
pMxDoc.UpdateContents

' Report the number of layers in the group layer
Set pCompLayer = pGroupLayer
MsgBox "Number of layers in the new group layer: " & _
      pCompLayer.Count
End Sub
```

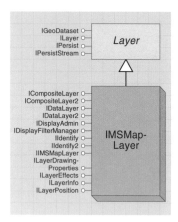

An Internet Map Server layer displays data from an image service on the Internet.

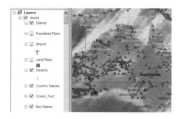

This map contains an IMSMapLayer called "World", which contains many IMS sublayers. The symbology for each layer is defined by the Internet service.

The Layers panel of the IMSMapLayer Properties dialog box lists all of the sublayers in the IMSMapLayer, and provides access to the properties of each sublayer.

The Internet is a vast resource for geographic data. Organizations can publish their data using ArcIMS® and serve it over the Internet. The Geography Network℠, which also uses ArcIMS, provides easy access to data on the Internet. You can view this data as layers in ArcMap.

ArcIMS provides two types of map services: an ArcIMS Feature Service and an ArcIMS Image Service.

An ArcIMS feature service is similar to a feature dataset that contains many feature classes. Each ArcIMS feature class represents a unique entity; the actual features are streamed to the client. When you add a feature service to the map, a group layer consisting of one or more feature layers is also added to the map. You can work with feature layers based on ArcIMS feature services in ArcMap the same way you work with feature layers based on local feature classes.

An ArcIMS image service is a raster representation of a complete map. When you add an image service to ArcMap, you'll see a new layer on your map. This layer is an Internet Map Server map layer (*IMSMapLayer*). You can turn off specific sublayers in the IMS map layer so you see only those that are of interest to you.

An *IMSMapLayer* is a composite layer consisting of IMS sublayers. You can use the *ICompositeLayer::Layer* property to get a reference to an IMS sublayer; the sublayer is of type *IIMSSubLayer*. From that, you can get a reference to the *ACLayer* (Arc Connection layer) on which the sublayer is based. An *ACLayer* does not implement *ILayer*; rather, it is an XML representation of the layer from the Internet service. *ACLayers* use the symbology defined on the Internet service for display in ArcMap.

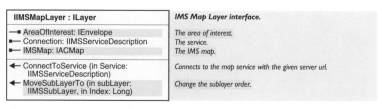

IIMSMapLayer : ILayer	IMS Map Layer interface.
▸■ AreaOfInterest: IEnvelope	The area of interest.
■— Connection: IIMSServiceDescription	The service.
■— IMSMap: IACMap	The IMS map.
◄— ConnectToService (in Service: IIMSServiceDescription)	Connects to the map service with the given server url.
◄— MoveSubLayerTo (in subLayer: IIMSSubLayer, in Index: Long)	Change the sublayer order.

The *IIMSMapLayer* interface indicates that the layer is an IMS map layer.

The *Connection* property and *Connect* method manage the connection to the Internet service.

The *MoveSubLayerTo* method allows you to rearrange the order of the sublayers in the *IMSMapLayer*.

The *IMSMap* property returns a reference to the *ACMap* (Arc Connection map), which is an XML representation of the map that was served over the Internet.

The following code loops through all the sublayers in the *IMSMapLayer* and reports the name of the sublayer.

```
Public Sub IMSLyrInfo()
    Dim pMxDoc As IMxDocument
    Dim pMap As IMap
```

```
Dim pIMSMapLyr As IIMSMapLayer
Dim pCompLyr As ICompositeLayer
Dim pIMSSubLyr As IIMSSubLayer
Dim pACLayer As IACLayer
Dim i As Integer

Set pMxDoc = Application.Document
Set pMap = pMxDoc.FocusMap

If TypeOf pMap.Layer(0) Is IIMSMapLayer Then
  Set pIMSMapLyr = pMap.Layer(0)
  Set pCompLyr = pIMSMapLyr
  For i = 0 To pCompLyr.Count - 1
    If TypeOf pCompLyr.Layer(i) Is IIMSSubLayer Then
      Set pIMSSubLyr = pCompLyr.Layer(i)
      Set pACLayer = pIMSSubLyr.IMSLayer
      MsgBox pACLayer.Name
    End If
  Next
End If
End Sub
```

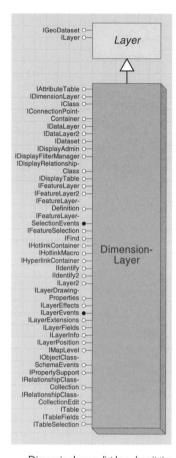

DimensionLayer *displays descriptive text and supporting graphics, such as leader lines, that are associated with map features.*

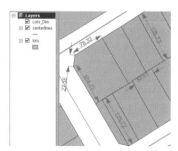

This map contains a dimension layer called "Lots_Dim". The green arrows and text are the dimension features.

Dimensions are a special kind of map annotation that show specific lengths or distances on a map. A dimension may indicate the length of a side of a building or land parcel or the distance between two features such as a fire hydrant and the corner of a building. Dimensions can be as simple as a piece of text with a leader line or more elaborate.

In the geodatabase, dimensions are stored in dimension feature classes. Like other feature classes in the geodatabase, all features in a dimension feature class have a geographic location and attributes and can either be inside or outside of a feature dataset. Like annotation features, each dimension feature knows what its symbology is and how it should be drawn.

A *DimensionLayer* object is a layer that is based on a dimension feature class. Feature classes of feature type *esriFTDimension* are dimension feature classes.

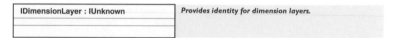

IDimensionLayer : IUnknown	*Provides identity for dimension layers.*

The *IDimensionLayer* interface indicates to the map that this layer is a dimension layer. There are no methods or properties on this interface. Most of the interfaces that are implemented by *Featurelayer* are available for use with the *DimensionLayer*.

The symbology used to display the dimension layer is defined in the geodatabase.

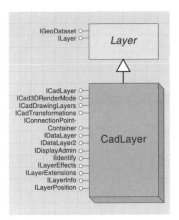

You can display a CAD drawing as a layer in ArcMap; you don't have to convert the data.

An ArcMap layer based on CAD drawing is either a CadLayer or a CadFeatureLayer.

In ArcMap, a CAD drawing is represented as either a CAD drawing or a CAD dataset. The CAD drawing represents all the layers in the drawing. The CAD dataset represents the drawing's features with individual feature classes (point, line, polygon, and annotation feature classes).

A CadLayer is based on the CAD drawing representation, and a CadFeatureLayer is based on CAD dataset representation.

Use a *CadLayer* if you want to add the CAD drawing as a layer for display only. In the map, this layer contains all of the layers in the drawing and uses the symbology defined in the drawing. You can choose which of the drawing's layers the layer in ArcMap displays.

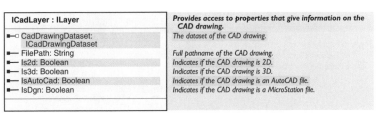

The *ICadLayer* interface has properties to determine if the CAD drawing is an AutoCAD® drawing (.dwg) file, a MicroStation® design (.dgn) file, a 2D drawing, or a 3D drawing. It also gives you the full pathname of the CAD drawing file used by the layer and the CAD drawing dataset.

This code reports some of the properties of the first CAD layers in the map:

```
Sub LayerProps()
  Dim pMxDoc As IMxDocument
  Dim pMap As IMap
  Dim pCadLayer As ICadLayer

  Set pMxDoc = Application.Document
  Set pMap = pMxDoc.FocusMap
  Set pCadLayer = pMap.Layer(0)

  MsgBox "File: " & pCadLayer.FilePath & vbNewLine & _
      "Is AutoCAD: " & pCadLayer.IsAutoCad & vbNewLine & _
      "Is Dgn: " & pCadLayer.IsDgn & vbNewLine & _
      "Is 3D: " & pCadLayer.Is3d & vbNewLine
End Sub
```

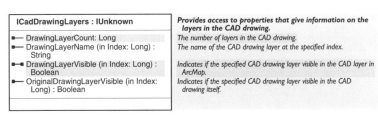

The *CadLayer* in this map represents all the CAD drawing layers. The symbology defined in the CAD drawing displays the layer in the map.

The *ICadDrawingLayers* interface manages the layers in the CAD drawing. These are the CAD drawing layers, not the layers in the map in ArcMap. You can get the count of the layers in the drawing and the name of the layer at the specified index in the drawing.

The *DrawingLayerVisible* property indicates if the specified drawing layer is visible in the *CadLayer* or *CadFeatureLayer* in ArcMap.

The *OriginalDrawingLayerVisible* property indicates if the drawing layer is visible in the CAD drawing itself.

The ICadTransformations *interface controls the settings in the Transformation panel of the layer's Properties dialog box for* CadLayer *and* CadFeatureLayer.

ICadTransformations : IUnknown	ICadTransformations Interface
■─■ EnableTransformations: Boolean	*Indicates if global transformations are enabled.*
■─■ TransformMode: tagesriCadTransform	*The transformation type.*
■─■ WorldFileName: String	*The pathname of the world file.*
← GetFromToTransform (out fromPoint1: _WKSPoint, out fromPoint2: _WKSPoint, out toPoint1: _WKSPoint, out toPoint2: _WKSPoint)	*Returns the points of a two point transformation.*
← GetTransformation (out from: _WKSPoint, out to: _WKSPoint, out Angle: Double, out Scale: Double)	*Returns the rotation, scale, and translation of a transformation.*
← SetFromToTransform (in fromPoint1: _WKSPoint, in fromPoint2: _WKSPoint, in toPoint1: _WKSPoint, in toPoint2: _WKSPoint)	*Sets the points of a two point transformation.*
← SetTransformation (in from: _WKSPoint, in to: _WKSPoint, in Angle: Double, in Scale: Double)	*Sets the rotation, scale, and translation of a transformation.*

The *ICadTransformations* interface allows you to transform the CAD data so that it matches other data in your map. You can perform the transformation using a two-point method, a rotation, a scale and translation method, or a World file. If a World file is used, there is a property to get and set the filename of the World file.

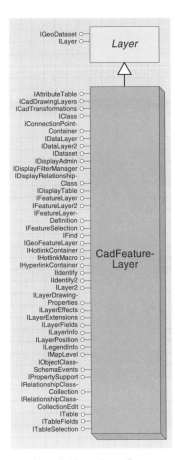

IGeoDataset
ILayer

Layer

IAttributeTable
ICadDrawingLayers
ICadTransformations
IClass
IConnectionPoint-
  Container
IDataLayer
IDataLayer2
IDataset
IDisplayAdmin
IDisplayFilterManager
IDisplayRelationship-
  Class
IDisplayTable
IFeatureLayer
IFeatureLayer2
IFeatureLayer-
  Definition
IFeatureSelection
IFind
IGeoFeatureLayer
IHotlinkContainer
IHotlinkMacro
IHyperlinkContainer
IIdentify
IIdentify2
ILayer2
ILayerDrawing-
  Properties
ILayerEffects
ILayerExtensions
ILayerFields
ILayerInfo
ILayerPosition
ILegendInfo
IMapLevel
IObjectClass-
  SchemaEvents
IPropertySupport
IRelationshipClass-
  Collection
IRelationshipClass-
  CollectionEdit
ITable
ITableFields
ITableSelection

CadFeature-
Layer

Use a CadFeatureLayer if you want to change symbology or analyze CAD data.

This map has three CadFeatureLayers. The PARCELS.DWG point layer contains all the point features in the CAD drawing, the PARCELS.DWG polyline layer contains all the polyline features in the CAD drawing, and the PARCELS.DWG polygon layer contains all the polygon features in the CAD drawing.

CAD data is treated as features in a *CadFeatureLayer*. CAD drawing files typically store different types of entities on different layers in a drawing file. There might be one layer in the CAD drawing for building footprints, another for streets, a third for well locations, and a fourth for textual annotation. However, CAD drawing files do not restrict the type of entities you can have on a drawing layer. Thus, building footprints might be on the same drawing layer as streets. When working with a CAD drawing as feature classes in ArcMap, all points are represented in one layer, all lines are represented in another layer, and all polygons are represented in a third layer. Therefore, you'll likely add several ArcMap layers from the same CAD drawing file and adjust what features display in those layers.

The *CadFeatureLayer* implements *ICadDrawingLayers* and *ICADTransformations*. Also, with *CadFeatureLayer* you can *QI* to most of the interfaces on *FeatureLayer*. Thus, you can perform the same operations on CAD feature layers as you can on feature layers.

The following code loops through all the drawing layers. If the drawing layer's name is BLDGS, then the layer is made visible in the *CadFeature-Layer*; otherwise, the drawing layer is made invisible. You can do this if, for example, you only want buildings in the polygon *CadFeatureLayer* for that CAD drawing.

```
Sub SetVisibleLayers()
  Dim pMxDoc As IMxDocument, pMap As IMap
  Dim pCadDrawLyrs As ICadDrawingLayers, i As Integer
  Set pMxDoc = Application.Document
  Set pMap = pMxDoc.FocusMap
  Set pCadDrawLyrs = pMap.Layer(0)
  For i = 0 To pCadDrawLyrs.DrawingLayerCount - 1
    If pCadDrawLyrs.DrawingLayerName(i) = "BLDGS" Then
      pCadDrawLyrs.DrawingLayerVisible(i) = True
    Else
      pCadDrawLyrs.DrawingLayerVisible(i) = False
    End If
  Next
  pMxDoc.ActiveView.PartialRefresh esriViewGeography, Nothing, _
    Nothing
End Sub
```

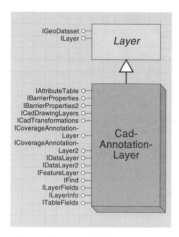

IGeoDataset
ILayer

Layer

IAttributeTable
IBarrierProperties
IBarrierProperties2
ICadDrawingLayers
ICadTransformations
ICoverageAnnotation-
Layer
ICoverageAnnotation-
Layer2
IDataLayer
IDataLayer2
IFeatureLayer
IFind
ILayerFields
ILayerInfo
ITableFields

Cad-
Annotation-
Layer

You would use a CadAnnotationLayer if you want to change the symbology of the annotation or have more control over which annotation entities get displayed in the ArcMap layer.

In a *CadAnnotationLayer*, CAD data is treated as annotation features. All the annotation entities in the CAD drawing file will be included in one *CadAnnotationLayer*.

Since the *CadAnnotationLayer* coclass implements *ICadDrawings*, you are able to specify what layers from the CAD drawing file are visible in the *CadAnnotationLayer*. Therefore, you are able to control which annotation entities from the drawing are actually displayed in the layer in ArcMap.

The *CadAnnotationLayer* coclass also implements all of the interfaces that are found on the *CoverageAnnotationLayer* coclass. Thus you can perform the same operations on CAD annotation layers as you can on coverage annotation layers.

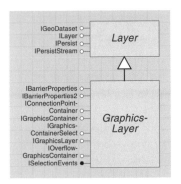

Graphics layers manage the graphics associated with a map.

Graphics layer objects manage the graphics associated with a map—graphic elements that were added in data view.

If you want more control over when graphics in a data frame draw in relation to other layers, or you want to draw graphics only when a particular layer is visible, you can create annotation. Annotation can be graphic elements but not frame elements.

When you add graphics to a data frame, you can choose which annotation target they're added to. By default, the annotation target is your map, so your graphics will be stored in the map and will always be drawn. Alternatively, you can create an annotation group and make that the target to which graphics will be added.

Each annotation group is a graphics layer. Annotation groups are useful for organizing a large number of graphics because they can be turned on and off individually.

If you want to use annotation on different maps, store it in a geodatabase as an annotation feature class and make that the target for graphics you add. Annotation feature classes that you create appear in your map as annotation layers (*FDOGraphicLayer* objects) in the table of contents.

All graphics layers implement *IGraphicsLayer, IGraphicsContainer,* and *ISelectionEvents.*

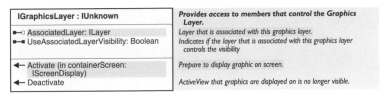

A graphics layer can be associated with another layer in the map; when that other layer changes visibility, the graphics layer can change visibility also. The *IGraphicsLayer* interface manages this.

The *AssociatedLayer* property specifies which layer the graphics layer is associated with—for example, this can be *Nothing*.

The *UseAssociatedLayerVisibility* property indicates if the graphics layer should use the same visibility setting as the associated layer.

The *IGraphicsLayer* interface also has methods to activate and deactivate the graphics layer. When a graphics layer is active, it is the current annotation target.

Note that the methods that add elements to the graphics container do not clone the elements. If the element that you are adding to a graphics container was retrieved from another graphics container, you should make sure that your code clones the element before you add it to the destination graphics container.

IGraphicsContainer : IUnknown	Provides access to members that control the Graphics Container.
← AddElement (in Element: IElement, in zorder: Long)	Add a new graphic element to the layer.
← AddElements (in Elements: IElementCollection, in zorder: Long)	Add new graphic elements to the layer.
← BringForward (in Elements: IEnumElement)	Move the specified elements one step closer to the top of the stack of elements.
← BringToFront (in Elements: IEnumElement)	Make the specified elements draw in front of all other elements.
← DeleteAllElements	Delete all the elements.
← DeleteElement (in Element: IElement)	Delete the given element.
← FindFrame (in frameObject: Variant) : IFrameElement	Find the frame that contains the specified object.
← GetElementOrder (in Elements: IEnumElement) : Variant	Private order object. Used to undo ordering operations.
← LocateElements (in Point: IPoint, in Tolerance: Double) : IEnumElement	Returns the elements at the given coordinate.
← LocateElementsByEnvelope (in Envelope: IEnvelope) : IEnumElement	Returns the elements that intersect with the given envelope.
← MoveElementFromGroup (in Group: IGroupElement, in Element: IElement, in zorder: Long)	Move the element from the group to the container.
← MoveElementToGroup (in Element: IElement, in Group: IGroupElement)	Move the element from the container to the group.
← Next: IElement	Returns the next graphic in the container.
← PutElementOrder (in order: Variant)	Private order object. Used to undo ordering operations.
← Reset	Reset internal cursor so that Next returns the first element.
← SendBackward (in Elements: IEnumElement)	Move the specified elements one step closer to the bottom of the stack of elements.
← SendToBack (in Elements: IEnumElement)	Make the specified elements draw behind all other elements.
← UpdateElement (in Element: IElement)	The graphic element's properties have changed.

A graphics layer is essentially a graphics container. The *IGraphics-Container* interface manages the elements in the graphics container. Use this interface to access and manipulate existing graphic elements or to add new ones.

ISelectionEvents : IUnknown	Provides access to events that occur when the selection changes.
← SelectionChanged	Fired when the selection changes.

The *ISelectionEvents* interface has one event, *SelectionChanged*, which occurs when the selection in the graphics layer changes.

The following code reports when the selection in the graphics layer of the map changes. The *StartListening* macro is used to initialize the events variable, *pSelEvents*.

```
Dim WithEvents pSelEvents As CompositeGraphicsLayer

Sub StartListening()
  Dim pMxDoc As IMxDocument, pMap As IMap
  Set pMxDoc = Application.Document
  Set pMap = pMxDoc.FocusMap
  Set pSelEvents = pMap.BasicGraphicsLayer
End Sub

Private Sub pSelEvents_SelectionChanged()
  MsgBox "Selection has changed."
End Sub
```

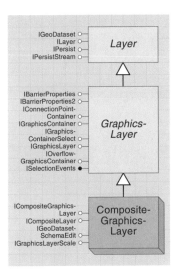

A CompositeGraphicsLayer *object is a graphics layer that can manage other graphics layers. The basic graphics container of a map is a composite graphics layer.*

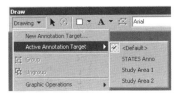

The Active Annotation Target menu shows which graphics layer is currently active.

The graphic elements in a *Map* are organized and stored in graphics layers.

By default, graphics are stored in the basic graphics layer (*IMap:: BasicGraphicsLayer* property). For example, when you label features or use the graphics tools, these elements are added to the basic graphics layer by default. The basic graphics layer has a graphics container to manage the graphic elements in that layer. If you *QI* from the *Map* coclass to *IGraphicsContainer*, you get the same container as the one on the basic graphics layer.

The basic graphics layer is also a composite graphics layer, so it can manage other graphics layers. The graphics layers that the *Composite-GraphicsLayer* manages are referred to as annotation groups or annotation target layers. The *IMap::ActiveGraphicsLayer* property specifies which graphics layer is currently active. By default, the basic graphics layer is the active layer, but any annotation group, or an *FDOGraphics-Layer*, can be set as the active graphics layer.

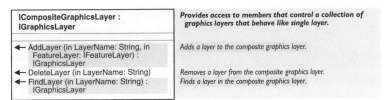

ICompositeGraphicsLayer : IGraphicsLayer	Provides access to members that control a collection of graphics layers that behave like single layer.
← AddLayer (in LayerName: String, in FeatureLayer: IFeatureLayer) : IGraphicsLayer	Adds a layer to the composite graphics layer.
← DeleteLayer (in LayerName: String)	Removes a layer from the composite graphics layer.
← FindLayer (in LayerName: String) : IGraphicsLayer	Finds a layer in the composite graphics layer.

The *ICompositeGraphicsLayer* interface provides methods for creating, finding, and deleting graphics layers. When you add a new graphics layer to the *CompositeGraphicsLayer*, you can specify what feature layer this new graphics layer is associated with.

From the ArcMap user interface, click the option to Convert Labels to Annotation from the feature layer context menu. Choose the Map as the annotation storage option. A new graphics layer is added to the *CompositeGraphicsLayer* and is associated with that feature layer. If you choose the New Annotation Target option from the Drawing menu on the Draw toolbar and choose to save annotation in the map, a new graphics layer is added to the *CompositeGraphicsLayer*, but it is not associated with any layer in the map.

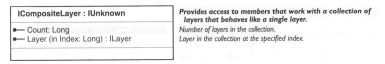

ICompositeLayer : IUnknown	Provides access to members that work with a collection of layers that behaves like a single layer.
■← Count: Long	Number of layers in the collection.
■← Layer (in Index: Long) : ILayer	Layer in the collection at the specified index.

The *CompositeGraphicsLayer* and its graphics layers (annotation groups) are not treated as other types of layers in that none of these layers can be accessed with the *IMap::Layer* or *IMap::Layers* properties. In addition, they are not included in the *IMap::LayerCount*, and they are not shown in the table of contents.

Use the *IMap::BasicGraphicsLayer* property to get access to the *Composite-GraphicsLayer*. Then, you can *QI* to the *ICompositeLayer* interface to get access to the individual layers and get a count of the graphics layers.

The basic graphics layer itself is not included in the count and cannot be accessed by the *Layer* property on *ICompositeLayer*; the reference you have to the *CompositeGraphicsLayer* is really the basic graphics layer itself.

The following code loops through all the layers in the basic graphics layer and reports whether the graphics layers are associated with a feature layer:

```
Sub CheckAssociation()
  Dim pMxDoc As IMxDocument
  Dim pMap As IMap
  Dim pBasicGraLyr As ICompositeLayer
  Dim pGraLyr As IGraphicsLayer
  Dim pAssocLayer As ILayer
  Dim i As Integer

  Set pMxDoc = Application.Document
  Set pMap = pMxDoc.FocusMap
  Set pBasicGraLyr = pMap.BasicGraphicsLayer

  For i = 0 To pBasicGraLyr.Count - 1
    Set pGraLyr = pBasicGraLyr.Layer(i)
    Set pAssocLayer = pGraLyr.AssociatedLayer
    If Not pAssocLayer Is Nothing Then
      MsgBox "Associated feature layer: " & pAssocLayer.Name
    Else
      MsgBox "Not associated with a feature layer."
    End If
  Next
End Sub
```

The *IGeoDatasetSchemaEdit* interface allows you to change the spatial reference associated with the graphics layer. For more information on this interface, refer to Volume 2, Chapter 8, 'Accessing the geodatabase'.

The *CompositeGraphicsLayer* coclass also implements *IGraphicsContainer-Select*. If you *QI* from the *CompositeGraphicsLayer* coclass to *IGraphicsContainerSelect*, you get the same object as you would with a *QI* from the *Map* coclass to *IGraphicsContainerSelect*.

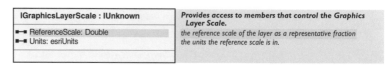

IGraphicsLayerScale : IUnknown	**Provides access to members that control the Graphics Layer Scale.**
■—■ ReferenceScale: Double	*the reference scale of the layer as a representative fraction*
■—■ Units: esriUnits	*the units the reference scale is in.*

The *IGraphicsLayerScale* has a *ReferenceScale* property that specifies the map scale to be used as a reference for the annotation size. The annotation will scale as you zoom the map. For example, if the reference scale is set to 1000 (1:1000), the same text will display twice as large at the mapscale 1:500 and, similarly, twice as small at 1:2000.

The *Units* property on this interface is not implemented.

IOverflowGraphicsContainer : IUnknown	Provides access to members that control the Overflow Graphics Container.
▬▢ OverflowElements: IElementCollection	the element collection.
◄— AddOverflowElement (pElement: IElement)	Add an element to the collection.
◄— DeleteAllOverflowElements	Delete all the element in the collection.
◄— DeleteOverflowElement (pElement: IElement)	Delete an element in the collection.

When you convert labels to annotation, the labels that overlap other labels can be placed in the overflow labels window. This enables you to decide whether you want them to appear on the map and, if so, place them manually on the map at the desired location. An overflow graphics container manages the collection of elements displayed in the overflow labels window.

The *IOverFlowGraphicsContainer* interface has properties and methods that control the overflow graphics container. There are methods to add an overflow label to the element collection, delete an overflow label from the element collection, or delete all the elements.

The Annotation panel of the Data Frame Properties dialog box lists all of the graphics layers available to the map. The following table shows what properties and methods are used by the controls on this property sheet.

The Annotation panel of the Data Frame Properties dialog box

Control	Property or Method
Group Name column	ICompositeLayer::Layer(i)::Name
Feature Layer Name column	IGraphicsLayer::AssociatedLayer
Reference Scale column	IGraphicsLayerScale::ReferenceScale
Toggle Visibilty button	ICompositeLayer::Layer(i)::Visible
Toggle Association button	IGraphicsLayer::UseAssociatedLayer
Delete Group button	ICompositeGraphicsLayer::DeleteLayer
Add Group button	ICompositeGraphicsLayer::AddLayer
Change Coord Sys button	IGeoDatasetSchemeEdit::AlterSpatialReference

The following code creates a new annotation group in the map and moves the selected graphics from the default graphics layer to the new annotation group. To accomplish this, a new graphics layer is added to the *CompositeGrapicsLayer* of the map.

```
Public Sub CreateAnnoGroup()
  Dim pMxDoc As IMxDocument
  Dim pMap As IMap
  Dim pBasicGraLyr As ICompositeGraphicsLayer
  Dim pBasicGraCont As IGraphicsContainer
  Dim pBasicGraContSel As IGraphicsContainerSelect
  Dim pEnumElement As IEnumElement
  Dim pNewAnnoGroup As IGraphicsLayer
  Dim pNewGraCont As IGraphicsContainer
```

```
Dim pElement As IElement
Dim pClone As IClone
Dim pElemClone As IClone

Set pMxDoc = Application.Document
Set pMap = pMxDoc.FocusMap
Set pBasicGraLyr = pMap.BasicGraphicsLayer
Set pBasicGraCont = pBasicGraLyr
Set pBasicGraContSel = pBasicGraLyr

' Create the new graphics layer group and associate it
' with the first feature layer in the map
Set pNewAnnoGroup = pBasicGraLyr.AddLayer("New Anno", pMap.Layer(0))
Set pNewGraCont = pNewAnnoGroup

' Get the selected elements from the default graphics layer
Set pEnumElement = pBasicGraContSel.SelectedElements
Set pElement = pEnumElement.Next

' Clone each selected graphic from the default graphics layer,
' add the clone to the new graphics layer, and delete original
' from the default graphcis layer
While Not pElement Is Nothing
  Set pClone = pElement
  Set pElemClone = pClone.Clone
  pNewGraCont.AddElement pElemClone, 0
  pBasicGraCont.DeleteElement pElement
  Set pElement = pEnumElement.Next
Wend
pMxDoc.ActivatedView.PartialRefresh esriViewGraphics, Nothing, Nothing
End Sub
```

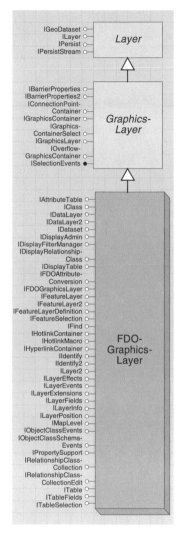

Annotation in a geodatabase is stored in special feature classes called annotation classes. An FDOGraphicsLayer (Feature Data Object graphics layer) is based on an annotation feature class stored in a geodatabase. Use an FDOGraphics-Layer if you want to use this annotation on different maps.

FDOGraphicsLayer objects are different from other graphics layers in that they are listed in the table of contents. However, they are also listed in the Active Annotation Target menu. To add elements to an *FDO-GraphicsLayer*, you must start editing the layer and set it as the active annotation target.

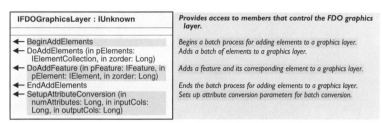

The *IFDOGraphicsLayer* interface indicates that the graphics layer is an *FDOGraphicsLayer*. If you have a reference to a graphics layer, you can try to *QI* for *IFDOGraphicsLayer* to check if you have an *FDOGraphics-Layer* object. This interface also has methods for batch loading annotation. These methods provide an optimized way to convert labels to annotation.

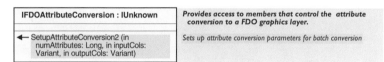

The *SetupAttributeConversion* method on *IFDOGraphicsLayer* will not work in Visual Basic; use the *SetupAttributeConversion2* method on *IFDOAttributeConversion* instead.

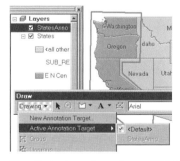

The *StatesAnno* layer is an *FDOGraphicsLayer*. This layer consists of the state labels and the red polygon, and shows up in both the table of contents and the active annotation target list.

ArcMap

ArcMap map surround objects

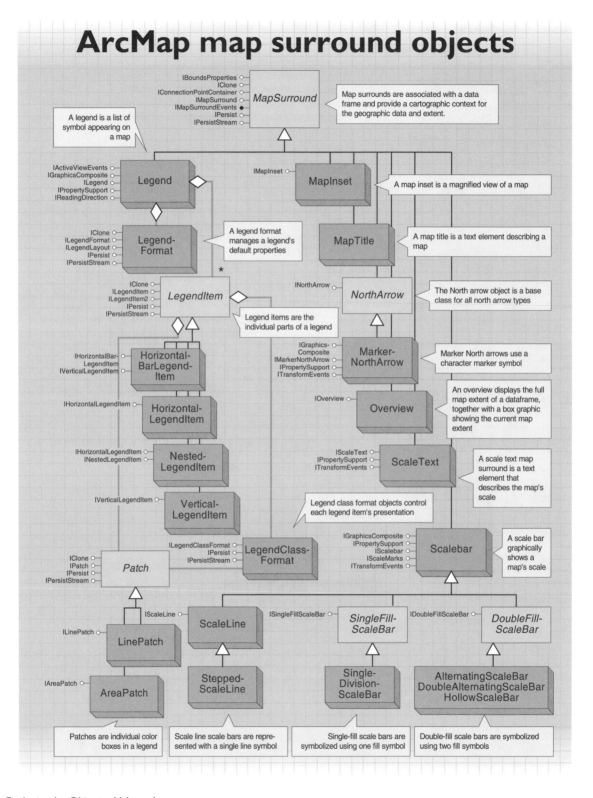

IBoundsProperties
IClone
IConnectionPointContainer
IMapSurround
IMapSurroundEvents
IPersist
IPersistStream

MapSurround

Map surrounds are associated with a data frame and provide a cartographic context for the geographic data and extent.

A legend is a list of symbol appearing on a map

IActiveViewEvents
IGraphicsComposite
ILegend
IPropertySupport
IReadingDirection

Legend

IMapInset

MapInset

A map inset is a magnified view of a map

IClone
ILegendFormat
ILegendLayout
IPersist
IPersistStream

Legend-Format

A legend format manages a legend's default properties

MapTitle

A map title is a text element describing a map

IClone
ILegendItem
ILegendItem2
IPersist
IPersistStream

LegendItem

Legend items are the individual parts of a legend

INorthArrow

NorthArrow

The North arrow object is a base class for all north arrow types

IHorizontalBar-
LegendItem
IVerticalLegendItem

Horizontal-BarLegend-Item

IGraphics-Composite
IMarkerNorthArrow
IPropertySupport
ITransformEvents

Marker-NorthArrow

Marker North arrows use a character marker symbol

IHorizontalLegendItem

Horizontal-LegendItem

IOverview

Overview

An overview displays the full map extent of a dataframe, together with a box graphic showing the current map extent

IHorizontalLegendItem
INestedLegendItem

Nested-LegendItem

IScaleText
IPropertySupport
ITransformEvents

ScaleText

A scale text map surround is a text element that describes the map's scale

IVerticalLegendItem

Vertical-LegendItem

Legend class format objects control each legend item's presentation

ILegendClassFormat
IPersist
IPersistStream

LegendClass-Format

IGraphicsComposite
IPropertySupport
IScalebar
IScaleMarks
ITransformEvents

Scalebar

A scale bar graphically shows a map's scale

IClone
IPatch
IPersist
IPersistStream

Patch

IScaleLine

ScaleLine

ISingleFillScaleBar

SingleFill-ScaleBar

IDoubleFillScaleBar

DoubleFill-ScaleBar

ILinePatch

LinePatch

Stepped-ScaleLine

Single-Division-ScaleBar

AlternatingScaleBar DoubleAlternatingScaleBar HollowScaleBar

IAreaPatch

AreaPatch

Patches are individual color boxes in a legend

Scale line scale bars are represented with a single line symbol

Single-fill scale bars are symbolized using one fill symbol

Double-fill scale bars are symbolized using two fill symbols

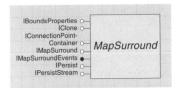

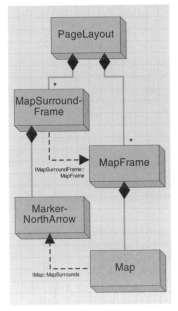

Map surrounds are a special class of elements that are contained by a map surround frame and associated with a Map.

This diagram shows the relationship between a North arrow map surround, its map surround frame, and its related Map. The PageLayout ultimately manages the frame objects but, when a Map is deleted, its related map surrounds, and their frames, are deleted as well.

Map surrounds are specific types of elements that are associated with a *Map* object. A good example of a map surround and its capabilities is the North arrow. North arrows are built as map surrounds so that they can respond to map rotation—when a map is rotated, its North arrow is rotated the same amount.

In ArcMap, map surrounds are always contained by a *MapSurround-Frame* object—a type of element. *MapSurroundFrames* are similar to *MapFrames*, which house a *Map* object, in that the *PageLayout* object manages both of them. In fact, the *PageLayout* manages all frame objects. Each *MapSurroundFrame* is also related to a *MapFrame*; if a *Map-Frame* is deleted, all of its *MapSurroundFrames* are deleted as well. Map surrounds are placed on the layout, not in a *Map*'s graphics layer.

Map surrounds can be moved anywhere on the layout, not just within the confines of a map frame. Because map surrounds are directly associated with a *Map*, the *Map* has a shortcut to all the map surrounds associated with it, *IMap::MapSurrounds*. This member, along with *IMap::MapSurroundCount*, allows you to loop through all of the available map surrounds for a given *Map* object.

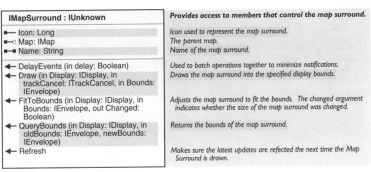

IMapSurround : IUnknown	Provides access to members that control the map surround.
■— Icon: Long	Icon used to represent the map surround.
■—□ Map: IMap	The parent map.
■—■ Name: String	Name of the map surround.
◄— DelayEvents (in delay: Boolean)	Used to batch operations together to minimize notifications.
◄— Draw (in Display: IDisplay, in trackCancel: ITrackCancel, in Bounds: IEnvelope)	Draws the map surround into the specified display bounds.
◄— FitToBounds (in Display: IDisplay, in Bounds: IEnvelope, out Changed: Boolean)	Adjusts the map surround to fit the bounds. The changed argument indicates whether the size of the map surround was changed.
◄— QueryBounds (in Display: IDisplay, in oldBounds: IEnvelope, newBounds: IEnvelope)	Returns the bounds of the map surround.
◄— Refresh	Makes sure the latest updates are reflected the next time the Map Surround is drawn.

All map surrounds implement the *IMapSurround* interface. This interface provides all the common functionality between all map surrounds. Use this interface to access the name of a particular map surround and the associated map. This interface also has methods for determining a surround's size and changing it.

IMapSurroundEvents : IUnknown	Provides access to events that occur when the state of the map surrounds changes.
◄— AfterDraw (in Display: IDisplay)	Fired after drawing completes.
◄— BeforeDraw (in Display: IDisplay)	Fired before drawing starts.
◄— ContentsChanged	Fired when the contents of the map surround changes.

IMapSurroundsEvents is the outbound interface for all map surround objects. This interface allows you to draw a map surround in a window. The events let the window know when to redraw.

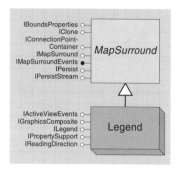

A legend is a list of symbols appearing on the map; legends include a sample of each symbol and text describing what feature each symbol represents.

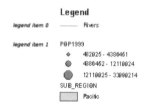

This image maps ArcMap layer rederers' legend groups and classes to a typical legend.

Legend

legend item 0 ——— Rivers

legend item 1 POP1999
◆ 482025 - 4386461
● 4386462 - 12110024
● 12110025 - 33090214
SUB_REGION
▭ Pacific

This image labels a legend's items. There is one legend item per map layer, just as there is one legend group per map layer (renderer).

The bottom area patch's style has been changed from a rectangular area patch to a natural area patch.

The *Legend* coclass is one of the most complicated map surround objects because it relies on several other objects to create a good-looking legend.

Legends are associated with the renderers that belong to each layer in a map. Each layer in a map has a separate renderer. Each renderer has one or more *LegendGroup* objects; the number of legend groups depends on the renderer's implementation. Each *LegendGroup*, in turn, has one or more *LegendClass* objects. A *LegendClass* object represents an individual classification and has its own symbol and label—a description and format are optional.

The diagram to the left illustrates this hierarchy. This legend has two map layers in it: USA Rivers and USA States. The symbology for the States layer is based on multiple attributes: SUB_REGION and POP1999. For simplicity, only the Pacific region has been added to the legend. Because the USA States layer is symbolizing on multiple items, there are two legend groups. The first legend group has three legend classes, and the second legend group has one legend class. The USA Rivers layer has one legend group and one legend class. For more details on legend groups and classes, see Chapter 5, 'Displaying graphics'.

Legends have a similar hierarchy. Each *Legend* object has one or more *LegendItem* objects. There is one legend item per map layer involved in the legend. Legend items control the presentation of the layers in a legend. There are several types of legend items, including *Horizontal-LegendItem, HorizontalBarLegendItem, VerticalLegendItem,* and *Nested-LegendItem.*

The symbology and classification scheme in a legend is almost entirely based on the map's renderers. For example, to change the color of an element in a legend, you must change the element's corresponding legend class. Legends automatically update in response to changes made in their related renderers. You can also customize the style of a legend patch. For example, you change regular rectangle area patches to natural area patches.

Legends have many more properties, including the gap size between the various parts of the legend, the title position, and default patches. Each *Legend* object automatically instantiates a *LegendFormat* object that manages all of these additional properties. Most legend properties have a default, making it very easy to create a new legend that looks good. When you change the properties of a legend after you have added it to the layout, you must call *ILegend::Refresh* to have changes reflected.

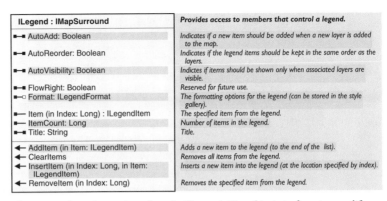

ILegend : IMapSurround	Provides access to members that control a legend.
■—■ AutoAdd: Boolean	Indicates if a new item should be added when a new layer is added to the map.
■—■ AutoReorder: Boolean	Indicates if the legend items should be kept in the same order as the layers.
■—■ AutoVisibility: Boolean	Indictes if items should be shown only when associated layers are visible.
■—■ FlowRight: Boolean	Reserved for future use.
■—□ Format: ILegendFormat	The formatting options for the legend (can be stored in the style gallery).
■—— Item (in Index: Long) : ILegendItem	The specified item from the legend.
■—— ItemCount: Long	Number of items in the legend.
■—■ Title: String	Title.
◄— AddItem (in Item: ILegendItem)	Adds a new item to the legend (to the end of the list).
◄— ClearItems	Removes all items from the legend.
◄— InsertItem (in Index: Long, in Item: ILegendItem)	Inserts a new item into the legend (at the location specified by index).
◄— RemoveItem (in Index: Long)	Removes the specified item from the legend.

The *Legend*'s primary interface is *ILegend*. Use this interface to modify a legend and access its subparts. For example, this interface provides access to the legend's items and its legend format object. *ILegend* also manages a few of the legend properties such as the title. Again, when changing the properties of an existing legend, you must call *ILegend::Refresh* to have the changes reflected in the layout.

Legend

• cities
▭ lakes
▭ province

Legend

cities •
lakes ▭
province ▭

The legend on the left has RightToLeft *set to* False, *and the legend on the right has* RightToLeft *set to* True.

IReadingDirection : IUnknown	Provides access to members that control the reading direction.
■—■ RightToLeft: Boolean	Reading direction.

The *IReadingDirection* interface has one property that controls whether the legend items are aligned along the left or right side. By default, this property is set to *False*.

ArcMap

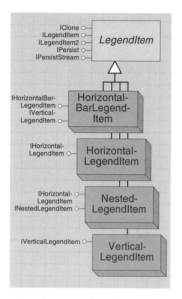

Legend items are the individual items in a legend. For example, a simple map with three layers typically has three legend items in its legend.

Legend map surrounds maintain a collection of associated layers. Each layer is represented by a *LegendItem*. *LegendItems* are responsible for formatting the legend information for a single layer. The *Legend* relies heavily on its associated *LegendItems* to lay out the legend. When the legend is refreshed, it creates a set of graphic elements to use for rendering itself.

The legend items do most of the work—each one pulls the legend information from its associated layer and formats it into a positioned set of graphic elements. The *Legend* simply positions the title and legend item graphics relative to one another.

All legend items have a *LegendClassFormat* object that optionally contains additional formatting information. For example, this object can control the text formatting, patch style, and patch size. In most cases, however, these properties are not set, and the *Legend* uses its *LegendFormat* object instead.

The *Legend's LegendFormat* object manages defaults for these properties. For example, legend patches are usually managed by the *LegendFormat* object and not by a *LegendClassFormat* object.

There are currently four types of legend items: *HorizontalLegendItem, VerticalLegendItem, HorizontalBarLegendItem,* and *NestedLegendItem*.

ILegendItem : IUnknown	Provides access to members that control how a layer appears in a legend. Can be stored in a style.
■— CanDisplay (in Layer: ILayer) : Boolean	Indicates if the style is compatible with the specified layer.
■—■ Columns: Integer	Number of columns in the legend item.
■— Graphics: IEnumElement	List of graphics that represent the legend item. Must call CreateGraphics first.
■—■ GroupIndex: Long	Zero-based index of the legend group shown by this item. Use -1 to show all legend groups using this item.
■—■ HeadingSymbol: ITextSymbol	Text symbol used to draw the heading.
■— Height: Double	Height of the item in points. Must call CreateGraphics first.
■—■ KeepTogether: Boolean	Indicates if classes must appear in a single column or whether they can be split across multiple columns.
■—□ Layer: ILayer	Associated layer.
■—■ LayerNameSymbol: ITextSymbol	Text symbol used to draw the layer name.
■—■ LegendClassFormat: ILegendClassFormat	Default formatting information for the legend classes. Renderer may override.
■— Name: String	Name of the style.
■—■ NewColumn: Boolean	Indicates if the item starts a new column in the legend.
■—■ ShowDescriptions: Boolean	Indicates if descriptions are visible.
■—■ ShowHeading: Boolean	Indicates if heading is visibile.
■—■ ShowLabels: Boolean	Indicates if labels are visible.
■—■ ShowLayerName: Boolean	Indicates if layer name is visible.
■— Width: Double	Width of the item in points. Must call CreateGraphics first.
←— CreateGraphics (in Display: IDisplay, in LegendFormat: ILegendFormat)	Rebuilds the list of graphics. Call whenever the associated layer changes.

All legend items implement the *ILegendItem* interface. The interface controls all of the properties a legend item has—the layer it is associated with; the number of columns it should span; whether it should be displayed in a new column; and whether the label, description, heading, and layer name should be displayed. This interface also provides access to the legend items *LegendClassFormat* object.

Enumeration esriLegendItemArrangement	Legend item arrangement options for the order of patches, labels, and descriptions.
0 - esriPatchLabelDescription	Patch followed by label followed by description.
1 - esriPatchDescriptionLabel	Patch followed by description followed by label.
2 - esriLabelPatchDescription	Label followed by patch followed by description.
3 - esriLabelDescriptionPatch	Label followed by description followed by patch.
4 - esriDescriptionPatchLabel	Description followed by patch followed by label.
5 - esriDescriptionLabelPatch	Description followed by label followed by patch.

All legend items use the *esriLegendItemArrangement* enumeration to specify the position of the label, patch, and description. The default is *esriPatchLabelDescription,* which translates to the patch on the far left, label to the right of the patch, then the description, if available, on the far right.

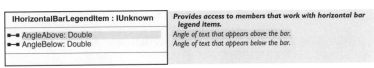

IHorizontalLegendItem : IUnknown	Provides access to members that work with legend item arrangement.
■—■ Arrangement: esriLegendItemArrangement	Legend item arrangement.

Horizontal legend items are the default and most commonly used class of legend items. The image to the left shows an example.

Horizontal legend items in a legend

IHorizontalBarLegendItem : IUnknown	Provides access to members that work with horizontal bar legend items.
■—■ AngleAbove: Double	Angle of text that appears above the bar.
■—■ AngleBelow: Double	Angle of text that appears below the bar.

The *IHorizontalBarLegendItem* interface supports additional properties for controlling the angle of the labels above and below the patch. The default is to display the labels at a 45-degree angle. The image to the left shows such an example.

Horizontal bar legend items in a legend

IVerticalLegendItem : IUnknown	Provides access to members that work with legend item arrangement.
■—■ Arrangement: esriLegendItemArrangement	Legend item arrangement.

Vertical legend items have the patches on top of the legend item text.

INestedLegendItem : IUnknown	Provides access to members that work with nested legend items.
■—■ AutoLayout: Boolean	Indicates if text automatically sizes to fit the markers.
■—■ HorizontalAlignment: tagesriTextHorizontalAlignment	Horizontal alignment of markers.
■—■ LabelEnds: Boolean	Indicates if only the first and last markers are labeled.
■—■ LeaderOverhang: Double	Distance that the leaders extend past the circles (points).
■—■ LeaderSymbol: ILineSymbol	Symbol used to draw the leader lines.
■—■ OutlineSymbol: IFillSymbol	Symbol used to draw outlines.
■—■ ShowOutlines: Boolean	Indicates if only the marker outlines are drawn.

Vertical legend items in a legend

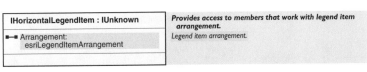

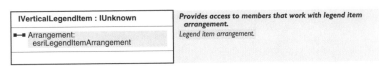

Nested legend items only work with graduated symbols. The image to the left shows a legend with a default nested legend item. The *INested-LegendItem* interface controls the many properties a nested legend item has, including whether or not to label the ends, the leader symbol, and the outline symbol.

Nested legend items in a legend

ArcMap

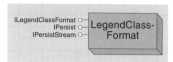

Legend class format objects control each legend item's presentation.

As mentioned earlier, each legend item has a *LegendClass* format object that controls the format of the individual legend item, including the symbols used for the label and description.

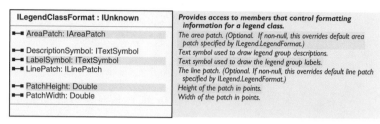

ILegendClassFormat : IUnknown	Provides access to members that control formatting information for a legend class.
■—■ AreaPatch: IAreaPatch	The area patch. (Optional. If non-null, this overrides default area patch specified by ILegend.LegendFormat.)
■—■ DescriptionSymbol: ITextSymbol	Text symbol used to draw legend group descriptions.
■—■ LabelSymbol: ITextSymbol	Text symbol used to draw the legend group labels.
■—■ LinePatch: ILinePatch	The line patch. (Optional. If non-null, this overrides default line patch specified by ILegend.LegendFormat.)
■—■ PatchHeight: Double	Height of the patch in points.
■—■ PatchWidth: Double	Width of the patch in points.

The renderer used to display the layer may also supply a default *LegendClassFormat* so that the legend formatting information gets stored with the layer (in a metadata-like fashion). By default, a layer's *LegendClassFormat* is set to *Nothing*. When a layer does not supply a *LegendClassFormat*, the legend's *LegendFormat* is used. The *LegendClassFormat* properties are optional. If they are not set, the default value from the *LegendFormat* object is used instead. This applies to *PatchWidth*, *PatchHeight*, *LinePatch*, and *AreaPatch*. This makes it easy to get all the patches in the legend to look the same even though they are controlled by different legend items. It also makes it possible to have different patch shapes for each layer if desired.

Each *Legend* has a *LegendFormat* object with which it works. The *LegendFormat* object controls many of the properties of a legend, particularly the spacing between the different parts in a legend.

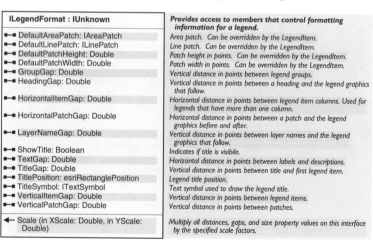

The legend format controls the spacing between the different parts in a legend.

Although LegendFormat is creatable, creating a new Legend object automatically creates a new LegendFormat. Access to the Legend's LegendFormat object is through ILegend::Format.

ILegendFormat : IUnknown	Provides access to members that control formatting information for a legend.
■—■ DefaultAreaPatch: IAreaPatch	Area patch. Can be overridden by the LegendItem.
■—■ DefaultLinePatch: ILinePatch	Line patch. Can be overridden by the LegendItem.
■—■ DefaultPatchHeight: Double	Patch height in points. Can be overridden by the LegendItem.
■—■ DefaultPatchWidth: Double	Patch width in points. Can be overridden by the LegendItem.
■—■ GroupGap: Double	Vertical distance in points between legend groups.
■—■ HeadingGap: Double	Vertical distance in points between a heading and the legend graphics that follow.
■—■ HorizontalItemGap: Double	Horizontal distance in points between legend item columns. Used for legends that have more than one column.
■—■ HorizontalPatchGap: Double	Horizontal distance in points between a patch and the legend graphics before and after.
■—■ LayerNameGap: Double	Vertical distance in points between layer names and the legend graphics that follow.
■—■ ShowTitle: Boolean	Indicates if title is visibile.
■—■ TextGap: Double	Horizontal distance in points between labels and descriptions.
■—■ TitleGap: Double	Vertical distance in points between title and first legend item.
■—■ TitlePosition: esriRectanglePosition	Legend title position.
■—■ TitleSymbol: ITextSymbol	Text symbol used to draw the legend title.
■—■ VerticalItemGap: Double	Vertical distance in points between legend items.
■—■ VerticalPatchGap: Double	Vertical distance in points between patches.
← Scale (in XScale: Double, in YScale: Double)	Multiply all distances, gaps, and size property values on this interface by the specified scale factors.

The *ILegendFormat* interface manages many legend properties, most notably the spacing between the different legend parts. There are also properties for default line and area patches, including their height and width, that are used when a legend item does not provide its own formatting information.

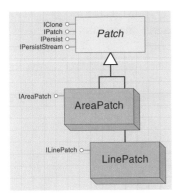

The patches help describe the features in each legend class.

Patches are the individual color boxes or lines associated with each legend class. Both the *LegendFormat* and *LegendFormatClass* objects manage area and line patches.

IPatch : IUnknown	Provides access to members that work with a legend patch.
━ Geometry: IGeometry	Patch geometry.
■━■ Name: String	Name of the patch.
■━■ PreserveAspectRatio: Boolean	Indicates if aspect ratio of patch is preserved.
◀━ get_Geometry (in Bounds: IEnvelope) : IGeometry	Patch geometry sized to fit the specified bounds.

Geometry and *PreserveAspectRatio* are two primary properties in a patch area. The *Geometry* property specifies the shape of the patch. The sample below shows one way to programmatically change a legend's area patches. The *PreserveAspectRatio* property controls how the geometry scales when the legend expands.

The sample below changes the *LegendFormat*'s default area patch to a shape similar to the selected element. To use, add a new polygon element (it doesn't matter what size) to the layout. Select the new element and then select a legend. Make sure the legend has area patches in it. Run the macro, and all the area patches in the specified legend item should adopt the new style. The code works with the last legend item; modify the code as necessary. Also, the color of the element has no bearing on the legend since the color comes from the renderer. You can modify the sample to also do line patches.

```
Public Sub CustomAreaPatch()
  Dim pMxDoc As IMxDocument
  Dim pGraphicsContainer As IGraphicsContainerSelect
  Dim pLegendSurround As IMapSurroundFrame
  Dim pLegend As ILegend
  Dim pLegendItem As ILegendItem
  Dim pPatch As IPatch
  Dim pElement As IElement
  Dim pLegendFormat As ILegendFormat

  Set pMxDoc = Application.Document
  Set pGraphicsContainer = pMxDoc.PageLayout
  Set pLegendSurround = pGraphicsContainer.SelectedElement(1)
  Set pLegend = pLegendSurround.MapSurround
  Set pLegendItem = pLegend.Item(pLegend.ItemCount - 1)
  Set pElement = pGraphicsContainer.SelectedElement(0)
  Set pPatch = New AreaPatch
  pPatch.Geometry = pElement.Geometry
  Set pLegendFormat = pLegend.Format
  pLegendFormat.DefaultAreaPatch = pPatch
  pLegend.Refresh
  pMxDoc.ActiveView.PartialRefresh esriViewGraphics, Nothing, Nothing
End Sub
```

Patches also implement indicator interfaces so that the patch type for a given object can easily be determined. Area patches implement *IAreaPatch*, and line patches implement *ILinePatch*. These interfaces have no members.

ArcMap

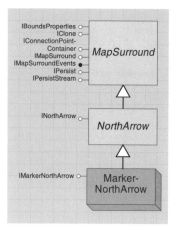

Marker North arrows are typical North arrows added to a layout.

MarkerNorthArrows are character marker symbols typically coming from the ESRI North font. However, any character from any font can be used as a North arrow.

MarkerNorthArrows implement two additional interfaces: *INorthArrow* and *IMarkerNorthArrow*.

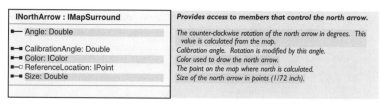

INorthArrow : IMapSurround	Provides access to members that control the north arrow.
■— Angle: Double	The counter-clockwise rotation of the north arrow in degrees. This value is calculated from the map.
■—■ CalibrationAngle: Double	Calibration angle. Rotation is modified by this angle.
■—■ Color: IColor	Color used to draw the north arrow.
■—□ ReferenceLocation: IPoint	The point on the map where north is calculated.
■—■ Size: Double	Size of the north arrow in points (1/72 inch).

The *INorthArrow* interface provides a common interface for North arrow properties, such as size, color, and reference location.

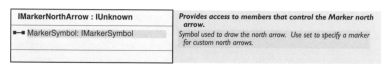

IMarkerNorthArrow : IUnknown	Provides access to members that control the Marker north arrow.
■—■ MarkerSymbol: IMarkerSymbol	Symbol used to draw the north arrow. Use set to specify a marker for custom north arrows.

IMarkerNorthArrow has one property, *MarkerSymbol*, that controls which marker symbol the North arrow uses. By default, the marker symbol belongs to the ESRI North font.

A *MapInset* map surround is another view of the current map extent. If you pan or zoom in on the map the *MapInset* is related to, the *MapInset* will mimic the change.

A map inset map surround is the surround found inside map inset data windows.

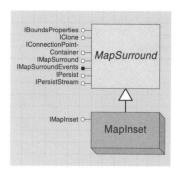

A map inset is a miniature map that typically shows a magnified view of an actual map.

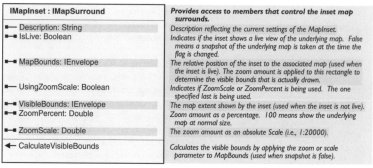

IMapInset : IMapSurround	Provides access to members that control the inset map surrounds.
■— Description: String	Description reflecting the current settings of the MapInset.
■—■ IsLive: Boolean	Indicates if the inset shows a live view of the underlying map. False means a snapshot of the underlying map is taken at the time the flag is changed.
■—■ MapBounds: IEnvelope	The relative position of the inset to the associated map (used when the inset is live). The zoom amount is applied to this rectangle to determine the visible bounds that is actually drawn.
■— UsingZoomScale: Boolean	Indicates if ZoomScale or ZoomPercent is being used. The one specified last is being used.
■—■ VisibleBounds: IEnvelope	The map extent shown by the inset (used when the inset is not live).
■—■ ZoomPercent: Double	Zoom amount as a percentage. 100 means show the underlying map at normal size.
■—■ ZoomScale: Double	The zoom amount as an absolute Scale (i.e., 1:20000).
◄— CalculateVisibleBounds	Calculates the visible bounds by applying the zoom or scale parameter to MapBounds (used when snapshot is false).

For more information on map inset windows (magnification windows), see 'ArcMap data window objects' earlier in this chapter.

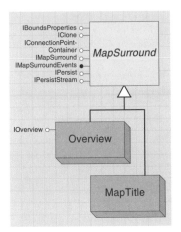

An Overview map surround is a map showing the full extent of the map to which it is related.

A map title holds text to label a map.

An overview map surround is the surround found in overview data windows.

IOverview : IMapSurround	Provides access to members that control the overview.
■—■ AoiFillSymbol: IFillSymbol	Fill symbol used to display the area of interest.
■—■ OverlayGridLabelSymbol: ITextSymbol	Text symbol used to label overlay grid cells with the layer's display field.
■—■ OverlayGridLayer: ILayer	Overlay grid layer for the overview.
← SetOverlayGridCell (in gridLayerFid: Long)	Sets the extent of the associated map to the specified overlay grid cell.
← UpdateDisplay (in windowWidth: Long, in windowHeight: Long)	Updates the display of the overview based upon the associated map's current settings.

For more information on overview windows, see 'ArcMap data window objects' earlier in this chapter.

The map title object is a map surround that holds a piece of text you can use to label a map. This may not be the title of the whole layout, but rather a subtitle for a specific map in the layout.

ArcMap

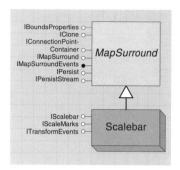

A scale bar shows a map's scale graphically.

There are many types of scale bar map surrounds, including several types of scale lines, single-fill scale bars, and double-fill scale bars. All scale bars implement *IScaleBar* and *IScaleMarks*.

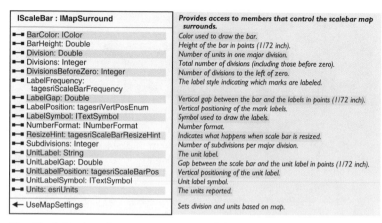

IScaleBar : IMapSurround	Provides access to members that control the scalebar map surrounds.
BarColor: IColor	Color used to draw the bar.
BarHeight: Double	Height of the bar in points (1/72 inch).
Division: Double	Number of units in one major division.
Divisions: Integer	Total number of divisions (including those before zero).
DivisionsBeforeZero: Integer	Number of divisions to the left of zero.
LabelFrequency: tagesriScaleFrequency	The label style indicating which marks are labeled.
LabelGap: Double	Vertical gap between the bar and the labels in points (1/72 inch).
LabelPosition: tagesriVertPosEnum	Vertical positioning of the mark labels.
LabelSymbol: ITextSymbol	Symbol used to draw the labels.
NumberFormat: INumberFormat	Number format.
ResizeHint: tagesriScaleBarResizeHint	Indicates what happens when scale bar is resized.
Subdivisions: Integer	Number of subdivisions per major division.
UnitLabel: String	The unit label.
UnitLabelGap: Double	Gap between the scale bar and the unit label in points (1/72 inch).
UnitLabelPosition: tagesriScaleBarPos	Vertical positioning of the unit label.
UnitLabelSymbol: ITextSymbol	Unit label symbol.
Units: esriUnits	The units reported.
← UseMapSettings	Sets division and units based on map.

The *IScaleBar* interface manages most of the properties a scale bar has, including bar color, bar height, division, and label frequency.

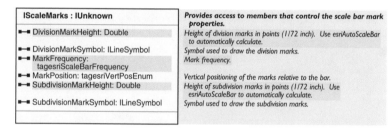

IScaleMarks : IUnknown	Provides access to members that control the scale bar mark properties.
DivisionMarkHeight: Double	Height of division marks in points (1/72 inch). Use esriAutoScaleBar to automatically calculate.
DivisionMarkSymbol: ILineSymbol	Symbol used to draw the division marks.
MarkFrequency: tagesriScaleBarFrequency	Mark frequency.
MarkPosition: tagesriVertPosEnum	Vertical positioning of the marks relative to the bar.
SubdivisionMarkHeight: Double	Height of subdivision marks in points (1/72 inch). Use esriAutoScaleBar to automatically calculate.
SubdivisionMarkSymbol: ILineSymbol	Symbol used to draw the subdivision marks.

The *IScaleMarks* interface manages all of the properties of a scale bar that relate to the individual marks, including the division mark height, division marker symbol, marker frequency, and marker position.

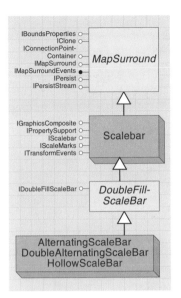

Double-fill scale bars are the most advanced scale bars. These use two symbols to create an attractive scale bar. There are currently three types of double-fill scale bars: alternating, double-alternating, and hollow. The graphic to the lower-left corner shows an example of each.

IDoubleFillScaleBar : IUnknown	Provides access to members that control a scale bar that uses two fill symbols to draw bar.
▪— FillSymbol1: IFillSymbol	Symbol used to draw the bar.
▪— FillSymbol2: IFillSymbol	Symbol used to draw the bar.

All double-fill scale bars implement the *IDoubleFillScaleBar* interface. This interface manages the two fill symbols used when rendering the scale bar.

Alternating scale bar

Double alternating scale bar

Double-fill scale bars are one style of scale bar that uses two fill symbols.

Hollow scale bar

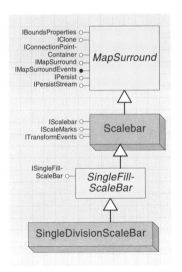

Single-fill scale bars are similar to double-fill scale bars except they use one fill symbol. ArcMap currently has one single-fill scale bar, the *SingleDivisionScaleBar*. The graphic to the left shows an example of a single-division scale bar.

ISingleFillScaleBar : IUnknown	Provides access to members that control a scale bar that uses a single fill symbol to draw bar.
▪— FillSymbol: IFillSymbol	Symbol used to draw the bar.

The *ISingleFillScaleBar* interface manages the single-fill symbol used by scale bars of this type.

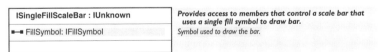

Single division scale bar

Single-fill scale bars are those scale bars symbolized with a single fill symbol.

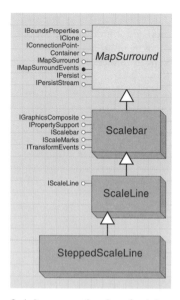

Scale line scale bars are the only class of scale bars that represent a scale bar as a line. ArcMap currently has one type of scale line scale bar—the stepped-line scale bar.

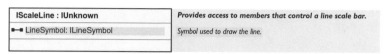

IScaleLine : IUnknown	Provides access to members that control a line scale bar.
■-■ LineSymbol: ILineSymbol	Symbol used to draw the line.

The *IScaleLine* interface manages the one line symbol used by scale lines.

Scale lines are another class of scale bars that are based on line work instead of polygons. The graphic below shows an example of a stepped-line scale bar.

Stepped-line scale bar

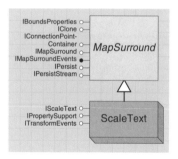

Scale text is essentially a text element that describes the map's scale. One example of scale text is "1 inch equals 2,400 miles".

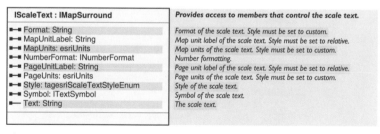

IScaleText : IMapSurround	Provides access to members that control the scale text.
■-■ Format: String	Format of the scale text. Style must be set to custom.
■-■ MapUnitLabel: String	Map unit label of the scale text. Style must be set to relative.
■-■ MapUnits: esriUnits	Map units of the scale text. Style must be set to custom.
■-■ NumberFormat: INumberFormat	Number formatting.
■-■ PageUnitLabel: String	Page unit label of the scale text. Style must be set to relative.
■-■ PageUnits: esriUnits	Page units of the scale text. Style must be set to custom.
■-■ Style: tagesriScaleTextStyleEnum	Style of the scale text.
■-■ Symbol: ITextSymbol	Symbol of the scale text.
■- Text: String	The scale text.

Scale text is a text element indicating a map's scale.

The *IScaleText* interface controls the format of the string that is added as a map surround element. This interface has properties such as *MapUnit* and *MapUnitLabel*—"miles", *PageUnit* and *PageUnitLabel*—"inches", and *Text,* which combines the label properties into a sentence.

ArcMap spatial bookmark objects

ISpatialBookmark ○—
IPersist ○—
IPersistStream ○—
Spatial-Bookmark

IAOIBookmark ○— **AOI-Bookmark**

An area of interest is a map extent you would create when zooming in or panning the display

IFeatureBookmark ○— A feature bookmark stores information about a particular feature so that it can be quickly found again

Feature-Bookmark

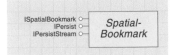

ISpatialBookmark ○—
IPersist ○—
IPersistStream ○—
Spatial-Bookmark

Spatial bookmarks are user-defined extents saved, along with a name identi-fying them, in an ArcMap document.

There are two types of spatial bookmarks in ArcMap: Area of Interest and Feature bookmarks. Both types of spatial bookmarks are managed by the *Map* object for which they store extents. Bookmarks are persisted in the map document saved to disk. You can access a *Map*'s spatial books using its *IMapBookmarks* interface. This interface has methods for accessing bookmarks, adding new ones, and deleting old ones.

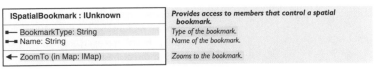

ISpatialBookmark : IUnknown	Provides access to members that control a spatial bookmark.
■— BookmarkType: String	Type of the bookmark.
■■ Name: String	Name of the bookmark.
◄— ZoomTo (in Map: IMap)	Zooms to the bookmark.

All spatial bookmarks implement the *ISpatialBookmark* interface. This interface defines all the common functionality between all bookmarks, particularly the name of the bookmark and a zoom function. Use this interface to check the name of a spatial bookmark and zoom to the extent stored in a bookmark. The *ZoomTo* function changes the map's extent via *IActiveView::Extent*. *ZoomTo* does not automatically invalidate the display.

Implement the *ISpatialBook* interface to create new custom spatial bookmarks.

Create a new *AOIBookmark* whenever you want to create an Area of Interest bookmark. This object persists an envelope holding an extent somewhere within the confines of the map's spatial extent. Like all spatial bookmarks, after creating an Area of Interest bookmark, you can later find it by name and set the map's current extent equal to the extent stored in the bookmark. In ArcMap, new Area of Interest bookmarks are created using the various commands found by clicking View and clicking Bookmarks.

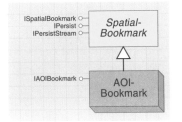

ISpatialBookmark ○—
IPersist ○—
IPersistStream ○—
Spatial-Bookmark

IAOIBookmark ○— **AOI-Bookmark**

This is the Area of Interest bookmark. An area of interest is a map extent that one would create when zooming in or panning the display.

IAOIBookmark : ISpatialBookmark	Provides access to members that control an AOI bookmark.
■—□ Location: IEnvelope	Location of the bookmark.

The only other interface that *AOIBookmark* implements is *IAOIBookmark*, which has one property for accessing the extent the object holds. All of the different spatial bookmark objects have a unique interface that actually inherits from *ISpatialBookmark*. This makes it easy to access the *ISpatialBookmark* members without performing a query interface. By inheriting the interface, the members appear as though they belong directly on the unique interface. For example, if you have a variable declared as an *IAOIBookmark*, you can directly call *ZoomTo* without querying the interface for *ISpatialBookmark*.

The script below creates a new Area of Interest bookmark and adds it to the focus map's bookmark collection:

```
Public Sub AddAreaOfInterestBookMark()
  Dim pMxDoc As IMxDocument
  Dim pMap As IMap
  Dim pActiveView As IActiveView
  Dim pAreaOfInterest As IAOIBookmark
  Dim pMapBookmarks As IMapBookmarks

  Set pMxDoc = Application.Document
  Set pMap = pMxDoc.FocusMap
  Set pActiveView = pMap 'QI

  'Create a new bookmark and set it's location to focus map's current extent
  Set pAreaOfInterest = New AOIBookmark
  Set pAreaOfInterest.Location = pActiveView.Extent
  'Give the bookmark a name
  pAreaOfInterest.Name = "My Bookmark"
  'Add the bookmark to the map's bookmark collection
  'This will add the bookmark to Bookmarks menu accessible from View menu
  Set pMapBookmarks = pMap
  pMapBookmarks.AddBookmark pAreaOfInterest
End Sub
```

This script searches for a specific bookmark and then zooms to its stored extent.

```
Public Sub FindSpatialBookMark()
  Dim pMxDoc As IMxDocument
  Dim pMap As IMap
  Dim pActiveView As IActiveView
  Dim pAreaOfInterest As IAOIBookmark
  Dim pMapBookmarks As IMapBookmarks
  Dim pEnumBookmarks As IEnumSpatialBookmark
  Dim pSpatialBookmark As ISpatialBookmark

  Set pMxDoc = Application.Document
  Set pMap = pMxDoc.FocusMap
  Set pMapBookmarks = pMap 'QI
  Set pActiveView = pMap 'QI

  Set pEnumBookmarks = pMapBookmarks.Bookmarks
  pEnumBookmarks.Reset
  Set pSpatialBookmark = pEnumBookmarks.Next
  'Loop through all the available bookmarks
  'to find the one we want to zoom to
```

ArcMap

```
Do While Not pSpatialBookmark Is Nothing
  If pSpatialBookmark.Name = "My Bookmark" Then
    'Zoom to the bookmark's extent
    pSpatialBookmark.ZoomTo pMxDoc.FocusMap
    'Refresh the display
    pActiveView.Refresh
    Exit Do
  End If
  Set pSpatialBookmark = pEnumBookmarks.Next
Loop
End Sub
```

Create a new *FeatureBookmark* whenever you want to quickly find a particular feature more than one time. This object stores the ID of a feature and the feature class it belongs to so that it can quickly discover and display the feature at any time.

In ArcMap, new Feature bookmarks are created using the Identify tool. Identify a feature and right-click the feature node in the Identify dialog box, then click Set Bookmark. Like all bookmarks, this new bookmark will be added to the map's collection of bookmarks and listed on the Bookmarks menu.

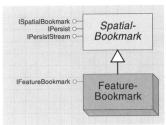

Where Area of Interest bookmarks store a user-specified extent, Feature bookmarks store information about a particular feature so that it may quickly be found and displayed over and over again.

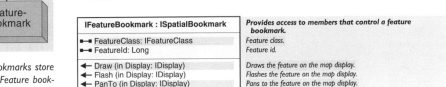

IFeatureBookmark : ISpatialBookmark	Provides access to members that control a feature bookmark.
■━ FeatureClass: IFeatureClass	Feature class.
■━ FeatureId: Long	Feature id.
← Draw (in Display: IDisplay)	Draws the feature on the map display.
← Flash (in Display: IDisplay)	Flashes the feature on the map display.
← PanTo (in Display: IDisplay)	Pans to the feature on the map display.

The *FeatureBookmark* object also implements the *IFeatureBookmark* interface, which provides the necessary properties for setting the feature class and feature ID. This interface also has methods for flashing the feature, panning to it, and drawing. These methods are not implemented at ArcGIS 8.1.

ArcMap style gallery objects

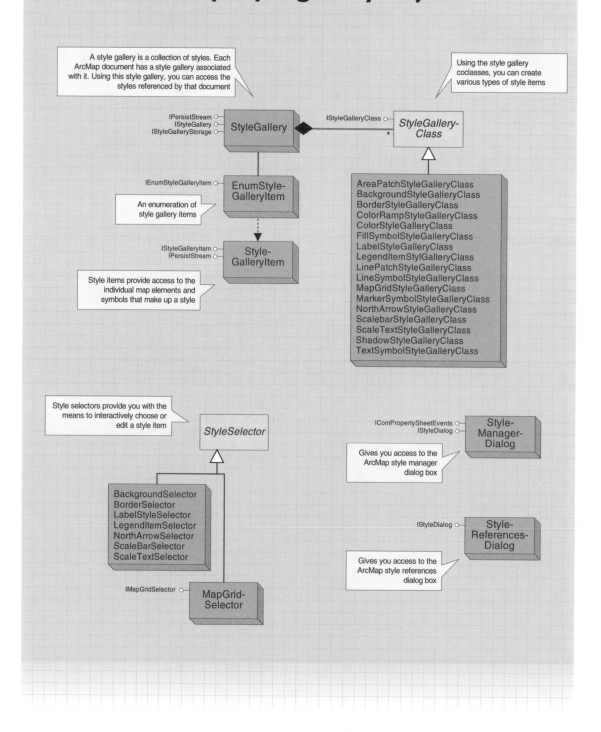

A style gallery is a collection of styles. Each ArcMap document has a style gallery associated with it. Using this style gallery, you can access the styles referenced by that document

Using the style gallery coclasses, you can create various types of style items

IPersistStream
IStyleGallery
IStyleGalleryStorage

StyleGallery

IStyleGalleryClass

StyleGallery-Class

IEnumStyleGalleryItem

EnumStyle-GalleryItem

An enumeration of style gallery items

IStyleGalleryItem
IPersistStream

Style-GalleryItem

Style items provide access to the individual map elements and symbols that make up a style

AreaPatchStyleGalleryClass
BackgroundStyleGalleryClass
BorderStyleGalleryClass
ColorRampStyleGalleryClass
ColorStyleGalleryClass
FillSymbolStyleGalleryClass
LabelStyleGalleryClass
LegendItemStylGalleryClass
LinePatchStyleGalleryClass
LineSymbolStyleGalleryClass
MapGridStyleGalleryClass
MarkerSymbolStyleGalleryClass
NorthArrowStyleGalleryClass
ScalebarStyleGalleryClass
ScaleTextStyleGalleryClass
ShadowStyleGalleryClass
TextSymbolStyleGalleryClass

Style selectors provide you with the means to interactively choose or edit a style item

StyleSelector

IComPropertySheetEvents
IStyleDialog

Style-Manager-Dialog

Gives you access to the ArcMap style manager dialog box

BackgroundSelector
BorderSelector
LabelStyleSelector
LegendItemSelector
NorthArrowSelector
ScaleBarSelector
ScaleTextSelector

IStyleDialog

Style-References-Dialog

Gives you access to the ArcMap style references dialog box

IMapGridSelector

MapGrid-Selector

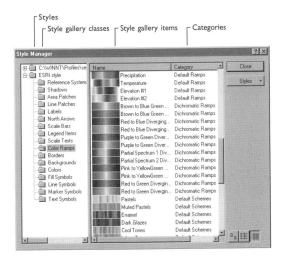

Styles
Style gallery classes
Style gallery items
Categories

Styles are collections of symbols and map elements that are often grouped by functionality. For example, symbols and map elements used by the transportation industry may be grouped into a Transportation Style.

Styles are stored in files that usually have a .style extension. ESRI provides several styles for you to use out of the box. These styles are found under <install_directory>\Bin\Styles. You will find commonly used symbols and map elements in ESRI.style, and more domain-specific style items in relevantly named .style files. The personal style file for each user is maintained in that user's Profile directory—for example, C:\WINNT\Profiles\user_name\Application Data\ESRI\ArcMap\user_name.style.

A style is composed of several style items. These style items provide access to individual map elements and symbols. Style items are organized into classes, which are types of style items. A class may have several groups of items organized into categories. In the style manager figure, Precipitation is a style item that belongs to the Color Ramps class and the Default Ramps category.

The *StyleGallery* coclass is a collection of the styles referenced by a map document. *StyleGallery* is a singleton class, which means that there is only one instance of this class per ArcMap session.

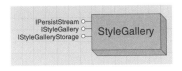

IPersistStream
IStyleGallery
IStyleGalleryStorage

StyleGallery

A style gallery is a collection of styles. Each ArcMap document has a style gallery associated with it. Using this style gallery, you can access the styles referenced by that document.

IStyleGallery : IUnknown	Provides access to members modify the Style Gallery.
Categories (in ClassName: String) : IEnumBSTR	The categories within the given class.
Class (in Index: Long) : IStyleGalleryClass	The class at the given index.
ClassCount: Long	Number of classes in the Style Gallery.
Items (in ClassName: String, in styleSet: String, in Category: String) : IEnumStyleGalleryItem	The style items from the specified style file, in the specified class and category. The style set and category may be blank to return all items.
AddItem (in Item: IStyleGalleryItem)	Adds an item to the target style file.
Clear	Removes all styles from the Style Gallery.
ImportStyle (in FileName: String)	Imports a style from a file other than a .style file.
LoadStyle (in FileName: String, in ClassName: String)	Loads a style from a file. If class is specified, only items in that class will be loaded.
RemoveItem (in Item: IStyleGalleryItem)	Removes an item from the target style file.
SaveStyle (in FileName: String, in styleSet: String, in ClassName: String)	Saves the specified style to a file. If class is specified, only items in that class will be saved.
UpdateItem (in Item: IStyleGalleryItem)	Updates an existing item in target style file.

The *IStyleGallery* interface provides access to the categories, classes, and items in a style. Using this interface, you can add, remove, and update style items. You can also load style files, save a style into another file, or import a style from a custom style file.

You can get to the style gallery used by a map document using the *IMxDocument::StyleGallery* property.

```
Dim pMxDoc As IMxDocument
Dim pStyleGallery As IStyleGallery
```

```
Set pMxDoc = ThisDocument
Set pStyleGallery = pMxDoc.StyleGallery
```

Using the *IStyleGallery::Categories* interface, you can get a listing of the categories in a particular style class. This property takes in the name of the class as an argument. This is the string after which style class folders are named in the style manager. This is also the string returned by *IStyleGalleryClass::Name* for the style gallery class of your interest.

```
Dim pEnumBstr As IEnumBSTR
Dim sCatList As String
Dim sCat As String

Set pEnumBstr = pStyleGallery.Categories("Fill Symbols")
sCatList = "Fill Symbol Categories: "
sCat = pEnumBstr.Next

Do
  sCatList = sCatList & " " & sCat
  sCat = pEnumBstr.Next
Loop While sCat <> ""
MsgBox sCatList
```

You can access the various classes available to the style gallery using *IStyleGallery::Class*.

```
Dim lClasses as Long
lClasses = pStyleGallery.ClassCount
Dim pClass As IStyleGalleryClass
Dim I As Long

For I = 0 To (lClasses - 1)
  Set pClass = pStyleGallery.Class(I)
  MsgBox pClass.Name
Next I
```

Using *IStyleGallery::Items*, you can access the style items in a style file. Using the *ClassName* and *Category* arguments, you can get the style items from a specific style gallery class and a specific category in that class. If you use blank strings for these arguments, you get all the style items in the style.

```
Dim pEnumStyleGall As IEnumStyleGalleryItem
Dim pStyleItem As IStyleGalleryItem

Set pEnumStyleGall = pStyleGallery.Items("Shadows", "D:\test.style", _
  "Default")
Set pStyleItem = pEnumStyleGall.Next
```

After accessing an item, you can make changes to it and update the item in the style file it comes from using *IStyleGallery::UpdateItem*.

```
'Make changes to the item
pStyleItem.Category = "My Category"
```

```
Dim pStyleStorage As IStyleGalleryStorage
Set pStyleStorage = pStyleGallery

Dim sOldFile As String
sOldFile = pStyleStorage.TargetFile

'Set the target style file for the changes
pStyleStorage.TargetFile = "D:\test.style"

'Update the item in the style
pStyleGallery.UpdateItem pStyleItem
pStyleStorage.TargetFile = sOldFile
```

Similarly, you can remove an item from a style file by first accessing it, then using *IStyleGallery::RemoveItem* to remove it.

```
Dim sOldFile As String
sOldFile = pStyleStorage.TargetFile

'Set the target style file for the changes
pStyleStorage.TargetFile = "D:\test.style"

'Remove the item from the style
pStyleGallery.RemoveItem pStyleItem
pStyleStorage.TargetFile = sOldFile
```

To add a style item, you would first have to create it. After creating the style item, you can add it using *IStyleGallery::AddItem*.

```
Dim sOldFile As String
sOldFile = pStyleStorage.TargetFile

'Set the target style file for the changes
pStyleStorage.TargetFile = "D:\test.style"

'Add the new item
pStyleGallery.AddItem pNewItem
pStyleStorage.TargetFile = sOldFile
```

The Style References dialog box shows referenced style files with checked check boxes and unreferenced style files with unchecked check boxes.

Using *IStyleGallery::ImportStyle*, you can load a style from a custom style file. This method looks for a custom style importer under the Style Importers category in the Category Manager. If the custom style importer's *IStyleImporter::CanImport* property returns *True*, this importer's *IStyleImporter::Import* method is used to import the file.

IStyleGalleryStorage : IUnknown	Provides access to members that manage the files used in the Style Gallery.
▪— CanUpdate (in Path: String) : Boolean	Indicates if the specified file can be updated.
▪— DefaultStylePath: String	The default file path for searching for standard styles.
▪— File (in Index: Long) : String	The file at the given index.
▪— FileCount: Long	The number of files in the Style Gallery.
▪—◾ TargetFile: String	The target output file for adding, updating and removing items.
◄— AddFile (in Path: String)	Adds a file to the Style Gallery.
◄— RemoveFile (in Path: String)	Removes a file from the Style Gallery.

The *IStyleGalleryStorage* interface provides access to the style files referenced in the style gallery. It also has methods that let you add and remove style files.

IStyleGalleryStorage::DefaultStylePath gives the location from which style files are read and listed for referencing in the Style References dialog box. This is currently <install_directory>\Bin\Styles. If you do not specify a path for a style file, this is the directory that ArcMap looks into for the file you specified.

The *IStyleGalleryStorage::TargetFile* property allows you to set a style file as the target for adding, removing, or updating items using the *IStyleGallery* interface. You can see this functionality illustrated in the *IStyleGallery* code samples. If the file you specify as *IStyleGalleryStorage::TargetFile* is not referenced by the style gallery, it gets referenced automatically. If this file does not exist, it gets created.

You can use *IStyleGalleryStorage::CanUpdate* to check if you have permissions to make changes to a style file before doing so.

```
pStyleStorage.AddFile pStyleStorage.DefaultStylePath & "Civic.style"
pStyleStorage.TargetFile = pStyleStorage.DefaultStylePath & "ESRI.style"
MsgBox "The target file now is " & pStyleStorage.TargetFile
```

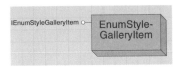

EnumStyleGalleryItem is an enumeration of style gallery items.

EnumStyleGalleryItem is an enumeration of style gallery items. It is created by the style gallery in response to *IStyleGallery::Items*.

IEnumStyleGalleryItem : IUnknown	Provides access to members that enumerate over a set of Style Gallery items.
← Next: IStyleGalleryItem	Gets the next Style Gallery item.
← Reset	Resets the enumerator.

Using *IEnumStyleGalleryItem*, you can access the style gallery items in the enumeration. *IEnumStyleGalleryItem::Reset* resets the enumeration so that the item accessed by *IEnumStyleGalleryItem::Next* will be the first item on the enumeration.

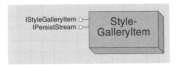

A StyleGalleryItem object contains a symbol or map element and the style item information associated with it.

The *StyleGalleryItem* coclass encapsulates a symbol or map element and the style information associated with it, such as its name, ID, and category.

IStyleGalleryItem : IUnknown	Provides access to members that defien items in the Style Gallery.
■—■ Category: String	The category of the item.
■— ID: Long	Id for the item in the Style Gallery.
■—■ Item: IUnknown Pointer	The symbol or map element to be stored in the Style Gallery item.
■—■ Name: String	The name of the item in the Style Gallery.

Using *IStyleGalleryItem*, you can access the category a style item belongs to and the name it is with. You can also find the ID of that item in the style file. But, most importantly, the *IStyleGalleryItem::Item* property allows you to access the symbol or map element of which the item is composed. *IStyleGalleryItem::Item* returns an *IUnknown* interface that you can *QI* for an interface supported by that symbol or map element.

The following example shows how you can access the marker symbols stored in a style:

```
Dim pStyleStorage As IStyleGalleryStorage
Dim pStyleGallery As IStyleGallery
Dim pStyleClass As IStyleGalleryClass
Dim pMxDoc As IMxDocument
Set pMxDoc = ThisDocument
Set pStyleGallery = pMxDoc.StyleGallery
Set pStyleStorage = pStyleGallery


Dim pEnumStyleGall As IEnumStyleGalleryItem
Dim pStyleItem As IStyleGalleryItem
Dim pMarkerSym As IMarkerSymbol


'Initialize the style gallery
Set pEnumStyleGall = pStyleGallery.Items("Marker Symbols", "ESRI.style", _
   "Default")
pEnumStyleGall.Reset
Set pStyleItem = pEnumStyleGall.Next


Do While Not pStyleItem Is Nothing    'Loop through and access each marker
   Set pMarkerSym = pStyleItem.Item
```

ArcMap

```
        Debug.Print pStyleItem.Name & " " & pMarkerSym.Size
        Set pStyleItem = pEnumStyleGall.Next
    Loop
```

You can create new style gallery items by first creating a symbol or map element relevant to this style gallery class. You can make this the Item for a newly created style gallery item. You can then add this item to a style gallery. Alternatively, you can use *IStyleGalleryClass::NewObject* to create the symbol/map element. The latter method is illustrated under *IStyleGalleryClass*.

```
'Create the new object
Dim pNewObject As IUnknown
Set pNewObject = New SimpleFillSymbol

'Assign properties specific to the style class
Dim pSimpleFillSymbol As ISimpleFillSymbol
Set pSimpleFillSymbol = pNewObject
pSimpleFillSymbol.Color = BuildRGB(55, 55, 200)

'Create new style item using object, and add it to the target style
Dim pNewItem As IStyleGalleryItem
Set pNewItem = New StyleGalleryItem
pNewItem.Item = pNewObject
pNewItem.Name = "My Fill Symbol"
pStyleGallery.AddItem pNewItem
```

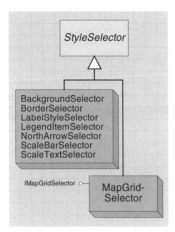

The Style Selector dialog box lets you choose a style item of a specific style class. For example, the BackgroundSelector allows you to choose a background style item.

The *StyleSelector* abstract class is inherited by several coclasses, all of which are dialog boxes you can use in your application to select a style item of the respective type.

IStyleSelector : IUnknown	Style Selector Dialog interface
← AddStyle (in Style: IUnknown Pointer) : Boolean	*Specify the original style. May specify more than one.*
← DoModal (in parentHWnd: Long) : Boolean	*Show the selector.*
← GetStyle (in Index: Long) : IUnknown Pointer	*Returns the updated style. Index is required when more than one style was originally added.*

The methods in the *IStyleSelector* interface allow you to bring up a Style Selector dialog box. You can use *IStyleSelector::DoModal* to bring up the dialog. Optionally, you can specify the style item that the Style Selector dialog box comes up with using *IStyleSelector::AddStyle*. This will allow you to control the default style item. You can get the user's choice with *IStyleSelector::GetStyle*.

```
Dim pSelector As IStyleSelector
Set pSelector = New BackgroundSelector

Dim bOK As Boolean
Dim pFill As IFillSymbol
Dim pBackground As ISymbolBackground

bOK = pSelector.DoModal(Application.hWnd)
If (bOK) Then
  Set pBackground = pSelector.GetStyle(0)
  Set pFill = pBackground.FillSymbol
  MsgBox pFill.Color.CMYK
End If

Set pBackground = New SymbolBackground
Set pFill = New SimpleFillSymbol
pFill.Color = BuildRGB(200, 90, 90)
pBackground.FillSymbol = pFill

pSelector.AddStyle pBackground
bOK = pSelector.DoModal(Application.hWnd)
If (bOK) Then
  Set pBackground = pSelector.GetStyle(0)
  Set pFill = pBackground.FillSymbol
  MsgBox pFill.Color.CMYK
End If
```

Style Gallery Class	Style Selector
AreaPatchStyleGalleryClass	None
BackgroundStyleGalleryClass	BackgroundSelector
BorderStyleGalleryClass	BorderSelector
ColorRampStyleGalleryClass	None
ColorStyleGalleryClass	ColorSelector
FillSymbolStyleGalleryClass	SymbolSelector
LabelStyleGalleryClass	LabelStyleSelector
LegendItemStyleGalleryClass	LegendItemSelector
LinePatchStyleGalleryClass	None
LineSymbolStyleGalleryClass	SymbolSelector
MapGridStyleGalleryClass	MapGridSelector
MarkerSymbolStyleGalleryClass	SymbolSelector
NorthArrowStyleGalleryClass	NorthArrowSelector
ScaleBarStyleGalleryClass	ScaleBarSelector
ScaleTextStyleGalleryClass	ScaleTextSelector
ShadowStyleGalleryClass	ShadowSelector
TextSymbolStyleGalleryClass	SymbolSelector

This table shows you the selectors you can use to interactively choose items of each style gallery class.

IMapGridSelector : IUnknown	Provides access to the map grid selector.
—□ MapFrame: IMapFrame	*The map frame whose map grids are edited.*

Map grid selectors need information on the data frame to which the map grid belongs. You can specify this using *IMapGridSelector*.

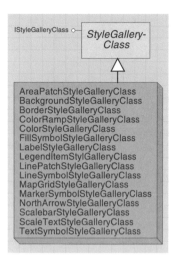

IStyleGalleryClass ○—□ **StyleGallery-Class**

AreaPatchStyleGalleryClass
BackgroundStyleGalleryClass
BorderStyleGalleryClass
ColorRampStyleGalleryClass
ColorStyleGalleryClass
FillSymbolStyleGalleryClass
LabelStyleGalleryClass
LegendItemStyleGalleryClass
LinePatchStyleGalleryClass
LineSymbolStyleGalleryClass
MapGridStyleGalleryClass
MarkerSymbolStyleGalleryClass
NorthArrowStyleGalleryClass
ScalebarStyleGalleryClass
ScaleTextStyleGalleryClass
TextSymbolStyleGalleryClass

You can instantiate new style items of a specific class with a style gallery class. The list of available style gallery classes is read from the ESRI Style Gallery Classes category in the Component Category Manager.

The various coclasses that inherit from the *StyleGallery* abstract class encapsulate functionality, creating style items of the respective type.

IStyleGalleryClass : IUnknown	Style Gallery Class interface
■← Description: String	*Description for the Style Gallery Class*
■← ItemClass: GUID	*Interface ID for the items in the class*
■← Name: String	*Name of the Style Gallery Class*
■← NewObject (in newType: String) : IUnknown Pointer	*Creates a new object of the specified type*
■← NewObjectTypes: IEnumBSTR	*Returns the available types of new items in this class*
■← PreviewRatio: Double	*The width ratio to 1 height.*
◄— EditProperties (in galleryItem: IUnknown Pointer, in listener: IComPropertySheetEvents, in hWnd: Long, out ok: Boolean)	*Edits the properties of a Style Gallery Item of the supported class*
◄— Preview (in galleryItem: IUnknown Pointer, in hDC: Long, in rectangle: tagRECT)	*Draws a preview of a Style Gallery Item of the supported class*

The *IStyleGalleryClass* interface gives you access to the class name, description, and type of new objects that can be created with the class. Using this interface, you can create new style items using edit properties of an item, then draw a preview of the item to a window.

The table below lists some of the properties exposed by *IStyleGallery-Class* for the coclasses that support it.

Style gallery class	Name	New object types	Preview ratio	Description
AreaPatchStyleGalleryClass	Area Patches	Area patches	2	Area patch—geometry used to draw symbol patches
BackgroundStyleGalleryClass	Backgrounds	Normal Background	2	Background
BorderStyleGalleryClass	Borders	Normal Border	4	Border
ColorRampStyleGalleryClass	Color Ramps	Random Color Ramp, Multi-part Color Ramp, Preset Color Ramp, Algorithmic Color Ramp	4	Color Ramps
ColorStyleGalleryClass	Colors	RGB, CMYK, HSV, Gray, Name	I	Colors
FillSymbolStyleGalleryClass	Fill Symbols	Fill Symbol	I	Fill Symbols
LabelStyleGalleryClass	Labels	Label	4	Labels—text symbol and placement option for labeling
LegendItemStyleGalleryClass	Legend Items	Horizontal Bar, Nested, Horizontal, Vertical	2	Legend Items—the part of the legend that corresponds to one layer
LinePatchStyleGalleryClass	Line Patches	Line Patches	2	Line Patch—geometry used to draw symbol patches
LineSymbolStyleGalleryClass	Line Symbols	Line Symbol	I	Line Symbols
MapGridStyleGalleryClass	Reference Systems	Graticule, Measured Grid, Index Grid	3	Reference Systems
MarkerSymbolStyleGalleryClass	Marker Symbols	Marker Symbol	I	Marker Symbols
NorthArrowStyleGalleryClass	North Arrows	North Arrow	I	North Arrows
ScaleBarStyleGalleryClass	Scale Bars	Scale Line, Stepped Scale Line, Hollow Scale Bar, Single Division Scale Bar, Alternating Scale Bar, Double Alternating Scale Bar	6	Scale Bars
ScaleTextStyleGalleryClass	Scale Texts	Scale Text	10	Scale Texts—display scale as formatted text
ShadowStyleGalleryClass	Shadows	Normal Shadow	2	Drop Shadow
TextSymbolStyleGalleryClass	Text Symbols	Text Symbol	3	Text Symbols

The code below illustrates how you can access the style gallery classes in a style:

```
Dim lClasses As Long
Dim sObjTypeList As String
Dim sObjType As String
lClasses = pStyleGallery.ClassCount
Dim pClass As IStyleGalleryClass
Dim i As Long
For i = 0 To (lClasses - 1)
  Set pClass = pStyleGallery.Class(i)
  sObjTypeList = pClass.Name & ":"
  Set pEnumBstr = pClass.NewObjectTypes
  sObjType = pEnumBstr.Next
 Do While Not sObjType = ""
    sObjTypeList = sObjTypeList & "," & sObjType
    sObjType = pEnumBstr.Next
  Loop
  Debug.Print sObjTypeList
Next i
```

When you create a new symbol item using *IStyleGalleryClass::NewObject*, the argument has to be one of the strings reported by *IStyleGalleryClass:: NewObjectTypes* for that class. You can *QI* the returned object for an interface supported by the new style gallery item, then add this as an item to the style gallery using *IStyleGalleryItem*.

This method of creating a new style gallery item is especially useful when you wish to create a new object based on your user's choice of object type from a list of object types that you create using *IStyleGalleryClass::NewObjectTypes*.

```
'Create the new object
Dim pClass As IStyleGalleryClass
Dim pNewObject As IUnknown
Set pClass = New FillSymbolStyleGalleryClass
Set pNewObject = pClass.NewObject("Fill Symbol")

'Assign properties specific to the style class
If TypeOf pNewObject Is ISimpleFillSymbol Then
  Dim pSimpleFillSymbol As ISimpleFillSymbol
  Set pSimpleFillSymbol = pNewObject
  pSimpleFillSymbol.Color = BuildRGB(55, 55, 200)
End If

'Create new style item using object, and add it to the target style
Dim pNewItem As IStyleGalleryItem
Set pNewItem = New StyleGalleryItem
pNewItem.Item = pNewObject
pNewItem.Name = "My Fill Symbol"
pStyleGallery.AddItem pNewItem
```

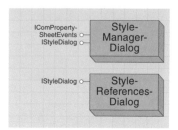

The *StyleManagerDialog* coclass is a dialog box that lets you manage the styles referenced by a map document and the style items in them. The *StyleReferencesDialog* coclass is a dialog box that lets you manage which style files ArcMap references.

The StyleManagerDialog and the StyleReferencesDialog allow you to bring up the Style Manager and the Style References dialog boxes, respectively.

IStyleDialog : IUnknown	*Style Dialog interface*
▪━▪ Title: String	*The title of the style dialog.*
◄— DoModal (in StyleGallery: IStyleGallery, Parent: Long) : Boolean	*Displays a style dialog for the given style gallery.*

Before calling *IStyleDialog::DoModal*, use *IStyleManager::Title* to change the title of the Style Manager dialog box.

```
Dim pMxDoc As IMxDocument
Dim pStyleGallery As IStyleGallery
Set pMxDoc = ThisDocument
Set pStyleGallery = pMxDoc.StyleGallery

Dim pStyleDialog As IStyleDialog
Set pStyleDialog = New StyleManagerDialog
pStyleDialog.DoModal pStyleGallery, Application.hWnd
```

ArcMap map grid objects

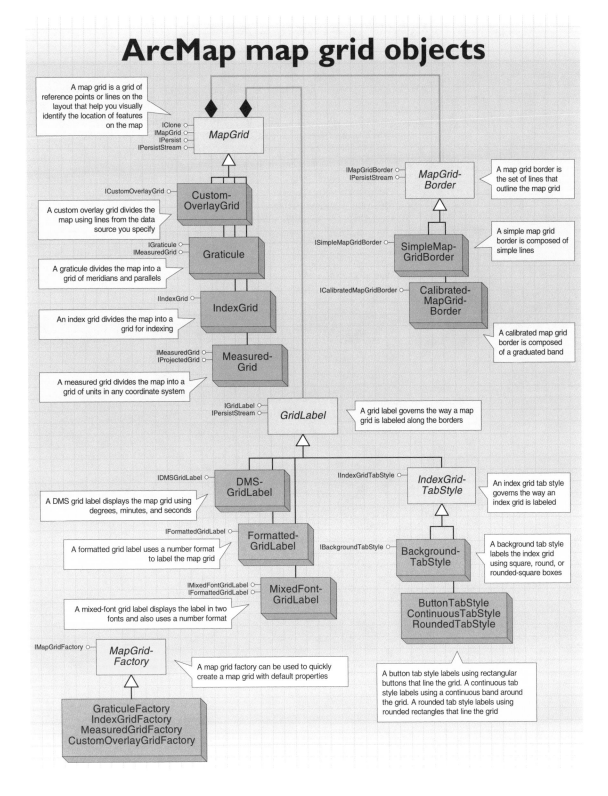

A map grid is a grid of reference points or lines on the layout that help you visually identify the location of features on the map

IClone
IMapGrid
IPersist
IPersistStream

MapGrid

IMapGridBorder
IPersistStream

MapGrid-Border

A map grid border is the set of lines that outline the map grid

ICustomOverlayGrid

Custom-OverlayGrid

A custom overlay grid divides the map using lines from the data source you specify

ISimpleMapGridBorder

SimpleMap-GridBorder

A simple map grid border is composed of simple lines

IGraticule
IMeasuredGrid

Graticule

A graticule divides the map into a grid of meridians and parallels

ICalibratedMapGridBorder

Calibrated-MapGrid-Border

IIndexGrid

IndexGrid

An index grid divides the map into a grid for indexing

A calibrated map grid border is composed of a graduated band

IMeasuredGrid
IProjectedGrid

Measured-Grid

A measured grid divides the map into a grid of units in any coordinate system

IGridLabel
IPersistStream

GridLabel

A grid label governs the way a map grid is labeled along the borders

IDMSGridLabel

DMS-GridLabel

A DMS grid label displays the map grid using degrees, minutes, and seconds

IIndexGridTabStyle

IndexGrid-TabStyle

An index grid tab style governs the way an index grid is labeled

IFormattedGridLabel

Formatted-GridLabel

A formatted grid label uses a number format to label the map grid

IBackgroundTabStyle

Background-TabStyle

A background tab style labels the index grid using square, round, or rounded-square boxes

IMixedFontGridLabel
IFormattedGridLabel

MixedFont-GridLabel

A mixed-font grid label displays the label in two fonts and also uses a number format

ButtonTabStyle
ContinuousTabStyle
RoundedTabStyle

IMapGridFactory

MapGrid-Factory

A map grid factory can be used to quickly create a map grid with default properties

A button tab style labels using rectangular buttons that line the grid. A continuous tab style labels using a continuous band around the grid. A rounded tab style labels using rounded rectangles that line the grid

GraticuleFactory
IndexGridFactory
MeasuredGridFactory
CustomOverlayGridFactory

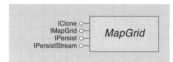

A map grid is a grid of reference points or lines on the layout.

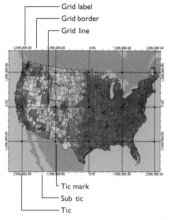

Parts of a map grid

A map grid can be a grid of geographic or projected coordinates, or a reference grid like those found in street maps. Map grids are part of the layout of a map and can only be seen in layout view.

You can use map grids to look at a map and figure out the approximate location of a feature. You can also use them to find features on the map when you know the location of the feature.

Map grids are essentially made up of three coclasses derived from the MapGrid, MapGridBorder, and GridLabel abstract classes. To create a MapGrid object, create instances of all of these. Associate the MapGridBorder and the GridLabel objects with the MapGrid object. Then, add the new MapGrid to the layout. We will see each of these steps in detail as we progress through this section.

To get to a map grid programmatically, navigate to the *PageLayout* Co-Class, then use its *IGraphicsContainer* interface's *FindFrame* method to get to the *Map's MapFrame*. The *MapFrame* coclass has an *IMapGrids* interface from which you can get to all the map grids for that dataframe.

```
Dim pMap As IMap, pMxDoc As IMxDocument
Dim pMapFrame As IMapFrame
Dim pGraphicsContainer As IGraphicsContainer
Dim pMapGrid As IMapGrid
Set pMxDoc = ThisDocument
Set pMap = pMxDoc.FocusMap
Set pGraphicsContainer = pMxDoc.PageLayout
Set pMapFrame = pGraphicsContainer.FindFrame(pMap)


Dim pMapGrids As IMapGrids
Set pMapGrids = pMapFrame
Set pMapGrid = pMapGrids.MapGrid(0)
```

IMapGrid : IUnknown	Provides access to members that control a map grid.
Border: IMapGridBorder	The map grid border.
ExteriorWidth (in pDisplay: IDisplay, in pMapFrame: IMapFrame) : Double	The width (in display units) of the portion of the grid that is outside of the frame.
LabelFormat: IGridLabel	The label format for map grid labels.
LineSymbol: ILineSymbol	The symbol used to draw grid lines - null will draw no lines.
Name: String	The name of the map grid.
SubTickCount: Integer	The number of subticks to draw between the major ticks.
SubTickLength: Double	The length of the subticks in points.
SubTickLineSymbol: ILineSymbol	The symbol used to draw the subtick lines.
TickLength: Double	The length of the major ticks in points.
TickLineSymbol: ILineSymbol	The line symbol used to draw the major ticks.
TickMarkSymbol: IMarkerSymbol	The symbol used to draw tick marks at the grid interval intersections - null will draw no tick marks.
Visible: Boolean	Indicates if the map grid is visible.
Draw (in Display: IDisplay, in pMapFrame: IMapFrame)	Draws the map grid for a map frame to the given display.
GenerateGraphics (in pMapFrame: IMapFrame, in GraphicsContainer: IGraphicsContainer)	Generates graphic elements corresponding to the grid lines and stores them in the specified graphics container.
PrepareForOutput (in hDC: Long, in dpi: Long, in PixelBounds: tagRECT, in pMapFrame: IMapFrame)	Prepares the map grid for output to a device.
QueryLabelVisibility (out leftVis: Boolean, out topVis: Boolean, out rightVis: Boolean, out bottomVis: Boolean)	Returns the visibility of the labels along all four sides of the map grid.
QuerySubTickVisibility (out leftVis: Boolean, out topVis: Boolean, out rightVis: Boolean, out bottomVis: Boolean)	Returns the visibility of the subticks along all four sides of the map grid.
QueryTickVisibility (out leftVis: Boolean, out topVis: Boolean, out rightVis: Boolean, out bottomVis: Boolean)	Returns the visibility of the ticks along all four sides of the map grid.
SetDefaults (in pMapFrame: IMapFrame)	Sets the properties of the map grid to default values.
SetLabelVisibility (in leftVis: Boolean, in topVis: Boolean, in rightVis: Boolean, in bottomVis: Boolean)	Sets the visibility of the labels along all four sides of the map grid.
SetSubTickVisibility (in leftVis: Boolean, in topVis: Boolean, in rightVis: Boolean, in bottomVis: Boolean)	Sets the visibility of the subticks along all four sides of the map grid.
SetTickVisibility (in leftVis: Boolean, in topVis: Boolean, in rightVis: Boolean, in bottomVis: Boolean)	Sets the visibility of the ticks along all four sides of the map grid.

IMapGrid holds the methods and properties common to all types of map grids. The *Draw* method can be used to draw a map grid to, for example, a *PictureBox* control that has a map and display associated with it. The *PrepareForOutput* method takes a device's *HDC* and should be called before the *Draw* method.

When you create a new map grid, you have to populate the properties of the grid that *IMapGrid* exposes. The following code illustrates how you can do this. After doing this, you can populate the properties exposed by interfaces specific to the grid type, then add the grid to a data frame.

```
Dim pMapGrid As IMapGrid 'Create the map grid
Set pMapGrid = New Graticule
pMapGrid.Name = "Map Grid" 'Set the map grid's name


'Set the line symbol used to draw the grid
Dim pLineSymbol As ISimpleLineSymbol
Set pLineSymbol = New SimpleLineSymbol
pLineSymbol.Style = esriSLSSolid
pLineSymbol.Width = 2
pLineSymbol.Color = BuildRGB(52, 52, 52)  'Soft Black
pMapGrid.LineSymbol = pLineSymbol


pMapGrid.TickLength = 15 'Set the Tick Properties
Set pLineSymbol = New SimpleLineSymbol
pLineSymbol.Style = esriSLSSolid
pLineSymbol.Width = 1.5
pLineSymbol.Color = BuildRGb(0, 0, 0)
pMapGrid.TickLineSymbol = pLineSymbol
pMapGrid.TickMarkSymbol = Nothing


pMapGrid.SubTickCount = 5 'Set the Sub Tick Properties
pMapGrid.SubTickLength = 10
Set pLineSymbol = New SimpleLineSymbol
pLineSymbol.Style = esriSLSSolid
pLineSymbol.Width = 0.2
pLineSymbol.Color = BuildRGb(0, 0, 0)
pMapGrid.SubTickLineSymbol = pLineSymbol


'Set the Tick, SubTick, Label Visibility along the 4 sides of the grid
pMapGrid.SetTickVisibility True, True, True, True
pMapGrid.SetSubTickVisibility True, True, True, True
pMapGrid.SetLabelVisibility True, True, True, True


'Make map grid visible, so it gets drawn when Active View is updated
pMapGrid.Visible = True
```

To avoid code repetition, the *BuildRGB* function is used in this section to create *Color* objects using red, blue, and green values and to get their *IColor* interface.

```
Public Function BuildRGB(lRed As Long, lGreen As Long, lBlue As Long) _
  As IRgbColor


Dim pRGBColor As IRgbColor
```

If you want tick marks in your grid, you can create a marker symbol and assign it to the IMapGrid::TickMarkSymbol property. If you do not want either a TickMarkSymbol or a TickLineSymbol, set these properties to 'Nothing'.

```
    Set pRGBColor = New RgbColor
    With pRGBColor
      .Red = lRed
      .Green = lGreen
      .Blue = lBlue
      .UseWindowsDithering = True
    End With
    Set BuildRGb = pRGBColor
End Function
```

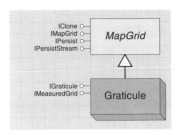

A graticule divides the map by meridians and parallels.

A graticule is a map grid with lines along longitudes and latitudes.

IGraticule : IMapGrid	Provides access to the members that control the graticule.
■—■ AutoInterval: Boolean	Indicates if the graticule automatically and interactively computes the interval size.
←— AddElement (in Label: String, in Location: Double, in IsLatitude: Boolean, in LabelSymbol: ITextSymbol)	Adds a grid line at custom location to the graticule.
←— RemoveElement (in Label: String)	Removes a grid line in a custom location.

The *IGraticule* interface is not implemented yet. The *AddElement* method is intended to be used for adding extra lines to the graticule. The *RemoveElement* method is intended to remove these lines. *AutoInterval* is intended to enable the computation of a suitable interval between grid lines based on the scale of display.

IMeasuredGrid : IUnknown	Provides access to the members that control the lines that make up the map grid.
■—■ FixedOrigin: Boolean	Indicates if the origin is read from the XOrigin and YOrigin properties (true) or if it is computed dynamically from the data frame (false).
■—■ Units: esriUnits	The units for the intervals and origin.
■—■ XIntervalSize: Double	The interval between grid lines along the X axis.
■—■ XOrigin: Double	The origin of the grid on the X axis.
■—■ YIntervalSize: Double	The interval between grid lines along the Y axis.
■—■ YOrigin: Double	The origin of the grid on the Y axis.

A graticule

The *IMeasureGrid* interface is implemented by the *MeasuredGrid* and *Graticule* coclasses. It exposes information on the origins, intervals, and units of the grid. If you set *IMeasuredGrid::FixedOrigin* to *False*, the origin is computed from the data frame instead of from the x- and y-origin properties. *IMeasuredGrid::Units* need not be populated for a graticule.

```
'Create graticule
Dim pMapGrid As IMapGrid
Dim pMeasuredGrid As IMeasuredGrid
Set pMeasuredGrid = New Graticule
Set pMapGrid = pMeasuredGrid

'Set the IMeasuredGrid properties
pMeasuredGrid.FixedOrigin = True
pMeasuredGrid.XIntervalSize = 10 'meridian interval
pMeasuredGrid.XOrigin = -180
pMeasuredGrid.YIntervalSize = 10 'parallel interval
pMeasuredGrid.YOrigin = -90
```

ArcMap

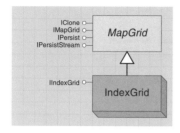

An index grid divides the map into a grid for indexing. A popular use for this is in street maps, where you locate a street in an alphabetic listing on the map, find the grid cell it is in, and use this information to locate the street on the map.

An index grid

An index grid is a map grid that divides the map into the specified number of columns and rows. It is mainly used to index a map.

IIndexGrid : IMapGrid	Provides access to members that control the index grid.
▪━ ColumnCount: Long	*The number of columns in the index grid.*
▪━ RowCount: Long	*The number of rows in the index grid.*
▪━ XLabel (in column: Long) : String	*The label for the given column in the index grid.*
▪━ YLabel (in Row: Long) : String	*The label for the given row in the index grid.*
◄━ QueryCellExtent (in Row: Long, in column: Long, in pMapFrame: IMapFrame, Extent: IEnvelope)	*Provides access to the cell extent in page space for the given row and column.*

IIndexGrid gives you access to the functionality common to all index grids. Using the *XLabel* and the *YLabel* properties, you can set or retrieve the label for each column and index in the grid. You can create an index grid as illustrated in the sample below:

```
'Create indexgrid
Dim pMapGrid As IMapGrid
Dim pIndexGrid As IIndexGrid
Set pIndexGrid = New IndexGrid
Set pMapGrid = pIndexGrid

'Set the IIndexGrid properties
pIndexGrid.ColumnCount = 5
pIndexGrid.RowCount = 5
'Set grid label strings for the x and y axes
Dim i As Integer
For i = 0 To (pIndexGrid.ColumnCount - 1)
  pIndexGrid.XLabel(i) = VBA.Chr(i + Asc("A"))
Next i
For i = 0 To (pIndexGrid.RowCount - 1)
  pIndexGrid.YLabel(i) = VBA.Str(i + 1)
Next i
```

IIndexGrid::QueryCellExtent is useful for finding the features that cross a cell in the grid. You can use the envelope returned by this method in a spatial filter after transforming it into map coordinates. Using *IDisplayTransformation::TransformRect*, you can use this filter to search for the features that cross this cell in the grid and to create an index listing of features and their location on the grid.

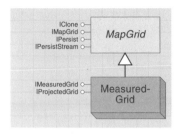

A measured grid divides the map into a grid of units in a coordinate system of your choice.

The grid can be in a projected coordinate system or in a geographic coordinate system. A measured grid in a geographic coordinate system is equivalent to a graticule. A measured grid can be in the same spatial reference system as the data frame or in a different one.

A measured grid

A measured grid is a map grid with grid lines on a coordinate system specified using the *IProjectedGrid* interface.

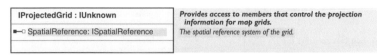

IProjectedGrid : IUnknown	Provides access to members that control the projection information for map grids.
▪—○ SpatialReference: ISpatialReference	The spatial reference system of the grid.

The *IProjectedGrid* interface holds the spatial reference information associated with a measured grid. If you want to create a measured grid in the same projection as the data frame it is in, you can set the *IProjectedGrid::SpatialReference* property using the data frame's *IMap::SpatialReference* property.

To create a measured grid with a different projection, you should first create an instance of a coclass that inherits from *SpatialReference*. You can then set the *IProjectedGrid::SpatialReference* property of the grid with the *ISpatialReference* interface of this object.

The following example shows how to create a measured grid and set the properties exposed through its specific interfaces.

```
'create measuredgrid
Dim pMapGrid As IMapGrid, pMeasuredGrid As IMeasuredGrid
Set pMeasuredGrid = New MeasuredGrid
Set pMapGrid = pMeasuredGrid

'Set the IMeasuredGrid properties
' Origin coordinates and interval sizes are in map units
pMeasuredGrid.FixedOrigin = True
pMeasuredGrid.Units = m_pMap.MapUnits
pMeasuredGrid.XIntervalSize = 1000000  'meridian interval
pMeasuredGrid.XOrigin = -3000000
pMeasuredGrid.YIntervalSize = 1000000 'parallel interval
pMeasuredGrid.YOrigin = -3000000

'Set the IProjectedGrid properties
Dim pProjectedGrid As IProjectedGrid
Set pProjectedGrid = pMeasuredGrid
Set pProjectedGrid.SpatialReference = m_pMap.SpatialReference
```

A custom overlay grid is a map grid with grid lines read from a feature class.

ICustomOverlayGrid : IMapGrid	Custom Overlay Grid interface
▪—▪ DataSource: IFeatureClass	Sets or returns the data source containing the grid cells
▪—▪ LabelField: String	Sets or returns the name of the field used to label the grid

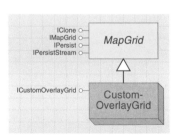

The custom overlay grid divides the map using lines from the data source you specify.

The *ICustomOverlayGrid* interface gives you access to the feature class that the grid lines are read from through the *ICustomOverlayGrid:: DataSource* property. It also lets you specify which field in this feature class will label the grid using the *ICustomOverlayGrid::LabelField* property.

ArcMap

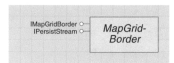

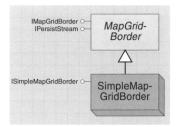

A map grid border is the set of lines that outline the map grid.

The map grid border coclasses determine how the outline of a map grid is drawn.

IMapGridBorder : IUnknown	Provides access to members that control the map grid border.
■— DisplayName: String	The display name for the map grid border.
■— Width: Double	The width of the map grid border in points.
◄— Draw (in Display: IDisplay, in frameGeometry: IGeometry, in mapGeometry: IGeometry)	Draws the border to the specified display, using the frame bounds and the map bounds in page space.

Type of MapGridBorder	Display Name
SimpleMapGridBorder	"Simple Border"
CalibratedMapGridBorder	"Calibrated Border"

Using the *IMapGridBorder* interface, you can find the width of the map grid border. Using the *DisplayName* property, you can report the type of the border object to which the *IMapGridBorder* interface is pointing. The table on the left lists the strings reported by this property for the two border types.

When you create a new map grid border, you don't need to use the *IMapGridBorder* interface. As you can see, all the properties exposed by this interface are read-only.

A simple map grid border is drawn using a line symbol specified with the *ISimpleMapGridBorder* interface.

A simple map grid border is composed of the lines that frame the map grid.

ISimpleMapGridBorder : IUnknown	Provides access to the members that control the simple map grid border.
■—■ LineSymbol: ILineSymbol	The line symbol used to draw the border.

The *ISimpleMapGridBorder* interface provides access to the line symbol used to draw the grid border through the *LineSymbol* property. The code below illustrates how you can create a simple map grid border.

```
'Create a simple map grid border
Dim pSimpleMapGridBorder As ISimpleMapGridBorder
Set pSimpleMapGridBorder = New SimpleMapGridBorder

'Set the ISimpleMapGridBorder properties
Dim pLineSymbol As ISimpleLineSymbol
Set pLineSymbol = New SimpleLineSymbol
pLineSymbol.Style = esriSLSSolid
pLineSymbol.Color = BuildRGb(0, 0, 0)
pLineSymbol.Width = 2
pSimpleMapGridBorder.LineSymbol = pLineSymbol

'Assign this border to the map grid
pMapGrid.Border = pSimpleMapGridBorder
```

A simple map grid border

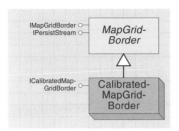

A calibrated map grid border is composed of a graduated band defining the edge of the map grid.

The *CalibratedMapGridBorder* coclass encapsulates the functionality required to draw a map grid outline composed of a graduated band.

ICalibratedMapGridBorder : IUnknown	Provides access to members that control the calibrated map grid border.
■━■ Alternating: Boolean	Indicates if the border pattern alternates across the width of the border.
■━■ BackgroundColor: IColor	The background color of the border pattern.
■━■ BorderWidth: Double	The width of the border in points.
■━■ ForegroundColor: IColor	The foreground color of the border pattern.
■━■ Interval: Double	The interval between border patterns in points.

You can use the *ICalibratedMapGridBorder* interface to set or retrieve the properties of a calibrated map grid border, such as the foreground and background color of the pattern, the interval of the pattern, the background color of the band, and the width of the border.

If you want the pattern to alternate in two bands across the width of the border, set the *Alternating* property to *True*. Setting this property to *False* will produce a border with a single band of the pattern.

The code below illustrates how you can create a calibrated map grid border.

```
'Create a calibrated map grid border
Dim pCalibratedBorder As ICalibratedMapGridBorder
Set pCalibratedBorder = New CalibratedMapGridBorder

'Set ICalibratedMapGridBorder properties
pCalibratedBorder.BackgroundColor = BuildRGb(255, 255, 255)
pCalibratedBorder.ForegroundColor = BuildRGb(0, 0, 0)
pCalibratedBorder.BorderWidth = 10
pCalibratedBorder.Interval = 72
pCalibratedBorder.Alternating = True   'Double alternating border

'Assign this border to the map grid
pMapGrid.Border = pCalibratedBorder
```

A calibrated map grid border

The interval of the pattern on the band is in points and page units. If you want to compute your border intervals in map units, you can use a *DisplayTransformation* to convert your interval from map units to page units. You can convert these to points, considering that there are 72 points to an inch.

For more information on using *DisplayTransformation*, see Chapter 5, 'Displaying graphics'.

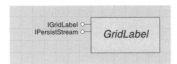

IGridLabel ○—
IPersistStream ○—   *GridLabel*

A grid label governs the way a map grid is labeled along the borders.

A grid label object is associated with every map grid object and provides the functionality required to draw labels around the map grid.

IGridLabel : IUnknown	Provides access to members that control the way a map grid is labeled.
▄— Applies (in grid: IMapGrid) : Boolean	Indicates if this grid label can be used with the specified map grid.
▄—▄ Color: IColor	The color of the grid label.
▄— DisplayName: String	The display name for the type of grid label.
▄—▄ EditObject: IUnknown Pointer	The interface to an object that can be edited with a property sheet. The object is either the grid label itself or a single editable property.
▄—▄ Font: Font	The font used by the grid label.
▄—▄ LabelAlignment (in axis: esriGridAxisEnum) : Boolean	Indicates if the grid label is horizontal (true) or vertical (false) on the specified axis.
▄—▄ LabelOffset: Double	The offset of the grid label from the border in points.
◄— Draw (in labelValue: Double, in Location: IPoint, in axis: esriGridAxisEnum, in Display: IDisplay)	Draws a label on the specified grid axis.
◄— Preview (in hDC: Long, in rectangle: tagRECT)	Draws a preview of the grid label into the specified hdc.
◄— QueryTextExtent (in labelValue: Double, in Location: IPoint, in axis: esriGridAxisEnum, in Display: IDisplay, Extent: IEnvelope)	Determines the extent of a label's text on the specified grid axis.

Grid	Label	DisplayName
Graticule	DMSLabel	Degrees Minutes Seconds
Measured-Grid	FormattedLabel	Formatted
	MixedFontLabel	Mixed Font
	ButtonTabStyle	Button Tabs
Index-Grid	RoundedTabStyle	Rounded Tabs
	ContinuousTabStyle	Continuous Tabs
	BackgroundTabStyle	Filled Background

The *IGridLabel* interface holds properties common to all types of grid labels. Not all grid labels can be used with all types of grids. The *Applies* property of *IGridLabel* returns *True* if the grid label can be used with the grid that you pass in as argument. The table to the left lists the types of labels that can be used with each grid type.

Using the *IGridLabel::DisplayName* property, you can list the type of label that the *IGridLabel* interface is pointing to. The strings returned for the various label types are also listed in the table to the left.

You can control the vertical or horizontal orientation of the labels along each of the four sides of the grid using the *IGridLabel::LabelAlignment* property. You specify which axis you are setting the property for using an *esriGridAxisEnum* enumeration.

Enumeration esriGridAxisEnum	Map grid axes.
0 - esriGridAxisNone	No axis.
1 - esriGridAxisTop	Top axis.
2 - esriGridAxisBottom	Bottom axis.
3 - esriGridAxisLeft	Left axis.
4 - esriGridAxisRight	Right axis.

Here's how you would populate the properties exposed by *IGridLabel* for a newly created *GridLabel*:

```
' Create grid label
Dim pGridLabel as IGridLabel
Set pGridLabel = New DMSGridLabel

' Set font and color
Dim pFont As IFontDisp
Set pFont = New StdFont
pFont.Name = "Arial"
pFont.Size = 24
pGridLabel.Font = pFont
pGridLabel.Color = BuildRGB(0, 0, 0)
```

ArcMap

```
'Specify Vertical Labels
pGridLabel.LabelAlignment(esriGridAxisLeft) = False
pGridLabel.LabelAlignment(esriGridAxisRight) = False
pGridLabel.LabelOffset = 6
```

You would then set the properties specific to the type of grid label you are creating. You would associate the newly created grid label to the grid using the grid's *IMapGrid::LabelFormat* property:

```
pMapGrid.LabelFormat = pGridLabel
```

IGridLabel::QueryTextExtent is used to check for labeling conflicts by ArcMap. The *IGridLabel::EditObject* method is used in the *MapGrid* property pages. It returns an interface that determines which dialog box is brought up when a user clicks Additional Properties under the Labels tab. The interfaces returned for each of the label types are listed in the table on the left.

Grid label	Edit object returned
DMSGridLabel	IDMSGridLabel
FormattedGridLabel	INumberFormat
MixedFontGridLabel	IMixedFontGridLabel
IndexFontGridLabel	IIndexGridTabStyle

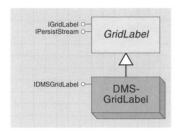

The *DMSGridLabel* coclass is used to label a map grid using degrees, minutes, and seconds.

A DMS grid label labels the map grid using degrees, minutes, and seconds. You can use this coclass to label graticules.

You can use a standard label to create a DMS label with the degrees, minutes, and seconds on the same line. A stacked label has the minutes stacked over the seconds, with both in smaller font size.

IDMSGridLabel : IUnknown	Provides access to members that control the DMS Grid Label.
■—■ LabelType: esriDMSGridLabelType	The type of the DMS grid label.
■—■ LatLonFormat: ILatLonFormat	The format with which the latitudes and longitudes are displayed.
■—■ MinutesColor: IColor	The color used to display the minutes.
■—■ MinutesFont: Font	The font used to display the minutes.
■—■ SecondsColor: IColor	The color used to display the seconds.
■—■ SecondsFont: Font	The font used to display the seconds.
■—■ ShowZeroMinutes: Boolean	Indicates if zero minutes are shown.
■—■ ShowZeroSeconds: Boolean	Indicates if zero seconds are shown.

IDMSGridLabel provides access to the font, color, and format information required to create a DMS grid label. The *LabelType* property can be set using the *esriDMSGridLabelType* enumeration, which is listed below. At ArcGIS 8.1, only the *esriDMSGridLabelStandard* and *esriDMSGridLabelStacked* values have been implemented.

Enumeration esriDMSGridLabelType	DMS grid label type options.
0 - esriDMSGridLabelStandard	Standard.
1 - esriDMSGridLabelStacked	Minutes stacked over seconds.
2 - esriDMSGridLabelDD	Decimal degrees.
3 - esriDMSGridLabelDM	Decimal minutes.
4 - esriDMSGridLabelDS	Decimal seconds.

The following code demonstrates how to create a DMS grid label:

```
'Create a DMS grid label
Dim pDMSLabel As IDMSGridLabel
Set pDMSLabel = New DMSGridLabel

'Set IDMSGridLabel properties
pDMSLabel.LabelType = esriDMSGridLabelStandard
pDMSLabel.ShowZeroMinutes = True
pDMSLabel.ShowZeroSeconds = True

Dim pLatLonFormat As ILatLonFormat
Set pLatLonFormat = New LatLonFormat
pLatLonFormat.ShowDirections = True
pDMSLabel.LatLonFormat = pLatLonFormat

Dim pFont As IFontDisp
Set pFont = New StdFont
pFont.Bold = False
pFont.Name = "Arial"
pFont.Italic = False
pFont.Underline = False
pFont.Size = 8
pDMSLabel.MinutesFont = pFont
pDMSLabel.MinutesColor = BuildRGB(0, 0, 0)
pDMSLabel.SecondsFont = pFont
pDMSLabel.SecondsColor = BuildRGB(0, 0, 0)
```

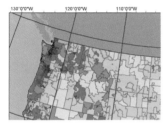

DMS grid label set to esriDMSGridLabelStandard

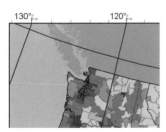

DMS grid label set to esriDMSGridLabelStacked

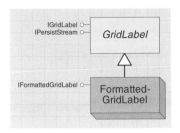

A formatted grid label uses any of the number format coclasses that support INumberFormat *to label the map grid.*

For more information on these classes, refer to the ArcMap number format objects topic in this chapter.

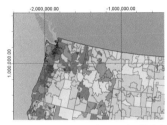

A measured grid with formatted grid labels

The *FormattedGridLabel* coclass makes use of one of the coclasses that inherits from the *NumberFormat* abstract class to create the grid labels.

IFormattedGridLabel : IUnknown	**Provides access to members controlling the number format of a grid label.**
■━■ Format: INumberFormat	*The format used to display the numbers in the grid label.*

This interface has a *Format* property that takes an *INumberFormat* interface. The following code illustrates the creation of a formatted grid label:

```
'Create the label
Dim pFormattedGridLabel As IFormattedGridLabel
Set pFormattedGridLabel = New FormattedGridLabel

'Set IFormattedGridLabel properties
Dim pNumericFormat As INumericFormat
Set pNumericFormat = New NumericFormat
pNumericFormat.AlignmentOption = esriAlignRight
pNumericFormat.RoundingOption = esriRoundNumberOfDecimals
pNumericFormat.RoundingValue = 2
pNumericFormat.ShowPlusSign = False
pNumericFormat.UseSeparator = True
pNumericFormat.ZeroPad = True
pFormattedGridLabel.Format = pNumericFormat
```

ArcMap

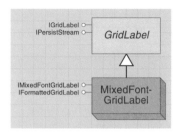

A mixed font grid label uses two fonts to display the label. It also uses a number format to format the label string.

Use the *MixedFontGridLabel* coclass to label map grids in two fonts and in the format specified using the *IFormattedGridLabel* interface.

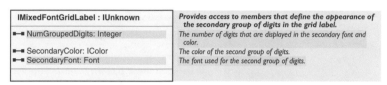

IMixedFontGridLabel : IUnknown	Provides access to members that define the appearance of the secondary group of digits in the grid label.
■← NumGroupedDigits: Integer	The number of digits that are displayed in the secondary font and color.
■← SecondaryColor: IColor	The color of the second group of digits.
■← SecondaryFont: Font	The font used for the second group of digits.

The *IMixedFontGridLabel::NumberOfDigits* property determines how the two fonts are applied to the label string. The last n digits of the label—where n is the number assigned as the *NumberOfDigits*—are displayed in the secondary font and color. The remaining digits are displayed in the primary font and color.

The primary font and color are set using *IGridLabel::Font* and *IGridLabel::Color*. The secondary font and color are set using *IMixedFontGridLabel::SecondaryFont* and *IMixedFontGridLabel::SecondaryColor*.

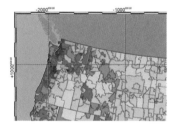

A measured grid with mixed font labels

The following code illustrates how you can create a mixed font grid label:

```
'Create the label
Dim pMixedFontLabel As IMixedFontGridLabel
Set pMixedFontLabel = New MixedFontGridLabel

'Set IMixedFontGridLabel properties
Dim pFont As IFontDisp
Set pFont = New StdFont
pFont.Name = "Arial"
pFont.Size = 12
pMixedFontLabel.SecondaryFont = pFont
pMixedFontLabel.SecondaryColor = BuildRGB(0, 0, 0)
pMixedFontLabel.NumGroupedDigits = 6 '-1 if not being used

'Set IFormattedGridLabel properties
Dim pFormattedGridLabel As IFormattedGridLabel
Set pFormattedGridLabel = pMixedFontLabel
Dim pNumericFormat As INumericFormat
Set pNumericFormat = New NumericFormat
pNumericFormat.AlignmentOption = esriAlignRight
pNumericFormat.RoundingOption = esriRoundNumberOfDecimals
pNumericFormat.RoundingValue = 2
pNumericFormat.ShowPlusSign = True
pNumericFormat.UseSeparator = False
pNumericFormat.ZeroPad = True
```

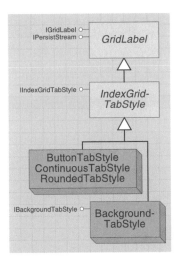

An index grid tab style governs the way an index grid is labeled.

Button tab style

Continuous tab style

Rounded tab style

The index grid tab style coclasses provide the means to label an index grid. These coclasses are described below.

IIndexGridTabStyle : IUnknown	Provides access to members that control the way an index grid's labels are drawn.
■─■ ForegroundColor: IColor	The foreground color of the tab.
■─■ OutlineColor: IColor	The outline color of the tab.
■─■ Thickness: Double	The thickness of the tab in points.
◄── PrepareDraw (in labelValue: String, in tabWidthPage: Double, in axis: esriGridAxisEnum)	Sets up the tab for drawing.

The *IIndexGridTabStyle* interface provides access to the color and thickness of the index grid's labels. The *PrepareDraw* method should be called before *IGridLabel::Draw* is called on index grid tab style labels.

You can create an index grid tab style label using a coclass that inherits from *IndexGridTabStyle*, as outlined in the following examples. The code illustrates how to populate the properties exposed by the *IIndexGridTabStyle* interface after you create the label:

```
'Set IIndexGridTabStyle properties
pIndexGridTabStyle.ForegroundColor = BuildRGB(255, 190, 190)
pIndexGridTabStyle.OutlineColor = BuildRGB(110, 110, 110)
pIndexGridTabStyle.Thickness = 20
```

Button tab style labels are rectangular buttons, each the width of the grid cell that it borders. The following code shows you how to create a button tab style grid label.

```
'Create the label
Dim pIndexGridTabStyle As IIndexGridTabStyle
Set pIndexGridTabStyle = New ButtonTabStyle
```

Continuous tab style labels form a continuous band around the map grid. The example below shows how you can create a label of this kind:

```
Dim pIndexGridTabStyle As IIndexGridTabStyle
Set pIndexGridTabStyle = New ContinuousTabStyle
```

Rounded tab style labels are rounded rectangles; each one is the width of the grid cell it borders. Using the example below, you can create your rounded tab style grid label.

```
Dim pIndexGridTabStyle As IIndexGridTabStyle
Set pIndexGridTabStyle = New RoundedTabStyle
```

ArcMap

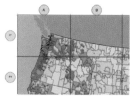

esriBackgroundTabRound

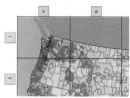

esriBackgroundTabRectangle

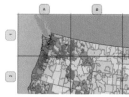

esriBackgroundTabRoundedRectangle

A background tab style labels the index grid using square, round, or rounded-square boxes. These boxes are centered outside the grid cells they border.

IBackgroundTabStyle : IUnknown	Provides access to members that control background tab style grid labels.
▪━■ BackgroundType: esriBackgroundTabType	The type of the background tab style.

IBackgroundTabStyle has a *BackgroundType* property you can use to determine the shape of the boxes that the *BackGroundTabStyle* label uses.

Enumeration esriBackgroundTabType	Types of background tabs for index grids.
0 - esriBackgroundTabRound	Round.
1 - esriBackgroundTabRectangle	Rectangle.
2 - esriBackgroundTabRoundedRectangle	Rounded rectangle.

The example below illustrates how you can create a background tab style label that uses round boxes to label a map grid.

```
Dim pIndexGridTabStyle As IIndexGridTabStyle
Set pIndexGridTabStyle = New BackgroundTabStyle

'Set IBackgroundTabStyle properties
Dim pBackgroundTabStyle As IBackgroundTabStyle
Set pBackgroundTabStyle = pIndexGridTabStyle
pBackgroundTabStyle.BackgroundType = esriBackgroundTabRound
```

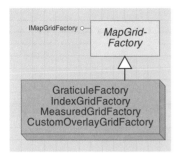

A map grid factory lets you quickly create a map grid with default properties.

You can use the *MapGridFactory* coclasses to quickly create map grids. The map grids created will have default properties applied.

Use one of the inheriting coclasses—*GraticuleFactory, IndexGridFactory, MeasuredGridFactory,* or *CustomOverlayGridFactory*—to create the respective map grid.

IMapGridFactory : IUnknown	*Provides access to members of the map grid factory.*
■— Name: String	*The name of the map grid class.*
◄— Create (in MapFrame: IMapFrame) : IMapGrid	*Creates a map grid.*

IMapGridFactory::Create takes a map frame as the argument and returns an *IMapGrid* interface to a newly created map grid. The map grid has default properties. This is similar to creating a map grid and using *IMapGrid::SetDefault* to assign properties to it. *IMapGridFactory::Name* returns the name of the map grid class to which the map grid factory object belongs. The following code shows you how to create a graticule using a map grid factory:

```
'Get the map frame for selected data frame
Dim pMap As IMap
Dim pMxDoc As IMxDocument
Dim pGraphicsContainer As IGraphicsContainer
Dim pMapFrame As IMapFrame
Set pMxDoc = ThisDocument
Set pMap = pMxDoc.FocusMap
Set pGraphicsContainer = pMxDoc.PageLayout
Set pMapFrame = pGraphicsContainer.FindFrame(pMap)
'Create a graticule
Dim pMapGrid As IMapGrid
Dim pMapGridFactory As IMapGridFactory
Set pMapGridFactory = New GraticuleFactory
Set pMapGrid = pMapGridFactory.Create(pMapFrame)
```

ArcMap

ADDING A MAP GRID TO A DATA FRAME

After creating your map grid, you can use the *IMapGrids::AddMapGrid* method to add it to the data frame. You can get the map frame as outlined in the previous example and *QI* it for the *IMapGrids* interface. If you want the change to be immediately apparent, refresh the active view. The following code illustrates this.

```
'Get the IMapGrids and IActiveView interfaces
Dim pMapGrids As IMapGrids
Set pMapGrids = pMapFrame
Set pMapGrid = pMapGrids.MapGrid(0)

Dim pActiveView As IActiveView
Set pActiveView = pMxDoc.PageLayout

pMapGrids.AddMapGrid pMapGrid   'Add map grid, and refresh active view
pActiveView.PartialRefresh esriViewBackground, Nothing, Nothing
```

REMOVING MAP GRIDS FROM A DATA FRAME

To remove map grids from a data frame, use *IMapGrids::DeleteMapGrid* as shown below.

```
Dim i As Long
Dim lCount As Long

lCount = m_pMapGrids.MapGridCount

For i = 0 To lCount - 1   'Delete all map grids
  'When you delete grid(0), then next grid becomes the new grid(0).
  Set pMapGrid = m_pMapGrids.MapGrid(0)
  m_pMapGrids.DeleteMapGrid pMapGrid
Next i

Set m_pActiveView = pMxDoc.ActiveView
m_pActiveView.PartialRefresh esriViewBackground, Nothing, Nothing
```

ArcMap number format objects

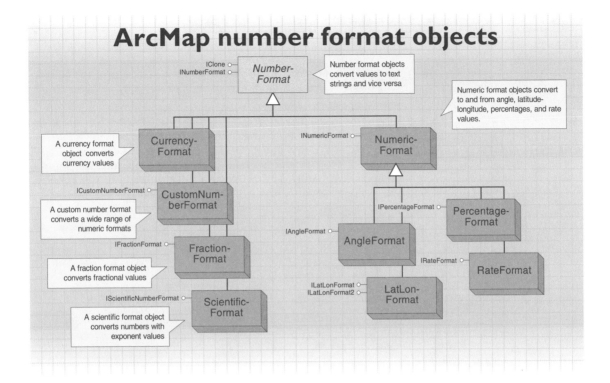

IClone ○—
INumberFormat ○— **Number-Format**

Number format objects convert values to text strings and vice versa

Numeric format objects convert to and from angle, latitude-longitude, percentages, and rate values.

INumericFormat ○— **Numeric-Format**

A currency format object converts currency values

ICustomNumberFormat ○— **CustomNumberFormat**

A currency format object converts currency values

Currency-Format

A custom number format converts a wide range of numeric formats

IFractionFormat ○— **Fraction-Format**

A fraction format object converts fractional values

IScientificNumberFormat ○— **Scientific-Format**

A scientific format object converts numbers with exponent values

IPercentageFormat ○— **Percentage-Format**

IAngleFormat ○— **AngleFormat**

IRateFormat ○— **RateFormat**

ILatLonFormat ○—
ILatLonFormat2 ○— **LatLon-Format**

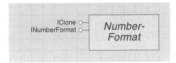

IClone ○—
INumberFormat ○— **Number-Format**

The number-format objects convert numerical values into strings and strings into numerical values using ValueToString and StringToValue methods. How this conversion takes place is normally dependent on the property settings of one or two other interfaces.

The *INumberFormat* interface exposes the two number-formatting methods (*ValueToString* and *StringToValue*) used by all the number format interfaces and coclasses.

INumberFormat : IUnknown	Provides access to members that format numbers.
← StringToValue (in str: String) : Double	Converts a formatted string to a numeric value.
← ValueToString (in Value: Double) : String	Converts a numeric value to a formatted string.

The *ValueToString* method transforms numerical values into a string. The *StringToValue* method returns numerical values from formatted strings, reversing the *ValueToString* operation.

The *ValueToString* method converts a numerical value into a formatted string. The string is formatted based on the property settings of the particular number-formatting interfaces used. For more information about property settings of number-formatting interfaces, refer to the number-formatting interface you're interested in later in this section. In some cases, the format produced by the *ValueToString* method depends on two interfaces' property settings. For example, *AngleFormat* uses *IAngleFormat* and *INumericFormat* to determine the formatting.

The *StringToValue* method converts a formatted string into a numerical value in the form of a *Double*. The string doesn't necessarily need to be formatted with the *ValueToString* method, but it does need to appear as if it were formatted with the associated interface's implementation of the *ValueToString* method. For more information, refer to the relevant number-formatting interface in which you're interested in the sections that follow.

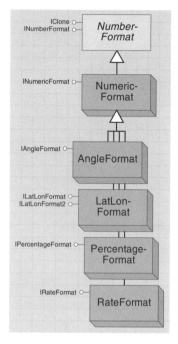

The following coclasses all support the INumericFormat *interface:*

AngleFormat

LatLonFormat

NumericFormat

PercentageFormat

RateFormat

The AngleFormat, LatLonFormat, PercentageFormat, *and* RateFormat *coclasses all support the* INumericFormat *interface as well as their own default interfaces (*IAngleFormat, ILatLonFormat, IPercentageFormat, *and* IRateFormat, *respectively).*

For each of the coclasses, the combination of properties on both interfaces is used to determine how numbers are formatted when using the ValueToString *and* StringToValue *methods from the associated* INumberFormat *interface.*

The format produced with the *NumericFormat* coclass object is determined solely by the *INumericFormat* interface property settings.

Formats produced with other coclasses that support *INumericFormat* depend on two interfaces' property settings: the *INumericFormat* interface as well as the implemented interface within the numeric format coclasses. This means that the *NumericFormat* coclass can be used to do general formatting of numbers (such as number of decimal places and plus sign), while the other coclasses that support *INumericFormat* can perform special formatting (such as rates, latitude/longitude, and percentages) by using a combination of *INumericFormat* and their own interface.

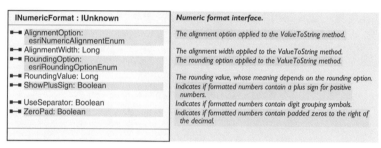

The *AlignmentOption* property sets or returns an option that tells the *ValueToString* method in the associated *INumberFormat* interface how to align formatted numbers. For example, the value "0.34", formatted as a string with an *AlignmentWidth* of 5, is returned as " 0.34" with an *AlignmentOption* of *esriAlignRight* and "0.34" with an *AlignmentOption* of *esriAlignLeft*.

The settings for *AlignmentOption* are as follows:

- With *esriAlignRight*, which is the default, numbers are aligned to the right. If the *AlignmentWidth* property is wider than the resulting formatted number, spaces are padded at the left to make the output *AlignmentWidth* characters wider.

- With *esriAlignLeft*, numbers are aligned to the left. No spaces are padded at the left or the right. If *AlignmentOption* is set to *esriAlignLeft*, the *AlignmentWidth* property is ignored. For both options, even if the *AlignmentWidth* is not sufficient to hold the formatted number, the number will not be truncated.

The *AlignmentWidth* property is used to set or return the width (the default is 12) of the resulting string produced by *ValueToString* from the associated *INumberFormat* interface.

If the *AlignmentOption* property is set to *esriAlignRight*, the formatted number will be *AlignmentWidth* characters wide; spaces will be padded to the left of the number as needed. If *AlignmentOption* is equal to *esriAlignLeft*, the *AlignmentWidth* property is ignored. The width includes plus signs and any decimal points. For example, +1,234.56 has a width of 9.

The *RoundingOption* property specifies how the *RoundingValue* property should be used to format a number using *ValueToString*. The two options are *esriRoundNumberOfDecimals,* which is the default, and *esriRoundNumberOfSignificantDigits.*

The *esriRoundNumberOfDecimals* option rounds values to the number of decimal places defined in the *RoundingValue* property. If *ZeroPad* is also set to *True*, decimal zeros are appended up to the number of places indicated in the *RoundingValue* property.

If *esriRoundNumberOfSignificantDigits* is used, then values are rounded to the number of significant digits indicated in the *RoundingValue* property.

To format numbers and express significant zeros at the right of the decimal, set *ZeroPad* to *True*. For example, the number 12.0345, formatted with a *RoundingValue*, is equal to 8, and *ZeroPad = True* becomes 12.034500, or simply 12.0345 if *ZeroPad = False*.

The *RoundingValue* property sets or returns the number of decimal places or significant digits to round a number to when the *ValueToString* method in the associated *INumberFormat* interface formats numbers. The default value is 6 for both rounding options.

The table below shows how the value of 123.456 is formatted as a string with various rounding settings.

Rounding option	Rounding value	ZeroPad	ValueToString result
esriRoundNumberOfDecimals	2	True	"123.46"
		False	"123.46"
	4	True	"123.4560"
		False	"123.456"
esriRoundNumberOfSignificantDigits	2	True	"120"
		False	"120"
	8	True	"123.45600"
		False	"123.456"

The *ShowPlusSign* property sets or returns a Boolean indicator that indicates whether or not a plus sign symbol (+) is to be prefixed to positive numbers when the *ValueToString* method in the associated *INumberFormat* interface is used.

The default value is *False*—positive numbers are formatted without a plus sign, and negative values are formatted with a minus sign (-). If this property is set to *True*, then positive numbers are formatted with a plus sign, and negatives behave as before. Zero values are never prefixed.

The *UseSeparator* property is used to specify whether to include a digit-grouping symbol when formatting numbers with the *ValueToString* method. *False* is the default, meaning that numbers are formatted without a digit-grouping symbol—for example, "1234567.89". However, if it is set to *True*, then a digit-grouping symbol is used as follows: "1,234,567.89". The formatting itself is determined using the current regional settings defined for the system at runtime. To change the sepa-

ArcMap

rator symbol or where the separator appears in the formatted number, change the settings on the Number tab of the Control Panel's Regional Settings applet.

ZeroPad is a Boolean property that states whether or not to pad zeros to the right of the decimal. If this property is left as the default value of *False*, then numbers will be formatted without padding decimal zeros. The last decimal digit (to the right of the decimal point) will be a nonzero digit. If set to *True*, however, zeros are appended to the right of the decimal point in accordance with the *RoundingValue* property.

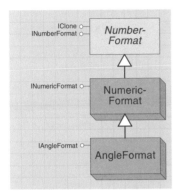

The angle format object is used for formatting numeric values that represent angles, such as 69°. It also allows the conversion between radians and degrees.

AngleFormat is the *IAngleFormat* interface coclass whose members determine how the *ValueToString* method in the associated *INumberFormat* interface formats numbers in an angular format.

IAngleFormat : IUnknown	Angle format interface.
■—■ AngleInDegrees: Boolean	*Indicates if the ValueToString argument is in degrees.*
■—■ DisplayDegrees: Boolean	*Indicates if the formatted number is an angle in degrees.*

The members in the *IAngleFormat* interface define how the *ValueToString* method in the associated *INumberFormat* interface formats numbers.

Use the *IAngleFormat* interface to format numbers that represent angles.

The *AngleInDegrees* property sets or returns whether the input angle represents degrees (*True*) or radians (*False*), which is the default value.

DisplayDegrees sets or returns whether the angle is displayed as degrees (*True*) or radians (*False*).

If the *AngleInDegrees* property is not set the same as the *DisplayDegrees* property (both of these are Boolean properties), a radian-to-degree or degree-to-radian conversion will take place when the *ValueToString* method formats the number. *AngleInDegrees* affects the *ValueToString* argument value. If the value is in degrees, then *AngleInDegrees* is set to *True*. If *AngleInDegrees* is *False*, the argument is assumed to be a radian value.

DisplayDegrees deals with the *ValueToString* result. If you want the resulting formatted number to be a degree value, set *DisplayDegrees* to *True*. A degree symbol (°) is also appended to the resulting formatted number. If *DisplayDegrees* is *False*, the formatted number is a radian value, and no degree symbol is appended.

The corresponding *StringToValue* method also uses these two properties. To obtain the numerical value that was used as a parameter to the *ValueToString* method, make sure the *AngleInDegrees* and *DisplayDegrees* properties are the same as they were when the *ValueToString* method was used. These settings may seem like they work in reverse when using the *StringToValue* method, but if you consider that *StringToValue* is intended to obtain numerical values from formatted strings, this makes more sense.

The *DisplayDegrees* property sets or returns an option that tells the *ValueToString* method in the associated *INumberFormat* interface whether or not the resulting formatted expression is in degrees or radians. If this property is set to *False,* the default, then the resulting format is a radian value, and a degree symbol is not appended. If the property is set to *True*, however, the resulting format is displayed as a degree value with a degree symbol appended to it.

ArcMap

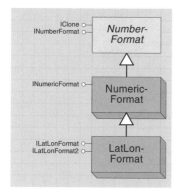

This LatLonFormat object formats numbers from decimal values to degrees, minutes, and seconds.

This *LatLonFormat* coclass formats numbers that represent latitude and longitude values. For example, the value 55.87 would be converted to the string '55°52'12"N'.

ILatLonFormat : IUnknown	Latitude/Longitude format interface.
→ IsLatitude: Boolean	Indicates if a formatted number is a latitude or not.
→ ShowDirections: Boolean	Indicates if a directional letter (N-S-E-W) is appended to the formatted number.
→ ShowZeroMinutes: Boolean	Indicates if zero minutes are included in formatted output.
→ ShowZeroSeconds: Boolean	Indicates if zero seconds are included in formatted output.
← GetDMS (in Value: Double, out degrees: Long, out minutes: Long, out seconds: Double)	Returns the degrees, minutes, and seconds for a lat/lon number.

Use the *ILatLonFormat* interface to format numbers that represent latitude or longitude. The members in the *ILatLonFormat* interface define how the *ValueToString* method in the associated *INumberFormat* interface formats numbers.

The *LatLonFormat* coclass also inherits the *INumericFormat* interface, which means both of these interfaces' properties determine how numbers are formatted. *GetDMS* is a utility method that returns the degrees, minutes, and seconds for a given latitude or longitude value. To use it you should pass in the input decimal degree value and also pass in three double values representing the output degrees, minutes, and seconds that will be populated by the method. The following code demonstrates this.

```
Sub LatLonTest()
 Dim pLatLonFormat As ILatLonFormat
 Set pLatLonFormat = New LatLonFormat

 dValue = 45.253
 Dim lDegrees As Long, lMinutes As Long, dSeconds As Double

 ' The GetDMS method calculates degrees, minutes and seconds
 pLatLonFormat.GetDMS dValue, lDegrees, lMinutes, dSeconds

 MsgBox lDegrees & " degrees" & vbNewLine & lMinutes & _
   "minutes" & vbNewLine & dSeconds & " seconds", , "DMS(" & dValue & ")"
End Sub
```

The *IsLatitude* property specifies whether subsequent values represent latitude (*True*) or longitude (*False*). If the value of the property is set to *False* and the *ShowDirections* property is set to *True*, then when the *ValueToString* method from the associated *INumberFormat* interface is used, a directional letter designation of either E (for positive values) or W (for negative values) is appended to the format. An example is "23°E". Also, when used with the *IDMSGridLabel* interface, it sets an indicator to specify that latitude labels will be placed on top of the data frame border, and longitude labels will be placed to the left of the data frame border.

If *True,* the directional letter will be either N or S; with *IDMSGridLabel,* latitude labels are placed below the data frame border, and longitude labels are placed to the right.

ShowDirections sets or returns a Boolean value specifying whether or not direction is shown with a letter (N, S, E, or W). It is useful only with the *ValueToString* method in the associated *INumberFormat* interface. The default value is *False.*

As an alternative, the *ShowPlusSign* property from *INumericFormat* can be used to show similar information since the *LatLonFormat* coclass also supports this interface.

The *ShowZeroMinutes* and *ShowZeroSeconds* properties simply set or return a Boolean value to specify whether or not a zero value in the minutes or seconds location is expressed when the *ValueToString* method in the associated *INumberFormat* interface formats numbers. For both properties, nonzero values are always expressed in the format. If *ShowZeroSeconds* is *True,* then zero values in the minutes location are also shown, regardless of the *ShowZeroMinutes* setting.

As an example, if *ShowZeroSeconds* is *True,* then *ValueToString* will return 17°0'0 from an input value of 17.0.

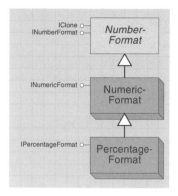

The percentage-format object formats values that represent percentages. For example, 56 is formatted to "56%", with an optional conversion from a fraction to a percentage, for example, 0.5 to "56%".

The *PercentageFormat* coclass allows the conversion between values and strings that represent percentages. The *PercentageFormat* coclass also supports the *INumericFormat* interface, so a combination of these interfaces' properties determines how numbers are formatted.

IPercentageFormat : IUnknown	Percentage format interface.
▪━ AdjustPercentage: Boolean	Indicates if ValueToString agument is treated as a fraction or a percentage.

The *AdjustPercentage* property allows the conversion to and from fractions. If it is set to *False*, the default, then the arguments to both the *ValueToString* and *StringToValue* methods are assumed to be in percentage format already. For *ValueToString* a percentage symbol is simply appended to the value, and for *StringToValue* this is removed. If this property is set to *True*, however, the argument to the *ValueToString* method is treated as a fraction. The value is multiplied by 100, and a percent symbol is appended. For *StringToValue,* the output is converted to a fraction (from a percentage)—it is divided by 100, and any percentage symbol is removed. This is demonstrated in the following code:

```
Sub PercentageFormatExample()
  Dim pPercentageFormat As IPercentageFormat
  Dim dValue As Double, sV2S As String, dS2V As Double
  Dim pNumberFormat As INumberFormat

  Set pPercentageFormat = New PercentageFormat
  Set pNumberFormat = pPercentageFormat

  dValue = 0.5 ' Set the input value

  'First try with a conversion between fractions and percentages
  pPercentageFormat.AdjustPercentage = True

  sV2S = pNumberFormat.ValueToString(dValue)
  dS2V = pNumberFormat.StringToValue(sV2S)

  MsgBox "ValueToString(" & dValue & ") = '" & sV2S & "'" & _
    vbNewLine & "StringToValue('" & sV2S & "') = " & dS2V, , _
    "PercentageFormat - AdjustPercentage = " & _
    pPercentageFormat.AdjustPercentage

  'Now try without converting between fractions and percentages
  pPercentageFormat.AdjustPercentage = False

  sV2S = pNumberFormat.ValueToString(dValue)
  dS2V = pNumberFormat.StringToValue(sV2S)

  MsgBox "ValueToString(" & dValue & ") = '" & sV2S & "'" & _
    vbNewLine & "StringToValue('" & sV2S & "') = " & dS2V, , _
    "PercentageFormat - AdjustPercentage = " & _
    pPercentageFormat.AdjustPercentage
End Sub
```

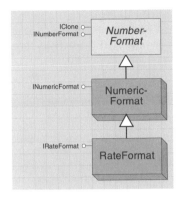

The rate-format object allows the formatting of values that represent rates. Using the associated ValueToString method on INumericFormat, it can be used to multiply the value by the RateFactor and append the RateString.

The *RateFormat* coclass and the *IRateFormat* interface format numeric values according to a given rate factor and string suffix.

IRateFormat : IUnknown	Rate format interface.
■–■ RateFactor: Double	The rate factor applied to the ValueToSring and StringToValue methods.
■–■ RateString: String	The label appended to the formatted rate number.

The interface's two properties (*RateString* and *RateFactor*) determine how the formatting takes place when using the *ValueToString* and *StringToValue* methods of the associated *INumberFormat* interface. This coclass supports *INumericFormat* so its members are also used in the formatting process.

When using the *ValueToString* method, any string defined in the *RateString* property (the default value is *Null*) is appended to the method's input value. Also, the value in the *RateFactor* property (the default value is 1000) is divided into the *ValueToString* argument value. For example, *ValueToString (300)* with a *RateFactor* of 3 and a *RateString* of "loaves" would return a formatted string of "100 loaves".

The corresponding *StringToValue* method also uses both these properties. The value from the input string is multiplied by the value in the *RateFactor* property when *StringToValue* converts the number back. Also, if set, the *RateString* is stripped from the result.

CurrencyFormat is a coclass that formats numbers to look like a currency. For example, the number 123456.789, when formatted with *CurrencyFormat* (default U.S. English regional settings), looks like $123,456.79. Note that the formatted number is rounded to the nearest cent. Negative numbers are typically depicted inside parentheses—for example, a negative number of the same value would be formatted as ($123,456.79).

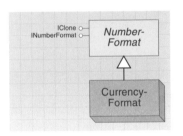

The CurrencyFormat coclass has no interface of its own—it simply uses the ValueToString and StringToValue methods from INumberFormat to convert between values representing currency and formatted strings. The formatting is taken from your system settings.

To format numbers as currency, create a *CurrencyFormat* object and use the *ValueToString* method.

CurrencyFormat does not have an *ICurrencyFormat* interface because there are no member properties to set. To use it, define an object as an *INumberFormat* and set it to a new *CurrencyFormat*. Numbers are formatted according to the current regional settings defined for the system at runtime. To change the way currency numbers are formatted, change the settings on the Currency tab of the Control panel's Regional Settings applet.

ArcMap

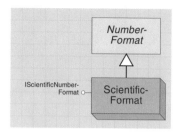

The scientific-format object allows the conversion of values to and from scientific (exponential) notation, for example, 19730 to "1.97e+006".

Use the *ScientificFormat* coclass when you want to express numbers in a scientific format, for example, to create a table of empirical values. *ScientificFormat* expresses numbers as a power of 10. For example, the value 1500 in scientific format to 3 significant digits is the expression 1.50e+003, where the number before "e" is the mantissa, and the number after "e" is the power of 10, or exponent. The meaning of this expression is 1.50 x 10^3. The number of digits in the exponent (+003) cannot be changed—it is always a plus or minus sign and 3 digits.

The *DecimalPlaces* property sets or returns a long representing the number of decimals to show in the mantissa. Since all digits in a scientific format expression are significant, set the *DecimalPlaces* property to the number of desired significant digits minus 1. For example, to express the value 1 to 3 significant digits (1.00e+000), set *DecimalPlaces* to 2. The default value is 6.

The power behind the scientific format expresses significant zeros. For example, a 1000-yard distance measured with a bicycle odometer may only be accurate to the nearest 10th mile (176 yards). In this case, 1000 is only significant to one place and should be expressed as 1 x 10^3. On the other hand, you may know the measurement is precise to the last zero (perhaps you carefully measured this distance with a yardstick)—in this case, you should express the measurement as 1.000 x 10^3.

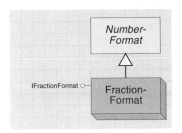

The fraction-format object converts from decimal values to fractions (using ValueToString) and vice versa (using StringToValue).

Use the *IFractionFormat* interface to either convert from a decimal fraction to a formatted fraction (using the *ValueToString* method) or to evaluate a formatted fraction as a decimal (using the *StringToValue* method). Basically, this means that *ValueToString* could convert an input of 0.75 to a string such as "3/4", and 2.5 could become "2 1/2", while *StringToValue* would do the reverse.

The properties *FractionOption* and *FractionFactor* give you more control over how the *ValueToString* conversion takes place because they allow you to use the *FractionFactor* to specify what denominator should be used for the output. The way in which this *FractionFactor* is used depends on which of the two settings (*esriFractionOptionEnum*) is used for the *FractionOption* property.

The default option for *FractionOption* is *esriSpecifyFractionDigits*, which means that the *FractionFactor* property specifies the maximum number of digits to which the numerator or denominator is calculated. If the value passed to *ValueToString* evaluates a fraction whose numerator or denominator has more digits than specified in the *FractionFactor* property, the formatted string will be rounded to represent the closest fraction to the number of digits specified. As an example, the fraction 893/1234 returns a decimal value of 0.723662884927066. *ValueToString* can format this decimal number back to "893/1234"; however, the maximum number of decimal places to be used in the output fraction is three (by default). Therefore, by default this returns a formatted result of 474/655 because this is the closest three-digit fraction to the decimal value. To calculate all four digits in the denominator and return to the original fraction, *FractionFactor* needs to be set to a value of 4. The caveat here is that the higher the *FractionFactor* setting, the more processing time it will take to figure out the fraction.

Alternatively, if *FractionOption* is set to *esriSpecifyFractionDenominator*, then the *FractionFactor* property value is used to explicitly specify the denominator. Since the *ValueToString* method doesn't have to calculate the denominator, the result is returned very quickly. For example, when using *esriSpecifyFractionDenominator*, if the *FractionFactor* is set to 8, then the resulting fraction would be given in eighths.

```
Public Sub FractionDemo()
  Dim pFraForm As IFractionFormat
  Dim pNumForm As INumberFormat

  Set pFraForm = New FractionFormat
  Set pNumForm = pFraForm

  'Specify denominator explicitly
  pFraForm.FractionOption = esriSpecifyFractionDenominator

  pFraForm.FractionFactor = 8 'Use eighths
  MsgBox pNumForm.ValueToString(0.75) 'Shows "6/8"
```

ArcMap

```
pFraForm.FractionFactor = 4 'Use fourths
MsgBox pNumForm.ValueToString(0.75) 'Shows "3/4"

pFraForm.FractionFactor = 4  'Use fourths
'Still shows "3/4" because result is rounded
MsgBox pNumForm.ValueToString(0.85)
```

End Sub

The result will be rounded to fit the denominator specified, as both 0.75 and 0.85 become "3/4" in the above example.

When using *StringToValue,* neither the *FractionOption* nor the *FractionFactor* properties are used; instead, a straightforward evaluation of the fraction is carried out. For example, "5/8" returns a value of 0.625, and "6 3/4" returns 6.75.

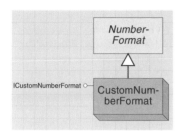

ICustomNumberFormat ○— CustomNumberFormat

The custom-number-format object and its default interface allow numeric values to be formatted as strings. It works by pattern matching and allows conversions, such as changing ValueToString(12345678.9) to "$12,345,678.90 big ones".

Use the *ICustomNumberFormat* interface to format numbers in a customized way using the *FormatString* member property. The associated *INumberFormat*'s *ValueToString* method is used to return a string formatted to fit whatever the *FormatString* property is set to. The *StringToValue* method reverses this formatting. The formatting is done based on the following sets of characters in the *FormatString*:

0   Digit placeholder. Displays a digit or a zero. If the expression has a digit in the position where the 0 appears in the format string, display it; otherwise, display a zero in that position. If the number has fewer digits than there are zeros (on either side of the decimal) in the format expression, display leading or trailing zeros. If the number has more digits to the right of the decimal separator than there are zeros to the right of the decimal separator in the format expression, round the number to as many decimal places as there are zeros. If the number has more digits to the left of the decimal separator than there are zeros to the left of the decimal separator in the format expression, display the extra digits without modification.

Digit placeholder. Displays a digit or nothing. If the expression has a digit in the position where the # appears in the format string, display it; otherwise, display nothing in that position. This symbol works like the 0-digit placeholder, except that leading and trailing zeros aren't displayed if the number has the same or fewer digits than there are # characters on either side of the decimal separator in the format expression.

.   Decimal placeholder. In some locales, a comma is used as the decimal separator. The decimal placeholder determines how many digits are displayed to the left and right of the decimal separator. If the format expression contains only number signs to the left of this symbol, numbers smaller than 1 begin with a decimal separator. To display a leading zero displayed with fractional numbers, use 0 as the first-digit placeholder to the left of the decimal separator. The actual character used as a decimal placeholder in the formatted output depends on the number format recognized by your system.

,   Thousand separator. In some locales, a period is used as a thousand separator. The thousand separator separates thousands from hundreds within a number that has four or more places to the left of the decimal separator. Standard use of the thousand separator is specified if the format contains a thousand separator surrounded by digit placeholders (0 or #). The actual character used as the thousand separator in the formatted output depends on the number format recognized by your system.

The actual characters used as decimal placeholders and thousand's separators in the formatted output depend on the number format recognized by the system at runtime; thus, it is dependent on your regional settings. To change the way numbers are formatted, change the settings on the Numbers tab of the Control panel's Regional Settings applet.

'ABC'   Literal string. You can place literal strings on either side of numeric placeholders. For example, you can define a format expression as, "The formatted number is: ###,###.#0".

All of the above can be combined to produce complex results. For example, using *ValueToString* with a value of 12345678.9 and a *FormatString* of '$#,###,###.#0 bucks', the output should be "$12,345,678.90 bucks".

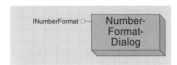

The Number Format dialog box gives a graphical user interface for setting up the number format objects in the above sections.

A *NumberFormatDialog* represents a graphical interface on the properties of the above interfaces. It allows you to set up one of the number format objects, which you may then use to format numeric values. The dialog box can be seen as a helper object since you are not required to use it, and you may wish to create your own VBA form to present the options to users in a different way.

The dialog box itself is split into two parts. On the left side is a list of all the categories available, each of which equates to roughly one of the *NumberFormat* coclasses. The right side shows the user interface particular to the category selected on the left-hand side.

For example, when *RateFormat* is selected from the left-hand side, the right side displays a dropdown box that allows the user to select and type in the factor (*IRateFactor::RateFactor*), and a text box where they can optionally type in a suffix (*IRateFactor::RateString*). Additionally, because the *RateFactor* coclass also supports *INumericFormat,* the Numeric Options button is also shown. If this button is pressed, then a second modal dialog box is displayed that allows access to the properties from *INumericFormat,* such as *ShowPlusSign, RoundingValue,* and *RoundingOption.*

The Number Format dialog box is used within ArcMap in several places, including:

Symbol property page: FormatLabels option in the ClassBreaksRenderer section

Scale bar property page: Number Format button in the Numbers & Marks tab

Layer property page: Format button in the Fields tab

It can also be used by developers to present number-formatting options to users.

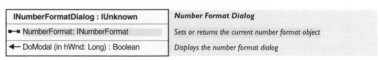

INumberFormatDialog : IUnknown	Number Format Dialog
▪━ NumberFormat: INumberFormat	*Sets or returns the current number format object*
◄━ DoModal (in hWnd: Long) : Boolean	*Displays the number format dialog*

The only interface supported by the *NumberFormatDialog* is *INumberFormatDialog*, which has one method, *DoModal*, and one read–write property, *NumberFormat*.

DoModal displays the dialog box on top of the window specified by the *hWnd* parameter. The method returns a Boolean to indicate which button was clicked when the dialog box was closed. *True* is returned if OK was clicked, and *False* is returned if either Cancel or the Close button was clicked. Because the dialog box is displayed modally, code execution does not continue until the dialog box has been closed.

The *NumberFormat* property allows you to set or get the *NumberFormat* object used by the dialog box. This has two uses: setting the *NumberFormat* object prior to calling *DoModal* (telling the dialog box which type of format object should be shown in the display initializing any settings) and getting the number-format object returned from the dialog box.

```
Private Sub UIButtonControl1_Click()
    Dim pApp As IApplication
    Dim pNumFrmDialog As INumberFormatDialog
    Dim pNumerForm As INumericFormat
    Dim pNumForm As INumberFormat
    Dim hWnd As OLE_HANDLE
```

```
' Get the application's window handle
hWnd = Application.hWnd
' Create a new NumberFormatDialog
Set pNumFrmDialog = New NumberFormatDialog
' Create a new NumericFormat
Set pNumerForm = New NumericFormat

' Setup the NumericFormat
With pNumerForm
  .RoundingOption = esriRoundNumberOfDecimals
  .RoundingValue = 3
  .ShowPlusSign = True
  .UseSeparator = True
End With

' Set the NumberFormatDialog's NumberFormat property
pNumFrmDialog.NumberFormat = pNumerForm

' Open the dialog on the application's window
If pNumFrmDialog.DoModal(hWnd) Then
  ' Get the returned INumberFormat and use to format a number
  Set pNumForm = pNumFrmDialog.NumberFormat
  MsgBox pNumForm.ValueToString(12345.6789)
End If
End Sub
```

Labeling objects

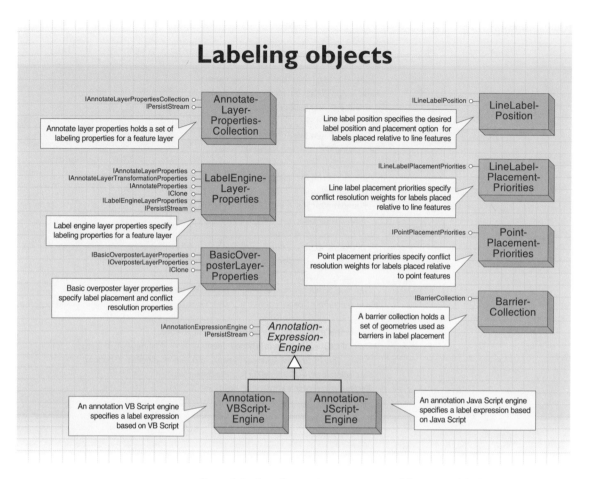

One of the key factors in creating a usable map is labeling (or annotating) features on the map. Labeling is the placing of text near a feature to purvey information about that feature. Normally the label is based on attribute values of the feature itself, but it doesn't have to be.

The ArcMap labeling environment offers a wide variety of methods for labeling features and for resolving conflicts when labels overlap each other. The labeling environment includes the ability to specify which features are to be labeled (all features, features identified by an SQL query, and so on); the expression that is used to label them (expressions can be simple or complex based on VB and Java scripting); placement options and weights for those placements; and priority specifications of one layer versus another. Depending on the requirements of the user, it is also possible to label one layer with multiple expressions.

The objects in this model provide the ability to access all of the parameters associated with the labeling of features. Advanced developers can also create their own expression-parsing engines to be used in the labeling process.

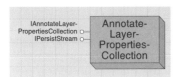

The AnnotateLayerPropertiesCollection object holds one or more labeling property objects for a feature layer. These objects in turn specify how the labels are to be rendered and placed relative to the features. Each object in the set can apply to a subset (query) of the features.

The *AnnotateLayerPropertiesCollection* holds a collection of the different labeling sets (*LabelEngineLayerProperties* objects) assigned to a particular feature layer. The collection can be created, or it can be retrieved from the *IGeoLayer::AnnotationProperties* property on a feature layer. It is possible to label a layer with more than one expression. The purpose of the *AnnotateLayerPropertiesCollection* object is to keep track of the set of expressions that have been assigned.

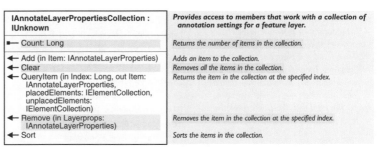

The *IAnnotateLayerPropertiesCollection* interface allows for the manipulation of the *IAnnotateLayerProperties* (*LabelEngineLayerProperties* coclass) objects held within the collection. Through the interface, the developer can add, remove, sort, and query the objects in the collection.

QueryItem provides access to the items in the collection as well as the placed and unplaced elements that go with each *LabelEngineLayerProperties* object.

The following VBA code gets the collection object from a layer and displays the expression defined for each property set within the collection.

```
Sub AnnoClasses()
  Dim pDoc As IMxDocument, pMap As IMap, lLoop As Long
  Dim pGeoLayer As IGeoFeatureLayer
  Set pDoc = ThisDocument
  Set pMap = pDoc.FocusMap
  For lLoop = 0 To pMap.LayerCount - 1
    If UCase(pMap.Layer(lLoop).Name) = "PIPES" Then
      Set pGeoLayer = pMap.Layer(lLoop)
      Exit For
    End If
  Next lLoop

  Dim pAnnoProps As IAnnotateLayerPropertiesCollection
  Dim pLabelEngine As ILabelEngineLayerProperties
  Set pAnnoProps = pGeoLayer.AnnotationProperties
  For lLoop = 0 To pAnnoProps.count - 1
    pAnnoProps.QueryItem lLoop, pLabelEngine
    Debug.Print pLabelEngine.Expression
  Next lLoop
End Sub
```

ArcMap

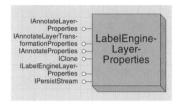

IAnnotateLayer-
Properties
IAnnotateLayerTrans-
formationProperties
IAnnotateProperties
IClone
ILabelEngineLayer-
Properties
IPersistStream

LabelEngine-
Layer-
Properties

The LabelEngineLayerProperties *object maintains one instance of labeling properties for a feature layer. These properties specify how the labels are to be rendered and placed relative to the features. These properties include on which attribute or expression you should base the labels, with which symbol to render the label text, the position relative to the features, and conflict resolution weights.*

A *LabelEngineLayerProperties* object maintains the set of properties associated with the labeling of a feature layer. Multiple *LabelEngine-LayerProperties* can be created for a single feature layer; they are stored within an *AnnotateLayerPropertiesCollection*. The object keeps track of which features to label, how to label them, what symbology to use, how to transform the labels based on the current scale, and what to do with unplaced labels.

The following VBA code demonstrates how to create a new *Label-EngineLayerProperties* object and add it to the *AnnotateLayerProperties-Collection* object retrieved from a line feature layer (for example, "PIPES"). The code also creates and employs *BasicOverposterLayer-Properties, LineLabelPlacementPriorities,* and *LineLabelPosition* objects.

```
Sub AddAnnoProps()
  Dim pDoc As IMxDocument, pMap As IMap, lLoop As Long
  Dim pGeoLayer As IGeoFeatureLayer
  Set pDoc = ThisDocument
  Set pMap = pDoc.FocusMap
  For lLoop = 0 To pMap.LayerCount - 1
    If UCase(pMap.Layer(lLoop).Name) = "PIPES" Then
      Set pGeoLayer = pMap.Layer(lLoop)
      Exit For
    End If
  Next lLoop

  Dim pAnnoProps As IAnnotateLayerPropertiesCollection
  Set pAnnoProps = pGeoLayer.AnnotationProperties
  Dim pAnnoLayerProps As IAnnotateLayerProperties
  Dim pPosition As IlineLabelPosition
  Dim pPlacement As ILineLabelPlacementPriorities
  Dim pBasic As IBasicOverposterLayerProperties
  Dim pLabelEngine As ILabelEngineLayerProperties
  Set pPosition = New LineLabelPosition
  pPosition.Parallel = False
  pPosition.Perpendicular = True

  Set pPlacement = New LineLabelPlacementPriorities
  Set pBasic = New BasicOverposterLayerProperties
  pBasic.FeatureType = esriOverposterPolyline
  pBasic.LineLabelPlacementPriorities = pPlacement
  pBasic.LineLabelPosition = pPosition

  Set pLabelEngine = New LabelEngineLayerProperties
  Set pLabelEngine.BasicOverposterLayerProperties = pBasic
  pLabelEngine.Expression = "[TONODE_]"
  Set pAnnoLayerProps = pLabelEngine
  pAnnoProps.Add pAnnoLayerProps
End Sub
```

ArcMap

IAnnotateLayerProperties : IUnknown	**Provides access to members that work with the display of dynamic labels (text) for a feature layer.**
■—■ AddUnplacedToGraphicsContainer: Boolean	Indicates if overflow labels are put into a graphics container.
■—■ AnnotationMaximumScale: Double	The maximum scale at which to display annotation.
■—■ AnnotationMinimumScale: Double	The minimum scale at which to display annotation.
■—■ Class: String	The class name.
■—■ CreateUnplacedElements: Boolean	Indicates if unplaced elements are created.
■—■ DisplayAnnotation: Boolean	Indicates if the layer displays annotation.
■—■ Extent: IEnvelope	The extent to perform labeling in.
■—□ FeatureLayer: IFeatureLayer	The annotated feature class.
■—■ FeatureLinked: Boolean	Indicates if the text is feature linked.
■—□ GraphicsContainer: IGraphicsContainer	The graphics container used to hold overflow labels.
■—■ LabelWhichFeatures: esriLabelWhichFeatures	The type of features labeled.
■—■ Priority: Long	Priority for labels of this feature class (0 is highest).
■—■ UseOutput: Boolean	Indicates if the output will be used.
■—■ WhereClause: String	SQL where clause that determines which features are labeled.

The *IAnnotateLayerProperties* interface is implemented only by the *LabelEngineLayerProperties* object and provides the answer to the question of which features to label and at what scales. Through this interface, the developer can specify the priority of the labels, a where clause to be applied to the feature layer, and a specification of what to do with unplaced elements.

FeatureLinked, *LabelWhichFeatures*, and *GraphicsContainer* properties apply only when the set of labels is being converted to annotation. The developer can use the *GraphicsContainer* property to specify where the converted labels will go.

FeatureLayer property is used internally during the labeling process. If you find it necessary to set this property, be sure to set it back to *Null* after labeling has completed.

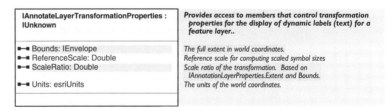

IAnnotateLayerTransformationProperties : IUnknown	**Provides access to members that control transformation properties for the display of dynamic labels (text) for a feature layer..**
■—■ Bounds: IEnvelope	The full extent in world coordinates.
■—■ ReferenceScale: Double	Reference scale for computing scaled symbol sizes
■—■ ScaleRatio: Double	Scale ratio of the transformation. Based on IAnnotationLayerProperties.Extent and Bounds.
■—■ Units: esriUnits	The units of the world coordinates.

The *IAnnotateLayerTransformationProperties* interface is implemented only by the *LabelEngineLayerProperties* object; it holds the settings that determine what size to draw the labels at different scales. Use this interface when you want to specify the reference scale and other transformation properties to use with a *LabelEngineLayerProperties* object.

The *ScaleRatio* is a ratio between the *IAnnotateLayerProperties::Extent* property and the *IAnnotateLayerTransformationProperties* property.

ILabelEngineLayerProperties : IUnknown	Provides access to some of the main properties for labeling features.
▪━○ BasicOverposterLayerProperties: IBasicOverposterLayerProperties	The overposter properties, which specify how labels are placed relative to features.
▪━■ Expression: String	The VBScript or JavaScript expression that evaluates and formats the label.
▪━○ ExpressionParser: IAnnotationExpressionEngine	The object that interprets the expression.
▪━■ IsExpressionSimple: Boolean	Indicates if the expression is simple.
▪━■ Offset: Double	The offset between the label and the feature.
▪━○ Symbol: ITextSymbol	The text symbol used to draw the label.
▪━■ SymbolID: Long	The ID of the group symbol used to draw the label.

The *ILabelEngineLayerProperties* interface is implemented only by the *LabelEngineLayerProperties* object and provides access to the expression, symbol, and overposting properties of the label engine object. Use this interface when you want to access the *AnnotationExpressionEngine* and *BasicOverposterLayerProperties* objects associated with the label engine object.

By default, the *ExpressionParser* property will return the *Annotation-VBScriptEngine* object. In general, the developer would not use this property unless they wanted to use Java scripting for labeling. In this case, an *AnnotationJScriptEngine* object would be created, and the *ExpressionParser* property would be set to this. The expression to use is always set through the *Expression* property.

The *IsExpressionSimple* property identifies whether a complex expression is being used in the *Expression* property. Complex expressions involve a parser object (ExpressionParser *property*) to parse the string.

The *SymbolID* property is used during the conversion of labels to annotation when a group symbol is being applied. A group symbol is applied when a feature-linked annotation class is being created and when converting coverage annotation to the geodatabase.

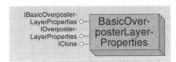

The BasicOverposterLayerProperties *object maintains properties that specify the desired label position relative to the features and weights for resolving conflict among labels and features from other layers.*

You can either create the *BasicOverposterLayerProperties* object, or you can retrieve it from the *ILabelEngineLayerProperties::BasicOverposter-LayerProperties* property.

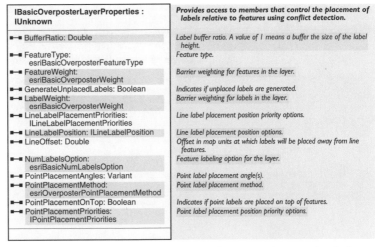

IBasicOverposterLayerProperties : IUnknown	Provides access to members that control the placement of labels relative to features using conflict detection.
■—■ BufferRatio: Double	Label buffer ratio. A value of 1 means a buffer the size of the label height.
■—■ FeatureType: esriBasicOverposterFeatureType	Feature type.
■—■ FeatureWeight: esriBasicOverposterWeight	Barrier weighting for features in the layer.
■—■ GenerateUnplacedLabels: Boolean	Indicates if unplaced labels are generated.
■—■ LabelWeight: esriBasicOverposterWeight	Barrier weighting for labels in the layer.
■—■ LineLabelPlacementPriorities: ILineLabelPlacementPriorities	Line label placement position priority options.
■—■ LineLabelPosition: ILineLabelPosition	Line label placement position options.
■—■ LineOffset: Double	Offset in map units at which labels will be placed away from line features.
■—■ NumLabelsOption: esriBasicNumLabelsOption	Feature labeling option for the layer.
■—■ PointPlacementAngles: Variant	Point label placement angle(s).
■—■ PointPlacementMethod: esriOverposterPointPlacementMethod	Point label placement method.
■—■ PointPlacementOnTop: Boolean	Indicates if point labels are placed on top of features.
■—■ PointPlacementPriorities: IPointPlacementPriorities	Point label placement position priority options.

The *IBasicOverposterLayerProperties* interface is implemented only by the *BasicOverposterLayerProperties* object—it provides access to the overposting resolution methods employed by the label engine object. Each set of labeling properties defines how conflict resolution (overposting) issues will be resolved for those labels. The *IBasic-OverposterLayerProperties* interface provides access to most of these properties.

FeatureType specifies whether labeling is being performed on point, line, or polygon features. Be sure to check this property before accessing any feature-type-specified property, such as *LineLabelPosition* or *PointPlacementAngles.*

FeatureWeight specifies whether labels can be placed on top of the features in a layer, while *LabelWeight* specifies whether the labels can conflict with other labels.

NumLabelsOption indicates how many labels to place per feature.

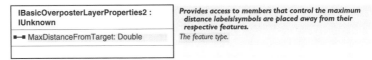

IBasicOverposterLayerProperties2 : IUnknown	Provides access to members that control the maximum distance labels/symbols are placed away from their respective features.
■—■ MaxDistanceFromTarget: Double	The feature type.

The *IBasicOverposterLayerProperties2* interface is implemented only by the *BasicOverposterLayerProperties* object and was added to allow you to set the maximum distance a label could be placed from its target (*MaxDistanceFromTarget* property).

ArcMap

IOverposterLayerProperties : IUnknown	*Provides access to members that control the placement of labels or symbols on top of features (barriers).*
■—■ IsBarrier: Boolean	*Indicates if features are treated as barriers to label/symbol placement.*
■—■ PlaceLabels: Boolean	*Indicates if labels are placed for the layer.*
■—■ PlaceSymbols: Boolean	*Indicates if symbols are placed for the layer.*

The *IOverposterLayerProperties* interface is implemented only by the *BasicOverposterLayerProperties* object and provides access to whether labels or symbols are placed.

The *IsBarrier* property indicates whether the features in the layer should serve as barriers for label placement (do not put labels on top of the features).

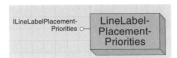

The LineLabelPlacementPriorities *object maintains the weights associated with label placement positions relative to the line start points and endpoints.*

The *LineLabelPlacementPriorities* object keeps track of the weight values assigned to the label engine object during the placement of labels along line features. The object is creatable, but it can also be retrieved from the *IBasicOverposterLayerProperties::LineLabelPlacementPriorities* property.

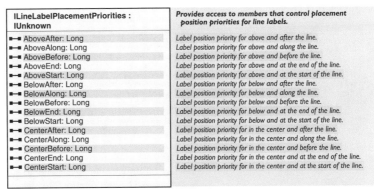

ILineLabelPlacementPriorities : IUnknown	Provides access to members that control placement position priorities for line labels.
━■ AboveAfter: Long	Label position priority for above and after the line.
━■ AboveAlong: Long	Label position priority for above and along the line.
━■ AboveBefore: Long	Label position priority for above and before the line.
━■ AboveEnd: Long	Label position priority for above and at the end of the line.
━■ AboveStart: Long	Label position priority for above and at the start of the line.
━■ BelowAfter: Long	Label position priority for below and after the line.
━■ BelowAlong: Long	Label position priority for below and along the line.
━■ BelowBefore: Long	Label position priority for below and before the line.
━■ BelowEnd: Long	Label position priority for below and at the end of the line.
━■ BelowStart: Long	Label position priority for below and at the start of the line.
━■ CenterAfter: Long	Label position priority for in the center and after the line.
━■ CenterAlong: Long	Label position priority for in the center and along the line.
━■ CenterBefore: Long	Label position priority for in the center and before the line.
━■ CenterEnd: Long	Label position priority for in the center and at the end of the line.
━■ CenterStart: Long	Label position priority for in the center and at the start of the line.

The *ILineLabelPlacementPriorities* interface is the only interface implemented by the *LineLabelPlacementPriorities* coclass. Use this interface when you want to change the weighting values for conflict resolution when labeling line features.

The *Start* weight (*AboveStart, BelowStart,* and *CenterStart*) values only come into play when the Label only at start option is selected. The same principle applies for the *End* weight values.

The *LineLabelPosition* object is used in conjunction with the *LineLabelPlacementPriorities* object to specify how labels are to be placed along line features. The *LineLabelPosition* object dictates the default position for labels along lines, while the *LineLabelPlacementPriorities* object dictates how the labels will be placed when there are conflicts. The *LineLabelPosition* coclass is creatable, but it can also be retrieved from the *IBasicOverposterLayerProperties::LineLabelPosition* property.

The LineLabelPosition *object maintains the flags associated with the possible label placement options. These include whether the labels should be placed horizontally, parallel (straight or curved), or perpendicular relative to the line, and whether the orientation should be determined by the line direction.*

ILineLabelPosition : IUnknown	Provides access to members that control the relative position of line labels.
■━■ Above: Boolean	Indicates if labels are placed above lines.
■━■ AtEnd: Boolean	Indicates if labels are placed at the start of lines.
■━■ AtStart: Boolean	Indicates if labels are placed at the start of lines.
■━■ Below: Boolean	Indicates if labels are placed below lines.
■━■ Horizontal: Boolean	Indicates if labels are placed horizontally.
■━■ InLine: Boolean	Indicates if labels are placed inside lines.
■━■ Left: Boolean	Indicates if labels are placed to the left of lines.
■━■ Offset: Double	Offset from the start/end of line.
■━■ OnTop: Boolean	Indicates if labels are placed on top of lines.
■━■ Parallel: Boolean	Indicates if labels are placed parallel to lines.
■━■ Perpendicular: Boolean	Indicates if labels are placed perpendicular to lines.
■━■ ProduceCurvedLabels: Boolean	Indicates if labels follow lines.
■━■ Right: Boolean	Indicates if labels are placed to the right of lines.

Use the *ILineLabelPosition* interface when you want to specify the default location of labels along line features. *AtEnd* and *AtStart* properties specify default locations that have weights attached to them in case there is a conflict, while *Parallel* and *Perpendicular* properties indicate options that are not changed by conflicts.

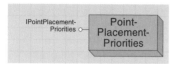

The PointPlacementPriorities object maintains the weights associated with label placement positions relative to point features.

The *PointPlacementPriorities* object keeps track of the weight values assigned to the label engine object during the placement of labels around point features.

The *PointPlacementPriorities* object is creatable, but it can also be retrieved from *IBasicOverposterLayerProperties::PointPlacementPriorities.*

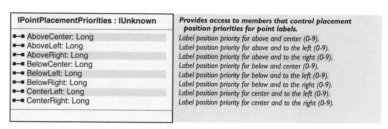

IPointPlacementPriorities : IUnknown	Provides access to members that control placement position priorities for point labels.
AboveCenter: Long	Label position priority for above and center (0-9).
AboveLeft: Long	Label position priority for above and to the left (0-9).
AboveRight: Long	Label position priority for above and to the right (0-9).
BelowCenter: Long	Label position priority for below and center (0-9).
BelowLeft: Long	Label position priority for below and to the left (0-9).
BelowRight: Long	Label position priority for below and to the right (0-9).
CenterLeft: Long	Label position priority for center and to the left (0-9).
CenterRight: Long	Label position priority for center and to the right (0-9).

The *IPointPlacementPriorities* interface is the only interface implemented by the *PointPlacementPriorities* coclass. Use this interface when you want to change the weighting values for conflict resolution when you are labeling point features. The interface provides weight settings for the eight positions around the point when the *IBasicOverposterLayerProperties:: PointPlacementMethod* is set to *esriAroundPoint*. A value of one sets the highest priority (preferred position), a value of 2 sets the second priority, and so on. A value of 0 means that the position should not be used.

AboveCenter identifies the weight to use when attempting to place labeling for a point at the "12:00" position.

The following VBA code shows how to change the placement options for the labeling of the feature layer "VALVES" to ensure labels are only placed in the *AboveCenter* position.

```
Sub PointLabelProps()
  Dim pDoc As IMxDocument, pMap As IMap, lLoop As Long
  Dim pGeoLayer As IGeoFeatureLayer
  Set pDoc = ThisDocument
  Set pMap = pDoc.FocusMap
  For lLoop = 0 To pMap.LayerCount - 1
    If UCase(pMap.Layer(lLoop).Name) = "VALVES" Then
      Set pGeoLayer = pMap.Layer(lLoop)
      Exit For
    End If
  Next lLoop

  Dim pAnnoProps As IAnnotateLayerPropertiesCollection
  Dim pLabelEngine As ILabelEngineLayerProperties
  Dim pBasic As IBasicOverposterLayerProperties
  Dim pProps As IPointPlacementPriorities
  Set pAnnoProps = pGeoLayer.AnnotationProperties
  pAnnoProps.QueryItem 0, pLabelEngine
  Set pBasic = pLabelEngine.BasicOverposterLayerProperties
  Set pProps = pBasic.PointPlacementPriorities
  pProps.AboveCenter = 1
  pProps.AboveLeft = 0
```

```
        pProps.AboveRight = 0
        pProps.BelowCenter = 0
        pProps.BelowLeft = 0
        pProps.BelowRight = 0
        pProps.CenterLeft = 0
        pProps.CenterRight = 0
        pBasic.PointPlacementPriorities = pProps
End Sub
```

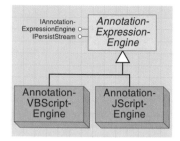

The AnnotationExpressionEngine *object parses an expression on which to base the label text. This can be a function based on either VB or Java script code.*

This interface is used internally to initially define and later validate labeling expressions entered by the user through the user dialog boxes. In general, developers will not need to use the properties and methods of this interface. However, if a developer chooses to write their own parser engine, then this interface must be implemented for defining the expression to use in generating labels.

The methods on this interface only need to be called when the developer wants to generate strings to use outside the core labeling environment.

The *AnnotationExpressionEngine* supports two types of objects for parsing the expressions used in labeling: the *AnnotationVBScriptEngine* (for VB scripting) and the *AnnotationJScriptEngine* (for Java scripting). On very rare occasions, a developer may want to write their own parser based on this abstract class.

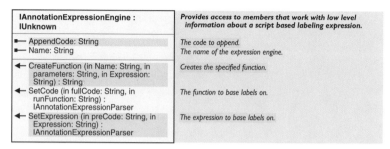

The *IAnnotationExpressionEngine* interface is implemented by all label parsing engines.

AppendCode indicates the string to use when appending multiple strings together to form the expression. For VB scripting, the *AppendCode* is set to"&", while for Java scripting it is "+".

Name identifies the type of engine being used as the parser ("VB Script" or "Java Script").

The *AnnotationVBScriptEngine* coclass is used for parsing VB scripting code during the labeling process. By default, VB scripting is used through this object to parse advanced labeling expressions. In general, a developer would only use an object of this type generating strings based on the defined expression for use outside the core labeling environment.

The *AnnotationJScriptEngine* coclass is used for parsing Java scripting code during the labeling process. A developer will create an object of this type when they want to perform labeling of features based on Java scripting code. Once the object is created, it can be applied through *ILabelEngineLayerProperties::ExpressionParser*.

Assuming an *IGeoLayer* object is present, the following code can be used to change the parser to Java Script (just make sure you also update the *Expression* as necessary):

```
Dim pAnnoProps As IAnnotateLayerPropertiesCollection
Set pAnnoProps = pGeoLayer.AnnotationProperties
Dim pAnnoLayerProps As IAnnotateLayerProperties
pAnnoProps.QueryItem 0, pAnnoLayerProps
Dim pLabelEngine As ILabelEngineLayerProperties
Set pLabelEngine = pAnnoLayerProps
Dim pAnnoEngine As IAnnotationExpressionEngine
Set pAnnoEngine = New AnnotationJScriptEngine
Set pLabelEngine.ExpressionParser = pAnnoEngine
```

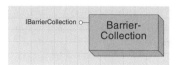

The BarrierCollection object holds one or more geometry collection objects, each with an associated label conflict resolution weight.

The *BarrierCollection* object keeps track of the set of barrier geometries being used during the placement of labels. As new labels are placed, their geometries are also added to the collection. When a new label to be placed conflicts with an existing barrier in the collection, the overposting engine will look for a new location for the label (depending on the settings defined in the *BasicOverposterLayerProperties* object). The object can either be created, or it can be retrieved from the *IMap::Barriers* or *IMapBarriers::Barriers2* properties.

ArcMap

IBarrierCollection : IUnknown	Provides access to members that control a collection of objects that act as barriers to label placement.
■— Count: Long	Returns the number of items in the collection.
◄— Add (in Barriers: IGeometryCollection, in Weight: esriBasicOverposterWeight)	Adds the specified item to the collection.
◄— Clear	Removes all the items in the collection.
◄— QueryItem (in Index: Long, out Barrier: IGeometryCollection, Weight: esriBasicOverposterWeight)	Returns the item in the collection at the specified index.

The *IBarrierCollection* interface allows for the manipulation of the geometries that make up the current set of barriers to label placement. Through this interface the developer can add, clear, and query the defined geometries and weights.

The *Add* and *QueryItem* properties add and return collections of geometries (*IGeometryCollection*) as a single barrier. Each *IGeometryCollection* represents a single graphics layer in the map.

The following VBA code shows how to access the *BarrierCollection* and the number of geometries for one entry in the collection based on the current extent of the map:

```
Sub LabelBarriers()
  Dim pDoc As IMxDocument, pMap As IMap, pBarriers As IBarrierCollection
  Dim pGeometry As IGeometryCollection, pActive As IActiveView
  Set pDoc = ThisDocument
  Set pMap = pDoc.FocusMap
  Set pActive = pMap
  Set pBarriers = pMap.Barriers(pActive.Extent)
  pBarriers.QueryItem 0, pGeometry
  Debug.Print pBarriers.count & " - " & pGeometry.GeometryCount
End Sub
```

In general, the model for extending ArcGIS applications is through in-process COM delivered as DLLs, such as extensions, commands, property pages, and so on. In some cases, however, it may be necessary to "drive" ArcGIS applications from a separate application, a practice commonly referred to as Automation.

In modern operating systems, such as UNIX® and Windows NT, all applications run in their own protected address space. Since memory is not directly accessible between these separate processes, calls made between them are necessarily slower due to the translations and remote invocations that must occur.

Normally, ArcGIS applications are extended by user customizations made available to the application through such mechanisms as component categories. For example, when ArcMap is launched, this application loads all properly registered extension objects into its process space. Since these objects then exist in ArcMap process space, access between them is direct and fast. The same is true for custom extensions, commands, and even VBA code running within ArcMap since they do not need to communicate between each other across process boundaries. COM communication in this case is generally referred to as "in-process" or simply "in-proc".

Conversely, it is possible to create a Visual Basic executable—a standalone application—that obtains a reference to and works with ArcMap "remotely" from its separate process space. In this case, there are two separate applications running and, therefore, two separate process spaces. COM communication in this case is referred to as "out-of-process" or simply "out-of-proc". This kind of access is also commonly called "automation". Although, as far as the client is concerned, things appear to be the same in automation as they are in the in-proc case, there are important differences of which programmers need to be aware.

PROBLEMS WITH AUTOMATION

Performance

Interapplication communication (whether through COM or some other mechanism) must cross process boundaries since all applications (in UNIX, Windows NT, and other operating systems) live in their own protected-address space. When a COM object is created in one process and accessed in another, interprocess marshaling (communication) must occur, and this is very expensive. In an application such as ArcMap, where large numbers of components are accessed over short periods of time (such as in drawing or query), this overhead can become extreme.

Process-confined types

Certain types, such as GDI handles and others, cannot be used within the context of a different process from which they were created in, or are restricted in what can be done with them in that foreign process. For instance, a bitmap created in one process and handed to another through COM (for example, as an OLE_HANDLE) cannot be rendered on a DC in the foreign-process space.

Deadlocks and other threading issues

Some areas of ArcGIS do not currently support access from a foreign-process space. For instance, map layers from one instance of ArcMap cannot be successfully rendered in a separate instance of ArcMap. Many of these limitations are due to limitations of what sorts of system objects can be shared between separate process spaces, and some are due to performance issues.

SOLUTION

In general, when "driving" ArcMap through automation, it is often the case that what you really want is for things to be as they are in the in-proc case. It would be desirable if there were some way that a request to create an object in one process space could be controlled so that the actual object instance could come into existence within the application being "driven" (ArcMap), instead of from where the request is actually made (the driving application). In reality, using VB's *New* statement simply creates the object in the driving application's process space, not in the ArcMap process.

This sort of control is made possible by the *IObjectFactory* interface, obtainable from the ArcMap *Application* object (which your process obtains through automation). This interface can be used to create an arbitrary object within the ArcMap process (in the main STA) by calling the *Create* method—passing in the ProgID/ClsID of the component you want to create. The caller receives a proxy to that object that now resides within ArcMap. Calls from within ArcMap to objects created in this way are local to the ArcMap process.

A useful example would be where an attempt is made to load a new feature layer into a map within ArcMap by a separate application written in Visual Basic, which uses automation to control the instance of ArcMap. Prior to ArcGIS 8.1, a new *FeatureLayer* object could only be created in the VB application's process space. In this case, the *FeatureLayer* would have to be remotely accessed by the ArcMap *Map* object, while the *Map* object itself would have to be remotely accessed by both the VB code in the separate executable as well as the *FeatureLayer* object.

This case is actually even more complex due to numerous other support objects that are involved in the interactions between *Map* and *FeatureLayer* objects. For example, for ArcMap to draw all the features represented in the feature layer, each feature would have to be remotely accessed through automation, creating an enormous bottleneck and a corresponding performance disaster. Note in the diagram to the left how the *FeatureLayer* object and the *Map* object exist in separate process spaces, and so must communicate through proxies.

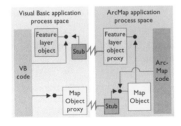

With the release of ArcGIS 8.1, it is possible to create the *FeatureLayer* object within ArcMap process space so that the interaction between these two objects is direct instead of through intra-application communication. Automation in still occurring in the sense that the VB code in the separate process is still calling remotely to these objects, which now exist in ArcMap's process, but these remote calls are minimal in number (setting a property or two, and so on). The numerous calls that normally occur as a result of drawing now occur solely within ArcMap. Note in the new diagram how both the *FeatureLayer* object and the *Map* object exist in ArcMap process space.

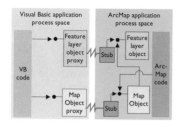

Visual Basic application process space

ArcMap application process space

The following example demonstrates how a feature layer can be loaded into ArcMap from a standalone Visual Basic application using the *IObjectFactory* interface.

```
Private m_pMxApp As IApplication

Private Sub Form_Load()
  frmIObjectFactory.MousePointer = vbHourglass

  ' Create an out-of-process instance of ArcMap
  Dim pDoc As IDocument
  Set pDoc = New MxDocument

  ' Hold on to this instance of ArcMap in a global in case
  ' we need it later.
  Set m_pMxApp = pDoc.Parent

  frmIObjectFactory.MousePointer = vbNormal
End Sub

Private Sub Form_Unload(Cancel As Integer)
  m_pMxApp.Shutdown
End Sub

Private Sub Command1_Click()
  Dim pObjFactory As IObjectFactory
  Dim pWorkspaceFactory As IWorkspaceFactory
  Dim pFeatureWorkspace As IFeatureWorkspace
  Dim pFeatureLayer As IFeatureLayer
  Dim pMxDocument As IMxDocument
  Dim pMap As IMap

  ' Show ArcMap
  m_pMxApp.Visible = True

  ' Obtain the object factory interface from the app
  Set pObjFactory = m_pMxApp

  ' Create a shapefile feature layer and add it to ArcMap.
  ' Note that we will use ArcMap's generic object factory to ensure that
  ' these objects exist in ArcMap's process space.

  ' Equivalent of Set pWorkspaceFactory = New ShapefileWorkspaceFactory
  Set pWorkspaceFactory = _
    pObjFactory.Create("esriCore.ShapefileWorkspaceFactory")

  Set pFeatureWorkspace = _
    pWorkspaceFactory.OpenFromFile("D:\Samples\Data\Usa", 0)
```

```
    ' Equivalent of Set pFeatureLayer = New FeatureLayer
    Set pFeatureLayer = pObjFactory.Create("esriCore.FeatureLayer")

    Set pFeatureLayer.FeatureClass = _
      pFeatureWorkspace.OpenFeatureClass("States")
    pFeatureLayer.Name = pFeatureLayer.FeatureClass.AliasName

    'Add the FeatureLayer to the focus map
    Set pMxDocument = m_pMxApp.Document
    Set pMap = pMxDocument.FocusMap

    pMap.AddLayer pFeatureLayer
    pMxDocument.ActiveView.PartialRefresh esriViewGeography, Nothing, Nothing
End Sub
```

5

Displaying graphics

Shelly Gill, Scott Campbell, Chris Davies, Steve Van Esch, Jim Clarke, Cory Eicher

ArcMap employs a rich palette of display objects to realize strong user interaction and sophisticated cartographic presentation. These are the components in ArcObjects for customizing ArcMap, making superior maps, and building custom map-centric applications.

The topics covered in this chapter include: drawing layers with feature renderers • defining colors for display and printing • drawing point features with marker symbols • drawing linear features with line symbols • drawing areas with fill symbols • labeling features with text symbols • displaying numeric data with chart symbols • adorning frame elements with frame decorations • controlling the display output • grouping numeric values into classes • customizing user interaction with rubber band objects, selection trackers, and display feedbacks

Feature renderer objects

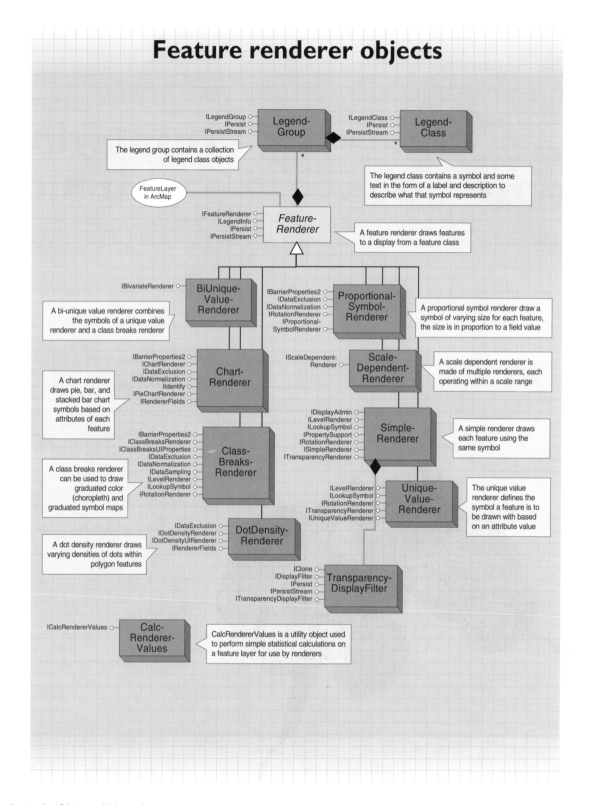

ILegendGroup ○—
IPersist ○—
IPersistStream ○—
Legend-Group

ILegendClass ○—
IPersist ○—
IPersistStream ○—
Legend-Class

The legend group contains a collection of legend class objects

The legend class contains a symbol and some text in the form of a label and description to describe what that symbol represents

FeatureLayer in ArcMap

IFeatureRenderer ○—
ILegendInfo ○—
IPersist ○—
IPersistStream ○—
Feature-Renderer

A feature renderer draws features to a display from a feature class

IBivariateRenderer ○—
BiUnique-Value-Renderer

A bi-unique value renderer combines the symbols of a unique value renderer and a class breaks renderer

IBarrierProperties2 ○—
IDataExclusion ○—
IDataNormalization ○—
IRotationRenderer ○—
IProportional-SymbolRenderer ○—
Proportional-Symbol-Renderer

A proportional symbol renderer draw a symbol of varying size for each feature, the size is in proportion to a field value

IBarrierProperties2 ○—
IChartRenderer ○—
IDataExclusion ○—
IDataNormalization ○—
IIdentify ○—
IPieChartRenderer ○—
IRendererFields ○—
Chart-Renderer

A chart renderer draws pie, bar, and stacked bar chart symbols based on attributes of each feature

IScaleDependent-Renderer ○—
Scale-Dependent-Renderer

A scale dependent renderer is made of multiple renderers, each operating within a scale range

IDisplayAdmin ○—
ILevelRenderer ○—
ILookupSymbol ○—
IPropertySupport ○—
IRotationRenderer ○—
ISimpleRenderer ○—
ITransparencyRenderer ○—
Simple-Renderer

A simple renderer draws each feature using the same symbol

IBarrierProperties2 ○—
IClassBreaksRenderer ○—
IClassBreaksUIProperties ○—
IDataExclusion ○—
IDataNormalization ○—
IDataSampling ○—
ILevelRenderer ○—
ILookupSymbol ○—
IRotationRenderer ○—
Class-Breaks-Renderer

A class breaks renderer can be used to draw graduated color (choropleth) and graduated symbol maps

ILevelRenderer ○—
ILookupSymbol ○—
IRotationRenderer ○—
ITransparencyRenderer ○—
IUniqueValueRenderer ○—
Unique-Value-Renderer

The unique value renderer defines the symbol a feature is to be drawn with based on an attribute value

IDataExclusion ○—
IDotDensityRenderer ○—
IDotDensityUIRenderer ○—
IRendererFields ○—
DotDensity-Renderer

A dot density renderer draws varying densities of dots within polygon features

IClone ○—
IDisplayFilter ○—
IPersist ○—
IPersistStream ○—
ITransparencyDisplayFilter ○—
Transparency-DisplayFilter

ICalcRendererValues ○—
Calc-Renderer-Values

CalcRendererValues is a utility object used to perform simple statistical calculations on a feature layer for use by renderers

Drawing a map with a single symbol

Drawing a map with proportional symbols

Drawing categories in a map with symbols

Drawing quantities in a map with symbols

Drawing value densities in a map with dots

Drawing multiple categories in a map

Drawing a map with pie charts

A feature renderer is a method for drawing feature layers. The feature renderers use symbols and colors to visually display features, possibly based on one or more attributes. There is one feature renderer associated with each feature layer. The scale breaks and biunique value renderers also contain other renderers. You can choose a renderer to display features differently depending on attribute values in the fields of a feature class. The following are types of feature renderers:

- *SimpleRenderer* uses the same symbol for each feature.

- *ClassBreaksRenderer* allows classes of numeric attribute values to be defined. A different symbol is specified for each class. The symbols typically vary in either color or size. This renderer can be used for ordinal, interval, or ratio data.

- *UniqueValueRenderer* uses a different symbol for each unique attribute value. A value can come from a single field or a combination of more than one field. This is used for nominal data.

- *ProportionalSymbolRenderer* modifies the size of the symbol in proportion to an attribute from a field.

- *DotDensityRenderer* displays a scattering of marker symbols in polygon features, the density of which reflects the value of an attribute.

- *ChartRenderer* displays pie, bar, or stacked bar charts that are comprised from one or more attribute fields.

- *ScaleBreaksRenderer* switches renderers depending on the map viewing scale.

- *BiUniqueValueRenderer* combines a unique-value renderer with a class-breaks renderer (either graduated colors or graduated symbol type symbology). This allows multiple attributes to be reflected in one symbol.

Display

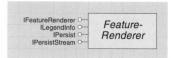

The feature renderer determines how a feature class is drawn. A renderer object describes the process of matching features and attributes to symbols.

To get to a feature renderer object in ArcMap from a layer, *QI* to *IGeo-FeatureLayer* and get the *Renderer* property. A simple renderer is the default renderer object when a new feature class is loaded.

```
' Check if the layer is a feature layer
If Not TypeOf pLayer Is IGeoFeatureLayer Then Exit Sub
Set pGeoFeatureLayer = pLayer


' Check if there is a simple renderer and get a reference to it
If Not TypeOf pGeoFeatureLayer.Renderer Is ISimpleRenderer Then Exit Sub
Set pSimpleRenderer = pGeoFeatureLayer.Renderer
```

All feature renderers implement the IFeatureRenderer interface; it is used by the framework to draw features from a feature class.

IFeatureRenderer : IUnknown	Provides access to members that control functionality common to all feature renderers.
ExclusionSet: IFeatureIDSet	Sets an object reference to a temporary drawing exclusion set.
RenderPhase (in drawPhase: tagesriDrawPhase) : Boolean	Indicates if renderer uses the specified draw phase.
SymbolByFeature (in Feature: IFeature) : ISymbol	Symbol used to draw the specified feature.
CanRender (in featClass: IFeatureClass, in Display: IDisplay) : Boolean	Indicates if the specified feature class can be rendered on the given display.
Draw (in Cursor: IFeatureCursor, in drawPhase: tagesriDrawPhase, in Display: IDisplay, in trackCancel: ITrackCancel)	Draws features from the specified cursor on the given display.
PrepareFilter (in fc: IFeatureClass, in QueryFilter: IQueryFilter)	Prepares the query filter for the rendering process.

The *ExclusionSet* is a list of feature IDs to be excluded from a drawing.

The default implementation of a feature takes the symbol supplied by the renderer and uses this to draw the feature. However, if this feature is a custom feature, the developer may have chosen to ignore the supplied symbol and used the custom feature's own symbology.

The *PrepareFilter* is called prior to the *Draw* method and gives the renderer a chance to adjust the query filter to incorporate extra constraints. For example, if a particular field is required for the renderer, it would add this field to the filter to ensure it is accessible during a draw.

The *Draw* method is typically called by the framework to renderer features to a display. This could be in response to a *Refresh* on the *Map*. The *Draw* method will iterate through all the features and render each feature with an appropriate symbol. The actual draw of the feature is normally performed by calling the *Draw* method on the feature's *IFeatureDraw* Interface; it simply uses the symbol created by the renderer.

To allow complex rendering to be canceled halfway through a draw, the renderer will typically check the *TrackCancel* object after each feature. If a cancel action has occurred, the renderer will exit.

There are two drawing phases: annotation and geography. For example, consider a proportional renderer for drawing a polygon layer. The proportional renderer draws the polygons with a fill symbol in the geography drawing phase and the proportional symbol in the annotation drawing phase. The renderer indicates in the RenderPhase method that it wants to draw both phases. Subsequently, the Draw method gets called twice.

For more discussion on drawing phases, refer to the topic 'Refreshing a map versus partial refresh' in Chapter 4.

SymbolByFeature is called to return the symbol corresponding to a feature. This is used to turn features into graphics.

If the renderer is not applicable to a feature layer, then it can return *False* in response to a *CanRender* method. For example, the dot-density renderer is only applicable to polygon feature layers and returns *False* in response to other feature layers. Similarly, if the renderer is not applicable to a particular draw phase, this can be indicated by returning *False* to the *RenderPhase* property. Typically, all renderers draw in the geography phase.

Remember that after changing symbology for a layer to update the display for that layer with code like this:

```
Dim pDoc As IMxDocument
pDoc.ActiveView.PartialRefresh esriDPGeography, pLayer, Nothing
```

Additionally, the table of contents needs to be updated, too.

```
pDoc.UpdateContents
```

After you have set up a new renderer object and assigned it to a feature layer, you will need to associate the correct property page (Layer properties/Symbology in ArcMap) with the renderer. The *IGeoFeatureLayer::RendererPropertyPageClassID* property needs to be initialized to the GUID of the appropriate property page.

One way to do this is to use the *UID* object and give it the GUID of the property page. The ProgID is not used because it is not guaranteed to be unique.

```
Dim pUID As New UID ' Create a new UID object
'ProgID is "esricore.BarChartPropertyPage"
pUID.Value = "{98DD7040-FEB4-11D3-9F7C-00C04F6BC709}"
pGeofeaturelayer.RendererPropertyPageClassID = pUID
```

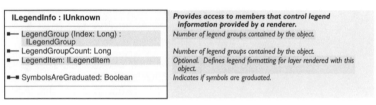

ILegendInfo : IUnknown	Provides access to members that control legend information provided by a renderer.
■— LegendGroup (Index: Long) : ILegendGroup	Number of legend groups contained by the object.
■— LegendGroupCount: Long	Number of legend groups contained by the object.
■— LegendItem: ILegendItem	Optional. Defines legend formatting for layer rendered with this object.
■—■ SymbolsAreGraduated: Boolean	Indicates if symbols are graduated.

The *ILegendInfo* interface is implemented by several layer types: feature, raster, and TIN. Although the feature layer object implements this interface, it just defers all methods and properties to the feature renderer's *ILegendInfo* interface.

Legend and other related objects such as *LegendItem* and *LegendFormat* are discussed in Chapter 4, 'Composing maps'.

The *ILegendInfo* interface has a property array of *LegendGroup* objects. The number of groups is determined by the implementation of the renderer. Consequently, these properties are read-only. For example, the simple renderer always has one group, but the biunique renderer can have any number of groups.

The simple, class breaks, and unique value renderers will update the legend class objects for you when you set the renderer's symbols. In fact, these renderers store their symbols there. However, with the proportional-symbol, chart, dot-density, and biunique renderers, you must call *CreateLegend* for the legend class objects to be set up and placed into appropriate groups.

The property *SymbolsAreGraduated* indicates whether the symbols used for the legend of this particular renderer vary by size. For example, the proportional-symbol renderer will return *True* for this property.

A renderer can override the legend appearance of a layer's legend by returning an *ILegendItem*.

The ILegendInfo *interface is used by the ArcMap framework to generate the symbols and labels for each layer shown in the table of contents and the* Legend *object.*

A legend group represents a collection of related symbols stored in legend classes.

Typically, all the symbols used in a group are of the same type. For example, a chart renderer that is being used to create pie charts has two groups—the first contains a single pie chart symbol, the second group contains fill symbols for each slice of the pie chart.

The *LegendGroup* object contains a collection of *LegendClass* objects.

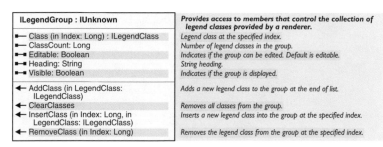

The *ILegendGroup* interface manages a property array of *LegendClass* objects. Inside a *LegendClass* object is one *Symbol* object. Classes can be looked up, but modifying the number of classes through addition, insertion, and deletion is the job of the renderer object. Some properties of the legend group can be retrieved.

The *Editable* property returns whether the symbols and text strings in the *LegendClass* objects of the group can be edited individually. You can see this in ArcMap by double-clicking the symbol in the table of contents. If the Symbol Properties dialog box appears, then the group has *Editable* set to *True*.

For example, a pie chart symbol in a group by itself returns *False*, and its symbol can't be edited. However, the fill symbols for each pie slice (this is in a second group) has *Editable* set to *True*, the fill symbol can be changed, and this is picked up by the renderer for all pie charts.

The *Visible* property controls if the group can be seen. Typically, this is in the table of contents. For example, setting *Visible* to *False* for all the legend groups of a layer will collapse and hide the symbols for a layer in the table of contents.

The *Heading* property of a group is a piece of text to describe what the group represents. For example, the field name is used when using the unique-value renderer.

There are many *LegendClass* objects in a *LegendGroup*. The legend class contains a symbol and some text in the form of a *Label* and *Description* to describe what that symbol represents. If the legend group is editable, then the symbol can be modified and the renderer will pick this up at the next draw phase.

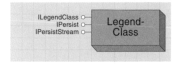

A legend class stores a symbol and text pair that is used in making legends.

However, the typical route for modifying renderer appearance is to go to the renderer objects themselves. For example, to change the simple renderer symbol, label and description fields, use the methods and properties of *ISimpleRenderer* in preference to the legend class object.

ILegendClass : IUnknown	**Provides access to members that control the legend/TOC entry for a renderer class.**
■—■ Description: String	*Legend class description.*
■—■ Format: ILegendClassFormat	*Optional. If non-null, then layer specifies class formatting information.*
■—■ Label: String	*Legend class label.*
■—□ Symbol: ISymbol	*Legend class symbol.*

Setting the *Format* property allows the appearance of the symbol to override the settings of the legend object.

Display

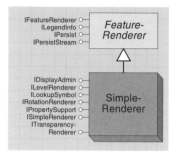

SimpleRenderer *draws each feature using a single symbol.*

In the Layer Properties/Symbology/Show list in ArcMap, the simple renderer corresponds to SingleSymbol under the type of Features.

A map drawn with the simple renderer and its legend.

The *SimpleRenderer* coclass draws each feature using a single symbol.

The symbol typically matches the geometry of the layer so that fill symbols are used for drawing polygons, line symbols for drawing lines, and marker symbols for drawing points. One exception is that a marker symbol can also be used with a polygon layer—this will draw a marker at the center of the polygon.

A symbol can also be rotated if it is a marker symbol (*IRotationRenderer*) or made transparent (*ITransparencyRenderer*) if it is a fill symbol. The amount of transparency or rotation is specified by attribute values associated with each feature.

ISimpleRenderer : IUnknown	Provides access to members that control a renderer which draws the same symbol for each feature.
■–■ Description: String	*Renderer description.*
■–■ Label: String	*Renderer label.*
■–□ Symbol: ISymbol	*Symbol used to draw each feature.*

By getting or setting the symbol property of *ISimpleRenderer,* the symbology of the whole layer can be changed. The label property states what that symbol means. For example, a black circular marker symbol represents "Cities". The description property provides further explanatory text. The symbol, label, and description can all appear and be arranged in a legend.

The simple renderer symbol is also accessible in the legend. It is the only symbol in the first legend class.

Here is an example VBA script to change the fill symbol of a simple renderer. (For code samples to get and refresh a simple renderer, see the documentation for the *FeatureRenderer* abstract class.)

```
'Set the color of Lilac
Set pColor = New RgbColor
pColor.Red = 235
pColor.Green = 202
pColor.Blue = 250

Set pFillSymbol = New SimpleFillSymbol
pFillSymbol.Color = pColor

Set pSimpleRenderer.Symbol = pFillSymbol
pSimpleRenderer.Label = "Label"
pSimpleRenderer.Description = "Description"
```

IDisplayAdmin : IUnknown	Provides access to members that control display administration.
■— UsesFilter: Boolean	*Indicates if the current object draws using a filter.*

The *IDisplayAdmin* interface is called by the framework to determine if the renderer is using a display filter. For the simple renderer, this will return *True* if a transparency field has been specified.

ILevelRenderer : IUnknown	Provides access to members that control the drawing of symbols for features, where symbols are separated into levels, and each level drawn separately.
—■ CurrentDrawLevel: Long	The current draw level, (set to -1 to draw all levels).
■— LevelArray (out levels: Variant)	Array that contains all levels used by the symbols, (symbols without a level get a level of 0).

The *ILevelRenderer* interface draws symbols on different levels. The renderers that support *ILevelRenderer* are *ClassBreaksRenderer*, *SimpleRenderer* coclass, and *UniqueValueRenderer*.

For more information on multilevel symbols, refer to the discussion on the IMapLevel interface under the Symbol abstract class documented later in this chapter.

This interface is used by the framework to draw multilevel symbols. This only happens if the property *IMap::UseSymbolLevels* is true. Multilevel symbols are enabled through the Advance Drawing Options dialog box on the data frame in ArcMap. This dialog box is also accessible through the *SymbolLevelDialog* object.

The *LevelArray* property returns an array of long integers listing all the levels of the symbols used by the render. The framework will iterate through all the available levels across all feature layers, thus ensuring that symbols of the same level will appear to join or merge.

The *CurrentDrawLevel* is set by the framework at draw time to specify which level of symbols the renderer is to draw.

The rotation renderer is very effective for displaying maps of wind direction. If combined with a proportional symbol renderer and arrow markers, locations of wind direction and magnitude can be clearly mapped.

esriRotateSymbolGeographic   esriRotateSymbolArithmetic

IRotationRenderer: IUnknown	Provides access to members that control the drawing of rotated marker symbols based on field values.
■—■ RotationField: String	Rotation field.
■—■ RotationType: esriSymbolRotationType	Rotation type.

The *IRotationRenderer* interface can be used in a renderer when applying marker symbols. The amount of rotation can be specified using an attribute field in the feature class specified with the *RotationField* property. The value in the attribute field should be in degrees and in the direction set by the *RotationType* property.

For an example of applying *IRotationRenderer* to making maps of wind direction, look in the ArcObjects Developer Help under ArcMap/Symbology/Renderers.

Enumeration esriSymbolRotationType	Marker symbol rotation options.
0 - esriRotateSymbolGeographic	Clockwise rotation with 0 at the positive y-axis.
1 - esriRotateSymbolArithmetic	Counter clockwise rotation with 0 at the positive x-axis.

The *esriSymbolRotationType* enumeration defines which one of two conventions for rotation angles is used.

The renderers that support *IRotationRenderer* are *ProportionalSymbolRenderer*, *ClassBreaksRenderer*, *UniqueValueRenderer*, and *SimpleRenderer* coclass.

Display

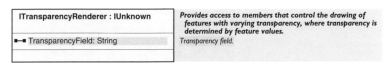

IPropertySupport : IUnknown	*Provides access to members that set a default property on an object.*
■— Current (in pUnk: IUnknown Pointer) : IUnknown Pointer	*The object currently being used.*
◄— Applies (in pUnk: IUnknown Pointer) : Boolean	*Indicates if the receiver can apply the given object at any given time.*
◄— Apply (in NewObject: IUnknown Pointer) : IUnknown Pointer	*Applies the given property to the receiver and returns the old object.*
◄— CanApply (in pUnk: IUnknown Pointer) : Boolean	*Indicates if the receiver can apply the given object at that particular moment.*

IPropertySupport is a generic interface implemented by most graphic elements and a few other objects. *IPropertySupport* is used for updating generic properties of an object. Through *IPropertySupport,* you can ask an object if another object, such as a color object, applies to it. If the object does apply, you can apply a new object of that type or ask for the current object.

ITransparencyRenderer : IUnknown	*Provides access to members that control the drawing of features with varying transparency, where transparency is determined by feature values.*
■—■ TransparencyField: String	*Transparency field.*

The *ITransparencyRenderer* interface is only used on layers that are based on polygon feature classes. The values in the *TransparencyField* modify the fill symbols (if they are of type *ISimpleFillSymbol*) such that the transparency of each symbol used to render each feature corresponds with the value in the field. The field values should range from 0 to 100. An attribute value of 100 is opaque, and a value of 0 is invisible.

If a transparency field is specified, the simple renderer will use the aggregated *TransparencyDisplayFilter* object to perform the changes to the display to achieve the transparency effect.

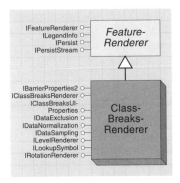

Use the class-breaks renderer to display data based on an attribute with values that represent ordinal, interval, or ratio data.

The *ClassBreaksRenderer* object can be set to break up one field of numeric data into arbitrary classes—for example, to separate population values into three classes of low, medium, and high. Classes are defined by specifying the break values between the classes; you can set these to be any values you like. However, you can use the *Classify* and *TableHistogram* objects to help calculate some useful breaks, such as "equal intervals".

A symbol is associated with each class, and this is used to draw features. For example, with a polygon feature class, a yellow fill symbol can represent low population, orange fill can represent medium, and red fill can represent high. The *ClassBreaksRenderer* works well with other feature types, too. For example, a line feature class representing roads with associated numeric values for traffic density can be rendered using different colors for high, medium, and low traffic. Cities, represented as points, could be classified with a range of circular marker symbols with different sizes and colors reflecting population.

The class-breaks renderer corresponds to GraduatedValues under the type of Quantities.

IClassBreaksRenderer : IUnknown	Provides access to members that control a renderer which is used to draw graduated color (choropleth) and graduated symbol maps.
■—■ BackgroundSymbol: IFillSymbol	Background fill symbol used when graduated marker symbols are draw on polygon features.
■—■ Break (in Index: Long) : Double	Break value at the specified index. Break(0) is the lowest break and represents the upper bound of the lowest class.
■—■ BreakCount: Long	Number of class breaks (equal to the number of classes).
■—■ Description (in Index: Long) : String	Description at the specified index.
■—■ Field: String	Classification field.
■—■ Label (in Index: Long) : String	Label at the specified index.
■—■ MinimumBreak: Double	Minimum break, i.e. the lower bound of the first class.
■—■ NormField: String	Normalization field.
■—■ SortClassesAscending: Boolean	Indicates if classes are displayed in increasing order in legends/TOC.
■—■ Symbol (in Index: Long) : ISymbol	Symbol at the specified index (used to draw features in the specified class).

The *Field* property specifies to which field in the feature class the class breaks apply. This field must be numeric.

To initialize some breaks, you just need to know how many breaks to set. This is set in *BreakCount* and corresponds to the number of classes. Once the *BreakCount* is set, the breaks, description, label, and symbol properties are initialized with the first index of 0 and the last index of *BreakCount* −1. Increasing *BreakCount* preserves existing breaks, but decreasing *BreakCount* removes excess break values.

```
Dim pClassBreaksRenderer As IClassBreaksRenderer
Set pClassBreaksRenderer = New ClassBreaksRenderer
pClassBreaksRenderer.Field = "POP1997"
pClassBreaksRenderer.BreakCount = 3
```

Before setting break values it is important to determine some characteristics of the data. If the field values have predefined intervals and related symbols, then these can be set without inspecting the data. For example, a temperature classification from freezing to boiling could be set up with breaks every 10 degrees Celsius.

If the classes are relative to the data (for example, classifying the data into equal intervals), then the data must be inspected to determine the

Display

classes. This could be done by iterating through the dataset and keeping a tally of the values found so far. Alternatively, the *TableHistogram* object can be used to extract data values and frequencies. These can then be passed to a *Classify* object to determine the breaks. These breaks may then be retrieved and set into the *ClassBreaksRenderer* object.

The lowest value in the dataset is specified via the *MinimumBreak* property. Values less than this will be considered outside the lowest class. Typically, this is set to the minimum data value. The value in *Break(0)* represents the upper value in the lowest class, and the break value is included. The highest value class is bounded by, and includes, the last break (*breakCount*-1). This is typically set to the maximum value.

Symbols are initialized and placed in indices corresponding to the breaks using the symbol property array. Consequently, the lowest class bounded by *Break(0)* will be depicted using *Symbol(0)*. Data values that are left out of the class breaks are drawn using the *BackgroundFill* symbol. The *BackgroundFill* symbol is also used to fill the polygon if the polygons are drawn with marker symbols.

The code below illustrates the setting up of three class breaks. The *maximumPopulation* variable has been previously calculated, and the function *GetRGBColor* is not shown, but it is used to return a color object with the supplied red, green, and blue values.

```
pClassBreaksRenderer.MinimumBreak = 0

' Low population class in yellow
Set pFillSymbol = New SimpleFillSymbol
pFillSymbol.Color = GetRGBColor(245, 245, 0)
pClassBreaksRenderer.Symbol(0) = pFillSymbol
pClassBreaksRenderer.Break(0) = maximumPopulation / 3
pClassBreaksRenderer.Label(0) = "Low"

' Medium population class in orange
Set pFillSymbol = New SimpleFillSymbol
pFillSymbol.Color = GetRGBColor(245, 122, 0)
pClassBreaksRenderer.Symbol(1) = pFillSymbol
pClassBreaksRenderer.Break(1) = maximumPopulation * (2 / 3)
pClassBreaksRenderer.Label(1) = "Medium"

' High population in red
Set pFillSymbol = New SimpleFillSymbol
pFillSymbol.Color = GetRGBColor(245, 0, 0)
pClassBreaksRenderer.Symbol(2) = pFillSymbol
pClassBreaksRenderer.Break(2) = maximumPopulation
pClassBreaksRenderer.Label(2) = "High"
```

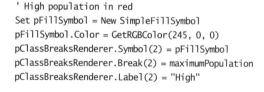

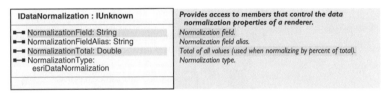

Break index	Break value	Corresponding Class	Fill symbol color
Break(2)	32,197,302	High (California)	
Break(1)	21,026,670	Medium (Texas and five others)	
Break(0)	11,066,153	Low (all other states, Wyoming at minimum)	
Minimum break	484,520		

The *Label* and *Description* fields are used to associate text with each class. These are used by the table of contents and map legends.

If *SortClassesAscending* is set to *False* (its default is *True*) the symbols used to draw the features are reversed in order. In the previous example, low population would be drawn in red.

The *NormField* allows a field to be specified to divide into the field specified for classification. Setting this property is the same as setting *IDataNormalization::NormalizationType = esriNormalizeByField* and setting *IDataNormalization::NormalizationField* equal to the field name.

IDataNormalization : IUnknown	Provides access to members that control the data normalization properties of a renderer.
■—■ NormalizationField: String	*Normalization field.*
■—■ NormalizationFieldAlias: String	*Normalization field alias.*
■—■ NormalizationTotal: Double	*Total of all values (used when normalizing by percent of total).*
■—■ NormalizationType: esriDataNormalization	*Normalization type.*

The *IDataNormalization* interface is used to map ratio data. This is used if you want to minimize differences based on the size of areas or numbers of features in each area. Ratios are created by dividing two data values; this is referred to as *normalizing* the data. For example, dividing the 18- to 30-year-old population by the total population yields the ratio of people aged 18 to 30. Similarly, dividing a value by the area of the feature yields a value-per-unit area, or density.

You can normalize your data in several ways by applying one of the following *esriDataNormalization* constants to the *NormalizationType* property.

Enumeration esriDataNormalization	Data normalization type.
0 - esriNormalizeByField	*Normalize by field.*
1 - esriNormalizeByLog	*Normalize by Log.*
2 - esriNormalizeByPercentOfTotal	*Normalize by percent of total.*
3 - esriNormalizeByArea	*Normalize by area.*
4 - esriNormalizeByNothing	*Do not Normalize.*

esriNormalizeByField requires the *NormalizationField* property to be set to a valid field name. This field is then divided into the data value.

esriNormalizeByLog will take a base 10 logarithm of the data values.

esriNormalizeByPercentageOfTotal requires the *NormalizationTotal* field to be set to the total data value. This is used to calculate percentage values by dividing the total into each data value and multiplying by 100.

esriNormalizeByArea is not implemented.

IDataExclusion: IUnknown	Provides access to members that control the exclusion of data values from a renderer.
ExclusionClause: String	Data exclusion where clause.
ExclusionDescription: String	Description for the excluded data.
ExclusionLabel: String	Label for the excluded data.
ExclusionSymbol: ISymbol	Symbol used to draw excluded values.
ShowExclusionClass: Boolean	Indicates if the exclusion symbol is used.

The *IDataExclusion* interface is implemented by *ChartRenderer, ClassBreaksRenderer, DotDensityRenderer,* and *ProportionalSymbolRenderer.*

This interface can be used to eliminate features from the renderer. These features may have erroneous attributes associated with them. An SQL expression set to the property *ExclusionClause* identifies these values— be careful to ensure the SQL syntax is valid, otherwise no features will be drawn.

Values that are excluded can optionally be symbolized with the symbol in *exclusionSymbol.* If this is not set, the feature will not be drawn.

If *ShowExclusionClass* is set to *False,* then excluded features will not be drawn with the *ExclusionSymbol.* This property controls the display of the map and the legend.

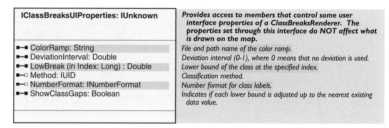

IClassBreaksUIProperties: IUnknown	Provides access to members that control some user interface properties of a ClassBreaksRenderer. The properties set through this interface do NOT affect what is drawn on the map.
ColorRamp: String	File and path name of the color ramp.
DeviationInterval: Double	Deviation interval (0-1), where 0 means that no deviation is used.
LowBreak (in Index: Long) : Double	Lower bound of the class at the specified index.
Method: IUID	Classification method.
NumberFormat: INumberFormat	Number format for class labels.
ShowClassGaps: Boolean	Indicates if each lower bound is adjusted up to the nearest existing data value.

The *IClassBreaksUIProperties* interface is used by the Layer/Properties/ Symbology dialog box to store additional values reflecting what the user has chosen in the dialog box. The properties of this interface are not parameters to rendering features. Keeping these values up-to-date helps keep the standard ArcMap dialog boxes consistent with the current settings. For example, when you set values into the LowBreak property, they will appear in the Range column of the classes.

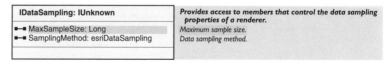

IDataSampling: IUnknown	Provides access to members that control the data sampling properties of a renderer.
MaxSampleSize: Long	Maximum sample size.
SamplingMethod: esriDataSampling	Data sampling method.

The *IDataSampling* interface is similarly used by the Layer/Properties/ Symbology dialog box to reflect values the user has chosen. If you programmatically update corresponding values in ArcObjects, update the values in this interface to keep the dialog box in synch with your application.

For documentation on the *IRotationRenderer* interface, see the previous topic on *SimpleRenderer.*

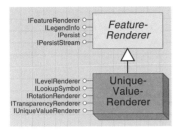

UniqueValueRenderer *is a way to symbolize the features of a layer based on the unique values of one or more attributes.*

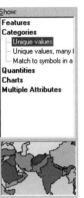

In the Layer Properties/Symbology/Show list in ArcMap, the unique-value renderer corresponds to Unique Values under the type of Categories.

Use the *UniqueValueRenderer* to display data that falls into distinct categories based on attribute values. If you have parcel data with land use types of residential, agriculture, and retail, you can use a different symbol to represent each unique land use type.

More than one category can be combined to give unique values. This is useful for differentiating features that are ambiguous in the individual categories but unique in their combination. When more than one attribute is specified, the combinations of unique values are used. Combinations of fields can be depicted, such as A|X, A|Y, A|Z, B|X, B|Y, B|Z, where | is a field delimiter.

IUniqueValueRenderer : IUnknown	Provides access to members that control a renderer where symbols are assigned to features based on unique attribute values.
ColorScheme: String	Color scheme (user interface property only).
DefaultLabel: String	Label used for unspecified values.
DefaultSymbol: ISymbol	Symbol used to draw any unspecified values (may be NULL).
Description (in Value: String) : String	Description for the specified label.
Field (in Index: Long) : String	Field at the specified index that is used to categorize features.
FieldCount: Long	Number of fields used by the renderer (0-3).
FieldDelimiter: String	Delimiter used to separate field values.
FieldType (in Index: Long) : Boolean	Indicates if the field at the specified index is a string.
Heading (in Value: String) : String	Heading that contains the specified value.
Label (in Value: String) : String	Label for the specified value.
LookupStyleset: String	Style used for matching (user interface property only).
ReferenceValue (in Value: String) : String	Reference value for the specified value.
Symbol (in Value: String) : ISymbol	Symbol associated with the specified value.
UseDefaultSymbol: Boolean	Indicates if DefaultSymbol is used for drawing unspecified values.
Value (in Index: Long) : String	Value at the specified index.
ValueCount: Long	Number of unique values used to categorize the data.
AddReferenceValue (in Value: String, in refValue: String)	Adds a value to the renderer to be grouped with refValue, which has already been added to the renderer.
AddValue (in Value: String, Heading: String, in Symbol: ISymbol)	Adds a value and corresponding symbol to the list. For multivariate cases, the specified value is a delimitted list of individual values.
RemoveAllValues	Removes all values from the renderer.
RemoveValue (in Value: String)	Removes a value from the renderer.

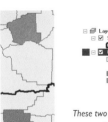

These two bitmaps show a map of two of the "Jefferson" counties distinguished by state name and the table of contents.

Use the *IUniqueValueRenderer* interface to specify the fields and then your unique values and corresponding symbols. Typically, you would specify one field as shown in this VBA code.

```
pUniqueValueRenderer.FieldCount = 1
pUniqueValueRenderer.Field(0) = "NAME"
```

You may also specify additional fields, which is valuable when a feature is ambiguous in the categories of the first field. For example, in the United States there are many counties in each state, and the county names are ambiguous to the United States as a whole. There are 26 counties called "Jefferson", and these would all get the same symbol unless they were distinguished by state name.

```
pUniqueValueRenderer.FieldCount = 2
pUniqueValueRenderer.Field(0) = "NAME"
pUniqueValueRenderer.Field(1) = "STATE_NAME"
pUniqueValueRenderer.FieldDelimiter = ","
```

Having set up the fields, the next step is to populate the unique values. The *AddValue* method creates a new value with a corresponding symbol and heading in the renderer object. You can retrieve and change the symbol at a later date by using the value as a lookup parameter to the *Symbol* property array.

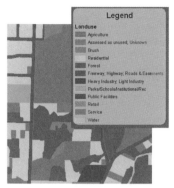

Sample ArcMap display of the UniqueValueRenderer

This also applies to the legend texts specified through the lookup parameter of *Label, Heading,* and *Description* property arrays. If a *Label* is not supplied, then it defaults to the same text as the value parameter. *Heading* defaults to the field name. The *Description* property is empty by default.

If a value and a new symbol are passed into *AddValue* and the value already exists in the renderer, then the symbol is replaced with the new symbol. The *ValueCount* property returns the number of unique values set up so far. The *Value* property array can be used to iterate through the existing values; the maximum index is *ValueCount*–1.

If multiple fields are involved, then the unique value must contain the two attribute values separated by the string specified in the *FieldDelimiter* property. This is typically set to a character that does not occur in the attribute string, for example, a comma.

```
pUniqueValueRenderer.AddValue "Jefferson,Montana", "", pSym1
pUniqueValueRenderer.AddValue "Jefferson,Idaho", "", pSym2
```

Values that have not been added to the renderer object can be drawn according to the symbol set in the *DefaultSymbol* property; remember to set the *UseDefaultSymbol* property to *True* first. The label for the default symbol is set in the *DefaultLabel* property.

If you would like two or more values to be in the same category and drawn with the same symbol, you can call the *AddReferenceValue* method, passing in the new value as the first parameter and an existing *refValue* as the second parameter. This will create a new unique value, but this value will not directly have an associated symbol—the symbol of the *refValue* is used to render the feature.

For example, the code below "Freeway" will be drawn using the symbol *pSymbol.* "Highway" is added as a reference to "Freeway" and will be drawn using the same symbol. Note that you cannot retrieve a symbol using *Symbol("Highway")* property—this will result in a VBA error exception. You can retrieve the reference value using the *ReferenceValue("Highway")* property. In this case, "Freeway" will be returned.

```
pUniqueValueRenderer.FieldCount = 1
pUniqueValueRenderer.Field(0) = "DESC"
pUniqueValueRenderer.AddValue "Freeway", "", pSymbol
pUniqueValueRenderer.AddReferenceValue "Highway", "Freeway"
```

pNextRow is a cursor to the current row. fieldNumber is the index of the field we are collecting values from. pEnumRamp enumerates colors from a color ramp object. codeValue is a string to hold the value read from the feature class.

The code snippets shown above put the values directly into *UniqueValueRenderer.* However, it is more likely you will scan the feature class for values and put them into the renderer object. Symbol colors to match the values can also be generated by iterating through a color ramp object. The VBA code below illustrates this loop.

It is also possible to use the IDataStatistics::UniqueValues method on the DataStatistics object to gather all the unique values in memory and then iterate through them.

```
Do While Not pNextRow Is Nothing
  Set pNextRowBuffer = pNextRow  'Get a value
  codeValue = pNextRowBuffer.Value(fieldNumber)
  Set pNextUniqueColor = pEnumRamp.Next 'Get a color
  If pNextUniqueColor Is Nothing Then 'Reset the ramp if out of colors
```

```
      pEnumRamp.Reset
      Set pNextUniqueColor = pEnumRamp.Next
    End If
    Set pSym = New SimpleFillSymbol 'Set the symbol to the new Color
    pSym.Color = pNextUniqueColor
    pUniqueValueRenderer.AddValue codeValue, "", pSym ' Add value and symbol
    Set pNextRow = pCursor.NextRow ' Advance to the next row
Loop
```

Display

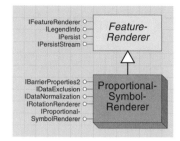

The proportional-symbol renderer draws symbols of varying size for each feature. The size is in proportion to a field value.

You can use the *ProportionalSymbolRenderer* to represent data values more precisely; the size of a proportional symbol reflects the actual data value.

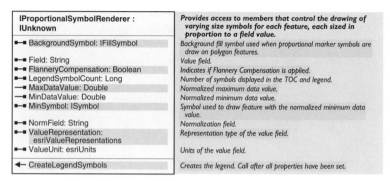

IProportionalSymbolRenderer : IUnknown	Provides access to members that control the drawing of varying size symbols for each feature, each sized in proportion to a field value.
■← BackgroundSymbol: IFillSymbol	Background fill symbol used when proportional marker symbols are draw on polygon features.
■← Field: String	Value field.
■← FlanneryCompensation: Boolean	Indicates if Flannery Compensation is applied.
■← LegendSymbolCount: Long	Number of symbols displayed in the TOC and legend.
─← MaxDataValue: Double	Normalized maximum data value.
─← MinDataValue: Double	Normalized minimum data value.
■← MinSymbol: ISymbol	Symbol used to draw feature with the normalized minimum data value.
■← NormField: String	Normalization field.
■← ValueRepresentation: esriValueRepresentations	Representation type of the value field.
■← ValueUnit: esriUnits	Units of the value field.
←─ CreateLegendSymbols	Creates the legend. Call after all properties have been set.

In the Layer Properties/Symbology/Show list in ArcMap, the proportional-symbol renderer corresponds to Proportional symbol under the type of Categories.

The symbol used to display the data is set with the property *MinSymbol*. This can be a marker or line symbol. Marker symbols can be used with polygon features. In this case, they are placed at the center of the polygon. An additional *BackgroundSymbol* property can also be specified to fill the polygons.

The *Field* property specifies the name of a numeric field; this is used to calculate each symbol's size on the map.

The *ValueUnit* specifies what distance units the data in the field represents (feet, meters, or other), or, for units that are not a distance (population counts, velocity, or other), this should be set to *esriUnknownUnits*.

If the *ValueUnit* is a distance, then the proportional-symbol renderer can take these values and change the size of the symbol supplied in *MinSymbol* to reflect this. There is no need to set the *MinDataValue* in this case. However, you should set the *ValueRepresentation* to specify how the symbol relates to the measurement. Marker symbols can be proportional by radius or area, whereas lines can be proportional by width or distance from the center line (half the width). Additionally, marker symbols should be circular or square for the radius and area settings to apply. If the *ValueRepresentation* is *esriValueRepUnknown*, then the symbol is proportional by width in both marker and lines.

An example of using the proportional-value renderer is where you have map tree locations as points and an attribute reflecting the radius of the tree canopy. By using proportional circles, the trees can be depicted by circles reflecting the actual ground covered by the tree.

Another application is a population map; the area of a circular marker can directly relate to the population value. Proportional symbols also apply well to line symbology; a river could be symbolized with a network of lines with different widths reflecting the river flow.

Enumeration esriValueRepresentations	Value representation type.
0 - esriValueRepUnknown	Value represents Unknown.
1 - esriValueRepRadius	Value represents Radius.
2 - esriValueRepArea	Value represents Area.
3 - esriValueRepDistance	Value represents Distance from Center.
4 - esriValueRepWidth	Value represents Width.

These are the values that can be set in the *ValueRepresentation* property.

If the *ValueUnit* is not known, then the proportional-symbol renderer must calculate an accurate scale for the symbols. In this case, the *MinDataValue* property must be set to the data value that relates to the size of the symbol set in *MinSymbol*. The symbols increase in proportion to the data values, with marker symbols increasing by the area and lines by width. So a value that is twice as big as the *MinDataValue* will have a marker twice the area of the smallest marker. In this case, the area is computed as if the marker was a square. With line symbols, a value that is twice the smallest value will have a line symbol twice as wide.

For marker symbols with unknown units, an appearance compensation can be specified. This will increase the marker size and is enabled by setting the *FlanneryCompensation* to *True*; this increase is an empirically derived result.

Similar to the class breaks renderer, you can specify a normalization field through the *NormField* property. This is exactly the same as setting the field in the *IDataNormalization::NormalizationField* property. Data is normalized before any calculations to set the symbol sizes are carried out. Normalization types for the proportional-symbol renderer can be by field value or by a base 10 logarithm.

As the proportional-symbol renderer does not use a fixed set of symbols, the symbols used in the legend must be created. Call *CreateLegendSymbols* to do this. If *ValueUnit* is set to a distance, then one symbol is used in the legend, and this is taken from *MinSymbol*.

This is a 1990 population map of the United States. The size area of the marker is in proportion to the population.

If the units are unknown, then a range of symbols are generated. The *MaxDataValue* should be set to represent the largest possible data value; this will correspond to the biggest symbol. *LegendSymbolCount* should be set to the number of required symbols in the legend. Be sure to set these two properties before calling *CreateLegendSymbols*. The symbols will be generated at powers of ten between the minimum and maximum values and then half- and quarter-values.

The VBA sample below illustrates setting up a proportional symbol renderer object for a population field for polygons of the United States. The units of population are not distance units; therefore, the *valueUnit* is set to be unknown. The *MinSymbol* is set to be a circular marker symbol and the *BackgroundSymbol* is a fill symbol. The minimum and maximum data values are calculated using a *DataStatistics* object that iterates a field and puts the results into the *IStatisticsResult* object.

```
Set pProportionalSymbolRenderer = New ProportionalSymbolRenderer
With pProportionalSymbolRenderer
  .ValueUnit = esriUnknownUnits
  .ValueRepresentation = esriValueRepUnknown
  .Field = "POP1990"
  .FlanneryCompensation = False
  .MinDataValue = pStatisticsResult.Minimum
  .MaxDataValue = pStatisticsResult.Maximum
  .BackgroundSymbol = pFillSymbol
  .MinSymbol = pSimpleMarkerSymbol
  .LegendSymbolCount = 3
  .CreateLegendSymbols
End With
```

Display

The proportional symbol renderer also supports the *IDataExclusion* interface—using this to exclude spurious data values can be an essential step for attributes that have unknown units.

For example, the population of the world has a large variation, from over a billion for China and India to some population values that are zero or unknown (-99999). In this case, even if the minimum symbol is one point in size, the maximum symbol can be huge. One way to avoid this problem is to exclude all countries with a population of less than a million persons.

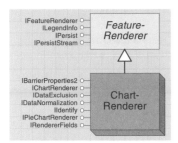

Charts are marker symbols and are placed at the center of polygons.

In the Layer Properties/Symbology/Show list in ArcMap, the chart renderer produces pie, bar, and stacked charts under the type of Charts.

The *ChartRenderer* object provides the ability to compare multiple attributes of a feature by depicting the attributes as elements of either a pie chart or bar chart.

Bar charts are available in two styles: a conventional bar chart, with a series of bars on a horizontal axis, and a stacked bar chart, where each bar is placed one above another. With pie charts, you can compare one feature to another by the relative size of the pie chart.

All the charts require a list of fields that are to be used in the chart; this is specified in the *IRendererFields* interface.

The chart renderers require specific marker symbols; these symbols implement *IChartSymbol*. A chart symbol contains further symbols that describe how each component of the chart is to be drawn.

For example, if a *BarChartSymbol* consists of two bars, then the object contains two fill symbols for each bar, and these correspond to two fields specified in *IRendererFields* in the *ChartRenderer*.

The available chart symbols are *BarChartSymbol*, *PieChartSymbol*, and *StackedBarChartSymbol*. By default, the chart symbols have a 3D appearance. For more information, see the section on chart symbols in this chapter.

Setting up a chart requires some properties to be set in *IChartRenderer*; additionally, there are some options for pie charts in *IPieChartRenderer* that can be set to size the pie chart.

The *IDataExclusion* and *IDataNormalization* interfaces are available in a similar way to the *ProportionalSymbolRenderer* object.

The VBA code below illustrates setting up a typical chart renderer object.

```
'Set up the chart marker symbol to use with the renderer
Dim pBarChartSymbol As IBarChartSymbol, pFillSymbol As IFillSymbol
Dim pMarkerSymbol As IMarkerSymbol, pSymbolArray As ISymbolArray
Dim pChartSymbol As IChartSymbol, pChartRenderer As IChartRenderer
Dim pRendererFields As IRendererFields

' Create a new bar chart symbol
Set pBarChartSymbol = New BarChartSymbol
' Set the width of each bar - units are points
pBarChartSymbol.Width = 6
Set pMarkerSymbol = pBarChartSymbol ' QI to marker symbol interface
Set pChartSymbol = pBarChartSymbol ' QI to chart symbol interface
pChartSymbol.maxValue = maxValue ' This is the biggest value of all bars
pMarkerSymbol.Size = 30 ' This is the maximum height of the biggest bar

Set pSymbolArray = pBarChartSymbol
Set pFillSymbol = New SimpleFillSymbol
pFillSymbol.Color = GetRGBColor(213, 212, 252) ' pastel green
pSymbolArray.AddSymbol pFillSymbol
Set pFillSymbol = New SimpleFillSymbol
```

Display

```
pFillSymbol.Color = GetRGBColor(193, 252, 179) ' pastel purple
pSymbolArray.AddSymbol pFillSymbol
Set pChartRenderer = New ChartRenderer ' Create a new chart renderer
' Set up the fields that comprise the components of a chart; a bar in
' a bar chart or a slice of a pie chart
Set pRendererFields = pChartRenderer
pRendererFields.AddField "MALES"
pRendererFields.AddField "FEMALES"

' Set the chart symbol into the renderer. This could also be a stacked
' bar or pie chart
Set pChartRenderer.ChartSymbol = pBarChartSymbol
Set pFillSymbol = New SimpleFillSymbol
pFillSymbol.Color = GetRGBColor(239, 228, 190)
Set pChartRenderer.BackgroundSymbol = pFillSymbol

' Disable so that charts appear in polygon centers
pChartRenderer.UseOverposter = False

pChartRenderer.CreateLegend ' Create the legend symbols

pChartRenderer.Label = "Population by Gender"
```

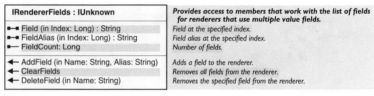

IRendererFields : IUnknown	Provides access to members that work with the list of fields for renderers that use multiple value fields.
■—■ Field (in Index: Long) : String	Field at the specified index.
■—■ FieldAlias (in Index: Long) : String	Field alias at the specified index.
■— FieldCount: Long	Number of fields.
← AddField (in Name: String, Alias: String)	Adds a field to the renderer.
← ClearFields	Removes all fields from the renderer.
← DeleteField (in Name: String)	Removes the specified field from the renderer.

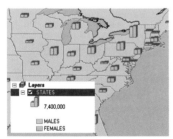

U.S. population by gender rendered with bar chart symbols

The *IRendererFields* interface allows you to specify the fields from the feature class that make up the chart. You can add in additional fields with *AddField* and then access and change individual fields using the *Field* property array. If you would like the text for the legend to be different from the field name, then set the *FieldAlias* array to the desired text.

IChartRenderer : IUnknown	Provides access to members that control the drawing of chart symbols (pie, bar, stacked bar) on a map to represent features.
■—□ BaseSymbol: ISymbol	Background fill symbol, (used when chart symbols are drawn for polygon features).
■—□ ChartSymbol: IChartSymbol	Chart symbol object.
■—■ ColorScheme: String	Color scheme (user interface property only).
■—■ FieldTotal (in Index: Long) : Double	Field total for the field at the specified index.
■—■ Label: String	Chart label.
■—■ UseOverposter: Boolean	Indicates if the overposter is used for positioning the chart symbols.
← CreateLegend	Creates the legend. Call after all properties are set.

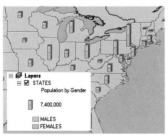

U.S. population by gender rendered with stacked bar chart symbols

The *IChartRenderer* interface specifies properties for pie, bar, and stacked bar charts. Pie charts require some additional properties to be set—see the *IPieChartRenderer* interface.

Charts are marker symbols and are placed at the center of polygons, so setting the *BackgroundSymbol* is a good idea so you can see the polygon shapes. The *ChartSymbol* property can be set to one of

BarChartSymbol, PieChartSymbol, or StackedBarChartSymbol. The chart symbol's ISymbolArray::SymbolCount must match the number of fields specified in the renderer's IRendererFields::FieldCount.

Setting UseOverposter to False will place the charts in the center of polygons; if this is set to True, the charts will be moved so that they do not overlap each other.

The symbols for the legend need to be explicitly created with the CreateLegend method. The Legend is composed of the chart symbol sized and labeled for half the maximum data value, followed by each fill symbol making up the chart with the text from ISymbolArray::FieldAlias (if this is empty, the field name is used). The Label property specifies what text appears above the chart in the legend; this must be set after calling CreateLegend.

If the normalization type is esriNormalizeByPercentOfTotal, the sum of the attribute values in a field has to be supplied in the FieldTotal property array.

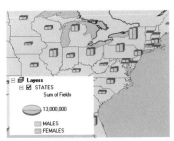

U.S. population by gender rendered with pie symbols

IPieChartRenderer : IUnknown	Provides access to members that work with additional chart renderer properties specific to pie charts.
■–■ FlanneryCompensation: Boolean	Indicates if Flannery Compensation is applied.
■–■ MinSize: Double	Symbol size (points) corresponding to the minimum value.
■–■ MinValue: Double	Minimum value (used for proportional sizing).
■–■ ProportionalBySum: Boolean	Indicates if the size of pie chart symbols is determined by the sum of the values.
■–■ ProportionalField: String	Field used to determine size of the pie chart symbols.
■–■ ProportionalFieldAlias: String	Field alias for the proportional field.

The pies can be sized by the sum of the values making up the pie. Set the *ProportionalBySum* property to *True* for this option to apply. Alternatively, the pie can be sized by a data value from another field. To do this, set the field name to *ProportionalField*. As with other data values, this field is normalized before the pie is sized. The legend text against the pie chart is taken from *ProportionalFieldAlias*, or, if this is empty, the proportional field name is used.

The overall size of a pie chart can be adjusted in a similar way to marker symbols with the proportional symbol renderer. If you want all the pies to appear as the same size, then leave all the properties in this interface set to their default values.

For both these options, you must set the *MinSize* property, which is the size in points of the width of the smallest pie chart. Additionally, you must set the minimum data value into *MinValue* property. Appearance compensation can also be specified to increase the size of the markers by setting *FlanneryCompensation* to *True*. For example, if the individual slices in a pie reflect population of males and population of females in a state, then the radius of the pie can represent the sum of the fields or population of the states as a whole.

```
Dim pPieChartRenderer As IPieChartRenderer
Set pPieChartRenderer = pChartRenderer
pPieChartRenderer.ProportionalBySum = True
pPieChartRenderer.MinSize = 6
pPieChartRenderer.MinValue = minFieldValue
```

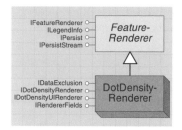

IFeatureRenderer
ILegendInfo
IPersist
IPersistStream

Feature-Renderer

IDataExclusion
IDotDensityRenderer
IDotDensityUIRenderer
IRendererFields

DotDensity-Renderer

A dot-density renderer places varying densities of dots within polygon features.

The *DotDensityRenderer* object requires a *DotDensityFillSymbol*. It fills a polygon layer with a scattering of marker symbols. The markers are randomly placed. The density of the marker symbols is determined by specifying the *DotValue*, or how much each dot represents.

Multiple attributes may be specified in one dot density fill symbol, where each attribute has a different marker symbol. However, this can lead to some confusing maps, so typically only one attribute is used.

Additionally, a mask layer of polygons can be specified, which can limit the areas where dots are placed.

The following sample code exercises a *DotDensityRenderer*.

In the Layer Properties/Symbology/Show list in ArcMap, the dot-density renderer corresponds to Dot Density under the type of Quantities.

The features of a polygon feature class are displayed with a number of dots corresponding to a value. This renderer is suitable for distribution throughout an area. For instance, a dot map depicting population will most likely have the strongest concentrations of dots along rivers and roads and near coastlines.

```
Dim pDotDensityRenderer As IDotDensityRenderer
Dim pDotDensityFillSymbol As IDotDensityFillSymbol
Dim pRendererFields As IRendererFields, pSymbolArray As ISymbolArray
Dim pColor As IColor, pMarkerSymbol As ISimpleMarkerSymbol

Set pDotDensityRenderer = New DotDensityRenderer
Set pRendererFields = pDotDensityRenderer 'QI to the fields
pRendererFields.AddField "POP1999" 'Add in the one population field

' Set up a new dot density fill symbol
Set pDotDensityFillSymbol = New DotDensityFillSymbol

' this is the size of each dot in points
pDotDensityFillSymbol.DotSize = 3

' The fill only has dots, the outline and background fill are removed
Set pColor = New RgbColor
pColor.NullColor = True
pDotDensityFillSymbol.BackgroundColor = pColor
pDotDensityFillSymbol.Outline = Nothing

' Put one circular marker into the dot density symbol
' use default color (black)
Set pSymbolArray = pDotDensityFillSymbol
Set pMarkerSymbol = New SimpleMarkerSymbol
pMarkerSymbol.Style = esriSMSCircle
pSymbolArray.AddSymbol pMarkerSymbol

' Put the dot density fill symbol into the renderer
Set pDotDensityRenderer.DotDensitySymbol = pDotDensityFillSymbol

pDotDensityRenderer.DotValue = 50000 'Each dot represents 50,000 people
pDotDensityRenderer.CreateLegend 'Create the symbols for the legend
```

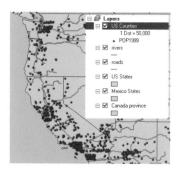

Map of the west coast of the U.S. Population density is drawn by county.

IDotDensityRenderer : IUnknown	Provides access to members that control the drawing of varying densities of dots within polygon features to represent different quantities.
■—■ ColorScheme: String	Color scheme, (user interface property only).
■—□ ControlLayer: IFeatureLayer	Control layer used for masking.
■—□ DotDensitySymbol: IDotDensityFillSymbol	The dot density symbol.
■—■ DotValue: Double	Value of each dot.
■—■ MaintainSize: Boolean	Indicates if dot size is preserved when zooming (the alternative is that density is preserved).
← CreateLegend	Creates the legend. Call after all properties are set.

The dot-density fill symbol is set into *DotDensitySymbol*. Additionally, you must set the *DotValue*, which represents the quantity of each dot. In combination with the area of the polygon, this value relates to the density of the dots. To increase the density of the dots, decrease the *DotValue*.

The symbols used in the legend must be explicitly created with a call to the *CreateLegend* method; the legend will contain a single marker symbol for each field, added using *IRendererFields::AddField*.

IDotDensityUIRenderer : IUnknown	Provides access to members that work with additional renderer properties which appear on the user interface.
■—■ maxArea: Double	Area in map units of the polygon with maximum density.
■—■ maxValueArea: Double	Maximum density.
■—■ meanArea: Double	Mean area in map units.
■—■ meanValueArea: Double	Mean density.
■—■ minArea: Double	Area in map units of the polygon with minimum density.
■—■ minValueArea: Double	Minimum density.

Set values in the *IDotDensityUIRenderer* interface if you wish to keep the settings in the renderer object consistent with the property page.

The *IRendererFields* interface stores a list of attribute field names used to draw dot densities, for example, population. The number of marker symbols in the *DotDensityFillSymbol* must match the number of renderer fields. See the description of this interface under the *ChartRenderer* coclass.

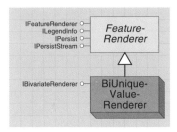

The biunique value renderer creates maps of multiple attributes.

The biunique value renderer is used to produce multivariate maps. Unlike maps that display one attribute, or characteristic, of the data—for example, a name or an amount—multivariate maps display two or more attributes at the same time. A multivariate map could use color to show the unique habitats of Africa and also display biodiversity of each region using a graduated symbol, where a larger symbol represents a greater diversity.

IBivariateRenderer : IUnknown	Provides access to members that control the rendering of bivariate symbology based on two constiuent renderers.
MainRenderer: IFeatureRenderer	Main renderer of a bivariate renderer.
VariationRenderer: IFeatureRenderer	Variation renderer of a bivariate renderer.
CreateLegend	Creates the legend. Call after all properties are set.

The *MainRenderer* property must be set to a *UniqueValueRenderer*, and the *VariationRenderer* must be a *ClassBreaksRenderer*. The *BiUniqueValueRenderer* takes the symbols of the unique value renderer and alters it by the size or color of the class-breaks renderer.

In the Layer Properties/Symbology/Show list in ArcMap, the biunique value renderer corresponds to Quantity by Category under the type of Multiple Attributes.

The *VariationRenderer* would typically be set up with a symbol type that matches the *MainRenderer*, for example, marker symbols in the main renderer and marker symbols in the variation renderer. The only exception to this is where the main renderer uses a fill symbol of varying colors for polygons, and the variation renderer uses markers varying in size. In this case, markers are placed at the polygon centers with varying background fills.

If variation renderer symbols vary in size, then the color of the main renderer is used and this is subdivided by size for the second attribute.

If the variation renderer symbols vary in color, then the colors of the main render are modified by the hue and saturation of the symbols of the variation renderer. In this case, it is wise to have your main renderer symbols colors, which have different hue values but the value and saturation do not really matter. The opposite applies to the variation renderer.

The *CreateLegend* method will generate legend symbols from both renderers that are related to the one layer. The legend typically consists of combinations of all possible values from the two renderers, unless different-sized maker symbols are used with polygon fills, in which case the marker sizes and fills are shown separately.

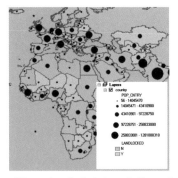

This map shows landlocked countries illustrated as two colors and population as a circular marker.

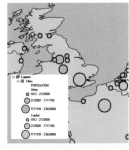

This map shows cities of the world sized by population—capital cities are in a different color than other cities.

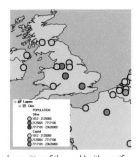

This map shows cities of the world with a uniform circular marker, capital cities distinguished by color, and population distinguished by lightness.

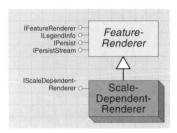

The scale-dependent renderer is made of multiple renderers, each operating within a scale range.

In the Layer Properties/ Symbology/Show list in ArcMap, the dot-density renderer corresponds to Dot Density under the type of Quantities.

The *ScaleDependentRenderer* is a renderer that contains other renderers. Its purpose is to allow you to specify different renderers for scale ranges. For example, when a user views a layer at its full extent, it will draw with one set of basic symbols, and when the user zooms in far enough, the symbols will change to become more detailed.

You can specify as many renderers and scale ranges as you need. One example would be showing road networks—when zoomed out to view a country, then roads would be drawn as simple lines with a *SimpleRenderer* coclass. But when zoomed in, the roads may be drawn using detailed line symbols reflecting the road type using a *UniqueValueRender*.

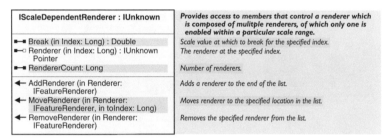

The *AddRenderer* method adds a feature renderer to the scale renderer. You must then set a corresponding *Break* array property to indicate map scale below which the renderer is used. For example, a renderer that displays at less than 1:10,000 would have a break value set to 10,000.

The following VBA sample combines the renderers from the second and third map layers into a scale-dependent renderer and sets this into the first map layer. Typically, you would add the same layer three times to ArcMap first, set some symbology on the second and third layers, then run this macro to set up the first layer.

```
Dim pDoc As IMxDocument, pLayer0 As IGeoFeatureLayer
Dim pLayer1 As IGeoFeatureLayer, pLayer2 As IGeoFeatureLayer
Dim pScaleDependentRenderer As IScaleDependentRenderer
Set pDoc = Document
Set pLayer0 = pDoc.FocusMap.Layer(0) ' Get a handle on each layer
Set pLayer1 = pDoc.FocusMap.Layer(1)
Set pLayer2 = pDoc.FocusMap.Layer(2)

Set pScaleDependentRenderer = New ScaleDependentRenderer
With pScaleDependentRenderer
  .AddRenderer pLayer1.Renderer ' Add in the detail renderer
  .Break(0) = 12000000
  .AddRenderer pLayer2.Renderer ' Add in the less detailed renderer
  .Break(1) = 1000000000
End With

' Set the scale break renderer into the first layer.
Set pLayer0.Renderer = pScaleDependentRenderer
```

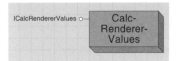

CalcRendererValues *is a utility object used to perform simple statistical calculations on a feature layer for use by renderers.*

The *CalcRendererValues* object is a utility object that can be used in combination with a chart renderer and a feature layer. It is used to calculate minimum and maximum data values and field totals.

First, set up your chart renderer object. You can set data exclusion and normalization properties, but do not set the *MinValue* or *FieldTotals* yet. Next, call the *ICalcRendererValues::SetData* method. This points the *CalcRendererValues* object at the chart renderer and feature layer objects. To simply calculate the maximum and minimum values, use the *CalcMinMax* method. This will do the job of iterating the feature layer, taking into account normalization and data exclusion to determine the minimum and maximum values.

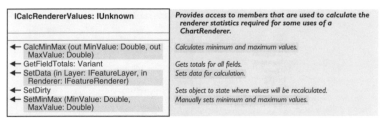

CalcMinMax also takes into account what minimum and maximum values the chart renderer requires. There are three possibilities.

1. When you are sizing pie charts in proportion to a single field, then the minimum and maximum value of the attribute values of this field are returned. This is the case when IChartRenderer::ProportionalField *has been set.*

2. When you are sizing a pie chart by the sum of all fields, then the minimum and maximum sums of all fields are returned. This is the case when IChartRenderer::ProportionalBySum *is set to True.*

3. When you are using a bar (or stacked bar) chart and you want to get the maximum and minimum attribute values, not caring which field these come from, then these values will be used to set into IChartSymbol::MaxValue *to size the biggest bar in all the charts.*

You can set your own minimum and maximum values with *SetMinMax*. If you call *CalcMinMax* a second time, the same minimum and maximum values will then be returned without rescanning the feature layer. To force a recalculation, call *SetDirty* before calling *CalcMinMax*.

If your chart renderer requires field totals (the normalization type is *esriNormalizeByPercentOfTotal*) and your chart renderer is for bar or stacked bar charts, you can call *GetFieldTotals* to work these out and return a safe array of the double values. You can then set the *IChartRenderer::FieldTotal* property array based on this array of doubles. Again, the *SetDirty* method is required to force a rescan of the feature layer.

The following VBA code illustrates how to calculate minimum and maximum values for a pie chart renderer where the pies are sized in proportion to the sum attribute values of the pie slices. In this code, *pFeatureLayer* is a feature layer, *pPieChartRenderer* is set to be a *IPieChartRenderer* and has *ProportionalBySum = True*. Because of this, using the *CalcRendererValues* object works out the minimum to be the sum of the data values of the smallest pie.

```
Dim pCalcRendererValues As ICalcRendererValues
Set pCalcRendererValues = New CalcRendererValues

' Point the CalcRendererValues at the feature layer
pCalcRendererValues.SetData pFeatureLayer, pPieChartRenderer
Dim minVal As Double, maxVal As Double

' This will scan all the features and return minimum and maximum values
pCalcRendererValues.CalcMinMax minVal, maxVal
' Now set the smallest pie value, other pies will be drawn in proportion
pPieChartRenderer.minValue = minVal
```

You can create your own renderer COM object. This is useful if you want complete control over drawing all the features for a feature layer.

There are several examples of custom renderers in the ArcObjects Developer Help under ArcMap/Symbology/Renderers.

The IFeatureRenderer interface is more fully documented with the FeatureRenderer abstract class at the beginning of this chapter section.

Custom feature drawing can be used to achieve a similar effect to custom renderers. However, custom features are more powerful. They can encapsulate behavior that is not related to symbology. Additionally, unlike custom renderers, the link between the custom feature and the behavior is stored in the geodatabase, not in map documents.

Another way to integrate a custom renderer and property page within the ArcGIS framework is by writing a FeatureClassExtension. Your class extension must implement IFeatureClassExtension and IFeatureClassDraw.

In brief, the GUID of the FeatureClassExtension object is stored as an entry in the geodatabase. Then, when the FeatureClass draws, it looks to the FeatureClassExtension and uses the renderer defined there (IFeatureClassDraw:: CustomRenderer), which can be either a custom renderer or one of the standard ESRI renderers. You can also associate a custom renderer property page through IFeatureClassDraw:: CustomRendererPropertyPageCLSID.

For more information about writing feature class extensions, see Volume 2, Chapter 8, 'Accessing the geodatabase', as well as the sample code under Geodatabase/Class Extensions.

The minimum interface you are required to implement for a functioning custom renderer is the *IFeatureRenderer* interface. However, it is usually recommended to implement additional interfaces. This topic is a summary of the typical interfaces that are implemented.

IFeatureRenderer : IUnknown	Provides access to members that control functionality common to all feature renderers.
ExclusionSet: IFeatureIDSet	Sets an object reference to a temporary drawing exclusion set.
RenderPhase (in drawPhase: tagesriDrawPhase) : Boolean	Indicates if renderer uses the specified draw phase.
SymbolByFeature (in Feature: IFeature) : ISymbol	Symbol used to draw the specified feature.
CanRender (in featClass: IFeatureClass, in Display: IDisplay) : Boolean	Indicates if the specified feature class can be rendered on the given display.
Draw (in Cursor: IFeatureCursor, in drawPhase: tagesriDrawPhase, in Display: IDisplay, in trackCancel: ITrackCancel)	Draws features from the specified cursor on the given display.
PrepareFilter (in fc: IFeatureClass, in QueryFilter: IQueryFilter)	Prepares the query filter for the rendering process.

The *IFeatureRenderer* interface is the core of the renderer. The main method that will be called by the framework is *Draw*. It is the job of your renderer to draw the feature layer anyway you specify. Your renderer is passed a feature cursor as well as a display on which to draw.

Before a *Draw* occurs, you are given an opportunity with *PrepareFilter* to modify the filter used to produce the feature cursor. At a minimum, you must add into the filter any fields you need for your renderer.

In response to a *IFeatureRenderer::Draw* method, a renderer will typically iterate through the feature cursor, taking each feature in turn. For each feature, the renderer works out a symbol to represent the feature and passes this off to *IFeatureDraw::Draw* for display. Calling the feature's *IFeatureDraw::Draw* allows custom features to use their own drawing methods.

If you want to restrict which layers your custom renderer can be applied to, such as being applicable only to line layers, then in your implementation of *IFeatureRenderer::CanRender*, you can test properties of the feature layer and return *True* if your renderer supports it and *False* if it does not.

IPersistStream : IUnknown	
GetSizeMax (out pcbSize: _ULARGE_INTEGER)	
IsDirty	
Load (in pstm: IStream)	
Save (in pstm: IStream, in fClearDirty: Long)	

Implement *IPersistStream* to preserve the symbology of your renderer in map documents (.mxd), layer files (.lyr), or anything else that persists object state. This gives you the opportunity to load and save any objects (typically symbols) you are using in your renderer. If the objects you are using also implement the *IPersistStream* mechanism (as do symbols), you can call on those objects to persist themselves.

IPersistVariant : IUnknown	Provides access to members used for storage of an object through VARIANTs.
■— ID: IUID	The ID of the object.
◀— Load (in Stream: IVariantStream)	Loads the object properties from the stream.
◀— Save (in Stream: IVariantStream)	Saves the object properties to the stream.

When programming in Visual Basic, use *IPersistVariant* instead of *IPersistStream* because *IPersistStream* contains types not supported in VB.

ILegendInfo : IUnknown	Provides access to members that control legend information provided by a renderer.
■— LegendGroup (Index: Long) : ILegendGroup	Number of legend groups contained by the object.
■— LegendGroupCount: Long	Number of legend groups contained by the object.
■— LegendItem: ILegendItem	Optional. Defines legend formatting for layer rendered with this object.
■—■ SymbolsAreGraduated: Boolean	Indicates if symbols are graduated.

Implement *ILegendInfo* to ensure the table of contents and legends show a list of what symbols, labels, and headings your renderer is using. Typically, you reuse the existing *LegendGroup* and *LegendClass* objects and use these to hold the symbols for your renderer. Implement your own interface to allow your renderer settings to be modified by a caller of your renderer. This could well be by a custom renderer property page.

To make your custom renderer object active on a layer, you could run a VBA script that creates your renderer object (you will need to add a reference in the VBA environment to your custom renderer's DLL), then replace an existing renderer in a particular layer.

```
' pGeoFeatureLayer is an interface pointer to the IGeoFeatureLayer
' interface on a Feature Layer object.

' Create a your custom renderer
Set pMyRenderer = New CustomRenderer.clsMyRenderer
' You could set some properties here

' Now set the custom renderer into the feature layer
Set pGeoFeatureLayer.Renderer = pMyRenderer

' Now refresh the active view and update the contents of the doc to _
' reflect the new symbology
```

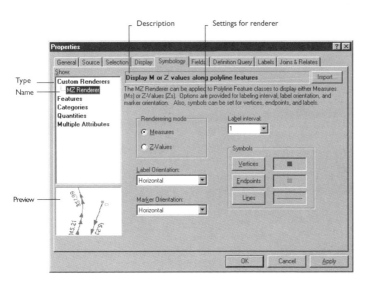

Description | Settings for renderer

Type
Name
Preview

Creating a custom property page provides a user interface for working with the settings of a custom object that is fully integrated within the ArcMap framework. This section provides an overview of how to implement a custom renderer property page that allows users to interact with the settings of a custom renderer. By registering the property page in the "ESRI Renderer Property Pages" component category, your custom user interface will appear in the Layer/Properties/Symbology page along with all of the standard symbology options. While this section provides a good overview, you should also look at the developer sample code before embarking on a custom property page implementation.

Define your custom renderer property page as a class that implements three interfaces: *IRendererPropertyPage*, *IComPropertyPage* (essentially a Visual Basic compatible version of the Microsoft interface *IPropertyPage*), and *IComEmbeddedPropertyPage*. Design your GUI on a form, placing all controls and descriptive text either directly on the form or on another object that supports a window handle, such as a Picture box control. Also, it is good practice to always reference this form through a private data member in your class module.

IRendererPropertyPage : IUnknown	Provides access to members that control renderer property pages.
■— ClassID: IUID	Property page class id (unique identifier object).
■— Description: String	Renderer description.
■— Name: String	Name of the renderer.
■— PreviewImage: Long	Preview bitmap for the renderer that appears on the page.
■— RendererClassID: IUID	Renderer class id (unique identifier object).
■— Type: String	Renderer type. Used to group renderers into categories.
◄— CanEdit (in obj: IFeatureRenderer) : Boolean	Indicates if the property page can modify the properties of the specified renderer.

Some properties in *IRendererPropertyPage* will appear on the ArcMap symbology property page (your page's parent) to help guide users when accessing your custom page. These include the *Description*, which will appear at the top of the page, and the *PreviewImage*, which will appear in the bottom left.

Name appears in the tree view on the left side of the symbology property page.

If you use an already existing *Type*, then your renderer will appear under that category. Or, you can use a new *Type*, in which case a new category will be created for your renderer.

Use *IComPropertyPage::Priority* to control where your renderer appears in the tree. Use a lower number to have your renderer and category

Type	Name	Priority
Features	Single symbol	100
Categories	Unique values	200
	Unique values, many fields	210
	Match to symbols in a style	300
	Graduated symbols	310
	Proportional symbols	320
	Dot density	330
Charts	Pies	400
	Bars	410
	Stacked	420
Multiple Attributes	Quantity by category	500

This table lists standard renderer property pages and their priorities.

appear toward the top of the list. Note that the priority of the first page in a category controls where that category fits in the list.

In *CanEdit* you should check the in parameter to make sure your custom page can edit the specified renderer. Typically, your custom property page will only edit your custom renderer. Follow similar logic in *IComPropertyPage::Applies*.

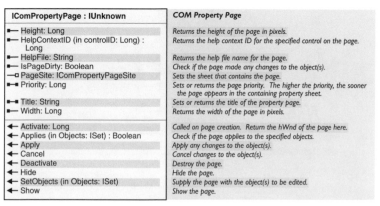

IComPropertyPage : IUnknown	COM Property Page
■— Height: Long	Returns the height of the page in pixels.
■— HelpContextID (in controlID: Long) : Long	Returns the help context ID for the specified control on the page.
■— HelpFile: String	Returns the help file name for the page.
■— IsPageDirty: Boolean	Check if the page made any changes to the object(s).
—□ PageSite: IComPropertyPageSite	Sets the sheet that contains the page.
■— Priority: Long	Sets or returns the page priority. The higher the priority, the sooner the page appears in the containing property sheet.
■—■ Title: String	Sets or returns the title of the property page.
■— Width: Long	Returns the width of the page in pixels.
← Activate: Long	Called on page creation. Return the hWnd of the page here.
← Applies (in Objects: ISet) : Boolean	Check if the page applies to the specified objects.
← Apply	Apply any changes to the object(s).
← Cancel	Cancel changes to the object(s).
← Deactivate	Destroy the page.
← Hide	Hide the page.
← SetObjects (in Objects: ISet)	Supply the page with the object(s) to be edited.
← Show	Show the page.

IComPropertyPage works with general property page settings. The typical behavior for a property page is to allow changes to a temporary object (that is, a renderer). Then if the Apply or Ok button is pressed, the temporary renderer replaces the "live" renderer object on the feature layer. If the Cancel button is pressed, then the temporary renderer is discarded. (In an alternate implementation, there is no temporary renderer object. Instead, the property page stores temporary changes to the renderer's settings. Then, if OK or Apply is clicked, the settings are applied to the renderer, and if Cancel is pressed, these settings are discarded.)

SetObjects is called by the framework as a renderer property page is opened. In this method you are passed a set of objects (map, feature layer, feature class, and feature renderer). You should find the renderer in this list, check for the proper type, and pass it to your page (that is, your form) for editing. The framework automatically handles cloning of the renderer object, so it is not necessary to make a copy before passing it to your page. (In the alternate implementation, instead of passing the renderer to your page for editing, simply initialize your page's controls using the renderer properties.)

Conversely, the *Apply* method is triggered when the user presses Apply or Ok on the layer properties property sheet. In this method, call *IComEmbeddedPropertyPage::QueryObject*, passing your renderer. If your page is directly editing the renderer, then do nothing in *QueryObject*, as the framework will automatically make all changes to the renderer permanent. (In the alternate implementation, you must instead manually update the renderer properties based on the settings from your page.)

For renderer property pages, the framework handles the cloning of the renderer as the page is opened and also the apply and cancel operations as the page is dismissed. This behavior holds true for renderers, but it can vary for other types of objects.

Activate is called as your page gains focus. Load the form here, and return your page's window handle (that is, either the handle of your form or your Picture box). Unload your form in *Deactivate*, which is called when the page loses focus. In ArcMap, this occurs when the user switches to another symbology option or to another tab on the Layer Properties dialog box or when this dialog box is closed. *Cancel* is triggered when the user presses Cancel on the layer properties property sheet.

PageSite allows your page to call back to its parent, telling it that a change has been made. In ArcMap, this gives a renderer property page control over the enabling of the Apply button on the layer properties property sheet. For a custom page, one implementation is to have a data member of type *IComPropertyPageSite* on your form, and set this in *PageSite*. In your form code, call *IComPropertyPageSite::PageChanged* on this member anytime a control changes. This will enable the Apply button.

Similarly, the framework also checks *IsPageDirty* to determine if your page needs to be redrawn. Avoid unnecessary redrawing by only conditionally returning *True*.

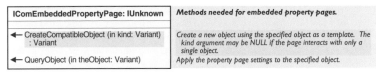

IComEmbeddedPropertyPage: IUnknown	Methods needed for embedded property pages.
←– CreateCompatibleObject (in kind: Variant) : Variant	Create a new object using the specified object as a template. The kind argument may be NULL if the page interacts with only a single object.
←– QueryObject (in theObject: Variant)	Apply the property page settings to the specified object.

Custom renderer property pages fall into the class of embedded property pages and thus must implement *IComEmbeddedPropertyPage*. Embedded property pages (as opposed to simple property pages) reside in the framework in a configuration that, as the property page is loaded, allows for the retention of properties from a previously edited object. *IComEmbeddedPropertyPage::CreateCompatibleObject* is used to manage the preservation of properties from the old object to the new object, which may or may not be of the same type.

For example, in ArcMap, users pick from different symbology options from the tree view on the Layer properties symbology tab. Because the internal representation of each option is a different renderer object, as the user picks a new option, a new renderer is being edited. In some cases, properties are preserved during this transition. For example, when a user switches between the Bar chart and Pie chart options, the renderer fields and symbols are preserved from the old to the new renderer. Other examples of embedded property pages in ArcMap include the *ColorBrowser* and *NumberFormatDialog*.

In addition to managing the retention of properties from an old renderer, you should also use *CreateCompatibleObject* to avoid unnecessary, excessive cloning of renderers. In this method check to see if the in parameter is an object of the type your page should edit. If so, return that same object. If not, create and return a new renderer object of the proper type, setting properties on the new object if you wish.

Designing a custom symbol property page provides an integrated user interface for working with the custom symbol settings. The implementation strategy for this page will be similar to that followed when designing a custom renderer property page.

Define your custom symbol property page as a class that implements four interfaces: *ISymbolPropertyPage, IComPropertyPage, IComPropertyPage2,* and *IPropertyPageContext.* Register your custom symbol object in the proper custom symbol category, for example, "Marker Symbols".

Register your custom property page object in the category "Symbol Property Pages". Your custom property page will then become available in the "Type" pulldown menu on the ArcMap symbol property editor property sheet.

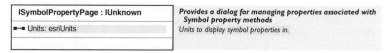

ISymbolPropertyPage : IUnknown	*Provides a dialog for managing properties associated with Symbol property methods*
■—■ Units: esriUnits	*Units to display symbol properties in.*

The *ISymbolPropertyPage* interface controls the measurement units that will appear on the page.

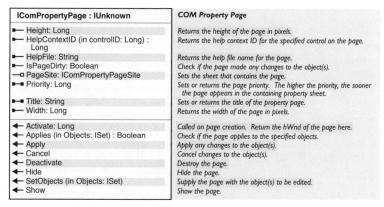

IComPropertyPage : IUnknown	COM Property Page
■— Height: Long	*Returns the height of the page in pixels.*
■— HelpContextID (in controlID: Long) : Long	*Returns the help context ID for the specified control on the page.*
■— HelpFile: String	*Returns the help file name for the page.*
■— IsPageDirty: Boolean	*Check if the page made any changes to the object(s).*
■—◻ PageSite: IComPropertyPageSite	*Sets the sheet that contains the page.*
■—■ Priority: Long	*Sets or returns the page priority. The higher the priority, the sooner the page appears in the containing property sheet.*
■—■ Title: String	*Sets or returns the title of the property page.*
■— Width: Long	*Returns the width of the page in pixels.*
← Activate: Long	*Called on page creation. Return the hWnd of the page here.*
← Applies (in Objects: ISet) : Boolean	*Check if the page applies to the specified objects.*
← Apply	*Apply any changes to the object(s).*
← Cancel	*Cancel changes to the object(s).*
← Deactivate	*Destroy the page.*
← Hide	*Hide the page.*
← SetObjects (in Objects: ISet)	*Supply the page with the object(s) to be edited.*
← Show	*Show the page.*

For more information about implementing *IComPropertyPage* and *IPropertyPageContext,* see the section on implementing a custom renderer property page.

IComPropertyPage2 : IUnknown	*Provides access to members that control a COM property page.*
← QueryCancel: Boolean	*Returns VARIANT_FALSE to prevent the cancel operation or VARIANT_TRUE to allow it.*

The *IComPropertyPage2* interface controls the Cancel operation on your page.

Color objects

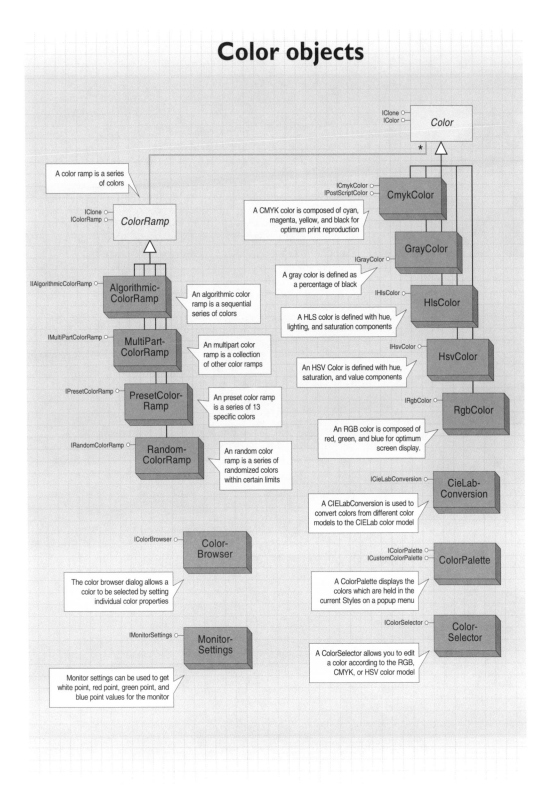

Color

IClone
IColor

A color ramp is a series
of colors

ColorRamp

IClone
IColorRamp

ICmykColor
IPostScriptColor

CmykColor

A CMYK color is composed of cyan,
magenta, yellow, and black for
optimum print reproduction

GrayColor

IGrayColor

A gray color is defined as
a percentage of black

IIAlgorithmicColorRamp

Algorithmic-
ColorRamp

An algorithmic color
ramp is a sequential
series of colors

IHlsColor

HlsColor

A HLS color is defined with hue,
lighting, and saturation components

IMultiPartColorRamp

MultiPart-
ColorRamp

An multipart color
ramp is a collection
of other color ramps

IHsvColor

HsvColor

An HSV Color is defined with hue,
saturation, and value components

IPresetColorRamp

PresetColor-
Ramp

An preset color ramp
is a series of 13
specific colors

IRgbColor

RgbColor

An RGB color is composed of
red, green, and blue for optimum
screen display.

IRandomColorRamp

Random-
ColorRamp

An random color
ramp is a series of
randomized colors
within certain limits

ICieLabConversion

CieLab-
Conversion

A CIELabConversion is used to
convert colors from different color
models to the CIELab color model

IColorBrowser

Color-
Browser

The color browser dialog allows a
color to be selected by setting
individual color properties

IColorPalette
ICustomColorPalette

ColorPalette

A ColorPalette displays the
colors which are held in the
current Styles on a popup menu

IMonitorSettings

Monitor-
Settings

Monitor settings can be used to get
white point, red point, green point, and
blue point values for the monitor

IColorSelector

Color-
Selector

A ColorSelector allows you to edit
a color according to the RGB,
CMYK, or HSV color model

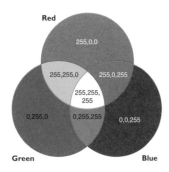

Red, green, blue (RGB) color model

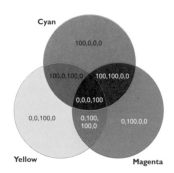

Cyan, magenta, yellow (CMY) color model

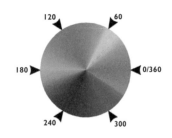

Color wheel for hue, saturation, and value
(HSV) color model

Color can be represented using a number of different models, which often reflect the ways in which colors can be created in the real world.

You may be familiar with the RGB color model, which is based on the primary colors of light—red, green, and blue. When red, green, and blue rays of light coincide, white light is created. The RGB color model is therefore termed *additive*, as adding the components together creates light.

By displaying pixels of red, green, and blue light, your computer monitor is able to portray hundreds, thousands, and even millions of different colors. To define a color as an RGB value, we give a separate value to the red, green, and blue components of the light. A value of 0 indicates no light, and 255 indicates the maximum light intensity.

Here are a few rules for RGB values:

- If all RGB values are equal, then the color is a gray tone.

- If all RGB values are 0, the color is black (an absence of light).

- If all RGB values are 255, the color is white.

Another common way to represent color, the CMYK model, is modeled on the creation of colors by spot printing. Cyan, magenta, yellow, and black inks are mingled on paper to create new colors. The CMYK model, unlike RGB, is termed *subtractive*, as adding all the components together creates an absence of light (black).

Cyan, magenta, and yellow are the primary colors of pigments—in theory you can create any color by mixing different amounts of cyan, magenta, and yellow. In practice, you also need black, which adds definition to darker colors and is better for creating precise black lines.

HSV, or the hue, saturation, and value color model, describes colors based around a color wheel that arranges colors in a spectrum.

The hue value indicates where the color lies on this color wheel and is given in degrees. For example, a color with a hue of 0 will be a shade of red, whereas a hue of 180 will indicate a shade of cyan.

Saturation describes the purity of a color. Saturation ranges from 0 to 100; therefore, a saturation of 20 would indicate a neutral shade, whereas a saturation of 100 would indicate the strongest, brightest color possible.

The value of a color determines its brightness, with a range of 0 to 100. A value of 0 always indicates black; however, a value of 100 does not indicate white, it just indicates the brightest color possible.

Hue is simple to understand, but saturation and value can be confusing. It may help to remember these rules:

- If value = 0, the color is black.

- If saturation = 0, the color is a shade of gray.

- If value = 255 and saturation = 0, the color is white.

The HLS, or hue, lightness, and saturation model, has similarities with the HSV model. Hue again is based on the spectrum color wheel, with a value of 0 to 360. Saturation again indicates the purity of a color, from 0 to 100. However, instead of value, a lightness indicator is used, again with a range of 0 to 100. If lightness is 100, white is produced, and if lightness is 0, black is produced.

The last color model is grayscale. 256 shades of pure gray are indicated by a single value. A grayscale value of 0 indicates black, and a value of 255 indicates white.

0   255

Grayscale color model

The CIELAB color model is used internally by ArcObjects, as it is device independent. The model, based on a theory known as opponent process theory, describes color in terms of three "opponent channels". The first channel, known as the *1* channel, traverses from black to white. The second, or *2* channel, traverses red to green hues. The last channel, or *3* channel, traverses hues from blue to yellow.

Display

Sample color values

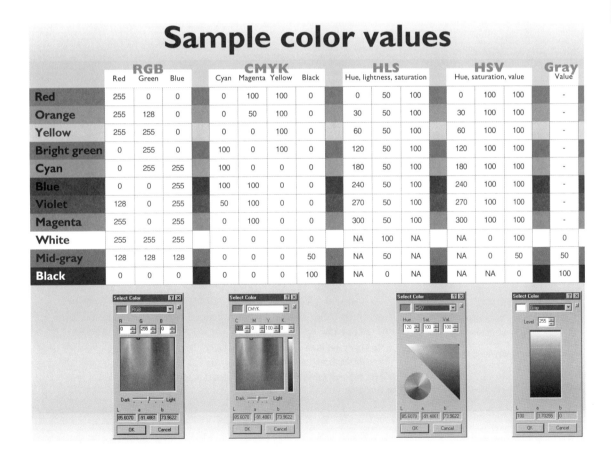

| | RGB | | | CMYK | | | | HLS | | | HSV | | | Gray |
	Red	Green	Blue	Cyan	Magenta	Yellow	Black	Hue, lightness, saturation			Hue, saturation, value			Value
Red	255	0	0	0	100	100	0	0	50	100	0	100	100	-
Orange	255	128	0	0	50	100	0	30	50	100	30	100	100	-
Yellow	255	255	0	0	0	100	0	60	50	100	60	100	100	-
Bright green	0	255	0	100	0	100	0	120	50	100	120	100	100	-
Cyan	0	255	255	100	0	0	0	180	50	100	180	100	100	-
Blue	0	0	255	100	100	0	0	240	50	100	240	100	100	-
Violet	128	0	255	50	100	0	0	270	50	100	270	100	100	-
Magenta	255	0	255	0	100	0	0	300	50	100	300	100	100	-
White	255	255	255	0	0	0	0	NA	100	NA	NA	0	100	0
Mid-gray	128	128	128	0	0	0	50	NA	50	NA	NA	0	50	50
Black	0	0	0	0	0	0	100	NA	0	NA	NA	NA	0	100

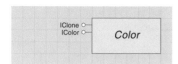

The color objects allow you to define colors simply and precisely. They also control color-related effects such as transparency.

Objects that support the *IColor* interface allow precise control over any color used within the ArcObjects model. You can get and set colors using a variety of standard color models—RGB, CMYK, HSV, HLS, and Grayscale.

Color is used in many places in ArcGIS applications—in feature and graphics symbols, as properties set in renderers, as the background for ArcMap or ArcCatalog windows, and as properties of a raster image.

The type of color model used in each of these circumstances will vary. For example, a window background would be defined in terms of an RGB color because display monitors are based on the RGB model. A map made ready for offset-press publication could have CMYK colors to match printer's inks.

"CMYK" stands for cyan, magenta, yellow, and black, the colors of the four inks used by offset presses. "RGB" stands for red, green, and blue, the three colors emitted in a monitor display.

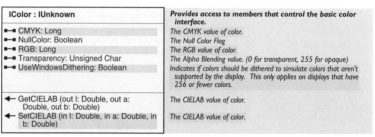

You can convert any color object to its representative value in the CIELAB color model, which is used internally by ArcObjects.

The properties available on the *IColor* interface define the common functionality of all color objects. Representations of colors are held internally as CIELAB colors, described in the color theory topic. The CIELAB color model is device independent, providing a frame of reference to allow faithful translation of colors between one color model and another. You can use the *GetCIELAB* and *SetCIELAB* methods of the *IColor* interface to interact directly with a color object using the CIELAB model.

One important point to note when reading the RGB property: the UseWindowsDithering property should generally be set to True. If UseWindowsDithering is False, the RGB property returns a number with a high byte of 2, indicating the use of a system color, and the RGB property will return a value outside of the range you would expect. If you write to the RGB property, the UseWindowsDithering property will be set to True for you.

Although colors are held internally as CIELAB colors, you don't need to deal directly with the CIELAB color model—you can use the *IColor* interface to simply read and define colors. For example, the *RGB* property can be used to read or write a *Long* integer representing the red, green, and blue values for any color object. You can use the Visual Basic *RGB* function to set the *RGB* property of a color object as follows.

```
colMyColor.RGB = RGB(intMyRedValue, intMyGreenValue, intMyBlueValue)
```

Or, you could use the following function, which essentially performs the same action but lets you see how the conversion is performed.

For more information on converting individual byte values to long integer representation, look for topics on color models and hexadecimal numbering in your development environment's online Help system.

```
Public Function RGBToLong(lngRed As Long, lngGreen As Long, _
    lngBlue As Long) As Long
    RGBToLong = lngRed + (&H100 * lngGreen) + (&H10000 * lngBlue)
End Function
```

If you are reading the *RGB* property, you can break down the RGB value into its component red, green, and blue values with an inverse function of the previously defined *RGBToLong* function, as follows:

```
Public Function ReturnRGBBytes(ByVal lngRGB As Long) As Byte()
  Dim bytArray(2) As Byte
  bytArray(0) = lngRGB Mod &H100
  bytArray(1) = (lngRGB \ &H100) Mod &H100
  bytArray(2) = (lngRGB \ &H10000) Mod &H100
  ReturnRGBBytes = bytArray
End Function
```

The *IColor* interface also provides access to colors through another color model—CMYK. The *CMYK* property can be used in a similar way as RGB to read or write a *Long* integer representing the cyan, magenta, yellow, and black components of a particular color—the difference being that the CMYK color model requires four values to define a color. Visual Basic does not have a function for creating a *CMYK Long* integer value, but the *RGBToLong* function can be adapted as shown.

```
Public Function CMYKToLong(lngBlack As Long, lngYellow As Long, _
             lngMagenta As Long, lngCyan As Long) As Long
  CMYKToLong = lngBlack + (&H100 * lngYellow) + _
             (&H10000 * lngMagenta) + (&H1000000 * lngCyan)
End Function
```

Setting the *NullColor* property to *True* will result in the set color being nullified. All items with color set to *Null* will not appear on the display. This only applies to the specific color objects—not all items with the same apparent color; therefore, you can have different null colors in one *Map* or *PageLayout*.

IColor also has two methods to convert colors to and from specific CIELAB colors, using the parameters of the CIELAB color model. You can set a color object to a specific CIELAB color by using *SetCIELab*, or read CIELAB parameters from an existing color by using *GetCIELab*. See also the *CieLabConversion* coclass.

Color transparency does not get used by the feature renderers; instead, a display filter is used. Setting the transparency on a color has no effect, unless the objects using the color honor this setting.

The *Color* class is only an abstract class—when dealing with a color object, you always interact with one of the color coclasses, which are described below. *RGBColor*, *CMYKColor*, *GrayColor* coclass, *HSVColor*, and *HLSColor* are all creatable classes, allowing new colors to be created programmatically according to the most appropriate color model.

Display

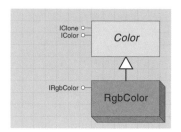

RGB colors are defined in terms of the amount of red, green, and blue.

The *RGBColor* coclass defines a simpler way to get and set the red, green, and blue components of a color, compared to using the *RGB* property of the *IColor* interface.

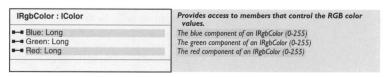

The *IRGBColor* interface defines colors by using 3 properties, *Red, Green,* and *Blue*, which may all be set to values between 0 and 255.

The *IRGBColor* interface defines a simpler way to get and set the red, green, and blue components of a color, compared to using the *RGB* property of the *IColor* interface as discussed earlier. The *Red, Green,* and *Blue* properties may all be set to values between 0 and 255.

For example, from the color theory discussed previously, we can see that if we mix red and green, we get yellow. Therefore, to create a new color that is bright yellow, we might do the following.

```
Dim pRGB As IRgbColor
Set pRGB = New RgbColor
pRGB.Red = 255    'Use the maximum amount of Red
pRGB.Green = 255 'Use the maximum amount of Green
```

There's no need to set the *Blue* property in this example, as the *Red, Green,* and *Blue* properties all default to zero. A darker yellow would be created by using equal, but smaller, values for *Red* and *Green*.

The *CMYKColor* coclass represents colors by using the CMYK color model, described on the color theory page. Colors can be specified for output in terms of *Cyan, Magenta, Yellow,* and *Black*.

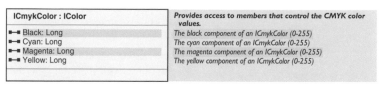

CMYK colors are defined in terms of the amount of cyan, magenta, yellow, and black.

The *ICMYKColor* interface allows you to define colors in terms of the CMYK color model by setting its four properties—*Cyan, Magenta, Yellow,* and *Black*—to values between 0 and 100. A value of 0 indicates the lack of a color, and a value of 100 indicates a maximum of a color. From the color theory, mixing magenta and yellow creates red; therefore, to create a red *CMYKColor,* we could write code like this:

```
Dim pCMYKCol As ICmykColor
Set pCMYKCol = New CmykColor
pCMYKCol.Yellow = 100
pCMYKCol.Magenta = 100
```

The *CMYKColor* coclass also includes the *IPostScriptColor* interface, but this interface is not supported at ArcGIS 8.1.

Display

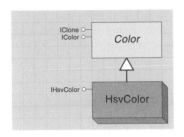

HSVColors are defined based on the HSV color model, which defines colors in terms of hue (color), saturation (purity), and value (brightness).

The *HSVColor* coclass represents colors by using the hue, saturation, and value color model described on the color theory page. *HSVColors* may be returned, for example, by a *RandomColorRamp* class.

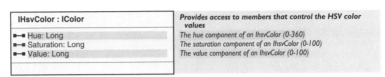

IHsvColor : IColor	Provides access to members that control the HSV color values
▪-▪ Hue: Long	The hue component of an IhsvColor (0-360)
▪-▪ Saturation: Long	The saturation component of an IhsvColor (0-100)
▪-▪ Value: Long	The value component of an IhsvColor (0-100)

The *HSVColor* coclass supports the *IHSVColor* interface. Colors are defined by three read–write properties: *Hue*, *Saturation*, and *Value*. The *Hue* property may be set to a number between 0 and 360, indicating in degrees where the hue lies on the color wheel. The *Saturation* property is a number between 0 and 100 indicating the saturation, or purity, of the color, and the *Value* property is a number between 0 and 100 indicating the value, or brightness, of a color. All of the properties have a default value of 0; therefore, the default *HSVColor* is black.

Using these properties, we can create a bright yellow *HSVColor* like this:

```
Dim pHSV As IHSVColor
Set pHSV = New HSVColor
pHSV.Hue = 60              'Yellow lies at 60 degrees on the color wheel
pHSV.Saturation = 100      'Use the maximum saturation for a bright color
```

The *HLSColor* coclass represents colors by using the hue, saturation, and lightness—a similar color model to HSV. However, HLS colors use *Lightness* instead of *Value*.

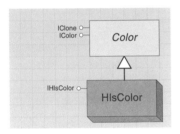

HLSColors are defined based on the HLS color model, similar to the HSV model, which defines colors in terms of hue (color), lightness, and saturation (purity).

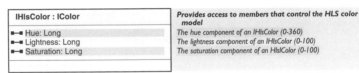

IHlsColor : IColor	Provides access to members that control the HLS color model
▪-▪ Hue: Long	The hue component of an IHlsColor (0-360)
▪-▪ Lightness: Long	The lightness component of an IHlsColor (0-100)
▪-▪ Saturation: Long	The saturation component of an IHlsIColor (0-100)

The *IHLSColor* interface defines colors by three read–write properties, *Hue, Saturation,* and *Lightness.* The *Hue* property may be set to a number between 0 and 360, indicating in degrees where the hue lies on the color wheel. The *Saturation* property is a number between 0 and 100 indicating the saturation, or purity, of the color, and the *Lightness* property is a number between 0 and 100 indicating the lightness, or paleness, of a color. Regardless of the other properties, a lightness of 0 is always black, and a lightness of 100 is always white. All of the properties have a default value of 0; therefore, the default *HSVColor* is black.

The *GrayColor* class represents the simplest of all the color models. Gray colors may be encountered, for example, in a grayscale bitmap.

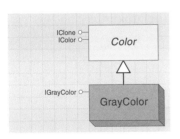

Gray colors are expressed as simple values from 0 to 255.

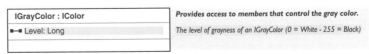

IGrayColor : IColor	Provides access to members that control the gray color.
▪-▪ Level: Long	The level of grayness of an IGrayColor (0 = White - 255 = Black)

The *Level* property can be set to a value representing a pure shade of gray, from 0, which is black, to 255, which is white.

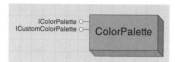

The ColorPalette is a popup menu displaying a choice of the colors defined by your currently selected Styles or, alternatively, a set of colors you specify.

The *ColorPalette* coclass defines a popup menu that can be used to allow interactive selection of colors. The colors included in the menu include all the colors in the *Styles* currently referenced by the Style-Gallery. By selecting the More Colors option on the menu, the Color-Selector will be displayed.

IColorPalette : IUnknown	Color Palette interface.
■— Color: IColor	Get Selected Color
◄— TrackPopupMenu (in rect: tagRECT, in currentColor: IColor, in Orientation: Boolean, in hParentWnd: Long) : Boolean	Show Color Palette

The *IColorPalette* interface allows you to display the *ColorPalette* to users, allowing them to select the colors they wish. The *TrackPopup-Menu* method controls the display of the palette with four parameters. The first parameter defines a rectangle, a *tagRect* structure, in screen coordinates (pixels) that the menu will align itself with—for example, the coordinates of the button that displays the popup menu. For more information about getting the onscreen coordinates of controls, see your development environment's documentation.

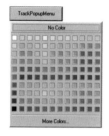

TrackPopupMenu, *Orientation = False*

The third parameter is a Boolean, which affects the orientation and location of the menu. If *False*, the menu will align beneath the rectangle specified; if *True,* the menu will appear to the right of the rectangle.

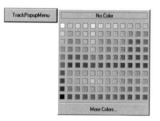

TrackPopupMenu, *Orientation = True*

The second parameter is a color object, which allows you to specify the current color. If the color exactly matches a color on the menu, that color will be displayed as selected initially. If the user cancels the palette rather than selecting a color, the read-only *Color* property will reflect the color passed in this parameter.

If the user selects a specific color, the *Color* property will return that selected color. If the user selects the More Colors option and selects a color from the *ColorSelector* that is then displayed, the *IColorPalette Color* property will return that color.

ICustomColorPalette : IUnknown	Interface for Setting or Creating a Custom Color Palette
—□ ColorSet: ISet	Set the Color Objects

The *ColorPalette* coclass also supports the *ICustomColorPalette* interface. This interface allows you to determine exactly which colors will be shown on the *ColorPalette* menu, instead of displaying the colors defined in the current Styles. To use the *ICustomColorPalette* interface, set the write-only property *ColorSet* to a *Set* coclass. The *Set* coclass, which supports the *ISet* interface required by the *ColorSet* property, should contain the *Color* objects you wish to display. For example, you could display a *ColorPalette* with four simple colors like this:

```
Dim pColorSet As ISet, pColor As IColor
Set pColorSet = New esriCore.Set
Set pColor = New RgbColor
```

```
pColor.RGB = 255       ' Red
pColorSet.Add pColor
Set pColor = New RgbColor
pColor.RGB = 65535     ' Yellow
pColorSet.Add pColor
Set pColor = New RgbColor
pColor.RGB = 65280     ' Green
pColorSet.Add pColor
Set pColor = New RgbColor
pColor.RGB = 16711680 ' Blue
pColorSet.Add pColor
```

The code produces this dialog box display.

```
Dim pCustomPalette As ICustomColorPalette, pPalette As IColorPalette, _
    pRect As tagRECT

Set pCustomPalette = New ColorPalette
Set pCustomPalette.ColorSet = pColorSet

Set pPalette = pCustomPalette
pPalette.TrackPopupMenu pRect, pColor, False, Me.hWnd
```

Note that since the *ISet Add* method passes the item by reference, you must create a new color object to pass into the method each time.

Display

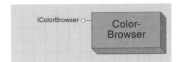

The ColorBrowser allows the user to select a color by specifying individual RGB, CMYK, HSV, HLS, or gray color properties.

Use the *ColorBrowser* coclass to display the ArcMap color browser dialog box. Note that this coclass should only be used from within the ArcMap framework.

IColorBrowser : IUnknown	Custom Color Dialog interface.
Color: IColor	Color edited by the browser.
DoModal (in hWnd: Long) : Boolean	Show the browser.

First, set the *Color* property to an existing *IColor* object—the type of coclass you use will determine what options the dialog displays for editing the color (see the pictures to the left).

Use the *DoModal* method as shown with the *ColorSelector* coclass, passing in the *hWnd* of the *Application* object of the ArcMap framework as this method's parameter.

Edit a color by specifying red, green, and blue proportions or by specifying cyan, magenta, yellow, and black proportions.

Edit a color by specifying hue, saturation, and value proportions or by specifying the degree of grayness.

Edit a color by specifying a name selected from all the available colors in your selected Styles.

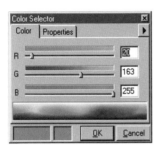

The ColorSelector is a dialog box that can be used to create new color objects. The dialog presents slider bars and check boxes that can be used to precisely set the properties of the new color.

The *ColorSelector* coclass contains a popup menu that can be used to allow interactive selection of a range of colors.

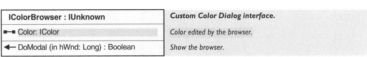

IColorSelector : IColorBrowser	*Custom Color Dialog interface.*
← InitPopupPosition (in parentLeft: Long, parentTop: Long, parentRight: Long, parentBottom: Long, aboveParent: Boolean)	*Initialize Popup Position*

IColorBrowser : IUnknown	*Custom Color Dialog interface.*
▪—▪ Color: IColor	*Color edited by the browser.*
← DoModal (in hWnd: Long) : Boolean	*Show the browser.*

Using the *IColorSelector* interface and the inherited *IColorBrowser* interface, you can present users with the *ColorSelector* dialog box.

First, you may want to specify the color that is already displayed by the dialog box when the user first sees it—you can do this by setting the read/write *Color* property to any color object, as shown in the following code.

```
Dim pColor As IColor
Set pColor = New RgbColor
pColor.RGB = 255  'Red
```

```
Dim pSelector As IColorSelector
Set pSelector = New ColorSelector
pSelector.Color = pColor
```

The *InitPopupPosition* method can be used to set the initial display location of the dialog box in screen coordinates.

To display the dialog box, you should call the *DoModal* method. The method takes one parameter, a handle to the parent Form, which is used to ensure the dialog box displays modally. The *DoModal* method returns a Boolean—you should check the result to determine if the user intended to cancel the action (the result is *False*) or click OK (the result is *True*). For example:

```
If Not pSelector.DoModal(Me.hWnd) Then
  Dim pOutColor As IColor
  Set pOutColor = pSelector.Color
  Me.BackColor = pOutColor.RGB
End If
```

To determine which color was selected, simply read the *Color* property.

Display

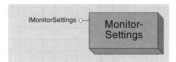

The monitor settings object can be used in conjunction with a device called a colorimeter to adjust the display of colors on a monitor.

The *MonitorSettings* coclass is not commonly used. It can be set to get and set *WhitePoint, RedPoint, GreenPoint,* and *BluePoint* values for the *Monitor*.

IMonitorSettings : IUnknown	Provides access to members that control the monitor settings.
■━■ Gamma: Double	The gamma value of the monitor. (1 <= gamma value <= 3).
■━■ MonitorName: String	The name of the monitor.
■━■ PhosphorName: String	The phosphor name of the monitor.
■━■ WhitePointName: String	The white point name of the monitor.
← GetBluePoint (out X: Double, out Y: Double)	The blue point of the monitor (0 <= x <= 1, 0 <= y <= 1.
← GetGreenPoint (out X: Double, out Y: Double)	The green point of the monitor (0 <= x <= 1, 0 <= y <= 1.
← GetRedPoint (out X: Double, out Y: Double)	The red point of the monitor (0 <= x <= 1, 0 <= y <= 1.
← GetWhitePoint (out X: Double, out Y: Double)	The white point of the monitor (0 <= x <= 1, 0 <= y <= 1.
← SetBluePoint (in X: Double, in Y: Double)	The blue point of the monitor (0 <= x <= 1, 0 <= y <= 1.
← SetGreenPoint (in X: Double, in Y: Double)	The green point of the monitor (0 <= x <= 1, 0 <= y <= 1.
← SetRedPoint (in X: Double, in Y: Double)	The red point of the monitor (0 <= x <= 1, 0 <= y <= 1.
← SetWhitePoint (in X: Double, in Y: Double)	The white point of the monitor (0 <= x <= 1, 0 <= y <= 1.

After using the *SetBluePoint, SetGreenPoint, SetRedPoint,* or *SetWhitePoint* methods to change monitor settings, the monitor settings should be reloaded.

CieLabConversion *provides information about colors within the CIELAB color space and can also be used to compare colors.*

The *CieLabConversion* coclass provides information about the location of colors within the CIELAB color space, the device independent color model used internally by ArcObjects. Colors can be converted from RGB and HSV models to the CIELAB model. It can also be used to compare the visual difference between two colors.

ICieLabConversion : IUnknown	Provides access to members that control the CIE Lab conversion.
■— SettingsVersion: Long	Gets monitor settings version
◄— GetDistance (in l1: Double, a1: Double, b1: Double, l2: Double, a2: Double, b2: Double) : Double	Gets visual difference between two CIELAB colors
◄— HsvToLab (in h: Integer, in s: Unsigned Char, in v: Unsigned Char, out l: Double, a: Double, b: Double)	Converts an RGB color to a CIELAB color
◄— LabToHsv (out h: Integer, in s: Unsigned Char, in v: Unsigned Char, in l: Double, a: Double, b: Double)	Converts a CIELAB color to an RGB color
◄— LabToRgb (out RGB: Long, in l: Double, a: Double, b: Double)	Converts a CIELAB color to an RGB color
◄— ReloadSettings	Reloads the monitor settings from the registry
◄— RgbToLab (in RGB: Long, out l: Double, a: Double, b: Double)	Converts an RGB color to a CIELAB color

The *ICieLabConversion* interface provides four methods for converting colors to and from the CIELAB color model (these methods are the ones used by the *IColor* interface's *SetCIELab* and *GetCIELab* methods). The methods *RGBtoLab, LabToRGB, HSVToLab,* and *LabToHSV* all take in parameters with which to populate the new converted values, as well as the value to convert. For example, to convert an HSV color representing yellow to CIELAB values, we might do the following:

```
Dim l As Double, a As Double, b As Double
Dim h As Integer, s As Byte, v As Byte

h = 60
s = 100
v = 100

Dim gConversion As ICieLabConversion
Set gConversion = New CieLabConversion
Call gConversion.HsvToLab(h, s, v, l, a, b)
MsgBox "L=" & l & " a=" & a & " b=" & b, 64, "CIELAB conversion from HSV"
```

The *GetDistance* function provides a useful indication of the visual difference of two colors by passing in two colors via their l, a, and b values. A distance of 4–10 may be indicative of two very similar, but just distinguishable colors—lighter colors tend to be more distinguishable. A distance of 20–30 may produce distinct but similar colors, whereas distances of > 30 indicate quite different colors.

Bear in mind that the difference between two colors will be affected by your monitor settings—if you have less than 24-bit color, two internally similar colors may be displayed exactly the same. If you have changed your monitor settings, call the *ReloadSettings* method to update your *CieLabConversion* object.

Display

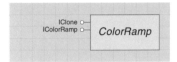

The color ramp objects offer a simple way to create a coherent or random range of colors. You may wish to use a color ramp as the fill when drawing polygons or to define the colors used by a renderer.

The objects supporting the *IColorRamp* interface offer a simple way to define a series of colors for use elsewhere in ArcObjects. For example, you can set a color ramp directly onto the *ColorRamp* property of the *IGradientFillSymbol* interface of a *FillSymbol*, or you might wish to create a color ramp to define the colors used in a *ClassBreaksRenderer*.

The individual *ColorRamp* objects offer different ways of defining the criteria that determine which colors will comprise the *ColorRamp*. Random colors can be created using the *RandomColorRamp*, and sequential colors can be created using the *AlgorithmicColorRamp*. The *PresetColorRamp* coclass contains 13 colors, allowing the creation of ramps mimicking ArcView GIS 3.x color ramps. In addition, the *MultiPartColorRamp* allows you to create a single color ramp that concatenates other color ramps, providing unlimited color ramp capabilities.

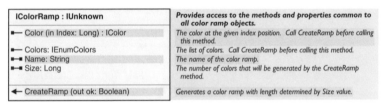

IColorRamp : IUnknown	Provides access to the methods and properties common to all color ramp objects.
■— Color (in Index: Long) : IColor	The color at the given index position. Call CreateRamp before calling this method.
■— Colors: IEnumColors	The list of colors. Call CreateRamp before calling this method.
■—■ Name: String	The name of the color ramp.
■—■ Size: Long	The number of colors that will be generated by the CreateRamp method.
◄— CreateRamp (out ok: Boolean)	Generates a color ramp with length determined by Size value.

ColorRamps are used in two different ways in ArcObjects: by accessing the individual colors in a ramp or by using the ramp object directly as a property or, in a method, of another object.

First, a color ramp can be set up and its individual colors accessed. For example, when a *UniqueValueRenderer* is created, each symbol in its symbol array should be set individually, perhaps using colors from a color ramp.

Note that if you set the Size property, then read it back before calling CreateRamp, you will find that Size = 0. This indicates that no Colors have been created. After calling CreateRamp, the Size property will equal 5.

To retrieve individual colors from a color ramp, first set the *Size* property according to the number of *Color* objects you wish to retrieve from the ramp. The *CreateRamp* method should then be called, which populates both the *Color* and the *Colors* properties. The *Color* property holds a read-only, zero-based array of *Color* objects, returned by index. The code fragment below shows the creation of a *RandomColorRamp* and the generation of 10 color objects from that ramp. Note that the Boolean parameter used in the *CreateRamp* method is checked after the method is called to ensure the colors were generated correctly.

```
Dim pColorRamp As esriCore.IRandomColorRamp
Set pColorRamp = New esriCore.RandomColorRamp
pColorRamp.Size = 10
Dim bOK As Boolean
pColorRamp.CreateRamp bOK
If bOK = True Then
  Dim i As Integer
  For i = 0 To pColorRamp.Size - 1
    ' Access the Color array here, for example, set the colors
    ' for an array of symbols, or map layers etc...
  Next i
End If
```

The *Colors* property returns an enumeration of colors and is useful as a lightweight object to pass around between procedures.

Second, a color ramp object may be used directly—for example, the *ColorRamp* property of the *IGradientFillSymbol* can be set to a specific color ramp object. The *MultiPartColorRamp* also uses color ramp objects directly by passing the object as a parameter in the *AddRamp* method. Below we can see a *GradientFillSymbol* object being created with an *AlgorithmicColorRamp* as its fill. The *IntervalCount* is set, which decides the amount of colors in the gradient fill.

```
Dim pAlgoRamp As IAlgorithmicColorRamp
Set pAlgoRamp = New AlgorithmicColorRamp

pAlgoRamp.FromColor = myFromColorObject
pAlgoRamp.ToColor = myToColorObject

Dim pGFill As esriCore.IGradientFillSymbol
Set pGFill = New esriCore.GradientFillSymbol
pGFill.ColorRamp = pAlgoRamp
pGFill.IntervalCount = 5
```

If the ramp will be used directly, as above, it is not necessary to set the *Size* property or to call the *CreateRamp* method yourself. In these cases, the parent object uses the information contained in the color ramp object to generate the number of colors it requires. The *Size* property will be ignored.

The name property simply stores a string, which you may want to use to keep track of your color ramps—it is not used internally by ArcObjects.

Each of the color ramp coclasses has one interface that inherits from the *IColorRamp* interface, allowing access to all of the *IColorRamp* properties and methods from the interface specific to the coclass you are using. The following pages detail each of these coclasses, with example code demonstrating their use.

Display

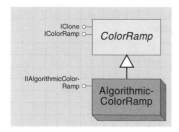

The algorithmic color ramp provides a series of sequential colors. After start and end colors are specified, intervening colors are interpolated by a choice of three different algorithms, providing an intuitive series of colors.

Using the esriHSVAlgorithm can often give the most vibrant or distinct results. The algorithm used to interpolate intervening colors traverses hues based on the HSV color model; therefore, if the FromColor and ToColor have very different hue values, the ramp will contain a large variety of hues. If the FromColor is red and the ToColor is the reddest PurpleRed, the result will look like the full spectrum of colors.

The other algorithms interpolate the FromColor and ToColor using other color models, producing results similar to those you might expect if you were mixing two colors of paint.

The CIELAB algorithm uses a shortest path between the FromColor and ToColor, based on the CIELAB color space. The result is an apparent blending of the start and end colors with no intervening colors.

LabLCh is also a shortest path type of algorithm but does not mute the intervening colors, often resulting in a brighter color ramp.

The *AlgorithmicColorRamp* class offers a way to produce a series of sequential colors and therefore is ideal for creating colors to represent sequential data in a layer—for example, when data is displayed using a *ClassBreaksRenderer*.

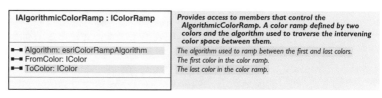

IAlgorithmicColorRamp : IColorRamp	Provides access to members that control the AlgorithmicColorRamp. A color ramp defined by two colors and the algorithm used to traverse the intervening color space between them.
■—■ Algorithm: esriColorRampAlgorithm	The algorithm used to ramp between the first and last colors.
■—■ FromColor: IColor	The first color in the color ramp.
■—■ ToColor: IColor	The last color in the color ramp.

The *IAlgorithmicColorRamp* interface allows you to specify how the series of colors is created using three properties. Colors created are *HSVColor* objects.

The read–write *FromColor* and *ToColor* properties specify the starting and ending color of the ramp using an object that supports the *IColor* interface. You can use any object that supports the *IColor* interface to set the *FromColor* or *ToColor* properties, although returning the *FromColor* or *ToColor* always gives an *HSVColor* object. For example, a simple color ramp starting at red and fading to white could be created as shown below. Note that the *FromColor* and *ToColor* properties are set by value; therefore, you cannot change the *RGB* values directly from the *IColor* interface returned by the *IAlgorithmicColorRamp* interface.

```
Dim pCol As IRgbColor
Set pCol = New RgbColor

Dim pAlgoRamp As esriCore.IAlgorithmicColorRamp
Set pAlgoRamp = New esriCore.AlgorithmicColorRamp

pCol.RGB = 255  'Red
pAlgoRamp.FromColor = pCol
pCol.RGB = 0    'White
pAlgoRamp.ToColor = pCol
```

The *Algorithm* property can be set to one of the three *esriColorRamp-Algorithm* constants. There is little to choose between the algorithms if the *FromColor* and *ToColor* are similar—the different algorithms may produce a color ramp slightly weighted to one end or the other. If the hues are significantly different, the algorithms produce very different results, as you can see in the diagrams to the left.

Enumeration esriColorRampAlgorithm	ESRI ColorRamp Algorithm.
0 - esriHSVAlgorithm	Use the HSV colorramp algorithm.
1 - esriCIELabAlgorithm	Use the CIE Lab colorramp algorithm.
2 - esriLabLChAlgorithm	Use the LabLCh colorramp algorithm.

The advantage of the CIELAB algorithm is that the colors of the ramp are visually equidistant, which produces a better ramp.

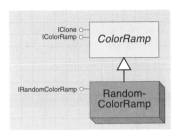

The random color ramp provides a series of randomly created colors. You can specify limits on the range of hues, values, and saturations possible to create "themed" random colors.

The *RandomColorRamp* class offers a way to produce a series of pseudo-random colors and therefore is ideal for creating a series of colors to represent nominal data based on unique values, for example, when a layer is displayed using a *UniqueValueRenderer*.

IRandomColorRamp : IColorRamp	Provides access to members that control the properties of a RandomColorRamp. A color ramp that is a list of randomly picked colors.
■—■ EndHue: Long	The end hue (0-360).
■—■ MaxSaturation: Long	The maximum saturation (0-100).
■—■ MaxValue: Long	The maximum value (0-100).
■—■ MinSaturation: Long	The minimum saturation (0-100).
■—■ MinValue: Long	The minimum value (0-100).
■—■ Seed: Long	The seed of the random number generator.
■—■ StartHue: Long	The start hue (0-360).
■—■ UseSeed: Boolean	Indicates if a seed is used when the ramp is generated. Set this property to True without changing the Seed to generate identical color ramps in succession.

The *IRandomColorRamp* interface allows you to control, to some degree, the randomness of the colors within a random color ramp. The *RandomColorRamp* is designed around the HSV color model and therefore the colors in a random color ramp may be restricted in terms of hue, saturation, and value. Setting the *StartHue* and *EndHue* properties to values between 0 and 360 will restrict the colors that may appear in the ramp. Setting *MinValue* and *MaxValue* to between 0 and 100 will restrict the brightness, and setting *MinSaturation* and *MaxSaturation* to between zero and 100 will restrict the purity of the colors in the ramp. Colors created are *HSVColor* objects.

You may wish to restrict the colors in the ramp to bright, light red, and yellow tones, creating a randomized color scheme of vibrant, warm colors. To achieve this effect, you could create a new *RandomColorRamp* and set the *StartHue* property to red (on the color wheel, red is zero), and the *EndHue* property to yellow (yellow has a *Hue* of 60, based on the color wheel). Then, you could restrict the *Saturation* and *Value* ranges. Here is some code to create a random color ramp:

```
Dim pRandomRamp As esriCore.IRandomColorRamp
Set pRandomRamp = New esriCore.RandomColorRamp
With pRandomRamp
  .StartHue = 0
  .EndHue = 60
  .MinSaturation = 60
  .MaxSaturation = 100
  .MinValue = 90
  .MaxValue = 100
End With
```

The code above produces a color ramp with warm colors like this:

If you wish to create a color scheme of dark, muted colors, try restricting the hue range to 160–240, the saturation range to 20–40, and the value range to 30–50, which produces a color ramp like this:

Perhaps a range of pastel colors would be more appropriate. Try using the full hue range of 0–360, a saturation range of 10–20, and a value range of 80–95. These values will produce a color ramp like this:

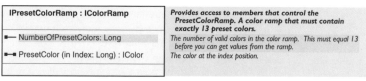

The *RandomColorRamp* creates colors based on a seed value, which is used to set the state of the pseudorandom number generator. For a specific seed value, the colors created are always the same.

Remember when you are setting your ranges that *StartHue* must always be less than the *EndHue*, *MinSaturation* less than *MaxSaturation*, and *MinValue* less than *MaxValue*. If the values are set incorrectly, the *RandomColorRamp* will use the full range of hue, saturation, or value.

By default, the *UseSeed* property of the *IRandomColorRamp* is *False*. In this case, the *RandomColorRamp* creates a new random number to use as the seed value for each call to *CreateRamp*, ensuring that the *Colors* created are random and different each time *CreateRamp* is called. If the *UseSeed* property is set to *True*, the seed used for the *RandomColorRamp* is taken from the *Seed* property, and therefore each time you call *CreateRamp* with a specific *Seed* value, the sequence of colors created is unchanged.

The *PresetColorRamp* class offers a way to store a series of 13 specific colors, which allows you to mimic ArcView GIS 3.x color ramps in order to preserve your symbology from older systems.

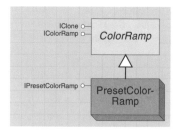

The algorithmic color ramp holds a series of 13 specific colors, which can be used to mimic ArcView GIS 3.x color ramps.

IPresetColorRamp : IColorRamp	Provides access to members that control the PresetColorRamp. A color ramp that must contain exactly 13 preset colors.
■— NumberOfPresetColors: Long	The number of valid colors in the color ramp. This must equal 13 before you can get values from the ramp.
■—■ PresetColor (in Index: Long) : IColor	The color at the index position.

The *IPresetColorRamp* interface provides simple access to the 13 colors in the ramp—the *NumberOfPresetColors* property always returns 13. By default, a *PresetColorRamp* contains 13 *RGBColor* objects ranging from red to green. The *PresetColor* property provides read–write access to the 13 colors in the ramp. For example, you might wish to use 13 random colors as your *PresetColorRamp*, which you could achieve like this:

```
Dim pRandomRamp As esriCore.IRandomColorRamp
Set pRandomRamp = New esriCore.RandomColorRamp
pRandomRamp.Size = 13
pRandomRamp.CreateRamp True

Dim pPresetRamp As esriCore.IPresetColorRamp
Set pPresetRamp = New esriCore.PresetColorRamp
Dim i As Integer
For i = 0 To 12
  'Here we set each PresetColor
  pPresetRamp.PresetColor(i) = pRandomRamp.Color(i)
Next i
```

To re-create ArcView predefined color ramps, you can use the ImportArcView ColorRamps sample from the ArcObjects Developer Help system.

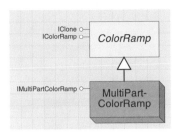

The multipart color offers a simple way to create more complex color ramps by adding together algorithmic, random, preset, or other multipart color ramps.

Although the algorithmic, preset, and random color ramp coclasses offer a wide range of options for defining color ramps, you may need to create specific ramps that cannot be created using these coclasses. By concatenating existing color ramps, the *MultiPartColorRamp* coclass offers a way to create highly complex color ramp schemes.

IMultiPartColorRamp : IColorRamp	Provides access to members that control the MultiPartColorRamp. A color ramp defined by a list of constituent color ramps.
■— NumberOfRamps: Long	The number of constituent color ramps.
■—■ Ramp (in Index: Long) : IColorRamp	The color ramp at the index position.
◀— AddRamp (in ColorRamp: IColorRamp)	Adds a color ramp to the list.
◀— RemoveRamp (in Index: Long)	Removes the color ramp located at the index position.

The *IMultiPartColorRamp* interface provides the framework for concatenating color ramps. After creating a *MultiPartColorRamp* object, you can add color ramps to it with the *AddRamp* method. You can add existing algorithmic, preset, random, or even other multipart color ramps.

As discussed in the *IColorRamp* section, member ramps are used here as properties of another object, and therefore you do not need to set a *Size* and call *CreateRamp* for any ramp set as a member of a *MultiPartColorRamp*—it is the *MultiPartColorRamp* itself that will create the colors when its *Size* property is set. A *MultiPartColorRamp* will try to use an equal number of colors from each member ramp to create its colors. In the illustrated code below, two different color ramps are added to a new *MultiPartColorRamp*, which is used to create 10 colors.

```
Dim pMPRamp As esriCore.IMultiPartColorRamp
Set pMPRamp = New esriCore.MultiPartColorRamp
With pMPRamp
  .AddRamp pAlgoRamp      ' added:
  .AddRamp pRandomRamp    ' added:
  .Size = 10
  .CreateRamp True      'results in:
End With
```

You can check the number of ramps in a *MultiPartColorRamp* by reading the *NumberOfRamps* property. You can access individual ramps by using the *Ramp* property array, which returns an individual ramp. You can also remove specfic ramps using the *RemoveRamp* method, which removes a ramp at a specific index, for example, to remove the last ramp in a *MultiPartColorRamp*:

```
pMPRamp.RemoveRamp pMPRamp.NumberOfRamps - 1
```

Display

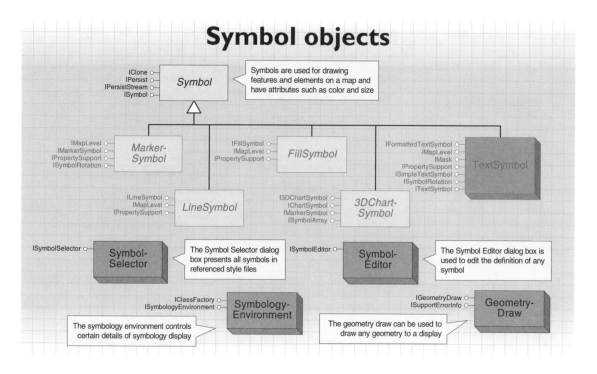

Symbol objects

Symbols are used for drawing features and elements on a map and have attributes such as color and size

The Symbol Selector dialog box presents all symbols in referenced style files

The Symbol Editor dialog box is used to edit the definition of any symbol

The symbology environment controls certain details of symbology display

The geometry draw can be used to draw any geometry to a display

ArcObjects uses three categories of symbols to draw geographic features: marker symbols, line symbols, and fill symbols. These same basic symbols are also used to draw graphic elements, such as neatlines and North arrows, on a *Map* or *PageLayout*. A fourth symbol, the *Text-Symbol*, is used to draw labels and other textual items. A fifth symbol, the *3DChartSymbol*, is used for drawing charts.

The size of a symbol is always specified in points (such as the width of a line), but the size of their geometry (such as the path of a line) is determined by the item they are used to draw. Most items, when created, have a default symbol, so instead of creating a new symbol for every item, you can modify the existing one.

In the case of a graphic element, a symbol is set as a property of each element. Layers, however, are drawn with a renderer, which has one or more symbols associated with it.

Another way to get a symbol is to use a style file. ArcObjects uses style files, which are distributable databases, to store and access symbols and colors. Many standard styles, offering thousands of predefined symbols, are available during the installation process. Using the *StyleGallery* and *StyleGalleryItem* classes, you can retrieve and edit existing symbols, which may be more efficient than creating symbols from scratch.

You might also wish to use the standard symbol editors found in ArcMap, which can be opened programmatically using the *SymbolEditor* coclass. The following pages describe how to create all the different symbols from first principles.

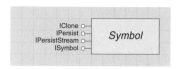

A symbol determines how any item is drawn on a map or page layout. Every item on a page layout or map has to have a symbol in order to be drawn.

The *Symbol* abstract class provides high-level functionality for all symbols. It allows you to draw any symbol directly to a device context (DC). A device context is an internal Windows structure—each window has a device context handle, or hDC.

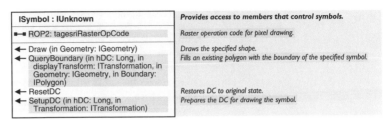

The *SetupDC, Draw,* and *ResetDC* methods can be used in conjunction with the *ROP2* property to draw a symbol to a device context, providing a familiar procedure for those who have worked with device context drawing before. Calling the *SetupDC* method selects the *Symbol* into the specified DC, and setting the *ROP2* property to one of the *esriRasterOpCodes* specifies how the *Symbol* is drawn (see below). Subsequently calling the *Draw* method will draw the *Symbol*, using the *Geometry* parameter from the *Draw* method, to the DC.

The following code demonstrates drawing to a device context, where *pDisplay* is a valid *Display* object, *pPoint* is a valid *Point* in display coordinates, and *pSymbol* is any valid *Symbol*. There are two important points to note.

- Call *StartDrawing* on the *Display* before using the *Draw* method, as this sets up the *Display*'s device context. Always ensure you call *FinishDrawing* on the *Display* after you have finished.

- Always make sure you call *ResetDC* after you finish drawing with a particular symbol, which restores the DC to its original state.

```
Sub DrawSymbol
    pDisplay.StartDrawing pDisplay.hDC, esriNoScreenCache
    pSymbol.SetupDC pDisplay.hDC, pDisplay.DisplayTransformation
    pSymbol.Draw pPoint
    pSymbol.ResetDC
    pDisplay.FinishDrawing
End Sub
```

The esriROPXOrPen or esriROPNotXOrPen are ideal for use in events where an item with a Symbol is being dragged around, as a repeat Draw at the same location will in effect erase the previous Draw.

Try setting the *ROP2* property to a different raster operation than the default, *esriROPCopyPen*, in which the color of each pixel is the color determined by the *Symbol*. A careful choice of pen can give many different results, for example, flashing symbols, drawing and erasing, silhouettes, and negative effects.

The example below demonstrates the use of this raster operation, where the *Symbol* is drawn twice in the *MouseMove* event, the first *Draw* erasing the existing symbol and the second *Draw* drawing the symbol in a new location. The *MouseUp* event erases the final symbol. The *m_Symbol* variable indicates any existing symbol.

```
Private m_Display As IDisplay
Private m_Symbol As ISymbol
Private m_newPoint As IPoint
Private m_DrawPhase As Boolean
```

```
Private Sub UIToolControl1_MouseDown(ByVal button As Long, ByVal shift As
Long, ByVal x As Long, ByVal y As Long)
  Dim pMxDoc As IMxDocument
  Set pMxDoc = ThisDocument
  Set m_Display = pMxDoc.ActiveView.ScreenDisplay
  Set m_newPoint = m_Display.DisplayTransformation.ToMapPoint(x, y)
  m_DrawPhase = True
  DrawSymbol
End Sub

Private Sub UIToolControl1_MouseMove(ByVal button As Long, ByVal shift As
Long, ByVal x As Long, ByVal y As Long)
  If m_DrawPhase Then
    DrawSymbol
    Set m_newPoint = m_Display.DisplayTransformation.ToMapPoint(x, y)
    DrawSymbol
  End If
End Sub

Private Sub UIToolControl1_MouseUp(ByVal button As Long, ByVal shift As
Long, ByVal x As Long, ByVal y As Long)
  If m_DrawPhase Then
    Set m_newPoint = m_Display.DisplayTransformation.ToMapPoint(x, y)
    DrawSymbol
    m_DrawPhase = False
  End If
End Sub
```

Enumeration tagesriRasterOpCode	Binary Raster op-codes for symbol drawing.
1 - esriROPBlack	Pixel is always 0.
2 - esriROPNotMergePen	Pixel is the inverse of the esriROPMergePen color.
3 - esriROPMaskNotPen	Pixel is a combination of the colors common to both the screen and the inverse of the pen.
4 - esriROPNotCopyPen	Pixel is the inverse of the pen color.
5 - esriROPMaskPenNot	Pixel is a combination of the colors common to both the pen and the inverse of the screen.
6 - esriROPNot	Pixel is the inverse of the screen color.
7 - esriROPXOrPen	Pixel is a combination of the colors in the pen and in the screen, but not in both.
8 - esriROPNotMaskPen	Pixel is the inverse of the esriROPMaskPen color.
9 - esriROPMaskPen	Pixel is a combination of the colors common to both the pen and the screen.
10 - esriROPNotXOrPen	Pixel is the inverse of the esriROPXOrPen color.
11 - esriROPNOP	Pixel remains unchanged.
12 - esriROPMergeNotPen	Pixel is a combination of the screen color and the inverse of the pen color.
13 - esriROPCopyPen	Pixel is the pen color.
14 - esriROPMergePenNot	Pixel is a combination of the pen color and the inverse of the screen color.
15 - esriROPMergePen	Pixel is a combination of the pen color and the screen color.
16 - esriROPWhite	Pixel is always 1.

You can select a value for the *ROP2* property from the *esriRasterOpCode* enumeration.

The IMapLevel *interface was designed for use by the* Advanced Drawing Options *dialog box in ArcMap, which allows you to join and merge multilayer symbols.*

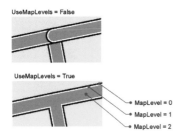

IMapLevel : IUnknown	*Provides access to memebers that control the map level.*
■—■ MapLevel: Long	*Current map level for drawing multi-level symbols.*

Display

Using the *IMapLevel* interface allows you to alter the draw order of the symbols used to draw feature layers. This functionality was originally designed for drawing cased roads and similar symbols but has been designed to offer flexibility and can be used on any symbol used by a renderer except 3D chart symbols. Graphic elements ignore *MapLevels*, as do *ISymbol::Draw* calls.

To draw layers in a map using map levels, first set the *IMap::UseSymbolLevels* property to *True*. Then, set up each individual symbol to have a *MapLevel*. Any symbols with *MapLevel* equal to 0 draw first (at the bottom), then any symbols with *MapLevel* equal to 1, until the highest *MapLevel* is reached. If more than one symbol has the same *MapLevel*, then when that *MapLevel* is reached those symbols are drawn in the normal layer order. A *MapLevel* of -1 on a multilayer symbol indicates that each of its symbol layers are drawn with their individual *MapLevel*.

The following code example demonstrates how you could "merge" a *MultiLayerLineSymbol* that belongs to a *SimpleRenderer* on the top map layer by setting the *MapLevel* symbols in the *MultiLayerLineSymbol*. The *SetMapLevel* function is called on each *Symbol* in the *MultiLayerLineSymbol*.

```
pMap.UseSymbolLevels = True

If TypeOf pMap.Layer(0) Is IGeoFeatureLayer Then
  Dim pFeatLyr As IGeoFeatureLayer
  Set pFeatLyr = pMap.Layer(0)

  If TypeOf pFeatLyr.Renderer Is ISimpleRenderer Then
    Dim pSimpleRend As ISimpleRenderer
    Set pSimpleRend = pFeatLyr.Renderer

    If TypeOf pSimpleRend.Symbol Is IMultiLayerLineSymbol Then
      Dim pMulti As IMultiLayerLineSymbol
      Set pMulti = pSimpleRend.Symbol
      SetMapLevel pMulti, -1
      Dim i As Long
      For i = 0 To pMulti.LayerCount - 1
        SetMapLevel pMulti.Layer(i), pMulti.LayerCount - (i + 1)
      Next i
    End If
  End If
End If

Sub SetMapLevel(pMapLevel As IMapLevel, lngLevel As Long)
  If Not pMapLevel Is Nothing Then
    pMapLevel.MapLevel = lngLevel
  End If
End Sub
```

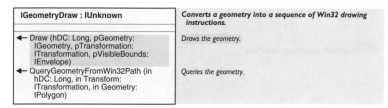

The geometry draw can be used to draw any geometry to a display.

The GeometryDraw object provides an alternative to using the ISymbol::Draw method, which draws a Symbol to a device context using a particular Geometry to provide the location.

The *GeometryDraw* coclass is used to draw an *IGeometry* object to an *IDisplay* object.

IGeometryDraw : IUnknown	Converts a geometry into a sequence of Win32 drawing instructions.
← Draw (hDC: Long, pGeometry: IGeometry, pTransformation: ITransformation, pVisibleBounds: IEnvelope)	Draws the geometry.
← QueryGeometryFromWin32Path (in hDC: Long, in Transform: ITransformation, in Geometry: IPolygon)	Queries the geometry.

Use the *Draw* method to draw a *Geometry* to a *Display*, as shown below.

```
Dim pMxDoc As IMxDocument
Set pMxDoc = ThisDocument

Dim pDisplay As IDisplay
Set pDisplay = pMxDoc.ActiveView.ScreenDisplay
pDisplay.StartDrawing 0, esriNoScreenCache

Dim pGeomDraw As IGeometryDraw
Set pGeomDraw = New GeometryDraw
'pGeom is an existing Geometry object
pGeomDraw.Draw pDisplay.hDC, pGeom, pDisplay.DisplayTransformation, _
  pGeom.Envelope
pDisplay.FinishDrawing
```

The *Geometry* is drawn using the current symbol set on the *Display*, which you can set by calling *IDisplay::SetSymbol*. Note the call to *StartDrawing*, which is necessary to set up the *Display* with a valid *hDC*.

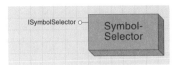

The Symbol Selector dialog box presents all the symbols in the currently referenced style files.

The *SymbolSelector* coclass is ideal for presenting the user with a choice of symbols, either marker, line, fill, or text symbols. The symbols in the selector are taken from all the currently referenced style files.

ISymbolSelector : IUnknown	Provides a dialog for Symbol Selection
← AddSymbol (in Symbol: ISymbol) : Boolean	Provides a dialog for Adding a symbol
← GetSymbolAt (in Index: Long) : ISymbol	Gets the symbol at the given index
← SelectSymbol (hWnd: Long) : Boolean	Displays a dialog that lets the user select a symbol

The *AddSymbol* method is used to define which type of symbols should be displayed in the *SymbolSelector*. For example, passing a *Marker-Symbol* will display all available *MarkerSymbols*. The *AddSymbol* method also determines which symbol is shown in the initial Preview frame when the dialog box opens.

The *SelectSymbol* method is used to display the dialog box; check the return value to determine if the user clicked OK (*True*) or Cancel (*False*).

Finally, the *GetSymbolAt* method is used to retrieve the selected symbol using an index of zero.

```
Dim pSymbolSelector As ISymbolSelector
Set pSymbolSelector = New SymbolSelector
Dim pMarker As ISimpleMarkerSymbol
Set pMarker = New SimpleMarkerSymbol
If Not pSymbolSelector.AddSymbol(pMarker) Then
  MsgBox "Could not add symbol"
Else
  If pSymbolSelector.SelectSymbol(0) Then
    Dim pSymbol As ISymbol
    Set pSymbol = pSymbolSelector.GetSymbolAt(0)
  End If
```

Display

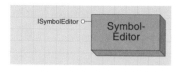

The SymbolEditor is the dialog box shown by ArcMap to edit the details of any given Symbol.

The pages shown on the dialog box will depend on the type of symbol used. For example, a cartographic line symbol has a slightly different dialog box than a marker line symbol.

The *SymbolEditor* provides an ideal way to allow a user to edit all the properties of a specific, preexisting symbol.

ISymbolEditor : IUnknown	**Symbol Editor**
▪━■ ShowUnits: Boolean	*Indicates whether to display the Units combo box.*
▪━■ Title: String	*The title of the Symbol Editor dialog.*
◀━ EditSymbol (Symbol: ISymbol, hWnd: Long) : Boolean	*Displays the Symbol Editor dialog for the given symbol and returns a flag indicating if the symbol changed.*

The *EditSymbol* method takes an *ISymbol* parameter, which must be an existing object that supports *ISymbol*. This object is passed by reference and will be directly changed depending on the selections made in the dialog box. Its coclass may even change.

The *EditSymbol* method call will open the *SymbolEditor* dialog box. To determine if the user clicked Cancel or OK, check the return value.

```
Dim pSymbol As IMarkerSymbol
Set pSymbol = New SimpleMarkerSymbol
Dim pSymbolEditor As ISymbolEditor
Set pSymbolEditor = New SymbolEditor
pSymbolEditor.Title = "Edit My Marker"
If Not pSymbolEditor.EditSymbol(pSymbol, 0) Then
  MsgBox "Use pressed Cancel"
Else
  'Do something with the edited Symbol
End If
```

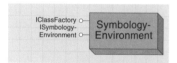

The symbology environment object is used internally by ArcMap when outputting maps.

The *SymbologyEnvironment* coclass is a Singleton and controls certain details of how symbols are drawn as Graphical Device Interface (GDI) objects. Most developers will find it unnecessary to change the default *SymbologyEnvironment* properties, as the coclass is used primarily by ArcMap to set symbology options for exporting and printing.

ISymbologyEnvironment : IUnknown	*Controls the environment for certain Symbol operations*
▪━■ GeometryClipping: Boolean	*Indicates if all geometry is clipped on output.*
▪━■ OutputGDICommentForCMYKColor: Boolean	*Indicates if a GDI comment is output for CMYK colors.*
▪━■ OutputGDICommentForGroupings: Boolean	*Indicates if a GDI comment is output for groupings.*
▪━■ OutputGDICommentForLayers: Boolean	*Indicates if a GDI comment is output for layers.*
▪━■ OutputGDICommentForText: Boolean	*Indicates if a GDI comment is output for text.*
▪━■ StrokeTrueTypeMarkers: Boolean	*Indicates if TrueType markers are stroked.*

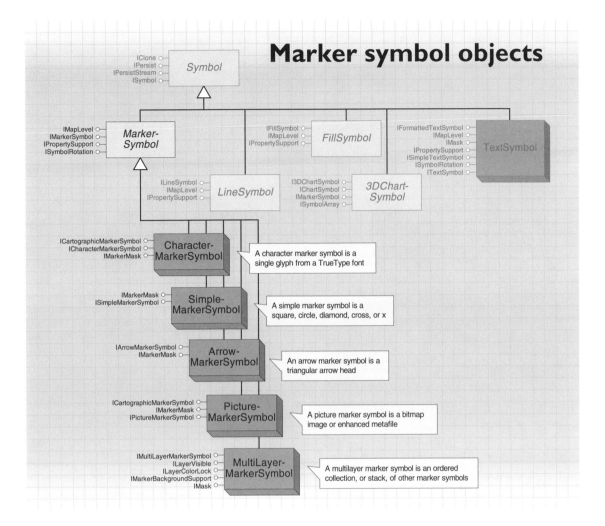

Marker symbol objects

A character marker symbol is a single glyph from a TrueType font

A simple marker symbol is a square, circle, diamond, cross, or x

An arrow marker symbol is a triangular arrow head

A picture marker symbol is a bitmap image or enhanced metafile

A multilayer marker symbol is an ordered collection, or stack, of other marker symbols

Display

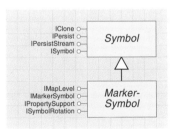

A MarkerSymbol *represents how a point or multipoint feature or graphic is drawn.*

The *MarkerSymbol* abstract class represents the properties all types of *MarkerSymbol* have in common. These are *Angle, Color, Size XOffset,* and *YOffset.*

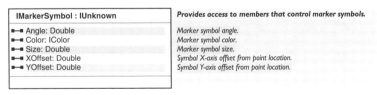

IMarkerSymbol : IUnknown	Provides access to members that control marker symbols.
■─■ Angle: Double	Marker symbol angle.
■─■ Color: IColor	Marker symbol color.
■─■ Size: Double	Marker symbol size.
■─■ XOffset: Double	Symbol X-axis offset from point location.
■─■ YOffset: Double	Symbol Y-axis offset from point location.

IMarkerSymbol is the primary interface for all marker symbols in ArcMap. All other marker symbol interfaces inherit the properties and methods of *IMarkerSymbol.* The interface has five read–write properties that allow you to get and set the basic properties of any *MarkerSymbol.*

The *Color* property can be set to any *IColor* object, and its effects will be dependent on the type of coclass you are using.

coclass	default color	color property sets
SimpleMarkerSymbol	black	the fill color of the marker
ArrowMarkerSymbol	black	the fill color of the arrow head
CharacterMarkerSymbol	black	the fill color of the text symbol
PictureMarkerSymbol I bit	black	parts of the boolean image which contain a color
PictureMarkerSymbol n bits	not set	no effect
MultiLayerMarkerSymbol	none	dependent on ILayerColorLock

The *Size* property sets the overall height of the symbol if the symbol is a *SimpleMarkerSymbol, CharacterMarkerSymbol, PictureMarkerSymbol,* or *MultiLayerMarkerSymbol.* For an *ArrowMarkerSymbol, Size* sets the length. The units are points. The default size is eight for all marker symbols except the *PictureMarkerSymbol*—its default size is 12.

The Size, XOffset, and YOffset of a marker symbol is in printer's points—1/72 of an inch.

The *Angle* property sets the angle in degrees to which the symbol is rotated counterclockwise from the horizontal axis; and its default is 0. The *XOffset* and *YOffset* properties determine the distance to which the symbol is drawn offset from the actual location of the feature. The properties are both in printer's points, both have a default of zero, and both can be negative or positive; positive numbers indicate an offset above and to the right of the feature, and negative numbers indicate an offset below and to the left.

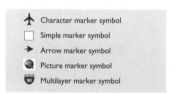

Character marker symbol
Simple marker symbol
Arrow marker symbol
Picture marker symbol
Multilayer marker symbol

The types of marker symbols.

Below, we create an *ArrowMarkerSymbol* and set only the properties inherited from *IMarkerSymbol.* This results in the symbol shown.

```
Dim pArrow As IMarkerSymbol
Set pArrow = New ArrowMarkerSymbol
With pArrow
  .Angle = 60
  .Size = 50
  .XOffset = 20
  .YOffset = 30
  .Color = pColor
End With
```

To the left are some examples of each of the marker symbol types.

Simple marker symbols

Arrow marker symbols

Character marker symbols

Picture marker symbols

Multilayer marker symbols

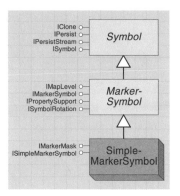

The simple marker symbol draws a circle, square, cross, x, or diamond.

The *SimpleMarkerSymbol* coclass can be used to display a point with simple characteristics. The *SimpleMarkerSymbol* determines the shape of the simple symbol and also its outline characteristics.

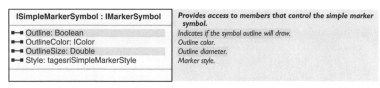

The *ISimpleMarkerSymbol* interface inherits from the *IMarkerSymbol* interface and has four read–write properties.

The *Style* property determines the basic shape of the symbol and can be set to one of five basic shapes using the *esriSimpleMarkerStyle* constants.

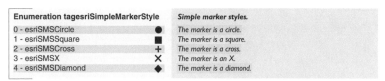

These simple shapes can be enhanced with outlines. Try setting the *Outline* property to *True* and setting an *IColor* onto the *OutlineColor* property.

The *OutlineSize* property determines the thickness of the outline in printer's points. Bear in mind that the outline is drawn on top of the symbol and will overlap the symbol by half its thickness. By default, a simple marker symbol will be a circle with no outline.

The default *OutlineColor* is black, and the default *OutlineSize* is 0.

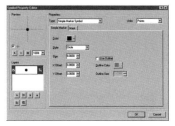

This is the ArcMap dialog box for editing simple marker symbols.

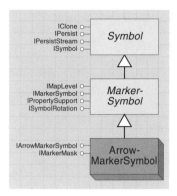

The *ArrowMarkerSymbol* coclass can be used to display a point as the head of an arrow.

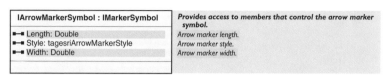

IArrowMarkerSymbol : IMarkerSymbol	Provides access to members that control the arrow marker symbol.
■—■ Length: Double	Arrow marker length.
■—■ Style: tagesriArrowMarkerStyle	Arrow marker style.
■—■ Width: Double	Arrow marker width.

The *IArrowMarkerSymbol* interface inherits from the *IMarkerSymbol* interface and allows you to set characteristics of the arrow marker. There is currently one style, a simple triangular arrowhead—the *Style* property therefore is always equal to the *esriArrowMarkerStyle* constant *esriAMSPlain*.

The *Length* and *Width* properties set the dimensions of the arrow. Note that the *Length* property equals the inherited *Size* property, so you can set the relative length and width of the arrow using the *Length* and *Width* properties and then scale the arrow marker using the *Size* property.

The ArrowMarkerSymbol *displays a feature as an arrowhead.*

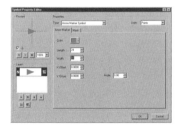

The ArcMap *dialog box for editing arrow marker symbols.*

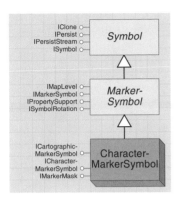

The CharacterMarkerSymbol displays a feature as a character from a font. You can use any font on your system and specify which glyph from the font should be used as the symbol.

A glyph is a single character from a font.

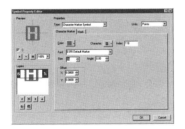

The ArcMap dialog box for editing character marker symbols.

To display a point as a glyph from a font, use the *CharacterMarkerSymbol* coclass.

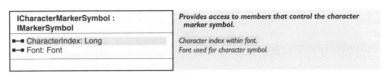

ICharacterMarkerSymbol : IMarkerSymbol	*Provides access to members that control the character marker symbol.*
■━ CharacterIndex: Long	*Character index within font.*
■━ Font: Font	*Font used for character symbol.*

The *ICharacterMarkerSymbol* interface inherits from the *IMarkerSymbol* interface and allows you to specify the characteristics of your chosen glyph. To choose a font from which to pick your glyph, create a standard OLE font object and set this onto the *Font* property. This is shown in the following code:

```
Dim pFont As New stdole.StdFont
With pFont
   .Name = "Arial"
   .Bold = True
   .Italic = True
End With
Dim pMarker As esriCore.ICharacterMarkerSymbol
Set pMarker = New esriCore.CharacterMarkerSymbol
pMarker.Font = pFont
pMarker.Size = 12.0
```

Now that you have set up the font to use, you should pick which glyph you require. Set the *CharacterIndex* property to the required glyph number. Each font has up to 256 glyphs. To work out which glyph you require, you may wish to use the Windows NT *CharacterMap* accessory. You can also use the *CharacterIndex* sample to work out all the character indices for a selected font. Use the *IMarkerSymbol* interface's *Size* property to set the size of the symbol, not the *Size* property of the font itself.

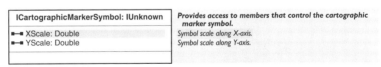

ICartographicMarkerSymbol: IUnknown	*Provides access to members that control the cartographic marker symbol.*
■━ XScale: Double	*Symbol scale along X-axis.*
■━ YScale: Double	*Symbol scale along Y-axis.*

To stretch a *PictureMarkerSymbol* or *CharacterMarkerSymbol*, use the *ICartographicMarkerSymbol* interface. The *ICartographicMarkerSymbol* interface inherits from the *IMarkerSymbol* interface and allows you to scale a marker symbol in the x and y directions independently by setting the *XScale* and *YScale* properties. For example, setting *XScale* and *YScale* to 1 (the default) indicates the symbol should remain at its original proportions; an *XScale* of 2 indicates the symbol is stretched to twice its original width.

Display

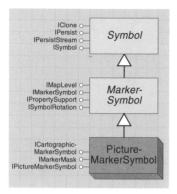

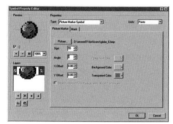

The PictureMarkerSymbol coclass draws a point as a bitmap or Windows metafile. Pictures can be 1-bit up to 24-bit (true color) images.

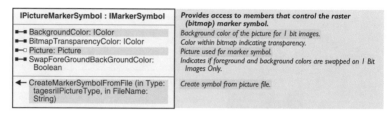

IPictureMarkerSymbol : IMarkerSymbol	Provides access to members that control the raster (bitmap) marker symbol.
■—■ BackgroundColor: IColor	Background color of the picture for 1 bit images.
■—■ BitmapTransparencyColor: IColor	Color within bitmap indicating transparency.
■—□ Picture: Picture	Picture used for marker symbol.
■—■ SwapForeGroundBackGroundColor: Boolean	Indicates if foreground and background colors are swapped on 1 Bit Images Only.
← CreateMarkerSymbolFromFile (in Type: tagesrilPictureType, in FileName: String)	Create symbol from picture file.

The PictureMarkerSymbol displays a feature as a bitmap. Use a PictureMarkerSymbol when you require a specific kind of symbol that cannot be created using the other marker types.

There are two ways to set the *Picture* of a *PictureMarkerSymbol*—calling *CreateMarkerSymbolFromFile* or setting the *Picture* property directly.

The *CreateMarkerSymbolFromFile* method has two parameters that specify a picture type and file path. Set the *FileName* parameter to the full path name of the picture you wish to use—an error is generated if the file path is incorrect. Set the *Type* parameter to one of the *esriPictureType* constants.

Enumeration tagesrilPictureType	IPicture Data Types.
0 - esriIPictureEMF	EMF.
1 - esriIPictureBitmap	BITMAP.

```
Dim pPicMarker As IPictureMarkerSymbol
Set pPicMarker = New PictureMarkerSymbol
pPicMarker.CreateMarkerSymbolFromFile esriIPictureBitmap, _
    "C:\Data\MyImage.bmp"
```

The ArcMap dialog box for editing picture marker symbols

If you already have a reference to an OLE picture, you can directly set the *Picture* property—note the *Picture* property is by reference. Below, the VB *LoadPicture* function returns an *IPictureDisp* interface.

```
Set pPicMarker.Picture = LoadPicture("C:\Data\MyImage.bmp")
```

The *Picture* property of a standard VBA Image control also returns an *IPictureDisp* interface.

```
Set pPicMarker.Picture = UserForm1.ImageControl1.Picture
```

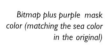

Bitmap plus purple mask color (matching the sea color in the original)

Your picture may have a solid filled background. You can display your marker without this background by setting the *BitmapTransparencyColor* property to the color of the background fill (or any other color in the image you wish to be transparent). You can decide to fill in any unfilled areas of your picture with a different color by setting the *BackgroundColor* property. If you have set the *BitmapTransparencyColor*, the background will be drawn in the transparent areas.

The original bitmap

To remove these color effects from your marker, set the *BitmapTransparencyColor* and *BackgroundColor* properties to *Nothing*.

The *SwapForeGroundBackGroundColor* property only affects the drawing of 1-bit images, where each pixel will either have a value of 0 or 1. When a 1-bit image is used as a *PictureMarkerSymbol*, the foreground equates to the "0" pixels, and the background equates to the "1" pixels.

Bitmap plus purple mask plus cyan background, which effectively replaces the purple

By default, the *Color* property is black, the *BackgroundColor* is also black but is a *NullColor*, and *SwapForeGroundBackGroundColor* is *True*.

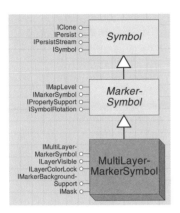

A MultiLayerMarkerSymbol is a collection of MarkerSymbols, all of which are used to display a single point feature.

Simple marker symbols are added to form a multilayer marker symbol.

The ArcMap dialog box for editing multilayer marker symbols.

Note the use of the Do...While loop. This is especially useful when removing an item from the collection that is being looped through—you could not use a For...Each here.

The *MultiLayerMarkerSymbol* coclass can be used to display a point by drawing a number of different marker symbols together, so complex marker symbols can be built up from simple marker symbols.

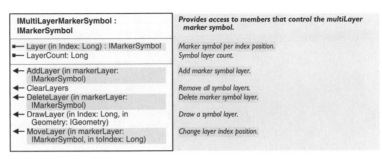

IMultiLayerMarkerSymbol : IMarkerSymbol	Provides access to members that control the multiLayer marker symbol.
Layer (in Index: Long) : IMarkerSymbol	Marker symbol per index position.
LayerCount: Long	Symbol layer count.
AddLayer (in markerLayer: IMarkerSymbol)	Add marker symbol layer.
ClearLayers	Remove all symbol layers.
DeleteLayer (in markerLayer: IMarkerSymbol)	Delete marker symbol layer.
DrawLayer (in Index: Long, in Geometry: IGeometry)	Draw a symbol layer.
MoveLayer (in markerLayer: IMarkerSymbol, in toIndex: Long)	Change layer index position.

The *IMultiLayerMarkerSymbol* interface refers to each symbol in the collection as a layer and provides a read-only *LayerCount* property summing the number of layers currently present.

The *Layer* property provides read-only access to each symbol within the *MultiLayerMarkerSymbol*.

Marker symbols can be added to the collection by passing the required symbol to the *AddLayer* method, which adds the symbols by value, for example:

```
Dim pMultiMarker As esriCore.IMultiLayerMarkerSymbol
Set pMultiMarker = New MultiLayerMarkerSymbol
pMultiMarker.AddLayer pSimpleMarker  'passing a valid SimpleMarkerSymbol
pMultiMarker.AddLayer pArrowMarker   'passing a valid ArrowMarkerSymbol
```

Now we have a *MultiLayerMarkerSymbol* with a *SimpleMarkerSymbol* and an *ArrowMarkerSymbol*—the *ArrowMarkerSymbol* was the last to be added, and therefore has an index of zero, and will be drawn last on top of the *SimpleMarkerSymbol*.

Each symbol can be moved to a different index by calling the *MoveLayer* method. For example, you may wish to move the largest symbols to the bottom of the *MultiLayerMarkerSymbol*. You can remove a symbol entirely from the *MultiLayerMarkerSymbol* by calling *DeleteLayer*, as shown in the following code:

```
Dim pRemove As IMarkerSymbol
Dim lngLayer As Long
Do While lngLayer < pMultiMarker.LayerCount
  If TypeOf pMultiMarker.Layer(lngLayer ) Is IArrowMarkerSymbol Then
    Set pRemove = pMultiMarker.Layer(lngLayer )
    pMultiMarker.DeleteLayer pRemove
    lngLayer = 0
  End If
  lngLayer = lngLayer + 1
Loop
```

To remove all the symbols from a *MultiLayerMarkerSymbol*, simply call the *ClearLayers* method. It's also possible to draw an individual layer

Display

from the *MultiLayerMarkerSymbol* straight to a specific device context by using the *DrawLayer* method. The use of this method is similar to the *ISymbol::Draw* method; you must call *SetupDC* before and *ResetDC* after your draw method. You may wish to use this capability, for example, if you are implementing your own multilayer symbol editor.

ILayerColorLock : IUnknown	Provides access to members that control the layer color locking.
■—■ LayerColorLock (in LayerIndex: Long) : Boolean	Color lock state per layer index.
←— SetAllColorLocked (allLocked: Boolean)	Indicates if the color is locked for all layers.

The *ILayerColorLock* interface determines which layers will be affected by setting the *IMultiLayerMarkerSymbol::Color* property. Layers with *LayerColorLock* equal to *True* will not be affected. Layers with *LayerColorLock* equal to *False* will have their *Color* property set to the color assigned in *IMultiLayerMarkerSymbol::Color*.

If you wish to set only the topmost layer of a *MultiLayerMarkerSymbol* (*pMultiLayerMarker*) to a new color (*pColor*), you could write code like this:

```
Dim pColorLock As ILayerColorLock
Set pColorLock = pMultiLayerMarker
pColorLock.SetAllColorLocked True
pColorLock.LayerColorLock(0) = False
pMultiLayerMarker.Color = pColor
```

Each symbol in the *MultiLayerMarkerSymbol* has a visibility property that determines whether or not each individual layer is drawn. This visibility property can be accessed by using the *ILayerVisible* interface.

ILayerVisible : IUnknown	Provides access to members that control the layer visibility.
■—■ LayerVisible (in LayerIndex: Long) : Boolean	Visibility of layer per layer index.
←— SetAllVisible (allVisible: Boolean)	Indicates if all the layers are visible or invisible.

You can alter a given *MultiLayerMarkerSymbol* by "turning off" every alternate symbol. You can set all the layers visible or invisible in one command by calling the *SetAllVisible* method.

```
Dim pLayerVisible As ILayerVisible, pLyr As Long
Set pLayerVisible = pMultiLayerMarker   'Existing Marker
For pLyr = 0 To pMultiLayerMarker.LayerCount - 1 Step 2
  pLayerVisible.LayerVisible(pLyr) = False
Next pLyr
```

IMask : IUnknown	Provides access to members that control the symbol mask.
■—■ MaskSize: Double	The mask size.
■—■ MaskStyle: tagesriMaskStyle	The mask style.
■—□ MaskSymbol: IFillSymbol	The mask symbol.

Use a contrasting color mask to highlight items that are a similar color to the features or their outlines underneath it.

The *IMask* interface provides a simple and efficient way to draw a symbol around the edge of your *Marker*. Set the *MaskStyle* property to an *esriMaskStyle* constant.

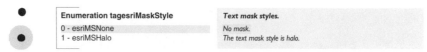

Enumeration tagesriMaskStyle	Text mask styles.
0 - esriMSNone	No mask.
1 - esriMSHalo	The text mask style is halo.

You can either fill the mask with a solid color by setting the *Color* property or with any other kind of *FillSymbol* by setting the *MaskSymbol* property. The *MaskSize* property indicates the width of the mask in points, measured from the marker edge.

Display

Line symbol objects

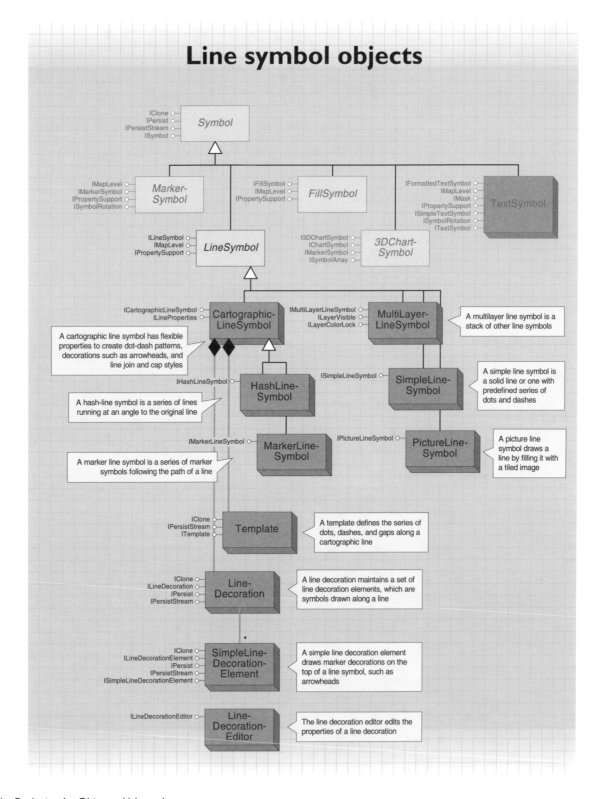

IClone
IPersist
IPersistStream
ISymbol

Symbol

IMapLevel
IMarkerSymbol
IPropertySupport
ISymbolRotation

Marker-Symbol

IFillSymbol
IMapLevel
IPropertySupport

FillSymbol

IFormattedTextSymbol
IMapLevel
IMask
IPropertySupport
ISimpleTextSymbol
ISymbolRotation
ITextSymbol

TextSymbol

ILineSymbol
IMapLevel
IPropertySupport

LineSymbol

I3DChartSymbol
IChartSymbol
IMarkerSymbol
ISymbolArray

3DChart-Symbol

ICartographicLineSymbol
ILineProperties

Cartographic-LineSymbol

IMultiLayerLineSymbol
ILayerVisible
ILayerColorLock

MultiLayer-LineSymbol

A multilayer line symbol is a stack of other line symbols

A cartographic line symbol has flexible properties to create dot-dash patterns, decorations such as arrowheads, and line join and cap styles

IHashLineSymbol

HashLine-Symbol

ISimpleLineSymbol

SimpleLine-Symbol

A simple line symbol is a solid line or one with predefined series of dots and dashes

A hash-line symbol is a series of lines running at an angle to the original line

IMarkerLineSymbol

MarkerLine-Symbol

IPictureLineSymbol

PictureLine-Symbol

A picture line symbol draws a line by filling it with a tiled image

A marker line symbol is a series of marker symbols following the path of a line

IClone
IPersistStream
ITemplate

Template

A template defines the series of dots, dashes, and gaps along a cartographic line

IClone
ILineDecoration
IPersist
IPersistStream

Line-Decoration

A line decoration maintains a set of line decoration elements, which are symbols drawn along a line

IClone
ILineDecorationElement
IPersist
IPersistStream
ISimpleLineDecorationElement

SimpleLine-Decoration-Element

A simple line decoration element draws marker decorations on the top of a line symbol, such as arrowheads

ILineDecorationEditor

Line-Decoration-Editor

The line decoration editor edits the properties of a line decoration

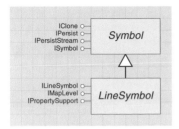

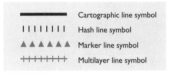

A line symbol represents how a one-dimensional feature or graphic is drawn. Straight lines, polylines, curves, and outlines can all be drawn with a line symbol. There are five different types of line symbol you can use.

▬▬▬▬▬▬	Cartographic line symbol
❘❘❘❘❘❘❘❘❘	Hash line symbol
▲ ▲ ▲ ▲ ▲ ▲	Marker line symbol
┼┼┼┼┼┼┼┼	Multilayer line symbol

The width of a line symbol is in printer's points— about 1/72 of an inch.

The *LineSymbol* abstract class represents the two properties—*Color* and *Width*—all types of line symbols have in common.

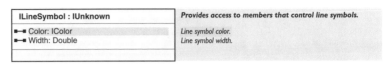

ILineSymbol : IUnknown	Provides access to members that control line symbols.
■━■ Color: IColor	Line symbol color.
■━■ Width: Double	Line symbol width.

ILineSymbol is the primary interface for all line symbols, which all inherit the properties and methods of *ILineSymbol*. The interface has two read–write properties that allow you to get and set the basic properties of any line symbol. The *Color* property controls the color of the basic line (it does not affect any line decoration that may be present—see the *ILineProperties* interface) and can be set to any *IColor* object. The *Color* property is set to black by default except for the *SimpleLineSymbol*, which has a default of mid-gray.

The *Width* property sets the overall width of a line, and its units are points. Note that for a *HashLineSymbol*, the *Width* property sets the length of each hash—see *HashLineSymbol* for more information. The default width is 1 for all line symbols except *MarkerLineSymbol*, which has a default width of 8.

To create a new symbol for a line, use one of the line symbol coclasses detailed in the following pages.

Display

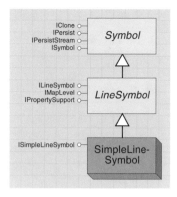

The simple line symbol displays a line with a simple symbol such as a solid line or a series of dots and/or dashes.

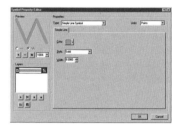

The ArcMap dialog box for editing simple line symbols.

The *SimpleLineSymbol* coclass can be used to display a line as a basic series of dots and dashes or as a solid line.

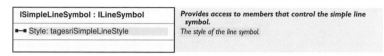

ISimpleLineSymbol : ILineSymbol	Provides access to members that control the simple line symbol.
▬ Style: tagesriSimpleLineStyle	The style of the line symbol.

The *ISimpleLineSymbol* interface inherits from the *ILineSymbol* interface, and its read–write *Style* property determines which style of line is used. It can be set to one of seven basic line patterns by using the *esriSimpleLineStyle* constants.

Enumeration tagesriSimpleLineStyle	Simple line styles.
0 - esriSLSSolid	The line is solid.
1 - esriSLSDash	The line is dashed ——
2 - esriSLSDot	The line is dotted ....
3 - esriSLSDashDot	The line has alternating dashes and dots _._._
4 - esriSLSDashDotDot	The line has alternating dashes and double dots _._.._
5 - esriSLSNull	The line is invisible.
6 - esriSLSInsideFrame	The line will fit into it's bounding rectangle, if any.

The default *Style* is *esriSLSSolid*. You should use only the *esriSLSSolid* style to draw lines with a *Width* greater than 1. Due to limitations of the Windows GDI routines used, dashed or dotted lines with a *Width* greater than 1 will be drawn as solid lines. In these cases, cartographic line symbols can be used instead to achieve the same effect.

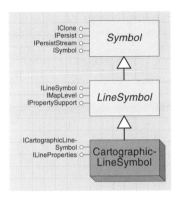

The cartographic line symbol is a general-purpose symbol used to display line features. More complex than the simple line symbol, it allows custom line patterns, offsets, and other characteristics to be set according to your requirements.

The *CartographicLineSymbol* coclass can be used to display one-dimensional features with a more complex symbology than *SimpleLineSymbol*. The *ICartographicLineSymbol* and *ILineProperties* interfaces offer precise control over the characteristics of the line.

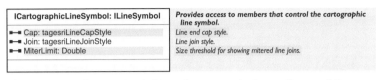

ICartographicLineSymbol: ILineSymbol	Provides access to members that control the cartographic line symbol.
■—■ Cap: tagesriLineCapStyle	Line end cap style.
■—■ Join: tagesriLineJoinStyle	Line join style.
■—■ MiterLimit: Double	Size threshold for showing mitered line joins.

The *ICartographicLineSymbol* interface controls the attributes of line symbol vertices.

The *MiterLimit* property determines the shape of a mitered join but does not affect lines with round or beveled joins. A miter length is defined as the distance from the intersection of the line walls on the inside of the join to the intersection of the line walls on the outside of the join. The *MiterLimit* property returns or sets the maximum allowed ratio of miter length to the line width. If a miter join exceeds the limit, the corner is not pointed but is cut off at the limit point. The default miter limit is 10.0.

The *Cap* property controls the appearance of line ends: butt, round, or square.

Enumeration tagesriLineCapStyle	Line cap styles.
0 - esriLCSButt	Line ends do not extend passed the end points.
1 - esriLCSRound	Line ends are rounded at the end points.
2 - esriLCSSquare	Line ends are squared off at the end points.

The *esriLineCapStyle* constants are used to set the line ends in the *Cap* property.

The *Join* property controls the appearance of any vertices of a line.

Enumeration tagesriLineJoinStyle	Line join styles.
0 - esriLJSMitre	Line joins are mitred.
1 - esriLJSRound	Line joins are round.
2 - esriLJSBevel	Line joins are beveled.

The *esriJoinCapStyle* constants are used to set the line join styles in the *Join* property.

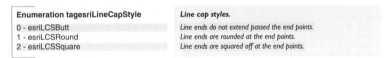

ILineProperties: IUnknown	Provides access to members that control the properties common to several line types.
■—■ DecorationOnTop: Boolean	Indicates if the decoration is drawn on top.
■—■ Flip: Boolean	Indicates if the line symbol is flipped.
■—□ LineDecoration: ILineDecoration	Line decoration element collection.
■—■ LineStartOffset: Double	The line start offset.
■—■ Offset: Double	The line offset value.
■—□ Template: ITemplate	The line template.

The *ILineProperties* interface precisely controls the dash–dot pattern of any line, where a dash may be a *MarkerSymbol* in the case of a *MarkerLineSymbol* coclass, a *LineSymbol* in the case of a

Display

HashLineSymbol coclass, or a simple dash in the case of a *CartographicLineSymbol* coclass. This interface also controls line pattern properties, such as offsets and line decoration elements.

The *Template* property sets or returns, by reference, a *Template* object that stores the pattern of dashes and dots along a cartographic line symbol.

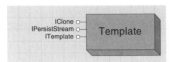

IClone ○—
IPersistStream ○—
ITemplate ○—

Template

A template defines the series of dots, dashes, and gaps along a cartographic line. It also determines where lines and markers appear on a hash line symbol and a marker line symbol.

The *Template* framework lets you design a common template for multiple *LineSymbol* objects in a *MultiLayerLineSymbol*, allowing you to synchronize multiple line patterns. You can use the same template to stack and center line dashes with markers or reverse the template to center a marker in each gap of a dashed line.

ITemplate : IUnknown	Provides access to members that control the template.
■—□ Geometry: IGeometry	The pattern geometry.
■—■ Interval: Double	The interval.
■— PatternElementCount: Long	Returns the number of pattern elements.
← AddPatternElement (in mark: Double, in Gap: Double)	Adds a pattern element.
← ClearPatternElements	Clears all pattern elements.
← DeletePatternElement (in Index: Long)	Removes the pattern element at the given index.
← GetPatternElement (in Index: Long, out mark: Double, out Gap: Double)	Gets pattern element properties for a given index.
← MovePatternElement (in fromIndex: Long, in toIndex: Long)	Moves a pattern element.
← QueryNextLine (in pGeometry: IGeometry)	Queries for the next line in the pattern.
← QueryNextPoint (in pPoint: IPoint, in pAngle: Double)	Queries for the next point in the pattern.
← Reset	Resets the enumerator.
← Setup (in hDC: Long, in Transformation: ITransformation, in lineSym: ILineSymbol)	Set up items needed by template.

A *Template* is built up by calling the *AddPatternElement* method. This method determines the size of an individual line dash and the following gap, measured in points. Together, each mark and following gap are known as a pattern element. Pattern elements can be any length, and setting the first mark to zero indicates the line starts with a gap.

```
Dim pTemplate as ITemplate
Set pTemplate = New Template
pTemplate.AddPatternElement 5,2
pTemplate.AddPatternElement 5,5
pTemplate.AddPatternElement 2,5
```

There is no specific limit to the number of elements you add, but you don't need to repeat the same one over and over again—the entire template is repeated over and over again, as required.

The *Interval* property affects the length that each element is drawn. The mark value times the interval equals the length of the mark. The gap value times the interval equals the length of the gap.

The *Interval* property defaults to zero, so always make sure to set this property greater than zero if you have a *MarkerLineSymbol* or *HashLineSymbol* (a *CartographicLineSymbol* will draw a solid line if *Interval* is zero). You can use *Interval* to produce similar patterns with one template or to scale up a template when the *LineSymbol's* *Width* is altered to maintain the proportions of the line pattern.

```
Dim pLineSymbol As ILineSymbol
' Set the LineSymbol here as required
Dim pLineProperties As ILineProperties
Set pLineProperties = pLineSymbol
pLineProperties.Template.Interval = pLineSymbol.Width * 0.7
```

Display

Use *ClearPatternElement, DeletePatternElement, GetPatternElement, PatternElementCount,* and *MovePatternElement* to maintain your template.

The code below takes one *Template* and produces a complementary *Template* containing the opposite gaps and marks, allowing you to create a *MultiLayerLineSymbol* with alternating colors or a dashed line with markers in the gaps.

```
Dim pTemplateNew As ITemplate
Set pTemplateNew = New Template
pTemplateNew.Interval = pTemplateOld.Interval
Dim i As Integer, dblMark As Double
Dim dblGap As Double, dblSaveGap As Double
pTemplateOld.GetPatternElement i, dblMark, dblGap
If dblMark > 0 Then
  pTemplateNew.AddPatternElement 0, dblMark
  For i = 1 To pTemplateOld.PatternElementCount - 1
    dblSaveGap = dblGap
    pTemplateOld.GetPatternElement i, dblMark, dblGap
    pTemplateNew.AddPatternElement dblSaveGap, dblMark
  Next i
  pTemplateNew.AddPatternElement dblGap, 0
End If
```

Note that this code only works where the template does not begin with a gap (that is, the first mark is zero), but this algorthim could be adapted to cover this.

The *Geometry, QueryNextPoint, QueryNextLine, Setup,* and *Reset* methods and properties can be used together to find out the actual location of each individual marker, hash, or line.

These methods are used internally by the *CartographicLineSymbol* coclasses but can also be called directly. The mechanism is similar to the *TextPath::Next* method, which is discussed later in this chapter.

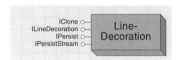

Line decorations are used for placing decorations such as arrowheads at particular places along a line symbol. A line decoration belongs to a cartographic line symbol and is not used as a line symbol itself.

The *LineDecoration* property of the *ILineProperties* interface, set by reference, stores symbols that are drawn on top of a marker line, hash line, or cartographic line. By default, no decoration is present on a line, so the first step to adding line decorations is to create a new line decoration coclass in this property:

```
Set pLineProperties.LineDecoration = New LineDecoration
```

ILineDecoration : IUnknown	Provides access to members that control the line decoration.
■— Element (in Index: Long) : ILineDecorationElement	*Returns the element at the given position.*
■— ElementCount: Long	*Returns the number of line decoration elements.*
← AddElement (in lineDecorationElement: ILineDecorationElement)	*Adds an element.*
← ClearElements	*Clears all line decoration elements.*
← DeleteElement (in Index: Long)	*Deletes the element at the given index.*
← Draw (in hDC: Long, in Transform: ITransformation, in LineGeometry: IGeometry)	*Draws the given line geometry.*
← MoveElement (in Element: ILineDecorationElement, in toIndex: Long)	*Moves a line decoration element to the given index.*
← QueryBoundary (in hDC: Long, in Transform: ITransformation, in LineGeometry: IGeometry, in Boundary: IPolygon)	*Queries for the boundary of the given line geometry.*

A LineSymbol with LineDecorations has advantages over a MultiLayerLineSymbol for producing arrows or similar symbols, as you can specify decorations to appear only at the ends, in the center of a line, or at any other proportion along a line. Therefore, if your line geometry changes, you do not need to update the location of any decoration element, as they are calculated internally.

The *ILineDecoration* interface maintains a collection of line decoration elements for a *LineSymbol*. Line decorations are symbols that display at certain locations along a line. Many decorations can be added to the collection by passing an *ILineDecorationElement* to the *AddElement* method—the most recently added elements display on top.

Use the *ClearElements, DeleteElement, Element, ElementCount,* and *MoveElement* methods to maintain the list of decorations like any other collection. To find out the boundary of the collection of line decorations, call the *QueryBoundary* method. You may wish to use this method to refresh specific areas of your display.

Display

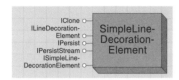

SimpleLine-Decoration-Element

IClone
ILineDecoration-Element
IPersist
IPersistStream
ISimpleLine-DecorationElement

A simple line decoration element draws marker decorations on the top of a line symbol. It's ideal for pleacing arrowheads at the start or end of a line.

The *SimpleLineDecorationElement* stores the decorations that are drawn on the top of a line symbol and defines how they appear. The *SimpleLineDecorationElement* is the only type of line decoration available currently in ArcObjects.

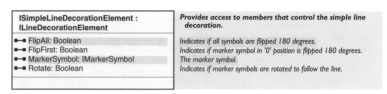

ISimpleLineDecorationElement : ILineDecorationElement	Provides access to members that control the simple line decoration.
■→ FlipAll: Boolean	Indicates if all symbols are flipped 180 degrees.
■→ FlipFirst: Boolean	Indicates if marker symbol in '0' position is flipped 180 degrees.
■→ MarkerSymbol: IMarkerSymbol	The marker symbol.
■→ Rotate: Boolean	Indicates if marker symbols are rotated to follow the line.

The *ISimpleLineDecorationElement* allows you to specify any *MarkerSymbol* as a line decoration. For each *SimpleLineDecorationElement*, this *MarkerSymbol* can be repeated at different positions along the line.

If *Rotate* is *False*, the decorations are drawn at a constant angle to the container. If it is *True*, they are rotated to follow the axis of the line. The default value is *True*.

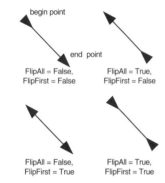

begin point

end point

FlipAll = False,
FlipFirst = False

FlipAll = True,
FlipFirst = False

FlipAll = False,
FlipFirst = True

FlipAll = True,
FlipFirst = True

These lines with simple line decorations have Rotate to True, Positions equal to 0 and 1, and PositionsAsRatio equal to True.

The *FlipAll* and *FlipFirst* properties are particularly useful when generating arrow line symbols. Consider a *LineDecoration* with arrowheads as decorations. If *Rotate* is *True*, the arrows are rotated along the axis of the line and will point toward the *ToPoint* of the line. If *FlipAll* is *True*, the arrows will point toward the *FromPoint*. Setting *FlipFirst* to *True* will make the first arrow point to the *FromPoint* and the rest point toward the *ToPoint*. Combining both would create arrows pointing toward the center of the line.

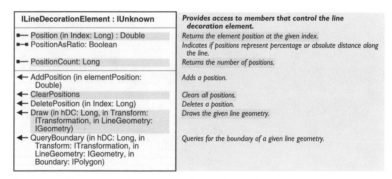

ILineDecorationElement : IUnknown	Provides access to members that control the line decoration element.
■— Position (in Index: Long) : Double	Returns the element position at the given index.
■→ PositionAsRatio: Boolean	Indicates if positions represent percentage or absolute distance along the line.
■— PositionCount: Long	Returns the number of positions.
←— AddPosition (in elementPosition: Double)	Adds a position.
←— ClearPositions	Clears all positions.
←— DeletePosition (in Index: Long)	Deletes a position.
←— Draw (in hDC: Long, in Transform: ITransformation, in LineGeometry: IGeometry)	Draws the given line geometry.
←— QueryBoundary (in hDC: Long, in Transform: ITransformation, in LineGeometry: IGeometry, in Boundary: IPolygon)	Queries for the boundary of a given line geometry.

Because of interface inheritance, all members of the *ILineDecorationElement* interface are available when working with the *ISimpleLineDecorationElement* interface.

If the *PositionAsRatio* property is *True*, then a *Position* of 1 indicates a decoration at the end of the line, and a *Position* of 0.5 indicates a decoration halfway along the line. If *PositionAsRatio* is False, positions are set as specific lengths along the line. Any decorations that have a position greater than the line length will not be displayed; if the line is subsequently edited to an even greater length, the decorations will then appear.

The code that follows creates a basic *CartographicLineSymbol* with small red circles repeated every quarter of the way along the line and larger green squares at the first whole unit along the line.

```
Dim pLineProperties As ILineProperties
Set pLineProperties = New CartographicLineSymbol
Set pLineProperties.LineDecoration = New LineDecoration

Dim pColor As IColor
Set pColor = New RgbColor
pColor.RGB = 255

Dim pMarker As ISimpleMarkerSymbol
Set pMarker = New SimpleMarkerSymbol
pMarker.Style = esriSMSCircle
pMarker.Size = 8
pMarker.Color = pColor
Dim pSimpleLineDec As ISimpleLineDecorationElement
Set pSimpleLineDec = New SimpleLineDecorationElement
With pSimpleLineDec
  .MarkerSymbol = pMarker
  .PositionAsRatio = True
  .AddPosition 0
  .AddPosition 0.25
  .AddPosition 0.5
  .AddPosition 0.75
  .AddPosition 1
End With
pLineProperties.LineDecoration.AddElement pSimpleLineDec

pColor.RGB = 655280
Set pMarker = New SimpleMarkerSymbol
pMarker.Style = esriSMSSquare
pMarker.Size = 12
pMarker.Color = pColor

Set pSimpleLineDec = New SimpleLineDecorationElement
With pSimpleLineDec
  .MarkerSymbol = pMarker
  .PositionAsRatio = False
  .AddPosition 1
End With
pLineProperties.LineDecoration.AddElement pSimpleLineDec
```

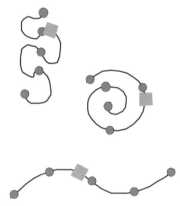

The cartographic line symbol created using the neighboring script

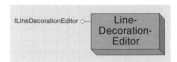

ILineDecorationEditor ○— Line-Decoration-Editor

The LineDecorationEditor is the dialog box used by ArcMap to allow the user to edit the properties of line decorations.

The *LineDecorationEditor* shows the dialog box used by ArcMap to allow a user to edit the properties of a *LineDecoration* of a *CartographicLineSymbol, HashLineSymbol,* or *MarkerLineSymbol.*

ILineDecorationEditor : IUnknown	Provides a dialog for managing properties associated with Line Decoration.
■— ShowUnits: Boolean	*Indicates whether to display the Units combo box.*
■— Title: String	*The title of the Line Decoration Editor dialog.*
← EditLineDecoration (LineDecoration: ILineDecoration, in previewLine: ILineSymbol, hWnd: Long) : Boolean	*Displays the Line Decoration Editor dialog for the given symbol and returns a flag indicating if the symbol changed.*

The *EditLineDecoration* method takes an *ILineDecoration* and an *ILineSymbol* parameter. The *LineDecoration* parameter, passed by reference, has its properties edited by the user. The *LineSymbol* is required to correctly display the line in the Preview frame of the dialog box.

If a user clicks the LineProperties button in the LineSymbolEditor, they can access the LineDecorationEditor and add decorations to the LineSymbol. However, using the LineDecorationEditor directly restricts the user to setting the properties of the decorations only for a specific LineSymbol object.

```
Dim pLineDec As ILineDecoration
Set pLineDec = pLineSymbol.LineDecoration
' pLineSymbol is a preexisting line symbol

Dim pLineDecEditor As ILineDecorationEditor
Set pLineDecEditor = New LineDecorationEditor
pLineDecEditor.Title = "Edit My Text Background"
pLineDecEditor.ShowUnits = False
If Not pLineDecEditor.EditLineDecoration(pLineDec, pLineSymbol, 0) Then
  MsgBox "User pressed Cancel"
Else
  'Do something with the edited Line Decoration
End If
```

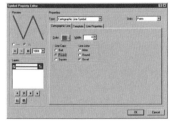

The ArcMap dialog box for editing simple line decoration elements

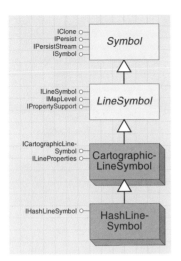

A HashLineSymbol is a line symbol made up of many short lines crossing the path of the line feature, such as part of a railroad symbol.

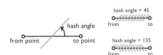

Using the *HashLineSymbol*, a line feature can be symbolized by a repeated line symbol, or hash, drawn across the path of the line feature.

IHashLineSymbol: ILineSymbol	Provides access to members that control the hash line symbol.
■—■ Angle: Double	Hash line angle.
■—□ HashSymbol: ILineSymbol	Line symbol used for hash pattern.

The *IHashLineSymbol* interface has two simple properties.

The *HashSymbol* property is used to return or set a *LineSymbol* that draws the hashes across the line path. The property is set by reference, so be careful with your object references.

The *Angle* property sets or returns the angle at which the hashes are drawn, relative to the path of the line feature. An angle of 90 degrees will draw all the hashes perpendicular to the path, angles of 0 to 89 degrees will tilt the hash toward the end vertex of the path, and angles of 91 to 180 degrees will tilt the hash toward the start vertex of the path.

The *Width* property, inherited from *ILineSymbol*, refers to the length of each hash line, and therefore the actual width of the symbol will be a function of both the *Width* and *Angle* properties.

Below, we set a *HashLineSymbol*'s *Width* by calculating the *LineSymbol Width* required to produce a symbol with an actual width of 20 points. The *SymbolWidth* function converts a value from a required perpendicular width to the required *LineSymbol Width*.

```
Dim pHashLineSym As IHashLineSymbol
Set pHashLineSym = New HashLineSymbol
pHashLineSym.Angle = 45
pHashLineSym.Width = SymbolWidth(20, 45)

Function SymbolWidth(dblPerpendicularWidth As Double, _
   pAngle As Double) As Double
  Const dblPi = 3.14159265
  SymbolWidth = dblPerpendicularWidth / Sin(pAngle * (dblPi / 180))
End Function
```

The default *HashSymbol* is a *SimpleLineSymbol* with a width of 1 and an angle of 90, but you could use any *LineSymbol*, even another *HashLineSymbol*.

Use the *ILineProperties* interface to set the pattern of the hashes, discussed in the *CartographicLineSymbol* abstract class. Note that for a *HashLineSymbol*, the *Template* marks how many dashes will occur in the pattern segment.

Display

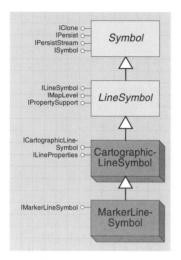

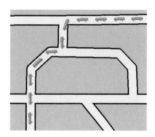

A line can be drawn as a repeated marker symbol by using a MarkerLineSymbol. For example, the path of a bus through a town may be shown as a repeated bus symbol.

Using the *MarkerLineSymbol*, a line feature can be drawn as a repeated *MarkerSymbol*.

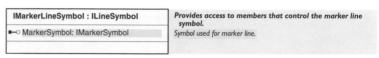

IMarkerLineSymbol : ILineSymbol	Provides access to members that control the marker line symbol.
▪—□ MarkerSymbol: IMarkerSymbol	Symbol used for marker line.

The *IMarkerLineSymbol* interface has one property, which sets the *MarkerSymbol* used to symbolize the line. Set this property to any *MarkerSymbol*, but be careful with your object references, as this property is set by reference.

```
Dim pMarkerLine As IMarkerLineSymbol
Set pMarkerLine = New MarkerLineSymbol

Dim pMarker As ISimpleMarkerSymbol
Set pMarker = New SimpleMarkerSymbol
Set pMarkerLine.MarkerSymbol = pMarker
pMarker.Size = 20
```

Note that the *MarkerSymbol*'s *Size* property equals the *MarkerLineSymbol*'s *Width* property.

You can set the pattern of the markers on your line by using the *ILineProperties* interface, discussed in the *CartographicLineSymbol* abstract class.

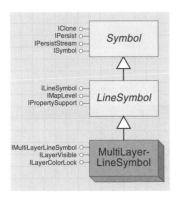

A multilayer line symbol allows a collection of different line symbols to be used to draw a single line feature.

The *MultiLayerLineSymbol* coclass can be used to display a line by stacking a number of different line symbols together, allowing more complex line symbols to be created from the basic building blocks provided. This is shown below.

IMultiLayerLineSymbol: ILineSymbol	Provides access to members that control the multilayer line symbol.
■— Layer (in Index: Long) : ILineSymbol	Line symbol per index value.
■— LayerCount: Long	The number of layers in the symbol.
◄— AddLayer (in lineLayer: ILineSymbol)	Adds a layer to the line symbol.
◄— ClearLayers	Removes all line symbol layers.
◄— DeleteLayer (in lineLayer: ILineSymbol)	Deletes a layer from the line symbol.
◄— DrawLayer (in Index: Long, in Geometry: IGeometry)	Draws a line symbol layer.
◄— MoveLayer (in lineLayer: ILineSymbol, in toIndex: Long)	Move line symbol layer to different layer position.

The *IMultiLayerLineSymbol* interface performs similar functions to the *IMultiLayerMarkerSymbol* interface. For more information, refer to the *MultiLayerMarkerSymbol* section earlier in this chapter.

The *MultiLayerLineSymbol* also supports the *ILayerColorLock* and *ILayerVisible* interfaces, also discussed earlier in this chapter.

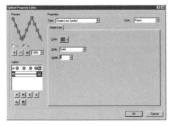

The ArcMap dialog box for editing multilayer line symbols.

Display

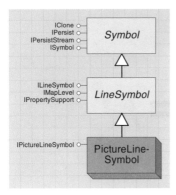

The PictureLineSymbol *draws a line by filling it with a tiled image.*

The *PictureLineSymbol* coclass provides a way to fill a *LineSymbol* with a tiled image, as if the boundary of the *LineSymbol* was a filled *Polygon*. This coclass can be used in preference to a *MarkerLineSymbol* using a *PictureMarkerSymbol*.

IPictureLineSymbol: ILineSymbol	Provides access to members that control the picture line symbol.
■━■ BackgroundColor: IColor	*Line background color.*
■━■ BitmapTransparencyColor: IColor	*Color within bitmap indicating transparency.*
■━■ Offset: Double	*Picture offset from center of line.*
■━□ Picture: Picture	*Picture used for line.*
■━■ Rotate: Boolean	*Indicates if the picture is rotated to follow the line.*
■━■ SwapForeGroundBackGroundColor: Boolean	*Indicates if the foreground and background colors are swapped on 1 Bit Images Only.*
■━■ XScale: Double	*Scale of picture along X-axis.*
■━■ YScale: Double	*Scale of picture along Y-axis.*
← CreateLineSymbolFromFile (in Type: tagesrilPictureType, in FileName: String)	*Create line symbol from picture file.*

Use the *CreateLineSymbolFromFile* method to set the picture that is to be used for the fill. This method sets the *Picture* property (note that this property is set by reference).

```
Dim pPictureLine As IPictureLineSymbol
Set pPictureLine = New PictureLineSymbol
pPictureLine.CreateLineSymbolFromFile esriIPictureBitmap,_
  "C:\MyIcons\Pattern.bmp"
```

Set the *Width* property to control the thickness of the line. The *Picture* is tiled to entirely fill the thickness of the line, but the size of each tile can be scaled using the *XScale* and *YScale* properties. For more information on the use of the *BackgroundColor, BitmapTransparencyColor,* and *SwapForeGroundBackGroundColor* properties, see the *PictureMarkerSymbol* coclass.

Fill symbol objects

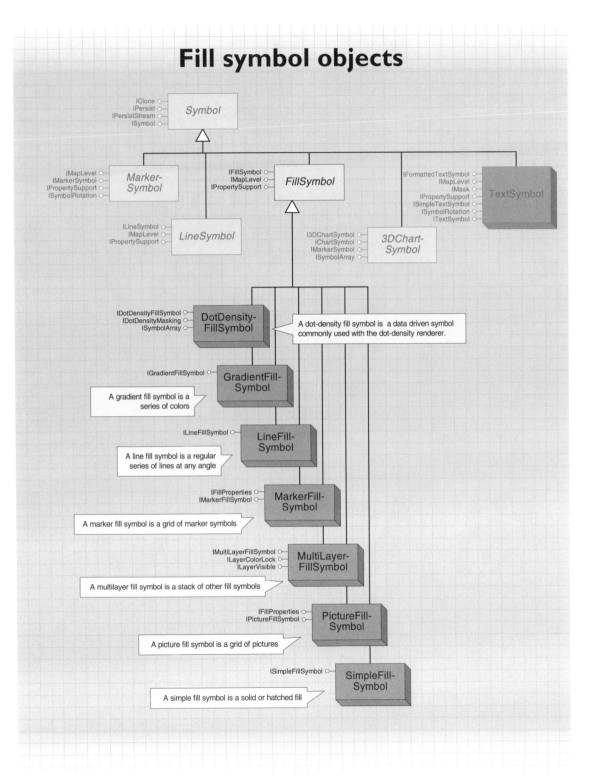

Symbol
- IClone
- IPersist
- IPersistStream
- ISymbol

Marker-Symbol
- IMapLevel
- IMarkerSymbol
- IPropertySupport
- ISymbolRotation

FillSymbol
- IFillSymbol
- IMapLevel
- IPropertySupport

TextSymbol
- IFormattedTextSymbol
- IMapLevel
- IMask
- IPropertySupport
- ISimpleTextSymbol
- ISymbolRotation
- ITextSymbol

LineSymbol
- ILineSymbol
- IMapLevel
- IPropertySupport

3DChart-Symbol
- I3DChartSymbol
- IChartSymbol
- IMarkerSymbol
- ISymbolArray

DotDensity-FillSymbol
- IDotDensityFillSymbol
- IDotDensityMasking
- ISymbolArray

A dot-density fill symbol is a data driven symbol commonly used with the dot-density renderer.

GradientFill-Symbol
- IGradientFillSymbol

A gradient fill symbol is a series of colors

LineFill-Symbol
- ILineFillSymbol

A line fill symbol is a regular series of lines at any angle

MarkerFill-Symbol
- IFillProperties
- IMarkerFillSymbol

A marker fill symbol is a grid of marker symbols

MultiLayer-FillSymbol
- IMultiLayerFillSymbol
- ILayerColorLock
- ILayerVisible

A multilayer fill symbol is a stack of other fill symbols

PictureFill-Symbol
- IFillProperties
- IPictureFillSymbol

A picture fill symbol is a grid of pictures

SimpleFill-Symbol
- ISimpleFillSymbol

A simple fill symbol is a solid or hatched fill

Display

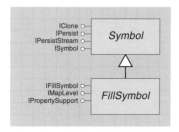

A fill symbol specifies how the area and outline of any polygon is to be drawn.

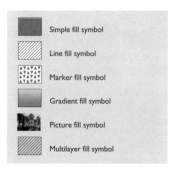

Simple fill symbol

Line fill symbol

Marker fill symbol

Gradient fill symbol

Picture fill symbol

Multilayer fill symbol

outline width = 1 pt   outline width = 5 pt

The *FillSymbol* abstract class represents the two properties—*Color* and *Outline*—all types of fill symbols have in common.

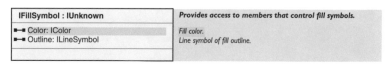

IFillSymbol : IUnknown	Provides access to members that control fill symbols.
▪━◼ Color: IColor	*Fill color.*
▪━◼ Outline: ILineSymbol	*Line symbol of fill outline.*

The *IFillSymbol* interface, inherited by all the specialist fill symbols in ArcObjects, has two read–write properties.

The *Color* property controls the color of the basic fill as described below and can be set to any *IColor* object.

Coclass	Default color	Color property
SimpleFillSymbol	black	color of the solid fill or pattern
MarkerFillSymbol	black	Color property of MarkerSymbol, see IMarkerSymbol for more details
GradientFillSymbol	blue	not used, set ColorRamp property instead
LineFillSymbol	mid-gray	Color property of the LineSymbol - See ILineSymbol for more details
PictureFillSymbol, 1 bit image	black	the parts of the boolean image which contain a color
PictureMarkerSymbol, >1 bit image	not set	no effect
MultiLayerFillSymbol	black	dependent on ILayerColorLock

The *Outline* property sets an *ILineSymbol* object, which is drawn as the outline of the fill symbol. By default, the outline is a solid *SimpleLineSymbol*, but you can use any type of line symbol as your outline.

Note that the outline is centered on the boundary of the feature; therefore, an outline with a width of 5 will overlap the fill symbol by a visible amount.

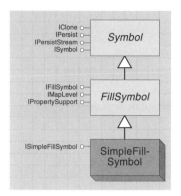

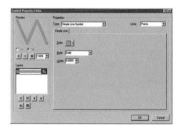

An areal feature can be filled with a solid flood fill or a simple pattern, such as cross-hatching or vertical lines.

The *SimpleFillSymbol* coclass is used to fill an areal shape with either a solid flood fill, a hollow fill (only the outline is drawn), or one of six simple line patterns.

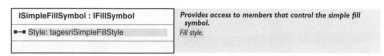

ISimpleFillSymbol : IFillSymbol	Provides access to members that control the simple fill symbol.
■─■ Style: tagesriSimpleFillStyle	Fill style.

The *ISimpleFillSymbol* interface allows you to specify the type of fill by setting the *Style* property to one of the *esriSimpleFillStyle* constants listed below.

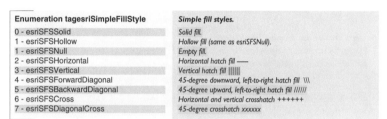

Enumeration tagesriSimpleFillStyle	Simple fill styles.
0 - esriSFSSolid	Solid fill.
1 - esriSFSHollow	Hollow fill (same as esriSFSNull).
1 - esriSFSNull	Empty fill.
2 - esriSFSHorizontal	Horizontal hatch fill ——
3 - esriSFSVertical	Vertical hatch fill ||||||
4 - esriSFSForwardDiagonal	45-degree downward, left-to-right hatch fill \\\
5 - esriSFSBackwardDiagonal	45-degree upward, left-to-right hatch fill //////
6 - esriSFSCross	Horizontal and vertical crosshatch ++++++
7 - esriSFSDiagonalCross	45-degree crosshatch xxxxxx

The *esriSimpleFillStyle* constants are used to set a simple fill style.

The ArcMap dialog box for editing simple fill symbols

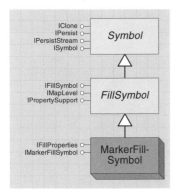

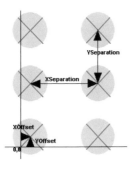

An areal feature can be filled by drawing MarkerSymbols in a regular grid or in random locations throughout the area.

The ArcMap dialog box for editing marker fill symbols

The *MarkerFillSymbol* coclass can be used to fill a polygon, rectangle, ellipse, or other two-dimensional shape with a repeated pattern of marker symbols.

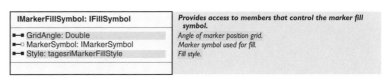

IMarkerFillSymbol: IFillSymbol	Provides access to members that control the marker fill symbol.
■—■ GridAngle: Double	Angle of marker position grid.
■—□ MarkerSymbol: IMarkerSymbol	Marker symbol used for fill.
■—■ Style: tagesriMarkerFillStyle	Fill style.

The *MarkerSymbol* property returns or sets the marker symbol that will be repeated throughout the fill—note that this property is set by reference, so watch your object references. You can use any *MarkerSymbol* for your fill, but note that the *PictureFillSymbol* may be more appropriate for your needs than using a *PictureMarkerSymbol* as the *MarkerSymbol*.

The *GridAngle* property is not yet functional.

The *Style* property offers options for the distribution of markers throughout the fill and can be set to one of the *esriMarkerFillStyle* constants.

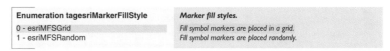

Enumeration tagesriMarkerFillStyle	Marker fill styles.
0 - esriMFSGrid	Fill symbol markers are placed in a grid.
1 - esriMFSRandom	Fill symbol markers are placed randomly.

If the grid style is chosen, then the *Marker* objects will be aligned on a grid starting at the origin of the containers coordinate system, with the center of a marker at (0,0); therefore, if the same fill is applied to many shapes in one container, the markers within every shape will align together.

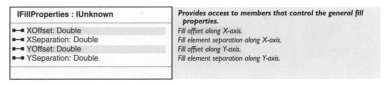

IFillProperties : IUnknown	Provides access to members that control the general fill properties.
■—■ XOffset: Double	Fill offset along X-axis.
■—■ XSeparation: Double	Fill element separation along X-axis.
■—■ YOffset: Double	Fill offset along Y-axis.
■—■ YSeparation: Double	Fill element separation along Y-axis.

The *IFillProperties* interface provides control over the distribution of *MarkerSymbol* objects within the fill shape. The *XOffset* and *YOffset* properties alter the alignment of grid-distributed symbols as defined above by shifting the start of the grid. The *XSeparation* and *YSeparation* properties determine the spacing of the markers on the grid. Remember that *Marker* objects represent zero-dimensional shapes, so a separation less than the marker size would result in overlapping markers. All four properties use points for units, and the default separation is 12 points. Setting separation values also determines the average spacing of *Marker* objects if the *Style* is *esriMFSRandom*.

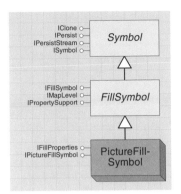

An areal feature can be filled with a repeated bitmap, which is ideal for adding a textural or pictorial fill to your map.

The *PictureFillSymbol* coclass allows us to specify the properties of a picture that is used to fill an areal feature.

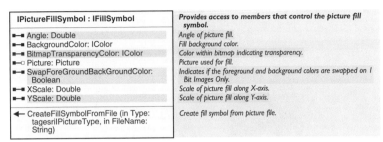

IPictureFillSymbol : IFillSymbol	Provides access to members that control the picture fill symbol.
■─■ Angle: Double	*Angle of picture fill.*
■─■ BackgroundColor: IColor	*Fill background color.*
■─■ BitmapTransparencyColor: IColor	*Color within bitmap indicating transparency.*
■─□ Picture: Picture	*Picture used for fill.*
■─■ SwapForeGroundBackGroundColor: Boolean	*Indicates if the foreground and background colors are swapped on 1 Bit Images Only.*
■─■ XScale: Double	*Scale of picture fill along X-axis.*
■─■ YScale: Double	*Scale of picture fill along Y-axis.*
◄─ CreateFillSymbolFromFile (in Type: tagesrilPictureType, in FileName: String)	*Create fill symbol from picture file.*

The first property you should set when creating a *PictureFillSymbol* is *Picture*, which you can set directly to an existing OLE picture. Note that the *Picture* property is set by reference. You may prefer to call the *CreateFillSymbolFromFile* method, which sets the *Picture* property for you. Using this method, you can set either an EMF or a BMP file as the *Picture* by using the correct *esriIPictureType* constant.

For information on the BackgroundColor, BitmapTransparencyColor, *and* SwapForeGroundBackGroundColor *properties, refer to these properties on the* IPictureMarkerSymbol *interface.*

Enumeration tagesriIPictureType	IPicture Data Types.
0 - esriIPictureEMF	*EMF.*
1 - esriIPictureBitmap	*BITMAP.*

You could use code like this:

```
Dim pPictureFill As IPictureFillSymbol
Set pPictureFill = New PictureFillSymbol
If UCase(Right(filename, 3)) = "EMF" Then
  pPictureFill.CreateFillSymbolFromFile esriIPictureEMF, filename
ElseIf UCase(Right(filename, 3)) = "BMP" Then
  pPictureFill.CreateFillSymbolFromFile esriIPictureBitmap, filename
End If
```

If the filename referenced is not a valid file and path, an error is raised by the *CreateFillSymbolFromFile* method.

After the *Picture* is set, the other properties can be set to adjust the appearance and pattern of the picture within the fill. The *Picture* is repeated on a grid, starting at the top left of the *Geometry* to which the fill is applied. The angle of the grid can be adjusted by setting the *Angle* property. A value of 45 will rotate the grid 45 degrees clockwise.

You can stretch the *Picture* in size by setting the *XScale* and *YScale* properties. For example, to make each picture in the fill twice as big as the original, set both properties to 2. *XScale* and *YScale* may also be set to values less than 1 to shrink the original image.

The *PictureFillSymbol* coclass also implements the *IFillProperties* interface, discussed previously with the *MarkerFillSymbol* coclass. Remember that a picture is two-dimensional; therefore, the *XSeparation* and *YSeparation* properties refer to the separation from the edge of one picture to the start of another. A separation of 0 (the default separation for a *PictureFillSymbol*) will result in a contiguous picture fill.

The ArcMap dialog box for editing picture fill symbols

Display

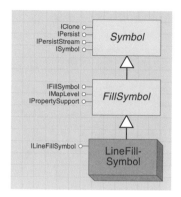

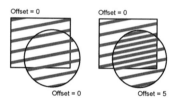

An areal feature can be filled with a repeated line.

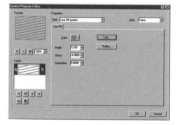

Setting the Offset property affects how overlapping line fill symbols are drawn.

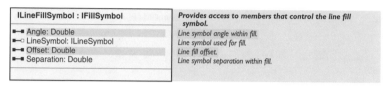

The ArcMap dialog box for editing line fill symbols

The *LineFillSymbol* coclass can be used to fill an areal shape with a repeated line, symbolized by any *LineSymbol* in ArcObjects.

ILineFillSymbol : IFillSymbol	Provides access to members that control the line fill symbol.
■─■ Angle: Double	Line symbol angle within fill.
■─□ LineSymbol: ILineSymbol	Line symbol used for fill.
■─■ Offset: Double	Line fill offset.
■─■ Separation: Double	Line symbol separation within fill.

The *ILineFillSymbol* interface is used to specify the type of *LineSymbol* used for a fill, its *Angle, Offset,* and *Separation.*

The *LineSymbol* property should be set to any *LineSymbol* object (see the section in this chapter on line symbols). Be careful with your object references, as this property is set by reference.

The *Angle* property indicates the number of degrees between the *LineSymbol* and a horizontal line and defaults to 0.

The first line will always be drawn through the origin (0, 0) of the container's coordinate system, unless the *Offset* property is set to a value other than zero. This means that line fill symbols can be aligned or offset as required between multiple shapes.

The *Separation* property, which is in points, determines the frequency of the line symbols within the areal feature. If the *Separation* is less than the *LineSymbol*'s *Width,* the lines will overlap, but a *Separation* greater than the *Width* will leave a transparent area between the *LineSymbols,* through which underlying symbols' elements can be seen.

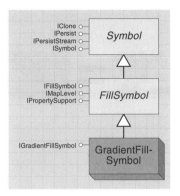

An areal feature can be filled with a series of colors, creating many different effects.

The *GradientFillSymbol* coclass can be used to fill an areal shape with colors from a *ColorRamp*.

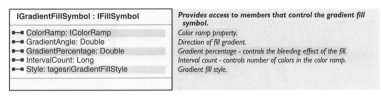

IGradientFillSymbol : IFillSymbol	Provides access to members that control the gradient fill symbol.
■—■ ColorRamp: IColorRamp	Color ramp property.
■—■ GradientAngle: Double	Direction of fill gradient.
■—■ GradientPercentage: Double	Gradient percentage - controls the bleeding effect of the fill.
■—■ IntervalCount: Long	Interval count - controls number of colors in the color ramp.
■—■ Style: tagesriGradientFillStyle	Gradient fill style.

Set any *IColorRamp* onto the *ColorRamp* property and it will be used to fill the areal feature. A graded effect can best be achieved by using an *AlgorithmicColorRamp* (see the topics in this chapter on *ColorRamps*).

You should note that you don't need to set a *Size* or call *CreateRamp* on your *ColorRamp*. Instead, the *IntervalCount* property defines the number of color steps required. Set the *IntervalCount* property depending on what kind of effect you wish to achieve.

You may wish to use the *GradientFillSymbol* to produce a smooth gradation of color in an area and therefore need an appropriate *IntervalCount*. The average computer screen has a resolution at least three times as coarse as the average printer at 300 dpi, as a rough guide. Although your printer may have a resolution of 600 or more dpi, an average person may not be able to distinguish between output at 300 dpi and 600 dpi when viewing regions of shifting color.

Therefore, a smooth fill on the screen may appear banded in the printed output. To produce a smooth progression of color in your fill for output to a printer, first set the 1:1 scale on the PageLayout view to account for differences in printed scale and onscreen scale. Next, experiment to find the *IntervalCount* at which the fill appears smooth on the screen—this will be dependent on the characteristics of your *ColorRamp*, the size of the area to be filled, and the *GradientPercentage* (see below). Then, multiply the *IntervalCount* by at least 3 times and try your output.

Decide how you want the gradient to fill your shape by setting the *Style* to one of the *esriGradientFillStyle* constants.

Enumeration tagesriGradientFillStyle	Gradient fill styles.
0 - esriGFSLinear	Linear Gradient Fill Style.
1 - esriGFSRectangular	Rectangular Gradient Fill Style.
2 - esriGFSCircular	Circular Gradient Fill Style.
3 - esriGFSBuffered	Buffered Gradient Fill Style.

The ArcMap dialog box for editing gradient fill symbols

For the *esriGFSLinear* or *esriGFSRectangular* styles, you can alter the fill by setting a *GradientAngle*. This is an angle, in degrees, between the vertical and the lines of fill.

You can also determine the percentage of the fill that has a gradient fill by setting *GradientPercentage* to a value between 0 and 1. A value of one indicates that the entire shape should be filled with the color ramp, but a value of 0.5 indicates only half the shape should be filled with the color ramp; the first half of the area is filled by the first color in the color ramp, and the remaining area is filled with the color ramp.

Display

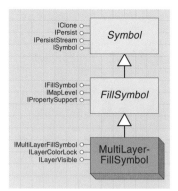

A MultiLayerFillSymbol *allows a collection of different fill symbols to be used to fill a single area feature, with lower fill patterns showing through the gaps in higher fill symbols.*

The ArcMap *dialog box for editing multilayer fill symbols*

The *MultiLayerFillSymbol* coclass can be used to create a complex fill pattern by stacking a number of different fill symbols together.

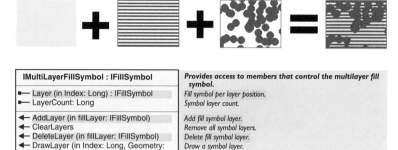

IMultiLayerFillSymbol : IFillSymbol	Provides access to members that control the multilayer fill symbol.
▪— Layer (in Index: Long) : IFillSymbol	Fill symbol per layer position.
▪— LayerCount: Long	Symbol layer count.
◄— AddLayer (in fillLayer: IFillSymbol)	Add fill symbol layer.
◄— ClearLayers	Remove all symbol layers.
◄— DeleteLayer (in fillLayer: IFillSymbol)	Delete fill symbol layer.
◄— DrawLayer (in Index: Long, Geometry: IGeometry)	Draw a symbol layer.
◄— MoveLayer (in fillLayer: IFillSymbol, in toIndex: Long)	Change symbol layer position index.

The *IMultiLayerFillSymbol* interface performs similar functions to the *IMultiLayerMarkerSymbol* interface discussed earlier in this chapter.

The *MultiLayerFillSymbol* also supports the *ILayerColorLock* and *ILayerVisible* interfaces, also discussed previously.

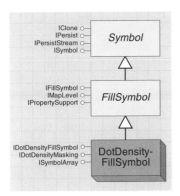

Dot-density fill symbols fill an areal shape with dots. When used in conjunction with a dot-density renderer, the density of dots is calculated from an attribute field.

The *Symbol* at index 0 is the first symbol to be added—it will be drawn first in the fill, below any other dots that may be specified.

Many different dots can be used in a DotDensityFillSymbol.

The *DotDensityFillSymbol* is a data-driven symbol typically used in conjunction with the *DotDensityRenderer* coclass. A *DotDensityFillSymbol* fills a shape with *MarkerSymbols* placed in random locations. The number of marker symbols drawn per unit area is calculated by the *DotDensity-Renderer*, giving a representation of the density of an attribute value.

In addition to the interfaces detailed below, *DotDensitySymbol* implements the *ISymbolArray* interface, discussed further with the 3D chart symbols. *DotDensitySymbols* can be filled with more than one type of dot, and the symbol array is used to store a *MarkerSymbol* for each type of dot.

If we intend to use the *DotDensitySymbol* in a *DotDensityRenderer* to draw dots of two types, indicating two different attributes, we might use code like this:

```
Dim pMarker As ISimpleMarkerSymbol, pSymArray As ISymbolArray
Set pSymArray = New DotDensityFillSymbol

Set pMarker = New SimpleMarkerSymbol
pMarker.Style = esriSMSDiamond
pSymArray.AddSymbol pMarker

Set pMarker = New SimpleMarkerSymbol
pMarker.Style = esriSMSCross
pSymArray.AddSymbol pMarker
```

We can also set other properties of each individual *MarkerSymbol* here, but we don't need to set the *Size* property, as the size of each marker is controlled by the *IDotDensityFillSymbol::DotSize property*.

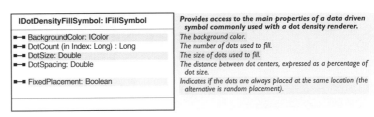

IDotDensityFillSymbol: IFillSymbol	Provides access to the main properties of a data driven symbol commonly used with a dot density renderer.
■← BackgroundColor: IColor	The background color.
■← DotCount (in Index: Long) : Long	The number of dots used to fill.
■← DotSize: Double	The size of dots used to fill.
■← DotSpacing: Double	The distance between dot centers, expressed as a percentage of dot size.
■← FixedPlacement: Boolean	Indicates if the dots are always placed at the same location (the alternative is random placement).

IDotDensityFillSymbol controls the appearance of the marker symbols within the dot-density fill.

BackgroundColor reflects the color used to fill areas that are not covered by dots—use a *NullColor* if you wish the underlying layers to be visible through the dots.

Color indicates the color of the dots, and *Outline* can be used to alter the appearance of the boundary of the shape.

Set *FixedPlacement* to *True* if you wish the dots to be always placed in the same location. The *DotSize* property indicates the size of each dot in points—using a small size, such as 1 to 3 points, is usually most suitable.

The *DotCount* property contains a zero-based array of values that determine the number of dots drawn in a filled shape. The *DotCount* at array index 0 indicates the number of dots drawn by *ISymbolArray::Symbol(0)*,

Display

and the size of the array is determined by the number of symbols that have been added to the *DotDensitySymbol*. If you are using a *DotDensityRenderer*, you do not need to set this property, as it will be set by the *DotDensityRenderer* to an appropriate value for each *Feature*, based on the specified attribute and the *IDotDensityRenderer::DotValue* property.

If you are using the *DotDensitySymbol* independently of a *DotDensityRenderer*, then the array should be set as required. You may wish to set the *DotCount* proportionally to the shape's area, and remember to scale up the *DotCount* if the item that uses the fill changes area.

DotSpacing is not implemented at ArcGIS 8.1.

IDotDensityMasking: IUnknown	Provides access to the masking properties of a dot density fill symbol.
■─■ ExcludeMask: Boolean	Indicates if the dots are to be excluded from the mask area.
■─□ MaskGeometry: IGeometry	The geometry used for masking (can be a geometry collection).
■─■ UseMasking: Boolean	Indicates if masking is used.

DotDensityFillSymbols can be slower to display than other fill symbols—a *DotDensityRenderer* must recalculate a new *DotCount* for each *Feature* whenever the *Map* is changed. Therefore, masking may be appropriate.

DotDensityMasking allows you to exclude certain areas of a fill when drawing—for example, you may wish to exclude all areas that are covered by another *MapLayer*.

If *UseMasking* is *True* then the *ExcludeMask* property should be set as required. *ExludeMask* equal to *False* indicates that only areas inside the specified *MaskGeometry* will be drawn with dots, while *True* indicates that only areas outside of the *MaskGeometry* will be drawn with dots.

The *MaskGeometry* property is set from the *IDotDensityRenderer:: ControlLayer* property. If using the *DotDensityFillSymbol* independently, you should set the *MaskGeometry* property yourself.

The code below specifies that only areas inside features in the *pControlLayer* are drawn with dots in a *DotDensityRenderer*.

```
Dim pDotDenSymbol As IDotDensitySymbol, pMasking As IDotDensityMasking
Set pDotDenSymbol = New DotDensityFillSymbol
' Set the properties of the symbol here
Set pMasking = pDotDensitySymbol
With pMasking
  .UseMasking = True
  .ExcludeMask = False
End With


Dim pDotDenRenderer As IDotDensityRenderer,
Set pDotDenRenderer = New DotDensityRenderer
Set pDotDenRenderer.DotDensitySymbol = pDotDenSymbol
pDotDenRenderer.ControlLayer = pControlLayer
```

Note that masking is only supported for *DotDensityFillSymbols* that are used in *DotDensityRenderers*.

Text symbol objects

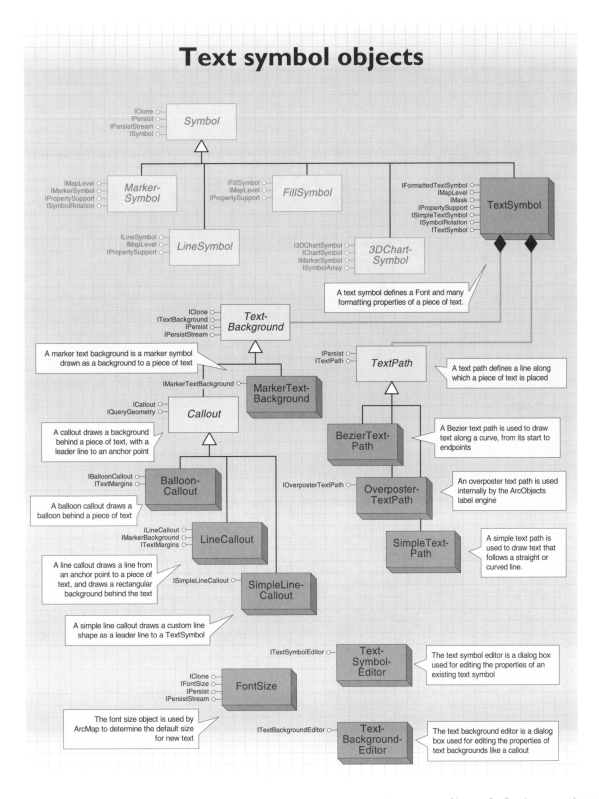

IClone ○
IPersist ○
IPersistStream ○
ISymbol ○
Symbol

IMapLevel ○
IMarkerSymbol ○
IPropertySupport ○
ISymbolRotation ○
Marker-Symbol

IFillSymbol ○
IMapLevel ○
IPropertySupport ○
FillSymbol

IFormattedTextSymbol ○
IMapLevel ○
IMask ○
IPropertySupport ○
ISimpleTextSymbol ○
ISymbolRotation ○
ITextSymbol ○
TextSymbol

ILineSymbol ○
IMapLevel ○
IPropertySupport ○
LineSymbol

I3DChartSymbol ○
IChartSymbol ○
IMarkerSymbol ○
ISymbolArray ○
3DChart-Symbol

A text symbol defines a Font and many formatting properties of a piece of text.

IClone ○
ITextBackground ○
IPersist ○
IPersistStream ○
Text-Background

IPersist ○
ITextPath ○
TextPath

A text path defines a line along which a piece of text is placed

A marker text background is a marker symbol drawn as a background to a piece of text

IMarkerTextBackground ○
MarkerText-Background

ICallout ○
IQueryGeometry ○
Callout

BezierText-Path

A Bezier text path is used to draw text along a curve, from its start to endpoints

A callout draws a background behind a piece of text, with a leader line to an anchor point

IBalloonCallout ○
ITextMargins ○
Balloon-Callout

IOverposterTextPath ○
Overposter-TextPath

An overposter text path is used internally by the ArcObjects label engine

A balloon callout draws a balloon behind a piece of text

ILineCallout ○
IMarkerBackground ○
ITextMargins ○
LineCallout

SimpleText-Path

A simple text path is used to draw text that follows a straight or curved line.

A line callout draws a line from an anchor point to a piece of text, and draws a rectangular background behind the text

ISimpleLineCallout ○
SimpleLine-Callout

A simple line callout draws a custom line shape as a leader line to a TextSymbol

ITextSymbolEditor ○
Text-Symbol-Editor

The text symbol editor is a dialog box used for editing the properties of an existing text symbol

IClone ○
IFontSize ○
IPersist ○
IPersistStream ○
FontSize

The font size object is used by ArcMap to determine the default size for new text

ITextBackgroundEditor ○
Text-Background-Editor

The text background editor is a dialog box used for editing the properties of text backgrounds like a callout

Display

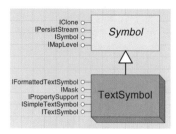

A text symbol is used for rendering cartographic and marginal text, such as annotation, labels, titles, text blocks, key legends, scale bars, graphs, graticule labels, and reports.

The *TextSymbol* coclass provides the object that is used to symbolize text in graphic elements, annotation, labels, and other places.

A *TextSymbol* defines much more than just a font. Its three main interfaces, *ITextSymbol, ISimpleTextSymbol,* and *IFormattedTextSymbol*, control exactly how the text appears and how the individual characters are displayed. Extended ASCII characters are supported by the *TextSymbol*.

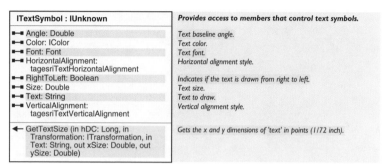

ITextSymbol : IUnknown	Provides access to members that control text symbols.
■—■ Angle: Double	Text baseline angle.
■—■ Color: IColor	Text color.
■—■ Font: Font	Text font.
■—■ HorizontalAlignment: tagesriTextHorizontalAlignment	Horizontal alignment style.
■—■ RightToLeft: Boolean	Indicates if the text is drawn from right to left.
■—■ Size: Double	Text size.
■—■ Text: String	Text to draw.
■—■ VerticalAlignment: tagesriTextVerticalAlignment	Vertical alignment style.
◄— GetTextSize (in hDC: Long, in Transformation: ITransformation, in Text: String, out xSize: Double, out ySize: Double)	Gets the x and y dimensions of 'text' in points (1/72 inch).

The *ITextSymbol* interface is the primary interface for defining the characteristics of a text and is inherited by the *ISimpleTextSymbol* and *IFormattedTextSymbol* interfaces and therefore may not need to be declared specifically. It contains the *Font* property, which is the first logical step to defining a new *TextSymbol*. To set a *Font*, you should first create a COM font object. Using the *IFontDisp* interface of your font, you should set the *Name* of the font. You should also set whether or not your *IFontDisp* is italic, bold, strike-through, or underlined and set its *CharacterSet* and weight. In Visual Basic, you can use the *StdFont* object, which provides VB's standard implementation of the COM font object.

Each font may include different character sets to allow for different alphabets and symbology. For most applications, you won't need to swap character sets from the default.

```
Dim pFnt As stdole.IFontDisp
Set pFnt = New stdole.StdFont
pFnt.Name = "ESRI Cartography"
pFnt.Bold = True
```

The StdFont object is defined in the stdole2.tlb type library, a reference to which is included, by default, in all standard VB projects. Other development environments should provide a similar implementation.

Now you can set the *Font* and also set the *Color* (as any coclass supporting *IColor*) and a *Size* (in points). The *Text* property is used for a standalone *TextSymbol* object only (such as a *TextSymbol* in a style file); a *TextElement* will draw text according to the *Text* property of the *TextElement* coclass. Set the *HorizontalAlignment* and *VerticalAlignment* relative to the text anchor as shown below.

Enumeration tagesriTextHorizontalAlignment	Horizontal text alignment options.
0 - esriTHALeft	The text is left justified.
1 - esriTHACenter	The text is center justified.
2 - esriTHARight	The text is right justified.
3 - esriTHAFull	The text is fully justified.

Enumeration tagesriTextVerticalAlignment	Vertical text alignment options.
0 - esriTVATop	The text is aligned at the top.
1 - esriTVACenter	The text is aligned at the center.
2 - esriTVABaseline	The text is aligned at the baseline.
3 - esriTVABottom	The text is aligned at the bottom.

If the *TextSymbol* is used to draw text to a point, not along a line (see *TextPath*), you can use the *Angle* property to rotate the text string. The *Angle* property specifies the angle of the text baseline, in degrees from the horizontal, and defaults to zero. For Hebrew and Arabic fonts, set the *RightToLeft* property to *True* to lay the text string out in a right-to-left reading order.

GetTextSize is useful for calculating text placements on a PageLayout or whether a text string should be truncated to fit within a certain space.

For any existing *TextSymbol*, the actual size in x and y directions can be calculated using the *GetTextSize* method. Having set a *Size* that defines the font height, the *GetTextSize* method will calculate the actual height and length of the symbol in points. Note that the *GetTextSize* method ignores the *TextPath* property if it is set through the *ISimpleTextSymbol* interface.

The use of this method is shown below, where *pDisplay* is the *IDisplay* of the *PageLayout* or *Map* that the *TextSymbol* belongs to, and *pTextSymbol* is a valid *TextSymbol*. Note that the *StartDrawing* and *FinishDrawing* calls are necessary to make sure the *hDC* of the display is valid. The *dblX* and *dblY* variables are populated respectively with the height and length of the text parameter when drawn with the *pTextSymbol* symbol.

```
Dim dblX As Double, dblY As Double
pDisplay.StartDrawing 0, esriNoScreenCache
pTextSymbol.GetTextSize pDisplay.hDC, pDisplay.DisplayTransformation,_
    "My Text", dblX, dblY
pDisplay.FinishDrawing
```

ISimpleTextSymbol : ITextSymbol	Provides access to members that control the simple text symbol.
■─■ BreakCharacter: Long	Character to be interpreted as text line end.
■─■ Clip: Boolean	Indicates if the text will be clipped per geometry.
■─□ TextPath: ITextPath	Path of text baseline.
■─■ XOffset: Double	Text offset along X-axis.
■─■ YOffset: Double	Text offset along Y-axis.

Remember that many properties, such as XOffset and YOffset, are set in Points—if the size is changed, you may want to change these properties to a percentage of the new size.

The *ISimpleTextSymbol* interface defines a further set of properties to graphically alter the appearance of a *TextSymbol*. The *BreakCharacter* property can be used to set the character code, which is interpreted as a line break character and is particularly useful if you are working with text from a different operating system. For example, the ASCII character code for "A" is 65; therefore, if you set *BreakCharacter* to 65, the text "My ArcMap and my ArcInfo" would appear as:

My
rcMap and my
rcInfo

Note that *BreakCharacter* objects are not used for splined text (for example, if a *TextElement*'s *Geometry* is of type *Line*).

The *XOffset* property sets a horizontal offset in points for the placement of the text from the text anchor, and the *YOffset* performs a similar function in the vertical direction.

The Boolean *Clip* property, if *True*, will clip the text string to fit inside an *Envelope* geometry. Note that at ArcGIS 8.1, there are no *TextElements* that support the *Envelope* geometry; however, this functionality will work with the *ISymbol::Draw* method.

The *TextPath* property is set by reference. For more information about this property, see the *TextPath* abstract class.

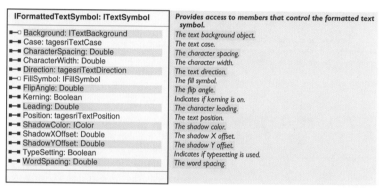

IFormattedTextSymbol: ITextSymbol	Provides access to members that control the formatted text symbol.
Background: ITextBackground	The text background object.
Case: tagesriTextCase	The text case.
CharacterSpacing: Double	The character spacing.
CharacterWidth: Double	The character width.
Direction: tagesriTextDirection	The text direction.
FillSymbol: IFillSymbol	The fill symbol.
FlipAngle: Double	The flip angle.
Kerning: Boolean	Indicates if kerning is on.
Leading: Double	The character leading.
Position: tagesriTextPosition	The text position.
ShadowColor: IColor	The shadow color.
ShadowXOffset: Double	The shadow X offset.
ShadowYOffset: Double	The shadow Y offset.
TypeSetting: Boolean	Indicates if typesetting is used.
WordSpacing: Double	The word spacing.

Examples of text symbols with various backgrounds and fill symbols

The *IFormattedTextSymbol* interface defines a further set of properties, relating mainly to details of exact character placement and the background properties of a *TextSymbol*. Many of the properties on *IFormattedTextSymbol* will be familiar to those with a background in printing or those who have used the Windows API for working with fonts.

Change the spread of characters in the text string by setting the *CharacterSpacing* property, which indicates the spacing between each character as a percentage. The default is 0, which indicates the standard character spacing, but values of -200 to 200 are valid. Lines of text can be spaced by setting the Leading property, whose units are Points.

You can change the case of every alphabetic character in the text string by setting the *Case* property to one of the *esriTextCase* constants.

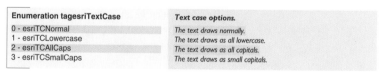

Enumeration tagesriTextCase	Text case options.
0 - esriTCNormal	The text draws normally.
1 - esriTCLowercase	The text draws as all lowercase.
2 - esriTCAllCaps	The text draws as all capitals.
3 - esriTCSmallCaps	The text draws as small capitals.

You can also create subscript and superscript text by setting the *Position* property.

Enumeration tagesriTextDirection	Text direction options.
0 - esriTDHorizontal	The text draws horizontally.
1 - esriTDAngle	The text draws along an angle.
2 - esriTDVertical	The text draws vertically.

A *TextSymbol*'s appearance can be changed dramatically by using a background or drawing with a *FillSymbol* instead of a simple *Color*. The *BackGround* and *FillSymbol* properties are both set by reference and are null by default (if the *FillSymbol* property is null, the *ITextSymbol*'s *Color* property is used to draw the symbol). For more information, see the *TextBackground* and *FillSymbol* abstract classes, respectively.

In addition to the background properties, you can add a shadow by using the *ShadowColor, ShadowXOffset,* and *ShadowYOffset* properties. For example, to create a gray shadow like in the graphic to the left, you could set the properties like this:

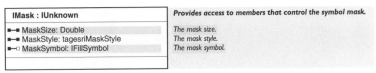

```
Dim pCOl As IColor
Set pCOl = New RgbColor
pCOl.RGB = 8421504
pFTS.ShadowColor = pCOl
pFTS.ShadowXOffset = pFTS.Size / 10
pFTS.ShadowYOffset = -pFTS.ShadowXOffset
```

To remove a shadow, simply set the *ShadowColor* to null.

The *CharacterWidth, WordSpacing, Kerning, FlipAngle, TypeSetting,* and *Direction* properties are not implemented at ArcGIS 8.1.

IMask : IUnknown	Provides access to members that control the symbol mask.
■—■ MaskSize: Double	The mask size.
■—■ MaskStyle: tagesriMaskStyle	The mask style.
■—□ MaskSymbol: IFillSymbol	The mask symbol.

Use a contrasting color Mask *to highlight text that is a similar color to the features or their outlines underneath it.*

The *IMask* interface provides a simple and efficient way to draw a symbol around the edge of your *Text*. For more information about masks, see the *IMask* interface remarks under the *MarkerSymbol* coclass.

A *Mask* differs from a *TextBackground* in that it immediately surrounds the characters in the text string in a limited and predefined way, whereas the *TextBackground* draws behind the entire text string in an extensible manner.

To create a rectangular block around your text, try a LineCallout *with no leader line or accent bar.*

Set the *MaskStyle* property to an *esriMaskStyle* constant.

Enumeration tagesriMaskStyle	Text mask styles.
0 - esriMSNone	No mask.
1 - esriMSHalo	The text mask style is halo.

You can either fill the mask with a solid color by setting the *Color* property, or you can fill it with any other kind of *FillSymbol* by setting the *MaskSymbol* property.

IPropertySupport : IUnknown	Provides access to members that set a default property on an object.
■— Current (in pUnk: IUnknown Pointer) : IUnknown Pointer	The object currently being used.
◄— Applies (in pUnk: IUnknown Pointer) : Boolean	Indicates if the receiver can apply the given object at any given time.
◄— Apply (in NewObject: IUnknown Pointer) : IUnknown Pointer	Applies the given property to the receiver and returns the old object.
◄— CanApply (in pUnk: IUnknown Pointer) : Boolean	Indicates if the receiver can apply the given object at that particular moment.

The *IPropertySupport* interface can be used to determine which interfaces are supported as properties of the *TextSymbol* interfaces. This interface was designed for use by the ArcMap Drawing toolbar. ArcObjects developers should use this interface with caution, as certain interfaces may not be supported by the *Applies* and *CanApply* methods.

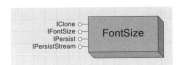

The font size object is used by ArcMap to determine the default size for new text.

The *FontSize* coclass is used by the *IMxDocument::DefaultTextFontSize* property to determine a default font size for ArcMap tools, such as the New Text tool on the Draw toolbar.

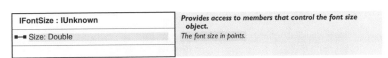

IFontSize : IUnknown	*Provides access to members that control the font size object.*
■—■ Size: Double	*The font size in points.*

For example, if you wish text added with the New Text tool to have a size of 30 points, use the following VBA code:

```
Dim pFontSize As IFontSize
Set pFontSize = New FontSize
pFontSize.Size = 30

Dim pMxDoc As IMxDocument
Set pMxDoc = ThisDocument
pMxDoc.DefaultTextFontSize = pFontSize
```

Display

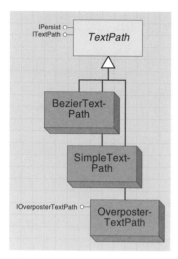

A piece of text can follow along a path (a series of connected lines) and is often known as splined text. A TextPath is the object used to calculate the position of each glyph along the path.

The ITextPath::Setup method sets the TextPath and its TextSymbol into the display device context, which allows it to calculate the coordinates based on the DisplayTransformation.

The *TextPath* abstract class defines the common functionality of the text path coclasses and provides the primary interface for creating splined text. Once a valid text path object is set as the *TextPath* property of the *ISimpleTextSymbol* interface, the text will be drawn splined along the path.

ITextPath : IUnknown	Provides access to members that control the text path.
▬○ Geometry: IGeometry	The geometry used for the path.
▬■ XOffset: Double	The X offset value.
▬■ YOffset: Double	The Y offset value.
◄■ Next (out X: Double, out Y: Double, out Angle: Double)	Returns the next coordinate.
◄■ Reset	Resets the coordinate enumerator.
◄■ Setup (in hDC: Long, in Transformation: ITransformation, in textSym: ITextSymbol)	Set up items needed by text path.

The *ITextPath* interface provides methods to calculate the exact location of each character along a text path, allowing you to investigate the exact placement of text and find out at which point the text string turns a corner or reaches a certain location. First, set the *Geometry* property to an object supporting the *ICurve* interface. Set the *XOffset* and *YOffset* properties if you want to offset your text from this curve (the units are points). Call the *Setup* method, passing parameters based on the *Display* to which the *Symbol* belongs. Then, call the *Next* method repeatedly to calculate the angle and x,y coordinates of each successive character in the text string.

The code below demonstrates the drawing of a symbol at the coordinates of each character in the *TextSymbol*, where *pPath* is its *TextPath*, *pDisplay* is a valid *ScreenDisplay*, and *pMark* is the *MarkerSymbol* used to draw the coordinates.

```
Dim i As Integer
Dim dblX As Double, dblY As Double, dblAngle As Double
Dim pPoint As IPoint
Set pPoint = New esriCore.Point

pDisplay.StartDrawing pDisplay.hDC, esriNoScreenCache
pDisplay.SetSymbol pMark

pPath.Setup pDisplay.hDC, pDisplay.DisplayTransformation, pSimpleTxtSym
pPath.Reset

For i = 1 To Len(strTheTextString)
  pPath.Next dblX, dblY, pAngle
  pPoint.PutCoords dblX, dblY
  pMark.angle = dblAngle
  pDisplay.DrawPoint pPoint
Next i
pDisplay.FinishDrawing
```

The *SimpleTextPath* coclass can be used to spline text along the path of any *ICurve*. Simply set a *SimpleTextPath* as the *TextPath* of a *TextSymbol* and ensure that the *Geometry* used to draw the *Symbol* is a type of *Geometry* that supports *ICurve*. For example, if you wish to use splined text as a graphics element on a *PageLayout*, the *Geometry* property of the *IElement* interface of the *TextElement* must support *ICurve*. The code below demonstrates how to create splined text, from an existing *TextSymbol* (*pTextSymbol*) and *BezierCurve* (*pCurve*). Note that we set the required *Geometry* onto the *TextElement*.

```
Dim pTextPath As ITextPath
Set pTextPath = New SimpleTextPath
Set pTextSymbol.TextPath = pTextPath

pTextElement.Symbol = pTextSymbol

Dim pElement As IElement
Set pElement = pTextElement

pElement.Geometry = pCurve
```

If you're creating a splined TextElement *or* AnnotationElement, *make sure you set the* IElement's Geometry *property to the required curve, as the* Geometry *of the* Element *is used to place the text.*

Experimenting with *ITextSymbol::VerticalAlignment* will result in text above, below, or on the line.

The *BezierTextPath* coclass has been superseded by the *SimpleTextPath*, which should generally be used in preference. It provided an early implementation of splined text along a Bézier curve before the *BezierCurve* class in geometry was introduced to ArcObjects. For a *BezierCurve*, a *BezierTextPath* takes the first, last, and midpoint of the given geometry and splines text along a Bézier curve calculated from those three points.

The *OverPosterTextPath* is used internally by the ArcObjects label engine. It is impractical for developers to use as it requires a specialized *Geometry* that is used within the label engine itself.

IOverposterTextPath : IUnknown	*Provides access to members that control the overposter text path.*

The *IOverPosterTextPath* is present only as a type-check mechanism; the coclass is used in a similar way to the *SimpleTextPath*. The specialized geometry required is a *PointCollection*, which contains two points for every character to be drawn. The first point of the two-point pair is the location at which the given character draws; the second point is used along with the first to determine the angle each character should be drawn at.

Display

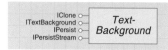

A background can be used to emphasize text or to aid clarity where text is obscured by features or other symbols. A background can also be part of the text symbology—for example, a highway feature can be labeled by a number drawn within a highway shield. Callouts can be applied to label features in cluttered areas of a map or layout by using a leader line. All of these examples are types of TextBackground.

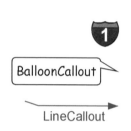

Examples of the three types of text background: marker text background, balloon callout, and line callout.

A leader line is a line from a piece of text that draws the viewer's eye from the label toward a specific place on the layout or map.

A text background will automatically grow to account for text size and shadows and move to account for offsets.

The *TextBackground* abstract class defines the common properties of the different types of background—*MarkerTextBackground, BalloonCallout,* and *LineCallout.* Use a *MarkerTextBackground* to draw text over a single glyph from a font (for example, a highway shield and number). A *BalloonCallout* draws a rectangular- or balloon-shaped background for a text string with a predefined leader line. A *LineCallout* is similar to a *BalloonCallout* but has a different leader line with a user-defined style and an accent bar.

Callout text backgrounds can be used for *TextSymbol* objects with a *TextPath* set, but note that the callout will produce a background to the envelope of the text, not one following the path.

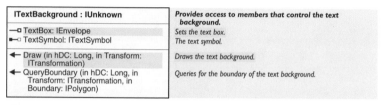

The *Draw* method is used in a similar way to the *ISymbol::Draw* method. Note that *ISymbol::Draw* called on a *TextSymbol* coclass will also call *ITextBackground::Draw*, if a *Background* is set, thus drawing both the background and the text. Note that there is no *Geometry* required in this method; the location and size of the *TextBackground* is determined by the *TextSymbol*.

Use the *QueryBoundary* method to find the shape of a callout. This method populates a *Polygon* with the boundary of the callout. For a *LineCallout*, this is the minimum bounding rectangle of the leader line and text background box. For a *BalloonCallout*, this is the shape of the balloon. For a *MarkerTextBackground*, this is the union of the bounding box of the *Marker* and the *Text*.

The *TextBox* property is write-only. It is set by a *TextSymbol* before a call to *ITextBackground::Draw* or *ITextBackground::QueryBoundary*. For this reason, the *ITextBackground* also has a *TextSymbol* property, which is the *TextSymbol* of which the *Background* is a property.

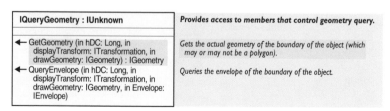

Use the *IQueryGeometry* to find out the exact boundary of a callout. The *GetGeometry* method returns the polygon boundary of a *BalloonCallout*, or a *Polyline* of the leader line, accent bar, and border for a *LineCallout* coclass. *QueryEnvelope* is not implemented at ArcGIS 8.1; instead, you can return the *Envelope* of the result of *GetGeometry*.

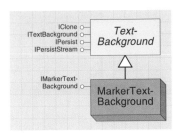

```
IClone ○─
ITextBackground ○─        Text-
IPersist ○─           Background
IPersistStream ○─


IMarkerText-
Background ○─         MarkerText-
                      Background
```

A MarkerTextBackground draws a single glyph as the background to a piece of text. This class is ideal for drawing highway shields as labels.

Earlier in this chapter, we saw that a *MultiLayerMarkerSymbol* provides the ability to draw one glyph on top of another but limits each layer to containing a single glyph. However, using a *MarkerTextBackground* coclass allows you to draw a string of text (many glyphs) with a single glyph as its background.

IMarkerTextBackground : ITextBackground	Provides access to members that control the marker text background.
■─■ ScaleToFit: Boolean	*Indicates if the marker symbol is scaled to fill the text box.*
■─○ Symbol: IMarkerSymbol	*The marker symbol.*

The *IMarkerTextBackground* interface provides two additional properties to the *ITextBackground* interface from which it inherits. Set the *MarkerSymbol* you wish to use as a background using the *Symbol* property—note that it is set by reference. The *ScaleToFit* property defaults to *False*—set this property to *True* if you want the *Symbol* to draw large enough to fit the entire text string. The *Symbol* object's *Size* property does not actually change, only its appearance when drawn.

The code below demonstrates how to create a *TextSymbol* resembling a highway route marker for Route 66 with a *MarkerTextBackground*. A *TextSymbol* is first created, then a *CharacterMarkerSymbol* is created to resemble a highway shield using the ESRI Transportation and Civic font. A *MarkerTextBackground* is created, and its *Symbol* property is set to the *CharacterMarkerSymbol*. Finally, the *MarkerTextBackground* is set as the *TextSymbol* object's *Background* property.

This symbol is created by the code sample.

```
Dim pFTS As IFormattedTextSymbol
Set pFTS = New TextSymbol
pFTS.Size = 50
pFTS.Text = "66"


Dim pFont As stdole.IFontDisp
Set pFont = New stdole.StdFont
pFont.Name = "ESRI Transportation & Civic"


Dim pCharMarker As ICharacterMarkerSymbol
Set pCharMarker = New CharacterMarkerSymbol
pCharMarker.Font = pFont
' The highway shield is the 33rd Glyph in the font
pCharMarker.CharacterIndex = 33
' Below we set any properties which need to be based on the
' size of the TextSymbol
pCharMarker.XOffset = pFTS.Size / 7


Dim pMarkerBack As IMarkerTextBackground
Set pMarkerBack = New MarkerTextBackground
Set pMarkerBack.Symbol = pCharMarker
' Setting the ScaleToFit property means we don't need
' to set a Size on the MarkerSymbol
pMarkerBack.ScaleToFit = True
Set pFTS.Background = pMarkerBack
```

Display

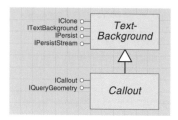

A callout is a graphic drawn behind a string of text that includes a leader line, indicating a particular area.

Creating a *TextSymbol* with a *Callout* background is done in much the same way:

```
Dim pBalloonCallout as IBalloonCallout
Set pBalloonCallout = New BalloonCallout
Set pFTS.Background = pBalloonCallout
```

The *Callout* abstract class defines the common properties of the *BalloonCallout* and *LineCallout* backgrounds.

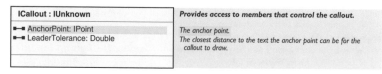

ICallout : IUnknown	Provides access to members that control the callout.
■→■ AnchorPoint: IPoint	The anchor point.
■→■ LeaderTolerance: Double	The closest distance to the text the anchor point can be for the callout to draw.

Use the *ICallout* interface to define an anchor point for a callout by setting the *AnchorPoint* property to an ESRI *Point* object. The *Leader-Tolerance* property indicates the minimum distance between the *Text-Background* and the *AnchorPoint* for which to display a leader line. Remember that an anchor point is independent of any geometry used to draw the *TextBackground*. An anchor point is the location at which a leader line begins.

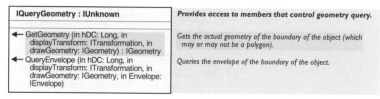

IQueryGeometry : IUnknown	Provides access to members that control geometry query.
← GetGeometry (in hDC: Long, in displayTransform: ITransformation, in drawGeometry: IGeometry) : IGeometry	Gets the actual geometry of the boundary of the object (which may or may not be a polygon).
← QueryEnvelope (in hDC: Long, in displayTransform: ITransformation, in drawGeometry: IGeometry, in Envelope: IEnvelope)	Queries the envelope of the boundary of the object.

The *BalloonCallout* coclass draws a rectangular graphic behind a *Text-Symbol* coclass. It has a leader line that ends by joining the callout at a predefined point.

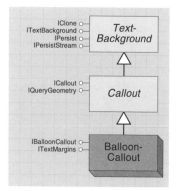

A balloon callout draws a background graphic behind text and includes a predefined leader line.

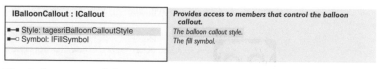

IBalloonCallout : ICallout	Provides access to members that control the balloon callout.
■→■ Style: tagesriBalloonCalloutStyle	The balloon callout style.
■→□ Symbol: IFillSymbol	The fill symbol.

The *Style* property defines the shape of the graphic drawn behind a *TextSymbol* and should be set to one of the *esriBalloonCalloutStyle* constants.

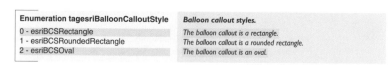

Enumeration tagesriBalloonCalloutStyle	Balloon callout styles.
0 - esriBCSRectangle	The balloon callout is a rectangle.
1 - esriBCSRoundedRectangle	The balloon callout is a rounded rectangle.
2 - esriBCSOval	The balloon callout is an oval.

Note that the oval callout style is not implemented in ArcGIS 8.1.

ITextMargins : IUnknown	Provides access to members that control the text margins.
■—■ BottomMargin: Double	Value for the bottom margin.
■—■ LeftMargin: Double	Value for the left margin.
■—■ RightMargin: Double	Value for the right margin.
■—■ TopMargin: Double	Value for the top margin.
◄— PutMargins (in Left: Double, in Top: Double, in Right: Double, in bottom: Double)	Sets the margins.
◄— QueryMargins (out Left: Double, out Top: Double, out Right: Double, out bottom: Double)	Returns the margins.

Use the *ITextMargins* interface to define the margins of a callout. The margins indicate the gap, in points, between the minimum bounding box of the text and the boundary of the *TextBackground*. The default value is 5 points for each margin. You can either write to the margin properties or use the *PutMargins* method to set all the margins with a single method call.

The callout balloon can be filled by setting the *Symbol* property to any class implementing *IFillSymbol*.

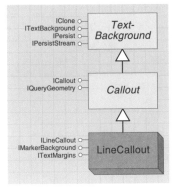

IClone ○—
ITextBackground ○—
IPersist ○—
IPersistStream ○—
Text-Background

ICallout ○—
IQueryGeometry ○—
Callout

ILineCallout ○—
IMarkerBackground ○—
ITextMargins ○—
LineCallout

A line callout draws a background graphic behind text, consisting of a user-defined leader line, accent bar, and border.

The *LineCallout* coclass draws a rectangular graphic behind a *TextSymbol* coclass and includes an optional leader line, accent bar, and border.

ILineCallout : ICallout	Provides access to members that control the line callout.
■—□ AccentBar: ILineSymbol	The line symbol used to render the accent bar.
■—□ Border: IFillSymbol	The fill symbol used to render the border.
■—■ Gap: Double	The gap.
■—□ LeaderLine: ILineSymbol	The line symbol used to render the leader line.
■—■ Style: tagesriLineCalloutStyle	The line callout style.

The *Style* property defines the shape of the leader line and should be set to one of the *esriLineCalloutStyle* constants.

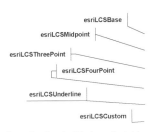

esriLCSBase
esriLCSMidpoint
esriLCSThreePoint
esriLCSFourPoint
esriLCSUnderline
esriLCSCustom

Examples of each of the line callout styles.

Enumeration tagesriLineCalloutStyle	Line callout styles.
0 - esriLCSBase	The line callout leader is a single line originating from the base or top of the accent bar.
1 - esriLCSMidpoint	The line callout leader is a single line originating from the midpoint of the accent bar.
2 - esriLCSThreePoint	The line callout leader is a 3-point line originating from the midpoint of the accent bar.
3 - esriLCSFourPoint	The line callout leader is a 4-point line originating from the midpoint of the accent bar.
4 - esriLCSUnderline	The line callout underlines the text.
5 - esriLCSCustom	A user defined line callout style.

Note that the custom callout style is not implemented at ArcGIS 8.1.

An accent bar is a line drawn at the start or end of a line callout's border, separated from the border by a user-defined gap. The leader line starts from a point on the accent bar.

The *LeaderLine* property sets the symbol used to draw the leader line and can be set to any *LineSymbol* object. For more information, see the *LineSymbol* abstract class. Similarly, you can change the appearance of the accent bar by setting the *AccentBar* property. Note that both properties are set by reference.

The spacing between the *Border* and *AccentBar* can be adjusted by setting the *Gap* property. This property indicates the separation between the center of the *AccentBar* and the edge of the *Border* as a distance in points and does not account for thick outlines on either the *AccentBar*

Display

or *Border*. To get the *AccentBar* to just touch the *Border*, you can use the following formula:

```
pLineCallout.Gap = (pLineCallout.Border.Outline.Width / 2) + _
                   (pLineCallout.AccentBar.Width / 2)
```

The *Border* property represents the rectangular background of the callout and can be filled by setting the *Border* property to any class implementing *IFillSymbol*.

The *SimpleLineCallout* coclass allows you to add a simple leader line to a *TextSymbol*. A *SimpleLineCallout* inherits from *ICallout* and is set onto a *TextSymbol* in the same way as the other callouts by setting the *Background* property of the *FormattedTextSymbol*.

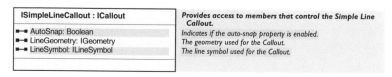

To determine the appearance of the leader line, set the *LineSymbol* property to any existing *ILineSymbol* object. Set the *LineGeometry* to a *Polyline* object—this will determine the shape of your leader line. The last vertex in your *Polyline* will be replaced by the existing *AnchorPoint* of the callout.

Use the *AutoSnap* property, in conjunction with the *LineGeometry* property, to determine if the *LineGeometry* will automatically change. If set to *True*, the first vertex of the *LineGeometry* will be drawn aligned to the current location of the *TextSymbol*. The existing vertex in the *LineGeometry* is not actually changed—only its position upon drawing.

A simple line callout draws a custom leader line to a text symbol.

You can use any shape of Polyline as your leader line by using the SimpleLineCallout. For more information on creating Polyline objects, see Volume 2, Chapter 9, 'Shaping features with geometry'.

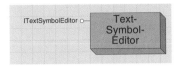

The text symbol editor is the dialog box shown by ArcMap for editing the details of a text symbol.

The ArcMap dialog box for editing text symbols.

The *TextSymbolEditor* provides an ideal way to allow a user to edit all the properties of a specific, preexisting *TextSymbol*.

ITextSymbolEditor : IUnknown	**Text Symbol Editor**
■─ ShowUnits: Boolean	*Indicates whether to display the Units combo box.*
■─ Title: String	*The title of the Text Symbol Editor dialog.*
◄─ EditTextSymbol (TextSymbol: ITextSymbol, hWnd: Long) : Boolean	*Displays the Text Symbol Editor dialog for the given text symbol and returns a flag indicating if it changed.*

The *EditTextSymbol* method takes an *ITextSymbol* parameter, which must be an existing *TextSymbol* object. This object is passed by reference and will be directly changed depending on the selections made in the dialog box. The *EditTextSymbol* method call will open the *TextSymbolEditor* dialog box. The *Title* property sets the title of the dialog box displayed, and the *ShowUnits* property determines if the *Units* option is shown to the user, allowing them to set size properties in units other than points.

```
Dim pTxtSym As ITextSymbol
Set pTxtSym = New TextSymbol
Dim pTextSymbolEditor As ITextSymbolEditor
Set pTextSymbolEditor = New TextSymbolEditor
pTextSymbolEditor.Title = "Edit My TextSymbol"
pTextSymbolEditor.ShowUnits = False
If Not pTextSymbolEditor.EditTextSymbol(pTxtSym, 0) Then
  MsgBox "User pressed Cancel"
Else
  'Do something with the edited TextSymbol, pTxtSym
End If
```

The text background editor is the dialog box shown by ArcMap to edit the details of a text symbol's background.

If a user clicks the Text Background button in the text symbol editor, they can access the text background editor and add a text background to the text symbol. However, using the text background editor directly restricts the user to setting the properties of the background for a specific text symbol object only.

The ArcMap dialog box for editing text backgrounds

The *TextBackgroundEditor* lets you edit all the properties of a pre-existing *TextBackground* object, for example, a *BalloonCallout* or a *LineCallout* coclass.

ITextBackgroundEditor : IUnknown	**Provides a dialog for managing properties associated with Text Background.**
■─ ShowUnits: Boolean	*Indicates whether to display the Units combo box.*
■─ Title: String	*The title of the Text Background Editor dialog.*
◄─ EditTextBackground (textBackground: ITextBackground, in previewSymbol: ITextSymbol, hWnd: Long) : Boolean	*Displays the Text Background Editor dialog for the given text background and returns a flag indicating if it changed.*

The *EditTextBackground* method takes an *ITextSymbol* parameter and an *ITextBackground* parameter. The *TextBackground* parameter, passed by reference, has its properties edited by the user. The *TextSymbol* is required to correctly display the *TextBackground* in the dialog box.

```
Dim pTxtBack As ITextBackground
Set pTxtBack = New BalloonCallout
Set pTxtBack.TextSymbol = pTxtSym ' pTxtSym is a pre-existing TextSymbol
Dim pTextBackgroundEditor As ITextBackgroundEditor
Set pTextBackgroundEditor = New TextBackgroundEditor
pTextBackgroundEditor.Title = "Edit My Text Background"
pTextBackgroundEditor.ShowUnits = False
If Not pTextBackgroundEditor.EditTextBackground(pTxtBack, pTxtSym, 0) Then
  MsgBox "User pressed Cancel"
Else 'Do something with the edited TextBackground
End If
```

Display

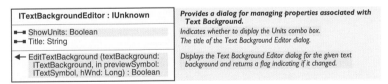

3D chart symbol objects

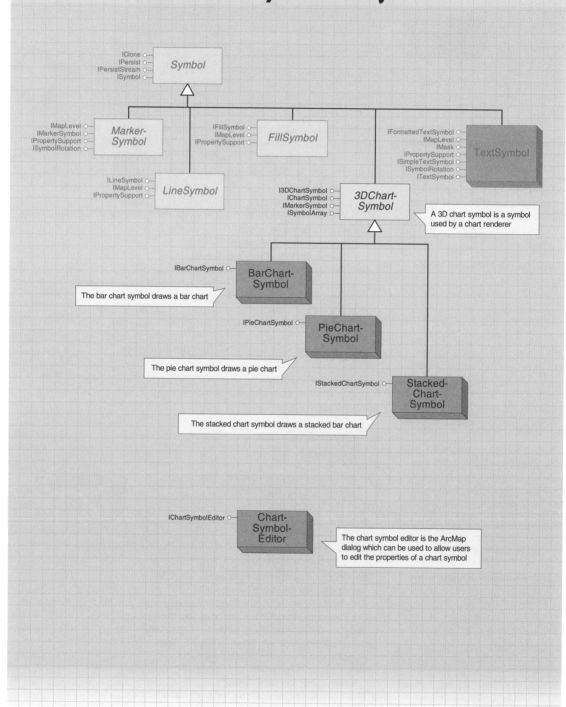

IClone ○
IPersist ○
IPersistStream ○
ISymbol ○

Symbol

IMapLevel ○
IMarkerSymbol ○
IPropertySupport ○
ISymbolRotation ○

Marker-Symbol

IFillSymbol ○
IMapLevel ○
IPropertySupport ○

FillSymbol

IFormattedTextSymbol ○
IMapLevel ○
IMask ○
IPropertySupport ○
ISimpleTextSymbol ○
ISymbolRotation ○
ITextSymbol ○

TextSymbol

ILineSymbol ○
IMapLevel ○
IPropertySupport ○

LineSymbol

I3DChartSymbol ○
IChartSymbol ○
IMarkerSymbol ○
ISymbolArray ○

3DChart-Symbol

A 3D chart symbol is a symbol used by a chart renderer

IBarChartSymbol ○

BarChart-Symbol

The bar chart symbol draws a bar chart

IPieChartSymbol ○

PieChart-Symbol

The pie chart symbol draws a pie chart

IStackedChartSymbol ○

Stacked-Chart-Symbol

The stacked chart symbol draws a stacked bar chart

IChartSymbolEditor ○

Chart-Symbol-Editor

The chart symbol editor is the ArcMap dialog which can be used to allow users to edit the properties of a chart symbol

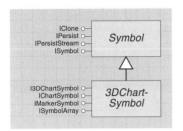

3D chart symbols are used by ChartRenderers to render FeatureClasses by drawing a pie chart, bar chart, or stacked bar chart for each Feature.

A *3DChartSymbol* is an abstraction of the three types of chart symbol. It represents a marker symbol, which can be used by a *ChartRenderer* to symbolize geographical data by multiple attributes. Although they are generally used by a *ChartRenderer*, if all the properties are set appropriately you can also use the symbol as a *MarkerSymbol* to symbolize an individual *Feature* or *Element*.

The following sections describe how to set up the different coclasses that implement *I3DChartSymbol*. For more information on using these coclasses as part of a *ChartRenderer*, see the sections on feature renderers in this chapter.

IChartSymbol : IUnknown	*Provides access to properties common to all type of chart symbols.*
▪━▪ MaxValue: Double	*The maximum value.*
▪━▪ Value (in Index: Long) : Double	*The value at the index position.*

IChartSymbol is used to calculate the size of bars or pie slices in a chart symbol.

The maximum attribute value that can be represented on the chart is used to scale the other attribute values in a chart. You should always set this property when creating a *3DChartSymbol*. When creating a *ChartRenderer*, you should have access to the statistics of your FeatureClass—you can use these statistics to set the *MaxValue* property to the maximum value of the attribute or attributes being rendered.

For example, if there are two fields rendered with a chart symbol, one containing attribute values from 0 to 5 and one containing attribute values from 0 to 10, set *MaxValue* to 10.

```
Dim pChartSymbol as IShartSymbol
Set pChartSymbol = New BarChartSymbol
pChartSymbol.MaxValue = 10
```

The *Value* property contains an array of values indicating the relative height of each bar or width of each pie slice. If using the *ChartSymbol* in a *ChartRenderer*, you do not need to set this property. The *Value* array is populated repeatedly during the draw process by the *ChartRenderer*, using attribute values from the specified attribute *Fields* from the *FeatureClass* coclass to create a slightly different symbol for each *Feature*. All *Values* are set back to 0 after the draw has completed.

If you wish to use the symbol independently of a *ChartRenderer*, you should set the *Value* array with the values you wish to use in the bar or pie chart.

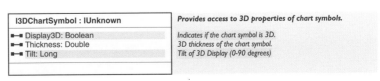

I3DChartSymbol : IUnknown	*Provides access to 3D properties of chart symbols.*
▪━▪ Display3D: Boolean	*Indicates if the chart symbol is 3D.*
▪━▪ Thickness: Double	*3D thickness of the chart symbol.*
▪━▪ Tilt: Long	*Tilt of 3D Display (0-90 degrees)*

I3DChartSymbol controls the characteristics of a chart symbol's 3D appearance. By default, *Display3D* is *True*, indicating that the chart will

Display

appear in 3D. Use *Thickness* and *Tilt* to control the 3D characteristics of the symbol.

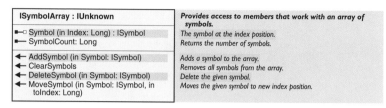

ISymbolArray stores the *FillSymbols* used to fill each bar or pie slice.

SymbolCount returns the number of symbols that have been added to the chart symbol using *AddSymbol*. Add a symbol for each attribute you intend to use in the *ChartRenderer*—check the *IRendererFields::FieldCount* property for the correct number of symbols to add. If you add too many symbols, these will be displayed by a bar chart as empty bars or by a pie chart as slices with zero thickness and may be visible in the *Legend*.

The code below demonstrates how you might use a *RandomColorRamp* to set the color of the symbols in a chart symbol, where *pRendererFields* is the *IRendererFields* interface of an existing *ChartRenderer*.

```
Dim pRandomCR As IRandomColorRamp, pFillSymbol as ISimpleFillSymbol
Set pRandomCR = New RandomColorRamp
pRandomCR.Size = 5
pRandomCR.CreateRamp True

Dim i As Integer
For i = 0 To pRendererFields.FieldCount - 1
  Set pFillSymbol = New SimpleFillSymbol
  pFillSymbol.Color = pRandomCR.Color(0)
  pSymbolArray.AddSymbol pFillSymbol
Next i
```

Use *ClearSymbols, DeleteSymbol,* and *MoveSymbol* to edit existing symbol arrays.

The chart symbols also implement *IMarkerSymbol*, which is discussed earlier in this chapter.

The *Size* property is used to specify the maximum height (or width if the bars are horizontal), in points, of the bar, stacked bar symbol, or the diameter of a pie chart symbol.

Note that if the symbols are scaled by the *ChartRenderer* (check *IStackedChartSymbol::Fixed, IPieChartRenderer::ProportionalBySum,* or *ProportionalByField*), the larger symbols may be larger than *Size*.

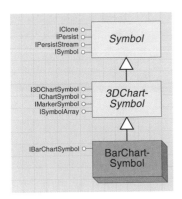

Features can be symbolized with a bar chart, each bar of which can represent the value of a different attribute.

A *BarChartSymbol* is most commonly used by a *ChartRenderer* to draw a bar chart for each *Feature* rendered, where the bar heights are derived from attribute fields.

IBarChartSymbol : IUnknown	Provides access bar chart symbol properties.
■─■ Axes: ILineSymbol	*The axis symbol.*
■─■ ShowAxes: Boolean	*Indicates if the axis are shown.*
■─■ Spacing: Double	*The spacing between bars in points.*
■─■ VerticalBars: Boolean	*Indicates if the bars are oriented vertically.*
■─■ Width: Double	*The width of each bar in points.*

Bars can be oriented either vertically or horizontally using the *VerticalBars* property.

The thickness of each bar and the spacing between bars can be altered as shown using the *Width* and *Spacing* properties—you may wish to set these properties proportional to *IMarkerSymbol::Size*.

The axes for each *BarChartSymbol* can also be displayed using the *ShowAxes* property—set a *LineSymbol* as the *Axes* property to determine their appearance.

VerticalBars = False   VerticalBars = True

Thickness = 20 and   Thickness = 5 and
Spacing = 0   Spacing = 5

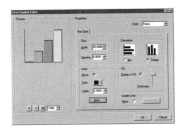

Bar axes drawn for a bar chart symbol

The ArcMap property page for the bar chart symbol

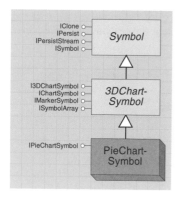

Features can be symbolized with a pie chart, where each slice can represent the value of a different attribute.

A *PieChartSymbol* is most commonly used by a *ChartRenderer* to draw a pie chart for each *Feature* rendered, where the proportion of each pie slice is derived from attribute fields.

IPieChartSymbol : IUnknown	Provides access to pie chart symbol properties.
Clockwise: Boolean	Indicates if the slices are drawn in a clockwise direction.
Outline: ILineSymbol	The chart outline symbol.
UseOutline: Boolean	Indicates if the outline symbol is drawn.

Use the properties of *IPieChartSymbol* to control the appearance of the pie chart. The pie chart symbol shown to the left was created by applying a *CartographicLineSymbol*, which had *LineDecorations* at each quarter length along the line.

You can also alter the orientation of the chart using the *Clockwise* property—use the *IMarkerSymbol::Angle* property to change the position of the first pie slice, if you wish.

Pie chart symbol drawn with an outline

Clockwise = True   Clockwise = False

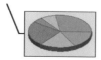

Pie chart symbol with background

The ArcMap property page for the pie chart symbol

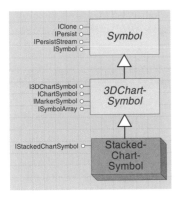

Features can be symbolized with a stacked bar chart, where each section of the bar can represent the value of a different attribute.

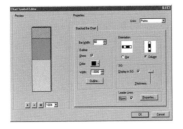

The ArcMap property page for the stacked chart symbol

A *StackedChartSymbol* is most commonly used by a *ChartRenderer* to draw a stacked bar chart for each *Feature* rendered, where the proportion of each section of the bar is derived from attribute fields.

IStackedChartSymbol : IUnknown	Provides access to stacked chart symbol properties.
■─■ Fixed: Boolean	Indicates if the bars are of a fixed length (the alternative is graduated length bars).
■─■ Outline: ILineSymbol	The symbol for the chart outline.
■─■ UseOutline: Boolean	Indicates if the outline symbol is drawn.
■─■ VerticalBar: Boolean	Indicates if the bar is oriented vertically.
■─■ Width: Double	The width of the bar in points.

Use *IStackedChartSymbol* to specify the appearance of the stacked bar chart.

The *Outline* and *UseOutline* properties are similar to those on the *PieChartSymbol*.

The *Width* and *VerticalBar* properties are similar to those on the *BarChartSymbol*.

If the *Fixed* property is *False*, a *ChartRenderer* will scale the stacked bar chart according to the total of the attributes for each feature. If *True*, each bar chart has the same height; if *VerticalBar* is *False*, each bar chart has the same width.

Display

The *ChartSymbolEditor* provides an ideal way to allow a user to edit all the properties of a specific, preexisting *ChartSymbol*. It is very similar to the *SymbolEditor* coclass.

The ArcMap Chart Symbol Editor dialog box edits the details of a chart symbol. The pages shown on the dialog box depend on the type of chart symbol used. For example, a bar chart symbol has a slightly different dialog box than a pie chart symbol.

IChartSymbolEditor : IUnknown	Provides access to members that control a dialog used to manage chart symbol properties .
■─■ ShowUnits: Boolean	Indicates if the units combo box is displayed.
■─■ Title: String	Title of the chart symbol editor dialog.
← EditChartSymbol (Symbol: IChartSymbol, hWnd: Long) : Boolean	Displays the chart symbol editor dialog for the given chart symbol and returns a value describing whether the symbol was changed.

The *EditChartSymbol* method takes an *IChartSymbol* parameter, which must be an existing object that supports *IChartSymbol* Interface. This object is passed by reference and will be directly changed depending on the selections made in the dialog box—its coclass may even change.

The *EditChartSymbol* method call will open the *ChartSymbolEditor* dialog. To determine if the user clicked Cancel or OK, check the return value.

```
Dim pBarSymbol As IBarChartSymbol, pChartSymEditor As IChartSymbolEditor
Set pBarSymbol = New BarChartSymbol
Set pChartSymEditor = New ChartSymbolEditor
If Not pChartSymEditor.EditChartSymbol(pBarSymbol, 0) Then
  'Do something with the edited Symbol
End If
```

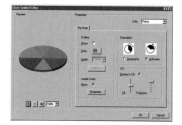

This is the Chart Symbol Editor dialog box for editing a pie chart symbol.

Frame decoration objects

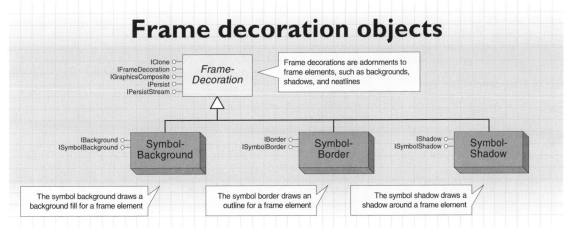

IClone
IFrameDecoration
IGraphicsComposite
IPersist
IPersistStream

Frame-Decoration

Frame decorations are adornments to frame elements, such as backgrounds, shadows, and neatlines

IBackground
ISymbolBackground

Symbol-Background

IBorder
ISymbolBorder

Symbol-Border

IShadow
ISymbolShadow

Symbol-Shadow

The symbol background draws a background fill for a frame element

The symbol border draws an outline for a frame element

The symbol shadow draws a shadow around a frame element

Frame decorations are used to determine how frame elements are displayed. You might use a frame decoration to alter the background of an active view, add a shadow to a group of graphic elements, or draw a neatline around a map.

Careful use of frame decorations can create a coherent and neat page layout for your maps. Use similar decorations to visually group related frames or try using shadows and fills to emphasize other frames.

A *FrameDecoration* is either a *SymbolBackground, SymbolBorder,* or *SymbolShadow* coclass used to draw a frame element. Use a *FrameDecoration* on any object supporting *IFrameProperties*, such as map surround frames or group elements.

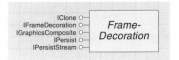

IClone
IFrameDecoration
IGraphicsComposite
IPersist
IPersistStream

Frame-Decoration

A frame decoration is used to draw a frame element.

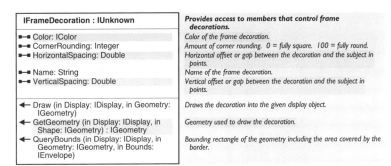

IFrameDecoration : IUnknown	Provides access to members that control frame decorations.
■→■ Color: IColor	Color of the frame decoration.
■→■ CornerRounding: Integer	Amount of corner rounding. 0 = fully square. 100 = fully round.
■→■ HorizontalSpacing: Double	Horizontal offset or gap between the decoration and the subject in points.
■→■ Name: String	Name of the frame decoration.
■→■ VerticalSpacing: Double	Vertical offset or gap between the decoration and the subject in points.
← Draw (in Display: IDisplay, in Geometry: IGeometry)	Draws the decoration into the given display object.
← GetGeometry (in Display: IDisplay, in Shape: IGeometry) : IGeometry	Geometry used to draw the decoration.
← QueryBounds (in Display: IDisplay, in Geometry: IGeometry, in Bounds: IEnvelope)	Bounding rectangle of the geometry including the area covered by the border.

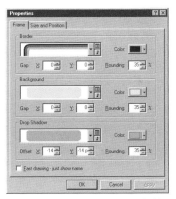

Frame decoration dialog box in ArcMap

The Draw and QueryBounds methods can be used in a similar way to the ISymbol::Draw method, which should be referred to for further information. For more information on the GetGeometry method, refer to the IQueryGeometry interface, described with the Callout classes.

Setting the *Color* property will fill a frame with a single color. The *CornerRounding* property alters the frame from its default rectangle shape to a rounded shape; the maximum value of 100 indicates that along the shorter edge of the frame, the corners will be rounded to the center of the edge. The *Name* property corresponds to the name of the style of the border, background, or shadow if it was set from a style file.

VerticalSpacing and *HorizontalSpacing* refer to the gap, in points, between the frame and its subject, positive values indicating the frame draws outside the subject, and negative values indicating that it draws inside the subject.

The code that follows uses the *IFrameDecoration* properties to change each frame in a graphics container (*pGraphics*) to a rounded frame filled with the color *pColor*. We use a *SymbolBackground* coclass to make the *FrameDecoration*, although we only use the *IFrameDecoration* properties.

```
Dim pElement As IElement
pGraphics.Reset
Set pElement = pGraphics.Next
Do While Not pElement Is Nothing

  If TypeOf pElement Is IFrameElement Then
    Dim pFrameElement As IFrameElement
    Set pFrameElement = pElement
    Dim pFrameDec As IFrameDecoration
    Set pFrameDec = New SymbolBackground
    pFrameDec.Color = pColor
    pFrameDec.CornerRounding = 50
    pFrameElement.Background = pFrameDec
    pGraphics.UpdateElement pElement
  End If
  Set pElement = pGraphics.Next
Loop
```

A MapFrame will only draw with unrounded corners, regardless of the CornerRounding property. However, the MapSurroundFrame can draw with a rounded frame.

A *SymbolBackground* is used to define how any frame element is filled. Set a *SymbolBackground* by value, as the *Background* property of any *IFrameElement* Interface.

```
Dim pSymbolBackground as ISymbolBackground
Set pSymbolBackground = New SymbolBackground
pFrameElement.Background = pSymbolBackground
```

Alternatively, you can set a *SymbolBackground* using the *IFrameProperties::Background* property, which has the same effect.

SymbolBackgrounds can be used to change the appearance of the interior of a frame.

IBackground : IUnknown	Provides access to members that control frame backgrounds.
▪━ Gap: Double	Gap between the frame background and the subject in points.
▪━ Name: String	Name of the frame background.
◄━ Draw (in Display: IDisplay, in Geometry: IGeometry)	Draws the background into the given display object.
◄━ GetGeometry (in Display: IDisplay, in Shape: IGeometry) : IGeometry	Geometry used to draw the frame background.
◄━ QueryBounds (in Display: IDisplay, in Geometry: IGeometry, in Bounds: IEnvelope)	Bounding rectangle of the geometry including area covered by the border.

The *Gap* property reflects the *HorizontalSpacing* and *VerticalSpacing* properties of the *IFrameDecoration* interface, with *HorizontalSpacing* taking preference if the properties contain different values. This provides a simple way to set an equal horizontal and vertical gap for the frame.

ISymbolBackground : IBackground	Provides access to members that control the SymbolBackground object.
▪—■ CornerRounding: Integer	Amount of corner rounding. 0 = fully square. 100 = fully round.
▪—■ FillSymbol: IFillSymbol	Symbol used to draw the background.

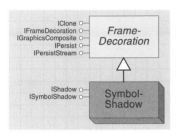

You can draw shadows around a frame by using a SymbolShadow object.

Set the *FillSymbol* property to any *IFillSymbol* object to draw a frame filled with the pattern of your choice, as shown in this example:

```
Dim pSimpleFill As ISimpleFillSymbol
Set pSimpleFill = New SimpleFillSymbol
pSimpleFill.Style = esriSFSCross
pSymbolBackground.FillSymbol = pSimpleFill
```

A *SymbolShadow* is used to create a dropped shadow. Set a *SymbolShadow* as the *Shadow* property on the *IFrameProperties* interface.

```
Dim pSymbolShadow as ISymbolShadow
Set pSymbolShadow = New SymbolShadow
pFrameElement.Shadow= pSymbolShadow
```

IShadow : IUnknown	Provides access to members that control frame drop shadows.
▪—■ HorizontalSpacing: Double	Horizontal offset between the drop shadow and the subject in points.
▪—■ Name: String	Name of the drop shadow.
▪—■ VerticalSpacing: Double	Vertical offset between the drop shadow and the subject in points.
← Draw (in Display: IDisplay, in Geometry: IGeometry)	Draws the drop shadow into the given display object.
← GetGeometry (in Display: IDisplay, in Shape: IGeometry) : IGeometry	Geometry used to draw the drop shadow.
← QueryBounds (in Display: IDisplay, in Geometry: IGeometry, in Bounds: IEnvelope)	Bounding rectangle of the geometry including the area covered by the border.

ISymbolShadow : IShadow	Provides access to members that control the SymbolBorder object.
▪—■ CornerRounding: Integer	Amount of corner rounding. 0 = fully square. 100 = fully round.
▪—■ FillSymbol: IFillSymbol	Symbol used to draw the shadow.

Setting the *HorizontalSpacing* and *VerticalSpacing* properties determines the offset, in points, of the shadow from the frame, with positive values indicating a shadow to the top-right corner of the frame.

Ideally, a suitable *FillSymbol* for a shadow is a simple fill used for emphasis, not for elaborate decoration.

A *SymbolBorder* is used to define the appearance of the line drawn around a frame, as shown in this code example:

```
Dim pSymbolBorder as ISymbolBorder
Set pSymbolBorder = New SymbolBorder
pFrameElement.Border = pSymbolBorder
```

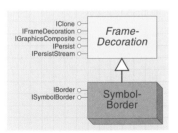

Neatlines can be drawn around frames using a SymbolBorder object.

IBorder : IUnknown	Provides access to members that control frame borders.
■—■ Gap: Double	Gap between the frame border and the subject in points.
■—■ Name: String	Name of the frame border.
← Draw (in Display: IDisplay, in Geometry: IGeometry)	Draws the frame border into the given display object.
← GetGeometry (in Display: IDisplay, in Shape: IGeometry) : IGeometry	Geometry used to draw the frame border.
← QueryBounds (in Display: IDisplay, in Geometry: IGeometry, in Bounds: IEnvelope)	Bounding rectangle of the geometry including the area covered by the border.

ISymbolBorder : IBorder	Provides access to members that control the SymbolBorder object.
■—■ CornerRounding: Integer	Amount of corner rounding. 0 = fully square. 100 = fully round.
■—■ LineSymbol: ILineSymbol	Symbol used to draw the border.

Set any *ILineSymbol* object as the *LineSymbol* property of a *SymbolBorder* coclass to emphasize the frame. This is shown in the following code example.

```
Dim pSimpleLine As ISimpleLineSymbol
Set pSimpleLine = New SimpleLineSymbol
pSimpleLine.Style = esriSLSSolid
pSymbolBorder.LineSymbol = pSimpleLine
```

To achieve a consistent look to your maps, you may wish to apply similar borders to related frame elements in a *PageLayout*. Remember that using too many elaborate and varied lines makes a layout look cluttered or confusing.

Display objects

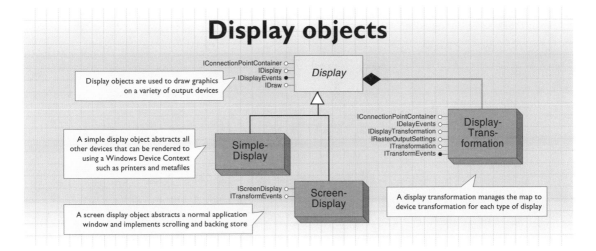

Display objects are used to draw graphics on a variety of output devices

A simple display object abstracts all other devices that can be rendered to using a Windows Device Context such as printers and metafiles

A screen display object abstracts a normal application window and implements scrolling and backing store

A display transformation manages the map to device transformation for each type of display

The Display objects are a set of objects that allow application developers to easily draw graphics on a variety of output devices. These objects allow you to render shapes stored in real-world coordinates to a screen, printer, or export file.

The display objects allow application developers to easily draw graphics on a variety of output devices. These objects allow you to render shapes stored in real-world coordinates to the screen, the printer, and export files. Application features such as scrolling, backing store, print "tiling", and printing to a frame can be easily implemented. If some desired behavior is not supported by the standard objects, custom objects can be created by implementing one or more of the standard display interfaces.

There are two standard display objects: *ScreenDisplay* and *SimpleDisplay*. The *ScreenDisplay* object abstracts a normal application window and implements scrolling and backing store. The *SimpleDisplay* abstracts all other devices that can be rendered to using a Windows Device Context, such as printers and metafiles.

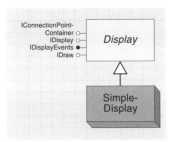

The Display object abstracts a drawing surface. A drawing surface is any hardware device, export file, or memory bitmap that can be represented by a Windows Device Context.

The SimpleDisplay object abstracts devices such as printers and metafiles.

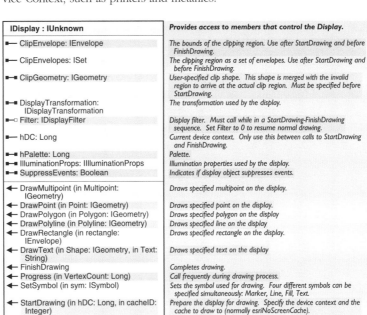

IDisplay : IUnknown	Provides access to members that control the Display.
ClipEnvelope: IEnvelope	The bounds of the clipping region. Use after StartDrawing and before FinishDrawing.
ClipEnvelopes: ISet	The clipping region as a set of envelopes. Use after StartDrawing and before FinishDrawing.
ClipGeometry: IGeometry	User-specified clip shape. This shape is merged with the invalid region to arrive at the actual clip region. Must be specified before StartDrawing.
DisplayTransformation: IDisplayTransformation	The transformation used by the display.
Filter: IDisplayFilter	Display filter. Must call while in a StartDrawing-FinishDrawing sequence. Set Filter to 0 to resume normal drawing.
hDC: Long	Current device context. Only use this between calls to StartDrawing and FinishDrawing.
hPalette: Long	Palette.
IlluminationProps: IIlluminationProps	Illumination properties used by the display.
SuppressEvents: Boolean	Indicates if display object suppresses events.
DrawMultipoint (in Multipoint: IGeometry)	Draws specified multipoint on the display.
DrawPoint (in Point: IGeometry)	Draws specified point on the display.
DrawPolygon (in Polygon: IGeometry)	Draws specified polygon on the display
DrawPolyline (in Polyline: IGeometry)	Draws specified line on the display
DrawRectangle (in rectangle: IEnvelope)	Draws specified rectangle on the display.
DrawText (in Shape: IGeometry, in Text: String)	Draws specified text on the display
FinishDrawing	Completes drawing.
Progress (in VertexCount: Long)	Call frequently during drawing process.
SetSymbol (in sym: ISymbol)	Sets the symbol used for drawing. Four different symbols can be specified simultaneously: Marker, Line, Fill, Text.
StartDrawing (in hDC: Long, in cacheID: Integer)	Prepare the display for drawing. Specify the device context and the cache to draw to (normally esriNoScreenCache).

Use the *IDisplay* interface to draw points, lines, polygons, rectangles, and text on a device. Access to the display object's *DisplayTransformation* object is provided by this interface.

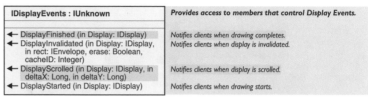

IDisplayEvents : IUnknown	Provides access to members that control Display Events.
← DisplayFinished (in Display: IDisplay)	Notifies clients when drawing completes.
← DisplayInvalidated (in Display: IDisplay, in rect: IEnvelope, erase: Boolean, cacheID: Integer)	Notifies clients when display is invalidated.
← DisplayScrolled (in Display: IDisplay, in deltaX: Long, in deltaY: Long)	Notifies clients when display is scrolled.
← DisplayStarted (in Display: IDisplay)	Notifies clients when drawing starts.

IDisplayEvents is the outbound interface of the *Display* abstract class. This interface enables developers to listen for specific events occurring inside a display. For example, you may wish to know whenever a particular display is scrolled. This is the case for the *Map* object that needs to perform some redrawing operations whenever its screen display is scrolled.

Several objects manage (cocreate) a *ScreenDisplay* object to help control their associated window. For example, both *Map* and *PageLayout* have their own associated *ScreenDisplay*, and so does the *MapInsetWindow*. The *AppDisplay* object does not instantiate a new *ScreenDisplay* object; instead, this object implements the *IScreenDisplay* interface. That is also what the *ScreenDisplay* object does.

A reference to a *ScreenDisplay* object is typically obtained via *IActiveView::ScreenDisplay* for the active views or *ILensWindow::ScreenDisplay* for the *MapInsetWindow*. *IAppDisplay* also has methods for returning a reference to the main screen of the application, the screen currently with focus, or any screen based on an index.

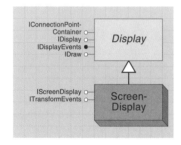

The ScreenDisplay *object is a display device that abstracts a normal application window. In addition to managing the display attributes for the screen, a* ScreenDisplay *also manages other issues specific to Microsoft Windows, including backing stores (caches), scrolling, and invalidation.*

The *ScreenDisplay* object is cocreateable; one instance when you may have to create a new *ScreenDisplay* object is when creating a custom active view. However, as discussed above, this object is typically created by another object, such as the *Map* or *PageLayout* objects.

To learn about working with all of the *ScreenDisplay* objects in an ArcMap application simultaneously, see the section on *AppDisplay* in Chapter 4, 'Composing maps'.

ITransformEvents : IUnknown	Provides access to members that control Transform Events.
← BoundsUpdated (sender: IDisplayTransformation)	Notifies clients when the bounds is updated.
← DeviceFrameUpdated (sender: IDisplayTransformation, sizeChanged: Boolean)	Notifies clients when the device frame is updated.
← ResolutionUpdated (sender: IDisplayTransformation)	Notifies clients when the resolution is updated.
← RotationUpdated (sender: IDisplayTransformation)	Notifies clients when the rotation angle is updated.
← UnitsUpdated (sender: IDisplayTransformation)	Notifies clients when the units are updated.
← VisibleBoundsUpdated (sender: IDisplayTransformation, sizeChanged: Boolean)	Notifies clients when the visible bounds is updated.

ITransformEvents is an outbound interface on the *ScreenDisplay* and *DisplayTransformation* objects. Use this interface to respond to changes made to these objects.

The IScreenDisplay *interface manages the display attributes of a screen.* IScreenDisplay *also handles other issues specific to Windows, including the backing store, scrolling, and invalidation. Use* IScreenDisplay *to pan or rotate the display, invalidate the display, and access or draw the caches created by the application.*

IScreenDisplay : IDisplay	Provides access to members that control Screen Display.
■—■ ActiveCache: Integer	Screen cache where drawing occurs. Use rarely. Change cache inside StartDrawing/FinishDrawing sequence.
■— CacheCount: Integer	Number of screen caches.
■— CacheMemDC (in Index: Integer) : Long	Memory device context for the specified screen cache.
■—□ CancelTracker: ITrackCancel	Cancel tracker that is associated with the display.
■—■ hWnd: Long	Associated window handle.
■—■ IsFirstCacheTransparent: Boolean	Indicates if the bottom cache is transparent.
■—■ IsFramed: Boolean	Indicates if drawing occurs in a frame rather than on the whole window.
■—■ ScaleContents: Boolean	Indicates if the contents of the screen scale when a resize occurs. True means scale contents to fit new window size. False means contents stays the same with more or less of it showing.
■—■ SuppressResize: Boolean	Indicates if display resizing is suppressed. True means the display doesn't resize with the window. False ensures that the display is the same size as the window.
■—■ UseScrollbars: Boolean	Indicates if scrollbars should appear.
■— WindowDC: Long	Device context that was specified to StartDrawing. Only use this between calls to StartDrawing and FinishDrawing.
← AddCache: Integer	Creates a new cache and return its ID. The ID can be specified to StartDrawing to direct output to the cache. It can also be used with a number of other methods such as DrawCache and Invalidate.
← DoScroll (in xDelta: Long, in yDelta: Long, in updateScreen: Boolean)	Scrolls the screen by the specified amount.
← DrawCache (in hDC: Long, in Index: Integer, in deviceRect: tagRECT, in cacheRect: tagRECT)	Draws the specified screen cache to the specified window device context. Pass an empty rectangle to copy the full bitmap to the DC origin
← Invalidate (in rect: IEnvelope, in erase: Boolean, in cacheIndex: Integer)	Indicates if the specified rectangle is refreshed.
← IsCacheDirty (in cacheIndex: Integer) : Boolean	Indicates if the specified cache needs refreshing.
← PanMoveTo (in mouseLocation: IPoint)	Pans to a new point.
← PanStart (in mouseLocation: IPoint)	Prepares display for panning.
← PanStop: IEnvelope	Stops panning and returns new visible bounds.
← RemoveAllCaches	Removes all caches.
← RemoveCache (in cacheID: Integer)	Removes the specified cache.
← RotateMoveTo (in pPoint: IPoint)	Rotates to new point.
← RotateStart (in mousePt: IPoint, in centerPt: IPoint)	Prepares display for rotating. If centerPt is NULL, the center of the visible bounds is used.
← RotateStop: Double	Stops rotating and returns new angle.
← RotateTimer	Draws the rotated display. Call in response to WM_TIMER.
← SetScrollbarHandles (in hWndHorzScrollbar: Long, in hWndVertScrollbar: Long)	Optionally specify application supplied scrollbars.
← StartRecording	Starts recording all output to the recording cache.
← StopRecording	Stops recording to the recording cache.
← TrackPan	Interactively pans the screen.
← TrackRotate	Interactively rotates the screen.
← UpdateWindow	Forces a redraw.

Two objects currently implement IScreenDisplay: *AppDisplay and Screen-Display. Both objects' implementation of* IScreenDisplay *is slightly different. For more details, see the component help for a particular member.*

Display

IScreenDisplay inherits from *IDisplay*. This means that all properties and methods on *IDisplay* are callable directly from *IScreenDisplay*.

This simple VBA script for a *UIToolControl MouseDown* event pans the map display.

```
Private Sub UIToolControl1_MouseDown(ByVal button As Long, _
   ByVal shift As Long, ByVal x As Long, ByVal y As Long)
 Dim pScreenDisplay As IScreenDisplay
 Dim pActiveView As IActiveView
 Dim pMxDoc As IMxDocument
 Set pMxDoc = Application.Document
 Set pActiveView = pMxDoc.FocusMap
 Set pScreenDisplay = pActiveView.ScreenDisplay
 pScreenDisplay.TrackPan
End Sub
```

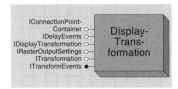

The display transformation defines how real-world coordinates are mapped to an output space.

As noted before, each *Display* object keeps a *DisplayTransformation* object to manage the map-to-device transformation. For example, units along the x-axis on the device actually represent map units along the y-axis. The *DisplayTransformation* also looks after the bounds of all the data loaded in the display as well as the visible bounds, which are used to pan and zoom the display.

In turn, each *Map*'s *DisplayTransformation* has a *SpatialReference* object that manages the *Map*'s current coordinate system. A reference to the *SpatialReference* object is set through *IDisplayTransformation:: SpatialReference*. Other objects with a *DisplayTransformation* coclass, such as the *PageLayout*, do not cocreate a *SpatialReference* object; in this case, the *SpatialReference* property returns nothing.

The *DisplayTransformation* object is cocreateable, but there is rarely a case when this is necessary. If you are creating your own *ScreenDisplay* or *DisplayTransformation*, see the steps under the *IDisplayTransformation* discussion for preparing a transform for use. Obtain a reference to a *DisplayTransformation* via *IDisplay::DisplayTransformation*. Since *IScreenDisplay* inherits from *IDisplay*, you can also use *IScreenDisplay::DisplayTransformation*.

Three rectangles define the transformation. The Bounds specifies the full extent in real-world coordinates. The VisibleBounds specifies what extent is currently visible. And the DeviceFrame specifies where the VisibleBounds appears on the output device. Since the aspect ratio of the DeviceFrame may not always match the aspect ratio of the specified VisibleBounds, the transformation calculates the actual visible bounds that fits the DeviceFrame. This is called the FittedBounds and is in real-world coordinates. All coordinates can be rotated about the center of the visible bounds by simply setting the transformation's Rotation property.

IDisplayTransformation : ITransformation	Provides access to members that control Display Transformation.
◼━◼ Bounds: IEnvelope	Full extent in world coordinates.
◼━ ConstrainedBounds: IEnvelope	Intersection of Bounds and VisibleBounds.
◼━◼ DeviceFrame: tagRECT	Visible extent in device coordinates.
◼━◼ FittedBounds: IEnvelope	Device frame in world coordinates.
◼━◼ ReferenceScale: Double	Reference scale for computing scaled symbol sizes.
◼━◼ Resolution: Double	Resolution of the device in dots (pixels) per inch.
◼━◼ Rotation: Double	Rotation angle in degrees.
◼━◼ ScaleRatio: Double	Scale between FittedBounds and DeviceFrame.
◼━◻ SpatialReference: ISpatialReference	Current spatial reference.
◼━◼ SuppressEvents: Boolean	Indicates if transformation object suppresses events.
◼━◼ Units: esriUnits	Units used by world coordinates.
◼━◼ VisibleBounds: IEnvelope	Visible extent in world coordinates.
◼━◼ ZoomResolution: Boolean	Indicates if resolution is tied to visible bounds. If true, zooming in magnifies contents (i.e., zoom in on page).
◀━ FromMapPoint (in mapPoint: IPoint, out X: Long, out Y: Long)	Calculates device coordinates corresponding to the map point.
◀━ FromPoints (in pointDistance: Double) : Double	Calculates a map distance corresponding to a point (1/72) distance.
◀━ ToMapPoint (in X: Long, in Y: Long) : IPoint	Calculates a point in map coordinates corresponding to the device point.
◀━ ToPoints (in mapDistance: Double) : Double	Calculates a distance in points (1/72 inch) corresponding to the map distance.
◀━ TransformCoords (in mapPoints: _WKSPoint, in devPoints: tagPOINT, in numPoints: Long, in options: Long)	Transforms a set of points or measurements from device to world space or vice versa. Use the flags specified by esriDisplayTransformEnum.
◀━ TransformRect (in mapRect: IEnvelope, in devRect: tagRECT, in options: Long)	Transforms a rectangle from device to world space or vice versa. Use the flags specified by esriDisplayTransformEnum.

Use *IDisplayTransformation* for converting coordinates between real-world and device space and back.

To prepare a transform for use, follow these steps:

1. Set the full map extent with the *Bounds* property.

2. Set the visible map extent (zoom rectangle) with the *VisibleBounds* property.

3. Set the output area of the device using the *DeviceFrame* property.

4. Set the resolution of the output device using the *Resolution* property.

The *Map* and *PageLayout* objects follow these steps after creating their display objects.

The transform is based on the ratio between the *VisibleBounds* and the *DeviceFrame*. Normally, the *DeviceFrame* is simply the full extent of the device with the origin equal to (0, 0). The transform object calculates the *FittedBounds* automatically, which is the visible map extent adjusted to fit the device.

```
Public Sub ZoomInCenter()
  Dim pMxDocument As IMxDocument
  Dim pActiveView As IActiveView
  Dim pDisplayTransform As IDisplayTransformation
  Dim pEnvelope As IEnvelope
  Dim pCenterPoint As IPoint

  Set pMxDocument = Application.Document
  Set pActiveView = pMxDocument.FocusMap
  Set pDisplayTransform = pActiveView.ScreenDisplay.DisplayTransformation
  Set pEnvelope = pDisplayTransform.VisibleBounds
  'In this case, we could have set pEnvelope to IActiveView::Extent
  'Set pEnvelope = pActiveView.Extent
  Set pCenterPoint = New Point

  pCenterPoint.x = ((pEnvelope.XMax - pEnvelope.XMin) / 2) + pEnvelope.XMin
  pCenterPoint.y = ((pEnvelope.YMax - pEnvelope.YMin) / 2) + pEnvelope.YMin
  pEnvelope.width = pEnvelope.width / 2
  pEnvelope.height = pEnvelope.height / 2
  pEnvelope.CenterAt pCenterPoint
  pDisplayTransform.VisibleBounds = pEnvelope
  pActiveView.Refresh
End Sub
```

Display

To help you understand how the various display objects work together to solve common development requirements, several application scenarios are given along with details on their implementation. Use these patterns as a starting point for working with the display objects.

THE APPLICATION WINDOW

One of the most common tasks is to draw maps in the client area of an application window with support for scrolling and backing store. The display objects are used as follows to make this possible.

Initialization

The DeviceFrame specifies the device rectangle where drawing takes place. Normally, it's the full pixel extent of the device or window, although it can be set to just a portion of the full device extent if desired.

Start by creating a *ScreenDisplay* when the window is created. You'll also need to create one or more symbols to use for drawing shapes. Forward the application's hWnd to *pScreenDisplay.hWnd*. Obtain from the *ScreenDisplay* its *IDisplayTransformation* interface and set the full and visible map extents using *pTransformation.Bounds* and *pDisplayTransform.VisibleBounds*. The visible bounds determines the current zoom level. *ScreenDisplay* takes care of updating the display transformation's *DeviceFrame*. The *ScreenDisplay* monitors the window's messages and automatically handles common events such as window resizing or scrolling.

Create a Visual Basic Standard EXE project. Add a reference to the ESRI Object Library, add a picture box control to the form, then open up the code window and enter the code opposite. This code initializes the screen display object and attaches it to the form's window.

```
Private m_pScreenDisplay As IScreenDisplay
Private m_pFillSymbol As ISimpleFillSymbol

Private Sub Form_Load()
  Set m_pScreenDisplay = New ScreenDisplay
  m_pScreenDisplay.hWnd = Picture1.hWnd

  Set m_pFillSymbol = New SimpleFillSymbol

  Dim pEnv As IEnvelope
  Set pEnv = New Envelope

  pEnv.PutCoords 0, 0, 50, 50

  m_pScreenDisplay.DisplayTransformation.bounds = pEnv
  m_pScreenDisplay.DisplayTransformation.VisibleBounds = pEnv
End Sub
```

Drawing

The display objects define a generic *IDraw* interface, which makes it easy to draw to any display. As long as you use *IDraw* or *IDisplay* to implement your drawing code, you don't have to worry about what kind of device you're drawing to. A drawing sequence starts with *StartDrawing* and ends with *FinishDrawing*.

For example, create a routine that builds one polygon in the center of the screen and draws it. The shape is drawn using the default symbol. Here are the sample routines:

You may want to add a Beep *function call in order to signal each time the* MyDraw *method is called. This will be useful when experimenting with caches later.*

```
Private Function GetPolygon() As IPolygon
  Set GetPolygon = New Polygon

  Dim pPointCollection As IPointCollection
  Set pPointCollection = GetPolygon

  Dim pPoint As IPoint
  Set pPoint = New Point

  pPoint.PutCoords 20, 20
  pPointCollection.AddPoint pPoint

  pPoint.PutCoords 30, 20
  pPointCollection.AddPoint pPoint

  pPoint.PutCoords 30, 30
  pPointCollection.AddPoint pPoint

  pPoint.PutCoords 20, 30
  pPointCollection.AddPoint pPoint

  GetPolygon.Close
End Function

Private Sub MyDraw(pDisplay As IDisplay, hDC As esriCore.OLE_HANDLE)
  ' Draw from Scratch
  Dim pDraw As IDraw
  Set pDraw = pDisplay

  pDraw.StartDrawing hDC, esriNoScreenCache

  Dim pPoly As IPolygon
  Set pPoly = GetPolygon()

  pDraw.SetSymbol m_pFillSymbol
  pDraw.Draw pPoly

  pDraw.FinishDrawing
End Sub
```

This routine can be used to draw polygons to any device context. The first place we need to draw, however, is to a window. To handle this, write some code in the *Paint* method of the Picture Box that passes the application's *ScreenDisplay* pointer and Picture Box *HDC* to the *yDraw* routine.

Notice that the routine takes both a display pointer and a Windows device context.

```
Private Sub Picture1_Paint()
  MyDraw m_pScreenDisplay, Picture1.hDC
End Sub
```

Forwarding the *DC* allows the display to honor the clipping regions that Windows sets into the paint *HDC*.

ADDING DISPLAY CACHING

Some drawing sequences can take a while to complete. A simple way to optimize your application is to enable display caching. This refers to *ScreenDisplay*'s ability to record your drawing sequence into a bitmap and then use the bitmap to refresh the picture box's window whenever *Paint* method is called. The cache is used until your data changes and you call *IScreenDisplay::Invalidate* to indicate that the cache is invalid.

There are two kinds of caches: recording caches and user-allocated caches. Use recording to implement a display cache in the sample application's *Paint* method.

```
Private Sub Picture1_Paint()
  If (m_pScreenDisplay.IsCacheDirty(esriScreenRecording)) Then
    m_pScreenDisplay.StartRecording

    MyDraw m_pScreenDisplay, Picture1.hDC

    m_pScreenDisplay.StopRecording
  Else
    Dim rect As tagRECT
    m_pScreenDisplay.DrawCache Picture1.hDC, esriScreenRecording, rect, rect
  End If
End Sub
```

When you execute this code you will see that nothing is drawn on the screen. This is due to the *ScreenRecording* cache not having its dirty flag set. To ensure that the *MyDraw* function is called when the first paint message is received, you must invalidate the cache. Add the following line at the end of the *Form_Load* method.

```
m_pScreenDisplay.Invalidate Nothing, True, esriScreenRecording
```

Some applications, ArcMap for example, may require multiple display caches. To utilize multiple caches, follow these steps:

1. Add a new cache using *IScreenDisplay::AddCache*. Save the cache ID that is returned.

2. To draw to your cache, specify the cache ID to *StartDrawing*.

3. To invalidate your cache, specify the cache ID to *Invalidate*.

4. To draw from your cache, specify the cache ID to *DrawCache*.

To change the sample application to support its own cache, make the following changes:

- Add a member variable to hold the new cache.

  ```
  Private m_lCacheID As Long
  ```

- Create the cache in the *Form_Load* method.

  ```
  m_lCacheID = m_pScreenDisplay.AddCache
  ```

- Change the appropriate calls to use the *m_lCacheID* variable and remove the start and stop recording from the *Paint* method.

Pan, zoom, and rotate

A powerful feature of the display objects is the ability to zoom in and out on your drawing. It's easy to implement tools that let users zoom in and out or pan. Scrolling is handled automatically. To zoom in and out on your drawing, simply set your display's visible extent.

For example, add a command button to the form and place the following code, which zooms the screen by a fixed amount, in the *Click* event of the button.

```
Private Sub Command1_Click()
  Dim pEnv As IEnvelope

  Set pEnv = m_pScreenDisplay.DisplayTransformation.VisibleBounds
  pEnv.Expand 0.75, 0.75, True
  m_pScreenDisplay.DisplayTransformation.VisibleBounds = pEnv

  m_pScreenDisplay.Invalidate Nothing, True, esriAllScreenCaches
End Sub
```

ScreenDisplay implements *TrackPan,* which can be called in response to a mouse down event to let users pan the display. You can also rotate the entire drawing about the center of the screen by setting the *DisplayTransformation*'s *Rotation* property to a nonzero value. Rotation is specified in degrees. *ScreenDisplay* implements *TrackRotate,* which can be called in response to a mouse down event to let users interactively rotate the display.

Printing

Printing is very similar to drawing to the screen. Since you don't have to worry about caching or scrolling when drawing to the printer, a *SimpleDisplay* can be used. Create a *SimpleDisplay* object and initialize its transform by copying the *ScreenDisplay*'s transform. Set the printer transformation's *DeviceFrame* to the pixel bounds of the printer page. Finally, draw from scratch using the *SimpleDisplay* and the printer's *HDC.*

Output to a metafile

The *GDIDisplay* object can be used to represent a metafile. There's hardly any difference between creating a metafile and printing. If you specify 0 as the *lpBounds* parameter to *CreateEnhMetaFile,* the

MyDraw routine can be used. Just substitute *hMetafileDC* for *hPrinterDC*. If you want to specify a bounds to *CreateEnhMetafFile* (in *HIMETRIC* units), set the *DisplayTransformation*'s *DeviceFrame* to the pixel version of the same rectangle.

Print to a frame

Some projects may require output to be directed to some subrectangle of the output device. It's easy to handle this by setting the *DisplayTransformation*'s device frame to a pixel bounds that is less than the full device extent.

Filters

Very advanced drawing effects, such as color transparency, can be accomplished using display filters. Filters work along with a display cache to allow a rasterized version of your drawing to be manipulated. When a filter is specified to the display (using *IDisplay::putref_DisplayFilter*), the display creates an internal filter cache that is used along with the recording cache to provide raster info to the filter. Output is routed to the filter cache until the filter is cleared (that is, *putref_DisplayFilter(0)*). At that point, the display calls *IDisplayFilter::Apply*. *Apply* receives the current background bitmap (recording cache), the drawing cache (containing all of the drawing that happened since the filter was specified), and the destination HDC. The transparency filter performs alpha blending on these bitmaps and draws them to the destination HDC to achieve color transparency. New filters can be created to realize other effects.

Classify objects

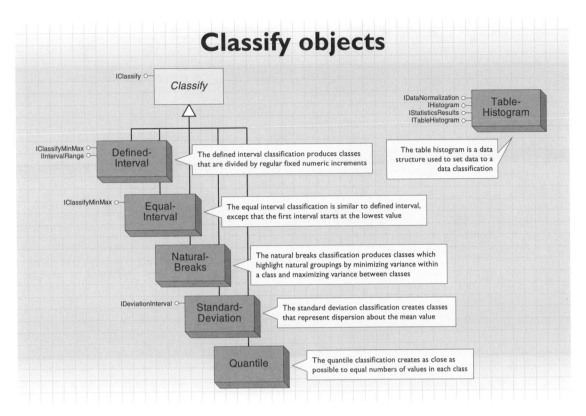

This group of closely related objects can be used to group numeric values into classes. There are five types of classification objects: *DefinedInterval, EqualInterval, NaturalBreaks, Quantile,* and *StandardDeviation* coclass.

The job of all classification objects is to take histogram data (values and frequencies) and, given a desired number of classes, compute appropriate break values between the classes. The breaks are in increasing value and, except for the first break, represent the highest value in the class. The range of values that a class covers can vary; this range is the class' interval.

If the values were from the attribute values of a feature layer, then, after determining the class breaks, you would typically setup a *ClassBreaksRenderer.* Also, the task of gathering the values and frequency counts from an attribute field can be made a lot easier by using the *TableHistogram* to retrieve the histogram data.

The histogram data is in the form of two arrays. The first of these is a sorted array of numeric values, and the second is a corresponding array of frequency counts of the values.

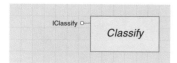

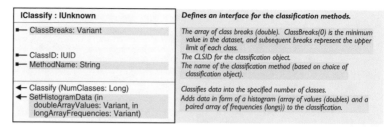

IClassify O—

Classify

Classify objects apply one of several methods to statistically subdivide a set of numeric values into classes.

The *Classify* abstract class defines the *IClassify* interface shared by all classify objects.

IClassify : IUnknown	Defines an interface for the classification methods.
■— ClassBreaks: Variant	The array of class breaks (double). ClassBreaks(0) is the minimum value in the dataset, and subsequent breaks represent the upper limit of each class.
■— ClassID: IUID	The CLSID for the classification object.
■— MethodName: String	The name of the classification method (based on choice of classification object).
◄— Classify (NumClasses: Long)	Classifies data into the specified number of classes.
◄— SetHistogramData (in doubleArrayValues: Variant, in longArrayFrequencies: Variant)	Adds data in form of a histogram (array of values (doubles) and a paired array of frequencies (longs)) to the classification.

The *IClassify* interface is implemented by all the data classification objects; this is the interface used to pass in histogram data and then classify it into breaks. The *ClassID* and *MethodName* properties are used by user interface dialog boxes to identify the classification object and establish what the classification is called.

To pass numeric data into the classify object, the *SetHistogramData* method is used. This takes two safe arrays that must have the same number of elements and an index of zero for their first element. The first array is the numeric data values, defined as an array of double. This array must be sorted in increasing value order. The second array represents the frequency of occurrence of the values, that is, an integer count of the number of times a value occurs.

For example, if the two arrays were called *DataValues* and *DataFrequency,* the lowest value would be stored in *DataValue(0),* and the number of times this value occurred would be stored in *DataFrequency(0).*

You could populate these arrays in code yourself, but if the data is available through the attribute field of a table, you can utilize the *TableHistogram* object to gather the data values and frequencies for you.

This VBA example illustrates populating a *NaturalBreaks* classify object with the numeric values from the 1997 population field of a feature class; this field is called "POP1997". The variable *pFeatureLayer* is initialized to an object implementing *IFeatureLayer.*

```
Dim pTable As ITable
Dim pClassify As IClassify
Dim pTableHistogram As ITableHistogram
Dim pHistogram As IHistogram

' QI to a ITable from a feature layer
Set pTable = pFeatureLayer

' Create and setup a table histogram object to point at the table and
' attribute field
Set pTableHistogram = New TableHistogram
pTableHistogram.Field = "Pop1997"
```

```
Set pTableHistogram.Table = pTable
' Dim some variants, these will hold the safe arrays
Dim DataValues As Variant
Dim DataFrequencies As Variant

' QI to the table histogram interface and go and retrieve the data values
Set pHistogram = pTableHistogram
pHistogram.GetHistogram DataValues, DataFrequencies

' Create a classify object of our choice - equal interval in this case
Set pClassify = New EqualInterval

' Put the values and frequencies into the classify object
pClassify.SetHistogramData DataValues, DataFrequencies
```

Having obtained the data values and frequencies, the next step is to compute some class breaks. Do this by calling the *Classify* method and specifying the number of classes you would like. You must supply the number of desired classes as a variable defined as a *Long*. Some classification algorithms will return a different number of class breaks to what you specified. The number of classes will be written back to the variable you supplied, so it is always best to recheck the number of class breaks after calling *Classify*.

```
Dim ClassBreaksArray() As Double ' Array to hold break values
Dim ClassCount As Long ' Now classify the data into 5 classes
ClassCount = 5
pClassify.Classify ClassCount

' ClassCount could have been modified so recheck this if necessary

' Retrieve the array of break values
ClassBreaksArray = pClassify.ClassBreaks
```

The array returned from the *ClassBreaks* method contains the break values between the classes. The first break value is the minimum break or lowest value in the lowest class, and other break values will be the last value in their class.

The following VBA code sets up a *ClassBreaksRenderer* object.

```
' Initialise a new class breaks renderer and supply the number of
' class breaks and the field to perform the class breaks on.
Dim pClassBreaksRenderer As IClassBreaksRenderer
Set pClassBreaksRenderer = New ClassBreaksRenderer
pClassBreaksRenderer.Field = "POP1997"

' First class break is the minimum value for the class breaks renderer
pClassBreaksRenderer.MinimumBreak = ClassBreaksArray(0)

' Set number of breaks to be number of classes returned from classification
pClassBreaksRenderer.BreakCount = ClassCount
```

Take care when using the ClassBreak property array against the Break and MinimumBreak properties in the ClassBreaksRenderer object.

Note that the *Breaks* property array on the *ClassBreaksRenderer* has one less entry than the array returned from *Classify*. The first break value in the array returned from *Classify* is put into the *ClassBreakRenderers'* *MinimumBreak* property. Next, copy the break values into the *Class-BreaksRenderer* object. You can set up the symbol property of the classes at the same time.

In this VBA example, *breakIndex* is a *Long*, *pColor* is an *IColor*, *pFillSymbol* is an *ISimpleFillSymbol*, and *pEnumColors* is a cursor from a color ramp.

```
' Iterate through each class break, setting values and corresponding
' fill symbols for each polygon,
For breakIndex = 0 To pClassBreaksRenderer.BreakCount - 1
    ' Retrieve a color and set up a fill symbol,
    ' put this in the symbol array corresponding to the class value
    Set pColor = pEnumColors.Next
    Set pFillSymbol = New SimpleFillSymbol
    pFillSymbol.Color = pColor
    pClassBreaksRenderer.Symbol(breakIndex) = pFillSymbol

    ' Set the break value - note this is the highest value in the class
    pClassBreaksRenderer.Break(breakIndex) = ClassBreaksArray(breakIndex +1)
Next breakIndex
```

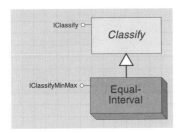

The equal interval classification is similar to defined interval, except that the first interval starts at the lowest value.

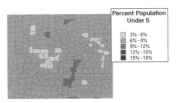

This map illustrates areas where there is differing population of infants relative to the population of the area. It is produced using an equal interval classification, where the minimum is 3 percent of the population being under 5, and then in bands of 3 percent, shows increasing numbers of under 5 (up to 18 percent of the population).

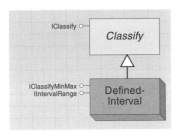

The defined interval classification produces classes that are divided by regular fixed numeric increments.

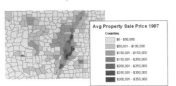

This uses a defined interval classification to illustrate average house prices in different counties. The interval is $50,000, and so the class breaks are at multiples of this amount.

The *EqualInterval* coclass subdivides the data range by the number of classes to produce the equal value intervals for each class. Optionally, you can use the *IClassifyMinMax* interface to specify just minimum and maximum values instead of setting the data values using *IClassify::SetHistogramData*.

This classification emphasizes how data values fall within uniform ranges of values. In practice, it is similar to defined intervals but has the advantage that the lowest and highest classes span the same range of values as the rest of the classes. An example of an application of this classification is a map that depicts homes for sale divided into equal ranges of purchase costs.

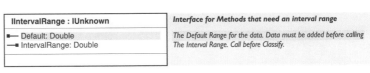

The *EqualInterval* object can additionally generate class breaks given only *Minimum* and *Maximum* values. In this case, you do not have to call *IClassify::SetHistogramData*. However, to be consistent with other classify objects, you can also call *IClassify::SetHistogramData*, which will override the minimum and maximum values. The *Minimum* and *Maximum* properties are write-only, and you must set both properties if you can use *IClassifyMinMax*.

The *DefinedInterval* coclass represents a defined interval classification; this divides a set of attribute values into classes that are divided by precise numeric increments, such as 10, 100, or 500.

This classification works well for values that people are accustomed to seeing in rounded numbers, such as age distribution, income level, or elevation ranges. The disadvantage is that some of the classes, particularly the first and last, may contain a disproportionate number of values.

Use the *IIntervalRange* interface to retrieve a default interval or to set a different interval. When you are calling *IClassify::Classify,* the number of classes returned depends on the maximum data value divided by the interval.

IIntervalRange : IUnknown	Interface for Methods that need an interval range
■— Default: Double	The Default Range for the data. Data must be added before calling
—■ IntervalRange: Double	The Interval Range. Call before Classify.

First, set up the data values with *IClassify::SetHistogramData*. After this, you can use the *Default* property to retrieve the default interval. This would typically be the maximum data value divided by five, so by default you will have five classes. To override this, set a different interval into the *IntervalRange* property.

Display

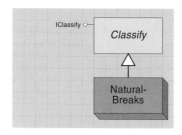

The natural breaks classification produces classes that highlight natural groupings by minimizing variance within a class and maximizing variance between classes.

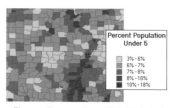

This map illustrates classes divided by the Jenks method into natural intervals. Since 6 percent to 8 percent of the population is infants under 5, this range has been split into two classes. Conversely, in only a few areas are infants more than 10 percent of the population, hence one class covers 10 percent to 18 percent.

The *NaturalBreaks* coclass uses a statistical formula to determine natural clusters of attribute values. The formula is known as Jenk's method. This attempts to minimize the variance within a class and to maximize the variance between classes. The natural-breaks classification is well suited to uneven distributions of attributes. Distinct natural groupings of attributes can be isolated and highlighted.

This classification only uses the *IClassify* interface, so there is nothing to set up other than calling *IClassify::SetHistogramData*.

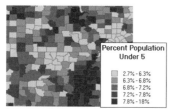

The quantile classification creates as close as possible to equal numbers of values in each class.

This map illustrates classes that contain equal numbers of features from the quantile classification.

The *Quantile* coclass creates an equal (or close to equal) number of values in each class. For example, if there were 12 values, then three classes would represent four values each.

This classification is particularly effective for ranked values. A company can measure sales performance of business locations and draw the respective businesses in their rank of sales performance. This classification yields visually attractive maps because all of the classes have the same number of features.

However, this classification might obscure the natural distribution of values; clusters of values may be split or combined with other values. This classification is best applied to values that have a linear distribution. If you have an even number of classes, the value delimiting the middle classes is the same as the median of statistical sampling.

Because features are grouped by the number in each class, the resulting map can be misleading. Similar features can be placed in adjacent classes, or features with widely different values can be put in the same class. You can minimize this distortion by increasing the number of classes.

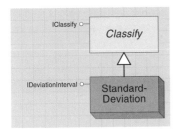

The standard deviation classification creates classes that represent dispersion about the mean value.

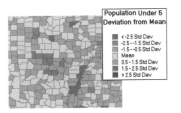

This classification scheme shows classes generated by the standard deviation classification. The class breaks are generated by successively adding or subtracting the standard deviation from the mean. A two-color ramp helps emphasize values above (shown in blue) and below (shown in red) the mean.

The *StandardDeviation* coclass represents dispersion about the mean, and this classification creates classes that represent this dispersion. The classes mainly have an interval that is either one whole or part (for example, a half or quarter) of a standard deviation. There will be one class (often labeled "the mean") that will straddle the mean value by the class interval. Other classes will be adjacent to this on either side, representing increasingly disperse values from the mean. The classes will all have the same interval except for the lowest and highest classes that cover the endpoints of the data range.

As with other classification objects, you put values into the classification with *IClassify::SetHistogramData*. Then you must use the *IDeviationInterval* interface to specify the mean and standard deviation values. Again, the *TableHistogram* object can be used here to calculate these values. Finally, you can produce the classes using the *IClassify::Classify* method.

The number of classes generated by *IClassify::Classify* is determined by the settings of the properties on *IDeviationInterval*, not by the value of the parameter passed to *IClassify::Classify*. However, you should still supply the parameter, as it will be modified to reflect the number of classes actually created.

This classification is intended for generally symmetric distributions of values that have a broad peak near the mean with the density of values diminishing away from the peak.

An example of a suitable map for this classification could be a population density or accident rates map. You would expect these values to have their greatest data density near a mean value, and values that vary significantly are scarce. The classic shape of this type of distribution is the bell curve.

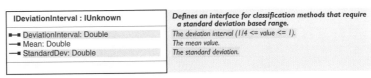

IDeviationInterval : IUnknown	Defines an interface for classification methods that require a standard deviation based range.
DeviationInterval: Double	The deviation interval (1/4 <= value <= 1).
Mean: Double	The mean value.
StandardDev: Double	The standard deviation.

When setting up a *StandardDeviation* classify object, you must set the *Mean* and *StandardDev* properties to be used for the class breaks before you call *IClassify::Classify*. By default, the classes will have an interval of one standard deviation. However, you can set the *DeviationInterval* property to give you more classes. The *DeviationInterval* property specifies what fraction of a standard deviation you want the class intervals to be. Typically, you would set this to be a half or quarter to give you twice or four times as many classes.

Display

This example VBA code uses the *IStatisticsResults* interface on the table histogram to get the mean and standard deviation values to populate the *StandardDeviation* classify object ready for classification.

In this example, *pTableHistogram* is an *ITableHistogram*. The data has already been gathered with *ITableHistogram::GetHistogramData* and placed into two arrays, *DataValues* and *DataFrequencies*.

```
' Create a classify object of our choice - StandardDeviation
Set pClassify = New StandardDeviation

' QI to the IDeviationInterval interface
Dim pDeviationInterval As IDeviationInterval
Set pDeviationInterval = pClassify

' DataValues and DataFrequencies are arrays that have already been
' populated using the TableHistogram object.
' Put the collected data into the classify object
pClassify.SetHistogramData DataValues, DataFrequencies

' QI to get the statistics result interface from the table
' histogram interface
Dim pStatisticsResult As IStatisticsResults
Set pStatisticsResult = pTableHistogram

' Set the mean and standard deviation into the classify object
pDeviationInterval.Mean = pStatisticsResult.Mean
pDeviationInterval.StandardDev = pStatisticsResult.StandardDeviation

' Our classes will be one standard deviation wide
pDeviationInterval.DeviationInterval = 1

' Now classify the data …
```

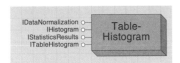

A histogram is a data structure mainly used to set data to a Classify *object.*

Generally, a histogram consists of two arrays, where the first array is an ordered list of values and the second is a paired list of frequencies. Though you can manually manage these arrays when working with a *Classify* object, typically, it is easier to use a histogram object, especially when mapping normalized data, excluding features, or working with a sample of features.

Use a *TableHistogram* object if your data is contained in an object that supports the ITable interface. Alternatively, use a *DataHistogram* object if your data is stored in an array or in another histogram object. Finally, a third type of histogram, *TinHistogram* coclass, can be used if your data source is a TIN.

This section provides an overview of how to prepare and use a *TableHistogram* object to set data to a *Classify* object.

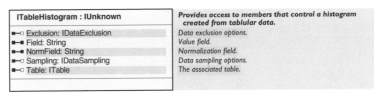

ITableHistogram : IUnknown	Provides access to members that control a histogram created from tablular data.
Exclusion: IDataExclusion	Data exclusion options.
Field: String	Value field.
NormField: String	Normalization field.
Sampling: IDataSampling	Data sampling options.
Table: ITable	The associated table.

Use *ITableHistogram::Table* and *ITableHistogram::Field* to specify the table and field that the histogram is based on.

Optionally, set *NormField* if you want to normalize by a field. Note that setting this property is equivalent to setting *IDataNormalization:: NormalizationField*.

Set the *Exclusion* object if you want to use a where clause to specify features that will not be included when the histogram is generated.

The *Sampling* property is also optional. Use this to specify a method for using only a subset of the features from the source table for the histogram.

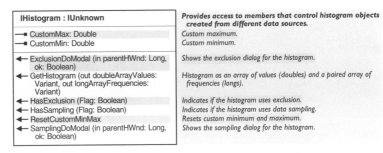

IHistogram : IUnknown	Provides access to members that control histogram objects created from different data sources.
CustomMax: Double	Custom maximum.
CustomMin: Double	Custom minimum.
ExclusionDoModal (in parentHWnd: Long, ok: Boolean)	Shows the exclusion dialog for the histogram.
GetHistogram (out doubleArrayValues: Variant, out longArrayFrequencies: Variant)	Histogram as an array of values (doubles) and a paired array of frequencies (longs).
HasExclusion (Flag: Boolean)	Indicates if the histogram uses exclusion.
HasSampling (Flag: Boolean)	Indicates if the histogram uses data sampling.
ResetCustomMinMax	Resets custom minimum and maximum.
SamplingDoModal (in parentHWnd: Long, ok: Boolean)	Shows the sampling dialog for the histogram.

IHistogram has properties and methods common to all histograms.

For a *TableHistogram*, use *GetHistogram* to generate the histogram based on the properties you set up via *ITableHistogram*. The method returns two arrays: the first is the values array (that is, the ordered list of values), and the second array contains the frequencies.

You can choose to use *CustomMin* and *CustomMax* to enforce end constraints on the data range.

HasExclusion and *HasSampling* provide feedback about whether or not a histogram is using exclusion or sampling, while *ExclusionDoModal* and *SamplingDoModal* open ArcGIS dialog boxes that allow users to work with exclusion and sampling properties, respectively.

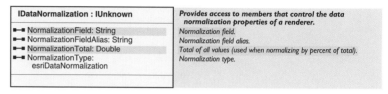

IDataNormalization : IUnknown	Provides access to members that control the data normalization properties of a renderer.
■—■ NormalizationField: String	*Normalization field.*
■—■ NormalizationFieldAlias: String	*Normalization field alias.*
■—■ NormalizationTotal: Double	*Total of all values (used when normalizing by percent of total).*
■—■ NormalizationType: esriDataNormalization	*Normalization type.*

Use *IDataNormalization* to set the normalization properties for your histogram.

As mentioned above, for a *TableHistogram* object, *NormalizationField* is the same as *ITableHistogram::NormField*.

Use *NormalizationType* to set the normalization flavor for your histogram.

IStatisticsResults : IUnknown	Provides access to members used for reporting statistics.
■— Count: Long	*The count of the values.*
■— Maximum: Double	*The maximum value.*
■— Mean: Double	*The arithmetic mean.*
■— Minimum: Double	*The minimum value.*
■— StandardDeviation: Double	*The standard deviation, based on sample flag.*
■— Sum: Double	*The sum of the values.*

Once you have set up a *TableHistogram*, you can use *IStatisticsResults* to calculate some values that are needed when working with some *Classify* objects.

For example, to set up a *StandardDeviation* object, use this interface to calculate *IDeviationInterval::Mean* and *IDeviationInterval::Standard-Deviation*.

Rubber band objects

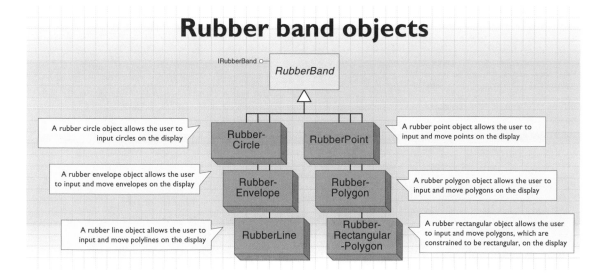

A rubber circle object allows the user to input circles on the display

A rubber envelope object allows the user to input and move envelopes on the display

A rubber line object allows the user to input and move polylines on the display

A rubber point object allows the user to input and move points on the display

A rubber polygon object allows the user to input and move polygons on the display

A rubber rectangular object allows the user to input and move polygons, which are constrained to be rectangular, on the display

The *RubberPoint, RubberEnvelope, RubberLine, RubberPolygon, RubberRectangularPolygon,* and *RubberCircle* coclasses, all implementing the *IRubberBand* interface, allow the user to digitize geometries on the display using the mouse—either to create whole new geometry objects or to update existing ones. As such, they can be viewed as simple versions of the feedback objects that are covered later in this chapter.

Some examples of uses for these rubberbanding objects include dragging an envelope, forming a new polyline, or moving a point. Each of the above classes supports the *IRubberBand* interface, but the behavior depends on the class used.

IRubberBand allows the user to interact with the display and either create new geometry objects using TrackNew or move existing ones with TrackExisting. Typically, this interface would be used in the Mouse_Down event of a tool.

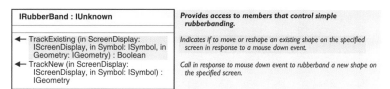

IRubberBand : IUnknown	Provides access to members that control simple rubberbanding.
← TrackExisting (in ScreenDisplay: IScreenDisplay, in Symbol: ISymbol, in Geometry: IGeometry) : Boolean	Indicates if to move or reshape an existing shape on the specified screen in response to a mouse down event.
← TrackNew (in ScreenDisplay: IScreenDisplay, in Symbol: ISymbol) : IGeometry	Call in response to mouse down event to rubberband a new shape on the specified screen.

The *IRubberband* interface has two methods, *TrackExisting* and *TrackNew,* which are used to move existing geometries and create new geometries, respectively. These methods would normally be called from within the code for a tool's *Mouse_Down* event, and they would then handle all subsequent mouse events themselves. They would capture subsequent mouse and keyboard events, such as *Mouse_Move, Mouse_Up,* and *Key_Down* events, and would complete when they received a *Mouse_Up* event or abort if the Esc key was pressed. Because the events are being trapped by the rubberband objects, no events will be raised in VBA.

This means that very little code is required to use them, although this comes at the expense of flexibility. Typically, these objects would be used for simple tasks such as dragging a rectangle or creating a new line. Operations that involve moving the vertices of existing geometries would require the feedback objects to be used instead.

The types of geometry that are returned for TrackNew by each of the rubber objects are as follows:

RubberCircle—ICircularArc

RubberEnvelope—IEnvelope

RubberLine—IPolyline

RubberPoint—IPoint

RubberPolygon—IPolygon

RubberRectangularPolygon—IPolygon

The *TrackNew* method takes two parameters: an *IScreenDisplay* object representing the *ScreenDisplay* to draw the *Rubberband* and an *ISymbol* object to use for drawing the rubberband. If no symbol is given, then the default symbol is used. The method returns a new geometry object—the type of geometry returned depends on which class was used. *RubberPolygon* class returns a *Polygon* object. If the method fails to complete (that is, if the user presses the Esc key), then *Nothing* is returned.

The following code shows how to use the *TrackNew* method of *IRubberBand* with a *RubberLine* object.

```
Private Sub UIToolControl1_MouseDown(ByVal button As Long, _
    ByVal shift As Long, ByVal x As Long, ByVal y As Long)
Dim pRubberLine As IRubberBand
Dim pGeom As IGeometry
Dim pMXDoc As IMxDocument

' QI for the MXDocument Interface
Set pMXDoc = ThisDocument
' Create a new Rubber Line object
Set pRubberLine = New RubberLine
' Track new polyline on current document's display using default symbol
Set pGeom = pRubberLine.TrackNew(pMXDoc.ActiveView.ScreenDisplay, Nothing)
End Sub
```

The *TrackExisting* method also takes *ScreenDisplay* and *Symbol* parameters as well as an *IGeometry* representing the input *Geometry*. This last parameter represents the geometry to move on the screen and is passed by reference so that it may be altered by the rubberband operation. The method returns a *Boolean,* which will be *True* unless the operation was interrupted by the user pressing the Esc key. The method will do nothing if the *Geometry* that is passed in does not intersect the current mouse location.

The types of geometry that are expected by TrackExisting for each of the rubber objects are as follows:

RubberCircle—Not implemented

RubberEnvelope—IEnvelope

RubberLine—IPolyline

RubberPoint—IPoint

RubberPolygon—IPolygon

RubberRectangularPolygon—IPolygon

The following code illustrates how to move an existing polygon using the *TrackExisting* method of *IRubberBand* with a *RubberPolygon* object. *pGeomPoly* is declared as an *IPolygon* and is used to represent the *Polygon* to be moved.

```
Private Sub UIToolControl1_MouseDown(ByVal button As Long, _
    ByVal shift As Long, ByVal x As Long, ByVal y As Long)
Dim pRubberPoly As IRubberBand
Dim pMXDoc As IMxDocument
Dim Success As Boolean

' QI for the MXDocument Interface
Set pMXDoc = ThisDocument
' Create a new Rubber Polygon object
Set pRubberPoly = New RubberPolygon
' Move an existing Polygon on current doc's display using default symbol
Success = pRubberPoly.TrackExisting(pMXDoc.ActiveView.ScreenDisplay, _
    Nothing, pGeomPoly)
End Sub
```

Selection tracker objects

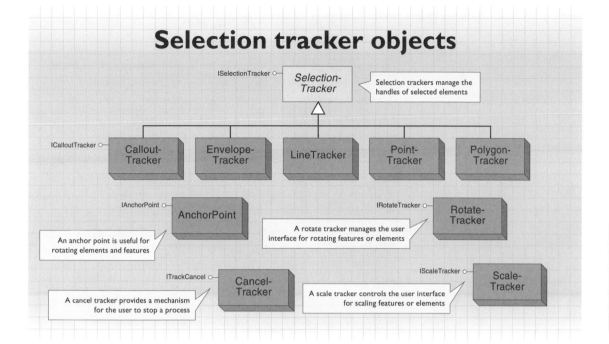

ISelectionTracker ○— **Selection-Tracker**

Selection trackers manage the handles of selected elements

ICalloutTracker ○— Callout-Tracker

Envelope-Tracker

LineTracker

Point-Tracker

Polygon-Tracker

IAnchorPoint ○— AnchorPoint

IRotateTracker ○— Rotate-Tracker

A rotate tracker manages the user interface for rotating features or elements

An anchor point is useful for rotating elements and features

ITrackCancel ○— Cancel-Tracker

A cancel tracker provides a mechanism for the user to stop a process

IScaleTracker ○— Scale-Tracker

A scale tracker controls the user interface for scaling features or elements

The envelope tracker operates on all element types.

The line tracker and polygon tracker lets the user manipulate the vertices of polylines and polygons.

The callout tracker lets the user manipulate text callouts.

There are three kinds of selection trackers; these can all be seen in ArcMap.

- An envelope tracker allows the user to move and resize the element. This functionality is implemented by the *EnvelopeTracker* object for all element types, including point, line, polygon, and group elements.

- A vertex edit tracker allows the user to move vertices of lines, polygons, curves, and curved text. This functionality is implemented by the *LineTracker* and *PolygonTracker* objects.

- A callout tracker allows the user to move a text callout. This functionality is implemented by the *CalloutTracker* objects.

The *PointTracker* object is not currently useful. Moving and resizing of point elements is handled by envelope trackers, the size of the envelope corresponding to the symbolized point.

Although the selection trackers are coclasses, you would only cocreate one if you were building your own custom element when implementing *IElement::SelectionTracker*.

ISelectionTracker : IUnknown	Provides access to members that control the managing of selection handle tracking.
■— Bounds (in Display: IDisplay) : IEnvelope	The area covered by the tracker including handles.
—◻ Display: IScreenDisplay	The display used by the tracker.
■—■ Geometry: IGeometry	Geometry used for tracking feedback.
■—■ Locked: Boolean	Indicates if the tracker is locked or not. Locked means nodes cannot be moved.
■—■ ShowHandles: Boolean	Indicates if the tracker is showing handles or not.
◀— Deactivate: Boolean	Cancel tracking.
◀— Draw (in Display: IDisplay, in hDC: Long, in Style: tagesriTrackerStyle)	Draw selection indicater. Usually a color outline with selection handles.
◀— HitTest (in Point: IPoint) : tagesriTrackerLocation	Check if mouse is over tracker. Return a TrackerLocation to indicate which handle mouse is over.
◀— OnKeyDown (in keyCode: Long, in Shift: Long) : Boolean	Special keypress processing while tracking.
◀— OnKeyUp (in keyCode: Long, in Shift: Long) : Boolean	Special keypress processing while tracking.
◀— OnMouseDown (in Button: Long, in Shift: Long, in X: Long, in Y: Long)	Begin tracking move or resize based on the location of the mouse over the tracker handles.
◀— OnMouseMove (in Button: Long, in Shift: Long, in X: Long, in Y: Long)	In process move or resize tracking.
◀— OnMouseUp (in Button: Long, in Shift: Long, in X: Long, in Y: Long)	Finish move or resize tracking.
◀— QueryCursor (in Point: IPoint) : Long	If the mouse is over the tracker, return an HCURSOR to indicate legal operations based on mouse's relation to selection handles: move resize, etc. Return 0 if mouse isn't over tracker.
◀— QueryMoveFeedback (in moveFeedback: IDisplayFeedback)	The move feedback for the selection tracker.
◀— QueryResizeFeedback (in resizeFeedback: IDisplayFeedback)	The resize feedback for the selection tracker.

The *ISelectionTracker* interface controls the selection handle user interface. You might use *ISelectionTracker* in order to provide different behavior than that of the standard ArcMap interface, for example, the Element Movement tool that snaps elements to a grid. However, it is more likely that you will use this interface when building a custom object such as an element.

You can gain access to selection trackers with *IElement::SelectionTracker*, *IElementEditVertices::GetMoveVerticesSelectionTracker,* or *IGraphicsContainerSelect::SelectionTracker*. When using *IElement*, you will get either an envelope tracker or edit vertices tracker, depending on the state of the element. This code example ensures that an envelope tracker is returned—if the element has a vertex edit tracker, it is changed to a envelope tracker and the document refreshed.

```
Public Sub EnsureEnvelopeTracker(pElement As IElement)
  Dim pMxDoc As IMxDocument
  Set pMxDoc = ThisDocument

  Dim pScreenDisplay As IScreenDisplay
  Set pScreenDisplay = pMxDoc.ActiveView.ScreenDisplay

  If TypeOf pElement Is IElementEditVertices Then
    Dim pElemVert As IElementEditVertices
    Set pElemVert = pElement
    If pElemVert.MovingVertices Then
      pElemVert.MovingVertices = False
      pMxDoc.ActiveView.PartialRefresh esriViewGraphicSelection, Nothing, _
        pElement.SelectionTracker.Bounds(pScreenDisplay)
    End If
  End If
End Sub
```

After obtaining a reference to a selection tracker, always set the *Display* property before using it.

The *Geometry* property of a selection tracker applies to the tracker, not the element: for envelope trackers, the geometry is a polygon created from the envelope shape; for vertex edit trackers, the geometry is a polygon or polyline as appropriate. The *Geometry* property is updated when the user finishes reshaping the element with the selection tracker.

The *HitTest* method provides information about the position of the mouse. The returned values are defined by *esriTrackerLocation*:

Enumeration esriTrackerLocation	ESRI mouse tracking location
0 - LocationNone	*Outside of tracker*
1 - LocationInterior	*Within tracker envelope*
2 - LocationTopLeft	*At top left tracker handle*
3 - LocationTopMiddle	*At top middle tracker handle*
4 - LocationTopRight	*At top right tracker handle*
5 - LocationMiddleLeft	*At middle left tracker handle*
6 - LocationMiddleRight	*At middle right tracker handle*
7 - LocationBottomLeft	*At bottom left tracker handle*
8 - LocationBottomMiddle	*At bottom middle tracker handle*
9 - LocationBottomRight	*At bottom right tracker handle*

The enumeration names are most relevant to envelope trackers, but *HitTest* can also be used with vertex edit trackers and callout trackers. In these cases, the returned values are LocationNone, LocationInterior, and LocationTopLeft.

Many of the *ISelectionTracker* methods—for example, *OnMouseDown*—correspond to user interface events. When controlling a selection tracker with a user interface tool, pass on the tool events to the selection tracker, for example:

```
Private Sub UIToolControl1_MouseMove(ByVal button As Long, _
   ByVal shift As Long, ByVal x As Long, ByVal y As Long)
  If Not m_pSelTracker Is Nothing Then
    ' Pass on the mouse move event to selection tracker
    m_pSelTracker.OnMouseMove button, shift, x, y
  End If
End Sub
```

QueryMoveFeedback and *QueryResizeFeedback* return the feedback objects that the selection tracker is using.

Draw is called by ArcMap if the element is selected, so normally you do not need to use this method (though it is important if you implement your own custom selection tracker).

ICalloutTracker : ISelectionTracker	*Provides access to members that control the callout feedback.*
▪─□ Symbol: ISymbol	*The symbol containing the callout the tracker will use.*
▪─▪ SymbolGeometry: IGeometry	*Geometry used for drawing the symbol.*

You would normally only use the *ICalloutTracker* interface when building custom elements since the symbol and its geometry can be obtained from the element or the *ISelectionTracker::Geometry* method.

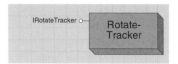

The rotate tracker object manages the user interface for rotating features or elements.

Note that the rotate tracker does not provide facilities for manipulation of the rotation origin—use the AnchorPoint object to do this.

RotateTracker manages the user interface for rotating features or elements.

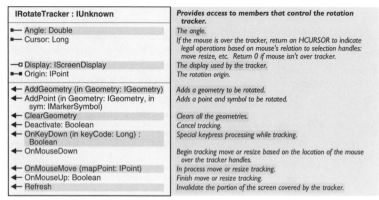

IRotateTracker : IUnknown	Provides access to members that control the rotation tracker.
▪— Angle: Double	The angle.
▪— Cursor: Long	If the mouse is over the tracker, return an HCURSOR to indicate legal operations based on mouse's relation to selection handles: move resize, etc. Return 0 if mouse isn't over tracker.
—▫ Display: IScreenDisplay	The display used by the tracker.
▪—▪ Origin: IPoint	The rotation origin.
◀— AddGeometry (in Geometry: IGeometry)	Adds a geometry to be rotated.
◀— AddPoint (in Geometry: IGeometry, in sym: IMarkerSymbol)	Adds a point and symbol to be rotated.
◀— ClearGeometry	Clears all the geometries.
◀— Deactivate: Boolean	Cancel tracking.
◀— OnKeyDown (in keyCode: Long) : Boolean	Special keypress processing while tracking.
◀— OnMouseDown	Begin tracking move or resize based on the location of the mouse over the tracker handles.
◀— OnMouseMove (mapPoint: IPoint)	In process move or resize tracking.
◀— OnMouseUp: Boolean	Finish move or resize tracking.
◀— Refresh	Invalidate the portion of the screen covered by the tracker.

The *IRotateTracker* interface controls the rotation user interface. After cocreating a *RotateTracker* object, use the members in the following order: *Display, Origin, ClearGeometry,* and then one or more calls to either *AddGeometry* or *AddPoint*. If you were rotating a single polygon element, you would need just one call to *AddGeometry* for the element geometry; however, a rotation tracker can handle a group of elements. Use *AddPoint* for features with marker symbology.

When using *AddGeometry* with elements whose size is determined by symbology, for example, text and marker elements, use the geometry of the element outline to get the correct feedback. This example function, given an element, returns a geometry suitable for *AddGeometry*:

```
Public Function GetElementGeometry(pElement As IElement, _
                                   pScreenDisplay As IScreenDisplay)
  Set GetElementGeometry = pElement.Geometry
  If TypeOf pElement Is IBoundsProperties Then
    Dim pBoundsProps As IBoundsProperties
    Set pBoundsProps = pElement
    If pBoundsProps.FixedSize Then
      Dim pPolygon As IPolygon
      Set pPolygon = New Polygon
      pElement.QueryOutline pScreenDisplay, pPolygon
      Set GetElementGeometry = pPolygon
    End If
  End If
End Function
```

You can QI directly from most elements to ITransform2D, which can be used to move, scale, and rotate them.

If you pass on the Key_Down event to OnKeyDown, pressing "a" will prompt the user for an angle.

The *OnMouseDown, OnKeyDown, OnMouseMove, OnMouseUp,* and *Deactivate* are all event handlers. Call these methods from the corresponding events in your tool. The *OnMouseMove* method will provide user interface feedback for the rotation.

Typically, you will choose to update the feature or element in question in conjunction with the *OnMouseUp* method. This returns a boolean indicating whether the element or feature was rotated. Get the amount of rotation from the *Angle* property; this can then be passed to *ITransform2D::Rotate*. For features, you may find *IFeatureEdit::RotateSet* useful.

The scale tracker manages the user interface for expansion or contraction of geometries by a scale ratio.

You can add the ArcMap Editor Scale Tool from the Customize dialog box.

In a similar way to the rotation tracker, the scale tracker can be applied to one or more elements or features.

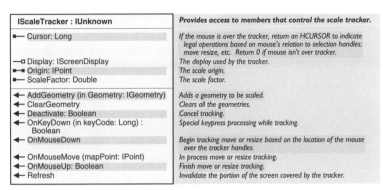

IScaleTracker : IUnknown	Provides access to members that control the scale tracker.
▪— Cursor: Long	If the mouse is over the tracker, return an HCURSOR to indicate legal operations based on mouse's relation to selection handles: move resize, etc. Return 0 if mouse isn't over tracker.
—▫ Display: IScreenDisplay	The display used by the tracker.
▪—▪ Origin: IPoint	The scale origin.
▪— ScaleFactor: Double	The scale factor.
◄— AddGeometry (in Geometry: IGeometry)	Adds a geometry to be scaled.
◄— ClearGeometry	Clears all the geometries.
◄— Deactivate: Boolean	Cancel tracking.
◄— OnKeyDown (in keyCode: Long) : Boolean	Special keypress processing while tracking.
◄— OnMouseDown	Begin tracking move or resize based on the location of the mouse over the tracker handles.
◄— OnMouseMove (mapPoint: IPoint)	In process move or resize tracking.
◄— OnMouseUp: Boolean	Finish move or resize tracking.
◄— Refresh	Invalidate the portion of the screen covered by the tracker.

The *IScaleTracker* interface controls the user interface for scaling objects. It works in a similar way to *IRotateTracker*.

The *ScaleFactor* property can be used to find out what scaling ratio was defined. If you pass on the key down event to *OnKeyDown*, pressing "F" will prompt the user for the scale factor.

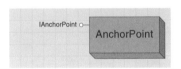

The anchor point represents a point that can be used when manipulating elements and features.

Anchor points can be useful in many situations— for rotating elements and features and moving the origin of a text callout.

When working with elements, anchor points can be considered a helper object, rather than an essential. You will first need to cocreate the anchor point and then manipulate it. This is useful when implementing your own tools and objects, for example, a custom rotation tool.

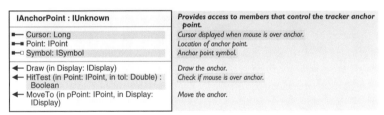

IAnchorPoint : IUnknown	Provides access to members that control the tracker anchor point.
▪— Cursor: Long	Cursor displayed when mouse is over anchor.
▪—▪ Point: IPoint	Location of anchor point.
▪—▫ Symbol: ISymbol	Anchor point symbol.
◄— Draw (in Display: IDisplay)	Draw the anchor.
◄— HitTest (in Point: IPoint, in tol: Double) : Boolean	Check if mouse is over anchor.
◄— MoveTo (in pPoint: IPoint, in Display: IDisplay)	Move the anchor.

The *IAnchorPoint* interface provides facilities for controlling anchor points.

IEditor::SelectionAnchor will return the anchor point being used by the editor, which you can subsequently manipulate.

Display

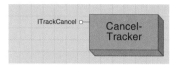

A cancel tracker provides a mechanism for the user to stop a process.

The *CancelTracker* object is the favorite class of many users, though most probably don't realize it. Have you ever started a process and realized as soon as you did that it wasn't what you wanted? If the process employed the *CancelTracker* object, then you would be able to hit the escape key and halt the process before it had completed. The *CancelTracker* object is the object used by ArcObjects to monitor the escape key (optionally, the space bar and mouse clicks as well) and terminate processes at the request of the user.

A *CancelTracker* is typically handed into or created just prior to functions that execute a lengthy operation. Just before such operations begin, *ITrackCancel::Reset* must be called; *Reset* sets the state of the *CancelTracker* to uncancelled and returns the internal counter, which is used to update progression to zero.

Within the innermost loop of the operation, *ITrackCancel::Continue* should be called to check whether the user has canceled the operation. By default, a cancellation occurs under the following circumstances:

- The Esc key has been pressed.
- The space bar has been pressed (disable with *CancelOnKeyPress* property).
- The left mouse button has been pressed (disable with *CancelOnClick* property).
- The right mouse button has been pressed (disable with *CancelOnClick* property).

If any of these actions occurs, the *ITrackCancel::Continue* method will return false and the operation's logic should then use this indicator to exit the loop.

Any object that exposes *IProgressor* or *IStepProgressor,* such as the *ProgressDialog* object, can be bound to the *CancelTracker* so that it will be updated correctly and efficiently and with no additional code within the operation itself. Once the progressor is connected to the *CancelTracker* via the *Progressor* property, it will be updated automatically as the operation is executed. If the progressor is a step progressor, the *MaxRange* should be set to equal the number of iterations that the operation will progress through; this number should also match the number of times *Continue* will be called in the operation's innermost loop.

In order for COM and various other parts of Windows to work correctly and responsively, Windows messages must be processed at regular intervals. For this reason, the *CancelTracker*'s implementation will process noninput (mouse, keyboard)-related messages every second during the operation if any such messages are pending. This default frequency may be changed utilizing the *ITrackCancel::CheckTime* property.

As a developer, you may use the *CancelTracker* several ways. Some ArcObjects commands (such as *IActiveView::Output*) take a

Display

CancelTracker object as an input parameter as the following code snippet demonstrates:

```
Dim pCancel as ITrackCancel
Set pCancel = New CancelTracker
IActiveView::Output <OLE_handle>, <screen resolution>, <pixel bounds>, _
  <visible bounds>, pCancel
```

In this case, you can provide cancel capabilities by simply creating a *CancelTracker* object and passing it in to the *Output* method. The *Output* method will then take care of monitoring the Esc button and canceling the process if the user chooses to.

Another way to use a *CancelTracker* object is similar to the process above, but you as the developer are responsible for monitoring the object. An approach of this type would be used when the execution of your code could take a considerable amount of time and you want to give the user the option of canceling out of the process. The following VBA code demonstrates this process. The code is designed to loop through a set of selected network features and run the *Connect* method on them to ensure they are connected to the network. The *CancelTracker* object is included for aborting the process if the user accidentally selects too many features or just wants the process to stop.

```
Dim m_pTrackCancel As ITrackCancel

Sub testCancel()
  Dim pEd As IEditor, pEnumSel As IEnumFeature, pFeat As IFeature
  Dim pNetFeat As INetworkFeature, pUID As New UID
  pUID = "esricore.editor"
  Set pEd = Application.FindExtensionByCLSID(pUID)
  Set pEnumSel = pEd.EditSelection
  Set pFeat = pEnumSel.Next

  Set m_pTrackCancel = New CancelTracker
  pEd.StartOperation
  Do While Not pFeat Is Nothing
    If TypeOf pFeat Is INetworkFeature Then
      Set pNetFeat = pFeat
      pNetFeat.Connect
    End If

    'Check for a cancel
    If Not m_pTrackCancel.Continue Then
      MsgBox "Canceled!"
      pEd.StopOperation "Connect network features."
      Exit Sub
    End If

    Set pFeat = pEnumSel.Next
  Loop
```

```
pEd.StopOperation "Connect network features."
End Sub
```

This code could also be used in conjunction with a *ProgressDialog* object to provide a dialog box with a Cancel button to the user. For an example of how to use a *ProgressDialog* object with a *CancelTracker* object, see the Developer Sample 'Convert AV3 to AV8 Attribute Indexes'.

A *CancelTracker* object can be retrieved through a couple of different methods (*IAppDisplay::CancelTracker*, *IScreenDisplay::CancelTracker*, and others), but it is not recommended that you attempt to use the object when obtained in this manner. The *CancelTracker* object used with these interfaces is for internal use.

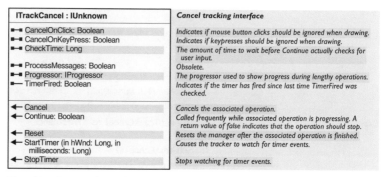

The *ITrackCancel* interface is the only interface implemented by the *CancelTracker* object and provides access to the properties of that object. Through this interface, the developer can monitor the *Cancel-Tracker* object to determine if a cancellation has been executed by the user. The *ITrackCancel* also allows the developer to specify what actions constitute a cancellation.

The *Continue* property is the key property of the interface. When writing code with an *ITrackCancel* object, you should check the *Continue* property often to know when the operation should be halted (a value of *False* indicates the operation should be ended).

CancelOnClick and *CancelOnKeyPress* are the properties that allow the developer to specify the user actions that constitute a cancellation (a cancellation changes the *Continue* property to *False*).

The *Progressor* property can be used with a progress object (*ProgressAnimation*, *ProgressBar*, or *ProgressDialog*) to display the progress of a lengthy operation.

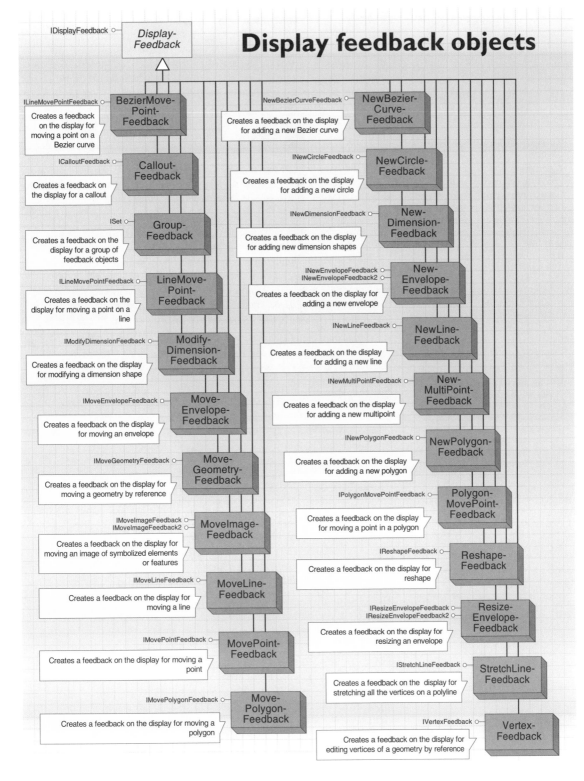

Display feedback objects

DisplayFeedback — IDisplayFeedback

BezierMovePointFeedback — ILineMovePointFeedback
Creates a feedback on the display for moving a point on a Bezier curve

CalloutFeedback — ICalloutFeedback
Creates a feedback on the display for a callout

GroupFeedback — ISet
Creates a feedback on the display for a group of feedback objects

LineMovePointFeedback — ILineMovePointFeedback
Creates a feedback on the display for moving a point on a line

ModifyDimensionFeedback — IModifyDimensionFeedback
Creates a feedback on the display for modifying a dimension shape

MoveEnvelopeFeedback — IMoveEnvelopeFeedback
Creates a feedback on the display for moving an envelope

MoveGeometryFeedback — IMoveGeometryFeedback
Creates a feedback on the display for moving a geometry by reference

MoveImageFeedback — IMoveImageFeedback, IMoveImageFeedback2
Creates a feedback on the display for moving an image of symbolized elements or features

MoveLineFeedback — IMoveLineFeedback
Creates a feedback on the display for moving a line

MovePointFeedback — IMovePointFeedback
Creates a feedback on the display for moving a point

MovePolygonFeedback — IMovePolygonFeedback
Creates a feedback on the display for moving a polygon

NewBezierCurveFeedback — NewBezierCurveFeedback
Creates a feedback on the display for adding a new Bezier curve

NewCircleFeedback — INewCircleFeedback
Creates a feedback on the display for adding a new circle

NewDimensionFeedback — INewDimensionFeedback
Creates a feedback on the display for adding new dimension shapes

NewEnvelopeFeedback — INewEnvelopeFeedback, INewEnvelopeFeedback2
Creates a feedback on the display for adding a new envelope

NewLineFeedback — INewLineFeedback
Creates a feedback on the display for adding a new line

NewMultiPointFeedback — INewMultiPointFeedback
Creates a feedback on the display for adding a new multipoint

NewPolygonFeedback — INewPolygonFeedback
Creates a feedback on the display for adding a new polygon

PolygonMovePointFeedback — IPolygonMovePointFeedback
Creates a feedback on the display for moving a point in a polygon

ReshapeFeedback — IReshapeFeedback
Creates a feedback on the display for reshape

ResizeEnvelopeFeedback — IResizeEnvelopeFeedback, IResizeEnvelopeFeedback2
Creates a feedback on the display for resizing an envelope

StretchLineFeedback — IStretchLineFeedback
Creates a feedback on the display for stretching all the vertices on a polyline

VertexFeedback — IVertexFeedback
Creates a feedback on the display for editing vertices of a geometry by reference

Display

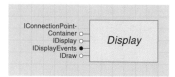

The display feedback objects and interfaces are used to digitize new and existing geometries, such as points, polylines, envelopes, or polygons, on a map or page layout. These objects are used internally within the ArcMap application in the drawing and editing tools as well as being available to developers.

The set of objects that implement the *IDisplayFeedback* interface gives you fine-grained control over customizing the visual feedback when using the mouse to form shapes on the screen display. You can direct the precise visual feedback for tasks, such as adding, moving, or re-shaping features or graphic elements. The objects can also be used without creating any features or elements for a task, such as measuring the distance between two points.

Typically, you would use the display feedback objects within code that handles the mouse events of a tool based on the *ITool* or *IUIToolControl* interfaces, such as *Mouse_Down* and *Mouse_Move*.

Which mouse events to program depends on the task at hand. For example, when adding a new envelope, you would program the display feedback objects in the *Mouse_Down*, *Mouse_Move*, and *Mouse_Up* events. Or, when digitizing a new polygon, you would program the *Mouse_Down*, *Mouse_Move*, and *Mouse_DblClick* events. When you are collecting points with the mouse to pass to the display feedbacks, you can use the *ToMapPoint* method on *IDisplayTransformation* to convert the current mouse location from device coordinates to map coordinates.

Although the feedback objects (excluding the *GroupFeedback* object) all have common functionality, their behavior does vary. These variations can be divided as follows:

The display feedback objects also provide some of the base functionality for the rubberband objects described earlier. You should use the rubberband objects first if they suit your requirements; select the display feedback objects if you want greater control over the user interface when modifying graphics or features. This greater control comes at the cost of more code.

1. Feedbacks that return a new geometry. The interfaces for these objects have a *Stop* method that returns the new geometry. These objects are *NewEnvelopeFeedback*, *NewBezierCurveFeedback*, *New-DimensionFeedback*, *NewLineFeedback*, *NewPolygonFeedback*, *Modify-DimensionFeedback*, *MoveEnvelopeFeedback*, *MoveLineFeedback*, *MovePointFeedback*, *MovePolygonFeedback*, *BezierMovePointFeedback*, *LineMovePointFeedback*, *PolygonMovePointFeedback*, *Reshape-Feedback*, *ResizeEnvelopeFeedback*, and *StretchLineFeedback*.

2. Feedbacks that are for display purposes only. The developer is required to calculate the new geometry. For example, you can use the start and end mouse locations and calculate the delta x and delta y shifts, and then you can update or create the geometry from this. These feedback objects are *MoveGeometryFeedback*, *MoveImageFeedback*, *NewMulti-PointFeedback*, and *VertexFeedback*.

Most of the interfaces contained in the display feedback objects are derived from the IDisplayFeedback interface.

The objects are used within the ArcMap application to allow graphic elements to be digitized and modified within the map (data view) and layout (layout view) and are also used by the ArcMap feature editing tools.

Some of the feedback objects have a *Constraint* property that determines how the feedback behaves. These constraints can specify, for example, that a *ResizeEnvelopeFeedback* maintains the aspect ratio of the input *Envelope*. The details of these constraints are given with the individual feedbacks.

IDisplayFeedback : IUnknown	Provides access to members that control the base display feedback.
—□ Display: IScreenDisplay	The display the feedback object will use.
■—□ Symbol: ISymbol	The symbol the feedback object will use.
◄— MoveTo (in Point: IPoint)	Move to the new point.
◄— Refresh (in hDC: Long)	Call this after a refresh to show feedback again.

The *IDisplayFeedback* interface is used to define the common operations on all of the display feedback operations. These include moving, symbolizing, and refreshing the display feedbacks as well as setting a display feedback object's *Display* property (for example, setting it to *IActiveView::ScreenDisplay*).

The *IDisplayFeedback* interface is useful only in combination with one of the display feedback objects and its derived interfaces, for example, the *NewPolygonFeedback* object and its *INewPolygonFeedback* interface. Nearly all of the display feedback interfaces employ interface inheritance from *IDisplayFeedback*; hence, there is no need to use *QueryInterface* to access its methods and properties.

Typically, the *Display* and *Symbol* properties would be set when a display feedback object is initialized, while the *MoveTo* method would be called in a mouse move event. Setting the *Symbol* property is optional. If not set, a default symbol is used.

The *Refresh* method is used to redraw the feedback after the window has been refreshed (for example, when it is activated again), and it should be called in response to the *Tool's Refresh* event. This would be *UIToolControl_Refresh* for *UIToolControl* in VBA, or *ITool_Refresh* if you are implementing *ITool* in VB or VC++. The *hDC* parameter, which is required by the *Refresh* method, is actually passed into the subroutine for you.

In the following example, a check is first made to see if *m_pNewPolyFeedback*, which is a member variable *NewPolygonFeedback* object, has been instantiated yet, that is, if the user is currently using the feedback. If it has been instantiated, then the *Refresh* method is called.

```
Private Sub UIToolControl_Refresh(byVal hDC As Long)
  If Not m_pNewPolyFeedback Is Nothing Then
    m_pNewPolyFeedback.Refresh hDC
  End If
End Sub
```

The following code example shows how to use the *IDisplayFeedback* interface with the *INewEnvelopeFeedback* interface to create a display feedback that will allow the user to add a new polygon. Note that this code simply demonstrates the visual feedback; further code is required if you wish to add that drawn shape as a map element or feature.

The new envelope feedback object is declared as a member variable as follows:

```
Private pNewEnvFeed As INewEnvelopeFeedback
```

Other objects are locally declared—*pEnv* as *IEnvelope*, *pScreenDisp* as *IScreenDisplay*, *pLineSym* as *ISimpleLineSymbol*, and *pStartPoint* and *pMovePoint* as *IPoint*.

The following code would be placed in the *Mouse_Down* event to set up the *Display* and *Symbol* properties and to call *INewEnvelopeFeedback::Start* with the current mouse location in map units.

```
Set pNewEnvFeed = new NewEnvelopeFeedback
Set pNewEnvFeed.Display = pScreenDisp
Set pNewEnvFeed.Symbol = pLineSym
pNewEnvFeed.Start pStartPoint
```

The following line of code would be placed in the *Mouse_Move* event to move the display feedback to the current mouse location in map units, using the *MoveTo* method from *IDisplayFeedback*.

```
pNewEnvFeed.MoveTo pMovePoint
```

The following line of code would be placed in the *Mouse_Up* event to return the result using the *Stop* method from *INewEnvelopeFeedback*.

```
Set pEnv = pNewEnvFeed.Stop
```

The *NewLineFeedback, NewBezierCurveFeedback,* and *NewPolygonFeedback* coclasses would normally be used in a similar way. To form one of these new geometries, the user would use the mouse to click on the shape's starting point, move to a new location, click for any intermediate vertices, then move to the endpoint and double-click to finish. Therefore, to support this behavior, three different mouse events—*Mouse_Down, Mouse_Move,* and *Mouse_DblClick*—would be handled. An outline of how the feedback's methods typically relate to these events is given below.

- *Mouse_Down—Start* adds the starting *Point,* or *Addpoint,* which adds subsequent *Points* and *Segments.*

- *Mouse_Move—MoveTo* is inherited from *IDisplayFeedback,* which moves the feedback onscreen.

- *Mouse_DblClick—Stop* returns the resulting single-part shape. For *NewLineFeedback* and *NewBezierCurveFeedback,* this would be a *Polyline* with one *Path.* For *NewPolygonFeedback,* this would be a *Polygon* with one *Ring.*

When the *Mouse_DblClick* event is fired, the *Mouse_Down* event is also fired only once, thus by simply clicking, moving, then double-clicking the mouse, a user will actually be firing *Mouse_Down* (*Start*), *Mouse_Move* (*MoveTo*), *Mouse_Down* (*AddPoint*), and *Mouse_DblClick* (*Stop*). Therefore, assuming that the convention shown above is used, a point will be added at the double-click location by the *Mouse_Down* event, even though the *Stop* method does not itself add a new point to the geometry.

The *NewLineFeedback* coclass allows the user to form a new *Polyline* geometry on the display. While the feedback is being used, the line shown on the screen is a series of segments made up of straight lines between each of the points clicked by the user. If the user opts to add no intermediate vertices, that is, they simply click at the start point (*Start*), move the mouse (*MoveTo*), and double-click at the end (*AddPoint* and *Stop*), then a polyline with only one segment will be generated.

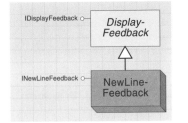

The new line feedback can be used to create a new single-part polyline object with as many vertices and segments as required.

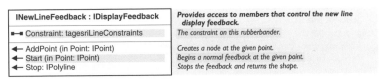

INewLineFeedback : IDisplayFeedback	Provides access to members that control the new line display feedback.
▪— Constraint: tagesriLineConstraints	The constraint on this rubberbander.
← AddPoint (in Point: IPoint)	Creates a node at the given point.
← Start (in Point: IPoint)	Begins a normal feedback at the given point.
← Stop: IPolyline	Stops the feedback and returns the shape.

This coclass uses *INewLineFeedback* to *Start, Stop, AddPoints,* and optionally apply a movement constraint. All other functionality is accessed through *IDisplayFeedback.*

The *Constraint* property is not functional at ArcGIS 8.1.

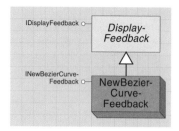

The new Bézier curve feedback can be used to create a new single-path polyline object in a similar manner to the new line feedback. The segments of this polyline will be Bézier curves rather than simple line segments.

The *NewBezierCurveFeedback* coclass behaves in the same basic way as a *NewLineFeedback* in that the user is required to digitize a start point and endpoint, as well as any intermediate vertices. However, the difference is the geometry of the line that is first displayed and then returned by the feedback.

In a case where the same user input was supplied for both a *NewLineFeedback* and a *NewBezierCurveFeedback*, both return geometries would be *PolyLine* objects with the same vertices. However, the segments forming these *Polyline* objects would be of type *Line* and *BezierCurve*, respectively.

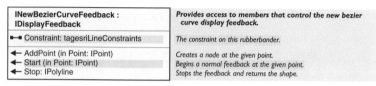

INewBezierCurveFeedback : IDisplayFeedback	Provides access to members that control the new bezier curve display feedback.
▪─■ Constraint: tagesriLineConstraints	The constraint on this rubberbander.
◀— AddPoint (in Point: IPoint)	Creates a node at the given point.
◀— Start (in Point: IPoint)	Begins a normal feedback at the given point.
◀— Stop: IPolyline	Stops the feedback and returns the shape.

Enumeration tagesriLineConstraints	ESRI line constraint.
0 - esriLineConstraintsNone	No line constraint.
1 - esriLineConstraintsVertical	Constrain line to vertical.
2 - esriLineConstraintsHorizontal	Constrain line to horizontal.

INewBezierCurveFeedback is used to *Start*, *Stop*, and *AddPoints* to a *NewBezierCurveFeedback* object. *Constraint* is not yet implemented at ArcGIS 8.1.

The use and behavior of the *NewPolygonFeedback* is again similar to the *NewLineFeedback*; however, the geometry that is displayed and returned is a closed *Polygon*. This means that when *Stop* is called, the start point will be added again as the finish point, thus closing the shape. At least three points should be added to the Feedback. *AddPoint* must be called a minimum of twice after the first point has been added using *Start*; otherwise a *Null Pointer* (*Nothing* in VB) is returned.

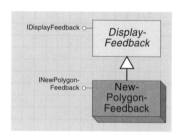

The new polygon feedback is used to create a new polygon in the same way as NewLineFeedback. The feedback will automatically close the polygon by adding a segment to join the first and last points entered.

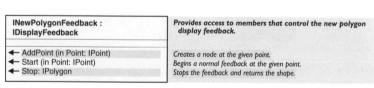

INewPolygonFeedback : IDisplayFeedback	Provides access to members that control the new polygon display feedback.
◀— AddPoint (in Point: IPoint)	Creates a node at the given point.
◀— Start (in Point: IPoint)	Begins a normal feedback at the given point.
◀— Stop: IPolygon	Stops the feedback and returns the shape.

Start, *Stop*, and *AddPoint* are the only three methods on this interface. *Start* will add the first point, while *AddPoint* will add subsequent points and segments, and *Stop* will return a *Polygon* if valid input, as described above, has been given.

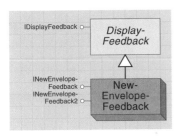

The new envelope feedback is perhaps the most useful and simplest of the feedbacks. It is used to allow the user to create a new envelope on the display, known as "dragging a rectangle".

The way in which INewEnvelopeFeedback2's methods would typically relate to mouse events is given below.

MouseDown—Start (adds first corner point)

MouseMove—MoveTo (inherited from IDisplayFeedback, moves the feedback onscreen)

MouseUp—Stop (returns the resulting geometry)

INewEnvelopeFeedback2 supersedes INewEnvelopeFeedback since it takes into consideration cases where the map's display is rotated. It does this by returning a rectangular IPolygon instead of an IEnvelope when Stop is called— when used with a rotated display it will return a polygon with sides parallel to the axes of the DisplayTransformation.

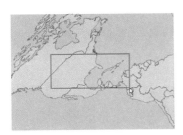

INewEnvelopeFeedback *being used to track a rectangle on a map display that is rotated by 45°*

In an application using the *NewEnvelopeFeedback* coclass, a user would typically define one corner of the envelope by pressing the mouse button down and then, while holding the mouse button down, move the mouse to the opposite corner and release it. This involves three events being handled (*Mouse_Down, Mouse_Move,* and *Mouse_Up*) and is a mechanism that is used in many areas with ArcMap, including the Zoom In, Zoom Out, and Select Features tools.

INewEnvelopeFeedback2 : IUnknown	Provides access to members that control the creation of a new envelope.
■—■ AspectRatio: Double	The aspect ratio for the custom constraint type.
■—■ Constraint: esriEnvelopeConstraints	The constraint on this rubberbander.
◄— Start (in Point: IPoint)	Begins a normal feedback at the given point.
◄— Stop: IGeometry	Stops the feedback and returns the shape.

INewEnvelopeFeedback2 has two methods, *Start* and *Stop,* and two properties, *AspectRatio* and *Constraint.* Other members, such as *Display, MoveTo,* and *Symbol,* which are common to all of the feedbacks, are inherited from *IDisplayFeedback.*

Start begins the feedback operation and takes the starting mouse location, while *Stop* completes the operation.

The inherited *MoveTo* method should typically be called for each *MouseMove* event between *Start* and *Stop.*

When the *Stop* method is called, it will return an *IGeometry* representing a rectangular polygon, that is, a polygon with four segments in a rectangle.

The maximum and minimum of this rectangle come from the coordinates of the point given with *Start* and the point from the last *MoveTo* method to be called. As a result, if *MoveTo* is never called, then an empty geometry will be returned; the *IsEmpty* property from *IGeometry* will return *True.*

The *Constraint* property allows you to specify how the feedback will behave and whether or not the feedback is forced to have a particular shape. The default value is zero, or no constraint.

If *esriEnvelopeConstraintsSquare* is applied, the feedback will be drawn with its width equal to its height, and only vertical movement of the mouse will affect the feedback's shape.

Alternatively, if *esriEnvelopeConstraintsAspect* is used, the feedback will be drawn using the current aspect ratio. In this case, if *AspectRatio* is greater than 1, only horizontal movement of the mouse will affect the feedback's shape, while if *AspectRatio* is less than or equal to 1, then the feedback's shape will be altered by vertical mouse movement only.

The *Constraint* property can be set at any time but will not have any effect until *MoveTo* is called.

Display

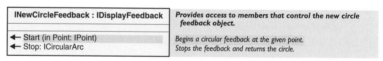

Enumeration tagesriEnvelopeConstraints	ESRI envelope constraint.
0 - esriEnvelopeConstraintsNone	No envelope constraint.
1 - esriEnvelopeConstraintsSquare	Constrain envelope to square.
2 - esriEnvelopeConstraintsAspect	Constrain envelope aspect ratio.

AspectRatio sets or returns the width to height ratio of a feedback that has an *AspectRatio* constraint, *esriEnvelopeConstraintsAspect*. *AspectRatio* is calculated as width divided by height, the default value is 1 (square), and it can only be altered by using the *AspectRatio* property.

For example, if you wished to constrain your feedback to show an envelope that is three times as long as it is high, you would first set the feedback's *AspectRatio* property to three, then set its *Constraint* property to *esriEnvelopeConstraintsAspect*. Note that this property is only useful with feedbacks that have their *Constraint* property set to *esriEnvelopeConstraintsAspect*; it will not set or return the aspect ratio of a feedback that has a constraint property set to either *esriEnvelopeConstraintsNone* or *esriEnvelopeConstraintsSquare*.

The *NewCircleFeedback* allows the user to create a circular geometry on the display. Typically, this would be done by clicking at the point where the circle's center is to be and then moving the mouse to specify the circle's radius.

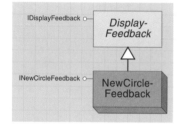

The new circle feedback is used to drag a Circle on the display by specifying a center point and a radius. It returns an ICircularArc.

INewCircleFeedback : IDisplayFeedback	Provides access to members that control the new circle feedback object.
← Start (in Point: IPoint)	Begins a circular feedback at the given point.
← Stop: ICircularArc	Stops the feedback and returns the circle.

This very simple interface has only two methods of its own: *Start* and *Stop*. Like the other feedback interfaces, all other functionality is inherited from *IDisplayFeedback*. The *Start* method is used to specify the circle's center point, and *Stop* returns a new *ICircularArc*. The radius of the circle created depends on the distance between the *Start* point and the last point used in the inherited *MoveTo* method.

Note that the *ICircularArc*, which is returned from *Stop*, can be converted into an *IPolygon* by creating a new *Polygon* object, then adding the *ICircularArc* using the *AddSegment* method on the *ISegmentCollection* interface.

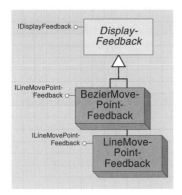

BezierMovePoint-Feedback *and* Line-MovePointFeedback *allow a vertex within an existing polyline object to be moved interactively and the line to be updated with the new vertex and segments. The updated segments will either be* Line *or* BezierCurve *objects depending on the coclass used.*

The *BezierMovePointFeedback* and *LineMovePointFeedback* coclasses allow the individual vertex of a *Polyline* object to be interactively moved on the display. They take an input *Polyline* and return a copy altered with the new vertex location. When the feedback is moved, the new vertex location is drawn along with the new locations of the adjacent segments—the type of segment used varies depending on which coclass is used.

With the *LineMovePointFeedback* object, these segments are simple *Line* objects, while with the *BezierMovePointFeedback* object, these segments are *BezierCurve* objects. This difference affects both the way in which the feedback is drawn and the returned geometry. Both of these coclasses use the *ILineMovePointFeedback* interface to *Start* and *Stop* the feedback. This interface inherits from *IDisplayFeedback*, which it uses for all other behavior.

ILineMovePointFeedback : IDisplayFeedback	Provides access to members that control the line move point display feedback.
← Start (in Polyline: IPolyline, in pointIndex: Long, in Point: IPoint)	Begins a move point feedback of the given shape. PointIndex is a zero based index into the polyline.
← Stop: IPolyline	Stops the feedback and returns the shape.

This interface is implemented by both *LineMovePointFeedback* and *BezierMovePointFeedback*. The *Start* method is used to initiate the feedback operations, taking the input polyline, the index of the vertex to be moved, and the starting point (mouse location from which to calculate the movement). If the vertex index is invalid, then an error will be raised. Each time *MoveTo* is called, the vertex in question will be positioned at the *MoveTo* point, and the segments immediately adjacent to the vertex will also be redrawn. As stated above, the type of segments that are created, and therefore the way in which these segments both move and are drawn, depend on the coclass being used.

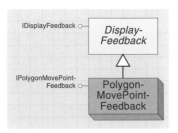

Like the *LineMovePointFeedback* and *BezierMovePointFeedback* coclasses, the *PolygonMovePointFeedback* coclass allows the user to move a vertex within an existing geometry—in this case, the geometry is a polygon. When the vertex is moved, the two adjoining segments are moved to use the new vertex location and are redrawn as lines.

The polygon move point feedback is for use with an existing polyline or polygon geometry. This feedback allows an individual point (vertex) to be moved along with its connecting segments.

IPolygonMovePointFeedback : IDisplayFeedback	Provides access to members that control the polygon move point display feedback.
← Start (in Polygon: IPolygon, in pointIndex: Long, in Point: IPoint)	Begins a move point feedback of the given shape. PointIndex is a zero based index into the polygon.
← Stop: IPolygon	Stops the feedback and returns the shape.

The *IPolygonMovePointFeedback* interface is very similar to *ILineMovePointFeedback*. It is used to start the feedback, which requires an input polygon, vertex index, and start location. It has a *Stop* method that stops the feedback and returns the new polygon geometry.

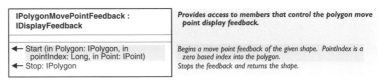

Display

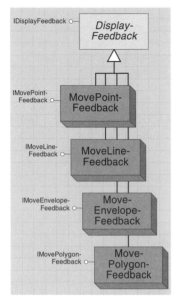

The feedbacks *MovePointFeedback, MoveLineFeedback, MoveEnvelopeFeedback,* and *MovePolygonFeedback* are used for moving existing geometries without altering their shapes. The geometries are offset from the current position, but no relative coordinates are altered.

Each of these feedbacks implements its own interface; these interfaces are very similar to one another among this set of feedbacks.

Each interface has two methods, *Start* and *Stop*, but like the other feedback interfaces, they make use of the methods and properties inherited from *IDisplayFeedback*, such as *MoveTo* and *Display*.

To *Start* a feedback requires an input shape, which is a geometry object of the correct type, and a starting mouse location, which is a *Point* object.

Each time *MoveTo* is called, the feedback draws a wireframe representation of the geometry, which is offset from the input shape by the difference between the starting location of the mouse and current location of the mouse.

When *Stop* is called, a new object is returned, which is the geometry of the wireframe drawn by the previous *MoveTo*.

The move point, line, envelope, and polygon feedbacks are used to allow users to move a geometry on the display. Upon completion, the feedback objects will return a copy of the moved shape.

These are the interfaces for moving entire geometries:

The *IMovePointFeedback* interface is used for moving points.

Applying the move point feedback

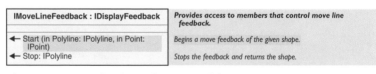

The *IMoveLineFeedback* interface is used for moving lines.

Applying the move line feedback

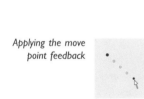

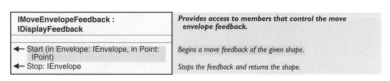

The *IMoveEnvelopeFeedback* interface is used for moving rectangles.

Applying the move envelope feedback

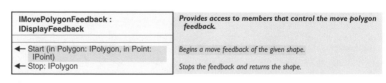

The *IMovePolygonFeedback* interface is used for moving polygons.

Applying the move polygon feedback

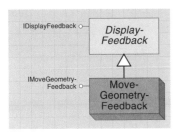

Allows multiple geometry objects of different types to be displayed and moved at the same time. This feedback is for display purposes only, and no objects are returned upon completion.

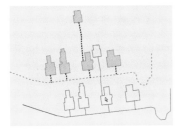

The feedback display from moving multiple geometries

You can use a *MoveGeometryFeedback* to interactively move multiple geometry objects on the display at the same time. Each geometry that is added to the feedback is drawn using a wireframe and is moved (along with any other geometry objects that have been added) in a similar way to the individual "Move" feedbacks, such as *MovePointFeedback* and *MoveLineFeedback*.

The objects that are added to the feedback may have different *GeometryTypes* so that a *Point* object may be moved along with *Polygon* objects and *Envelope* objects. However, the behavior of the feedback differs from the simple "Move" feedbacks since it does not return a new object on completion. Therefore, if you wished to move the elements' or features' geometries, you would have to calculate the offset of the feedback (difference between the start and end mouse locations) and apply this offset to each of the geometries in turn.

For example, this could be done by caching the starting mouse location, comparing this to the final mouse location to calculate the delta x and delta y, and moving each of the geometries in question using the *Move* method on the *ITransform2d* interface.

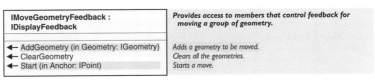

IMoveGeometryFeedback : IDisplayFeedback	Provides access to members that control feedback for moving a group of geometry.
← AddGeometry (in Geometry: IGeometry)	Adds a geometry to be moved.
← ClearGeometry	Clears all the geometries.
← Start (in Anchor: IPoint)	Starts a move.

IMoveGeometryFeedback is implemented by the *MoveGeometryFeedback* coclass and has three methods, *AddGeometry*, *Start*, and *ClearGeometry*. Other functionality is handled by the inherited *IDisplayFeedback* interface and its members, *MoveTo*, *Refresh*, *Display*, and *Symbol*.

AddGeometry is used to add an *IGeometry* to an existing *MoveGeometryFeedback* and should be called for each geometry object that you wish to include in the feedback operation.

Start begins the feedback process, taking a starting anchor point (*IPoint*). This anchor point is used to calculate the delta x and delta y offset the first time *MoveTo* is called—subsequent offsets being calculated using the current and previous *MoveTo* points. Geometries cannot be added after *Start* has been called.

ClearGeometry simply removes any previously added geometries from the feedback but does not remove the feedback itself.

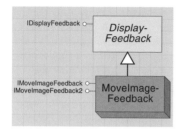

The move image feedback allows the creation of a feedback that shows map elements (or features) being moved along with their symbolization by drawing these objects into an offscreen display and then drawing this display each time the feedback is moved to a new location.

Care should be taken when using the Display property since there is also a Display property on the inherited IDisplayFeedback interface that serves a very different purpose. In order to access the Display property for the IDisplayFeedback interface, you should explicitly QI for that interface; otherwise, it will default to the IMoveImageFeedback version of the property.

IMoveImageFeedback2 supersedes IMove-ImageFeedback since it has all of the methods and properties provided by the original interface as well as providing one additional property itself.

The *MoveImageFeedback* coclass is used to interactively move a symbolized version of a geometry or geometries on the display. The feedback has its own offscreen display into which you can draw your symbolized geometries. Each time the feedback is moved, this offscreen display is drawn centered at the new location. This means that to the user, the geometries will appear to be moving, for example, a *Tree* or a *Pipe* rather than simply a *Point* or a *Line*. Features, map elements, and selections may all be added to the feedback.

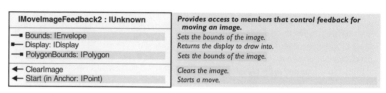

IMoveImageFeedback2 is implemented by the *MoveImageFeedback* coclass, and it has three properties, *Display*, *Bounds*, and *PolygonBounds* and two methods, *Start* and *ClearImage*.

Display is a Get property that allows access to the feedback's offscreen display. When a new *MoveImageFeedback* is created, it automatically creates a new one of these displays—it is to this that the various things to be moved (elements, features, and others) are drawn.

The feedback's offscreen display can be accessed as shown below, where *pDisp* is an object declared as *IDisplay* and *pMvImageFeed* is an *IMoveImageFeedback*.

```
Set pDisp = pMvImageFeed.Display
```

Then, the mechanism for drawing to this display depends on what is to be drawn.

For map elements, the *Draw* method on the *IElement* interface may be used as follows, where *pDrawElem* is an *IElement* that you wish to add to the feedback:

```
pDrawElem.Draw pDisp, Nothing
```

For features, it is slightly more complex since a *Symbol* should be provided and a *QI* will be required for *IFeatureDraw* on the *Feature* so that the *Draw* method may be called. In the following code example, *pFeat* is an *IFeature* that is to be added to the feedback.

```
Dim pFeatDraw As IFeatureDraw
Dim pSimpleFillSym As ISimpleFillSymbol
Set pSimpleFillSym = New SimpleFillSymbol
Set pFeatDraw = pFeat
pFeatDraw.Draw 1, pDisp, pSimpleFillSym, False, Nothing, esriDSNormal
```

The *Bounds* and *PolygonBounds* properties define the area to be covered by the feedback on the screen when the feedback operation begins. These are also used to determine the size of the offscreen display in map units. These two properties serve a similar purpose, so only one or the other should be used.

Bounds is the more simplistic of the two since it expects the input bounds as an *IEnvelope* and is therefore less suited for a situation where the map display is rotated.

PolygonBounds effectively supersedes *Bounds* and takes an *IPolygon*, thus allowing the bounds of geometries to be used, even if they are rotated.

For situations where multiple geometries are to be added to the feedback, the shapes or envelopes of these can be combined in a union to create a larger polygon or envelope that covers all of them. If neither of these properties is set, then an offscreen display will be created that corresponds in size to the whole of the *Map* object's *Display*; this may adversely affect performance and therefore is not recommended.

IMoveImageFeedback2 supersedes *IMoveImageFeedback* since it has all of the methods and properties provided by the original interface as well as providing one additional property itself.

Start begins the feedback operation. It should be called once all of the drawing has been done to the feedback's display. Once *Start* has been called, the feedback can be moved using the inherited *MoveTo* method, which causes it to be redrawn at a new location.

The *ClearImage* method clears the offscreen display of the *MoveImageFeedback* object. Once this has been called, the feedback will no longer be visible but will still accept *MoveTo* requests. It is often used in combination with the inherited *Refresh* method, which is useful if the user has cancelled the feedback operation (for example, by pressing the Esc key) or when the feedback operation is complete.

The following code shows how a *MoveImageFeedback* might be used to show the movement of an *IElement* using the *MouseDown* and *MouseMove* events of a *UIToolControl*. This code does not actually move the element itself—this could be done in the *MouseUp* event by comparing the start and finish mouse locations to calculate the delta x and delta y and using the *Move* method on the *IGraphicElement* interface.

These objects are member variables: *m_pMvImageFeed* as *IMoveImageFeedback*. The feedback itself, *m_pSelElem* As *IElement*, is assumed to be a valid element that you wish to show in the feedback, such as from the ActiveView's *BasicGraphicsLayer*.

```
Private Sub UIToolControl1_MouseDown(ByVal button As Long, _
  ByVal shift As Long, ByVal x As Long, ByVal y As Long)
 Dim pPnt As IPoint ' The current mouse location in map units
 Dim pMXDoc As IMxDocument ' The current document
 Dim pEnvBnds As IEnvelope ' Bounds of the element (including symbology)
 Dim pDispFeed As IDisplayFeedback, pDisp As IDisplay
 Set pMXDoc = ThisDocument ' QI for the MXDocument interface

 ' Transform the current mouse location into map coordinates
 Set pPnt = _
 pMXDoc.ActiveView.ScreenDisplay.DisplayTransformation.ToMapPoint(x, y)
```

Display

```
                        ' Create a new feedback object
                        Set m_pMvImageFeed = New MoveImageFeedback

                        ' QI for the IDisplayFeedback interface (because of ambiguity between
                        ' the Display property of IMoveImageFeedback and IDisplayFeedback)
                        Set pDispFeed = m_pMvImageFeed

                        ' Use this interface to set the Display property to point to the
                        ' ActiveView's Screendisplay
                        Set pDispFeed.Display = pMXDoc.ActiveView.ScreenDisplay

                        ' Now we can get a handle on the new feedback's Display. This display is
                        ' then used to draw the element into (causing the element to be drawn
                        ' when moving the feedback)
                        Set pDisp = m_pMvImageFeed.Display

                        ' Create a new envelope and use this to get the element's bounds
                        ' (includes symbology) based upon the feedback's display
                        Set pEnvBnds = New Envelope
                        m_pSelElem.QueryBounds pDisp, pEnvBnds
                        m_pMvImageFeed.Bounds = pEnvBnds ' Set the feedback's bounds
                        m_pSelElem.Draw pDisp, Nothing ' Draw the element into off-screen display
                        m_pMvImageFeed.Start pPnt ' Start at the current mouse location
                    End Sub

                    Private Sub UIToolControl1_MouseMove(ByVal button As Long, _
                      ByVal shift As Long, ByVal x As Long, ByVal y As Long)

                        ' Check that we are using a feedback
                        If Not m_pMvImageFeed Is Nothing Then
                          Dim pPnt As IPoint
                          Dim pMXDoc As IMxDocument
                          Set pMXDoc = ThisDocument ' QI for the MXDocument Interface

                          ' Transform the current mouse location into map coordinates
                          Set pPnt = _
                          pMXDoc.ActiveView.ScreenDisplay.DisplayTransformation.ToMapPoint(x, y)
                          m_pMvImageFeed.MoveTo pPnt ' Move the feedback to the current location
                        End If
                    End Sub
```

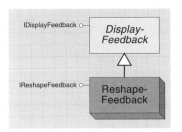

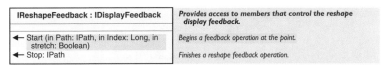

The reshape feedback reshapes an IPath by either rotating and shifting the whole shape or just the segments adjacent to a given vertex.

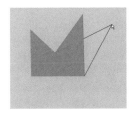

Reshaping feedback with the stretch option set

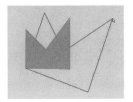

Reshaping feedback with the stretch option off

The *ReshapeFeedback* allows the user to reshape an object that supports the *IPath* interface. Such objects are the *Path* and *Ring* objects, which can represent one part of a *Polyline* or *Polygon*, respectively. The reshaping process can behave in two quite separate ways depending on how the *stretch* parameter is set.

IReshapeFeedback : IDisplayFeedback	*Provides access to members that control the reshape display feedback.*
← Start (in Path: IPath, in Index: Long, in stretch: Boolean)	*Begins a feedback operation at the point.*
← Stop: IPath	*Finishes a reshape feedback operation.*

The *IReshapeFeedback* interface has two methods, *Start* and *Stop*.

The *Start* method takes the input geometry as an *IPath*, the index of the vertex that is being used, and a Boolean describing how the feedback should behave. The *Stop* method returns an *IPath*, which is a new object.

Both *Path* and *Ring* objects, which represent single parts of *Polyline* objects and *Polygon* objects, respectively, support the *IPath* interface. Therefore, the object underlying the returned *IPath* will be either a *Ring* or a *Path*, depending on the input object's class. Like the other feedback interfaces, *IReshapeFeedback* inherits from *IDisplayFeedback*, which it uses for moving, refreshing, symbolizing, and setting up the display. The behavior of the feedback depends on the combined factors of vertex index, stretch parameter, and whether the input object is a *Path* or a *Ring*.

If stretching is set (a *True* value for the *Stretch* parameter) then the whole shape may be scaled or rotated by the feedback and all of the segments may be altered. Conversely, if *Stretch* is *False*, then only one vertex and its adjacent segments may be altered. If stretching is used, then the shape is rotated and/or scaled around the start and endpoints of the path. For a *Ring,* these two points will be coincident and the shape can therefore only undergo a translation—it will maintain its relative shape. For a *Path*, however, this may not be the case and, as a result, the shape may become transformed or have its actual "shape" changed.

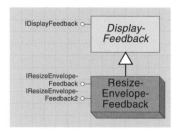

The resize envelope feedback is used for resizing an existing Envelope *object. Use the* ResizeEdge *property to specify which edge or corner to move. Constraints may optionally be used to further control the behavior of the feedback.*

A *ResizeEnvelopeFeedback* is used for resizing an existing *IGeometry* that is either an *IEnvelope* or a (rectangular) *IPolygon*. These geometries can be resized by moving their edges and corners. The corner or edge to be moved by the feedback operation must be specified, and you can also optionally apply a movement constraint, such as forcing the feedback's shape to be square.

IResizeEnvelopeFeedback2 : IUnknown	Provides access to members that control the resize of an envelope.
▬■ AspectRatio: Double	The aspect ratio for the custom constraint type.
▬■ Constraint: tagesriEnvelopeConstraints	The constraint on this rubberbander.
▬■ ResizeEdge: tagesriEnvelopeEdge	The edge to rubberband.
◄ Start (in Envelope: IGeometry, in Point: IPoint)	Begins a resize feedback of the given shape.
◄ Stop: IGeometry	Stops the feedback and returns the shape.

The *IResizeEnvelopeFeedback2* interface has two methods, *Start* and *Stop*.

Start is used to begin the feedback operation onscreen; it takes the starting mouse location as an *IPoint* and an input geometry as either an *IEnvelope* or a rectangular *IPolygon* (an *IPolygon* with four segments and a rectangular shape).

The *Stop* method completes the operation and returns an *IGeometry* that represents a rectangular *Polygon* coclass. The interface also has three properties: *ResizeEdge, Constraint,* and *AspectRatio*.

Enumeration tagesriEnvelopeEdge	ESRI envelope edge location.
0 - esriEnvelopeEdgeTopLeft	Top left envelope edge.
1 - esriEnvelopeEdgeTopMiddle	Top middle envelope edge.
2 - esriEnvelopeEdgeTopRight	Top right envelope edge.
3 - esriEnvelopeEdgeMiddleLeft	Middle left envelope edge.
4 - esriEnvelopeEdgeMiddleRight	Middle right envelope edge.
5 - esriEnvelopeEdgeBottomLeft	Bottom left envelope edge.
6 - esriEnvelopeEdgeBottomMiddle	Bottom middle envelope edge.
7 - esriEnvelopeEdgeBottomRight	Bottom right envelope edge.

IResizeEnvelopeFeedback2 supersedes IResizeEnvelopeFeedback since it takes into consideration cases where either the map's display or the input geometry is rotated and allows the rotation of the input geometry to be maintained. As a result, some of the interfaces used as input and return types differ from those used in IResizeEnvelopeFeedback. For example, the Stop method returns an IGeometry representing an IPolygon, rather than an IEnvelope.

ResizeEdge simply allows you to specify which edge or corner is to be moved by the feedback.

The *Constraint* property allows you to specify how the feedback will behave and whether or not the feedback is forced to have a particular shape. The default value is no constraint, or *esriEnvelopeConstraintsNone*.

If *esriEnvelopeConstraintsSquare* is applied, the feedback will be drawn with its width equal to its height, and only vertical movements of the mouse will affect the feedback's shape.

Alternatively, if *esriEnvelopeConstraintsAspect* is used, the feedback will be drawn, maintaining the aspect ratio of the input *IGeometry*. The *Constraint* property can be set at any time but will not have any effect until *MoveTo* is called. Note that the *AspectRatio* property is not fully implemented at this release, and therefore its value will not affect the feedback operation.

IResizeEnvelopeFeedback being used to resize a RectangleElement that is rotated by 60°

Enumeration tagesriEnvelopeConstraints	*ESRI envelope constraint.*
0 - esriEnvelopeConstraintsNone	*No envelope constraint.*
1 - esriEnvelopeConstraintsSquare	*Constrain envelope to square.*
2 - esriEnvelopeConstraintsAspect	*Constrain envelope aspect ratio.*

Like other feedback interfaces, *IResizeEnvelopeFeedback* inherits from *IDisplayFeedback* and uses that interface for common feedback functionality, such as symbolizing, moving, and setting the display property.

Display

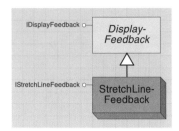

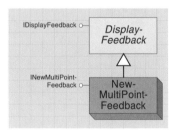

The stretch line feedback can be used to scale and rotate a polyline object about its FromPoint or ToPoint.

You can use a *StretchLineFeedback* object to scale or rotate an existing *Polyline* object. The scaling and rotation is done about an anchor point. The feedback is moved by shifting the nonanchored end of the polyline by the difference (delta x and delta y) between the current and original mouse locations. The whole polyline is moved to match up with this using a rigid stretch and, as a result, may be both scaled and rotated.

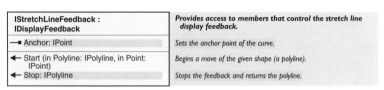

The *IStretchLineFeedback* interface has two methods, *Start* and *Stop*, and a write-only property, *Anchor*. Like other feedbacks, *Start* begins the feedback operation and takes an input *Polyline* object and a *Point*, which represents the starting mouse location in map units. *Stop* simply completes the feedback operation and returns a new *Polyline* object, which is a copy of the input that has been scaled and rotated as necessary.

The *Anchor* property is used to specify which end to use as the fixed point and can be set to either the *Polyline* object's *FromPoint* or *EndPoint*. If this property is not specified, then the default is to use the *FromPoint* as the anchor. The *Anchor* property should only be set after the *Start* method has been called. Other functionality is inherited from the *IDisplayFeedback* interface.

A *NewMultiPointFeedback*, unlike many other feedback objects, does not return a new geometry or alter the input geometry. Instead, it is used for visual feedback only and relies on you to update a geometry when appropriate. It takes a multipoint object as input and then, when *MoveTo* is called, it draws a line segment between the current mouse location and each of the points in the multipoint. It should not be confused with the other "New" feedbacks, such as *NewLineFeedback*, as it serves a very different purpose.

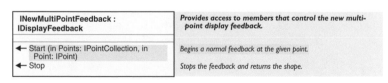

The new multipoint feedback draws a line between each point of multipoint and the mouse location.

INewMultiPointFeedback has only two methods, *Start* and *Stop*.

Start takes two input parameters: an object that supports *IMultipoint* and a starting location as an *IPoint*. When *Start* is called, a series of line segments are drawn onto the display, joining each point within the *IMultipoint* to the starting location. Each time *MoveTo* (inherited from *IDisplayFeedback*) is called, these lines are updated to join the multipoint points to the new mouse location. The *Stop* method does not return any objects but simply tells the feedback that operation is complete and to stop drawing and moving.

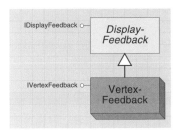

Vertex feedbacks are used to alter paths and rings by moving their vertices and any adjacent segments. Segments are added one by one with either their FromPoint or ToPoint as an anchor. Multiple segments, which may come from different geometry objects, can be moved at the same time. No geometry objects are returned on completion.

A *VertexFeedback* object allows one or more individual segments to be moved on the display by the user. Like the *NewMultiPointFeedback*, the *VertexFeedback* does not return an object at the end of the operation and is used for visual feedback only. The segments in question don't need to belong to the same geometry or even type of geometry. This allows, for example, a segment from a polygon to be moved along with some segments from a polyline or, alternatively, the moving of vertices (and segments) that are part of a shared polygon boundary.

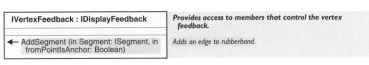

IVertexFeedback : IDisplayFeedback	*Provides access to members that control the vertex feedback.*
← AddSegment (in Segment: ISegment, in fromPointIsAnchor: Boolean)	*Adds an edge to rubberband.*

The *IVertexFeedback* interface has only one member, the *AddSegment* method, which adds the segments and specifies which end to use as the anchor point.

Each time *AddSegment* is called, a check is made to see if the segment has already been added; if it has, then it is not added a second time. The methods used to move, symbolize, refresh, and setup the display are accessed through the inherited *IDisplayFeedback* interface. Since there is no *Start* method, the first call to *MoveTo* will begin the feedback operation, that is, draw the feedback, and the feedback will be redrawn with each subsequent *MoveTo*. To finish the operation, the feedback object should be cleared and the display refreshed.

The following Visual Basic example shows how you can use the *IVertexFeedback* interface to move segments from two different *Polyline* geometries. *m_pVertexFeed* represents the feedback object itself and is a member variable declared as *IVertexFeedback*, so it can be accessed in all of the tool's mouse events. The code assumes that you already have two pairs of segments (one pair from each of polylines A and B) that you wish to add to the feedback. These are represented by *pLnASeg1*, *pLnASeg2, pLnBSeg1,* and *pLnBSeg2*, which are declared as *ISegment*.

The following code would be placed in a tool's *Mouse_Down* event to initiate the feedback operation.

```
Dim pMXDoc As IMxDocument
Dim pPnt As IPoint

' QI for the IMXDocument interface
Set pMXDoc = ThisDocument

' Get the current mouse location in Map Units
Set pPnt = _
    pMXDoc.ActiveView.ScreenDisplay.DisplayTransformation.ToMapPoint(x, y)

' Create a new VertexFeedback
Set m_pVertexFeed = New VertexFeedback

' Set the Feedback's display property (to the ActiveView's ScreenDisplay)
```

Display

```
Set m_pVertexFeed.Display = pMXDoc.ActiveView.ScreenDisplay

' Add the required segments to the feedback...
' Line A, Segment 1, using FromPt as anchor
m_pVertexFeed.AddSegment pLnASeg1, True
' Line A, Segment 2, using ToPt as anchor
m_pVertexFeed.AddSegment pLnASeg2, False

' Line B, Segment 1, using FromPt as anchor
m_pVertexFeed.AddSegment pLnBSeg1, True
' Line B, Segment 2, using ToPt as anchor
m_pVertexFeed.AddSegment pLnBSeg2, False

' Start the feedback operation by moving to the start point
m_pVertexFeed.MoveTo pPnt
```

The code below is used to move the feedback and should be placed in the *Mouse_Move* event of a tool.

```
If Not m_pVertexFeed Is Nothing Then ' Check that user is using feedback
    Dim pMXDoc As IMxDocument
    Dim pPnt As IPoint

    ' QI for the IMXDocument interface
    Set pMXDoc = ThisDocument
    ' Get the current mouse location in Map Units and move the feedback
    Set pPnt = _
        pMXDoc.ActiveView.ScreenDisplay.DisplayTransformation.ToMapPoint(x, y)
    m_pVertexFeed.MoveTo pPnt
End If
```

The *Mouse_Up* event of the tool would be used to complete the feedback operation using the following code:

```
If Not m_pVertexFeed Is Nothing Then 'Check that user is using feedback
    Dim pMXDoc As IMxDocument

    ' QI for the IMXDocument interface
    Set pMXDoc = ThisDocument

    ' Refresh the ActiveView
    pMXDoc.ActiveView.Refresh

    ' Clear feedback object
    Set m_pVertexFeed = Nothing
End If
```

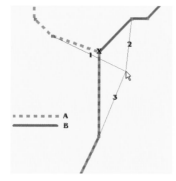

In this example, the user has hit point X, which is the endpoint of four different segments (two each from polylines A and B). Two of these segments are identical, while the other two are different.

The two different segments are both added to the feedback and become 1 and 2 in the feedback. Conversely, one of the duplicate segments is automatically rejected by AddSegment, the remaining one becoming 3 in the feedback object. This rejection is useful because if two identical segments were added, the feedback would not draw correctly. However, care should still be taken when adding segments that are the reverse of one another, as these will not be rejected.

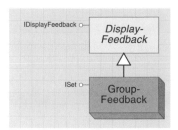

The group feedback is a special feedback that allows many different feedbacks to be controlled together. Any properties set or methods called through IDisplayFeedback are passed on to every member, thus reducing the amount of code.

The *GroupFeedback* is different from the other feedback objects—rather than being a feedback in its own right, it is simply a holder for one or more member *Feedback* objects.

The *GroupFeedback* supports the *ISet* interface, which allows these member feedbacks to be added, removed, found, and iterated through. All of the *Feedback* objects themselves support the *IDisplayFeedback*, which is used to handle common areas of functionality, such as refreshing, moving, and symbolizing. The *GroupFeedback* also supports the *IDisplayFeedback* interface, but when one of these methods or properties is called, the *GroupFeedback* simply passes this on to its member objects.

For example, if the *MoveTo* method was called on a *GroupFeedback*, then it would in turn call *MoveTo* on each of its member *Feedback* objects. This avoids having to call the method multiple times (once for each feedback) and can be very useful if two or more feedbacks are being used in conjunction—for example, if you wished to show two *Envelope* objects being resized simultaneously or to move a vertex that was shared by multiple geometries. The *Feedback* objects that can be added to the *GroupFeedback* should be instantiated before they are added.

The following code shows a new *GroupFeedback* being created along with two member feedbacks (a *NewLineFeedback* and a *NewBezierCurveFeedback*). The two member feedbacks are started individually and then added to the *GroupFeedback*, which is then used to collectively set up their *Display* and *Symbology* properties. This same mechanism could be used for applying the *MoveTo* method in the *MouseMove* event. In this code, *pPnt* is an *IPoint* representing the starting point in map units, and *pDisp* is an *IDisplay* representing the *ActiveView*'s *ScreenDisplay*.

```
Dim pGrpFeedDisp As IDisplayFeedback
Dim pGrpFeedSet As ISet
Dim pNewLineFeedback As INewLineFeedback
Dim pNewBzFeedback As INewBezierCurveFeedback

' Create a new GroupFeedback object (with the IDisplayFeedback interface)
Set pGrpFeedDisp = New GroupFeedback
Set pGrpFeedSet = pGrpFeedDisp ' QI for the ISet interface

' Create 2 new feedbacks to add to GroupFeedback
Set pNewLineFeedback = New NewLineFeedback
Set pNewBzFeedback = New NewBezierCurveFeedback
' Set the new member Feedback's StartPoints
pNewLineFeedback.Start pPnt
pNewBzFeedback.Start pPnt

' Add the new member Feedbacks to the GroupFeedback
pGrpFeedSet.Add pNewLineFeedback
pGrpFeedSet.Add pNewBzFeedback
Set pGrpFeedDisp.Display = pDisp
```

Display

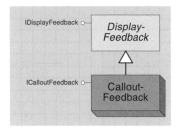

A callout feedback is used to modify a callout object. For example, you can modify the display of a TextElement by moving either the body of the callout or the AnchorPoint.

A callout is a graphic that may be drawn as a background behind a *TextElement*. The *Callout* may also have a leader line to an anchor point.

A *CalloutFeedback* may be used to move either the *Callout* itself or the *AnchorPoint*. It returns a *Polyline* representing the new outline of the callout. This *Polyline* can be useful; however, in order to move the *Callout*, it is simpler to calculate the shift in x and y between the start and endpoints of the feedback operation, then move the callout by the specified amount.

ICalloutFeedback : IDisplayFeedback	Callout feedback object.
← MoveAnchorTo (in Point: IPoint)	*Moves the anchor point to the given point.*
← Start (in Symbol: ISymbol, in Geometry: IGeometry, in Point: IPoint)	*Begins a feedback of the given symbol.*
← Stop: IPolyline	*Stops the feedback and returns the shape.*

The *ICalloutFeedback* interface has three methods: *Start, Stop,* and *MoveAnchorTo*, as well as all of those that it inherits from *IDisplayFeedback* Interface. As mentioned above, the *CalloutFeedback* can be used in two distinct ways—moving the *Callout* itself and moving the *AnchorPoint*.

Using a CalloutFeedback object to move the anchorpoint of a TextElement's Callout

The *Start* and *Stop* methods are used for both types of operation, while *MoveAnchorTo* is only used as an alternative to *MoveTo* when manipulating the *AnchorPoint*. Typically, an application detects whether or not a user has hit the *Callout* or its *AnchorPoint*, and this determines what operation is carried out.

The code below demonstrates how to use the *ICalloutFeedback* interface. The variables *m_pCalloutfeedback* and *m_PtStart* are declared as *ICalloutFeedback* and *IPoint*, respectively. *m_pSelElem* is declared as an *IElement* and represents a *TextElement* with an *IPoint* geometry and a *Callout* background that you wish to move. *m_BoolHitAnchor* represents a Boolean that specifies whether to move the *Callout* or the *AnchorPoint*.

Using a CalloutFeedback object to move the body of Callout box

```
Private Sub UIToolControl1_MouseDown(ByVal button As Long, _
    ByVal shift As Long, ByVal x As Long, ByVal y As Long)
  Dim pMxDoc As IMxDocument
  Dim pTxtElem As ITextElement
  Dim pGeom As IGeometry
  Dim pHitTest As IHitTest
  Dim pFormTextSym As IFormattedTextSymbol

  'Get the document's BasicGraphicsLayer
  Set pMxDoc = ThisDocument
  ' Get the current mouse location in Map Units
  Set m_PtStart = _
    pMxDoc.ActiveView.ScreenDisplay.DisplayTransformation.ToMapPoint(x, y)
  ' QI for ITextElement from IElement
  Set pTxtElem = m_pSelElem
  ' Get the TextSymbol and QI for IFormattedTextSymbol
  Set pFormTextSym = pTxtElem.Symbol
```

```
' Get the Element's geometry (either an IPoint or IPolyline)
Set pGeom = m_pSelElem.Geometry
' Create a new CalloutFeedback
Set m_pCalloutfeedback = New CalloutFeedback
'Set the feedback's display
Set m_pCalloutfeedback.Display = pMxDoc.ActiveView.ScreenDisplay
' Start the feedback, supplying the Callout's TextSymbol,
' Geometry and Starting location
m_pCalloutfeedback.Start pFormTextSym, pGeom, m_PtStart

End Sub

Private Sub UIToolControl1_MouseMove(ByVal button As Long, _
      ByVal shift As Long, ByVal x As Long, ByVal y As Long)
  If Not m_pCalloutfeedback Is Nothing Then
    Dim pPnt As IPoint
    Dim pMxDoc As IMxDocument

    ' QI for MXDocument
    Set pMxDoc = ThisDocument
    ' Get the current mouse location in Map Units and...
    Set pPnt = _
      pMxDoc.ActiveView.ScreenDisplay.DisplayTransformation.ToMapPoint(x, y)
    If m_BoolHitAnchor Then ' Move the AnchorPoint
      m_pCalloutfeedback.MoveAnchorTo pPnt
    Else ' Move the Feedback itself
      m_pCalloutfeedback.MoveTo pPnt
    End If
  End If
End Sub
```

The *MouseUp* event of the *UIToolControl* can be used to modify the
TextElement with the updated *Callout.*

Display

The following dimension feedback objects are used to create and modify *DimensionShape* objects. They are similar in some respects to other feedback objects, such as the *NewPolylineFeedback* and *PolygonMovePoint-Feedback*, but differ in other ways, including the following:

- The dimension feedback interfaces do not inherit from *IDisplay-Feedback*. Instead, the coclasses support this interface; therefore, a *QueryInterface* is required when moving between the interfaces.

- The dimension feedback objects and interfaces are useful only in creating modifying (dimension) *Features* in a *FeatureClass*.

- The dimension feedback objects require knowledge of dimension objects rather than of geometry objects; therefore, reference should be made to the section covering *IDimensionShape* in Volume 2, Chapter 9, 'Shaping features with geometry'.

The *NewDimensionFeedback* is used for creating new *DimensionShape* objects. It is shown as a dimension object, which changes dynamically as the mouse is moved. Also, the text for the dimension is updated with each movement to reflect the size of the dimension in map units.

The *NewDimensionFeedback* coclass supports the *INewDimensionFeedback* interface, which has members specifically used for creating dimensions. This coclass also supports the *IDisplayFeedback* interface, which it uses for general feedback operations, specifically the *Display* property and the *MoveTo* and *Refresh* methods. Unlike many other feedback interfaces, *INewDimensionFeedback* does not inherit from *IDisplayFeedback*, and so a *QueryInterface* is required when switching between both interfaces.

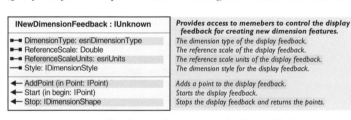

New dimension feedbacks allow the user to create a new DimensionShape object by entering points on the display using the mouse. As the points are entered, a representation of the dimension being created is shown on the display—this dimension is dynamically updated with each mouse movement or click, including the value of the dimension's text.

INewDimensionFeedback : IUnknown	Provides access to memebers to control the display feedback for creating new dimension features.
▪→ DimensionType: esriDimensionType	The dimension type of the display feedback.
▪→ ReferenceScale: Double	The reference scale of the display feedback.
▪→ ReferenceScaleUnits: esriUnits	The reference scale units of the display feedback.
→ Style: IDimensionStyle	The dimension style for the display feedback.
← AddPoint (in Point: IPoint)	Adds a point to the display feedback.
← Start (in begin: IPoint)	Starts the display feedback.
← Stop: IDimensionShape	Stops the display feedback and returns the points.

INewDimensionFeedback uses the *Start* method to add the *BeginDimensionPoint*, taking an *IPoint* in *MapUnits*. *AddPoint* should then be used for each subsequent point to be added.

Stop ends the feedback operation and returns an *IDimensionShape*, which can then be added to a *FeatureClass*.

The *DimensionType* property can be set to either aligned (the default) or linear. The type chosen affects the resulting geometry. The linear type constrains the angle of the dimension line to 0 or 90 degrees.

If the *DimensionType* is aligned (*esriDimensionTypeAligned*), then the required number of points is either two or three. The order in which the feedback expects these points to be added is *BeginDimensionPoint*, *EndDimensionPoint*, and optionally a *DimensionLinePoint* (to indicate the length of the extension lines).

Dimension type of esriDimensionTypeAligned

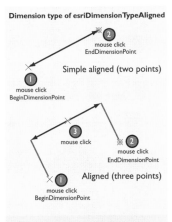

Simple aligned (two points)

Aligned (three points)

Dimension type of esriDimensionTypeLinear

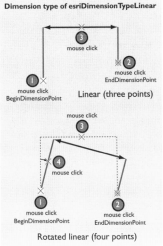

Linear (three points)

Rotated linear (four points)

For linear dimensions (*esriDimensionTypeLinear*), the required number of points is three. These are the *BeginDimensionPoint*, *EndDimensionPoint*, and *DimensionLinePoint*. Optionally, a fourth point may be added to represent the *ExtensionLineAngle*. If entered, this fourth point is taken in combination with the third point to calculate a new *DimensionLinePoint*—length of the extension line coming from the third point and the angle from the fourth.

The feedback's *ReferenceScale* and *ReferenceScaleUnits* properties determine at what map scale the text and symbology will be set (at which scale it will appear as intended). If this property is not set, then the reference scale of the *Map* will be used if set. If you are unable to see the symbology or text for your feedback, then it is likely that the reference scale properties are not correctly set.

Below is some VB code illustrating one method of creating a (simple) *LinearDimensionFeedback*. The code requires the *Mouse_Down* event to start the feedback (*BeginDimensionPoint*), *Mouse_Move* to move the feedback, and *Mouse_Down* again to complete the feedback (*EndDimensionPoint*). The variable *m_pNewDimFeed* is a member variable declared as an *INewDimensionFeedback*.

The following code should be placed in the *Mouse_Down* event of a *ITool* or *UIToolControl*.

```
Dim pPnt As IPoint
Dim pDispFeed As IDisplayFeedback
Dim pMXDoc As IMxDocument
Dim pDimShp As IDimensionShape


' QI for MXDocument
Set pMXDoc = ThisDocument
' Get the current mouse location in Map Units
Set pPnt = pMXDoc.ActiveView.ScreenDisplay. _
  DisplayTransformation.ToMapPoint(x, y)


' If user is not currently using the feedback then...
If m_pNewDimFeed Is Nothing Then
  ' Create a new NewDimensionFeedback object
  Set m_pNewDimFeed = New NewDimensionFeedback
  ' Set up the NewDimensionFeedback
  m_pNewDimFeed.DimensionType = esriDimensionTypeLinear
  m_pNewDimFeed.ReferenceScale = 100000
  m_pNewDimFeed.ReferenceScaleUnits = esriMeters
  ' QI for IDisplayFeedback
  Set pDispFeed = m_pNewDimFeed
  'Set the Feedback's Display
  Set pDispFeed.Display = pMXDoc.ActiveView.ScreenDisplay
  ' Then start at the current mouse location (BeginDimensionPoint)
  m_pNewDimFeed.Start pPnt
Else
  ' If the user is already using the feedback then...
  ' Add the current mouse location (EndDimensionPoint)
  m_pNewDimFeed.AddPoint pPnt
```

Display

```
                                 ' Stop the feedback and get the DimensionShape returned
                                 Set pDimShp = m_pNewDimFeed.Stop
                                 ' TODO: Now the result can be added to a Dimension FeatureClass
                                 ' Set the feedback to nothing for the next use
                                 Set m_pNewDimFeed = Nothing
                              End If
```

This code is for the *Mouse_Move* event.

```
    ' Check that the user is currently using the feedback
    If Not m_pNewDimFeed Is Nothing Then
        Dim pMXDoc As IMxDocument
        Dim pPnt As IPoint
        Dim pDispFeed As IDisplayFeedback

        ' QI for MXDocument
        Set pMXDoc = ThisDocument
        ' Get the current mouse location in map units
        Set pPnt = pMXDoc.ActiveView.ScreenDisplay _
        .DisplayTransformation.ToMapPoint(x, y)
        ' QI for IDisplayFeedback and use this to move the feedback
        Set pDispFeed = m_pNewDimFeed
        pDispFeed.MoveTo pPnt
    End If
```

The *Style* property takes and returns an *IDimensionStyle* that determines how the feedback should be drawn when it is being used. If this property is not set, the default style is used. Typically, if you were to set this property, you would set it to match the dimension style of the *FeatureClass* (if a feature class is being used). For example, the following function retrieves the default *DimensionStyle* for the *Editor*'s current layer.

```
Private Function GetFCDefaultStyle() As IDimensionStyle
    ' This function assumes that the current
    ' edit layer is a Dimension FeatureClass

    Dim pEditLyrs As IEditLayers
    Dim pFClass As IFeatureClass
    Dim pDimClassExt As IDimensionClassExtension
    Dim StyleId As Integer

    Set pEditLyrs = Application.FindExtensionByName("ESRI Object Editor")
    Set pFClass = pEditLyrs.CurrentLayer.FeatureClass
    Set pDimClassExt = pFClass.Extension
    StyleId = pDimClassExt.DimensionStyles.DefaultStyleID
    Set GetFCDefaultStyle = pDimClassExt.DimensionStyles.GetStyle(StyleId)
End Function
```

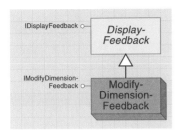

You can use a ModifyDimensionFeed-*back to change an existing* Dimension-*Shape by moving one of its handles:* BeginDimensionPoint, EndDimensionPoint, DimensionLinePoint, *or* TextPoint.

The *ModifyDimensionFeedback* coclass is similar to the *NewDimensionFeedback* in that it allows you to move a dynamic representation of a *Dimension* on the display and return the *DimensionShape* at the end of the operation. However, it differs in that it is used for editing an existing dimension shape object.

The *ModifyDimensionFeedback* coclass supports the *IModifyDimensionFeedback* and *IDisplayFeedback* interfaces and uses the latter for general feedback behavior—setting the *Display* and calling *MoveTo* and *Refresh*.

IModifyDimensionFeedback : IUnknown	Provides access to memebers to control the display feedback for modifying existing dimension features.
▪━▫ DimensionShape: IDimensionShape	The Dimension shape
▪━▪ DimensionType: esriDimensionType	The dimension type of the display feedback.
▪━▪ ReferenceScale: Double	The reference scale of the display feedback.
▪━▪ ReferenceScaleUnits: esriUnits	The reference scale units of the display feedback.
━▪ Style: IDimensionStyle	The dimension style for the display feedback.
◀━ GetHandles: IPointCollection	The display feedback's handles.
◀━ Start (in Handle: IPoint)	Starts the feedback
◀━ Stop: IDimensionShape	Stops the feedback and returns the points.

The *IModifyDimensionFeedback* shares several of the members of the *INewDimensionFeedback*, namely *DimensionType, ReferenceScale, ReferenceScaleUnits, Stop,* and *Style*. For information on these members, refer to the *INewDimensionFeedback* interface earlier in this chapter.

IModifyDimensionFeedback has the following members, which differ from *INewDimensionFeedback*: *DimensionShape, GetHandles,* and *Start*.

The *DimensionShape* property is used to specify the input dimension. It takes an *IDimensionShape* and needs to be set before starting the feedback operation.

Handle index	Meaning
0	BeginDimensionPoint
1	EndDimensionPoint
2	DimensionLinePoint
3	TextPoint

GetHandles returns an *IPointsCollection* representing all four of the editable points in the input *DimensionShape*. These points are the *BeginDimensionPoint, EndDimensionPoint, DimensionLinePoint,* and *TextPoint*. Note that this method can only be used once the *IDisplayFeedback::Display* property is set to a valid *IDisplay*.

The *Start* method allows the feedback method to commence and takes one of the *IPoint* objects from *GetHandles*. The behavior of the feedback depends on which member of the *PointsCollection* is used. For example, the following VB code fragment shows how a *ModifyDimensionFeedback* could be used to move the *EndDimensionPoint* of an existing *DimensionShape* by using the second *IPoint* returned from the *GetHandles* method.

The following code is extracted from the *Mouse_Down* event of a *UIToolControl* or *ITool*. *pModDimFeed* is a member variable declared as an *IModifyDimensionFeedback*, and *pDimShp* is locally declared as *IDimensionShape* representing an existing dimension that is being used as input to the feedback operation.

```
Dim pDispFeed As IDisplayFeedback
Dim pPtHndl As IPoint
```

Display

```
Dim pMXDoc As IMxDocument
' QI for IMXdocument
Set pMXDoc = ThisDocument

' Create a new ModifyDimensionFeedback
Set m_pModDimFeed = New ModifyDimensionFeedback

' Set the ReferenceScale, ReferenceScaleUnits
m_pModDimFeed.ReferenceScale = 100000
m_pModDimFeed.ReferenceScaleUnits = esriMeters

' Set the DimensionType, and input DimensionShape
m_pModDimFeed.DimensionType = esriDimensionTypeAligned
Set m_pModDimFeed.DimensionShape = m_pDimShp

' QI for the IDisplayFeedback and set the Display
Set pDispFeed = m_pModDimFeed
Set pDispFeed.Display = pMXDoc.ActiveView.ScreenDisplay

' Now get the second handle (EndDimensionPoint)
Set pPtHndl = m_pModDimFeed.GetHandles.Point(1)

' Start the feedback operation to move the EndDimensionPoint
m_pModDimFeed.Start pPtHndl
```

Like the *INewDimensionFeedback* example in the previous section, the *Mouse_Move* event of the tool would be used to move the feedback by calling *MoveTo* on the associated *IDisplayFeedback* interface, and the operation would be completed by calling the *Stop* method to return an *IDimensionShape* representing the new shape.

6

Directing map output

Larry Young

One of the primary tasks of a GIS professional is to make maps. The common requirement of these maps is to present information from geographic databases on a printed page. These printed maps range from large wall plots for display to smaller prints for inclusion into reports, magazines, and textbooks.

The ArcMap objects are used to display data and other information on the page; the Output objects are used to direct the information on that page to an output device or file.

This chapter discusses how to apply the Output objects to a hardcopy device—a plotter or printer—or to a file in formats such as JPEG, PostScript, and Enhanced Metafile. The two key Output objects are Printer, which supports output to hardcopy devices, and Exporter, which controls output to a file. Files are used when the goal is to incorporate that information into another document or Web page.

Printer objects

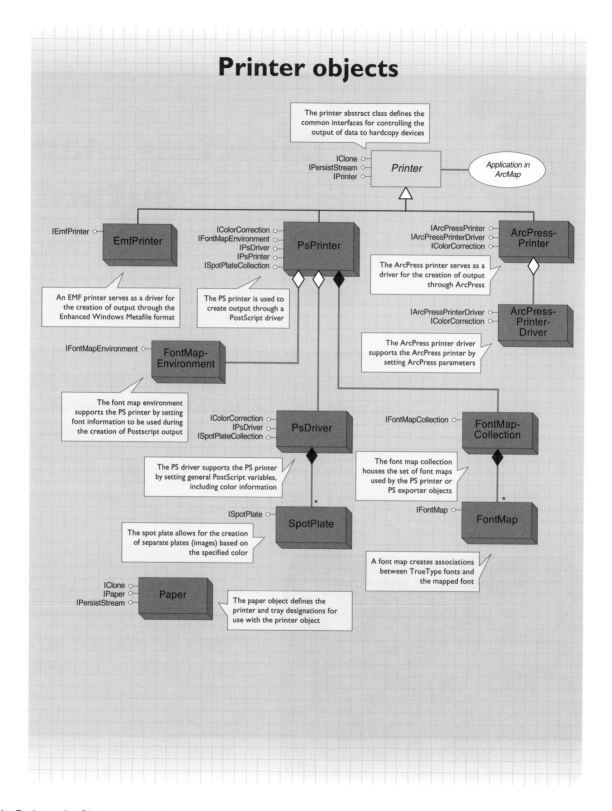

The printer abstract class defines the common interfaces for controlling the output of data to hardcopy devices

IClone
IPersistStream
IPrinter

Printer

Application in ArcMap

IEmfPrinter — **EmfPrinter**

IColorCorrection
IFontMapEnvironment
IPsDriver
IPsPrinter
ISpotPlateCollection

PsPrinter

IArcPressPrinter
IArcPressPrinterDriver
IColorCorrection

ArcPress-Printer

The ArcPress printer serves as a driver for the creation of output through ArcPress

An EMF printer serves as a driver for the creation of output through the Enhanced Windows Metafile format

The PS printer is used to create output through a PostScript driver

IArcPressPrinterDriver
IColorCorrection

ArcPress-Printer-Driver

IFontMapEnvironment — **FontMap-Environment**

The ArcPress printer driver supports the ArcPress printer by setting ArcPress parameters

The font map environment supports the PS printer by setting font information to be used during the creation of Postscript output

IColorCorrection
IPsDriver
ISpotPlateCollection

PsDriver

IFontMapCollection — **FontMap-Collection**

The PS driver supports the PS printer by setting general PostScript variables, including color information

The font map collection houses the set of font maps used by the PS printer or PS exporter objects

ISpotPlate — **SpotPlate**

IFontMap — **FontMap**

The spot plate allows for the creation of separate plates (images) based on the specified color

A font map creates associations between TrueType fonts and the mapped font

IClone
IPaper
IPersistStream

Paper

The paper object defines the printer and tray designations for use with the printer object

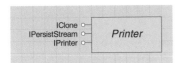

IClone ○—
IPersistStream ○—
IPrinter ○—   *Printer*

The Printer *abstract class specifies interfaces that control the output of data to hardcopy devices.*

Three printer objects inherit from the *Printer* abstract class: *EmfPrinter, ArcPressPrinter,* and *PsPrinter* object. Each object supports printing to a hardcopy device, but they all have different methods for achieving that goal.

The printer object you select to send output depends on the type of printing device you wish to use and what drivers you have available.

IPrinter : IUnknown	**Provides access to members that control the Printer Driver Interface.**
■— DriverName: String	*Indicates the name of Windows Printer Driver.*
■— FileExtension: String	*Indicates the File Extension associated with the Printer Driver.*
■— Filter: String	*Indicates the Filter used in CFileDialog.*
■— Name: String	*Indicates the Name of the IPrinter Driver.*
■—□ Paper: IPaper	*Provides access to members that control the IPaper interface.*
■— PrintableBounds: IEnvelope	*Indicates the area of the printer page that can be printed on.*
■—■ PrintToFile: String	*Indicates the named used for Print to File.*
■—■ Resolution: Integer	*Indicates the Printer Driver Resolution.*
■—■ SpoolFileName: String	*Indicates the Spool File Name which is from the Print Manager.*
—■ StepProgressor: IStepProgressor	*Indicates that Updates to the Progress Bar is set.*
■— Units: esriUnits	*Indicates the units for PaperSize and PrintableBounds.*
◄— DoesDriverSupportPrinter (in PrinterName: String) : Boolean	*Indicates if the Printer Name passed into function is supported by the IPrinter Driver.*
◄— FinishPrinting	*Finishes Printing.*
◄— QueryPaperSize (out Width: Double, out Height: Double)	*Returns the Page Size for the Printer.*
◄— StartPrinting (in PixelBounds: IEnvelope, in hDcPrinter: Long) : Long	*Initializes Printing.*
◄— VerifyDriverSettings: Boolean	*Indicates if the Printer Driver should validate the Printer Driver's local settings.*

The *IPrinter* interface is implemented by all printer objects.

The *Paper* property is initialized to the default printer of the system upon application startup. Create your own *Paper* object to use a different printer.

The *PrintToFile* property makes it possible to send output to a file.

The *DoesDriverSupportPrinter* method allows the developer to determine if the specified printer can be used with the current driver object.

Use the *StartPrinting* method to return an hDC (handle to the device context of the printer) that can then be used with *IActiveView::Output* to send output to a printer. *IPrinter::FinishPrinting* should then be issued to flush everything out to the printer or plotter.

This sample VBA code demonstrates the use of the *EmfPrinter* object to produce output.

```
Public Sub PrintLayout ()
   'To test, add a layer to the map, and run procedure
   Dim pMxApp As IMxApplication
   Dim pMxDoc As IMxDocument
   Set pMxApp = Application
   Set pMxDoc = ThisDocument

   Dim pPrinter As IPrinter
   Dim pPaper As IPaper
   Dim pPageLayout As IPageLayout
   Set pPrinter = pMxApp.Printer
   Set pPrinter.Paper = pMxApp.Paper
```

Output

```
            Set pPageLayout = pMxDoc.PageLayout

            Dim pActiveView As IActiveView
            Set pActiveView = pMxDoc.ActiveView

            Dim deviceframe As tagRECT
            Dim pDeviceFrame As IEnvelope

            ' Now set the printer object with the correct properties
            Set pDeviceFrame = New Envelope
            pPageLayout.Page.GetDeviceBounds pPrinter, 1, 0, pPrinter.Resolution, _
              pDeviceFrame
            deviceframe.Left = pDeviceFrame.xmin
            deviceframe.top = pDeviceFrame.ymin
            deviceframe.Right = pDeviceFrame.XMax
            deviceframe.bottom = pDeviceFrame.YMax

            ' Get the Visible Bounds if we are in Page Layout View
            Dim pVisibleBounds As IEnvelope
            Dim pPageLayoutView As IActiveView
            Set pPageLayoutView = pPageLayout
            If TypeOf pActiveView Is IPageLayout Then
              Set pVisibleBounds = New Envelope
              pPageLayout.Page.GetPageBounds pPrinter, 0, 0, pVisibleBounds
            End If

            Dim pEmfPrinter As IEmfPrinter
            Set pEmfPrinter = pPrinter

            ' Need to offset deviceBounds by xmin and ymin margins only for EmfPrinter
            If TypeOf pPrinter Is IEmfPrinter Then
              Dim pPrintableBounds As IEnvelope
              Set pPrintableBounds = pPrinter.PrintableBounds

              Dim dXmin As Double
              Dim dYmin As Double
              dXmin = pPrintableBounds.xmin
              dYmin = pPrintableBounds.ymin

              deviceframe.Left = deviceframe.Left - (dXmin * pPrinter.Resolution)
              deviceframe.top = deviceframe.top - (dYmin * pPrinter.Resolution)
              deviceframe.Right = deviceframe.Right - (dXmin * pPrinter.Resolution)
              deviceframe.bottom = deviceframe.bottom - (dYmin * pPrinter.Resolution)
            End If

            Dim lHDC As Long
            lHDC = pPrinter.StartPrinting(pDeviceFrame, 0)
            pActiveView.Output lHDC, pPrinter.Resolution, deviceframe, _
              pVisibleBounds, Nothing

            ' finishing the printing will flush everything out to the print spooler
            pPrinter.FinishPrinting
          End Sub
```

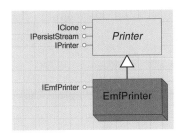

An EMF printer serves as a driver for the creation of output through the Windows Enhanced Metafile format.

The *EmfPrinter* coclass is a type of printer object that serves as a driver for the Windows Enhanced Metafile format.

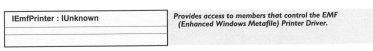

IEmfPrinter : IUnknown	Provides access to members that control the EMF (Enhanced Windows Metafile) Printer Driver.

IEmfPrinter is the only interface for the *EmfPrinter* coclass. The interface has no properties or methods; it is used to identify whether or not your printer object is of type *EmfPrinter*.

The following VBA code demonstrates that process. *pPrinter* is an object of type *IPrinter*.

```
If TypeOf pPrinter is IEmfPrinter then
  Dim pEmf as IEmfPrinter
  Set pEmf = pPrinter
End If
```

Output

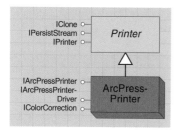

The ArcPress printer serves as a driver for the creation of output through ArcPress.

The *ArcPressPrinter* coclass is a type of printer object that represents the ArcPress™ printer driver.

ArcPress is ESRI's Graphics Rasterizer. ArcPress is composed of three basic modules: a graphics interpreter, a rasterizer, and several output filters.

The graphics interpreter accepts PostScript files, CGM files, and all ESRI formats. The graphics interpreter translates the input to intermediate PostScript metafiles. The rasterizer then takes the intermediate files and converts them into a pure raster metafile. This raster metafile is then filtered through the printer driver or bitmap export driver (these are listed under the *Exporter* object) of your choice.

Do not attempt to use this object unless you have ArcPress installed on your system. The *ArcPressPrinter* coclass provides access to the driver but offers little control over the process. The *ArcPressPrinterDriver* (discussed next) can be used with the *ArcPressPrinter* object to set additional input parameters.

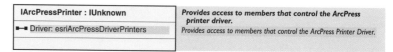

The *IArcPressPrinter* interface lets you identify a printer object as type *ArcPressPrinter*.

The lone property on the interface, *Driver*, allows you to set and retrieve which driver to use when outputting through ArcPress.

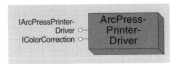

The ArcPress printer driver supports the ArcPress printer by setting ArcPress parameters.

ArcPressPrinterDriver is the coclass that does the work when you direct output through ArcPress. Through the supported interfaces on the object, you can set all the necessary parameters, from color to resolution, to ensure proper output from the ArcPress object. Use this object in conjunction with *ArcPressPrinter* when you want to control the parameters used by ArcPress to create hardcopy output.

IArcPressPrinterDriver: IUnknown	*Provides access to members that control the ArcPress printer driver formats.*
■—■ ArcPressSeparateImage: Boolean	*Indicates if the ArcPress Driver is using the Separate Image option.*
■— DitherDescription (in dither: esriArcPressDriverDithers) : String	*Indicates a description of the selected dither pattern.*
■— DitherDescriptionHelpText (in dither: esriArcPressDriverDithers) : String	*Indicates the help text description of the selected dither.*
■— DriverDescription (in Driver: esriArcPressDriverPrinters) : String	*Indicates a description of the ArcPress Printer Driver.*
■— DriverDescriptionHelpText (in Driver: esriArcPressDriverPrinters) : String	*Indicates the help text description of the ArcPress Printer Driver.*
■—■ DriverDither: esriArcPressDriverDithers	*Indicates the dither pattern of the ArcPress Printer Driver.*
■— DriverResolution (in Driver: esriArcPressDriverPrinters, in Index: Integer) : Integer	*Indicates the resolution of the selected ArcPress Printer Driver at the specified index.*
■— DriverResolutionCount (in Driver: esriArcPressDriverPrinters) : Integer	*Indicates the number of resolutions available for the selected ArcPress Printer Driver.*
■— InternalDriverName (in Driver: esriArcPressDriverPrinters) : String	*Indicates the internal ArcPress Printer Driver name.*
■—■ Orientation: Integer	*Indicates whether the page orientation is 1 = portrait or 2 = landscape.*
■—■ PaperSizeHeight: Double	*Indicates the height of the selected paper size.*
■—■ PaperSizeWidth: Double	*Indicates the width of the selected paper size.*
■—■ PrintableBounds: IEnvelope	*Indicates the Printer Margins.*
■—■ Resolution: Integer	*Indicates the resolution of the ArcPress Printer Driver.*
—■ StepProgressor: IStepProgressor	*Indicates the progress bar to update.*
◀— CreateRaster (in Driver: esriArcPressDriverPrinters, in InputFileName: String, in OutputFileName: String)	*Creates a Printer Format file from a PostScript input file.*

The *IArcPressPrinterDriver* interface sets a variety of input parameters for use with the ArcPress driver.

CreateRaster is used to create a printer format file based on an input PostScript file. The file that is created can then be sent to a plotter for output.

DitherDescription, DitherDescriptionHelpText, and *DriverDither* pertain to the method of dithering when the output device does not support as many colors as you are sending. Dithering refers to the display of colors, specifically, any color that should be solid but looks like it has small spots of another color. Use the *DriverDither* parameter to specify the type of dithering algorithm to apply when the output device does not support a sufficient number of colors (as is the case with a black-and-white printer).

Use the *Resolution* and *PrintableBounds* properties with the *IActiveView::Output* statement to match the resolution and page size of the output to the device.

Output

IColorCorrection : IUnknown	Provides access to members that control the Color Correction Interface.
►—■ CMYKCorrection (in dataType: esriColorCorrectionDataType, in Index: esriCMYKIndex) : Integer	Indicates the Color Correction for the CMYK color model.
►—■ Lightness (in dataType: esriColorCorrectionDataType) : Integer	Indicates the Lightness Value of the HLS Color Model.
►—■ Saturation (in dataType: esriColorCorrectionDataType) : Integer	Indicates the Saturation Value of the HLS Color Model.
►— SupportedColorCorrections: Integer	Indicates the dataType supported: 1 Total, 2 Raster, and 4 Vector.
►—■ UnderColorRemoval (in dataType: esriColorCorrectionDataType) : Integer	Indicates the Under Color Removal Value.

The *IColorCorrection* interface is implemented by the *ArcPressPrinterDriver* coclass and several other classes. It lets you manipulate the color parameters within the ArcPress driver through the CMYK and HLS models. Use this interface when you want to adjust the default color settings for the ArcPress driver.

SupportedColorCorrections returns which data types are supported by the current object. The other properties use this value as input, so it is good practice to check this value before trying to access any other values.

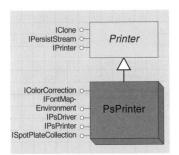

The PsPrinter is used to create output through a PostScript driver.

The *PsPrinter* coclass is a type of printer object used to create output through a PostScript device driver. The coclass is an aggregation of the *PsDriver* and *FontMapEnvironment* classes. Use this coclass when you want to create hardcopy output through a PostScript driver.

IPsPrinter : IUnknown	Provides access to members that control the PostScript Printer Driver.
⬝▬ PPDFile: String	Indicates the PPD file used for the PostScript file.

The *IPsPrinter* interface allows you to identify a printer object as type *PsPrinter* and allows for the setting of a filename to receive output (as opposed to sending output directly to a hardcopy device).

The VBA code that follows sends map data to an output device using the *PsPrinter* and *Printer* objects. The *ConvertRWToPixels* routine converts from the current units to pixels.

```
Dim pPsPrinter As IPsPrinter
Dim pPrinter As IPrinter
Dim lScreenResolution As Long
Dim hDc As OLE_HANDLE
Dim userRECT As tagRECT
Dim pMxDoc As IMxDocument
Dim pPaper As IPaper
Dim lDrvResolution As Long
Dim pMxApp As IMxApplication
Dim pDriverBounds As IEnvelope, pEnv As IEnvelope

Set pMxApp = Application
Set pMxDoc = ThisDocument
Set pPsPrinter = New PsPrinter
Set pPrinter = pPsPrinter
Set pPrinter.Paper = pMxApp.Paper

lScreenResolution = _
  pMxDoc.ActiveView.ScreenDisplay.DisplayTransformation.Resolution
lDrvResolution = screenResolution
pPrinter.Resolution = drvResolution

Set pEnv = pMxDoc.ActiveView.Extent
userRECT.Top = 0
userRECT.Left = 0
userRECT.Right = ConvertRWToPixels(pEnv.Width)
userRECT.bottom = ConvertRWToPixels(pEnv.Height)

Set pDriverBounds = New Envelope
pDriverBounds.PutCoords userRECT.Left, userRECT.bottom, _
                        userRECT.Right, userRECT.Top
hDc = pPrinter.StartPrinting(pDriverBounds, 0)
pMxDoc.ActiveView.Output hDc, lScreenResolution, userRECT, pEnv, Nothing
pPrinter.FinishPrinting
```

ISpotPlateCollection : IUnknown	Provides access to members that control the Collection of Spot Plates.
■— Count (Count: Long)	Indicates the count of the Spot Plate collection.
■— SpotPlate (Index: Long, SpotPlate: ISpotPlate)	Indicates an ISpotPlate from the Spot Plate collection.
◀— Add (SpotPlate: ISpotPlate)	Adds an ISpotPlate to the Spot Plate collection.
◀— Insert (Index: Long, SpotPlate: ISpotPlate)	Inserts an ISpotPlate into the Spot Plate collection at position index.
◀— Remove (Index: Long)	Removes ISpotPlate at index from the Spot Plate collection.
◀— RemoveAll	Removes all ISpotPlates from the Spot Plate collection.

Spot plates are used for color separation to produce CMYK plates.

The *ISpotPlateCollection* makes it possible to create plates based on the individual colors in the CMYK color model. The plates can then be used by publishers in the generation of printed material.

The *ISpotPlateCollection* interface contains a collection of individual *SpotPlate* objects. You can use this interface to add, remove, and generally keep track of the *SpotPlate* objects that have been defined. For more information, see the topic *SpotPlate* and *FontMapEnvironment* later in this chapter.

The *IFontMapEnvironment* interface is documented with the *FontMapEnvironment* coclass.

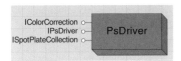

The PsPrinter is used to create output through a PostScript driver.

The *PSDriver* coclass, along with *FontMapEnvironment*, is aggregated into the *PsPrinter* coclass. This class provides access to all of the different parameters that can be set when outputting through a PostScript driver (excluding *Font* control).

Since the *PsPrinter* coclass aggregates the *PSDriver* coclass, the interfaces from *PSDriver* can be accessed from the *PsPrinter*.

For example, if you have an object named *pPsPrinter* defined as an *IPSPrinter*, the following VBA code allows you to access the *IPsDriver* interface on the *PSDriver* coclass.

```
Dim pPsDriver as IPSDriver
Set pPsDriver = pPsPrinter
```

IPSDriver : IUnknown	Provides access to members that control the PostScript Driver.
■—■ ArcPressSeparateImage: Boolean	Indicates the ArcPress Separate Image File flag to create a separate Image file for ArcPress.
■—■ ArcPressSeparateImageRotate: Boolean	Indicates the ArcPress Separate Image Rotate flag to Rotate Image 90 degress for ArcPress.
■—■ Emulsion: esriPSDriverEmulsion	Indicates the Emulsion setting for the PostScript Driver.
■—□ FontMapCollection: IFontMapCollection	Provides access to members that control the Font Map Collection for Font Mapping.
■—■ FormName: String	Indicates the printer page form. Uses Win32 DMPAPER_xxx constants.
■—■ HalfTone (in HalfTone: esriPSDriverHalfTone) : Long	Indicates the HalfTone DPI / LPI is being used.
■—■ Image: esriPSDriverImage	Indicates whether the Image setting for the PostScript Driver is Positive or Negative.
■—■ ImageCompression: esriPSDriverImageCompression	Provides access to members that control the Image Compression of the PostScript Driver.
■—■ Marks: Integer	Indicates if the PostScript Marks are being used.
■—■ OneBitImageTransparency: Boolean	Indicates the 1 Bit Image Transparency setting for the PostScript Driver.
■—■ Orientation: Integer	Indicates whether the printer page orientation is either 1 = portrait or 2 = landscape.
■—■ PPDFile: String	Indicates the PPD file to be used.
■—■ PrintableBounds: IEnvelope	Indicates the printers Printable Bounds that are used for Marks.
■—■ PSLanguageLevel: esriPSDriverPSLanguageLevel	Indicates the PostScript Driver Language Level.
—■ StepProgressor: IStepProgressor	Indicates that the PostScript Driver will update a Progress Bar.
■—■ UseEMFFrameBoxForPSBoundingBox: Boolean	Indicates the PostScript Driver to use the ENHMETAHEADER rclFrame instead of rclBounds for the PostScript Bounding Box.
← CreatePS (in InputFileName: String, in OutputFileName: String)	Indicates the Conversion of the EMF file to a EPS File.

Through aggregation, the *IPSDriver* interface is also supported by the *PsPrinter* object. The interface provides access to the set of parameters that can be used to alter the output being produced by the PostScript driver.

The *ArcPressSeparateImage* and *ArcPressSeparateImageRotate* properties can be used to create separate images for use with ArcPress.

CreatePS takes an EMF file as input and outputs a PostScript file.

The *IColorCorrection* interface is documented with the *ArcPressPrinterDriver* coclass.

Output

The spot plate allows for the creation of separate plates (images) based on the specified color.

The *SpotPlate* coclass allows for the creation of separate plates (images) based on the specified color. Each plate contains the plotting information for a single specified color.

The *SpotPlate* objects are managed by the *ISpotPlate* interface object on the *PSDriver* coclass. Use this coclass when you need to create color separates of your plots for publishing purposes.

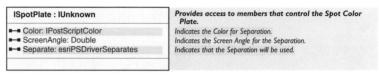

ISpotPlate : IUnknown	Provides access to members that control the Spot Color Plate.
■━ Color: IPostScriptColor	*Indicates the Color for Separation.*
■━ ScreenAngle: Double	*Indicates the Screen Angle for the Separation.*
■━ Separate: esriPSDriverSeparates	*Indicates that the Separation will be used.*

ISpotPlate is the only interface supported by the *SpotPlate* coclass. This interface allows specification of the color separation (cyan, yellow, magenta, or black) to create with the PostScript driver.

The *Color* property takes an *IPostScriptColor* object, which sets saturation and overprint parameters for the separation.

Enumeration esriPSDriverSeparates	Provides access to members that control the PostScript Driver Color Separation settings.
1 - esriPSDriverSeparateCyan	*Provides access to members that control the Cyan Plate.*
2 - esriPSDriverSeparateMagenta	*Provides access to members that control the Magenta Plate.*
3 - esriPSDriverSeparateYellow	*Provides access to members that control the Yellow Plate.*
4 - esriPSDriverSeparateBlack	*Provides access to members that control the Black Plate.*
5 - esriPSDriverSeparateCustom	*Provides access to members that control the Custom Spot Color Plate.*

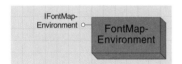

The font map environment supports the PS printer by setting font information to be used during the creation of PostScript output.

The *FontMapEnvironment* coclass is one of the aggregated coclasses (along with *PSDriver*) that make up the *PsPrinter* coclass. The object is used to determine the set of fonts used by the PostScript driver to produce the desired output.

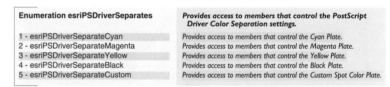

IFontMapEnvironment : IUnknown	Provides access to members that control the Font Mapping Environment.
■━ ApplyDefaultMappingDesc: String	*Indicates the Font Mapping checkbox description string.*
■━ DefaultMapping: String	*Indicates the Default Font Mapping string.*
■━ DefaultMappingsChoices: Variant	*Indicates the Default Mapping Choices for Font Substitution.*
■━ FontMapCollection: IFontMapCollection	*Provides access to members that control the FontMap Collection.*
■━ SaveMappings: Boolean	*Indicates whether to save font mappings.*

The *IFontMapEnvironment* interface tracks the collection of *FontMap* objects that have been defined and allows for additional settings for the default font mapping to use with the PostScript driver. Use this interface when you want to control the set of fonts used by the PostScript driver.

The *FontMapCollection* property returns a collection object to allow the developer to add and remove *FontMap* objects. Since the *FontMapCollection* property is read-only, you cannot create your own *FontMapCollection* object; you must instead manipulate the existing one.

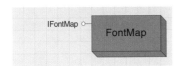

The font map collection houses the set of font maps used by the PS printer or PS exporter objects.

The *FontMapCollection* is a collection object whose life cycle is tied to that of the object that created it, such as *PsPrinter* or *PsExporter*. This object controls the set of *FontMap* objects defined for use with the PostScript driver. An object of this type is returned by *IFontMapEnvironment::FontMapCollection*. Use this object to make your adjustments to the font mapping environment.

By default, the collection returned by *IFontMapEnvironment-::FontMapCollection* will have some values in it. These default values are defined by the system. You can then add additional *FontMap* objects to the collection.

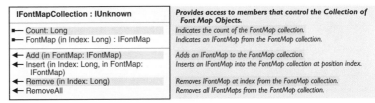

IFontMapCollection : IUnknown	Provides access to members that control the Collection of Font Map Objects.
•— Count: Long	*Indicates the count of the FontMap collection.*
•— FontMap (in Index: Long) : IFontMap	*Indicates an IFontMap from the FontMap collection.*
◄— Add (in FontMap: IFontMap)	*Adds an IFontMap to the FontMap collection.*
◄— Insert (in Index: Long, in FontMap: IFontMap)	*Inserts an IFontMap into the FontMap collection at position index.*
◄— Remove (in Index: Long)	*Removes IFontMap at index from the FontMap collection.*
◄— RemoveAll	*Removes all IFontMaps from the FontMap collection.*

IFontMapCollection is the only interface implemented by the *FontMapCollection* object. This interface is a typical collection interface that allows *FontMap* objects to be added and removed from the collection. The interface also provides a count of and access to the individual objects contained in the collection.

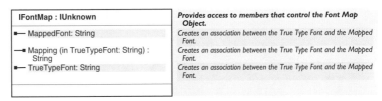

A font map creates associations between TrueType™ fonts and the mapped font.

FontMap objects are created for inclusion in a *FontMapCollection* object. The life cycle of the *FontMap* object is based on the life cycle of the *FontMapCollection* object (which, in turn, has its life cycle based on that of the object that created it). The purpose of the object is to allow for the setting of font mapping properties for individual fonts. These properties are then used by the PostScript driver to create the hardcopy output.

Objects of this type are creatable, but the developer does not have the ability to set the necessary parameters for the object that is created.

IFontMap : IUnknown	Provides access to members that control the Font Map Object.
•— MappedFont: String	*Creates an association between the True Type Font and the Mapped Font.*
—● Mapping (in TrueTypeFont: String) : String	*Creates an association between the True Type Font and the Mapped Font.*
•— TrueTypeFont: String	*Creates an association between the True Type Font and the Mapped Font.*

IFontMap is the only interface implemented by the *FontMap* object. This interface allows the developer to examine the font mapping that has been defined. The C++ programmer can define additional mapping through the *IFontMap::Mapping* property. The VB programmer will need to use the *IFontMap2::SetMapping* method to define additional font mapping.

IFontMap2 : IUnknown	Provides access to members that control the Font Map 2 Object.
◄— SetMapping (in TrueTypeFont: String, in MappedFont: String)	*Creates an association between the True Type Font and the Mapped Font.*

Output

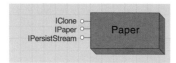

The paper object defines the printer and tray designations to use with the printer object.

The *Paper* object is a key object required by the *Printer* object. The *Paper* object is responsible for maintaining properties related to the paper and printer used with the *Printer* object.

When the application is started, a *Paper* object is automatically created based on the default printer for the system. To use another printer on the system, you must define a new *Paper* object and set it to the printer or plotter through the *PrinterName* property. The *Paper* object can then be associated with the *Printer* object through the *IPrinter::Paper* property.

The *Paper* object is basically a wrapper for the Microsoft *DevMode* and *DevNames* parameters. These two operating system wrappers define the printing environment through application programming interface (API) structures.

The *DevNames* structure contains strings that identify the driver, device, and output port names for a printer. The *DevMode* data structure contains information about the device initialization and environment of a printer.

The *PrinterInfo* property and *Attach* method use these structures in the form of pointers to OLE_HANDLEs. Because of the nature of these two parameters, VB developers cannot take advantage of them.

The following VBA code demonstrates how to create a *Paper* object, assign it to a particular device, then pass that object to a printer object.

```
Dim pPaper As IPaper
Dim pPrinter As IPrinter
Dim pPsPrinter As IPsPrinter

Set pPaper = New Paper
pPaper.PrinterName = "\\OMNI\Oakland"
Set pPsPrinter = New PsPrinter
Set pPrinter = pPsPrinter
Set pPrinter.Paper = pPaper
```

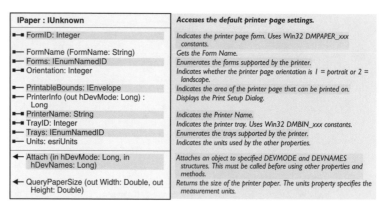

The *IPaper* interface allows the developer to create an association between the *Paper* object and the hardcopy device. Once that association is created, form and paper properties can be retrieved and set through the interface.

Use the *PrinterName* property to specify which printer you want to use with the *Paper* object (see the coding example on the previous page).

The *PrinterInfo* property returns the information that serves as input to the *Attach* method. However, the parameters returned by *PrinterInfo* are not handled correctly by Visual Basic at this time. Do not try to use the *PrinterInfo* property with Visual Basic.

Output

Exporter objects

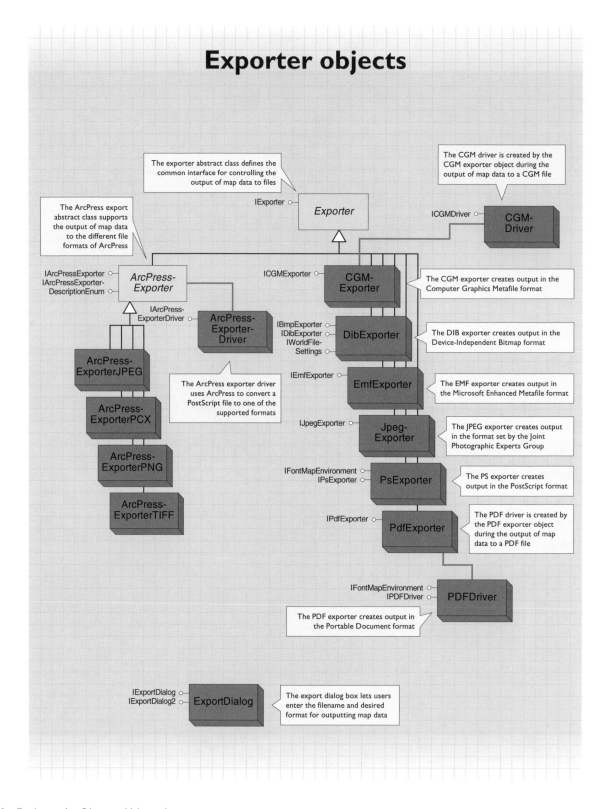

The exporter abstract class defines the common interface for controlling the output of map data to files

The CGM driver is created by the CGM exporter object during the output of map data to a CGM file

IExporter ○— *Exporter*

ICGMDriver ○— **CGM-Driver**

The ArcPress export abstract class supports the output of map data to the different file formats of ArcPress

IArcPressExporter ○—
IArcPressExporter-
DescriptionEnum ○— *ArcPress-Exporter*

ICGMExporter ○— **CGM-Exporter**

The CGM exporter creates output in the Computer Graphics Metafile format

IArcPress-
ExporterDriver ○— **ArcPress-Exporter-Driver**

IBmpExporter ○—
IDibExporter ○—
IWorldFile-
Settings ○— **DibExporter**

The DIB exporter creates output in the Device-Independent Bitmap format

ArcPress-ExporterJPEG

IEmfExporter ○— **EmfExporter**

The EMF exporter creates output in the Microsoft Enhanced Metafile format

The ArcPress exporter driver uses ArcPress to convert a PostScript file to one of the supported formats

ArcPress-ExporterPCX

IJpegExporter ○— **Jpeg-Exporter**

The JPEG exporter creates output in the format set by the Joint Photographic Experts Group

ArcPress-ExporterPNG

IFontMapEnvironment ○—
IPsExporter ○— **PsExporter**

The PS exporter creates output in the PostScript format

ArcPress-ExporterTIFF

IPdfExporter ○— **PdfExporter**

The PDF driver is created by the PDF exporter object during the output of map data to a PDF file

IFontMapEnvironment ○—
IPDFDriver ○— **PDFDriver**

The PDF exporter creates output in the Portable Document format

IExportDialog ○—
IExportDialog2 ○— **ExportDialog**

The export dialog box lets users enter the filename and desired format for outputting map data

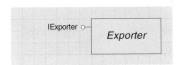

The exporter abstract class defines the common interface for controlling the output of map data to files.

The *Exporter* object class controls the production of softcopy output (files of different formats). The main purpose of the object is to support the coclasses underneath it.

There are seven file formats supported through specific drivers (DIB, CGM, EMF, JPEG, PostScript, PDF, and TIFF), and four formats supported through the ArcPress driver (JPEG, PCX, PNG, and TIFF). Each of these creatable subclasses inherits from the *Exporter* object.

It is possible to create file output from the descendants of the *Printer* abstract class, but you should only use this method when you plan to send the file to an output device at a later time. The printer objects create some printer-dependent files that you do not need unless you are going to direct the file to an output device.

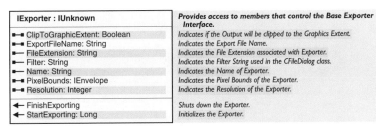

The *IExporter* interface is supported by all of the exporter objects, such as *CGMExporter*. The interface provides all the common parameters (such as filename and resolution) needed to export map data to a file. It will be necessary to use this interface to complete any exporting procedures.

The *FileExtension, Filter,* and *Name* properties are based on the type of exporter object you create. For example, if you create a *JpegExporter* object, the *FileExtension* will be ".jpg".

PixelBounds specifies a destination rectangle in the output file.

StartExporting must be run during an exporting procedure, and it returns an hDC value that should be used with subsequent *IActiveView::Output* operations.

Here is some sample VBA code for using the *IExporter* interface through a *JpegExporter* object.

```
Sub Export()
  Dim pExporter As IExporter
  Dim pDriverBounds As IEnvelope
  Dim lScreenResolution As Long
  Dim hDc As OLE_HANDLE
  Dim userRECT As tagRECT
  Dim pMxDoc As IMxDocument
  Dim pActive As IActiveView
  Dim pEnv As IEnvelope

  Set pMxDoc = ThisDocument
```

Output

```
        Set pEnv = pMxDoc.ActiveView.Extent

        lScreenResolution = _
          pMxDoc.ActiveView.ScreenDisplay.DisplayTransformation.Resolution

        Set pExporter = New JpegExporter
        pExporter.ExportFileName = "C:\temp\ArcMapExport2.jpg"
        pExporter.Resolution = screenResolution

        userRECT.top = 0
        userRECT.Left = 0
        userRECT.Right = ConvertRWToPixels(pEnv.Width)
        userRECT.bottom = ConvertRWToPixels(pEnv.Height)

        Set pDriverBounds = New Envelope
        pDriverBounds.PutCoords userRECT.Left, _
                          userRECT.bottom, _
                          userRECT.Right, _
                          userRECT.top
        pExporter.PixelBounds = pDriverBounds
        hDc = pExporter.StartExporting

        pMxDoc.ActiveView.Output hDc, screenResolution, userRECT, pEnv, Nothing
        pExporter.FinishExporting
End Sub

Private Function ConvertRWToPixels(RWUnits As Double) As Double
  Dim realWorldDisplayExtent As Double
  Dim pixelExtent As Long
  Dim sizeOfOnePixel As Double
  Dim pDT As IDisplayTransformation
  Dim deviceRECT As tagRECT
  Dim pEnv As IEnvelope
  Dim pMxDoc As IMxDocument

  Set pMxDoc = ThisDocument

  Set pDT = pMxDoc.ActiveView.ScreenDisplay.DisplayTransformation
  deviceRECT = pDT.DeviceFrame
  pixelExtent = deviceRECT.Right - deviceRECT.Left
  Set pEnv = pDT.VisibleBounds

  realWorldDisplayExtent = pEnv.Width
  sizeOfOnePixel = realWorldDisplayExtent / pixelExtent
  ConvertRWToPixels = RWUnits / sizeOfOnePixel
End Function
```

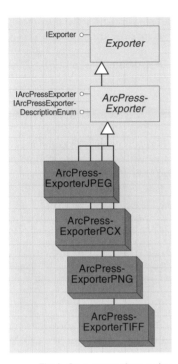

The ArcPress export abstract class supports the output of map data to the different file formats of ArcPress.

The *ArcPressExporter* abstract class supports the file formats that are supported through the ArcPress driver, which are JPEG, PCX, PNG, and TIFF.

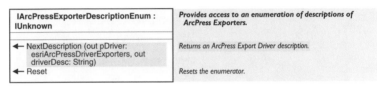

IArcPressExporter: IUnknown	Provides access to members that control the ArcPress Exporter Driver.
■← Driver: esriArcPressDriverExporters	Indicates the Driver for the ArcPress Exporter.
■← DriverResolution: Integer	Indicates the ArcPress Printer Driver Resolution.

The *IArcPressExporter* interface is supported by all of the ArcPress coclasses that produce output files through the ArcPress driver. The purpose of this interface is to provide generic properties (*Driver* and *DriverResolution*) for the ArcPress driver.

The *Driver* property sets or retrieves the output option for the type of driver you have. Use *IExporter::Name* to determine the type of object you have, then use the *Driver* property to determine the format option within the output object.

IArcPressExporterDescriptionEnum : IUnknown	Provides access to an enumeration of descriptions of ArcPress Exporters.
←■ NextDescription (out pDriver: esriArcPressDriverExporters, out driverDesc: String)	Returns an ArcPress Export Driver description.
←■ Reset	Resets the enumerator.

The *IArcPressExporterDescriptionEnum* interface is also supported by all of the file format-specific ArcPress drivers. This interface provides an enumeration of the supported file formats for the specific object.

For example, if you have an *ArcPressExporterTiff* object, then the enumeration will include the supported TIFF formats (*TIFF3_BW, TIFF4_BW,* and *TIFF6_RGB*). This interface would commonly be used when the developer wished to create a dialog box to allow the user to specify the type of output desired. To do this, choose between the object types (BIL, BIP, and so on), then use this interface to display the available options within that format.

The *NextDescription* method returns a driver that can be plugged into the *IArcPressExporter::Driver* property to produce output in the desired format.

Each of these ArcPress coclasses—*ArcPressExporterJPEG, ArcPressExporter-PCX, ArcPressExporterPNG,* and *ArcPressExporterTIFF*—are used to create output files in the respective formats. They only support the interfaces inherited from the *Exporter* and *ArcPressExporter* abstract classes. Use the *IExporter::Name* property to determine if you have a class of this type.

This is a summary of each of the formats supported by ArcPress:

Tag Image File Format (TIFF), developed by Aldus® Corporation, is an industry standard for data storage and data transfer across operating system environments and applications. It is one of the most versatile bitmaps available. At this time, ArcPress supports groups 3 and 4, which use CCITT Encoding for compression to encode 1-bit image data. The

Output

TIFF 3 and TIFF 4 formats provide an excellent format for the transmission of high-quality monochrome images in modem and facsimile protocol used in machines and modems. TIFF 6 is an uncompressed group 6 for 24-bit RGB color images. ArcPress can generate:

- 1-bit (Monochrome)—Group 3 TIFF
- 1-bit (Monochrome)—Group 4 TIFF
- 24-bit (True Color)—Group 6 TIFF

The Joint Photographic Experts Group (JPEG) is a combined committee of researchers from ISO and ANSI. Their goal is to set industry standards "for the transmission of graphics and image data over digital communications networks." Their result is "a compression method that is capable of compressing continuous-tone image data with pixel depth of 6 to 24 bits with reasonable speed and efficiency." (*Encyclopedia of Graphics File Formats*, 1994). The ArcPress-created JPEG format does not have any legal restrictions.

ArcPress can generate:

- 8-bit (Grayscale) JPEG
- 24-bit (True Color) JPEG

PCX (PC Paintbrush File Format), developed by Z-soft, also known as DCX and PCC, is a common exchange and storage format for MS–DOS® and Microsoft Windows applications. It is used with PC Paintbrush and Microsoft Paintbrush for Windows. It is also commonly used for clip art in many desktop publishing applications. PCX provides hardware-dependent formats designed for specific types of display hardware. Image data is compressed using a variation of Run Length Encoding (RLE), which is quick and efficient at file size reduction.

ArcPress can generate:

- 1-bit (Monochrome) PCX
- 8-bit (Grayscale) PCX
- 8-bit (256 Colors) PCX
- 24-bit (True Color) PCX

The Portable Network Graphics (PNG) format was originally developed to replace GIF to overcome the legal entanglements of the LZW compression scheme; it is rising in popularity. The PNG, or "ping", format provides several useful features that include stream ability, progressive display, and 100 percent loss-less compression. PNG is also completely hardware and platform independent.

ArcPress can generate:

- 1-bit (Monochrome) PNG
- 8-bit (Grayscale) PNG
- 8-bit (256 Colors) PNG
- 24-bit (True Color) PNG

The ArcPress exporter driver uses ArcPress to convert a PostScript file to one of the supported formats.

The *ArcPressExporterDriver* class is a standalone class (does not inherit from any other class) used to convert a PostScript file to one of the supported ArcPress file formats. This object is cocreated internally by the core functionality as part of the output process through the ArcPress drivers.

IArcPressExporterDriver: IUnknown	*Provides access to members that control the ArcPress exporter driver formats.*
■—■ Resolution: Integer	*Indicates the Resolution of the ArcPress Exporter Driver.*
← CreateRaster (in Driver: esriArcPressDriverExporters, in InputFileName: String, in OutputFileName: String)	*Creates an Export Format file from the PostScript input file.*

The purpose of the *IArcPressExporterDriver* interface is to allow you to set a resolution, then use the *CreateRaster* method to convert a PostScript file to one of the supported ArcPress file formats (BIL, BIP, and so on).

Output

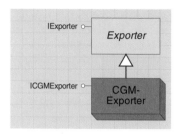

The CGM exporter creates output in the Computer Graphics Metafile format.

The CGM driver is created by the CGM exporter object during the output of map data to a CGM file.

The *CgmExporter* coclass creates output files in the Computer Graphics Metafile (CGM) format. Create an object of this type when you want to generate your map output as a CGM file. The *CgmExporter* coclass internally cocreates the *CgmDriver* coclass. The *CgmDriver* coclass does all the work in producing an output file in the CGM format.

ICGMExporter : IUnknown	Provides access to members that control the CGM (Computer Graphics Metafile) Exporter Interface.
← QueryCGMDriver: ICGMDriver	*Returns Interface ICGMDriver.*

The *ICgmExport* interface provides the ability to query for the CGM driver being used with the object. The *CgmDriver* object can then be used to set additional parameters to use when outputting to the CGM format.

The *CgmDriver* coclass is creatable by the developer, but it is also internally created by the *CgmExporter* object. The *CgmDriver* object does all the work in producing CGM files as output.

ICGMDriver : IUnknown	Provides access to members that control the CGM (Computer Graphics Metafile) Driver.
■→ CGMProfile: esriCGMProfile	*Indicates the CGM profile.*
■→ CGMVersion: esriCGMVersion	*Indicates the CGM version.*
■→ PolygonizeText: Boolean	*Indicates whether text is to be converted to polygons.*
← CreateCGM (in InputFileName: String, in OutputFileName: String)	*Indicates the Conversion of the EMF file to a CGM File.*

ICGMDriver is the only interface supported by the *CgmDriver* coclass. This interface allows the developer to set additional parameters before outputting map data to the CGM format.

CreateCGM requires the input of an EMF file to produce the CGM output file. The developer can avoid having to create the EMF file by using the *CgmExporter* object (and the inherited *IExporter* interface) to generate output.

This is some VBA code for exporting through the *CGMExporter* object. The *ConvertRWToPixels* routine can be found with the *IExporter* sample code.

```
Sub CGMExport()
  Dim pExporter As IExporter, pCGMDriver As ICGMDriver
  Dim pDriverBounds As IEnvelope, pCGMExporter As ICGMExporter
  Dim screenResolution As Long
  Dim hDc As OLE_HANDLE
  Dim userRECT As tagRECT
  Dim pMxDoc As IMxDocument
  Dim pActive As IActiveView
  Dim pEnv As IEnvelope

  Set pMxDoc = ThisDocument
  Set pEnv = pMxDoc.ActiveView.Extent

  screenResolution = _
    pMxDoc.ActiveView.ScreenDisplay.DisplayTransformation.Resolution
```

```
          Set pExporter = New CGMExporter
          pExporter.ExportFileName = "C:\temp\ArcMapExport2.cgm"
          pExporter.Resolution = screenResolution
          Set pCGMExporter = pExporter
          Set pCGMDriver = pCGMExporter.QueryCGMDriver
          pCGMDriver.PolygonizeText = True

          userRECT.top = 0
          userRECT.Left = 0
          userRECT.Right = ConvertRWToPixels(pEnv.Width)
          userRECT.bottom = ConvertRWToPixels(pEnv.Height)

          Set pDriverBounds = New Envelope
          pDriverBounds.PutCoords userRECT.Left, userRECT.bottom, _
                              userRECT.Right, userRECT.top
          pExporter.PixelBounds = pDriverBounds
          hDc = pExporter.StartExporting

          pMxDoc.ActiveView.Output hDc, screenResolution, userRECT, pEnv, Nothing
          pExporter.FinishExporting
      End Sub
```

Output

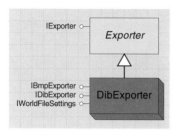

IExporter ○— Exporter

IBmpExporter ○—
IDibExporter ○— DibExporter
IWorldFileSettings ○—

The DIB exporter creates output in the device-independent bitmap format.

The *DibExporter* coclass creates output files in the DIB (device-independent bitmap) format. BMP files store graphics in the DIB format; the default file extension for this object type is .bmp. Create an object of this type when you want to generate your map as a BMP file.

The *IExporter::Resolution* property cannot be set when using an object of this type.

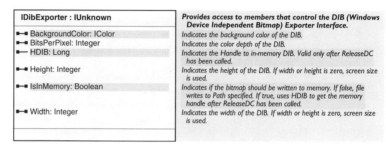

IDibExporter : IUnknown	Provides access to members that control the DIB (Windows Device Independent Bitmap) Exporter Interface.
■—■ BackgroundColor: IColor	Indicates the background color of the DIB.
■—■ BitsPerPixel: Integer	Indicates the color depth of the DIB.
■— HDIB: Long	Indicates the Handle to in-memory DIB. Valid only after ReleaseDC has been called.
■—■ Height: Integer	Indicates the height of the DIB. If width or height is zero, screen size is used.
■—■ IsInMemory: Boolean	Indicates if the bitmap should be written to memory. If false, file writes to Path specified. If true, uses HDIB to get the memory handle after ReleaseDC has been called.
■—■ Width: Integer	Indicates the width of the DIB. If width or height is zero, screen size is used.

IDibExporter is implemented only by the *DibExporter* coclass and the only object that implements this interface. This interface provides DIB- or BMP-specific properties the developer can set before outputting map data to files in this format.

IBmpExporter : IUnknown	Provides access to members that control the BMP (Bitmap) Exporter Interface.
■— Bitmap: Long	Indicates the Windows Bitmap handle.
■— Palette: Long	Indicates the Windows Bitmap color palette.

The *IBmpExporter* interface provides access to the OLE_Handles used during the export process. These handles can be used to send additional information to the BMP file.

IWorldFileSettings : IUnknown	Provides access to members that control the World File Exporter Interface.
■—■ MapExtent: IEnvelope	Indicates the Map Extent.
■—■ OutputWorldFile: Boolean	Indicates if a World File will be created.

The *IWorldFileSettings* interface is implemented exclusively by the *DibExporter* and *TiffExporter* coclasses. The interface allows the developer to specify whether a world file (a file containing information about the spatial extent of the data within the file) will be created during the output process.

The *MapExtent* property sets the spatial extent of the map data being outputted.

This VBA code uses the *DibExporter* object and its *IDibExport* and *IWorldFileSettings* interfaces to output a BMP file with a related world file:

```
Sub BMPExport()
    Dim pExporter As IExporter, pDibExporter As IDibExporter
    Dim pDriverBounds As IEnvelope, pWorldFile As IWorldFileSettings
```

```
Dim hDc As OLE_HANDLE
Dim userRECT As tagRECT
Dim pMxDoc As IMxDocument
Dim pActive As IActiveView
Dim pEnv As IEnvelope

Set pMxDoc = ThisDocument
Set pEnv = pMxDoc.ActiveView.Extent
Set pExporter = New DibExporter
pExporter.ExportFileName = "C:\temp\ArcMapExport.bmp"
Set pDibExporter = pExporter
pDibExporter.IsInMemory = False
Set pWorldFile = pExporter
pWorldFile.OutputWorldFile = True
pWorldFile.MapExtent = pEnv

userRECT.top = 0
userRECT.Left = 0
userRECT.Right = ConvertRWToPixels(pEnv.Width)
userRECT.bottom = ConvertRWToPixels(pEnv.Height)

Set pDriverBounds = New Envelope
pDriverBounds.PutCoords userRECT.Left, _
                  userRECT.bottom, _
                  userRECT.Right, _
                  userRECT.top
pExporter.PixelBounds = pDriverBounds
hDc = pExporter.StartExporting

pMxDoc.ActiveView.Output hDc, pExporter.Resolution, userRECT, pEnv, _
  Nothing
pExporter.FinishExporting
End Sub
```

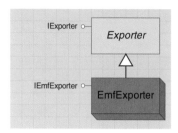

The *EMF exporter creates output in the Microsoft Enhanced Metafile format.*

The *EmfExporter* coclass creates output files in the EMF format. Create an object of this type when you want to generate your map output as an EMF file.

IEmfExporter : IUnknown	Provides access to members that control the EMF (Enhanced Windows Metafile) Exporter Interface.
■—■ Description: String	*Indicates a description string to embed in the file.*
■—— HENHMETAFILE: Long	*Indicates the Handle to in-memory metafile. Valid only after ReleaseDC has been called.*
■—■ IsInMemory: Boolean	*Indicates if the metafile will be written to memory.*
◄— TakeHENHMETAFILE: Long	*Returns the handle to the in-memory metafile. Valid only after ReleaseDC has been called. Ownership of the handle is transferred to the client who must call DeleteEnhMetafile on the returned handle. Subsequent calls to this routine will return 0.*

IEmfExporter is implemented only by the *EmfExporter* coclass and the only object that implements this interface. This interface provides EMF-specific properties the developer can set or retrieve before outputting map data in this format.

The *IsInMemory* property sets or returns whether the Metafile will be written to memory. Be sure this property is set to *True* before trying to use the *HENHMETAFILE* or *TakeHENHMETAFILE* properties.

The *JpegExporter* coclass will create output files in the JPEG format. Create an object of this type when you want to generate your map output as a JPG file.

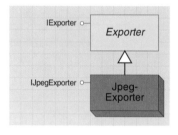

The *JPEG exporter creates output in the format set by the Joint Photographic Experts Group.*

IJpegExporter : IUnknown	Provides access to members that control the JPEG (Joint Photographic Experts Goup) Exporter Interface.
■—■ BackgroundColor: IColor	*Indicates the background color of the JPEG.*
■—■ Height: Integer	*Indicates the height of the JPEG. If width or height is zero, screen size is used.*
■—■ Quality: Integer	*Indicates the JPEG compression / image quality.*
■—■ Width: Integer	*Indicates the width of the JPEG. If width or height is zero, screen size is used.*

IJpegExporter is implemented only by the *JpegExporter* coclass and the only object that implements this interface. This interface provides JPEG-specific properties the developer can set or retrieve before outputting map data in this format.

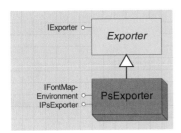

The PsExporter *creates output in the PostScript format.*

The *PsExporter* coclass creates output files in the PostScript format. Create an object of this type when you want to generate your map output in the PostScript format.

IPsExporter : IUnknown	Provides access to members that control the EPS (Encapsulated PostScript) Exporter Interface.
← QueryPSDriver: IPSDriver	Returns Interface IPSDriver.

IPsExporter is implemented only by the *PsExporter* coclass. *PsExporter* is the only object that implements this interface. The interface provides the ability to query for the PostScript driver being used by the object.

The *IFontMapEnvironment* interface is documented with the *FontMapEnvironment* coclass.

The *PsDriver* coclass is internally created by the *PsExporter* coclass and is documented earlier in this chapter.

Output

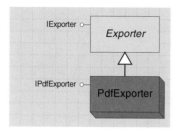

The PDFExporter *creates output in the Portable Document Format.*

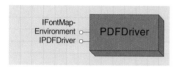

The PDF driver is created by the PDFExporter object during the output of map data to a PDF file.

The *PDFExporter* coclass generates output files in the Portable Document Format (PDF). Create an object of this type when you want to generate your map output in PDF.

This object internally creates the *PDFDriver* coclass to generate output in PDF.

IPDFExporter : IUnknown	Provides access to members that control the PDF (Portable Document Format) Exporter Interface.

IPDFExporter is implemented only by the *PDFExporter* coclass. This interface doesn't support any properties or methods, but you can use it to identify the object as being type *PDFExporter*.

The *PDFDriver* coclass is creatable by the developer, but it is also internally created by the *PDFExporter* object. The *PDFDriver* object does all the work in producing PDF files as output.

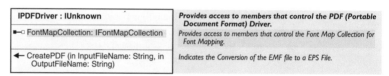

IPDFDriver : IUnknown	Provides access to members that control the PDF (Portable Document Format) Driver.
▪─▫ FontMapCollection: IFontMapCollection	Provides access to members that control the Font Map Collection for Font Mapping.
◄─ CreatePDF (in InputFileName: String, in OutputFileName: String)	Indicates the Conversion of the EMF file to a EPS File.

IPDFDriver is implemented only by the *PDFDriver* coclass. This interface allows the developer to set additional parameters before outputting map data to PDF.

CreatePDF requires the input of an EMF file to produce the PDF output file. The developer can avoid having to create the EMF file by using the *PDFExporter* object (and the inherited *IExporter* interface) to generate output.

The *IFontMapEnvironment* interface is documented with the *FontMapEnvironment* coclass.

IExportDialog o—
IExportDialog2 o— **ExportDialog**

The Export dialog box displays a dialog box for users to enter filename and desired format for outputting map data.

The *ExportDialog* coclass creates a dialog box for the user to enter in the export filename and desired format. After qualified entries have been made in the dialog box, the appropriate exporter object is created; you can get that object through the *IExportDialog::Exporter* property for further processing.

As the VBA code below demonstrates, the *ExportDialog* object presents the simplest method for the developer to write code to allow the user to produce output in the desired file format.

```
Sub OutputInFileFormat()
  Dim pDialog As IExportDialog, bOut As Boolean, pEnv As Ienvelope
  Dim hDc As OLE_HANDLE, pMxDoc As IMxDocument
  Dim pExporter As IExporter, pDriverBounds As IEnvelope
  Dim userRECT As tagRECT, lRes As Long, screenResolution As Long
  Set pEnv = New Envelope
  Set pMxDoc = ThisDocument
  Set pDialog = New ExportDialog
  bOut = pDialog.DoModal(pEnv, lRes)
  If Not bOut Then Exit Sub

  Set pEnv = pMxDoc.ActiveView.Extent
  userRECT.top = 0
  userRECT.Left = 0
  userRECT.Right = ConvertRWToPixels(pEnv.Width)
  userRECT.bottom = ConvertRWToPixels(pEnv.Height)
  screenResolution = _
    pMxDoc.ActiveView.ScreenDisplay.DisplayTransformation.Resolution

  Set pExporter = pDialog.Exporter
  pExporter.Resolution = screenResolution
  Set pDriverBounds = New Envelope
  pDriverBounds.PutCoords userRECT.Left, userRECT.bottom, _
                          userRECT.Right, userRECT.top
  pExporter.PixelBounds = pDriverBounds

  hDc = pExporter.StartExporting
  pMxDoc.ActiveView.Output hDc, screenResolution, userRECT, pEnv, Nothing
  pExporter.FinishExporting
End Sub

Private Function ConvertRWToPixels(RWUnits As Double) As Double
  Dim realWorldDisplayExtent As Double
  Dim pixelExtent As Long
  Dim sizeOfOnePixel As Double
  Dim pDT As IDisplayTransformation
  Dim deviceRECT As tagRECT
  Dim pEnv As IEnvelope
  Dim pMxDoc As IMxDocument

  Set pMxDoc = ThisDocument
```

Output

```
Set pDT = pMxDoc.ActiveView.ScreenDisplay.DisplayTransformation
deviceRECT = pDT.DeviceFrame
pixelExtent = deviceRECT.Right - deviceRECT.Left
Set pEnv = pDT.VisibleBounds

realWorldDisplayExtent = pEnv.Width
sizeOfOnePixel = realWorldDisplayExtent / pixelExtent
ConvertRWToPixels = RWUnits / sizeOfOnePixel
End Function
```

IExportDialog : IUnknown	Provides access to members that export a map to another file format.
▪━ ClipToGraphicExtent: Boolean	*Indicates if Clip To Graphic Extent option is selected.*
▪━ DisableClipGrahicsCheckBox: Boolean	*Indicates if Clip To Graphic Extent checkbox is enabled.*
━▪ DocumentName: String	*Name of the Active Document.*
▪━ Exporter: IExporter	*The Exporter to be used.*
◄━ DoModal (in pPixelBounds: IEnvelope, in res: Integer) : Boolean	*Displays Export Dialog.*

IExportDialog is implemented only by the *ExportDialog* object. The interface provides a method for capturing user input specifying output file parameters.

The *Exporter* property returns the *IExporter* interface on the object created based on the user selection in the dialog box. Be sure to determine the type of exporter before trying to perform specific operations on the object.

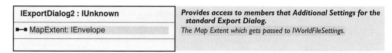

IExportDialog2 : IUnknown	Provides access to members that Additional Settings for the standard Export Dialog.
▪━ MapExtent: IEnvelope	*The Map Extent which gets passed to IWorldFileSettings.*

The *IExportDialog2* interface was added at ArcGIS 8.1 to allow for the setting and retrieval of the map extent. The map extent gets passed to the *IWorldFileSettings::MapExtent* property when output is being sent through the *TiffExporter* and *DibExporter* objects and is ultimately saved with the file.

7

Working with the Catalog

Larry Young, Aleta Vienneau, Keith Ludwig

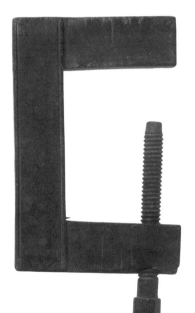

The Catalog is the place where you can assemble connections to all the data you need to use. When you choose a connection, you can access the data to which it's linked, whether it's a folder on a local disk or a database on the network. Together, your connections create a catalog of geographic data sources.

This chapter reveals how the ArcObjects components let you: browse for maps and data • inspect features with the contents view • explore the data through thumbnails • look at geographic data with geography view • inspect the attributes of a geographic data source with a table view • view and create metadata • search for maps and data • use data in ArcMap and ArcToolbox • manage data sources • create layers with the Catalog

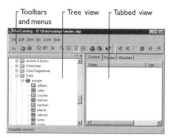

Toolbars and menus | Tree view | Tabbed view

When you select an item in the tree view, that becomes the selection location—the items you select in the contents view become the selected set of objects at that location.

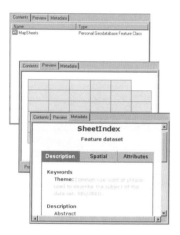

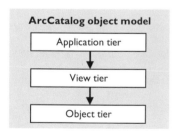

ArcCatalog object model

Application tier → View tier → Object tier

The Gx prefix through ArcCatalog refers to an early internal prerelease name of ArcCatalog: "GX", short for the "geographic explorer".

ArcCatalog is the application you use to browse and manage all of your local and remote GIS data. It is patterned after Windows Explorer to promote rapid familiarity and ease of use.

The user interface consists of three main elements: a tree view, a tabbed view, and a set of toolbars and menus. The tree view depicts your data holdings in a hierarchical structure of names and icons. The tabbed view is really a set of data views, each of which appears on its own tab, and one of which is active at any given time. These data views let you visualize your data in a variety of ways. The toolbars and menus contain all the tools and commands that enable you to manipulate and work with your data.

The three primary data views are contents view, metadata view, and preview view:

- Contents view displays an iconic list of all the children of the selection location, just like its counterpart in Windows Explorer. By default, this is the active view when you start up ArcCatalog.

- Metadata view shows all the metadata associated with the current selection. By default, the format comes from an ESRI style sheet, but this can be customized.

- Preview view is a set of data views, one of which may be active at any given moment (just like the tabbed view). By default, preview chooses whichever data view is most natural and appropriate for displaying the current selection. For example, if you've selected a shapefile, Preview will show you its geography by default. However, a dropdown menu at the bottom of the preview allows you to override this and explicitly pick the view you wish to use.

ARCHITECTURE

The object model for ArcCatalog closely mirrors the actual user interface experience. The running application is represented by the *GxApplication* object. Its major purpose is to manage the three main interface elements—the tree view (*GxTreeView*), the active tabbed view (*IGxApplication::View*), and the toolbars and menus. It also represents the starting point for developers that wish to customize or augment the standard application behavior. From the application object, you can navigate to all the objects within ArcCatalog and execute methods on them.

The object model consists of three separate but related tiers of functionality—the object tier, the view tier, and the application tier.

Object tier

The object tier is the bottom level in the object model. *GxObjects* represent individual data items and are as they appear in the tree view and the contents view. Different types of *GxObjects* are used for different types of data. For example, the *GxLayer* object represents layer files,

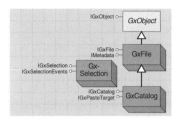

Behind the user interface, two objects serve as the heart and soul of ArcCatalog—the catalog object, GxCatalog, and the current selection object, GxSelection. The Catalog represents your actual tree of data and is shown through the tree view. The selection itself is really composed of two parts: a location and a set of objects at that location.

whereas the *GxMap* object encapsulates map documents. Within the *GxObject* tier, two objects are of supreme importance: the catalog object (*GxCatalog*) and the current selection (*GxSelection*).

The Catalog represents your actual tree of data, as is shown in the tree view. From the *GxCatalog* object, you can navigate to any of its descendants to access and manipulate them. Most often, however, you will work with the selection, which is composed of two parts: a location and a set of selected objects at that location. When you select an item in the tree view, that becomes the selection location; the items you select in the contents view become the selected set of objects at that location. Most operations in ArcCatalog work on the current selection.

The object tier is extensible. To add custom *GxObjects*, create an object that supports at least *IGxObject*. (Typically, you'll also want to implement *IGxObjectUI* and *IGxObjectEdit*.) You also need to write a *GxObjectFactory* that knows how to manufacture your custom *GxObjects*. This factory is used by *ArcCatalog* as folders are expanded to detect what objects exist within that folder.

View tier

The view tier is the middle tier. Its views display individual *GxObjects* in a host of different ways. They represent different user interfaces on the *GxObjects*. Different *GxViews* are used for different tasks. For example, to rapidly browse for a data set, you might use the *GxContentsView* because it has different list styles. To look for data with certain attributes, use the *GxDocumentationView*. *GxGeographicView* is extremely useful for seeing what the dataset actually looks like before you use it.

ArcCatalog offers a simple framework for hosting *GxViews*. The tree view is always available (even though it can be shown and hidden by the user as desired). It is the primary navigation tool within ArcCatalog and is used to establish the current selection location. The selection location governs what is shown by the other *GxViews*.

ArcCatalog offers two ways to show the other views: as tabbed views or as previews. Tabbed views show up as individual tabs within the main ArcCatalog window. By default, there are three: Contents, Preview, and Metadata. However, a developer can add as many as they want.

Previews show up as combo box choices within the Preview tab and are generally used for those views that show static views of the data (such as geography, table, 3D, and so on). Regardless of the view style chosen, the actual implementation of the *GxView* is not affected. It is the same for either. However, other than the visual differentiation, there is a minor functional difference between the two view types.

Tabbed views can only be chosen manually. However, previews are automatically chosen depending on what kind of object is currently selected. If the Preview tab is active, when the user changes the selection location, ArcCatalog uses the *IGxView::Applies* method to ask each registered preview if it can handle the type of object selected. If the

ArcCatalog

current preview supports it, no switching occurs. However, if the current preview does not support it, the first view that says that it can support it is chosen as the active preview. Users may, of course, switch the preview to a different one afterwards, but the automatic switching logic still occurs when the selection changes.

Application tier

The top tier of ArcCatalog, the application tier, is dominated by the *GxApplication* and its associated menus and toolbars. It manages the lifetime of the *GxCatalog* and its descendants and manages all the *GxViews*.

When the application starts up, ArcCatalog creates *GxDisk-Connection* objects for each folder connected at the root and populates the Catalog tree.

If this is the first time you've started ArcCatalog, it will add all your local drives as folder connections to get you started. Also at this level, ArcCatalog creates and adds any *GxObject* objects that are registered in the *CATID_GxRootObjects ("ESRI Gx Root Objects")* component category.

Several root objects are supplied by default—the Database Connections folder, the Coordinate Systems folder, the Geocoding Services folder, the Internet Servers folder, and the Search Results folder. Typically, these root objects act as containers of other objects and therefore implement *IGxObjectContainer*, but this is not a requirement.

When any container object is expanded in ArcCatalog, its children are retrieved via the *Children* property of *IGxObjectContainer* and are then shown in the tree view (and possibly the contents view). Most container objects have hardwired knowledge about what their children are. A notable exception is the *GxFolder*. It discovers its list of children dynamically using a set of *GxObjectFactory* objects.

When a *GxFolder* is first asked for its children, it loops over all the registered *GxObjectFactory* objects (in the *CATID_GxObjectFactories* component category) and calls their *GetChildren* methods, passing in the directory path and a list of filenames. The object factory responds by returning an enumeration of *GxObject* objects for everything that it recognizes within that folder. For example, the *GxObjectFactory* for shapefiles looks for all files that have a .shp extension and creates and returns *GxShapefile* objects for each one of them.

As an optimization, ArcCatalog actually calls *HasChildren* first on the factory before calling *GetChildren*—in response, the factory should do a quick scan of the folder first to see if there are any children. This saves looping over all the filenames, since *HasChildren* can return *True* once the first valid file is found.

Then, using the *IGxObjectUI* interface, ArcCatalog asks each child for an icon to use for display purposes. If the object doesn't support this interface, a default icon is used instead. Its name is shown next to the icon, and, in details view, its type information (derived from the *IGxObject::Category* property) is also displayed.

DATA TRANSFER (VIA DRAG/DROP AND COPY/PASTE)

ArcCatalog uses the standard OLE data transfer mechanism for both drag and drop and copy and paste. This is always the case, whether or not it is acting as the source of the operation, the destination, or both. To fully understand how drag/drop and copy/paste works, it is best to look at how ArcCatalog behaves when it is both the source and destination.

ArcCatalog

DRAG/DROP WITHIN ArcCatalog

When it detects that a drag operation has started, ArcCatalog packages the selected *GxObjects* into a data object (*IDataObject*) and passes this to OLE.

ArcCatalog packages the selected *GxObjects* up as follows. First, the current selection of *GxObjects* is identified (via the *GxSelection* object). Then, each *GxObject* in the selection is asked for its internal name object via the *InternalNameObject* property. Those that return nothing for this property aren't considered. All of the internal *Name* objects are then persisted into a stream that is placed into an OLE data object. To persist them into this stream, ArcCatalog creates a *NameFactory* utility object, then invokes its *PackageNames* method. This data object is then passed over to OLE to let it proceed with the operation.

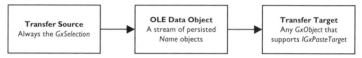

Then OLE takes over. If the operation is a drag/drop, OLE enters a modal event loop while the drag takes place. During this event loop, OLE checks to see where the mouse is currently located. If the mouse enters an *hWnd* that is registered as a drop target, OLE invokes the *IDropTarget* interface on it, first calling *DragEnter*, then *DragOver*, and *DragLeave* as necessary. (To register an *hWnd* as a potential drop target, call the Win32 method *RegisterDragDrop*.) If the user releases the mouse over the *hWnd*, OLE calls the *Drop* method.

Since ArcCatalog is the destination for the data transfer in this example, ArcCatalog handles the *IDropTarget* requests from OLE. It does so as follows. As the mouse moves within the tree or contents view, ArcCatalog checks to see if target *GxObject* is a valid recipient for the data transfer. Any object that supports *IGxPasteTarget* is considered. Here's that interface:

```
interface IGxPasteTarget:
Function CanPaste(names as IEnumName, moveOperation as Boolean) as Boolean
Function Paste(names as IEnumName, moveOperation as Boolean) as Boolean
```

ArcCatalog transforms the drag data into a more usable form, namely, an enumeration of *Name* objects (*IEnumName*). It then calls *CanPaste* to determine if the drop target can accept the *Names* being dragged. In response, the potential target enumerates through the list of *Names* to see if it can handle them. For example, the *GxDatabase* object checks to make sure all the *Name* objects are actually *DatasetNames* (that is, they support *IDatasetName*). Other objects might check to make sure the *Name* objects support *IFileName*. If the target *GxObject* decides it can accept a drop, it returns *True*. If the data isn't supported, it returns *False*. The *GxObject* must also indicate if the drag operation represents a move or a copy. It does so by setting the value of the *moveOperation* parameter to *True* or *False*.

When the user releases the mouse button, OLE calls *IDropTarget::Drop*. ArcCatalog responds by calling the *IGxPasteTarget::Paste* method on the *GxObject*, again passing in the list of *Names*. It also passes in *True* or *False* for *moveOperation* to indicate if the operation is to be a move or just a copy. At this point, the target *GxObject* must carry out the actual data transfer operation in whatever fashion makes sense for the data. (For example, *GxDatabase* handles data transfers by issuing geodatabase schema changes and cursor requests to physically move rows from one place to another. Other transfer targets might behave similarly, or do something entirely different, depending on the kind of data involved.) If the data transfer involves changes that should be reflected in the ArcCatalog tree or contents views, be sure to call *Refresh* to make those changes visible.

The target *GxObject* also needs to indicate whether or not an actual move was carried out if *moveOperation* was initially *True*. It does so by setting this parameter to *True* or *False* before returning. Finally, if the data transfer operation succeeded, the function returns *True*; otherwise it returns *False*.

COPY/PASTE IN ArcCatalog

If the transfer operation is a copy/paste instead of a drag/drop, the situation is very similar—only a few things are different. First, when the copy is initiated, ArcCatalog packages up the selected *GxObjects* into a data object as before (by asking them for their internal *Names*). It then places this data object onto the OLE clipboard, where it remains available for other applications to paste it.

Whenever the current selection location changes in ArcCatalog (either manually or programmatically), ArcCatalog needs to check to see if the *Paste* command should be enabled. It does this by calling *IGxPasteTarget::CanPaste* on the current location. The desirable aspect of this behavior is that the implementation for *IGxPasteTarget* is the same for the target, regardless of the type of data transfer operation (copy/paste or drag/drop). It responds in exactly the same way as it does for the drag/drop case. If the user selects the *Paste* command, ArcCatalog invokes the *Paste* method on the current location.

ArcCatalog

GxView objects

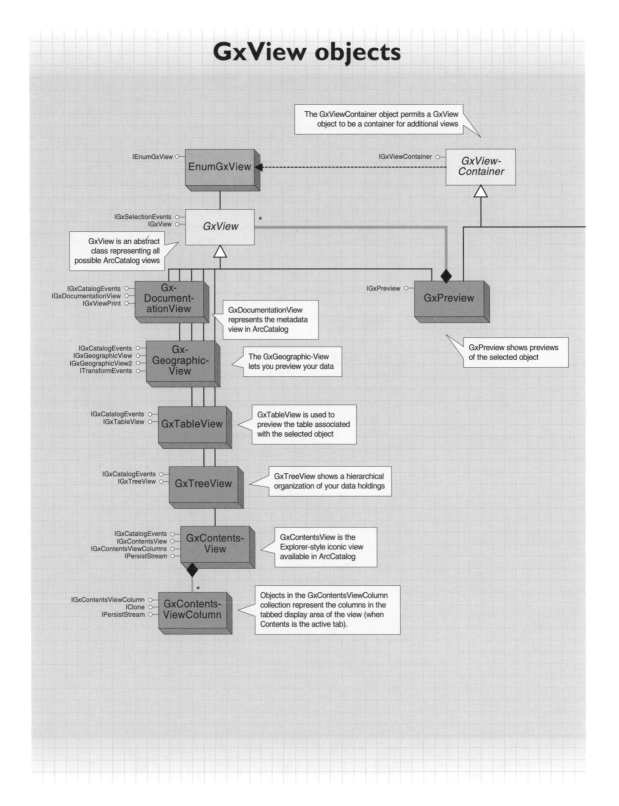

The GxViewContainer object permits a GxView object to be a container for additional views

IEnumGxView ○— **EnumGxView**

IGxViewContainer ○— **GxView-Container**

IGxSelectionEvents ○—
IGxView ○— *GxView*   *

GxView is an abstract class representing all possible ArcCatalog views

IGxCatalogEvents ○—
IGxDocumentationView ○—
IGxViewPrint ○— **Gx-Documentation-View**

GxDocumentationView represents the metadata view in ArcCatalog

IGxPreview ○— **GxPreview**

GxPreview shows previews of the selected object

IGxCatalogEvents ○—
IGxGeographicView ○—
IGxGeographicView2 ○—
ITransformEvents ○— **Gx-Geographic-View**

The GxGeographic-View lets you preview your data

IGxCatalogEvents ○—
IGxTableView ○— **GxTableView**

GxTableView is used to preview the table associated with the selected object

IGxCatalogEvents ○—
IGxTreeView ○— **GxTreeView**

GxTreeView shows a hierarchical organization of your data holdings

IGxCatalogEvents ○—
IGxContentsView ○—
IGxContentsViewColumns ○—
IPersistStream ○— **GxContents-View**

GxContentsView is the Explorer-style iconic view available in ArcCatalog

IGxContentsViewColumn ○—
IClone ○—
IPersistStream ○— **GxContents-ViewColumn**   *

Objects in the GxContentsViewColumn collection represent the columns in the tabbed display area of the view (when Contents is the active tab).

GxApplication and related objects

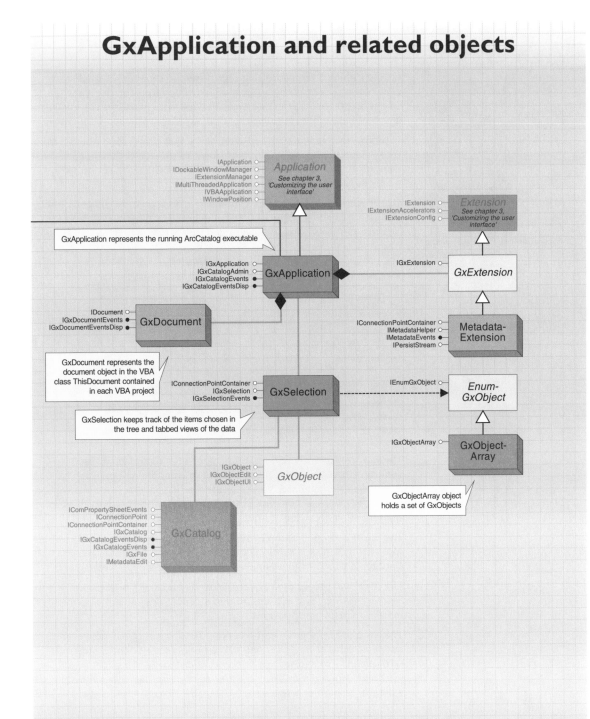

IApplication
IDockableWindowManager
IExtensionManager
IMultiThreadedApplication
IVBAApplication
IWindowPosition

Application
See chapter 3, 'Customizing the user interface'

IExtension
IExtensionAccelerators
IExtensionConfig

Extension
See chapter 3, 'Customizing the user interface'

GxApplication represents the running ArcCatalog executable

IGxApplication
IGxCatalogAdmin
IGxCatalogEvents
IGxCatalogEventsDisp

GxApplication

IGxExtension

GxExtension

IDocument
IGxDocumentEvents
IGxDocumentEventsDisp

GxDocument

IConnectionPointContainer
IMetadataHelper
IMetadataEvents
IPersistStream

Metadata-Extension

GxDocument represents the document object in the VBA class ThisDocument contained in each VBA project

IConnectionPointContainer
IGxSelection
IGxSelectionEvents

GxSelection

IEnumGxObject

Enum-GxObject

GxSelection keeps track of the items chosen in the tree and tabbed views of the data

IGxObject
IGxObjectEdit
IGxObjectUI

GxObject

IGxObjectArray

GxObject-Array

IComPropertySheetEvents
IConnectionPoint
IConnectionPointContainer
IGxCatalog
IGxCatalogEventsDisp
IGxCatalogEvents
IGxFile
IMetadataEdit

GxCatalog

GxObjectArray object holds a set of GxObjects

ArcCatalog

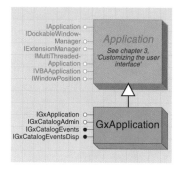

GxApplication *represents the running ArcCatalog application.*

GxApplication is the object that represents the running ArcCatalog executable. It creates and manages the user interface—the tree view, the tabbed views, and the menus and toolbars—and initializes the Catalog tree by creating the *GxCatalog* root object.

Typically, developers will start their navigation of the object model from *GxApplication* and work their way down to the object they need to manipulate. All commands and tools are passed a reference to the *GxApplication* in their *OnCreate* method.

GxApplication supports *IApplication* and *IGxApplication*. *IApplication* is common to both ArcMap and ArcCatalog and is described in detail in Chapter 3, 'Customizing the user interface'.

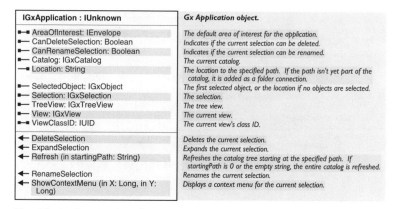

The *IGxApplication* interface is unique to ArcCatalog and is used to control certain aspects of its behavior. For example, through the *IGxApplication* interface, you can delete or expand the current selection (through *DeleteSelection* and *ExpandSelection*) or force a refresh of a certain part of the Catalog tree (through *Refresh*).

The *Catalog* property returns the *GxCatalog* object, which represents the root of the Catalog data tree. From there, you can use *IGxObject-Container::Children* to enumerate through the Catalog's descendants.

The *TreeView* property gives you access to ArcCatalog's tree view. From this *GxTreeView*, you can ensure that a certain descendant is visible or initiate a renaming operation.

The *View* property gives you access to the active *GxView*, whatever it happens to be. It might be one of the built-in views—for example, *GxContentsView, GxPreview,* or *GxMetadataView*—or it might be a developer-added one. From here, you can manipulate the active view in whatever fashion is native to it.

IGxCatalogEvents : IUnknown	Provides access to events that the catalog can fire.
← OnObjectAdded (Object: IGxObject)	Called when an object has been added to some part of the catalog.
← OnObjectChanged (Object: IGxObject)	Called when an object in some part of the catalog has been changed.
← OnObjectDeleted (Object: IGxObject)	Called when an object has been deleted from some part of the catalog.
← OnObjectRefreshed (Object: IGxObject)	Called when an object in some part of the catalog has been refreshed.
← OnRefreshAll	Called when the whole catalog has changed.

IGxCatalogEvents interface is the events interface implemented by *GxApplication*. This interface allows developers to attach code to the various events fired by ArcCatalog, such as when objects are added or deleted.

When a refresh is performed on ArcCatalog (when the user clicks the View menu and clicks Refresh), only the *Location* object (the selected object in the tree view) is passed to the *OnObjectRefreshed* event. However, everything underneath this object is refreshed.

GxSelection *keeps track of items chosen in the tree view.*

The *GxSelection* object keeps track of the items chosen in the tree and tabbed views of the data. A *GxSelection* object can be created, but more commonly it is retrieved from the *GxApplication* (*IGxApplication::- Selection*). What is selected is key in determining what context menus to display when the user right-clicks and in determining copy/paste capabilities of the objects.

Here is some VBA code that uses the *GxSelection* object to loop through the selected set of objects and display their categories:

```
Dim pApp As IGxApplication, pGxSel As IGxSelection, _
  pEnumGxObj As IEnumGxObject
Dim pGxObj As IGxObject
Set pApp = Application
Set pGxSel = pApp.Selection
Set pEnumGxObj = pGxSel.SelectedObjects
Set pGxObj = pEnumGxObj.Next
Do While Not pGxObj Is Nothing
  Debug.Print pGxObj.Category
  Set pGxObj = pEnumGxObj.Next
Loop
```

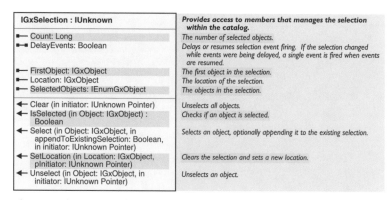

IGxSelection : IUnknown	Provides access to members that manages the selection within the catalog.
■— Count: Long	The number of selected objects.
■—■ DelayEvents: Boolean	Delays or resumes selection event firing. If the selection changed while events were being delayed, a single event is fired when events are resumed.
■— FirstObject: IGxObject	The first object in the selection.
■— Location: IGxObject	The location of the selection.
■— SelectedObjects: IEnumGxObject	The objects in the selection.
◄— Clear (in initiator: IUnknown Pointer)	Unselects all objects.
◄— IsSelected (in Object: IGxObject) : Boolean	Checks if an object is selected.
◄— Select (in Object: IGxObject, in appendToExistingSelection: Boolean, in initiator: IUnknown Pointer)	Selects an object, optionally appending it to the existing selection.
◄— SetLocation (in Location: IGxObject, pInitiator: IUnknown Pointer)	Clears the selection and sets a new location.
◄— Unselect (in Object: IGxObject, in initiator: IUnknown Pointer)	Unselects an object.

The *IGxSelection* interface is implemented by the *GxSelection* object and provides access to the objects selected in the tree and tabbed views of ArcCatalog. Use this interface when you want to determine what is selected or make changes to what is selected.

The *Location* method returns the *IGxObject* selected in the tree view (there can be only one), while the *SelectedObjects* method returns an enumeration of objects selected in the tabbed view.

FirstObject returns the first object selected in the tabbed view.

The methods that change the selection require an initiator parameter, which can be set to nothing. Calling one of these methods will fire the *SelectionChanged* event, and *SelectionChanged* will pass on the initiator parameter. The initiator is the object initiating the change.

The selection methods (*Clear, IsSelected, Select,* and *Unselect*) all operate on the selected objects in the tabbed view.

The following VBA code demonstrates how to use the *SetLocation* method to change the selection in tree view:

```
Dim pApp As IGxApplication
Dim pSel As IGxSelection
Dim pObject As IGxObject
Dim ln As Long
Set pApp = Application
Set pObject = pApp.Catalog.GetObjectFromFullName _
 ("d:\tools\various\labeling.txt", ln)
Set pSel = pApp.Selection
pSel.SetLocation pObject, Nothing
```

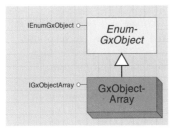

The GxObjectArray *object holds a set of* GxObjects.

The *GxObjectArray* object holds a set of *GxObjects*. The object is not returned by a method on any other object; therefore, it is up to the developer to create and manipulate an object of this type.

A few of the methods in the ArcCatalog object model take *IEnumGxObject* variables as input. Without the *GxObjectArray* class, developers would need to create their own custom class to implement *IEnumGxObject*.

IGxObjectArray : IUnknown	Provides access to members that manage an array of GX objects.
●— Count: Long	The number of objects in the array.
◄— Empty	Removes all objects from the array.
◄— Insert (in Index: Long, in gxObject: IGxObject)	Inserts an object into the array before the specified index. If index is -1, the object is inserted at the end.
◄— Item (in Index: Long) : IGxObject	The object at the given index in the array.
◄— Remove (in Index: Long)	Removes the object at the specified index in the array.

The *IGxObjectArray* interface is implemented by the *GxObjectArray* class and provides the ability to manipulate the set of *GxObjects* maintained by the class. Through this interface, the developer can insert, remove, and retrieve the objects within the array.

ArcCatalog

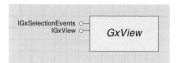

GxView *is an abstract class that represents all possible ArcCatalog views. There are five types of GxViews: Gx-ContentsView, GxGeographicView, GxPreview, GxTableView, and GxTreeView.*

There are two types of views: tabbed views and previews. They are implemented exactly the same but are registered in separate component categories depending on the look and feel desired.

Tabbed views show up as individual tabs in the ArcCatalog main window. They are always available regardless of the type of the current selection.

Previews are different—they are only available under the Preview tab and only show up if they are appropriate for the type of the current selection. The *Applies* property determines this. If the view does apply, it shows up as a possible choice in the preview dropdown combo box. If it doesn't apply, it does not show up. *Applies* has no effect when the view is registered as a tabbed view.

At the appropriate times, ArcCatalog calls *Activate* and *Deactivate* on the *GxView* to inform it that it is becoming active or inactive. In response, the view typically should refresh itself and establish or release references to any resources that it needs for interaction with the user.

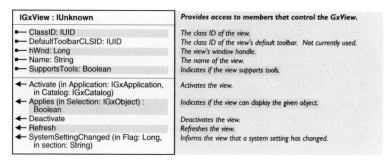

A *GxView* must minimally support the *IGxView* interface, which ArcCatalog uses to negotiate with the view. It asks the view for an *hWnd* to display through the *hWnd* property. It reparents this *hWnd* so that it is a child of an ArcCatalog *hWnd*. It also guarantees events are passed to the *hWnd* correctly and that it is resized when the ArcCatalog window is resized. Developers that wish to create their own custom views must implement this interface.

Use the *Activate* property to hold on to the *GxApplication* and *GxCatalog* objects that are passed in as parameters. The *Deactivate* property releases these references.

DefaultToolbarCLSID provides a reference to the default toolbar for the particular view. The default toolbar for a view contains tools that are appropriate for the current type of *GxView*.

If the *SupportsTools* property returns *True*, ArcCatalog will intercept mouse events normally destined for the view and instead send them to the active tool.

The following VBA code uses the *Name* property of the *IGxView* interface to determine if you are looking at a preview. If you are, then the class ID of the preview is changed to a table view.

```
Dim pApp As IGxApplication, pGxView As IGxView
Set pApp = Application
Set pGxView = pApp.View
If UCase(pGxView.Name) = "PREVIEW" Then
'The above line could be replaced with "If TypeOf pGxView Is IGxPreview  Then"
  Dim pPrev As IGxPreview, pUID As New UID
  Set pPrev = pGxView
  Debug.Print pPrev.ViewClassID
  pUID = "{9C34344D-99DC-11D2-AF6A-080009EC734B}"
  pPrev.ViewClassID = pUID
End If
```

IGxViewPrint : IUnknown	Provides access to members that control the printing of a GxView object.
■— IsPrintable: Boolean	Indicates if the view can be printed.
◄— Print	Prints the view.

GxViews optionally support the *IGxViewPrint* interface to allow the user to print the current display. This is especially handy for the metadata view, as it allows users to create scripts to print nicely formatted metadata for a batch of objects at once.

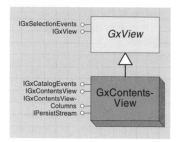

The Explorer-style iconic view available in ArcCatalog is the GxContentsView.

The *GxContentsView* coclass shows the children of the current selection location in a variety of styles: large icons, list, report, and thumbnails. You can set the style it uses by changing the *DisplayStyle* property on *IGxContentsView*.

Here is some VBA code for checking the current view to determine if it is a *GxContentsView*. This code also accesses properties associated with that view.

```
Sub test1()
  Dim pApp As IGxApplication, pView As IGxView
  Dim pContView As IGxContentsViewColumns, pCol As IGxContentsViewColumn
  Set pApp = Application
  Set pView = pApp.View
  If TypeOf pView Is IGxContentsViewColumns Then
    Set pContView = pView
    Set pCol = pContView.ColumnByIndex(0)
    Debug.Print pCol.Caption & ", " & pCol.PropertyName
  End If
End Sub
```

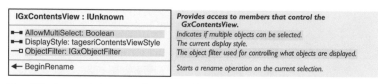

IGxContentsView : IUnknown	Provides access to members that control the GxContentsView.
▪━ AllowMultiSelect: Boolean	Indicates if multiple objects can be selected.
▪━ DisplayStyle: tagesriContentsViewStyle	The current display style.
━□ ObjectFilter: IGxObjectFilter	The object filter used for controlling what objects are displayed.
← BeginRename	Starts a rename operation on the current selection.

The *IGxContentsView* interface is implemented by the *GxContentsView* object. It provides the ability to change how users interact with a view of that type. What types of files are displayed, how they are displayed, and whether more than one can be selected at a time are all controlled through the interface.

Constrain the set of objects displayed by supplying an object filter through the *ObjectFilter* property. For a discussion of what filters are available and how to create your own, see the introductory section in this chapter on *GxDialog* and *GxObjectFilters*.

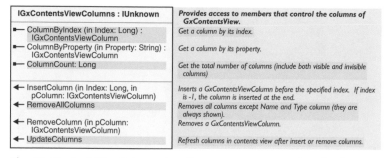

IGxContentsViewColumns : IUnknown	Provides access to members that control the columns of GxContentsView.
■━ ColumnByIndex (in Index: Long) : IGxContentsViewColumn	Get a column by its index.
■━ ColumnByProperty (in Property: String) : IGxContentsViewColumn	Get a column by its property.
■━ ColumnCount: Long	Get the total number of columns (include both visible and invisible columns)
← InsertColumn (in Index: Long, in pColumn: IGxContentsViewColumn)	Inserts a GxContentsViewColumn before the specified index. If index is -1, the column is inserted at the end.
← RemoveAllColumns	Removes all columns except Name and Type column (they are always shown).
← RemoveColumn (in pColumn: IGxContentsViewColumn)	Removes a GxContentsViewColumn.
← UpdateColumns	Refresh columns in contents view after insert or remove columns.

The *IGxContentsViewColumns* interface serves as a container for the *GxContentsViewColumn* objects contained within the *GxContentsView* object. The objects in the collection represent the columns in the tabbed display area of the view (when Contents is the active tab).

After using the *InsertColumn* method to add your new column, execute the *UpdateColumn* method to refresh the column list.

RemoveAllColumns will not remove the *Name* and *Type* columns. These columns cannot be removed. Keep in mind that removal of columns is not just for that session; it is permanent.

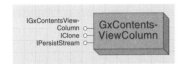

GxContentsViewColumn objects represent the columns of information displayed when the Contents tab is the active view. The developer has the ability to create and add additional columns of information to customize the contents view for displaying specific information.

GxContentsViewColumn *objects represent the columns of information displayed when the Contents tab is the active view.*

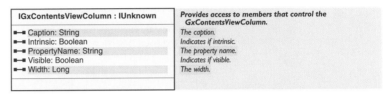

IGxContentsViewColumn : IUnknown	Provides access to members that control the GxContentsViewColumn.
▪─▪ Caption: String	The caption.
▪─▪ Intrinsic: Boolean	Indicates if intrinsic.
▪─▪ PropertyName: String	The property name.
▪─▪ Visible: Boolean	Indicates if visible.
▪─▪ Width: Long	The width.

The *IGxContentsViewColumn* interface provides access to the properties of the columns contained within the *GxContentsView* object. The column properties allow you to set the width, visibility, and caption of the column.

Intrinsic properties (*Intrinsic* property set to *True*) are properties such as *Name, Category,* and *Size.* These are not really useful unless you add your own *GxObject* through a new workspace factory; if you do this, you have the ability to add object-specific special properties.

The *PropertyName* property is based on keywords within the metadata for the object. Make sure you have metadata with the specific keyword before using it as a *PropertyName*.

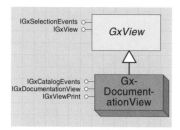

The GxDocumentationView *object opens the Metadata Properties dialog box.*

The metadata view in ArcCatalog is represented by *GxDocumentationView*. Since it is a *GxView*, it naturally supports *IGxView*. However, to manipulate it, you will want to work with *IGxDocumentationView*. This interface allows you to do three things: edit the metadata using a custom editor through *Edit*, edit the metadata properties with a default editor via *EditProperties*, and force the metadata to be updated with respect to the object's current attributes through *Synchronize*.

To build a custom editor, create an object that implements *IMetadataEditor* Interface, then inform the metadata extension object to use it through its *IMetadataHelper::Editor property*.

GxDocumentationView also implements *IGxViewPrint* to enable you to print the well-formatted metadata.

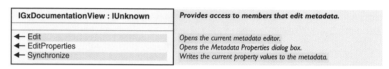

IGxDocumentationView : IUnknown	Provides access to members that edit metadata.
← Edit	Opens the current metadata editor.
← EditProperties	Opens the Metadata Properties dialog box.
← Synchronize	Writes the current property values to the metadata.

The *IGxDocumentationView* is implemented by *GxDocumentationView*. It provides a set of methods for manipulating the metadata associated with an object. Through this interface, the developer can open the editor associated with the metadata, access the metadata properties, or apply the edits made to the metadata.

The following VBA code brings up the default editor for the metadata associated with the selected object:

```
Dim pApp As IGxApplication, pGxView As IGxView, _
  pDocView As IGxDocumentationView
Set pApp = Application
Set pGxView = pApp.View
If TypeOf pGxView Is IGxDocumentationView Then
  Set pDocView = pGxView
  pDocView.Edit
End If
```

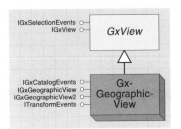

The GxGeographicView appears on the Preview tab.

When you want to preview your data, use *GxGeographicView*. It is available through the Preview tab in ArcCatalog. It displays the geography of the selected dataset in its window. By default, the *GxGeographicView* object shows up on the Preview tab page; however, the object implements *IGxView* like the other *GxView* objects and can be used as its own tab.

A set of standard manipulation tools is provided for zooming, panning, and performing identify. However, you can easily add your own tools, which can work with this view in whatever fashion you would like. You can do this by accessing the map or map display objects from the *IGxGeographicView* interface. Internally, the view uses the services of these two objects to display the selected item, and you can manipulate them as well.

The following VBA method accesses the geographic view's map (as an *IActiveView*) and zooms in a fixed amount:

```
Public Sub ZoomIn()
    Dim pApp As IGxApplication
    Set pApp = Application
    If Not TypeOf pApp.View Is IGxPreview Then Exit Sub

    Dim pPreview As IGxPreview
    Set pPreview = pApp.View
    If Not TypeOf pPreview.View Is IGxGeographicView Then Exit Sub

    Dim pGeoView As IGxGeographicView
    Set pGeoView = pPreview.View
    Dim pActiveView As IActiveView
    Set pActiveView = pGeoView.Map

    Dim pExtent As IEnvelope
    Set pExtent = pActiveView.Extent
    pExtent.Expand 0.75, 0.75, True
    pActiveView.Extent = pExtent
    pActiveView.Refresh
End Sub
```

Newer versions of ArcCatalog also support previewing a map document's page layout within the geographic view. In these cases, you can use the new *IGxGeographicView2* interface and access its *ActiveView* property. It will contain a reference to a page layout object if the selected item refers to a map document (*GxMap*). You can manipulate this object in any way you desire.

IGxGeographicView : IUnknown	Provides access to members that control the GxGeographicView.
■— DisplayedLayer: ILayer	*The layer object currently being displayed.*
■— Map: IMap	*The map object that is used to draw the layer.*
■— MapDisplay: IScreenDisplay	*The display object that is used to draw the layer.*

The *IGxGeographicView* interface is implemented by the *GxGeographicView* object. It provides access to the map and screen display that preview the currently selected object. Through this interface, the developer can retrieve the layer being displayed, then use the map and screen display properties to show additional information within the view.

The *DisplayedLayer* property is set to *Nothing* when the selected object cannot be previewed in the *GxGeographicView*. The following VBA code demonstrates how you might check for this condition:

```
Sub GxGeographicViewDisplayLayer()
  Dim pApp As IGxApplication
  Dim pView As IGxView
  Dim pPreview As IGxPreview
  Dim pGeo As IGxGeographicView

  Set pApp = Application
  Set pView = pApp.View

  If TypeOf pView Is IGxPreview Then
    Set pPreview = pView
    If TypeOf pPreview.View Is IGxGeographicView Then
      Set pGeo = pPreview.View
      If pGeo.DisplayedLayer Is Nothing Then
        Debug.Print "nothing is displayed"
      Else
        Debug.Print "something is there"
      End If
    End If
  End If
End Sub
```

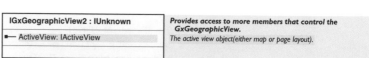

IGxGeographicView2 : IUnknown	Provides access to more members that control the GxGeographicView.
ActiveView: IActiveView	The active view object(either map or page layout).

The *IGxGeographicView2* interface provides access to the *IActiveView* of the map being used to preview the current selection.

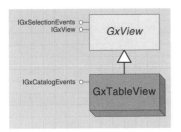

GXTableView *is accessed via the preview viewer. It shows a table view of the class.*

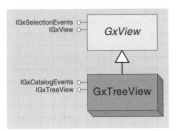

The tree view displays your data holdings in a parent–child structure.

The *GxTableView* object is similar to the *GxGeographicView* in that it is used to preview data. By default, it is accessed through the Preview tab. As the name implies, the *GxTableView* coclass is used to preview the table associated with the selected object. The coclass is a type of *GxView*, so it implements the *IGxView* interface, but it does not implement any additional interfaces.

The tree view is represented by *GxTreeView*; it shows a hierarchical organization of your data holdings as parents and children. It is unlikely you will need to interact programmatically with the tree view other than to force it to reveal a particular *GxObject* (through the *IGxTreeView::EnsureVisible* method) or to initiate a renaming operation (through *BeginRename*).

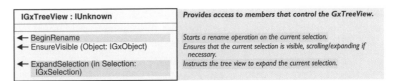

The *IGxTreeView* interface is implemented only by the *GxTreeView* object. It provides the ability to manipulate the object selected in the tree view. Through this interface, the developer can begin a rename process, ensure the visibility of the object, or expand the node in the tree view.

The following VBA code begins the rename process for the selected object in the tree view:

```
Dim pApp As IGxApplication, pTreeView As IGxTreeView
Set pApp = Application
Set pTreeView = pApp.TreeView
pTreeView.BeginRename
```

ArcCatalog

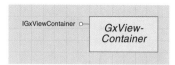

The GXViewContainer *supports holding more than one GXView within it.*

The *GxViewContainer* object permits a *GxView* object to be a container for additional views. The *GxPreview* coclass is the only type of *GxViewContainer* object currently implemented in ArcCatalog. Out of the box, the *GxPreview* object contains the *GxGeographicView* and *GxTableView* objects. This functionality is exposed in the user interface through the Geography and Table options on the Preview tab in ArcCatalog.

IGxViewContainer : IUnknown	Provides access to members that control the GxViewContainer.
■— Views: IEnumGxView	All gx views in the application.
◄— FindView (in pUID: IUID, bRecursive: Boolean) : IGxView	Finds a view by CLSID. If recursive is true, it will return views in a container view.

The *IGxViewContainer* interface provides access to the views within the container. It is not possible to add additional views to the container through this interface. Additional views must be added by registering a component in the ESRI GxPreviews category.

The *Views* property returns an enumeration of all the valid views in the container for the currently selected object.

The following VBA code demonstrates how to find the table view through the *IGxViewContainer* interface when the Preview tab is active:

```
Dim pApp As IGxApplication, pGxView As IGxView
Set pApp = Application
Set pGxView = pApp.View
If TypeOf pGxView Is IGxViewContainer Then
  Dim pViewCont As IGxViewContainer, pUID As New UID, pView As IGxView
  Set pViewCont = pGxView
  pUID = "{9C34344D-99DC-11D2-AF6A-080009EC734B}"
  Set pView = pViewCont.FindView(pUID, False)
  If pView Is Nothing Then
    MsgBox "could not find it"
  End If
End If
```

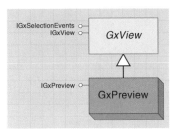

The GXPreview *coclass contains the geographic and table views as well as any user-defined views.*

The *GxPreview* coclass is the only type of *GxView* that is also a type of *GxViewContainer.* The class is implemented as a tab within ArcCatalog, but within that tab is a container for additional views. These views provide previews of the selected object, depending on which ones are applicable. For example, the geography and table previews are available for a shapefile, while only the table preview is available for a table.

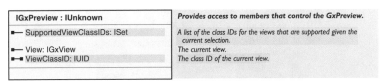

IGxPreview : IUnknown	Provides access to members that control the GxPreview.
SupportedViewClassIDs: ISet	A list of the class IDs for the views that are supported given the current selection.
View: IGxView	The current view.
ViewClassID: IUID	The class ID of the current view.

The *IGxPreview* interface is implemented by the *GxPreview* object. It provides access to the supported views for the selected object. Use this interface when you want to find out what the supported views are, or to retrieve or set the current view.

The *ViewClassID* property sets and retrieves the current view through its UID. Setting the UID is the only way to change the current view within the *GxPreview* object.

The following VBA code updates the *ViewClassID* to the *GxTableView* preview (your code should make sure the *GxTableView* view is one of the support views before setting the property):

```
Sub UpdateViewClassID()
  Dim pApp As IGxApplication, pGxView As IGxView
  Set pApp = Application
  Set pGxView = pApp.View
  If TypeOf pGxView Is IGxPreview Then
    Dim pPrev As IGxPreview, pUID As New UID
    Set pPrev = pGxView
    Debug.Print pPrev.ViewClassID
    pUID = "{9C34344D-99DC-11D2-AF6A-080009EC734B}" 'GUID for GxTableView
    pPrev.ViewClassID = pUID
  End If
End Sub
```

ArcCatalog

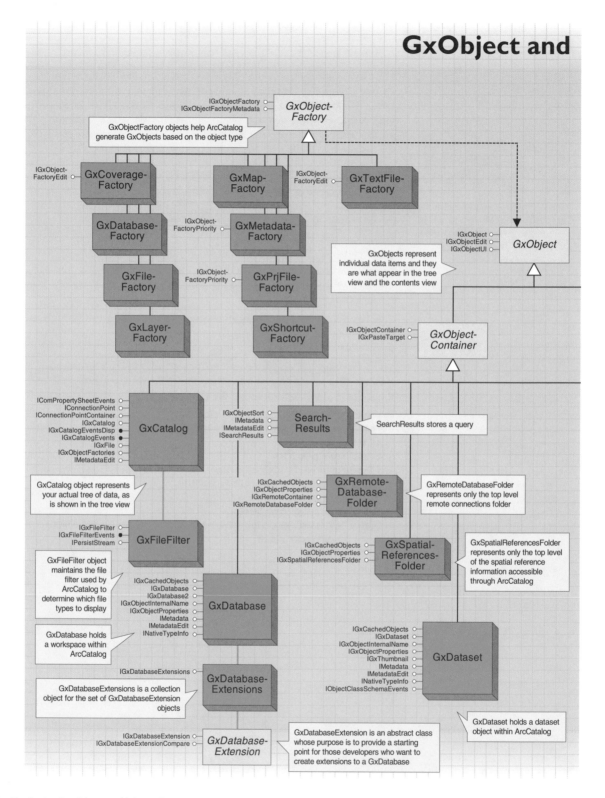

IGxObjectFactory
IGxObjectFactoryMetadata

GxObject-Factory

GxObjectFactory objects help ArcCatalog generate GxObjects based on the object type

IGxObject-FactoryEdit

GxCoverage-Factory

GxMap-Factory

IGxObject-FactoryEdit

GxTextFile-Factory

GxDatabase-Factory

IGxObject-FactoryPriority

GxMetadata-Factory

IGxObject
IGxObjectEdit
IGxObjectUI

GxObject

GxObjects represent individual data items and they are what appear in the tree view and the contents view

GxFile-Factory

IGxObject-FactoryPriority

GxPrjFile-Factory

GxLayer-Factory

GxShortcut-Factory

IGxObjectContainer
IGxPasteTarget

GxObject-Container

IComPropertySheetEvents
IConnectionPoint
IConnectionPointContainer
IGxCatalog
IGxCatalogEventsDisp
IGxCatalogEvents
IGxFile
IGxObjectFactories
IMetadataEdit

GxCatalog

IGxObjectSort
IMetadata
IMetadataEdit
ISearchResults

Search-Results

SearchResults stores a query

GxCatalog object represents your actual tree of data, as is shown in the tree view

IGxCachedObjects
IGxObjectProperties
IGxRemoteContainer
IGxRemoteDatabaseFolder

GxRemote-Database-Folder

GxRemoteDatabaseFolder represents only the top level remote connections folder

IGxFileFilter
IGxFileFilterEvents
IPersistStream

GxFileFilter

GxFileFilter object maintains the file filter used by ArcCatalog to determine which file types to display

IGxCachedObjects
IGxObjectProperties
IGxSpatialReferencesFolder

GxSpatial-References-Folder

GxSpatialReferencesFolder represents only the top level of the spatial reference information accessible through ArcCatalog

IGxCachedObjects
IGxDatabase
IGxDatabase2
IGxObjectInternalName
IGxObjectProperties
IMetadata
IMetadataEdit
INativeTypeInfo

GxDatabase

GxDatabase holds a workspace within ArcCatalog

IGxCachedObjects
IGxDataset
IGxObjectInternalName
IGxObjectProperties
IGxThumbnail
IMetadata
IMetadataEdit
INativeTypeInfo
IObjectClassSchemaEvents

GxDataset

IGxDatabaseExtensions

GxDatabase-Extensions

GxDatabaseExtensions is a collection object for the set of GxDatabaseExtension objects

GxDataset holds a dataset object within ArcCatalog

IGxDatabaseExtension
IGxDatabaseExtensionCompare

GxDatabase-Extension

GxDatabaseExtension is an abstract class whose purpose is to provide a starting point for those developers who want to create extensions to a GxDatabase

related objects

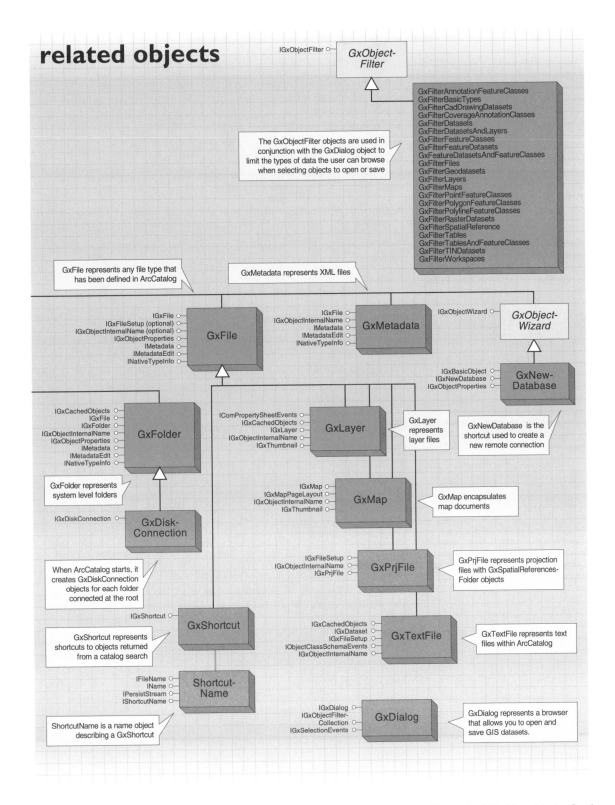

IGxObjectFilter — **GxObject-Filter**

The GxObjectFilter objects are used in conjunction with the GxDialog object to limit the types of data the user can browse when selecting objects to open or save

GxFilterAnnotationFeatureClasses
GxFilterBasicTypes
GxFilterCadDrawingDatasets
GxFilterCoverageAnnotationClasses
GxFilterDatasets
GxFilterDatasetsAndLayers
GxFilterFeatureClasses
GxFilterFeatureDatasets
GxFeatureDatasetsAndFeatureClasses
GxFilterFiles
GxFilterGeodatasets
GxFilterLayers
GxFilterMaps
GxFilterPointFeatureClasses
GxFilterPolygonFeatureClasses
GxFilterPolylineFeatureClasses
GxFilterRasterDatasets
GxFilterSpatialReference
GxFilterTables
GxFilterTablesAndFeatureClasses
GxFilterTINDatasets
GxFilterWorkspaces

GxFile represents any file type that has been defined in ArcCatalog

GxMetadata represents XML files

IGxFile
IGxFileSetup (optional)
IGxObjectInternalName (optional)
IGxObjectProperties
IMetadata
IMetadataEdit
INativeTypeInfo
— **GxFile**

IGxFile
IGxObjectInternalName
IMetadata
IMetadataEdit
INativeTypeInfo
— **GxMetadata**

IGxObjectWizard — **GxObject-Wizard**

IGxBasicObject
IGxNewDatabase
IGxObjectProperties
— **GxNew-Database**

IGxCachedObjects
IGxFile
IGxFolder
IGxObjectInternalName
IGxObjectProperties
IMetadata
IMetadataEdit
INativeTypeInfo
— **GxFolder**

IComPropertySheetEvents
IGxCachedObjects
IGxLayer
IGxObjectInternalName
IGxThumbnail
— **GxLayer**

GxLayer represents layer files

GxNewDatabase is the shortcut used to create a new remote connection

GxFolder represents system level folders

IGxDiskConnection — **GxDisk-Connection**

IGxMap
IGxMapPageLayout
IGxObjectInternalName
IGxThumbnail
— **GxMap**

GxMap encapsulates map documents

When ArcCatalog starts, it creates GxDiskConnection objects for each folder connected at the root

IGxFileSetup
IGxObjectInternalName
IGxPrjFile
— **GxPrjFile**

GxPrjFile represents projection files with GxSpatialReferences-Folder objects

IGxShortcut — **GxShortcut**

IGxCachedObjects
IGxDataset
IGxFileSetup
IObjectClassSchemaEvents
IGxObjectInternalName
— **GxTextFile**

GxTextFile represents text files within ArcCatalog

GxShortcut represents shortcuts to objects returned from a catalog search

IFileName
IName
IPersistStream
IShortcutName
— **Shortcut-Name**

ShortcutName is a name object describing a GxShortcut

IGxDialog
IGxObjectFilter-Collection
IGxSelectionEvents
— **GxDialog**

GxDialog represents a browser that allows you to open and save GIS datasets.

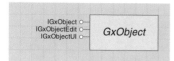

GxObject *is perhaps the most important abstract class in ArcCatalog. Every item that shows up in the tree and list views is a GxObject of one sort or another. There are several dozen types of GxObjects, ranging from GxDatabase to GxPrjFile.*

GxObjects *should be viewed as a means to an end, meaning you should always work with the objects that they are encapsulating. This is very important if objects are to be stored in data structures for later use. For example, when using the GxDialog to access datasets on a disk, you should not store the GxObjects returned for later use; instead, store the dataset objects that are encapsulated by the GxObject.*

If you want to create your own custom GxObject, you need to first implement IGxObjectFactory, which actually returns GxObjects. Then, you need to implement the IGxObject and IGxObjectUI interfaces to show the GxObject within ArcCatalog.

You can implement various methods under the IGxObject interface to provide specific operations on this object. For example, the Category property would show the category in the Type column in details view.

The IGxObjectUI interface allows you to specify a bitmap for your custom GxObject so that it shows up in the tree view. There are methods to show small icons and large icons so that they show up accordingly in the details/list/icons view types in the contents view.

Using the *IGxObject* interface, ArcCatalog calls *Attach* to initialize the object, passing in references to its parent and the *GxCatalog* object. The object should hold onto these references, then release them when ArcCatalog calls the *Detach* method. This behavior is necessary to guarantee that no circular dependencies develop between the object and its parent, or the *GxCatalog* coclass.

ArcCatalog relies on three separate properties to retrieve information about the textual name of the object:

- *Name* indicates the short name of the object including its extension (if any).

- *BaseName* returns the name without the filename extension (if it has one).

- *FullName* returns a string identifying the fully qualified pathname of the object starting at the root level. This is not necessarily a path to a file on disk since the object might exist within a database hierarchy somewhere. It is a fully qualified path within the context of ArcCatalog. It is made up of the names of all its *GxObjects* parents, each separated from the other with a backslash ("\") character.

The easiest way for an object to assemble and return this path is to call the *ConstructFullName* utility method on the *GxCatalog* object, passing in itself as a parameter.

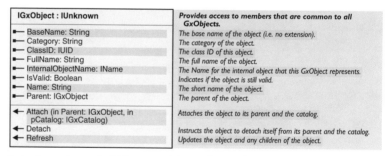

IGxObject : IUnknown	Provides access to members that are common to all GxObjects.
BaseName: String	The base name of the object (i.e. no extension).
Category: String	The category of the object.
ClassID: IUID	The class ID of this object.
FullName: String	The full name of the object.
InternalObjectName: IName	The Name for the internal object that this GxObject represents.
IsValid: Boolean	Indicates if the object is still valid.
Name: String	The short name of the object.
Parent: IGxObject	The parent of the object.
Attach (in Parent: IGxObject, in pCatalog: IGxCatalog)	Attaches the object to its parent and the catalog.
Detach	Instructs the object to detach itself from its parent and the catalog.
Refresh	Updates the object and any children of the object.

In order to be a *GxObject*, an object only needs to support *IGxObject*, though it will usually implement a number of other interfaces as well. To start with, however, it must support *IGxObject* since ArcCatalog uses this interface to setup and tear down the object, as well as to retrieve certain critical information from it during its lifetime. The *IGxObject* interface provides read-only access to the description of the object, such as name, parent, and category.

InternalObjectName is used for data-transfer operations. If you want your object to participate in drag and drop or copy and paste operations, you need to return something for this property. This property represents the actual data object that your *GxObject* manages. For example, database objects, such as *GxDatabase* and *GxDataset*, wrap underlying geodatabase entities, such as workspaces and datasets. It is these underlying objects that *InternalObjectName* references, not the

GxObject itself. Moreover, this property indirectly references these underlying objects via a *Name* object (sometimes also called a moniker).

ArcCatalog calls *Refresh* on your object whenever it needs to ensure your state is up to date. Mostly, this happens as a direct result of the user forcing a refresh of a part of the *GxCatalog* tree. It is your object's responsibility to release and re-create its internal state, then propagate the *Refresh* call onto any children you have.

IsValid is called periodically by ArcCatalog to verify that your object is in a legitimate state. Typically, it does so prior to performing critical operations involving your object, such as data transfer or the like.

Here is some VBA code to loop through the selected objects in the tabbed view and print their categories.

```
Dim pApp As IGxApplication, pGxSel As IGxSelection, _
  pEnumGxObj As IEnumGxObject
Dim pGxObj As IGxObject
Set pApp = Application
Set pGxSel = pApp.Selection
Set pEnumGxObj = pGxSel.SelectedObjects
Set pGxObj = pEnumGxObj.Next
Do While Not pGxObj Is Nothing
  Debug.Print pGxObj.Category
  Set pGxObj = pEnumGxObj.Next
Loop
```

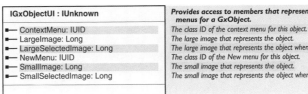

During an object's lifetime, ArcCatalog uses the *SmallImage, SmallSelectedImage, LargeImage,* and *LargeSelectedImage* properties of the optional *IGxObjectUI* interface to determine what images to use when displaying the object in the tree and contents views. Your object should return HBITMAPs for these properties.

Since these properties are requested frequently, you should load the images only once and cache them for later retrieval, rather than loading them each time they are requested. If you choose not to implement *IGxObjectUI*, ArcCatalog can still display and work with your object, but it will use a generic icon in the various views.

ContextMenu and *NewMenu* return GUIDs that indicate the menus that will display when the user attempts to manipulate the object through the ArcCatalog user interface.

IGxObjectEdit : IUnknown	Provides access to members that edit/modify a GxObject.
← CanCopy: Boolean	Indicates if the object can be copied.
← CanDelete: Boolean	Indicates if the object can be deleted.
← CanRename: Boolean	Indicates if the object can be renamed.
← Delete	Deletes the object.
← EditProperties (in hParent: Long)	Presents a modal dialog to allow editing the object's properties.
← Rename (in newShortName: String)	Renames the object.

An object should implement the *IGxObjectEdit* interface if its properties can be edited by the user within the context of ArcCatalog. This interface consists of several important properties and methods.

Rename assigns a new short name to the object (if you return *True* for the *CanRename* property).

If you return *True* for the *CanDelete* property, *Delete* physically deletes the object and all its associated underlying data—ArcCatalog handles deleting the *GxObject*, but it is the object's responsibility to delete all underlying and associated data that the object represents or wraps.

CanCopy indicates if the object is a valid source for a copy operation; a return value of *True* enables the *Copy* command/menu item in ArcCatalog. (However, to fully enable an object to participate in data-transfer operations, you also need to implement the *IGxObject::InternalObjectName* property as described in the earlier discussion on data transfer.)

The *EditProperties* method brings up a dialog box appropriate to the object that allows the user to manipulate its internal properties and state. It is entirely up to you to decide what can and cannot be manipulated through this dialog box, but a good rule of thumb is that properties about the object, not the actual data contained by the object, should appear here.

For example, if the object is a table, this dialog box might show a list of all the columns present and their data types and permit the user to edit this information. However, the actual rows of data in the table would not be presented in this dialog box.

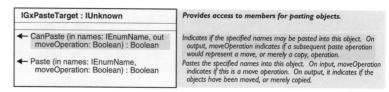

IGxPasteTarget : IUnknown	Provides access to members for pasting objects.
← CanPaste (in names: IEnumName, out moveOperation: Boolean) : Boolean	Indicates if the specified names may be pasted into this object. On output, moveOperation indicates if a subsequent paste operation would represent a move, or merely a copy, operation.
← Paste (in names: IEnumName, moveOperation: Boolean) : Boolean	Pastes the specified names into this object. On input, moveOperation indicates if this is a move operation. On output, it indicates if the objects have been moved, or merely copied.

The *IGxPasteTarget* interface is implemented by those *GxObjects* that can have other objects pasted into them. For example, the *GxDataset* implements *IGxPasteTarget* because it is possible to paste feature classes into an object of this type through the ArcCatalog user interface. The interface provides methods for testing whether or not a set of name objects can be pasted and methods to actually perform the paste.

Use *CanPaste* to determine if at least one object in the current set can be pasted before executing the *Paste* method.

IGxObjectInternalName : IUnknown	Provides access to members that manage the name object that the GX object represents.
►—□ InternalObjectName: IName	Returns a Name for the internal object that this GxObject represents.

IGxObjectInternalName is an optional interface for the different types of *GxObjects*. This interface provides access to the internal name of the object that implements it through the *InternalObjectName* interface.

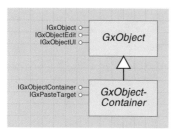

GxObjectContainer provides access to members that manage child GxObjects.

Some types of *GxObjects* may also be supported by the *GxObjectContainer* abstract class. This container class is for *GxObjects* that contain other *GxObjects* within them. For example, the *GxDatabase* object can contain *GxDataset* objects (among other things), so the *GxDatabase* object is also a type of *GxObjectContainer.*

IGxObjectContainer : IUnknown	Provides access to members that manage child GxObjects.
AreChildrenViewable: Boolean	Indicates if the objects children are available for viewing in the tree-view.
Children: IEnumGxObject	An enumeration of the child objects.
HasChildren: Boolean	Indicates if the object has any children.
AddChild (in child: IGxObject) : IGxObject	Adds a new child and returns a reference to it. However, if a duplicate already exists, the function returns the existing child instead.
DeleteChild (in child: IGxObject)	Deletes the specified child object.

If an object can contain other objects as children, it must implement the *IGxObjectContainer* interface. This interface exposes methods and properties to access and manipulate the children of the object.

The *HasChildren* property indicates if the object presently has any children.

Children returns an enumeration of the current set of children.

AreChildrenViewable indicates if the children should show up as items in the tree view within ArcCatalog; usually, this makes sense, but in certain cases you might want to prevent this from happening.

The last two methods, *AddChild* and *DeleteChild*, do not have to be implemented—they are only used when a container is up and running in ArcCatalog and the user wishes to either create new items in that container or remove items from it. They aren't required since doing a *Refresh* on the container (or one of its ancestors) will refresh its set of children as well.

The following VBA code demonstrates how to loop through the children of a *GxObjectContainer* object:

```
Dim pApp As IGxApplication, pGxSel As IGxSelection, pGxObj As IGxObject
Set pApp = Application
Set pGxSel = pApp.Selection
Set pGxObj = pGxSel.Location
If TypeOf pGxObj Is IGxObjectContainer Then
  Dim pGxObjCont As IGxObjectContainer, pEnum As IEnumGxObject
  Dim pObject As IGxObject
  Set pGxObjCont = pGxObj
  Set pEnum = pGxObjCont.Children
  Set pObject = pEnum.Next
  Do While Not pObject Is Nothing
    Debug.Print pObject.Category
    Set pObject = pEnum.Next
  Loop
End If
```

IGxRemoteContainer : IUnknown	*Identifies an object that contains objects from a remote source.*

GxObjectContainer objects that are based on remote connections implement the *IGxRemoteContainer* interface. The *GxRemoteDatabaseFolder* object is an example of a container object for remote database connections. The interface has no properties or methods, but it does identify the implementing object as a remote container object.

ArcCatalog

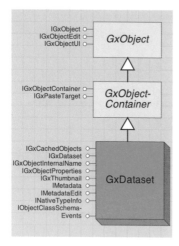

GxDataset *holds a dataset object within ArcCatalog.*

The *GxDataset* object holds an *IDatabase* object within ArcCatalog. The coclass is a descendant of both *GxObject* and *GxObjectContainer.*

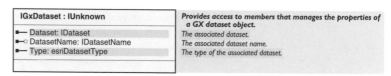

The *IGxDataset* interface provides access to the dataset itself. Through this interface, the developer can retrieve the *IDataset* or the *IDatasetName* object along with the type of dataset. This interface is implemented by several different types of dataset objects including *GxCadDataset, GxCoverageDataset, GxShapefileDataset,* and *GxVpf-Dataset.*

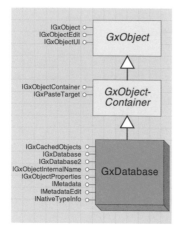

GxDatabase *represents a database in ArcCatalog.*

The *GxDatabase* object holds an *IWorkspace* object within ArcCatalog. The coclass is a descendant of both *GxObject* and *GxObjectContainer.* The *GxDatabase* object pertains to a geodatabase database.

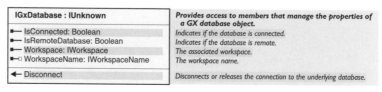

The *IGxDataset* interface provides access to the workspace itself. Through this interface, the developer can retrieve the *IWorkspace* or the *IWorkspaceName* object along with the type of dataset. This interface is implemented by several different types of database objects including *GxCoverageDatabase, GxPcCoverageDatabase,* and *GxPre70Coverage-Database.*

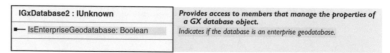

The *IGxDatabase2* is implemented by the *GxDatabase* object. It provides access to the *IsEnterpriseGeodatabase* property. As the name implies, the property indicates whether or not the database is an enterprise database (an ArcSDE database).

The GxDatabaseExtensions *object is a collection object for the set of* GxDatabaseExtension *objects.*

Each geodatabase can have a set of extensions associated with it (such as the *GxGeocodingServiceExtension*). The *IGxDatabaseExtensions* interface allows access to those extensions.

To obtain a *GxDatabaseExtensions* object, simply create one. The following VBA code shows you how to do that.

```
Dim pGxDataExts As IGxDatabaseExtensions
Set pGxDataExts = New GxDatabaseExtensions
Debug.Print pGxDataExts.Count
```

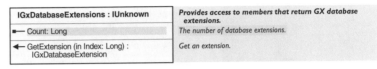

The *IGxDatabaseExtensions* interface is implemented by the *GxDatabaseExtensions* object. It provides access to the extensions held within the collection.

GxDatabaseExtension is an abstract class that provides a starting point for those developers who want to create extensions to a *GxDatabase*. The Geocoding service (*GxGeocodingServiceExtension*) is an example of a *GxDatabaseExtension* that supports the creation of address-matching services for use with ArcMap. Developers might want to develop their own extensions to support custom services.

GxDatabaseExtension *provides a starting point for developers who want to create extensions to a GxDatabase.*

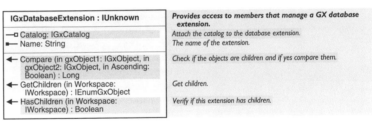

All *GxDatabaseExtension* objects implement the *IGxDatabaseExtension* interface. The *GxGeocodingServiceExtension* object is an example of an extension that allows the creation of address-matching services. The interface provides the ability to check whether or not an extension has children defined for it and to compare selected objects.

The *Compare* method determines whether or not objects are being displayed in the correct order. If the *Long* value returned is positive, then item one should be listed before item two; if zero, then the items are the same item; if negative, then item two should be listed before item one. As an example, if the only difference between two objects is the name, then the result will be positive if item one's name is alphabetically before item two's; otherwise, the result will be negative (unless reverse sorting—*Ascending* is *True*—is turned on).

ArcCatalog

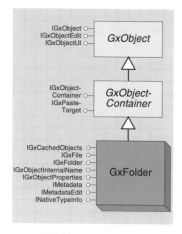

GxFolder *represents system-level folders.*

The *GxFolder* object represents system-level folders (directories). These folders represent workspaces if they contain ArcCatalog-supported data (such as coverages, shapefiles, or CAD drawings).

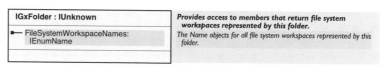

IGxFolder : IUnknown	Provides access to members that return file system workspaces represented by this folder.
■— FileSystemWorkspaceNames: IEnumName	The Name objects for all file system workspaces represented by this folder.

The *GxFolder* object implements the *IGxFolder* interface. The purpose of the interface is to provide access to the workspace *Name* objects that may be part of the folder.

FileSystemWorkspaceNames returns an enumeration of *Name* objects. *Name* objects only apply when the folder contains coverages. For more information on *Name* objects, see Volume 2, Chapter 8, 'Accessing the geodatabase'.

The following sample VBA code uses the *IGxFolder* interface to display the *Name* objects within a selected folder:

```
Dim pApp As IGxApplication, pGxSel As IGxSelection, _
  pEnumGxObj As IEnumGxObject
Dim pGxObj1 As IGxObject, pGxFolder As IGxFolder, pEnumName As IEnumName
Dim pName As IName
Set pApp = Application
Set pGxSel = pApp.Selection
If pGxSel.Count > 0 Then
  Set pEnumGxObj = pGxSel.SelectedObjects
  Set pGxObj1 = pEnumGxObj.Next
  If Not TypeOf pGxObj1 Is IGxFolder Then Exit Sub
  Set pGxFolder = pGxObj1
  Set pEnumName = pGxFolder.FileSystemWorkspaceNames
  Set pName = pEnumName.Next
  Do While Not pName Is Nothing
    Debug.Print pName.NameString
    Set pName = pEnumName.Next
  Loop
End If
```

The *GxSpatialReferencesFolder* object represents the top level of the spatial reference information that is accessible through ArcCatalog. The *Type* of folder, as listed in ArcCatalog, is Coordinate Systems Folder. This is a root-level folder that contains additional folders that hold the different types of supported spatial references.

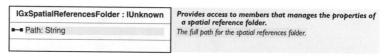

IGxSpatialReferencesFolder : IUnknown	Provides access to members that manages the properties of a spatial reference folder.
■—■ Path: String	The full path for the spatial references folder.

GxSpatialReferencesFolder *represents the top level of the spatial reference information that is accessible through ArcCatalog.*

The *GxSpatialReferencesFolder* object implements the *IGxSpatialReferencesFolder* interface. The interface allows for the retrieval and setting of the path to the spatial reference files on the system.

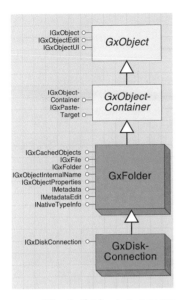

When ArcCatalog starts, it creates GxDiskConnection *objects for each folder connected at the root.*

The *GxDiskConnection* object represents the top-level disk connections. For example, the c:\ and d:\ drives on your local machine are *GxDiskConnection* objects (as well as *GxObjects*). Also, any additional remote folders the user adds with the Connect to Folder button are *GxDiskConnection* objects.

IGxDiskConnection : IUnknown	*Identifies an object that represents a connection to disk.*

Only the *GxDiskConnection* object implements the *IGxDiskConnection* interface. The interface does not support any properties or methods but allows the developer to determine whether or not the current *GxObject* is also a *GxDiskConnection* object. This can be accomplished through the following VBA code:

```
Dim pApp As IGxApplication, pGxSel As IGxSelection, pGxObj As IGxObject
Set pApp = Application
Set pGxSel = pApp.Selection
Set pGxObj = pGxSel.FirstObject
If TypeOf pGxObj Is IGxDiskConnection Then
  Debug.Print "The user picked a GxDiskConnection object"
End If
```

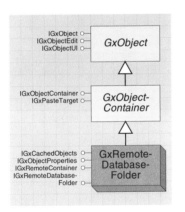

GxRemoteDatabaseFolder *represents the top-level remote connections folder.*

The *GxRemoteDatabaseFolder* object represents the top-level remote connections folder. There is only one object of this type. The *Type* of folder, as listed in ArcCatalog, is Database Connections Folder. This is a root-level folder that contains connection files to remote databases (for example, SDE® or OLE DB). The remote part is intended to correspond to the Feature Database Object (FDO) remote database type, *esriRemoteDatabaseWorkspace*, but it's possible to create an OLE DB connection to something local on your machine, as well as a remote machine.

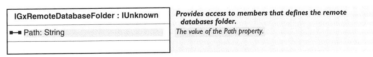

IGxRemoteDatabaseFolder : IUnknown	*Provides access to members that defines the remote databases folder.*
■→■ Path: String	*The value of the Path property.*

The *GxRemoteDatabaseFolder* object implements the *IGxRemoteDatabaseFolder* interface. The interface allows for the retrieval and setting of the path to the connection files for the remote databases.

ArcCatalog

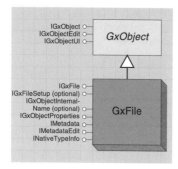

A GxFile object represents any file type that has been defined in ArcCatalog.

The user can define file types that they want to have displayed in Arc-Catalog through the File Types tab on the Options dialog box (or through *IGxFileFilter::AddFileType*). The files that are then displayed in the Catalog are *GxFile* objects.

For example, you may choose to have .txt files displayed within ArcCatalog. Using the *IGxFile* interface, *GxFile* objects can be manipulated based on the application associated with the file. For example, .doc files could be opened inside of Microsoft Word.

The following VBA code creates a new *GxFile* object and opens it in edit mode based on the application associated with the file (Microsoft Word, in the case of a .doc file):

```
Dim pFile As IGxFile
Set pFile = New GxFile
pFile.Path = "d:\tools\various\labeling.doc"
pFile.Edit
```

IGxFile : IUnknown	Provides access to members that manages a file object.
▪—▪ Path: String	The full path for the file.
← Close (in saveChanges: Boolean)	Closes the file, optionally saving changes.
← Edit	Opens an editor to modify the file.
← New	Creates a new file.
← Open	Opens the file.
← Save	Saves changes without closing the file.

The *GxFile* object and several other types of *GxObjects* implement the *IGxFile* interface. The interface allows for the writing of information onto disk. Be sure methods that you attempt to apply to the selected object are valid for that object. For example, *IGxFile::Open* has no effect on a .txt file associated with the NotePad application, while *IGxFile::Edit* opens the file in edit mode.

Updating the *Path* property changes the file associated with the current instance of the *GxObject*, but it does not change what is selected in ArcCatalog.

The *Close, Edit, New, Open,* and *Save* methods have varying affects on the object, depending on the application associated with it. Be sure you are applying the correct methods based on the *IGxFile* you are manipulating. Use error checking to ensure your application will not fail when one of the methods does.

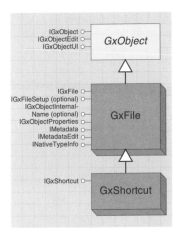

GxShortcut *represents shortcuts to objects returned from a Catalog search.*

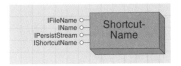

ShortcutName *is a name object that describes a GxShortcut.*

The *GxShortcut* objects represent shortcuts to objects returned from a Catalog search; they do not represent system shortcut files. *GxShortcut* objects are found under the Search Results heading in tree view.

These objects provide a way to access the *GxObjects* returned by a search without having to copy the data to a new location. The *GxShortcut* objects provide a path to the location of the real object and allow you to access the object directly.

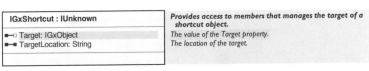

The *IGxShortcut* interface is implemented by the *GxShortcut* object. It provides access to the path and the actual object associated with the shortcut. Use this interface when you want to access the object returned by a search or when you want to determine the path to the object.

A *ShortcutName* is a name object that describes a *GxShortcut*. If you call *IGxObject::InternalObjectName* on a *GxShortcut*, you will get a *ShortcutName* CoClass.

GxShortcuts have a special name object because the layer factories need to know how to deal with them. The *CanCreate* and *Create* methods on a layer factory take a name object. In the case of a shortcut, this name object needs to delegate to the target's name object so that a layer is created on the *GxObject* to which the shortcut is pointing.

IShortcutName : IUnknown	Provides access to members that define the target for the shortcut name.
■–▫ TargetName: IName	The value of the TargetName property.

The *IShortcutName* interface is implemented by the *ShortcutName* object. It provides access to the *Name* object for the layer to which the shortcut points. The majority of developers will not use this object and interface.

ArcCatalog

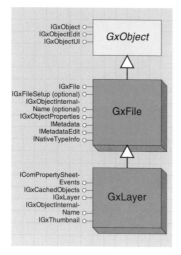

GxLayer *encapsulates a map layer.*

The *GxLayer* object represents a layer file that points to a data source. Layer files do not represent the data source itself but, instead, the layer file created for that data source. Through the *GxLayer* object, the developer can access the layer and the system path to that layer (*IGxFile::PathName*).

The following VBA code demonstrates how to create a *GxLayer* object (in this case pointing to a CAD file) from the selected item:

```
Dim pLayerFactory As ILayerFactory, pApp As IGxApplication, _
  pGxObject As IGxObject
Dim pName As IName

Set pLayerFactory = New CadLayerFactory
Set pApp = Application

Set pGxObject = pApp.SelectedObject
' Use GetObjectFromFullName if you want to specify a path to a file on disk
Set pName = pGxObject.InternalObjectName

If Not pLayerFactory.CanCreate(pName) Then
  MsgBox "Cannot create layer"
  Exit Sub
End If

Dim pEnum As IEnumLayer, pLayer As ILayer, pGxLayer As IGxLayer, _
  pFile As IGxFile
Set pEnum = pLayerFactory.Create(pName)
Set pGxLayer = New GxLayer
Set pFile = pGxLayer
pFile.Path = "C:\temp\mylayer.lyr"
Set pGxLayer.layer = pEnum.Next
pFile.Save
```

IGxLayer : IUnknown	Provides access to members that manage a GX layer object.
▪□ Layer: ILayer	The associated layer.

The *GxLayer* object implements the *IGxLayer* interface. It provides access to the *ILayer* the object represents. Use this interface when you want to access or update the properties of the layer.

The following VBA code demonstrates how to update the renderer for a layer through the *IGxLayer* interface:

```
Sub ChangeLayerProps()
  Dim pGxCat As IGxCatalog
  Dim pGxLayer As IGxLayer
  Dim pGxObj As IGxObject
  Dim pEnumGxObj As IEnumGxObject

  Set pGxCat = New GxCatalog
  Dim lNum As Long
```

```
    Dim v As Variant

    Set v = pGxCat.GetObjectFromFullName("d:\data\uslakes layer.lyr", lNum)
    If TypeOf v Is IEnumGxObject Then
      Set pEnumGxObj = v
      Set pGxObj = pEnumGxObj.Next
    Else
      Set pGxObj = v
    End If
    Set pGxLayer = pGxObj
    Dim pGFLayer As IGeoFeatureLayer
    Set pGFLayer = pGxLayer.Layer
    Set pGFLayer.Renderer = MakeFillRenderer

    Dim pEvent As IComPropertySheetEvents
    Set pEvent = pGxLayer
    pGxLayer.Layer.Visible = True
    pEvent.OnApply
  End Sub
```

The last three lines of the routine (use of *IComPropertySheetEvents*) are important because they force *Save* to be called for the layer. Without them, the changes to the renderer would not be persisted.

ArcCatalog

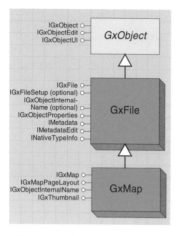

GxMap *encapsulates map documents.*

The *GxMap* object represents a map document that has been stored to a file (.mxd). The object provides browsing support for map documents within ArcCatalog and provides access to the page layout within the document. The page layout can be displayed as a thumbnail when browsing map documents.

IGxMap : IUnknown	*Identifies a GX object that corresponds to an ArcMap document.*

The *GxMap* object implements the *IGxMap* interface. This interface doesn't have any properties or methods, but it can be used to identify an object as type *GxMap*. The following VBA code demonstrates how this can be accomplished:

```
Dim pApp As IGxApplication, pSel As IGxSelection, pObj As IGxObject
Set pApp = Application
Set pSel = pApp.Selection
Set pObj = pSel.FirstObject
If pSel.Count < 1 Then Exit Sub
If TypeOf pObj Is IGxMap Then
  MsgBox "You selected a map!!"
End If
```

IGxMapPageLayout : IUnknown	*Provides access to members that returns the page layer for a map document.*
▪— PageLayout: IPageLayout	*The page layout object in the map document.*

The *GxMap* object implements the *IGxMapPageLayout* interface. The interface provides access to the page layout within the map document. The page layout can then be examined to determine the data within it and the extent of the data.

The *GxPrjFile* object represents projection files with *GxSpatialReferencesFolder* objects. While browsing in ArcCatalog, you will find *GxPrjFile* objects within folders under the Coordinate Systems heading. These files represent one defined projection.

IGxPrjFile : IUnknown	*Provides access to members that returns the properties of a PRJ file.*
▪— SpatialReference: ISpatialReference	*The spatial reference property of the PRJ file.*

GxPrjFile *represents projection files with* GxSpatialReferencesFolder *objects.*

The *IGxPrjFile* interface is implemented by the *GxPrjFile* object. It provides access to the projection information for the file. The projection information is returned as an *ISpatialReference*. The following VBA code demonstrates one method for determining if a *GxPrjFile* object is selected:

```
Dim pApp As IGxApplication, pSel As IGxSelection, pObj As IGxObject
Set pApp = Application
Set pSel = pApp.Selection
Set pObj = pSel.FirstObject
If pSel.Count < 1 Then Exit Sub
If TypeOf pObj Is IGxPrjFile Then
  MsgBox "You selected a project file!!"
End If
```

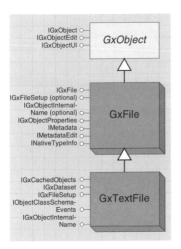

GxTextFile *represents text files within ArcCatalog.*

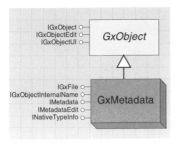

The GxMetadata *object represents XML files.*

The *GxTextFile* object represents .txt files within ArcCatalog. *GxTextFile* objects are also a type of *GxFile* object, but this type of object must have the .txt extension.

The following VBA code creates a new *GxTextFile* object and opens it in edit mode based on the application associated with the file (NotePad, in the case of a .txt file):

```
Dim pFile As IGxFile
Set pFile = New GxTextFile
pFile.Path = "d:\tools\various\labeling.txt"
pFile.Edit
```

The following VBA code demonstrates one method for determining whether or not a *GxTextFile* object is selected:

```
Dim pApp As IGxApplication, pSel As IGxSelection, pObj As IGxObject
Set pApp = Application
Set pSel = pApp.Selection
Set pObj = pSel.FirstObject
If pSel.Count < 1 Then Exit Sub
If TypeOf pObj Is IGxTextFile Then
  MsgBox "You selected a text file!!"
End If
```

In general, metadata for the different types of objects is stored in XML files associated with the object. For example, metadata for a parcels shapefile (parcels.shp) is stored in a file called parcels.shp.xml. Metadata files of this type (associated with a data type supported by ArcCatalog) will not show up in the tree and tabbed views of ArcCatalog. In order to see metadata objects within ArcCatalog, they cannot be associated with another support object.

IMetadata : IUnknown	Provides access to members that manage and update metadata.
■—■ Metadata: IPropertySet	*The PropertySet containing metadata.*
← Synchronize (in Action: tagesriMetadataSyncAction, in Interval: Long)	*Updates metadata with the current properties; may create metadata if it doesn't already exist.*

The *GxMetadata* object implements the *IMetadata* interface and all other objects that support metadata (the majority of *GxObject* types). Use this interface when you want to access the set of metadata associated with an object or when you want to create new metadata for the object.

The *Synchronize* method updates metadata for an object after changes have been made, but it also generates a new set of metadata if it doesn't already exist.

ArcCatalog

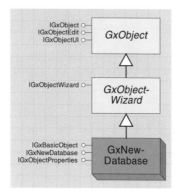

GxNewDatabase *provides funtionality to define the workspace factory object to use when creating a workspace.*

The *GxNewDatabase* object is the shortcut used to create a new remote connection. There's one instance of this object for each type of FDO remote workspace factory (for example, ArcSDE™ or OLE DB). It's the icon that invokes the wizard to create a new connection file.

IGxNewDatabase : IUnknown	Provides access to members that defines a new database shortcut.
—□ WorkspaceFactory: IWorkspaceFactory	The value of the workspace factory property.

The *IGxNewDatabase* interface is implemented by the *GxNewDatabase* object. It provides the ability to specify the *WorkspaceFactory* object to use. Developers only use this interface when they want to create a shortcut in ArcCatalog for users to create a connection to a custom data type.

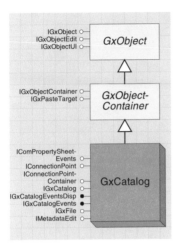

The GxCatalog object represents your actual tree of data, as is shown in the tree view.

The *GxCatalog* object represents your actual tree of data, as is shown in the tree view (the top-level object in the tree view). From the *GxCatalog* object, you can navigate to any of its descendants to access and manipulate them. The *GxCatalog* object is a type of *GxObject* and a type of *GxObjectContainer* because it is an item in the tree view and it contains additional *GxObjects*.

The *GxCatalog* object is also an event source, as it monitors the adding, deleting, and changing of the *GxObjects* within the Catalog through the *IGxCatalogEvents* interface.

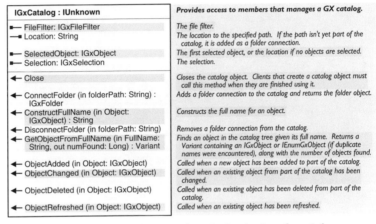

The *GxCatalog* object implements the *IGxCatalog* interface. It lets you connect and disconnect folder objects. It also maintains the file filter associated with ArcCatalog.

GetObjectFromFullName returns a variant because it is possible to get more than one *GxObject* back from this method. For example, if you use this method on a CAD file, it returns two objects: one for the CAD file and one for the CAD dataset.

The *SelectedObject* method returns the first selected object in the tabbed view of ArcCatalog.

The following VBA code uses the *Location* property to change the selected folder in the tree view to "d:\tools":

```
Dim pApp As IGxApplication, pCat As IGxCatalog
Set pApp = Application
Set pCat = pApp.Catalog
pCat.Location = "d:\tools"
```

ArcCatalog

IGxObjectFactories : IUnknown	Provides access to members that manage a collection of GX object factories.
■— Count: Long	The number of registered Gx object factories.
■— EnabledGxObjectFactories: IEnumGxObjectFactory	The enabled Gx object factories (sorted by priority).
■— GxObjectFactory (in Index: Long) : IGxObjectFactory	The specified Gx object factory.
■— GxObjectFactoryCLSID (in Index: Long) : IUID	The CLSID of the specified Gx object factory.
■— IsEnabled (in Index: Long) : Boolean	Indicates if a specific Gx object factory is enabled.
◄— EnableGxObjectFactory (Index: Long, bEnabled: Boolean)	Enables or disables a Gx object factory.

The *IGxObjectFactories* interface is implemented by the *GxCatalog* object. It provides access to the *GxObjectFactory* objects registered in the ESRI GX Object Factories category. Developers use this interface when they want to enable or disable an object factory or simply get access to one of the defined object factories.

The *EnableGxObjectFactory* method can enable or disable an object factory based on the value that is passed in.

The following VBA code demonstrates how to loop through the defined object factories and display their enabled properties:

```
Dim pObjFactories As IGxObjectFactories, lLoop As Long
Dim pObjFact As IGxObjectFactory
Set pObjFactories = New GxObjectFactories
For lLoop = 0 To pObjFactories.Count - 1
  Set pObjFact = pObjFactories.GxObjectFactory(lLoop)
  If pObjFact Is Nothing Then
    Debug.Print "Nothing at Index " & lLoop
  Else
    Debug.Print pObjFact.Name & " - " & pObjFactories.IsEnabled(lLoop)
  End If
Next lLoop
```

The GxFileFilter object maintains the file filter used by ArcCatalog to determine which file types to display.

The *GxFileFilter* object maintains the file filter used by ArcCatalog to determine which file types to display. Use this object when you want to manipulate the file types being displayed. The *GxFileFilter* object monitors changes made to the file filter through the *IGxFileFilterEvents* interface.

IGxFileFilter : IUnknown	Provides access to members that manages the properties for filtering file types.
▪— FileTypeCount: Long	The number of file types for the filter.
◄— AddFileType (in Extension: String, in Description: String, in filePathImage: String)	Add the file type to the collection.
◄— DeleteFileType (in Index: Long)	Remove the file type.
◄— Filter (in FilePath: String) : Boolean	Checks to see if the indicated file passes the filter.
◄— FindFileType (in Extension: String) : Long	The index of the file filter or -1.
◄— GetFileType (in Index: Long, out Extension: String, out Description: String, out imageFile: String, out SmallBitmap: Long, out largeBitmap: Long)	Returns a file type information by index.

The *GxFileFilter* object implements the *IGxFileFilter* interface. It lets you manipulate the file types displayed by ArcCatalog. Through this interface, you can add additional file types to the filter, remove file types, and determine whether or not a particular file will be displayed.

The *Filter* method returns a *Boolean* that indicates whether or not the specified file will be displayed in ArcCatalog based on the current file filter.

The *FindFileType* method returns an index that indicates the position of the specified file extension within the filter list. A value of -1 indicates the extension was not found. Do not include the "." when passing in the extension.

The following VBA code demonstrates how to use the *AddFileType* method to add the ".aml" file type to the filter. The file type is displayed with the default icon since you are not specifying one with the last parameter of *AddFileType*.

```
Dim pApp As IGxApplication, pCat As IGxCatalog, pFileFilter As IGxFileFilter
Set pApp = Application
Set pCat = pApp.Catalog
Set pFileFilter = pCat.FileFilter
pFileFilter.AddFileType "aml", "Workstation ArcInfo Macro files", " "
```

IGxFileFilterEvents : IUnknown	Provides access to events that the ArcCatalog file filter can fire.
◄— OnDefinitionChanged	Called when the file filter definition has changed.

The *GxFileFilter* object implements the *IGxFileFilterEvents* interface. It monitors when the file filter is changed. Developers might want to attach code to this event based on what file types have been added or removed from the filter.

ArcCatalog

GxDialog allows you to bring up a "mini-catalog" browser that allows you to open or save GIS datasets.

The *GxDialog* object controls the browser functionality of ArcCatalog. For example, when a user right-clicks a dataset, points to Import, then clicks Coverage to Geodatabase, the *GxDialog* object is employed in the browser that pops up, allowing the user to select a coverage.

The *GxDialog* object can be used within ArcCatalog and ArcMap to provide browser capabilities. The Intersect sample tool provides the capability to intersect two layers in the map and create a new geodatabase layer or a shapefile. The *GxDialog* object is used in that tool to allow the user to browse to a location for the layer or shapefile to create.

What the user can select or specify when using a *GxDialog* browser is based on the filters (*GxObjectFilter*) held by the object. The *GxDialog* object maintains a collection of these filters, and the developer has the ability to create his or her own filter to add to the collection. As an example, the Intersect sample tool uses a custom filter to specify that output must go to a geodatabase layer or a shapefile.

IGxDialog : IUnknown	Provides access to members that control the GxDialog.
AllowMultiSelect: Boolean	Indicates if multiple items may be selected. False, by default.
ButtonCaption: String	The caption to use for the Open or Save button.
FinalLocation: IGxObject	The dialog's final location.
InternalCatalog: IGxCatalog	The catalog object used internally by the GxDialog.
Name: String	The text in the Name text box (only for DoModalSave).
ObjectFilter: IGxObjectFilter	The object filter.
RememberLocation: Boolean	Indicates if the dialog should use the final location as the next starting location. True, by default.
ReplacingObject: Boolean	Indicates if an object already exists with the name supplied by the user, and is being replaced.
StartingLocation: Variant	The dialog's starting location. This can be an IGxObject or a text-string containing the full name of an object.
Title: String	The dialog's title.
DoModalOpen (in parentWindow: Long, out Selection: IEnumGxObject) : Boolean	Opens the dialog to choose data.
DoModalSave (in parentWindow: Long) : Boolean	Opens the dialog to save data.

The *IGxDialog* interface is implemented by the *GxDialog* object and provides access to the properties of the dialog box object and methods for displaying the dialog box during open or save operations. Use this interface when you want to access the properties of the dialog box or when you wish to display the dialog box for input from the end user.

ObjectFilter returns the filter that is currently active in the dialog box. If the dialog box is not currently open (through *DoModalOpen* or *DoModalSave*), this property will return the default filter.

IGxObjectFilterCollection : IUnknown	Provides access to members that manages a collection of GX object filters.
AddFilter (in Filter: IGxObjectFilter, in defaultFilter: Boolean)	Add a filter to the filter collection, and specify if it is to selected by default.
RemoveAllFilters	Remove all filters from the filter collection.

The *GxDialog* object implements the *IGxObjectFilterCollection* interface. It provides access to the set of filters used by the *GxDialog* object. Even though a collection of filters can be attached to a *GxDialog* object, only one filter is actually active at a time. The active filter is specified through the dialog box when *DoModalOpen* or *DoModalSave* is executed through the *IGxDialog* interface. Use the *IGxObjectFilterCollection* interface when you want to remove all of the filters or when you want to add an additional filter to the object.

The following VBA code demonstrates how to use the *IGxObjectFilterCollection* interface to add existing filters to a *GxDialog* object:

```
Dim pGxDialog As IGxDialog
Dim pShpFilter As IGxObjectFilter
Dim pLyrFilter As IGxObjectFilter
Dim pFilterCol As IGxObjectFilterCollection
Dim pEnumGx As IEnumGxObject

Set pShpFilter = New GxFilterShapefiles
Set pLyrFilter = New GxFilterLayers

Set pGxDialog = New GxDialog
Set pFilterCol = pGxDialog

pFilterCol.AddFilter pShpFilter, False
pFilterCol.AddFilter pLyrFilter, True 'pLyrFilter is the default filter.
pGxDialog.Title = "Browse Data"
pGxDialog.DoModalOpen 0, pEnumGx
```

ArcCatalog

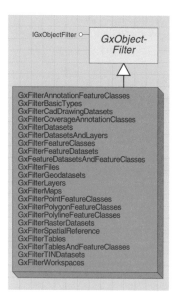

IGxObjectFilter ○—	GxObject-Filter

GxFilterAnnotationFeatureClasses
GxFilterBasicTypes
GxFilterCadDrawingDatasets
GxFilterCoverageAnnotationClasses
GxFilterDatasets
GxFilterDatasetsAndLayers
GxFilterFeatureClasses
GxFilterFeatureDatasets
GxFeatureDatasetsAndFeatureClasses
GxFilterFiles
GxFilterGeodatasets
GxFilterLayers
GxFilterMaps
GxFilterPointFeatureClasses
GxFilterPolygonFeatureClasses
GxFilterPolylineFeatureClasses
GxFilterRasterDatasets
GxFilterSpatialReference
GxFilterTables
GxFilterTablesAndFeatureClasses
GxFilterTINDatasets
GxFilterWorkspaces

The GxObjectFilter objects are used in conjunction with the GxDialog object to limit the types of data the user can browse when selecting objects to open or save.

There are over thirty types of *GxObjectFilter* objects the developer can use in the code. They can also create their own code depending on how they want their users to apply the *GxDialog* object. Through the use of objects of this type, the developer can determine which types of objects the user can choose for open and save operations when browsing data.

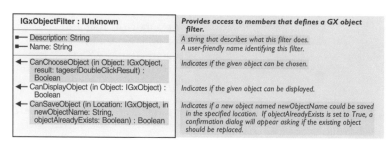

IGxObjectFilter : IUnknown	Provides access to members that defines a GX object filter.
■— Description: String	A string that describes what this filter does.
■— Name: String	A user-friendly name identifying this filter.
◄— CanChooseObject (in Object: IGxObject, result: tagesriDoubleClickResult) : Boolean	Indicates if the given object can be chosen.
◄— CanDisplayObject (in Object: IGxObject) : Boolean	Indicates if the given object can be displayed.
◄— CanSaveObject (in Location: IGxObject, in newObjectName: String, objectAlreadyExists: Boolean) : Boolean	Indicates if a new object named newObjectName could be saved in the specified location. If objectAlreadyExists is set to True, a confirmation dialog will appear asking if the existing object should be replaced.

All *GxObjectFilter* objects implement the *IGxFileFilter* interface. The interface allows for the specification of the file types that can be chosen for open and save operations when using a *GxDialog* browser object. Developers normally only access this interface when they are implementing it as part of a custom object filter. (Review the Intersect sample for an example of a custom *GxObjectFilter*.)

The following Visual Basic code demonstrates how to create a custom filter within a class:

```
Option Explicit

Implements IGxObjectFilter

Dim basicFilter As IGxObjectFilter

Private Sub Class_Initialize()
  Set basicFilter = New GxFilterBasicTypes
End Sub

Private Sub Class_Terminate()
  Set basicFilter = Nothing
End Sub

Private Function IGxObjectFilter_CanChooseObject(ByVal Object As _
  esriCore.IGxObject, result As esriCore.esriDoubleClickResult) As Boolean
  Dim canChoose As Boolean
  canChoose = False
  If TypeOf Object Is IGxFile Then
    Dim ext As String
    ext = GetExtension(Object.Name)
    If LCase(ext) = ".shd" Or LCase(ext) = ".pal" Then canChoose = True
  End If
  IGxObjectFilter_CanChooseObject = canChoose
End Function
```

```
Private Function IGxObjectFilter_CanSaveObject(ByVal Location As _
  esriCore.IGxObject, ByVal newObjectName As String, _
  objectAlreadyExists As Boolean) As Boolean

End Function

Private Property Get IGxObjectFilter_Name() As String
  IGxObjectFilter_Name = "Custom filter"
End Property

Private Property Get IGxObjectFilter_Description() As String
  IGxObjectFilter_Description = "Browses for .shd and .pal files."
End Property

Private Function IGxObjectFilter_CanDisplayObject(ByVal Object As _
  esriCore.IGxObject) As Boolean
  Dim canDisplay As Boolean
  canDisplay = False
  If basicFilter.CanDisplayObject(Object) Then
    canDisplay = True
  ElseIf TypeOf Object Is IGxFile Then
    Dim ext As String
    ext = GetExtension(Object.Name)
    If LCase(ext) = ".shd" Or LCase(ext) = ".pal" Then canDisplay = True
  End If
  IGxObjectFilter_CanDisplayObject = canDisplay
End Function

Private Function GetExtension(fileName As String) As String
  Dim extPos As Long
  extPos = InStrRev(fileName, ".")
  If extPos > 0 Then
    GetExtension = Mid(fileName, extPos)
  Else
    GetExtension = ""
  End If
End Function
```

ArcCatalog

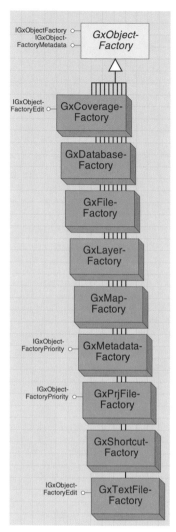

IGxObjectFactory ○
IGxObject-
FactoryMetadata ○

GxObject-
Factory

IGxObject-
FactoryEdit ○
GxCoverage-
Factory

GxDatabase-
Factory

GxFile-
Factory

GxLayer-
Factory

GxMap-
Factory

IGxObject-
FactoryPriority ○
GxMetadata-
Factory

IGxObject-
FactoryPriority ○
GxPrjFile-
Factory

GxShortcut-
Factory

IGxObject-
FactoryEdit ○
GxTextFile-
Factory

GxObjectFactory objects help ArcCatalog generate GxObjects based on the object type.

At the top level, the *Catalog* object is made up of a set of *GxObjects*. All these objects support the *IGxObject* interface along with some other interfaces.

There are a core set of *GxObjects* within ArcCatalog, such as catalog, disk connections, folders, and files. Basically, whenever a folder is asked for its children, it iterates over all registered *GxObjectFactories* to return *GxObjects*. Object factories know what types of files to return as *GxObjects*. These returned *GxObjects* are then populated in the Catalog by implementing *IGxObject* interface. Developers can easily extend the core set of *GxObjects* by implementing their own *GxObjectFactories*. After creating your own *GxObjectFactory*, the class must be registered under ESRI GX Object Factories for it to be considered.

The implementation of a custom *GxObjectFactory* class for .txt files may look something like this in Visual Basic:

```
Option Explicit

Implements IGxObjectFactory

Private Property Set IGxObjectFactory_Catalog(ByVal RHS As _
    esriCore.IGxCatalog)

End Property

Private Function IGxObjectFactory_GetChildren(ByVal parentDir As String, _
  ByVal fileNames As esriCore.IFileNames) As esriCore.IEnumGxObject
  Dim f As String
  Dim children As IGxObjectArray
  Set children = New GxObjectArray
  Do
    f = fileNames.Next
    If f <> "" Then
      If UCase(Right(f, 4)) = ".TXT" Then
        Dim child As IGxObject
        Set child = New GxTextFile
        f = child.Name
        children.Insert -1, child
        Set child = Nothing
        fileNames.Remove
      End If
    End If
  Loop Until f = ""
  Set IGxObjectFactory_GetChildren = children
End Function

Private Function IGxObjectFactory_HasChildren(ByVal parentDir As String, _
  ByVal fileNames As esriCore.IFileNames) As Boolean
  Dim f As String
  Do
    f = fileNames.Next
```

```
    If f <> "" Then
      If UCase(Right(f, 4)) = ".TXT" Then
        IGxObjectFactory_HasChildren = True
        Exit Do
      End If
    End If
  Loop Until f = ""
End Function


Private Property Get IGxObjectFactory_Name() As String
  IGxObjectFactory_Name = "GxSatishFactory"
End Property
```

IGxObjectFactory : IUnknown	Provides access to members that define a GX object factory.
—□ Catalog: IGxCatalog	Attach the catalog to the object factory.
■— Name: String	The name of the object factory.
◄— GetChildren (in parentDir: String, in fileNames: IFileNames) : IEnumGxObject	Returns an enumeration of objects corresponding to one or more of the given file names supported by the object factory.
◄— HasChildren (in parentDir: String, in fileNames: IFileNames) : Boolean	Indicates if any of the specified files are supported by the object factory.

All *GxObjectFactory* classes implement the *IGxObjectFactory* interface. The interface allows *GxObjectFactory* objects to return the name of the factory and information about the potential children of the object.

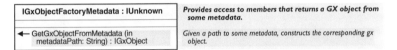

IGxObjectFactoryMetadata : IUnknown	Provides access to members that returns a GX object from some metadata.
◄— GetGxObjectFromMetadata (in metadataPath: String) : IGxObject	Given a path to some metadata, constructs the corresponding gx object.

All *GxObjectFactory* classes that support metadata implement the *IGxObjectFactoryMetadata* interface. The interface allows *GxObjectFactory* objects to return *GxObjects* when metadata paths are sent in. When creating your own *GxObjectFactory*, implement this interface if you want to support the defining of metadata on your custom objects.

ArcCatalog

FindDialog and related objects

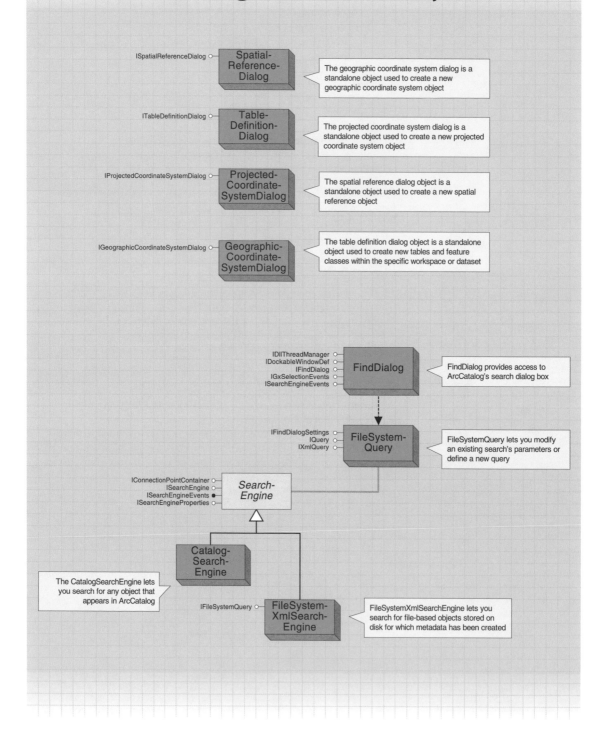

ISpatialReferenceDialog ○— **Spatial-Reference-Dialog**

The geographic coordinate system dialog is a standalone object used to create a new geographic coordinate system object

ITableDefinitionDialog ○— **Table-Definition-Dialog**

The projected coordinate system dialog is a standalone object used to create a new projected coordinate system object

IProjectedCoordinateSystemDialog ○— **Projected-Coordinate-SystemDialog**

The spatial reference dialog object is a standalone object used to create a new spatial reference object

IGeographicCoordinateSystemDialog ○— **Geographic-Coordinate-SystemDialog**

The table definition dialog object is a standalone object used to create new tables and feature classes within the specific workspace or dataset

IDllThreadManager ○—
IDockableWindowDef ○—
IFindDialog ○—
IGxSelectionEvents ○—
ISearchEngineEvents ○—
FindDialog

FindDialog provides access to ArcCatalog's search dialog box

IFindDialogSettings ○—
IQuery ○—
IXmlQuery ○—
FileSystem-Query

FileSystemQuery lets you modify an existing search's parameters or define a new query

IConnectionPointContainer ○—
ISearchEngine ○—
ISearchEngineEvents ●—
ISearchEngineProperties ○—
Search-Engine

Catalog-Search-Engine

The CatalogSearchEngine lets you search for any object that appears in ArcCatalog

IFileSystemQuery ○— **FileSystem-XmlSearch-Engine**

FileSystemXmlSearchEngine lets you search for file-based objects stored on disk for which metadata has been created

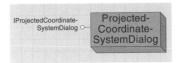

The projected coordinate system dialog box is a standalone object that creates a new projected coordinate system object.

The *ProjectedCoordinateSystemDialog* object is a standalone object used to create a new *IProjectedCoordinateSystem* object. As a developer, you should create an object of this type when you need to create a custom projection under the Projected Coordinate System category.

IProjectedCoordinateSystemDialog : IUnknown	*Provides access to members that control the Projected Coordinate System Dialog.*
← DoModalCreate (in hParent: Long) : IProjectedCoordinateSystem	*Prompts the user to define a new projected coordinate system.*

The *IProjectedCoordinateSystemDialog* interface is implemented by the *ProjectedCoordinateSystemDialog* object. It displays a dialog box for creating a new custom projection.

The following VBA code demonstrates how to use the dialog box to create a new projection and store it in the appropriate folder:

```
Dim pProjD As IProjectedCoordinateSystemDialog
Dim pProj As IProjectedCoordinateSystem
Set pProjD = New ProjectedCoordinateSystemDialog
Set pProj = pProjD.DoModalCreate(0)

Dim spRefEnviron As ISpatialReferenceFactory
Set spRefEnviron = New SpatialReferenceEnvironment

Dim pSpatialReference As ISpatialReference
Set pSpatialReference = pProj
spRefEnviron.ExportESRISpatialReferenceToPRJFile & "c:\arcgis\arcexe81" &_
    "\Coordinate Systems\projected coordinate systems\polar\abc.prj", _
    pSpatialReference
```

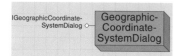

The geographic coordinate system dialog box is a standalone object used to create a new geographic coordinate system object.

The *GeographicCoordinateSystemDialog* object is a standalone object used to create a new *IGeographicCoordinateSystem* object. As a developer, you should create an object of this type when you need to create a custom projection under the Project Coordinate System category.

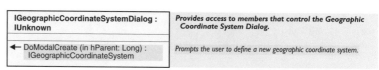

The *IGeographicCoordinateSystemDialog* interface is implemented only by the *GeographicCoordinateSystemDialog* object. It displays a dialog box for creating a new custom projection.

The following VBA code demonstrates how to use the dialog box:

```
Dim pGeoD As IGeographicCoordinateSystemDialog
Dim pGeo As IGeographicCoordinateSystem0
Set pGeoD = New GeographicCoordinateSystemDialog
Set pGeo = pGeoD.DoModalCreate(0)
```

The spatial reference dialog box object is a standalone object used to create a new spatial reference object.

The *SpatialReferenceDialog* object is a standalone object that creates a new *ISpatialReference* object. As a developer, you should create an object of this type when you need to generate or edit a spatial reference object.

As an example, *ISpatialReference* objects are needed in ArcCatalog when creating a new feature dataset, as the following VBA code demonstrates:

```
Dim pApp As IGxApplication, pSel As IGxSelection, pGxObj As IGxObject
Set pApp = Application
Set pSel = pApp.Selection
Set pGxObj = pSel.Location
'Make sure object selected in the tree view is a database object
If Not TypeOf pGxObj Is IGxDatabase Then Exit Sub

Dim pFeatWork As IFeatureWorkspace
Dim pSpatDiag As ISpatialReferenceDialog
Dim pSpat As ISpatialReference, pGxData As IGxDatabase2
Set pGxData = pGxObj
Set pFeatWork = pGxData.Workspace
Set pSpatDiag = New SpatialReferenceDialog
Set pSpat = pSpatDiag.DoModalCreate(True, False, False, 0)

If Not pSpat Is Nothing Then
  pFeatWork.CreateFeatureDataset "My New Dataset", pSpat
End If
```

ISpatialReferenceDialog : IUnknown	*Provides access to members that control the Spatial Reference Dialog.*
← DoModalCreate (in hasXY: Boolean, in HasZ: Boolean, in HasM: Boolean, in hParent: Long) : ISpatialReference	*Prompts the user to define a new spatial reference.*
← DoModalEdit (in inputSpatialReference: ISpatialReference, in hasXY: Boolean, in HasZ: Boolean, in HasM: Boolean, in coordPageReadOnly: Boolean, in domainPageReadOnly: Boolean, in hParent: Long) : ISpatialReference	*Displays/edits the properties of the given spatial reference.*

The *ISpatialReferenceDialog* interface is implemented by the *SpatialReferenceDialog* object. It displays dialog boxes for editing and creating *ISpatialReference* objects. Use this interface when you want to present your users with the standard dialog box for manipulating a spatial reference.

DoModalEdit and *DoModalCreate* arguments limit the pages of the wizard that will be displayed. For example, passing a *HasZ* value of *True* displays the page that sets z-values.

ArcCatalog

The table definition dialog box object is a standalone object used to create new tables and feature classes within the specific workspace or dataset.

The *TableDefinitionDialog* object is a standalone object that creates new tables (*ITable*) and feature classes (*IFeatureClass*) within the specific workspace or dataset. As a developer, you should create an object of this type when you want to give your users the capability to create new tables or feature classes through the standard dialog box.

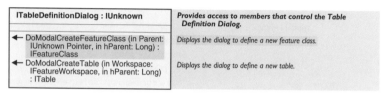

The *ITableDefinitionDialog* interface is implemented by the *TableDefinitionDialog* object. It displays a dialog box for creating a new table of a feature class.

For the first parameter of *DoModalCreateFeatureClass*, pass in an *IFeatureDataset* or an *IFeatureWorkspace*, depending on whether or not you want the feature class to be created within a dataset.

The following VBA code demonstrates how to create a new feature class within the dataset selected in the tree view of ArcCatalog:

```
Dim pApp As IGxApplication, pSel As IGxSelection, pGxObj As IGxObject
Set pApp = Application
Set pSel = pApp.Selection
Set pGxObj = pSel.Location
If Not TypeOf pGxObj Is IGxDataset Then Exit Sub

Dim pDataset As IDataset, pGxData As IGxDataset
Dim pTableDiag As ITableDefinitionDialog, pFeatClass As IFeatureClass
Set pGxData = pGxObj
Set pDataset = pGxData.Dataset
Set pTableDiag = New TableDefinitionDialog
Set pFeatClass = pTableDiag.DoModalCreateFeatureClass(pDataset, 0)
```

IDllThreadManager
IDockableWindowDef
IFindDialog
IGxSelectionEvents
ISearchEngineEvents

FindDialog

FindDialog provides access to the ArcCatalog Search dialog box.

The *FindDialog* provides access to the ArcCatalog Search dialog box.

IFindDialog : IUnknown	*IFindDialog.*
■— IsVisible: Boolean	*Determines if the find dialog is visible.*
◄— DoSearch (in pQuery: IQuery)	*Start the search given the query.*
◄— GetNumSearchEngines (in num: Long)	*Get the number of search engines.*
◄— GetSearchEngine (in Index: Long) : ISearchEngine	*Get the nth search engine.*
◄— Initialize (in pQuery: IQuery)	*Initialize the Find Dialog UI using a query.*
◄— Show (in bShow: Boolean)	*Show the find dialog.*
◄— StopSearch	*Stop the search.*

The *IFindDialog* interface lets you execute a search programmatically.

The *IsVisible* property indicates whether or not the Search dialog box is open.

The *Show* method lets you open and close the Search dialog box. On opening, the dialog box is initialized based on the selected object in ArcCatalog; if the object is a search result, the dialog box represents its search criteria. The *Initialize* method can be used to initialize the dialog box to represent the search parameters defined by a separate query (the use of *FileSystemQuery* is discussed in detail later in this section). The example below shows how to open the Search dialog box.

```
Dim pFindDialog As IFindDialog
Set pFindDialog = New FindDialog
pFindDialog.Show true
```

You can change the query's parameters by setting its properties with the *IQuery* and *IFindDialogSettings* interfaces, with the exception of the search engine used and the location in which the search should begin. You must set those properties separately by enabling the appropriate search engine and then setting its location string (use of *SearchEngine* is discussed later in this chapter).

The Search dialog box must have been shown once before the available search engines can be retrieved; however, if the *Show* command is used with the parameter *False*, the dialog box will be initialized but will not appear. The following example shows how this can be accomplished:

```
Dim pSearchEngine As ISearchEngine
Dim pSEProperties As ISearchEngineProperties
Dim i As Long

pFindDialog.Show False
For i = 0 To (pFindDialog.GetNumSearchEngines - 1)
  Set pSearchEngine = pFindDialog.getSearchEngine (i)
  Select Case pSearchEngine.Name
    Case "Catalog"
      pSearchEngine.Enabled = True
      Set pSEProperties = pSearchEngine
      pSEProperties.LocationString = "C:\Temp\data"
    Case "File system"
      pSearchEngine.Enabled = False
  End Select
Next
```

ArcCatalog

The *DoSearch* method initiates a search using the parameters defined by the input *FileSystemQuery* object. Before the search starts, the query is saved as a *SearchResults* object in the Search Results folder in ArcCatalog. The new search is selected in the Catalog tree, and when objects are found, shortcuts to those objects are automatically added to the search results, which are listed in the Contents tab. The Search dialog box must have been opened once before the search will execute successfully.

It is important to note that when one search engine is enabled, other search engines are not disabled automatically. If more than one search engine is enabled, the search will be executed once with each enabled search engine. The results from all search engines will appear in the Contents tab.

You can use *StopSearch* to halt the search at any point in time after the search has started. If *StopSearch* immediately follows *DoSearch*, the query is saved but the search does not execute.

Metadata objects

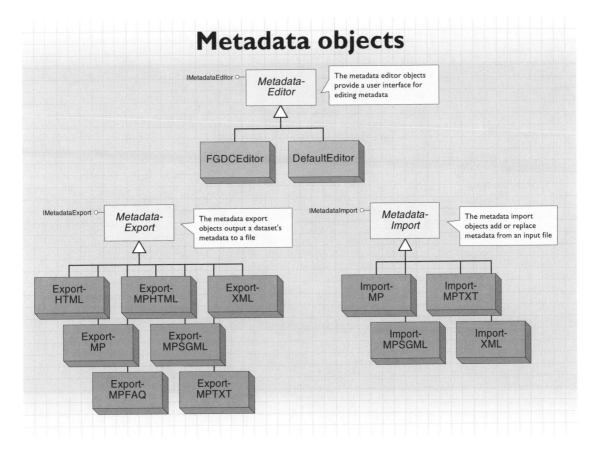

IMetadataEditor — **Metadata-Editor**

The metadata editor objects provide a user interface for editing metadata

FGDCEditor

DefaultEditor

IMetadataExport — **Metadata-Export**

The metadata export objects output a dataset's metadata to a file

Export-HTML

Export-MPHTML

Export-XML

Export-MP

Export-MPSGML

Export-MPFAQ

Export-MPTXT

IMetadataImport — **Metadata-Import**

The metadata import objects add or replace metadata from an input file

Import-MP

Import-MPTXT

Import-MPSGML

Import-XML

Most objects that appear in ArcCatalog can have metadata. However, you cannot create metadata or read metadata that already exists for datasets accessed using an OLE DB, ArcSDE 3, or an ArcSDE for Coverages database connection. For all other datasets and files (except standalone XML documents), ArcCatalog will by default create and update metadata automatically when you view metadata in the Metadata tab in ArcCatalog; this process, known as synchronization, is described in detail in Volume 2, Chapter 8, 'Accessing the geodatabase'. The only requirement is that the location of the data is writable. For example, you can create metadata for a coverage that is stored on your computer but not for one that resides on a CD–ROM. Within a geodatabase, you must be the owner of an object to be able to create or update its metadata.

Metadata can be created for folders, folder connections, and geodatabases themselves manually or programmatically, but they don't support synchronization. Metadata can be edited manually in ArcCatalog using a metadata editor, a metadata importer, or the Metadata Properties dialog box. The contents of standalone XML documents can be modified the same way. For example, you might use a metadata editor to describe the project for which a folder or personal geodatabase was created.

ArcCatalog organizational objects—the root of the Catalog tree and the Database Connections, Internet Servers, Geocoding Services, Coordinate Systems, and Search Results folders—don't support metadata. The objects you use to create database and Internet server connections and new geocoding services don't support metadata either.

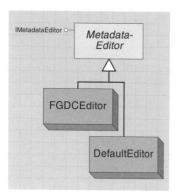

A MetadataEditor object provides a user interface for editing metadata. You can create your own custom metadata editor.

Two metadata editors are supplied with ArcCatalog: the *FGDCEditor* and the *DefaultEditor*.

The *FGDCEditor* allows you to create metadata following the FGDC standard; it is the metadata editor that is available by default when you click the Edit Metadata button in ArcCatalog.

The *DefaultEditor* is the Options page in the Metadata Properties dialog box; it works differently from other metadata editors.

You can build your own custom metadata editor, which can be opened in place of the *FGDCEditor* when the Edit Metadata button is clicked. You might do this to allow users to create metadata following a different metadata standard or to add specific information used by your organization to the metadata, such as the current state of a data-creation project. To build your own editor, create a class that implements *IMetadataEditor* and register it with the Component Categories Manager utility in the Metadata Editors category. There is an example of a custom metadata editor in the ArcObjects Developer Samples.

IMetadataEditor : IUnknown	Provides access to members that define a metadata editor.
■— Name: String	Name of the metadata editor.
◄— Edit (in props: IPropertySet, in hWnd: Long) : Boolean	Shows the metadata editor and indicates if the metadata property set was modified.

The *IMetadataEditor* interface controls a metadata editor.

When using a metadata editor, the *Name* property is read-only. This property is defined when the *IMetadataEditor* interface is implemented. The name value will appear in the Metadata Editors dropdown list in the Metadata tab in the ArcCatalog Options dialog box.

One way to open a metadata editor programmatically is to use *IMetadataHelper::Editor* to control which editor will appear, then *IGxDocumentationView::Edit* to show the editor. *IGxDocumentationView::Edit* in turn calls the *Edit* method on the *IMetadataEditor* interface.

When using the *Edit* method directly, two parameters must be passed in: an XML property set whose contents will be modified and the number zero. *Edit* also returns a value indicating whether or not the contents of the XML property set were modified; if this value is true, the changes should be saved to the original object. The DLL that contains the metadata editor must be referenced as part of your project. This example opens the FGDC editor.

```
Dim pPS As IPropertySet
Set pPS = pMetadata.Metadata

Dim pMetaEdit As IMetadataEditor
Set pMetaEdit = New MetaEditor.MetaEdit

Dim bModified As Boolean
bModified = pMetaEdit.edit(pPS, 0)
If bModified Then pMetadata.Metadata = pPS
```

The MetaEditor DLL contains the class named *MetaEdit*, which implements the *IMetadataEditor* interface. An XML property set containing metadata is retrieved from a *GxObject* or a *Name* object, and then passed to the *Edit* method, which opens a form. If you modify any values with the form, a flag is set. When the dialog box is closed, the *Edit* method's return value is set to the value of the flag. Your code should check the return value and then act accordingly; if the return value is true, save the changes to the metadata with the original object.

When the *Edit* method is implemented, you define how the editor will modify the XML property set. It may open a form where each control on the form lets users set the value of a specific metadata element. It may also set the value of several additional elements automatically, such as the time when the changes were saved or the name of the user who made the changes.

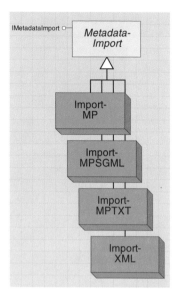

The metadata import objects are used to replace the existing metadata with new definitions from a file.

The *MetadataImport* objects work in the same way as the Import Metadata button in ArcCatalog, with one exception. The Import Metadata dialog box provides the option to synchronize imported metadata with the dataset after the importing is complete. When importing is initiated programmatically, this option isn't available; setting the appropriate *Sync* attributes and initiating synchronization must also be accomplished programmatically.

Each *MetadataImport* coclass corresponds to a different format of metadata in the input file. The following table summarizes the supported metadata import and export formats.

Import coclass	Export coclass	Metadata format
ImportMP	ExportMP	FGDC CSDGM (XML): the XML format that can be imported and exported by the FGDC metadata parser utility.
ImportMPSGML	ExportMPSGML	FGDC CSDGM (SGML): the SGML format that can be imported and exported by mp; mp is used to generate the result.
ImportMPTXT	ExportMPTXT	FGDC CSDGM (TXT): the text format that can be imported and exported by mp; mp is used to generate the result.
ImportXML	ExportXML	XML: imports and exports XML documents as-is; essentially creates a copy of the XML document.
	ExportMPHTML	FGDC CSDGM (HTML): the HTML output that can be generated by mp; mp is used to generate the result.
	ExportMPFAQ	FGDC CSDGM (FAQ): the FAQ-style HTML output that can be generated by mp; mp is used to generate the result.
	ExportHTML	HTML: HTML output is created by using ArcCatalog's current stylesheet to transform the metadata.

There are more export than import formats because XML can be readily presented as HTML, but not vice versa. For more information about the FGDC's metadata parser utility, mp, see http://geology.usgs.gov/tools/metadata/tools/doc/mp.html.

You can build your own custom metadata importer by creating a class that implements *IMetadataImport*, then registering it with the Component Categories Manager utility in the Metadata Importers category. There is an example custom metadata importer in the ArcObjects Developer Samples.

IMetadataImport : IUnknown	*Provides access to members that define a metadata importer.*
■─ DefaultFilename: String	*Default filename (including the file extension) from which to import.*
■─ Name: String	*Name of the metadata importer.*
◄─ Import (in source: String, in destination: IMetadata)	*Imports metadata from the specified location.*

The *IMetadataImport* interface lets you import existing metadata from a file.

When using a metadata importer, the properties *DefaultFileName* and *Name* are read-only. These properties are defined when the *IMetadataImport* interface is implemented.

The *Name* value appears in the Format dropdown list in the Import Metadata dialog box. If an importer's default filename is "aFile.abc", for example, then after choosing an importer in the Format list, the extension of the filename in the Location text box changes to match the extension of the default filename, which in this example is "abc". Also, when you click the Browse button, the default filename of the selected metadata format appears in the File name text box, and its file extension appears as the default option in the Files of type dropdown list.

The default location in which to look for input files is initially C:\Temp and thereafter is the ArcCatalog current working directory.

When the *Import* method is used, two parameters must be passed in: the path of the file whose contents will be imported and the *IMetadata* interface, which provides access to the metadata that should be modified as a result of importing metadata. The following example imports metadata for an ArcCatalog object from a text file that is formatted according to mp's requirements.

```
Dim pApp As IGxApplication
Dim pGxObject As IGxObject

Set pApp = Application
Set pGxObject = pApp.SelectedObject

Dim pMetadata as IMetadata
Set pMetadata = pGxObject

Dim pMetadataImport as IMetadataImport
Set pMetadataImport = New ImportMPTXT

pMetadataImport.Import "C:\stuff\fgdc_metadata.txt", pMetadata
MsgBox "Finished import in format: " & pMetadataImport.Name
```

When the *Import* method is implemented, it defines exactly what is recorded in the metadata when the importer is used. For example, it may open a file, extract some information, set specific elements in the original metadata document, then save the results.

Or, the importer may set specific elements in the metadata without opening a file at all; this is one possible method for adding standard blocks of information, such as contact information, to metadata documents. The metadata importers that are provided replace all existing metadata with the contents of the imported file.

ArcCatalog

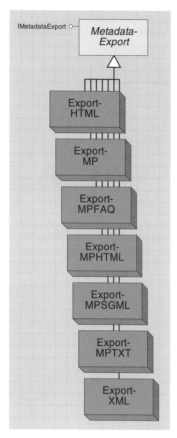

The MetadataExport objects are used to make an output file of a dataset's metadata.

The *MetadataExport* objects work in the same way as the Export Metadata button in ArcCatalog. Each *MetadataExport* coclass corresponds to a different format for the output file (see the table in the *MetadataImport* section).

You can build your own custom metadata exporter by creating a class that implements *IMetadataExport*, then registering it with the Component Categories Manager utility in the "Metadata Exporters" category. There is an example custom metadata importer in the ArcObjects Developer Samples.

IMetadataExport : IUnknown	*Provides access to members that define a metadata exporter.*
■— DefaultFilename: String	*Default filename (including the file extension) to create on export.*
■— Name: String	*Name of the metadata exporter.*
◄— Export (in source: IMetadata, in destination: String)	*Exports metadata to the specified location.*

The *IMetadataExport* interface lets you export information in the metadata document to an output file.

When using a metadata exporter, the properties *DefaultFileName* and *Name* are read-only. These properties are defined when the *IMetadataExport* interface is implemented. The name value appears in the Format dropdown list in the Export Metadata dialog box. The default filename defines the filename and extension, which are used by default in the same way as is described for the *IMetadataImport* interface. The default location in which output files will be placed is initially C:\Temp and thereafter is the ArcCatalog current working directory.

When the *Export* method is used, two parameters must be passed in: the *IMetadata* interface, which references the information that will be exported, and the path of the output file that will be created. The following example exports metadata for an ArcCatalog object to an XML file that satisfies mp's requirements.

```
Dim pApp As IGxApplication
Set pApp = Application

Dim pGxObject As IGxObject
Set pGxObject = pApp.SelectedObject

Dim pMetaData As IMetadata
Set pMetaData = pGxObject

Dim pMetadataExport As IMetadataExport
Set pMetadataExport = New ExportHTML

pMetadataExport.Export pMetaData, pMetadataExport.DefaultFilename
MsgBox "Finished export in format: " & pMetadataExport.Name
```

ExportMP uses *IXmlPropertySet::SaveAsFile* to create an output XML file in the manner that they are created by mp. The _MPXML stylesheet is used to transform the elements in the original metadata XML property set. It orders the metadata elements according to the hierarchy defined by the FGDC standard and removes the elements defined in the ESRI Profile. *ExportMP* also specifies a header that adds the XML version notation and a reference to the FGDC's DTD to the top of the output file. For the resulting XML to be valid, its elements must be ordered and their values must conform to the rules defined by the DTD. Since the ESRI profile elements are not defined in the FGDC's DTD, their presence would cause validation to fail. The other MP exporters also transform the metadata using the _MPXML style sheet. They pass the resulting XML file to mp. In turn, mp processes the XML and then writes an output file in the appropriate format to disk.

When exporting with the *ExportMP, ExportXML, ExportMPHTML, Export-MPFAQ,* and *ExportHTML* coclasses, do not use their default filenames, "metadata.xml" and "metadata.htm", respectively. When files with these names are placed inside a folder, they are assumed to contain metadata for that folder; their contents appear in the Metadata tab when the folder is selected in the Catalog tree, and incorrect assumptions may be made.

When the *Export* method is implemented, it defines exactly what is recorded in the output file. For example, it might create a new file, extract some information from the metadata, store it in an appropriate format within that file, then save the results.

ArcCatalog

FileSystemQuery *lets you modify an existing search's parameters or define a new query.*

The *FileSystemQuery* coclass lets you modify an existing search's parameters or define a new query. The *FileSystemQuery* coclass has three interfaces: *IFindDialogSettings, IQuery,* and *IXmlQuery.* The *IXmlQuery* interface builds the XSL Patterns expressions that correspond to the query parameters that are used to evaluate whether or not a dataset's metadata satisfies the search criteria. Typically, you would not use this interface.

You can build your own custom query object by creating a class that implements *IQuery.* You might do this to support a custom searching application in which additional properties or methods are required to define the search parameters.

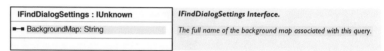

The *IFindDialogSettings* interface lets you specify which dataset will be used as a map when the geographic extent of the search is defined using the Search dialog box.

The *BackgroundMap* property specifies the complete path that identifies the dataset.

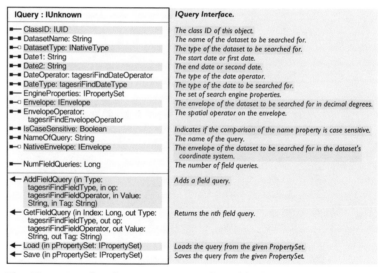

The *IQuery* interface lets you access and modify the search parameters.

The *ClassID* property is read-only. It identifies the type of query object that is represented by the search parameters. This information is essential if parameters are being retrieved from a query that was saved to disk. For example, if you define a new query using the *FileSystemQuery* coclass, the *ClassID* property reflects the UID of that coclass. If the query was instead defined using a custom query object, the appropriate object would be indicated by the *ClassID* property.

When creating a new *FileSystemQuery*, you are required to set only two parameters using the *IQuery* interface: *DatasetName*, which establishes the name of the object you want to find, and *NameQuery*, which defines the name of the query itself; all other properties are set to their default values. The dataset name may include an asterisk (*) as a wildcard character; use the dataset name "*" to select objects with any name. The following code demonstrates how to create a new query.

```
Dim pQuery As IQuery
Set pQuery = New FileSystemQuery

pQuery.DatasetName = "*"
pQuery.NameOfQuery = "My Search"
```

In addition to the *DatasetName* and *FileSystemQuery* properties, the query's search engine properties must be set or the search will not run. The query's *EngineProperties* property returns a property set. Modify the property set in order to change which search engine will be used to execute the query or how the search engine operates.

When a new query object is created, its *EngineProperties* property set doesn't contain any properties. An easy way to define the property set's contents is by creating the appropriate search engine, setting its properties, and then saving them to the *EngineProperties* property set. The example below shows how to change the location where the search will begin.

```
Dim pCatalogSE As ISearchEngineProperties
Set pCatalogSE = New CatalogSearchEngine
pCatalogSE.LocationString = "D:\Data"
pCatalogSE.Save pPS
```

The Catalog search engine adds the "EngineCLSID" and "CatalogLocation" properties. The file system XML search engine adds the "EngineCLSID", "FileSystemLocation", and "IncludeSubFolders" properties. The Catalog location property can identify any location in the Catalog, such as a database connection, for example, "Database Connections\My ArcSDE Connection.sde". The file system location property can identify any disk location on the network, for example, "\\aComputer\public".

The methods defined in the *IPropertySet* interface can also be used to add and remove properties and modify their values. The example below shows how to retrieve a previously defined query from an existing *SearchResults* object, modify its start location, and then execute the query.

```
Dim pGxApp As IGxApplication
Dim pGxObject As IGxObject
Set pGxApp = Application
Set pGxObject = pGxApp.SelectedObject

Dim pSearchResults As ISearchResults
Dim pQuery As IQuery
```

```
Set pSearchResults = pGxObject
Set pQuery = pSearchResults.Query

Dim pPropSet As IPropertySet
Set pPropSet = pQuery.EngineProperties
pPropSet.SetProperty "FileSystemLocation", "C:\mystuff"

pFindDialog.DoSearch pQuery
```

Other properties of the *IQuery* interface may optionally be set. For keyword-style searches, use *NumFieldQueries*—it returns the current number of field queries that have been defined. *GetFieldQuery* returns the parameters of the appropriate field query. Use the *AddFieldQuery* method to add to the list of field queries.

To search for a value in one of the predefined query fields, specify the appropriate field type, operator, and value and provide an empty string for the *Tag* parameter. To search for a value in another metadata element that isn't in the predefined list, specify the user-defined field type and the appropriate operator and value, and for the *Tag* parameter, specify the name string that identifies the metadata element.

The example below adds two field queries, one that looks for "roads" in the abstract and another that looks for the name of the project, "My Project", in the supplemental information element. For information about how to construct your own name string, see Volume 2, Chapter 8, 'Accessing the geodatabase'.

```
pQuery.AddFieldQuery esriFindFieldTypeAbstract, _
  esriFindFieldOperatorIncludes, "roads", ""
pQuery.AddFieldQuery esriFindFieldTypeUserDefined, _
  esriFindFieldOperatorIncludes, "My Project", "idinfo/descript/supplinf"
```

To search using date information in the metadata, set the *DateType, DateOperator, Date1,* and *Date2* properties appropriately. The date type defines whether you are looking for a date, how current the data is, when the metadata was last updated, or when the data was published.

The date operator defines how to compare the date in the metadata with the dates provided; for example, you might want to look for objects whose metadata was updated during the previous 30 days. For after, before, during, and equal date comparisons, dates must be specified in the format yyyymmdd; for example, "20000601" refers to the date June 1, 2000. For after, before, and equal comparisons, only the *Date1* property is used. For previous searches, *Date1* should be the appropriate number of days, such as "30".

Set the *DatasetType* property if you want to search for specific objects or data formats. To search by the geographic location of the dataset, you need to set the *Envelope* and *NativeEnvelope* properties appropriately.

The *Envelope* property defines the search extent in decimal degrees, while the *NativeEnvelope* property defines the search extent in a dataset's projected coordinates. Both search extents should be defined. If appropriate, both the native search extent and the decimal degrees search extent may contain decimal degrees values.

These extent values will be compared against the Bounding Coordinate and Local Bounding Coordinate metadata elements, which contain decimal degrees extent and native extent values, respectively.

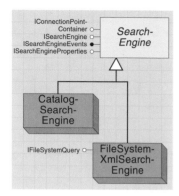

IConnectionPoint-
Container ○—
ISearchEngine ○—
ISearchEngineEvents ●—
ISearchEngineProperties ○—

Search-
Engine

Catalog-
Search-
Engine

IFileSystemQuery ○—

FileSystem-
XmlSearch-
Engine

The CatalogSearchEngine *lets you search for any object that appears in ArcCatalog.*

FileSystemXmlSearchEngine lets you search for file-based objects stored on disk for which metadata has been created.

Two search engines are supplied with ArcCatalog: the *CatalogSearchEngine* and the *FileSystemXmlSearchEngine*.

The *CatalogSearchEngine* lets you search for any object that appears in ArcCatalog including objects that are stored within geodatabases and are available on ArcIMS services. It is the default search engine. When searching by the dataset's name, type, and extent, metadata need not be created.

The *FileSystemXmlSearchEngine* lets you search for file-based objects stored on disk for which metadata has been created. It is faster than the *CatalogSearchEngine*.

Use the search engine object directly rather than through the Find dialog box if you want to define and run the search using a custom search interface or if you want to customize how the search results are compiled. For example, a custom search interface might use terminology that is specific to your organization. Similarly, you might create an HTML page listing the search results, rather than have ArcCatalog generate shortcuts to the datasets that were found.

You can build your own custom search engine by creating a class that implements *ISearchEngine* and registering it with the Component Categories Manager utility in the ESRI GX Search Engines category. You might do this to support a custom searching application that communicates with metadata stored within a relational database rather than with XML files on disk.

ISearchEngine : IUnknown	**ISearchEngine Interface.**
■—■ Enabled: Boolean	*Indicates if this search engine is enabled.*
■— IsExecuting: Boolean	*Indicates if the find operation is currently executing.*
■— Name: String	*The name of the search engine.*
—□ Query: IQuery	*<<< No help string specified >>>*
← ExecuteAsynchronous	*Executes the query asynchronously.*
← Stop	*Stops the query from executing (if it is currently executing).*

The *ISearchEngine* interface provides access to the search engine itself.

The *Enabled* property lets you enable or disable a search engine that has been retrieved from the Find dialog box.

The *Name* property returns the name of the search engine.

IsExecuting indicates whether or not the search engine is currently working.

If you are using the search engine independently from the Find dialog box, *Query* lets you set the query that will be executed, *ExecuteAsynchronous* starts the query, and *Stop* ends it. The query's engine properties must be set to use this search engine object.

ISearchEngineEvents : IUnknown	ISearchEngineEvents Interface.
← ObjectFound (in anObject: IGxObject, in Location: String)	Called when the find operation has found an object.
← SearchCanceled	Called when the find operation was explicitly canceled.
← SearchFailed	Called when the find operation has terminated prematurely.
← SearchFinished	Called when the find operation has finished executing.
← SearchLocationChanged (in Location: String)	Called when the find operation searches a new folder/container.

While the search is continuing, you may listen and respond to events using the *ISearchEngine* interface.

The *ObjectFound* event occurs when an object is found whose properties or metadata satisfies the search criteria.

The *SearchCancelled* event occurs when the search is stopped.

The *SearchFailed* event occurs when an error has occurred.

The *SearchFinished* event occurs when the search is complete.

The *SearchLocationChanged* event occurs when the search begins looking inside a new folder.

ISearchEngineProperties : IUnknown	ISearchEngineProperties Interface.
⊶ LocationString: String	A string describing the starting location of a search.
← Edit (in parentHWnd: Long)	Returns the name of the search engine.
← Load (in pPropertySet: IPropertySet)	Loads the search engine properties from the given PropertySet.
← Save (in pPropertySet: IPropertySet)	Saves the search engine properties to the given PropertySet.

The *SearchEngineProperties* interface can set a search engine's properties after the search engine has been retrieved from the Find dialog box.

The *LocationString* property can set the location in which the search should begin.

Alternatively, the *Edit* method can be used to open a dialog box that provides an interactive method for defining the search engine's properties. For the Catalog search engine, a *GxDialog* appears that lets you define its location string. For the file system XML search, a dialog appears; in addition to letting you set the location string, you can check a box indicating whether or not subfolders should be searched.

Save will record all of the search engine's properties in a property set (not an XML property set), which can then be modified using the *IPropertySet* interface.

Load will set the search engine's properties using the parameters defined in an existing property set.

ArcCatalog

Index

Symbols

#import 165, 172

A

AbridgedMolodenskyTransformation coclass 1107
Abstract class 11, 79
Accelerator table
    accessing 211, 216
    adding accelerators to
        example 216
        described 216
    removing accelerators from
        example 216
Accelerators
    accessing 216
    creating 216
        example 216
    removing
        example 216
ACMap coclass 356
Active Server Pages (ASP) 1278
Active Template Library. See ATL
Active tool
    accessing 188
    setting 188
Active view. See Views
ActiveX Data Objects (ADO) 1271
    library file 1274
ActiveX Data Objects model
    command 1273
    connection 1273, 1276, 1278
        openschema 1276
    error 1273
    field 1273
    parameter 1273
    property 1273
    record 1273
    recordset 1273, 1276, 1278
        edit 1276
        filter 1276
    stream 1273
ActiveX DLL 120–121
Addref method. See IUnknown
ADO (ActiveX Data Objects) 1271
Advanced Drawing Options dialog box 503
AffineTransformation2D coclass 1053, 1054, 1055

Aggregation. See also COM: aggregation
    in CASE tools 1286
AlgorithmicColorRamp coclass 494, 495, 496, 537
AnchorPoint coclass 552, 618
AngleFormat coclass 415, 419
Angles 984, 1007, 1020, 1029
AngularUnit coclass 1070, 1088
Animation progressor 210, 241
AnnotateLayerPropertiesCollection coclass 431, 432
Annotation 302
    adding layers to ArcMap example 444–445
    creating from labels 365
    groups 363, 365
        creating example 367–368
    in layers
        annotation feature classes in a geodatabase 363, 369
        coverages 350–352
        graphics 363
    levels in coverage 350
    scale 366–367
    subclasses in coverages 350
    target 363, 365, 369
Annotation class. See Annotation feature class
Annotation feature 845–846, 847
    example 847
    splined 549
Annotation feature class 740, 845–846, 847
    adding elements to 369
    in ArcMap layers 369
Annotation layers. See FDO graphics layers
AnnotationFeature coclass 740, 845, 847
AnnotationFeatureClassExtension coclass 740, 845
AnnotationJScriptEngine coclass 434, 440
AnnotationVBScriptEngine coclass 434, 440
AOIBookmark coclass 383
Apartment 85–86
AppDisplay coclass 252, 254, 260, 568
Application
    active tool 188
    ArcMap 249
    discussion 187–190
    display built-in dialog boxes 188
    exiting 188
    extending 191–201
    getting a reference to 207, 230, 235–236
    handling global data 197–199
    in ArcCatalog 187
    in ArcMap 187
    locking 188
    managing threads 188–189
    multithreaded 188–189
    persisting data 199–201
    start up sequence 197
    unlocking 188
    window. See Application window

D

Data conversion. *See* Feature data converter
Data exporting. *See* Feature data converter
Data Frame. *See* Map Frame
Data graph window 315
  creating example 315
Data loading. *See* Feature data converter. *See also* Cursor:
    insert
Data sources
  nonrelational 1271
  relational 1271
Data types 95–96
Data views. *See* Views
Data windows
  accessing example 253
  data graph 315
  discussion 314–315
  magnifier 316
  map inset 316
  object model diagram 314
  overview 317
  table 319–320
Database
  as an ArcCatalog object 680, 686
  schema
    modify 1279
  transaction 743, 781
DataGraph coclass 315, 321, 322
DataGraphElement coclass 305, 315
DataGraphWindow coclass 314, 315, 321
DataHistogram coclass 585
Dataset
  access control 759, 764
  as an ArcCatalog object 680, 686
  browsing for 736
  copying 763
  coverage 912
  creating a feature class within 710
  defined 762
  deleting 741, 763
  editing 763
  grant access example 759
  IDataset example 762
  locking 764
    example 764
  metadata. *See* Metadata
  move example 770
  name objects 758. *See also* Name object
    example 756, 758
  opening 736, 737
  privileges 759

Dataset (continued)
  referenced in a document 256
  register as versioned 891
  renaming 763
  spatial properties 789
  spatial reference 767
  specifying before creation 758
  types of 762
  version 891
  zoom to example 767
DataStatistics coclass 465
Datum
  described 1090
  user-defined 1091
Datum coclass 1070, 1071, 1077, 1078, 1087,
    1088, 1089, 1090
DblPnt coclass 1225, 1260
DCE 78, 82
Debugging. *See* Visual Basic: debugging. *See also* ATL:
    debugging; Visual C++: debugging
DefaultProduct property 1293
DefinedInterval coclass 577, 581
DefineEx method 1089
Definition query
  on layers 336
Deleting data. *See* Editing
Deleting features example 1132–1133
Delphi 98
Deployment object models 1292–1299
Device context 500, 501, 567, 575
Device units 570–571
Device-independent bitmap format. *See* DIB
Dialog boxes
  coordinate 243
  display in application 188
  list 246
  message 247
  number 248
  progress 241
  string 244
  user and password 245
DIB
  exporting to 641, 648
    example 648, 648–649
  World file 648
DibExporter coclass 648, 654
Difference of shapes 1045
DifferenceCursor coclass 890
DigitizerExtension coclass 1157
Digitizing 1157
  programming puck button 1157–1158
    example 1158
  streaming tolerance 1139
Digitizing shapes. *See* Feedbacks. *See also* Rubber band

E

Edge feature. *See* Geometric network: edge feature
EdgeConnectivityRule coclass 859, 865
EdgeFlag coclass 1187
EdgeFlagDisplay coclass 1196, 1197
Edit box controls
    creating 232
    creating in VBA 228
Edit cache 749
Edit events 1127, 1128, 1136
    example 1137
Edit extensions 1134, 1142
    attributes window 1154
    conflicts window 1156
    digitizer 1157
    topology editor 1159–1160
Edit operations 93–94, 1132
    delete feature example 1132–1133
Edit sessions 1129
Edit sketch 1130–1131, 1141
    add point example 1130
    context menu 1130, 1131
    delete vertex and fire event example 1146–1147
    delete vertex example 1131–1132
    extensions 1131, 1153
    operations 1131, 1146–1147
    symbology example 1139
Edit tasks 1127, 1128, 1143–1144
    changing example 1135–1136
    custom edit task example 1143
    relation to current layer 1138
    relation to edit sketch 1130, 1141
EditEvents2 coclass 1136, 1137
Editing
    appending data 903
    attribute domains 857
    conflicts. *See* Version: conflicts
    custom configuration 838
    customizing attribute editing 833
    direct updates 743, 785
    event handling 748, 797
    feature caching 749
    multiuser issues 746
    original values 799
    outside of edit session 780
    performance 748, 836
    reconcile and post 887
    route event source 967
    rules for geodatabase integrity 93–95, 747
    Store method 780, 785, 797
    topological features 867
    undo and redo 745
    without editing tools in ArcMap 745
    workspace edit example 746
    XY events 975

Editing features 1125
    attributes 1134, 1154
    delete feature example 1132–1133
    edit events. *See* Edit events
Editing features
    edit sessions 1129
    edit tasks. *See* Edit tasks
    extending the system overview 1127–1128
    object model diagram 1126
    resolving conflicts 1156
    start edit session example 1129
    topological associations 1159–1160
Editing properties 1139–1140
Editor coclass 93, 192, 272, 672, 833, 893,
        1127, 1128, 1130, 1133, 1135, 1136,
        1137, 1141, 1142, 1148, 1154
Editor extensions. *See* Edit extensions
EditSelection coclass 109
EditSelectionCache coclass 1151
EID. *See* Logical network: element ID (EID)
Element ID (EID). *See* Logical network: element ID (EID)
Elements
    accessing selection 288
    adding text example 286–287
    custom 589
    custom properties 300
    discussion 299
    fill shape elements 310–311
        circle 310
        ellipse 310
        polygon 311
        rectangle 311
    frame elements 306, 307–308
        background 564
        decoration 563–566
        example 564
        map frame 307–308
        map surround frame 308
        OLE frame 307
    graphic elements 301, 302, 303, 304
        adding to a graphics container 364
        group 304
        line 303
        marker 303
        storing in a geodatabase 369
        text 302
    map surrounds. *See* Map surrounds
    moving example 287
    object model diagram 298
    picture elements
        adding to layout example 313
        bitmap 312–313
        enhanced metafile 312–313
    positioning
        with grid 292, 296

G

GDI 506
Generalization. *See* Geometry
Generic customization environment 191–192
GeocentricTranslation coclass 1105, 1107, 1118
Geocoding
    services folder 659
Geodatabase. *See also* Workspace
    compress 885, 891
    customization 832
    editing rules 93–95, 747
    get user example 735
    integrity. *See* Validation rules
    load-only mode 784
    loading feature data. *See* Feature data converter. *See also*
      Cursor: insert
    performance 736, 741, 748, 749, 765, 775, 815,
      816, 817, 819, 824, 836, 845
    privileges 759
    release 752
    security 759
    versioning 885
Geographic Coordinate System. *See* Spatial reference
Geographic query. *See* Query: spatial
GeographicCoordinateSystem coclass 1070, 1071,
    1075, 1086, 1087, 1095, 1096
GeographicCoordinateSystemDialog coclass 708
Geography Network
    used for layers in ArcMap 356
Geometric network
    accessing features example 869
    building 1186. *See also* Geometric network: creating
    complex edge feature 876, 883
    complex junction examples 879
    complex junction feature 875–879
    connectivity rule 862
    creating 769, 1185, 1186
    custom feature 872, 873, 875, 877, 878
    default junction 863, 865
    defined 868, 1164
    edge feature 881
    edges at junction example 874
    enabling features 872, 876
    error detection 870
    event handling 872
    feature classes 769, 784, 843
    junction feature 873, 874, 875–879
    moving features 804
    name object 760
    navigating 881
    rebuilding connectivity 871
    snapping 879
    validate connectivity example 863
GeometricNetwork coclass 784, 868, 872, 875, 876

GeometricNetworkName coclass 760
Geometry 1276. *See also* Envelopes; Polygons; Polylines
    attributes 983, 1040
    build query shape example 824
    column 1276
    described 980, 985, 1056
Geometry
    digitizing. *See* Rubber band. *See also* Feedbacks: for new
      shapes
    drawing 501, 504, 981
    empty 981, 985
    errors 988
    example of digitizing 588
    finding locations on 990, 1046, 1050
    generalization 992, 993, 1000
    in fields 789
    multipart 983, 994, 1002, 1032, 1038
    objects 1276, 1277
    projecting 982, 986, 987, 1121
    simplicity 984, 989, 995, 999, 1030, 1041
    simplification 998, 1044
    spatial operations 982, 983, 1025, 1027, 1030, 1044
    spatial operators 1049
    spatial reference of 982, 985, 986, 1030
    splitting features example 805
    three-dimensional 1056
    topology 997, 1044
    transforming the shape of 1000, 1024, 1051
    user interaction 587–588
    WKB 1277
GeometryBag coclass 980, 981, 1028, 1030, 1031, 1044
GeometryDef coclass 739, 769, 789, 790, 791, 803
GeometryDraw coclass 504, 982
GeometryEnvironment coclass 1027, 1049
Geotransformation
    creating 1082, 1104, 1107, 1111, 1113
    described 1102, 1104
    direction 1103, 1112, 1113
    grid-based 1105, 1110, 1111
    HARN 1110
    NADCON 1110
    on-the-fly 1112, 1114
    parameters for 1097, 1105–1106, 1107, 1108
    two-stage 1112
    user-defined 1107, 1118
GeoTransformationOperationSet coclass 1081, 1114
GetStringDialog coclass 244
GetUserAndPasswordDialog coclass 245
Globally unique identifier. *See* GUID
GradientFillSymbol coclass 495, 537
Graphic elements 301, 302, 303, 304
Graphical Device interface. *See* GDI
Graphics. *See* Elements; Graphics container

I

V

Validation 1136
   customizing validation example 834
Validation rule
   applying 779, 800
      example 779
   attribute rule 861
   customizing validation 833
   described 859
   example 859
   managing 779
   network connectivity example 863
   network connectivity rule 862
   relationship rule 861
   types of 859
VB. *See* Visual Basic
VBA. *See* Visual Basic for Applications. *See also* Visual Basic
VBScript 84
VBVM. *See* Visual Basic: Virtual Machine (VBVM)
Vector3D coclass 1063, 1064, 1065
Version
   access control example 886
   accessing 885
      example 885
   and edit sessions 746
   conflicts 889, 892, 893–894
   conflicts window 893
   creating 885
   differences 890, 892
   manager window 895
   managing 885–886, 895
   posting 887
   properties 885–886, 890
   reconcile and post example 887
   reconciling 887, 889, 892, 893–894
VersionedWorkspace coclass 885
VersionInfo coclass 886, 890
Versioning
   resolving feature conflicts 1156
VersionManager coclass 895
VertexFeedback coclass 615
VerticalLegendItem coclass 372, 374
Views
   3D 657
   active view 673, 674
      example 673
   changing the layout 256
   check active view example 255
   custom view 668
   data view
      described 254
   GxViews
      contents view 656, 661, 670, 671, 681
      contents view example 670

Views (continued)
   GxViews (continued)
      geographic 673, 676
      geographic view 657
      geographic view example 673
      metadata view 656
      preview view 656, 658, 676, 677
      preview view example 669
      table view 657, 675, 676
      table view by UID example 676
      tree view 656, 657, 659, 661, 664,
         666, 675, 681, 684, 691, 695, 697
      tree view rename example 675
      ViewClassID example 677
   introduced 254
   layout view
      described 254
   previews 657, 658, 668
   tabbed view 656, 657, 664, 666, 668, 695
   table 324–325
Visual Basic 11
   add-ins
      align control creation with tab index 139
      automatic reference 128
      compile and register 128–130
      error handler 135–137
      error handler remover 137
      interface implementer 130–131
      line number 137–138
      line number remover 138
   and interfaces 103–106
   arrays 101
   bibliography 180
   callback model 157–159
   coding guidelines 100–113
   coding standards
      ambiguous type matching 102
      arrays 101–102
      bitwise operators 102
      default properties 101
      indentation 101
      intermodule referencing 101
      multiple property operations 101
      order of conditional determination 101
      parantheses 100–101
      type suffixes 102
      variable declaration 100
      while wend constructs 103
   collection object 113
   collections 112
   Command Creation Wizard 132–135
   creating COM components 120
   data types 96
   debugging 124–127
   debugging with ATL helper object 126–127

X

Z